THE VAN NOSTRAND CHEMIST'S DICTIONARY

D. VAN NOSTRAND COMPANY, INC.

TORONTO   NEW YORK   LONDON

NEW YORK

D. Van Nostrand Company, Inc., 250 Fourth Avenue, New York 3

TORONTO

D. Van Nostrand Company (Canada), Ltd., 25 Hollinger Rd., Toronto

LONDON

Macmillan & Company, Ltd., St. Martin's Street, London, W.C. 2

PRINTED IN THE UNITED STATES OF AMERICA

PREFACE

THE CHEMIST'S DICTIONARY is designed to provide the widest possible coverage of the terms in which chemists are most commonly interested. The book includes, therefore, definitions of all the group terms of chemical substances; the elements, the ions, the radicals, the type-compounds and the classes of chemical substances are defined in light of present-day nomenclature. The book also gives definitions of the laws, reactions, mathematical equations and fundamental entities; the presentation extends into physics and other sciences when necessary to meet the needs of the chemist. Proper names are included as well as common names—a policy that has been followed not only in regard to the scientific terms, but for the many applications of chemistry.

A feature that facilitates ready reference is the KEY WORD PLAN of indexing. Each topic is defined as far as possible in basic terms, and then every word important to the explanation that is further defined elsewhere in the book is printed in bold-face type to serve as a reference to the article on that subject.

The applications of chemistry include names of industrial processes and plant and laboratory equipment. Coverage of definitions of the chemical tests, solutions, and reagents is provided. Since very many important tests and solutions, as well as laws, equations and reactions, are best known by the names of the men to whom they are accredited, the large number (more than 5000) of proper-name entries are a valuable feature of this book. Both the common-name and the proper-name terms basic to many phases of pure and applied chemistry are brought together for convenient reference.

While the inclusion of the terms of applied chemistry, even though they number several thousand, has required the most exacting and often arbitrary selections, the result will be, it is hoped, sufficiently useful to the vast majority of chemists to justify the obvious omissions if the book is viewed from the standpoint of a single, highly specialized field. In fact, the primary objective of this Dictionary is to furnish to the specialist in any one field the information in all fields up to the level of the specialist. To accomplish this purpose the definitions have been written, as far as possible, in the most commonly used terms; atomic entities, for example, are discussed either in the language of quantum mechanics or the "classical language" in accordance with the most common usage of the particular term. The same pragmatic viewpoint has determined the other editorial policies in the preparation of the book; structural formulas are employed only when necessary to clarify the structure of the compound or the course of the reaction under discussion. The numerical values of the various fundamental and derived constants are those deemed the best single values at the time of writing.   The definitions of the terms range in length from a few words to comprehensive articles, several pages long.

The Editors wish to acknowledge their indebtedness to all those who have assisted in the many tasks involved in the preparation of this Dictionary, not the least of which has been the choice of the terms to be included.   The Editors sincerely trust that the chemists who use this book will feel free to communicate their comments on the selections that have been made or the scope of their treatment.

THE EDITORS

A. Symbol for the element **argon** (A). Symbol for the **Angstrom unit** (A). Symbol for **van der Waals constant** (a). Symbol for **acceleration** (A or a). Symbol for **activity** (a). Symbol for specific **rotation** [a]. Symbol for **accommodation coefficient** (a). Symbol for refracting angle of a prism (A). Symbol for **amplitude** (A). Symbol for area (A). Symbol for **atomic weight** (A). Symbol for **Helmholtz function,** or maximum isothermal work function: per atom or molecule, a or a_m, per mole, a, A, or A_M, per unit mass, a, total value A. A factor in **Richardson equation** A. Symbol for width of slit (transparent portion) a. See also **alpha.**

ABBE THEORY. A relationship derived for the limiting width of an object visible under the microscope, which is expressed as directly proportional to the wave length of the light, and inversely proportional to the **aperture.**

ABDERHALDEN-KAUTZSCH TEST REACTION. On treatment with an ammoniacal copper solution, pyrrolidone carboxylic acid gives a precipitate, then a deep blue solution.

ABDERHALDEN REACTION. A serum test used in medical diagnosis, especially in pregnancy.

ABDERHALDEN TEST REACTION FOR CYSTINE. Treatment of cystine with β-naphthalene thiochloride and sodium hydroxide solution yields naphthalene-sulfocystine.

ABDERHALDEN-SCHMIDT REAGENT. A solution of 0.1 g. ninhydrin in 300 ml. water, used in testing for adrenalin, for proteins and for hydrolysis products derived from proteins. A blue color, obtained on warming a solution of the substance with a small quantity of the reagent, is given by these compounds.

ABDERHALDEN-WEIL TEST REACTION. Glutamic acid gives a blue color with ninhydrin.

ABEGG RULE. If the maximum positive **valence** exhibited by an element be numerically added to its maximum negative valence, there appears to be a tendency for the sum to equal 8. This tendency is exhibited especially by the elements of the 4th, 5th, 6th, and 7th groups and is known as the Abegg rule.

ABEL-PENSKY APPARATUS. A closed apparatus used in determining the flash point of liquids. (See also **Pensky-Martens Apparatus.**)

ABEL REAGENT. A solution of chromic acid (10% CrO_3) used as an etching reagent in metallography.

ABEL TEST REACTIONS FOR ETHYL SULFIDE. (1) Upon addition of mercuric chloride to the aqueous or alcoholic solution of ethyl sulfide, the addition product (m.p. 119° C.) precipitates. (2) Ethyl sulfide in sulfuric acid solution gives with 1 drop normal aqueous iodine solution a precipitate of the iodine addition product, which settles as oily, brown drops.

ABELIN TEST FOR ARSPHENAMINE. Arsphenamine in aqueous solution containing a few drops hydrochloric acid gives with $\frac{1}{2}$% aqueous sodium nitrite solution a greenish yellow fluorescent liquid, which becomes red when added to an alkaline 10% resorcinol solution.

ABENSOUR TESTS FOR QUININE. (1) To a quinine solution, bromine water is added until the fluorescence disappears, then the addition of an equal volume of ethyl alcohol and two drops of ammonia produces a green color. (2) 10 ml. of slightly acid quinine solution, with 1 drop bromine water, 1 drop potassium ferrocyanide solution, and 1 drop 10% ammonia gives to chloroform, after shaking, a pink to red color.

ABERRATION, CHROMATIC. Unequal **refraction** of beams of **radiation** of more than one frequency producing a certain degree of **dispersion.**

ABERRATION, SPHERICAL. Unequal **refraction** of **radiation** attributable to variation in the degree of curvature of the medium, resulting in distortion of the image produced.

ABRAHAM THEORY. A mathematical analysis yielding the relationship:

$$M = \frac{3M_0\left(\dfrac{1+B^2}{2B} \cdot \log \dfrac{1+B}{1-B} - 1\right)}{4B^2}$$

where M_0 = electromagnetic mass of the **electron** for infinitely small velocities; M = transverse mass for a velocity v; $\dfrac{v}{c} = B$ in which c is the velocity of light.

ABRAHAMSON REAGENT. A reagent prepared by mixing a solution of 11.1 g. sodium tungstate dihydrate and 5 g. sodium citrate in 700 ml. water; with a solution of 13.6 g. sodium hydrogen sulfate in 200 ml. water. It is made up to 1 l., and is used to precipitate proteins from blood.

ABRASION. Erosion or grinding by friction, or shearing action.

ABRASIVE. A material used for wearing away a surface by friction, as in polishing. Sandpaper, steel wool, emery, and pumice are abrasives.

ABSCISSA. The distance between points measured along a horizontal scale; commonly the coordinate of the distance of a point from an origin, measured along the x-axis.

ABSOLUTE. Independent or unlimited, as an absolute condition, or completely pure or unadulterated, as a perfume base or alcohol.

ABSOLUTE DENSITY. See **density, absolute.**

ABSOLUTE HUMIDITY. See **humidity, absolute.**

ABSOLUTE PRESSURE. See **pressure, absolute.**

ABSOLUTE TEMPERATURE. See **temperature, absolute.**

ABSOLUTE TEMPERATURE SCALE. See **temperature scale, absolute.**

ABSOLUTE UNIT. See **unit, absolute.**

ABSOLUTE ZERO. The temperature at which the volume of an ideal gas would become zero. The value calculated from the limiting value of the coefficient of expansion of various real gases is $-273.16°$ C.

ABSORBANCE. The logarithm to the base 10 of the reciprocal of the **transmittance.** Generally, pure solvent is the reference material. $A = \log_{10}(1/T)$. See **Law of Beer.**

ABSORBENT. A substance, material, or solution able to **imbibe,** or "attract into its mass," or trap liquids or gases, commonly to remove them from a given medium or region.

ABSORBENT, GAS. A substance, solution, or mixture used for the selective **absorption** of gases, as in **gas analysis** or purification.

ABSORBENT, LIGHT. A substance or material that transmits **radiations** of some frequencies and absorbs others.

ABSORPTIOMETER. A graduated tube, closed at one end, used for the analysis of gases, performed by introducing an absorbing agent and noting the decrease in volume at constant pressure of the contents of the tube. Often incorrectly termed an eudiometer. Also an apparatus used to control the thickness of a film of liquid in **spectrophotometry.**

ABSORPTION. The imbibing or attracting into its mass of one substance (or form of energy) by another substance so that the absorbed substance or energy disappears physically. The phenomenon may be due to either molecular or chemical action. It is not to be confused with "**adsorption**" which is characterized by surface tension and condensation. In physiology, the term absorption connotes the conversion of ingested materials into part of the organism.

ABSORPTION APPARATUS. Certain forms of apparatus used especially in gas analysis by means of which a portion of the sample under examination is absorbed and its quantity subsequently determined.

ABSORPTION BAND. A region of the **absorption spectrum** in which the **absorptivity** passes through a maximum or inflection.

ABSORPTION CELL. A glass vessel used to hold liquids for the determination of their **absorption spectra.**

ABSORPTION COEFFICIENT OF GASES. In general, the volume of gas dissolved by a specified volume of **solvent.** A widely-used coefficient is the volume of gas, reduced to standard conditions, dissolved by unit volume of solvent when the **partial pressure** of the gas is one atmosphere.

ABSORPTION COEFFICIENT, LINEAR. A substance is said to possess a linear absorption coefficient if, in traversing a very small distance through the absorbing medium, the change of **intensity** of the incident **radiation** is proportional to the (small) distance traversed. Under these conditions the intensity of the emerging radiation falls exponentially with the thickness of the medium.

ABSORPTION COEFFICIENT, MASS. The quantity obtained by dividing the linear absorption coefficient (see **absorption coefficient, linear**) by the density of the absorbing medium.

ABSORPTION COEFFICIENT OF LIGHT, MOLAR. A constant that appears in one of the forms of statement of the **Law of Beer** (q.v.), which relates the light intensity at a selected frequency passing through a solution to the concentration of solute and the thickness of the absorbing layer. In the quantitative expression of Beer's law, $I = I_0 e^{-\alpha c d}$, I is the intensity of light transmitted and I_0 is the intensity of incident light (both for a given wave length); e is the natural logarithmic base; c is the concentration of the solution in moles per liter; d is the thickness of the transmitting layer; and α is the molar absorption coefficient.

ABSORPTION FACTOR. In any absorbing system, especially in the case of absorption of **radiation,** the ratio of the total unabsorbed radiation to the total incident radiation, or to the total radiation transmitted in the absence of the absorbing substance. Cf. **absorptivity.**

ABSORPTION LAGOON. An artificial pond, used as a basin for the disposal of industrial waste water. The size must be sufficiently great, in relation to the porosity of the soil, that the loss of water by evaporation and ground infiltration is at least equal to the average inflow.

ABSORPTION OF GASES. The solution of gases in liquids is termed absorption. Such solutions obey the **laws of Dalton** and **Henry** (q.v.) unless the dissolved gas reacts with the **solvent** or forms a **constant-boiling mixture** with it.

ABSORPTION OF LIGHT. When a compound beam of light is passed through a medium, one or more of the component **frequencies** may disappear, so that the light which issues from the medium is changed in composition. The frequencies which have disappeared are said to have been absorbed. The property of absorbing certain frequencies is characteristic of a large number of substances and is a function of their constitution.

ABSORPTION PAPER. A specially-prepared filter paper used in fat determination.

ABSORPTION SPECTRUM. See **spectrum, absorption.**

ABSORPTION TUBE. An apparatus for the **absorption of gases,** totally or selectively.

ABSORPTION VALUE. See **iodine value.**

ABSORPTION, UNILATERAL AND BILATERAL. The degree of **absorption of light** in absorbent media varies with the **wave length** of the light. When the absorption increases or decreases steadily with the wave length, the condition is termed unilateral absorption; when, however, there occurs a minimum absorption at a certain frequency or frequency range with increased absorption at higher or lower frequencies, the condition is termed bilateral absorption.

ABSORPTIVE POWER. A mathematical expression of the capacity of a substance to absorb another substance or form of energy: absorption being defined as the apparent disappearance of the second substance, or the form of energy, into the first substance. When applied to radiant energy, this term denotes the fraction of the **radiant energy** incident upon a surface which is absorbed, and transformed into heat. The reciprocal term is reflective power.

ABSORPTIVITY. The ratio of the **absorbance** to the product of concentration and length of optical path. It is the absorbance per **unit** concentration and thickness — i.e., the specific absorbance. (See **Law of Beer.**)

ABSORPTIVITY, MOLAR. The **absorptivity** expressed in units of liter/(mole cm.); the concentration is in mole per liter and the cell length in centimeters.

ABUNDANCE RATIOS. The proportions of the various **isotopes** making up a particular specimen of an **element.**

ABUNDANCE OF ELEMENTS. The percentage distribution of the **elements** in the earth or the earth's crust. Tables have been prepared showing separately this distribution of the elements in the solid portion of the earth (commonly in the crust), in the liquid portion of the earth (i.e., oceans, seas, etc.), and in the gaseous portion of the earth (i.e., the atmosphere).

Ac (1) Symbol for the element **actinium.** (2) The prefix *ac-*, commonly italicized, is used as an abbreviation for **alicyclic.** (3) Abbreviation for **acetyl, acyl,** or **acetate.**

ACCELERATION. The rate of change of the velocity of an entity or a chemical reaction. When the acceleration is positive the reaction is increasing in velocity; when negative, the reaction is diminishing in velocity.

ACCELERATOR. (1) In general, any agent which increases the speed of a chemical **reaction,** but the term is used today in a more restricted sense. It is applied, for example, to materials used in the rubber industry to increase the speed of **vulcanization** and to improve the quality of the product; to substances used to increase the effectiveness of catalysts, which are better known as **promotors** (q.v.); and to substances used to increase the speed of a penetrant, which are better known as **introfiers** (q.v.).

(2) A particle accelerator, an apparatus which gives charged particles high speeds and imparts large amounts of energy. See **betatron, cyclotron, synchrotron,** etc.

ACCEPTOR. (1) A substance whose **rate of reaction** with another substance is accelerated by the occurrence of a reaction in which the second substance is involved. (2) An **electron acceptor** (q.v.).

ACCESSORY FACTOR. See **vitamin.**

ACCOMMODATION COEFFICIENT. A quantity defined by the equation:

$$a = \frac{T_3 - T_1}{T_2 - T_1}$$

where T_1 is the temperature of gas molecules striking a surface which is at temperature T_2, and T_3 is the temperature of the gas molecules as they leave the surface, a is the accommodation coefficient. It is, therefore, a measure of the extent to which the gas molecules leaving the surface are in thermal equilibrium with it.

ACCUMULATION COEFFICIENT. A term sometimes used specifically to denote the rate of increase in the concentration of **adsorbed** molecules upon a surface, in relation to the concentration of that molecular species in the phase in contact with the surface.

ACCUMULATOR. See **cell, secondary.**

ACE-. A word fragment derived from **acetic,** as used in acenaphthene.

ACENAPHTHENYL. The radical $C_{12}H_9-$, derived from acenaphthene, H_2C——CH_2.

ACET-. Prefix denoting the presence of the radical $CH_3C\equiv$.

ACETAL. A dialkyl ether of a hypothetical **glycol.** These glycols, if they existed, would contain two hydroxyl groups attached to one carbon atom, as occurs in chloral hydrate. Acetals are formed by the union of two alcoholic molecules with one of an aldehyde.

ACETAMIDO. The radical CH_3CONH-.

ACETATE. An ester or salt of acetic acid containing the radical CH_3COO-.

ACETATE PROCESS. A process for the preparation of a synthetic fiber from cotton linters, wood pulp, and other sources of cellulose. The material is acetylated, dissolved in acetone, and forced through spinnerets into a coagulating solution.

ACETENYL. See **ethynyl.**

ACETIC. Related to acetic acid, CH_3COOH.

ACETIFIER. Equipment used for the production of acetic acid, commonly by accelerated oxidation of fermented organic materials.

ACETIMETER. An instrument for **acetimetry** (q.v.).

ACETIMETRY. The process of determining the acetic acid strength of a solution.

ACETIMIDO. The radical $CH_3C(:NH)-$.

ACETO-. Prefix denoting the presence of the radical CH_3CO-.

ACETOACETIC. Related to acetoacetic acid, $CH_3 . CO . CH_2 . COOH$.

ACETOACETIC ESTER CONDENSATION. See **condensation, acetoacetic.**

ACETOLYSIS. Reaction with a substance containing an **acetyl** group, as acetic acid or acetic anhydride. A decomposition reaction in which one of the reacting substances breaks up so as to yield an acetyl radical. Symbolically, a reaction of the type $AB + CAc = AAc + CB$, in which A, B, and C are various radicals, and Ac is the acetyl group, CH_3CO-.

ACETOMETER. Apparatus used in **acetimetry** (q.v.).

ACETONE NUMBER. The weight of a substance insoluble in acetone (CH_3—CO—CH_3), useful in estimating the degree of **polymerization** and certain other properties of organic materials.

ACETONITRIOLIC. Related to acetonitriolic acid, $CH_3(NO_2)C=NOH$.

ACETONYL. The radical CH_3COCH_2-.

ACETONYLIDENE. The radical

$$CH_3COCH=.$$

ACETOXY. The radical CH_3COO-.

ACETYL. The radical CH_3CO-.

ACETYL NUMBER OR VALUE. A constant determined in oil and fat analysis, by treating the sample with acetic anhydride, saponifying the product, and titrating the acetic acid obtained, with potassium hydroxide. Specifically, the number of milligrams of potassium hydroxide required to neutralize the acetic acid liberated by saponification from 1 g. oil, fat, or wax acetylated with acetic anhydride.

ACETYLACETONE REAGENT. A solution of 0.5 g. acetylacetone in 100 g. alcohol or water, used as a test reagent for ferric iron. An orange-red color, best obtained in slightly acid solution, indicates the presence of ferric iron.

ACETYLAMINO. The radical

$$CH_3CONH-.$$

ACETYLATION OR ACETYLIZATION.
A reaction or process whereby an **acetyl** radical, CH_3CO-, is introduced into an organic compound. Reagents often used for acetylation are acetic anhydride, acetyl chloride, acetic acid, etc.

ACETYLBENZOIC. Related to acetyl-benzoic acid, $CH_3 . CO . C_6H_4 . COOH$.

ACETYLENE. The compound $CH\!:\!CH$, which is the first member of the **acetylene series** (q.v.). The radical $=CHCH=$ is sometimes termed the acetylene radical, as in acetylene tetrachloride, $Cl_2CHCHCl_2$, tetrachloroethane.

ACETYLENE SERIES, ALKYNES. A series of unsaturated hydrocarbons having the general formula C_nH_{2n-2}, and containing a triple bond between two carbon atoms, as $-C\equiv C-$. The name of the series is that of the simplest member, acetylene $(HC\equiv CH)$. The members of this series are also designated by changing the "yl" termination of the alcohol radicals of like carbon content to "yne"; e.g., acet-ylene, C_2H_2, is thus named ethyne; propy-lene, C_3H_4, is named propyne; butylene, or crotonylene, C_4H_6, is named butyne, etc.

ACETYLFORMIC. See **pyruvic.**

ACETYLIDE. The anion C_2^- or HC_2^-, or a compound containing one of these anions.

ACETYLSALICYLIC. Related to ace-tylsalicylic acid, $CH_3COO . C_6H_4COOH$.

ACHROMATIC. Transmitting white light without resolution; or correcting such reso-lution as has already been caused by lenses and other optical elements or systems.

ACHROMATIC CONDENSER. See **con-denser, achromatic.**

ACHROMIC. Free from color.

ACHROMIC PERIOD. The time re-quired for complete **fermentation** of starch, as shown by its failure to produce a blue color with iodine. This period is used as a measure of enzymatic activity, with a standard starch solution, commonly 1%, in water.

ACI-. A prefix used to indicate the acid form, as aci-acetoacetic ester.

ACICULAR. Shaped like a needle.

ACID. I. **Any** substance that may ionize in solution to yield hydrogen ions, or, in more general terms, any substance that acts as a proton — hydrogen ion — donor. II. Any substance that contains hydrogen capable of being replaced by basic radicals. Acids are classified as monobasic, dibasic, tribasic, polybasic, etc., according to the number (one, two, three, many, etc.) of hydrogen atoms, replaceable by bases, contained in a molecule. They are further classified as (1) organic when the molecule contains carbon; (2) normal, if they are derived from nitrogen, phos-phorus, or arsenic, and contain three hy-droxyl groups; (3) ortho, meta, or para, according to the location of the carboxyl group in relation to another substituent in a cyclic compound, or (4) ortho, meta, or pyro, according to their composition.

ACID, ALICYCLIC. See **alicyclic acid.**

ACID AMIDE. Any organic compound containing the formamyl group $-CONH_2$. The general formula is $RCONH_2$, in which R is an organic radical in all cases except that of the simplest acid amide, formamide, $HCONH_2$.

ACID ANHYDRIDE. A compound de-rived from an **acid** by the elimination of one or more molecules of water from one or more molecules of the acid. The cor-responding acids may commonly be re-generated from them by the addition of water, the process being often accompanied by an evolution of heat. In the early periods of chemical theory, the acid an-hydrides were regarded as the true acids; e.g., SO_3 was considered the formula of sulfuric acid.

ACID CAPACITY. The neutralizing power of a base expressed as the number of hydroxyl ions available per molecule.

ACID CHLORIDE. A compound con-taining the radical $-COCl$.

ACID DYE OR STAIN. Dyes or stains of an acidic nature, or those which require an acid to set them. This term "acid stain" is often applied to water-soluble stains.

ACID EGG. An egg-shaped vessel of fitted heavy construction with appropriate piping which is used to move or raise corrosive liquids by the application of air pressure.

ACID ESTER. An ester of a polybasic organic acid in which one or more of the acidic hydrogen atoms are free, i.e., not replaced.

ACID-FORMING ELEMENT. See **element, acid-forming.**

ACID FUNCTION. **Proton** or **hydrogen ion.**

ACID GROUP, CARBOXYLIC. The radical –COOH.

ACID HALIDE. A compound containing the radical –COX, in which X is a **halogen** atom.

ACID, HALOID. An acid that contains no oxygen, but is composed of **hydrogen** and a **halogen** element.

ACID HEAT. The **heat of reaction** with an **acid**; a term used specifically to denote the heat formed in the reaction of organic compounds with sulfuric acid, an approximate measure of their degree of unsaturation.

ACID HYDRAZIDE. A compound containing the radical –CONHNH$_2$.

ACID HYDROGEN. The **hydrogen** atom in the acid group –COOH.

ACID ION. An ion which combines with one or more **protons** (hydrogen ions) to form molecules of **acids.**

ACID NUMBER. A term used in the analysis of fats or waxes to designate the number of milligrams of potassium hydroxide required to neutralize the free fatty acids in 1 g. of substance. The determination is performed by **titrating** an alcoholic solution of the wax or fat with tenth or half-normal alkali, using phenolphthalein as indicator.

ACID PEROXIDE. A compound containing the radical
$$-\overset{\overset{\displaystyle O}{\|}}{C}-O-O-\overset{\overset{\displaystyle O}{\|}}{C}-.$$

ACID PUMP. Any pump of resistant materials used to pump acids; or a special small pump used to fill or empty shipping containers used for acids.

ACID RADICAL. (1) The portion of the **acid** molecule apart from the hydroxyl group. Thus, –NO$_2$ is the acid radical of nitric acid. (2) The negative ion of an acid, i.e., SO$_4^=$, Cl$^-$.

ACID SALT. A salt of a polybasic acid, in which not all of the acidic hydrogen atoms have been neutralized.

ACID SOLUTION. A solution having a **pH** value less than 7.0.

ACID SULFATE. A compound containing the radical
$$\overset{\displaystyle O\qquad OH}{\underset{\displaystyle O\qquad O-}{S}}$$
or yielding the ion [HSO$_4$]$^-$.

ACID VALUE. The **acidity** of a **solution,** commonly in terms of **normality.** Also see **acid number.**

ACIDIC SOLVENT. A **solvent** which is strongly protogenic, i.e., which has a strong tendency to donate **protons** and little tendency to accept them. Liquid hydrogen chloride and hydrogen fluoride are acidic solvents, and in them even such normally strong acids as nitric acid do not exhibit acidic properties, since there are no molecules which can accept protons; but, on the contrary, behave to some extent as bases by accepting protons yielded by the dissociation of the HCl or the H$_2$F$_2$.

ACIDIFY. To increase the acidity of a **solution** or other system, commonly by adding acid, until the **pH** reaches a value less than 7.0.

ACIDIMETER. (Obs.) A term formerly applied to a form of **hydrometer** used to determine the specific gravity of acid liquids.

ACIDIMETRY. The process of determining the amount of an **acid** present in a sample by titration against a standard alkaline solution; or, more broadly, the system of analysis by **titration** whose end point is recognized by a change in **hydrogen ion** concentration.

ACIDITY. The amount of **acid** present, expressed for a solution either as the molecular concentration of acid, in terms of normality, molality, etc., or the ionic concentration (hydrogen ions or **protons**) in terms of **pH** (the logarithm of the reciprocal of the hydrogen ion concentration). The acidity of a **base** is the number of molecules of monoatomic acid which one molecule of the base can neutralize.

ACIDITY, DEGREE OF. The **hydrogen ion** concentration of an acid.

ACIDOPHILE. Easily stained by acid dyes. This term is used commonly in bacteriology, biology, and medicine.

ACID, PSEUDO. See **pseudo acid.**

ACIDULATE. See **acidify.**

ACIDYLATE. See **acylate.**

ACIDYLATION. See **acylation.**

ACI-NITRO. See **isonitro.**

ACI-NITRO COMPOUND. One of a class of **isomers** of true **nitro compounds,** in which one of the two oxygen atoms that are joined to the nitro nitrogen by a double bond has become joined by one valence bond to another atom or radical, as by a tautomeric shift within the molecule. The nitrogen atom is then joined to the molecule by a double, instead of a single bond.

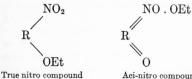

True nitro compound   Aci-nitro compound

Cf. **acid pseudo.**

ACKER PROCESS. A method of manufacturing sodium hydroxide from molten salt by **electrolysis,** with the addition of steam, and a cathode of molten lead.

ACKERMANN TEST FOR GUANIDINE. On heating 3 parts guanidine with 30 parts water, 6 parts 33% sodium hydroxide, and 4 parts benzenesulfonylchloride, white needles (m.p. 212° C.) are obtained.

ACKERMANN TEST FOR THIO-*p*-TOLYL-β-NAPHTHYLAMINE. With concentrated sulfuric acid a violet-blue color is formed, changed to red-violet by addition of nitric acid.

ACME BURNER. A special type of Bunsen burner.

ACREE-ROSENHEIM TEST REACTION. A test for **proteins** and tryptophane characterized by the formation of a purple ring in the interface between a solution of the sample containing formaldehyde and a layer of concentrated sulfuric acid.

ACRIDYL. The radical $C_{13}H_8N-$ (from acridine).

ACRINYL. The radical *p*-hydroxybenzyl, $OH-C_6H_4-CH_2-$.

ACROMETER. A special **hydrometer** used for oils.

ACRYL. The radical $-CH:CHCHO$ or $CH_2:C(CHO)-$.

ACRYLIC. (1) Related to acrylic acid, $CH_2:CH.COOH$. (2) Related to one of a series of **acids** of the type formula, $C_nH_{2n-1}COOH$.

ACRYLYL. The radical $CH_2:CHCO-$.

ACTINIC RAYS. **Radiations** effective in producing chemical changes and biological action. This term is usually applied to the violet and ultraviolet portion of the **electromagnetic spectrum** which consists of radiations relatively effective in causing these changes, as contrasted with radiation in the long wave-length portion of the spectrum.

ACTINIDE SERIES. A term derived by analogy to the **lanthanide series** (q.v.), to denote elements of mass number 89–98 inclusive, **actinium, thorium, protactinium, uranium, neptunium, plutonium, americium, curium, berkelium,** and **californium.** The justification for this grouping is found in the existence in the higher elements of (III) oxidation states similar to actinium, and (IV) oxidation states similar to thorium. Certain similarities also exist between the atomic spectra and magnetic properties in the two series.

ACTINIUM. Radioactive element. Symbol Ac. Atomic number 89. It is a member of the actinium family in which it occurs as an atomic species of mass number 227, and a half-period of 21.7 years. It is formed from protactinium by α-particle emission and emits in turn a β-particle to form radioactinium. Isotopes of actinium include mesothorium 2 which has a mass number of 228 and a half-period of 6.14 hours. It is a member of the thorium series being formed from mesothorium 1 by β-particle emission, and forms in turn, radiothorium, also by β-particle emission. Other actinium isotopes are known with mass numbers 222, 223, 224, 225, 226, 229, and 230. Valence 3.

ACTINIUM SERIES. See **element, radioactive series.**

ACTINOMETER. An instrument which measures the **intensity** of photochemically active radiation, by determining the **fluorescence** of a screen or the extent of a chemical decomposition reaction initiated by the incident radiation.

ACTINOMETRY. The determination of the photochemical intensity of light.

ACTINON. Isotope of radon. Symbol An. Atomic number 86. Mass number 219. Half-period 3.92 seconds. Produced as an emanation of actinium. See **radioactive elements.**

ACTION. As a physical concept, action is an expression for the product of twice the mean total **kinetic energy** of a system of particles, during a specified interval of time, by the length of the interval. It is expressed by

$$S = 2 \int^{t} E_K \, dt,$$

in which E_K is the kinetic energy and t_0 and t are the times of beginning and ending of the interval. **Planck's constant h** is the designation of the elementary quantum of action.

Maupertuis enunciated a law, known as the "principle of least action," which states that when a dynamic system is left to itself, unaffected by outside forces, so that its total energy cannot alter, any spontaneous change within the system takes place in such fashion that the action has the least possible value during the interval covered by the change.

In chemistry, the term action is frequently used as a synonym for **reaction** (q.v.).

ACTION, INTERMOLECULAR, PRINCIPLE OF. In determining the constitution of molecules by studying their decomposition products, it is assumed that radicals found in the cleavage products occupy contiguous positions in the original substance. This principle applies in such cases as the resolution of atropine into tropine and tropic acid.

ACTIVATED ADSORPTION. See **adsorption, activated.**

ACTIVATED ATOM. See **atom, activated.**

ACTIVATED MOLECULE. See **molecule, activated.**

ACTIVATED SLUDGE. A sediment produced by sewage, which contains various **bacteria** effective in breaking up organic materials, and therefore useful in breaking up and partly digesting fresh sewage, as in the activated sludge process.

ACTIVATION. The transformation of any material into a more **reactive** form, or into a form in which it functions more effectively, as in the **regeneration** of a metallic or inorganic catalyst, the transformation of an enzyme from inactive form to active form, the treatment of various forms of finely-divided silica or carbon to render them more adsorbent, and the **excitation** of atoms or molecules.

ACTIVATION ANALYSIS. A method of analysis by means of **isotopes** in which a small quantity of an element that is difficult to determine is exposed to activating particles (e.g., **deuterons** in a cyclotron or **neutrons** in a nuclear reactor). One or more of the stable isotopes of the element are thus converted to **radioisotopes** which can be detected by their characteristic radiations and half-lives. By treating similarly a comparison sample containing a known proportion of the given element the analysis can be made quantitative.

ACTIVATION ENERGY. The excess energy over the **ground state** which must be acquired by molecules in order to take part in a particular reaction. The most common source of this additional energy is believed to be energy interchange occurring in **collisions.**

ACTIVATION, ENTROPY OF. The difference in entropy between the activated complex and the reactants, all of which are referred to their standard states. This quantity occurs in certain equations developed in the application of the theory of absolute reaction rates.

ACTIVATION, HEAT. The difference in **heat content** between the activated complex and the reactants, all of which are referred to their **standard states.**

ACTIVATOR. A substance which renders a material or a system **active;** commonly a **catalyst** (q.v.). A special use of this term occurs in the **flotation process,** where an activator assists the action of the **collector** (q.v.).

ACTIVE. Potent, effective — especially with the connotation of in motion, or producing motion or change.

ACTIVE ALKALI. A general term in various processes for the total content of various alkali metal salts, often expressed as the equivalent NaOH that is available for a particular reaction.

ACTIVE CENTER. Atoms which by their position on a surface, such as at the apex of a peak or on the edge or corner of a crystal, share with neighboring atoms an abnormally small portion of their **electrostatic field** and, therefore, have a large residual field available for **catalytic** activity or for **adsorption.**

ACTIVE DEPOSIT. Solid radioactive material, deposited by radioactive emanations on surfaces in contact with them.

ACTIVE EARTH. An adsorbent prepared from a naturally occurring mineral, especially one that is found in a disintegrated solid state, i.e., as an earth.

ACTIVE IMMUNIZATION. Any process by which means of protection against bacteria or their products is elaborated by an organism.

ACTIVE MASS. Mass per unit volume, usually expressed in moles per liter (a concentration factor).

ACTIVE OXYGEN TEST. See **oxygen test, active.**

ACTIVE PRINCIPLE. The chemical compound, or group of compounds, to which the physiological action of a **drug** is attributed.

ACTIVITY. (1) The apparent effective **concentration** of a substance in a reacting system. In many relationships involving concentrations, it has been found that the use of actual concentrations does not give calculated results which agree with observed results, because of the attraction between molecules or ions due to the disturbing influence of interionic or intermolecular attraction. Consequently, in such calculations activities are used instead of concentrations. (2) The term activity is also applied to an expression of the magnitude of interionic forces. (3) Activity is also the rate at which an agent operates.

ACTIVITY COEFFICIENT. A multiplying factor applied to the **concentrations** of a **component** in a nonideal **solution** to convert to activities. This factor is a measure of the departure of the solution from ideal behavior.

ACTIVITY CONSTANT. In a reversible **reaction** which has reached equilibrium, the product of the activities of the substances produced by the direct reaction, divided by the product of the activities of the substances produced by the reverse reaction. Thus in the reaction,

$$mA + nB \cdots \rightleftarrows pC + qD \cdots$$
$$K = \frac{a_C^p a_D^q \cdots}{a_A^m a_B^n \cdots}$$

where K is the activity constant.

ACTIVITY, OPTICAL. See **optical activity.**

ACTOR. In coupled or sympathetic **reactions,** the substance which takes part in both primary and secondary reactions as distinguished from the "inductor" and the "acceptor," both of which take part in but one of the reactions.

ACYCLIC. Not of cyclic or ring structure.

ACYL. An organic radical of the general formula, RCO–. These radicals are also called acid radicals, because they are often produced from organic acids by loss of a hydroxyl group. Typical acyl radicals are acetyl, CH_3CO–, benzoyl C_6H_5CO–, etc.

ACYLATION. A reaction or process whereby an **acyl** radical (q.v.), such as acetyl, benzoyl, etc., is introduced into an organic compound. Reagents often used for acylation are the acid anhydride, acid chloride, or the acid of the particular acyl radical to be introduced into the compound.

ACYLOIN CONDENSATION. See **condensation, acyloin.**

ADAMANTINE COMPOUND. A compound having in its crystal structure an arrangement of atoms essentially that of diamond, in which every atom is linked to its four neighbors by covalent bonds. An example is zinc sulfide, but it is to be noted that the eight electrons involved in forming the four bonds are not provided equally by the zinc and sulfur atoms, the sulfur yielding its six valency electrons, and the zinc, two.

ADAMKIEWICZ TEST REACTION. Proteins dissolved in glacial acetic acid give a red-violet color and a green fluorescence when floated on concentrated sulfuric acid.

ADAMS-HALL-BAILEY REAGENT. A saturated aqueous solution of cobalt acetate and zinc acetate, which is then saturated with the mixture of the vapors obtained by treating copper with nitric acid. It is used as an analytical reagent for potassium and for sodium. With potassium, it gives a yellow precipitate, and with sodium, after filtration and the addition of uranyl acetate solution gives a yellowish-green precipitate.

ADAPTOR, ADOPTER. A piece of apparatus in the shape of a gradually narrowing tube, commonly bent in an obtuse angle, used to connect distillation and other apparatus, as a condenser and receiver.

ADATOM. A mobile, adsorbed atom.

ADDITION. See **addition reaction.**

ADDITION AGENT. A substance added to a process which, without entering into the main reaction, improves the quality or uniformity of the product.

ADDITION COMPOUND. See **compound, addition.**

ADDITION POLYMERIZATION. See **polymerization, addition.**

ADDITION REACTION. When two or more molecules react to produce but one product, the reaction is termed "addition" or, less commonly, a synthetical reaction. The direct union of carbon and hydrogen to produce acetylene or of sulfur and oxygen to produce sulfur dioxide are addition reactions.

ADDITIVE COMPOUND. See **compound, additive.**

ADDITIVE PROPERTY. A property of a system which is equal to the sum of the values of that property for the constituents of the system.

ADDITIVITY, PRINCIPLE OF. The properties of a solution of a strong **electrolyte** are the sum of the individual properties of its ions.

ADELOMORPHIC. Of indefinite structure.

ADHESION. In general, a condition in which two discrete entities or particles remain in close contact, or the force by which such a condition is maintained. Specifically, the term adhesion is often used in chemistry to denote the attraction between two unlike substances, as distinguished from **cohesion,** which is the internal force of attraction, molecular or otherwise, within a single substance or phase.

ADHESION TENSION. The work required to enlarge the surface between a solid and a liquid is called the adhesion energy, and it may be expressed as the adhesion tension in units of force per unit of surface.

ADIABATIC. Occurring without change in heat content, i.e., without gain or loss of heat by the system involved.

ADIABATIC CALORIMETER. See **calorimeter, adiabatic.**

ADIABATIC ELASTICITY. A term invented by Hugoniot to express the change of elasticity of the medium which is propagating an explosion wave, assuming that the medium is discontinuous in the vicinity of the wave.

ADIABATIC EXPANSION. Expansion without gain or loss of heat from outside the substance or system.

ADIABATIC PROCESS. Any process conducted without evolution or absorption of heat by the system involved.

ADIACTINIC. Not transmitting photochemically active rays.

ADION. An **ion** adsorbed on a surface that is held so that it is free to move on the surface but not away from it.

ADIPIC. Related to adipic acid, $COOH(CH_2)_4COOH$.

ADIPYL. The radical $-OC(CH_2)_4CO-$.

ADJACENT POSITION. In an organic compound having a **ring** structure, the position occupied by two or more **atoms** or **radicals** which are joined by **valence** forces to consecutive atoms in the ring.

ADJUVANT. A drug which assists the action of another drug.

ADLER TEST REACTION FOR PENTOSES. On heating a mixture of equal parts aniline (or toluidine) and glacial acetic acid with pentoses, an intense red color is obtained.

ADLER TEST REACTION FOR WOOD. On treatment with a hot solution of phenylhydrazine hydrochloride in glacial acetic acid, wood becomes green, and bark red to brown.

ADLER TESTS FOR BLOOD. (1) On acidulating with acetic acid an aqueous solution containing blood, and adding benzidine solution and hydrogen peroxide, a blue color is produced.

(2) Blood stains or spots on saturation with a solution of malachite green (leuco base form), and moistening with hydrogen peroxide, develop the green color of the dye.

Many modifications of these tests have been described.

ADRIAN TEST FOR NITRITE. Nitrites in acid solution give an orange-yellow color with guaiacol.

ADRIAN TEST FOR OIL OF WINE. On shaking with water, ether containing oil of wine gives a turbidity.

ADRIAN TEST REACTION FOR ALDEHYDES. To test ether for aldehydes, saturate with gaseous ammonia. A precipitate of aldehyde ammonia is positive. The ether must be neutral before testing.

ADSORBATE. A substance which is adsorbed.

ADSORBENT. A substance or material which adsorbs.

ADSORPTION. A process in which a substance or entity concentrates or holds another substance upon its surface. The absorbate is concentrated on the surface of the adsorbent by adhesive forces.

ADSORPTION, ACTIVATED. Chemisorption (adsorption involving forces of chemical nature) in which the activation energy is relatively high.

ADSORPTION ANALYSIS. See **analysis, adsorption.**

ADSORPTION, APOLAR. Adsorption of nonpolar substances on nonpolar media.

ADSORPTION CATALYSIS. Catalysis of a chemical reaction effected by **adsorption** of reactants on surfaces.

ADSORPTION, DISPLACEMENT. Displacement from a surface of one adsorbed substance by another.

ADSORPTION EQUILIBRIUM. Equilibrium between a substance that is adsorbed upon a surface, and the same substance in a solution or other medium that is in contact with the surface.

ADSORPTION EXPONENT. The exponential term n in the (classical) **adsorption isotherm** (q.v.).

ADSORPTION, HEAT OF. See **heat of adsorption.**

ADSORPTION INDICATOR. Dyestuffs or other chemicals which are used to detect the the end point of a precipitation **titration.** These substances are dissolved in the solution to be titrated and lend color to it. The end point of the titration is signaled by disappearance of the color from the solution, or a change of color in the solution, attributable to adsorption of the indicator by the precipitate.

ADSORPTION ISOSTERE. A graph showing the variation with temperature of the pressure required to keep a predetermined quantity of gas adsorbed on a given solid surface.

ADSORPTION ISOTHERM. A relationship between the mass of substance adsorbed at a given temperature and the mass of adsorbent. The Freundlich adsorption isotherm is of the form:

$$\frac{x}{m} = kp^{1/n}$$

in which x is the mass of gas adsorbed, m is the mass of adsorbent, p is the gas pressure, and k and n are constants for the temperature and system. Numerous isotherm equations have been proposed in the chemical literature in the last fifty years.

ADSORPTION, NEGATIVE. A phenomenon exhibited by certain solutions in which the concentration of solute is less in the surface than it is throughout the solution. This behavior is shown by solutes that increase the surface tension.

ADSORPTION, NONPOLAR. See **adsorption, apolar.**

ADSORPTION, ORIENTED. State of adsorption in which the adsorbed molecules are uniformly (or partially) ordered with respect to orientation.

ADSORPTION, POLAR. Adsorption of electrically unequal amounts of ions, so that the adsorbed film has an over-all electrical charge. Also adsorption chiefly attributable to attraction between polar groups of adsorbent and adsorbate.

ADSORPTION POTENTIAL. The energy change experienced by a molecule (ion) in passing from the gas (or solution) phase to the surface of the adsorbent.

ADSORPTION, PREFERENTIAL. See **adsorption, specific.**

ADSORPTION SPACE. The thickness of an adsorbed layer.

ADSORPTION, SPECIFIC. (1) Preferential **adsorption** of one substance over another. (2) Quantity of adsorbate held per unit area of adsorbent.

ADULTERANT. A substance of inferior quality or lower cost that is used in a mixture or other preparation. Its presence may be due to improper handling as well as to intentional addition. Thus, a dirty material is also considered adulterated.

ADULTERATE. To substitute one substance for another, partly or entirely. The term connotes a deterioration of the quality of the product caused by the substitution. The substitution may be due to dirt, i.e., to impurities present in the material because of careless handling or processing.

ADVECTION. Transfer of heat by convection.

AEOLOTROPISM. The property possessed by certain solids (as crystals) and some liquids, of exhibiting differences in the physical properties of a spherical portion of the body when it is tested in different directions. Cf. **isotropism.**

AEROBE. An organism whose metabolism demands free (uncombined) oxygen.

AEROBIC. Taking place through the agency of, and in the presence of, oxygen.

AEROBIC BACTERIA. Certain single-celled microorganisms that need gaseous oxygen for the maintenance of their vitality.

AEROBIOSCOPE. An apparatus for counting bacteria in air or other gases.

AERODYNAMICS. The science of gases in motion. Cf. **aerostatics,** the science of gases at rest (mechanical equilibrium).

AEROGEL. A colloidal solution of a gaseous phase in a solid phase, obtained usually by replacement of the liquid in the dispersed phase by air or gas.

AEROMETER. An instrument used to measure the density of gases.

AEROSOL. A colloidal system in which a gas, usually air, is the continuous medium, and particles of solid or liquid are dispersed in it.

AEROSTATICS. The science of gases at rest (mechanical equilibrium). Cf. **aerodynamics,** the science of gases in motion.

AFANASIEV TEST. To test for cyclopentadiene, mix 1 drop of the liquid with 1 ml. chloroform and 1 ml. glacial acetic acid, then add 2 or 3 drops sulfuric acid. A violet color is positive.

AFFINATION. A process in the sugar industry, in which the sucrose crystals obtained from the crude molasses are freed from residual molasses by treatment with a solvent and centrifuging.

AFFINITY, CHEMICAL. Barchusen in 1698 proposed this term to name the attractive force between elements by means of which compounds may be formed. The conception was extended by Thomsen and Bertholet, who thought that the heat evolved in a chemical reaction was a measure of the "affinity" of the substances involved in the reaction. A more recent view (Gibbs and Helmholtz) is that affinity is the **intensity factor** of chemical energy, the capacity factor being the equivalent weight of the element. The affinity determines the course of reaction in a mixture where many reactions are possible. Also termed chemical activity, avidity, intensity: or potential.

AFFINITY COEFFICIENT. See **reaction rate constant.**

AFFINITY CURVE. A graph obtained by plotting the heats of formation of various binary compounds of an element against the atomic number of the various elements with which it combines (or any regular arrangement of those elements).

AFTER-FLOW. The flow of a very viscous liquid or a plastic solid, which continues after the pressure causing it has been removed.

AFTER-GLOW. The emission of light or other **radiation** by a gas or other system persisting after the discharge, reaction, or other process causing it has terminated.

Ag Symbol for the element silver.

AGENT. A force or substance that acts to produce a change.

AGGLOMERATION. The gathering together of particles.

AGGLUTINATION. (1) The gathering of particles. (2) The clumping together of bacteria or cells, resulting often from their reaction with the corresponding immune or modified serum.

AGGLUTININ. One of a class of substances found in blood to which certain foreign substances or organisms have been added or admixed. As the name indicates, agglutinins have the characteristic property of causing agglutination, especially of the foreign substances or organisms responsible for their formation.

AGGREGATION. The gathering of particles, especially in the sense of their formation into larger entities.

AGGREGATION, STATE OF. A term used to denote the properties of a mass resulting from its physical condition, as solid, liquid, or gaseous.

AGGRESSIN. A product of bacterial **metabolism** which impairs the defensive mechanisms of the blood of the host.

AGING. Maturing with the passage of time. Natural aging takes place without addition of other substances, directed change of environment, or other intervention. Artificial aging involves such intervention to hasten ripening or to obtain the effects of aging in a shortened time, as in the case of alcoholic beverages.

AGITATOR. A stirrer or other device to start and maintain motion in fluids.

AGLYCONE. The noncarbohydrate portion of a glucosidic molecule. See **glucoside.**

AGON. The active portion of an **enzyme** molecule.

AGOSTINI TEST FOR MAGNESIUM. Add 2 drops of a saturated solution of thio-diphenylcarbazide to 10 ml. of the solution to be tested, then add a large excess of ammonia. A red color or precipitate on standing indicates the presence of magnesium.

AGRAZ TEST REACTION. A dilute solution of pyrrole, when mixed with a normal solution of iodine in potassium iodide and shaken with potassium hydroxide and ether, gives an intense blue color (violet with chloroform). Upon shaking the blue test-mixture with zinc dust, a green color is produced.

AGRESTINI TEST. A solution of alloxan or alloxantin in sulfuric acid, upon addition of a solution of pyrocatechol, gives a blue-green color which changes to green upon addition of water. Using resorcinol instead of pyrocatechol, a wine-red color is obtained, changing to indigo blue upon addition of water.

AGRICULTURAL CHEMISTRY. See **chemistry, agricultural.**

AGULHON SOLUTION. A solution of 0.5 g. potassium dichromate in 100 ml. concentrated nitric acid, used as a test reagent for certain reducing substances, such as alcohols, aldehydes, or carbohydrates. A blue color, changing to green on heating, is given by the various reducing substances.

AIR BATH. An apparatus providing a current of uniformly heated air used for controlling the temperature of a process, such as **drying.**

AIR COMPRESSOR. Mechanical apparatus for supplying air or other gases under increased pressure.

AIR CONDITIONING. The control of air temperature and humidity, and the removal of dust. The process is usually accomplished by scrubbing with water at lower temperatures and filtering.

AIR DRYING. Drying by the evaporative action of atmospheric air currents.

AIR ELUTRIATION. The same as **air separation** (q.v.).

AIR HORSEPOWER. The delivered power of a fan and compressor equal to the product of the rate of gas flow (in cubic feet per minute) and the pressure in pounds per square foot, divided by 33,000.

AIR LIFT. A method of elevating liquids through the medium of compressed air admitted by a small compressed air pipe into a larger pipe which dips into the liquid, and extends up to the tank or level to which the liquid is to be delivered.

AIR PREHEATER. An apparatus used to preheat air for use in an industrial or technological process, such as in a blast furnace or a steam-boiler furnace.

AIR PUMP. A mechanical appliance designed to move or compress air.

AIR SEPARATION. A process for the **classification** of particles by the action of air currents.

Al (1) Symbol for the element aluminum. (2) A suffix designating an **aldehyde** (q.v.).

ALABAMINE. The name that was assigned to the element of atomic number 85 when its discovery was claimed by the magneto-optic method (see **astatine**).

ALANYL. The radical $CH_3CH(NH_2)CO-$.

ALBEDO. (1) Whiteness or a white tissue or substance. (2) In photometry the ratio of the amount of radiation reflected by a surface to the amount incident upon it. (3) The ratio of the neutron current density out of a (nonsource) medium to the neutron current density into it.

ALBER STARCH TEST. The starch is shaken for 3 minutes with a mixture of 2 parts hydrochloric acid (sp. gr. 1.12) and 1 part water. Unadulterated arrowroot starch is unchanged; if wheat starch or potato starch is present, a gelatinous mass is formed.

ALBERGER PROCESS. A method of producing high-quality sodium chloride from crude brine by fractional crystalliza-tion of calcium sulfate that is present, and **flash evaporation** (q.v.) of the purified brine.

ALBERTI TEST. To test for solanine and solanidine, dissolve the material in 1 drop glacial acetic acid, add 1 or 2 drops concentrated sulfuric acid and then 1 drop 0.5% hydrogen peroxide or 1% formaldehyde. A purple-red color indicates the presence of solanine or solanidine.

ALBUMEN. The white portion of eggs, in either the liquid (fresh) or the dried form.

ALBUMIN. (1) One of a large class of **proteins** intimately associated with the structure of living organisms of which they compose the protoplasm. They are coagulated by heat and soluble in water. See **protein.** (2) A simple protein, having the formula, $C_{72}H_{112}N_{18}O_{22}S$, and occurring widely in Nature. It is the chief constituent of egg albumen and is characterized by coagulation on heating, content of sulfur, etc.

ALBUMIN, ACID. A modification of **albumin** which is insoluble in pure water but dissolves in dilute acids. A correlative modification, alkali albumin, is known.

ALBUMINATE. A compound of **albumin.**

ALBUMINOID. One of a class of **proteins** that are insoluble in neutral solvents.

ALBUMINOID AMMONIA. Ammonia obtained by decomposition of albuminous material. The quantity present is utilized in water analysis to determine the percentage of organic nitrogen in the sample.

ALBUMINOMETER. A graduated glass vessel used in the determination of **albumin.**

ALBUMOSCOPE. A glass tube used in conducting a ring test for **albumin.** A common method of performing this test is the superimposition of the solution to be tested upon concentrated nitric acid. The appearance of a white ring at the interface indicates the presence of albumin.

ALBUMOSE. (Peptone) A product obtained by the digestion of **proteins** with pepsin or dilute acids.

ALCHEMY. (1) Medieval chemistry. (2) A term applied to the ancient attempts to transmute the base metals into gold and silver and to prepare the panacea for all diseases or the elixir of life. The most famous alchemists were Geber, Albertus Magnus, Roger Bacon, Raymond Lully, Basil Valentine, Paracelsus, Libavius, and Glauber.

ALCHLOR PROCESS. A process for the purification treatment of lubricating oil, using aluminum chloride.

ALCOCK REACTION FOR CHRO-MIUM. On treatment with an excess of sodium hydroxide solution, and then with sodium peroxide, chromium salts form yellow chromates. Addition of acetic acid to the solution containing hydrogen peroxide yields a violet or blue color.

ALCOCK-WILKIN TEST REACTION. On heating 0.01 g. acetophenetidin with 5 ml. concentrated sulfuric acid a brown color is obtained, which turns to red upon addition of water and ammonia.

ALCOGEL. See **colloidal solutions.**

ALCOHOL. (1) The common name for ethyl alcohol (ethanol). (2) Any one of a class of organic substances derived from the aliphatic hydrocarbons by the substitution of one or more hydroxyl groups for an equal number of hydrogen atoms, except that in rare cases, and only where modifying constitutional influences are present, two hydroxyl groups or more are never united to the same carbon atom. The alkyl residue of the alcohol may be further substituted by aromatic nuclei, as in benzyl alcohol $C_6H_5CH_2OH$, thus forming the alcoholic derivatives of the carbocyclic series, but the alcoholic hydroxyl may not be directly united to a carbon atom which is a member of the aromatic ring, because in that case, the compound is considered a phenol, which has certain distinctive properties. The alcohols are named according to the Geneva plan by the substitution of ol for the final e of the parent hydrocarbon name: i.e., ethane — ethanol; propane — propanol. The number of hydroxyl groups is indicated by the insertion of numerical prefixes be-

tween the hydrocarbon root and the ol suffix: i.e., glycerol is propanetriol, glycol is ethanediol. In more complicated cases the position of the alcoholic groups is designated by the arabic numerals placed before the name of the compound.

Alcohols are classified, 1st, according to their content of hydroxyl groups as monatomic, diatomic, triatomic, etc., or monohydric, dihydric, trihydric, etc., if they have one, two, three, etc., hydroxyl groups of alcoholic character; 2nd, according to the environment of the carbon atom to which the alcoholic hydroxyl is united as primary, secondary, or tertiary. Primary alcohols are characterized by the grouping $-CH_2OH$; secondary alcohols by $=CHOH$; and tertiary alcohols by $\equiv COH$. It is evident that some compounds may contain all of these groups at once and so do not fall under any single one of the above classifications.

ALCOHOL ACID. An organic compound which contains alcoholic groups and either **carboxyl** or **sulfonic acid** radicals in the same molecule.

ALCOHOL ALDEHYDE. An organic compound containing both an alcoholic hydroxyl and an **aldehyde** radical (q.v.).

ALCOHOL AMINE. An organic compound containing both an alcoholic hydroxyl and an **amino** radical.

ALCOHOL, DENATURED. Ethyl alcohol containing sufficient methyl alcohol, acetone, methyl isobutyl ketone, hydroxybutyraldehyde, or other organic compounds to render it unsuitable for beverage use.

ALCOHOL KETONE. An alcohol which contains the **ketone** (carbonyl) group.

ALCOHOL PHENOL. An organic compound containing an alcoholic hydroxy radical in a side chain, and a hydroxyl radical attached to a carbon atom in a benzene ring.

ALCOHOLATE. A compound derived from an alcohol by replacement of the hydrogen in the hydroxyl group by a metal, commonly one that forms a strong base.

ALCOHOLIC FERMENTATION. The process of converting certain sugars, notably dextrose and fructose, into ethyl alcohol through the action of an enzyme.

ALCOHOLOMETER. A form of **hydrometer** graduated in percentages of absolute alcohol or in degrees of proof spirit or both, used to determine the alcoholic strength of mixtures of alcohol and water and commonly referred to a definite temperature, 15.6° C. or 60° F. Some forms of the instrument are equipped with a thermometer and table of corrections so that the reading at any temperature may be reduced to that at 15.6° C.

ALCOHOLYSIS. See **reaction, alcoholysis.**

ALCOHOMETRY. (Alcoholometry) The process of determining the alcoholic content of a mixture.

ALCOSOL. See **colloidal solutions.**

ALD-, ALDO-. A prefix derived from **aldehyde.**

ALDEHYDE. (1) Acetaldehyde. (2) Any one of a class of compounds derived from the primary alcohols by oxidation and characterized by the group –CHO. They are named (a) from the corresponding acids by combining the root of the acid with the word aldehyde, e.g., formaldehyde, butyraldehyde, and (b) according to the Geneva plan by substituting "al" for the final e in the name of the parent hydrocarbon, e.g., ethanal, butanal.

ALDEHYDE AMMONIA. One of a class of compounds formed by the condensation with ammonia of an **aldehyde.**

ALDEHYDE GROUP. The radical

$$-C\begin{smallmatrix} \diagup H \\ \diagdown\diagdown O \end{smallmatrix} \cdot$$

ALDEHYDE KETONE. A compound containing both the **aldehyde** group and the **ketone** group (q.v.).

ALDEHYDE REACTION, ANGELI. See **reaction, Angeli aldehyde.**

ALDEHYDES, STEPHEN PREPARATION OF. See **Stephen preparation of aldehydes.**

ALDIME. A compound containing the

$$-C\begin{smallmatrix} \diagup H \\ \diagdown\diagdown NH \end{smallmatrix}$$

group which may be derived from an **aldehyde** by replacement of the **carbonyl** oxygen by an **imido** group.

ALDOHEXOSE. One of a class of **sugars** that contain six carbon atoms and an **aldehyde** group; e.g., glucose, mannose.

ALDOKETENE. A compound containing

the $$\begin{smallmatrix} H \\ \diagdown \\ C=C=O \\ \diagup \end{smallmatrix}$$ group.

ALDOL CONDENSATION. See **condensation, aldol.**

ALDOPENTOSE. One of a class of **sugars** that contain five carbon atoms and an **aldehyde** group; e.g., arabinose, ribose.

ALDOSE. One of a class of **sugars** belonging to the monosaccharide group, and which contain an **aldehyde** group.

ALDOSE DEGRADATION, WOHL. See **Wohl aldose degradation.**

ALDOSIDE. A compound resulting from the union of an **aldose** and an **alcohol,** a **phenol** or other hydroxylated substance by the elimination of water. The true glucosides belong to this class, as do also the mannosides, galactosides, rhamnosides, arabinosides, xylosides, etc.

ALDOXANE. A condensation compound of an **aldol** and a **carbonyl** compound.

ALDOXIME. One of a series of compounds containing the group $$\begin{smallmatrix} \diagdown \\ C=NOH, \\ \diagup \end{smallmatrix}$$ or its tautomeric form.

ALEKSEEVKII TEST. Chloropicrin in aqueous solution, when reduced with metallic calcium, gives a red precipitate with β-naphthylamine and sulfuric acid.

ALEMBIC. A form of **retort** with a removable cap and neck used by early chemists and alchemists.

ALEUROMETER. A cylindrical apparatus used to measure expansion of the gluten in flour on baking.

ALIAMET TEST. In this test for copper, a solution of the metallic salt is added to a concentrated solution of sodium sulfite containing pyrogallol. A red-yellow to red color indicates the presence of copper.

ALICYCLIC. Pertaining to organic compounds which contain saturated rings, such as the **cycloparaffins,** or other **hydroaromatic** compounds.

ALICYCLIC ACID. One of a group of acids having a saturated ring in their molecular structures; e.g.,

$$CH_2 \diagdown$$
$$CH_2—CHCOOH,$$

which is cyclopropanemonocarboxylic acid.

ALICYCLIC NUCLEUS. An **hydroaromatic** ring.

ALIMARIN-FRIED REAGENT. A strongly-acid solution of phenylarsonic acid, containing tartaric acid, used in the determination of columbium and tantalum. White precipitates are produced.

ALIPHATIC. Pertaining to carbon compounds, or portions of carbon compounds whose carbon atoms are arranged in chains only.

ALIQUOT PART. A fractional portion of a sample or solution taken for analysis, of a size such that the results obtained may be calculated for the whole sample by a simple multiplication.

ALKALESCENT. Slightly alkaline.

ALKALI. A term that was originally applied to the **hydroxides** and **carbonates** of sodium and potassium but since has been extended to include the hydroxides and carbonates of the other **alkali metals** (q.v.) and ammonium. Alkali hydroxides are characterized by ability to form soluble soaps with fatty acids, to restore color to litmus which has been reddened by acids, and to unite with carbon dioxide to form soluble compounds.

ALKALI BUILDER. An alkali added to **soap** which increases the **alkalinity** of materials to be washed. Among the alkali builders used for this purpose are the following: caustic soda, soda ash, various soluble basic salts such as trisodium phosphate, sodium orthosilicate and various mixtures of some of the above substances.

ALKALI, FIXED. Sodium or potassium hydroxide.

ALKALI METAL. Any one of the elements **lithium, sodium, potassium, rubidium, cesium,** and **francium,** which constitute the first group of the periodic system.

ALKALI, VEGETABLE. An **alkaloid;** the term is also applied at times to potash or potassium carbonate.

ALKALI, VOLATILE. Ammonia; ammonium hydroxide.

ALKALIMETER. A laboratory apparatus for the determination of the carbon dioxide evolved from solids.

ALKALIMETRY. The process of determining the amount of an alkali present in a sample by titration against a standard acid solution, or, more broadly, the system of analysis by titration whose end point is recognized by a change in hydrogen-ion concentration. [Acidimetry (q.v.).]

ALKALINE. Exhibiting some or all of the properties of an **alkali** (q.v.); or an aqueous solution having an excess of **hydroxyl** over **hydrogen ions** (**pH** greater than 7.0).

ALKALINE EARTH METALS. The elements **barium, strontium,** and **calcium. Magnesium** is sometimes included.

ALKALINE EARTHS. Oxides of the alkaline earth metals. (See **metal, alkaline earth.**)

ALKALINE REACTION. Any reaction characteristic of **alkalies** (q.v.), as the changes in a substance or system which are brought about by increase of its **pH** to values above 7.0.

ALKALINITY. (1) Possessing properties of **alkalies.** (2) In aqueous solution having a **pH** of more than 7.0.

ALKALIZATION. The act of communicating **alkalinity** to a compound or system.

ALKALIZE. To render **alkaline.**

ALKALOIDS. Any member of a class of organic compounds characterized by content of nitrogen and the property of combining with acids to form salts. The term is now limited to basic substances derived from plants and excludes the simpler amino derivatives, as aniline, quinoline, propylamine, etc., which were formerly included in the classification. Certain other substances, i.e., the purine bases, as caffeine, theobromine, etc., although products of vegetable organisms, are not now included among the alkaloids. In *Organic Chemistry* by Whitmore (D. Van Nostrand Co., Inc.), the following classification of alkaloids is given:

Derivatives of aryl-substituted amines.
Examples: tyramine, ephedrine, adrenaline, benzedrine, neosynephrine.

Derivatives of pyrrole.
Examples: nicotine, hygrine, carpaine.

Imidazole derivatives.
Example: pilocarpine.

Derivatives of pyridine and piperidine.
Examples: ricinine, coniine, anabasine.

Complex alkaloids (containing condensed or fused ring systems).

All the complex alkaloids may be classified on the basis of whether nitrogen is present in one or more rings, and the presence of fused rings having two or three carbon atoms in common, or nitrogen atoms in common. By further detailing this structural classification, the complex alkaloids are grouped in the following categories.

Alkaloids containing pyrrole rings fused with other rings.
Examples: physostigmine, yohimbine, vasicine, gelsemine.

Tropine alkaloids.
Examples: ecgonine, cocaine, atropine, tropine, scopolamine.

Alkaloids containing a fusion of two piperidine rings.
Examples: pseudopelletierine, isopelletierine.

Lupine alkaloids.
Examples: sparteine, lupanine.

Berberine alkaloids.
Examples: berberine, emetine.

Cryptopine alkaloids.
Examples: cryptopine, protopine.

Quinoline alkaloids.
Examples: galipoline, dictamine, lycorine.

Cinchona alkaloids.
Examples: cinchonine, quinine, quinidine.

Isoquinoline alkaloids.
Examples: pellotine, sarsoline, anhalidine.

Papaverine alkaloids.
Examples: papaverine, homolaudanosine, codamine.

Phthalide isoquinoline alkaloids — narcotine alkaloids.
Examples: narcotine, narceine, hydrastine.

Aporphine alkaloids.
Examples: apomorphine, isothebaine, corydine.

Bis-benzylisoquinoline alkaloids.
Examples: bebeerine, trilobine.

Morphine and related alkaloids.
Examples: morphine, codeine, thebaine.

Other alkaloids.
Examples: solanidine, strychnine, brucine.

ALKALOID, CADAVERIC. See **ptomaine.**

ALKALOID REAGENT. See **alkaloidal reagent.**

ALKALOID, VEGETABLE. An **alkaloid** obtained from materials of vegetable origin.

ALKALOIDAL REAGENT. A substance or mixture of substances used to separate or detect **alkaloids,** as by precipitating them, by giving characteristic color reactions with them, etc. Representative alkaloidal reagents are solutions of phosphomolybdic acid, potassium mercuric iodide, tannic acid, and chloroplatinic acid.

ALKAMINE. A compound containing both the **alcoholic** hydroxyl group and the **amine** group.

ALKANE. One of the group of **hydrocarbons** of the paraffin series, e.g., methane, ethane, propane, etc.

ALKANIZATION. A term applied in the petroleum industry to a particular reaction. It consists of the condensation, usually catalytic, of isobutane and various butenes, to form trimethyl butene and isooctane.

ALKENE. One of a group of **hydrocarbons** having one double bond and the type formula C_nH_{2n}, e.g., ethylene, propylene, etc.

ALKINE. See **alkyne.**

ALKONE. One of a group of **hydrocarbons** which have the type formula C_nH_{2n-4}, as by the possession of one triple bond and one double bond, as in butone, pentone, hexone, etc. See also **terpenes.**

ALKOXIDE. One of a group of compounds in which a hydrogen atom of an **alcohol** or **phenol** hydroxide group is replaced by a metal.

ALKOXY. A radical of the type RO–, in which R is an **alkyl** radical.

ALKYL. A generic name for any organic group or radical formed from an **hydrocarbon** by elimination of one atom of hydrogen and so producing a univalent unit. The term is usually restricted to those radicals derived from the aliphatic hydrocarbons, those owing their origin to the aromatic compounds being termed "aryl." Usually, saturated radicals, such as methyl,

ethyl, propyl, etc., containing, respectively, one hydrogen atom less than the corresponding saturated hydrocarbons — methane, ethane, propane, etc. — are understood.

ALKYLATION PROCESS. In general, any process which results in the addition or the substitution of an alkyl group in a compound. Specifically, the term is applied to various methods, including both thermal and catalytic processes, for bringing about the union of paraffin hydrocarbons with olefins. The process is especially effective in yielding gasolines of high **octane number** and low boiling range (aviation fuels). The thermal method uses temperatures around 500° C., and pressures as great as 500 pounds per square inch; in the catalytic method, concentrated sulfuric acid is frequently used, at temperatures close to 0° C., as the catalyst.

ALKYLENE. Any radical related to an **alkene** by a difference of one hydrogen atom, e.g., the ethylene radical C_2H_3–, the propylene radical C_3H_5–, etc.

ALKYLIDE. A compound of one or more **alkyl** radicals and a metal.

ALKYLIDENE. A radical related to an **alkane,** or saturated aliphatic compound, by a difference of two hydrogen atoms, both from the same carbon atom, as ethylidene, $CH_3CH\diagdown$, propylidene, $CH_3CH_2CH\diagdown$, etc.

ALKYLOGEN. An **alkyl** ester of a halogen acid, as ethyl chloride; these compounds may also be regarded as the monohalogen substitution products of the aliphatic hydrocarbons, as monochloroethane.

ALKYLOLAMINE. An **aliphatic** compound containing both hydroxy (–OH) and amino (–NH₂) groups.

ALKYNE. One of a group of **hydrocarbons** having one triple bond, and the type formula C_nH_{2n-2}, e.g., acetylene, allylene, etc.

ALLAN-ROBINSON CONDENSATION. See **Kostanecki-Robinson reaction.**

ALLELOMORPH. (1) One of two or more **isomorphic** substances which consist of the same atoms having the same valences, but differing in their linkages. (2) The first of two or more **isomers** to be recovered or separated from a system.

ALLELOTROPISM. The property by virtue of which, under certain conditions, a tautomeric substance (see **tautomerism**) is partly converted into its isomeric form and an equilibrium is established, the proportion of each isomer present depending upon the temperature, the solvent, and the degree of dilution.

ALLEN AND SCOTT-SMITH TEST REACTIONS. Emetine and cephaeline give a blue color, changing to green, on mixture with a solution of ferric chloride. With **Froehde reagent**, emetine gives a dirty green color, and cephaeline a purple-red color.

ALLEN-MOORE CELL. An electrolytic cell used in the industrial production of chlorine and caustic soda from sodium chloride solution.

ALLEN TEST FOR PHENOL. A few drops of the liquid to be tested are mixed with hydrochloric acid and 1 drop concentrated nitric acid is added. A red color indicates the presence of phenol.

ALLEN TEST FOR PHENOL IN CREOSOTE. The creosote is mixed in a dry tube with an equal volume of collodion. The formation of a coagulum shows the presence of phenol.

ALLEN TEST OF VINEGAR. An extract of 2 g. logwood in 100 ml. boiling water is spotted on a porcelain plate, and 1 drop vinegar added. A color change from yellow to red, on drying, shows the presence of free mineral acids in the vinegar.

ALLEN TEST REACTION FOR STRYCHNINE. With manganese dioxide and concentrated sulfuric acid, strychnine gives a deep violet color.

ALLERGY. Abnormal sensitivity of an organism to an **antigen** (q.v.), or, in general, to a substance causing an **anaphylactic** (q.v.) reaction.

ALLIGATION. A simple mathematical method for calculating the correct proportioning of the ingredients of a mixture or, in general, the value of a property of a mixture from the values of that property in its components. It is based upon the formula

$$P_{xy} = \frac{xX + yY}{x + y}$$

in which P_{xy} is the value of a property of the mixture, X and Y are its values in the components, and x and y are the proportions of the components. It assumes, of course, no change in properties on mixing.

ALLO-. A prefix indicating close relation, often applied to one of two isomeric compounds. As used specifically, it designates the more stable of two **geometrical isomers.**

ALLOCHROMY. Any fluorescence, or re-radiation of light, in which the wave length (and hence color) of the emitted light differs from that of the absorbed light.

ALLOISOMERISM. See **geometrical isomerism.**

ALLOMERISM. A property of substances that differ in chemical composition but have the same crystalline form.

ALLOMORPHISM. A property of substances that differ in crystalline form but have the same chemical composition.

ALLOTRIOMORPHIC. Characterized by absence of typical crystal faces.

ALLOTROPE. One of the isomeric forms of an element. See **allotropy.**

ALLOTROPIC TRANSFORMATION. The change from one allotropic form to another. This change in form commonly associated with a change in energy, accompanied by absorption of heat, and occurring at a definite temperature (the transition temperature).

ALLOTROPY. (Allotropism) The isomerism of the elements (Richter). A property of certain substances existing in two or more modifications distinct in physical, and some chemical, properties. A good example of allotropy is furnished by carbon, which exists in three forms — amorphous carbon or lamp-black, graphite, and diamond — that differ in hardness, luster, specific gravity, and heat of combustion. The distinction here is due to differences in the bonding of the atoms in the solid.

ALLOTROPY, DYNAMIC. A class of allotropic phenomena in which the transition from one form to another is reversible but with no definite transition temperature. The proportions of the allotropes depend upon the temperature.

ALLOTROPY, ENANTIOMORPHIC. A class of allotropic phenomena in which the transition from one form to another is reversible and takes place at a definite temperature, above or below which only one form is stable, e.g., the alpha and beta forms of sulfur.

ALLOTROPY, MONOTROPIC. A class of allotropic phenomena in which the transition is irreversible. One allotrope is metastable at all temperatures, e.g., explosive antimony.

ALLOXAN REAGENT. A mixture of 2 g. of uric acid and 2 ml. of nitric acid is heated with 2 ml. water until clear, and diluted with water to a volume of 100 ml. A characteristic color reaction occurs with certain cations, such as those of magnesium, cadmium, and zinc, and also with glycine.

ALLOXANIC. Related to alloxanic acid, $NH_2 . CO . NH . CO . CO . COOH$.

ALLOXANTIN REAGENT. A solution of 1 g. alloxan in 100 ml. normal sodium hydroxide solution. It gives a characteristic blue color with ferric iron.

ALLOY. Any mixture or combination of metals formed by fusing the components together, as brass, bronze, type metal, etc. In practice the metal whose melting point is the highest is first fused and to it are then added the other components in the order of diminishing melting point. Where mercury is an ingredient the product is called an **amalgam** (q.v.). Alloys are to be regarded as mixtures of the metals rather than as compounds, although often metallic compounds are present in the mixture and may crystallize out; some alloys are solid solutions of one metal or metallic compound in another, others are mixtures of mutually insoluble metals. The melting point of an alloy is constant for a definite composition and is commonly lower than that of any of the components. Hydrogen and ammonium may form alloys.

ALLYL. The radical $CH_2:CHCH_2-$. For β-allyl, see **isopropenyl.**

ALLYLIC REARRANGEMENT. See **rearrangement, allylic.**

ALLYLTHIOUREA SOLUTION. A solution of 5 g. allylthiourea in 100 ml. water, used in testing for cadmium. One drop of the reagent and 1 drop 30% sodium hydroxide solution gives a yellow precipitate with 1 drop of the unknown solution, if it contains cadmium.

ALMÉN ALBUMIN SOLUTION. A solution of 5 g. tannic acid in 10 ml. 25% acetic acid and 240 ml. 50% ethyl alcohol. It gives a characteristic turbidity with urine containing albumin.

ALMÉN GLUCOSE SOLUTION. A solution of 10 g. Rochelle salt and 5 g. bismuth subnitrate in 250 ml. 35% potassium hydroxide solution. This reagent gives a characteristic black precipitate on boiling with urine containing glucose.

ALMÉN-SCHONBEIN SOLUTION. A mixture of equal volumes of tincture of guaiac and oxidized oil of turpentine. This reagent gives a characteristic blue ring upon contact with a solution containing blood.

ALMÉN TEST REACTION FOR CYANIDE. The solution to be tested is mixed with yellow ammonium sulfide and evaporated to dryness; then water and hydrochloric acid are added, followed by ferric chloride solution. An orange-red color is given if cyanide is present.

ALOY-LAPRADE REAGENT. A solution of 10 g. uranium nitrate in 60 ml. water, that is neutralized with ammonium hydroxide, and diluted with water to 100 ml. It gives a red color with phenols in neutral solution.

ALOY-RABAUT TEST. In this modification of the Lamal test, a few drops of methanol and a crystal of uranyl nitrate give a red color with morphine (if the morphine is present as its hydrochloride, uranyl acetate is used instead). Phenols give the same reaction.

ALOY REAGENT FOR ALKALOIDS. A neutral solution of uranium nitrate or acetate, which precipitates most alkaloids from solution.

ALOY TEST REACTION FOR MORPHINE. With a solution of uranium nitrate exactly neutralized with ammonia, morphine gives a characteristic red color.

ALOY TESTS FOR URANIUM AND HYDROGEN PEROXIDE. With hydrogen peroxide and solid potassium carbonate, uranium compounds give a red solution, and a red precipitate on addition of alcohol. This reaction is also used in testing for hydrogen peroxide.

ALOY-VALDIGUIÉ MORPHINE REAGENT. A solution of 1 ml. 0.1% formaldehyde in 100 ml. 1% aqueous uranium acetate solution. It gives characteristic colors with alkaloids in the presence of concentrated sulfuric acid — blue with codeine, violet with morphine, etc.

ALOY-VALDIGUIÉ STRYCHNINE REAGENT. A solution in 100 g. sulfuric acid of 2 g. ammonium uranate or 1 g. uranic oxide. It gives a violet color, changing to red, with strychnine.

ALOY-VALDIGUIÉ TEST FOR COPPER AND HYDROQUINONE. Heat 10 ml. of a solution of 0.2 g. hydroquinone in 100 ml. water, to which 20 drops 0.01 N hydrochloric acid has been added, for 20–30 seconds in a boiling water bath, then add 1 or 2 drops of the dilute solution to be tested. A rapidly deepening blue color indicates the presence of copper. The reaction can also be used for hydroquinone.

ALOY-VALDIGUIÉ TEST REACTION FOR FORMALDEHYDE, TRIOXYMETHYLENE AND METHENAMINE. To a mixture of 2 ml. concentrated sulfuric acid, 2 or 3 drops 1% alcoholic codeine solution and 1 drop 1% ferric acetate solution, add 1 to 3 drops of a dilute solution of the sample. An immediate blue color shows the presence of one of the above compounds.

ALPHA (A OR α). The first letter of the Greek alphabet, used as a prefix to denote (1) the carbon atom in a straight chain compound to which the principal group is attached, or a derivative in which a substituted group is attached to that carbon atom (α-); (2) in a polycyclic compound, a carbon atom closest to one of the carbon atoms shared by two rings, or a derivative in which a substituted group is attached to that carbon atom (α-); (3) in a heterocyclic compound, a carbon atom closest to the heterocyclic atom, or a derivative in which a substituted group is attached to that carbon atom (α-); (4) a stereoisomer of a sugar (α-); (5) the first isomer to be discovered of a series of isomers (α-), or one of a group of substances occurring together, of unknown constitution, as the α, β, and γ resins of *Cascara sagrada*; (6) a symbol for absorptivity of radiation (α); (7) a symbol for angle (α); (8) a symbol for the coefficient of linear expansion (α); (9) a symbol for thermal diffusibility (α); (10) a symbol for specific resistance of filter cake (α); (11) a symbol for angular acceleration (α); (12) a symbol for aperture in optics (α); (13) a symbol for attenuation constant (α); (14) a symbol for fine-structure or Sommerfeld constant (α); (15) a symbol for thermal coefficient of resistance (α); (16) a symbol for most probable speed (α); (17) a symbol for degree of electrolytic dissociation (α); coefficient of recombination (α). See also **alpha particles** and **alpha rays.**

ALPHA CHANGE. A nuclear change consisting of the emission of an α- particle.

ALPHA PARTICLES. Positively charged helium nuclei, in other words, helium atoms which have lost their two electrons. The term was applied originally to helium nuclei emitted, with high velocity, by radium and other radioactive substances.

ALPHA RAYS. A stream or beam of α-particles (helium atomic nuclei), moving at similar speeds and in roughly the same direction.

ALPHATOPIC. Pertaining to a relationship wherein the masses or composition of two nuclei differ by an α-particle.

ALPHYL. An abbreviation for alkylphenyl, or a radical which contains both an alkyl and a phenyl group, as $CH_3 . C_6H_4^-$ (methylphenyl or toluyl).

ALTERATIVE. A drug that stimulates **metabolism,** aids in restoring general health, or improves appetite without apparently influencing any particular organ.

ALTERNATION, LAW OF. See **law of alternation.**

ALTMAN SOLUTION. A mixture of equal parts of a 5% aqueous solution of potassium dichromate, and a 2% aqueous solution of osmic acid. It is used as a fixative.

ALTMANN SOLUTION. A volume of 100 ml. of a saturated aqueous solution of aniline, containing 20 g. acid fuchsin, used as a staining solution.

ALUDEL. A pear-shaped vessel open at both ends and arranged so that several such vessels may be fitted into one another in succession to form a series. Used in the sublimation of iodine, the distillation of nitric acid, etc.

ALUM. One of a class of double **salts** of the general formula $M'''_2(SO_4)_3R'_2SO_4 . 24 H_2O$, in which M may be any one of the three elements aluminum, iron, or chromium, and R may be either potassium, sodium, cesium, lithium, rubidium, thallium, silver, or ammonium. Alums crystallize in octahedra or cubes and have many other properties in common. The name of the class is taken from common alum, potassium aluminium sulfate, $K_2Al_2(SO_4)_4 . 24 H_2O$.

ALUM, PSEUDO. See **pseudo alum.**

ALUM TANNING. See **tanning process, alum.**

ALUMETIZE. To coat with aluminum, as by spraying the molten metal on a cleaned metal surface.

ALUMINATE, HYDROXO-. The anion $Al(OH)_4^-$, or a compound containing it.

ALUMINATE (META-). The anion AlO_2^-, or a compound containing it.

ALUMINATE (ORTHO-). The anion AlO_3^{3-}, or a compound containing it.

ALUMINIZE. The same as **alumetize** (q.v.).

ALUMINON SOLUTION. An aqueous solution of 1 g. of the ammonium salt of aurintricarboxylic acid in 1 liter of water, used in the colorimetric determination of aluminum.

ALUMINUM. Metallic element. Symbol Al. Atomic number 13. Atomic weight 26.97. Density 2.702. Specific heat 0.217. Melting point 658.7° C. Boiling point 1800° C. Valence 3. Aluminum forms but one series of compounds; oxide Al_2O_3; the hydroxide is amphoteric. It occurs naturally in the ruby and sapphire, as corundum, in emery, various clays, feldspar, mica, cryolite, and most crystalline rocks.

ALVAREZ CHOLIC ACID REAGENT. A solution, in 100 ml. of concentrated sulfuric acid, of 0.1 g. β-naphthol and 0.1 g. diphenylamine, used as a test reagent for cholic acid.

ALVAREZ NITRATE REAGENT. A solution, in 100 ml. concentrated sulfuric acid, of 1 g. resorcinol and 1 g. diphenylamine, used as a test reagent for nitrates and nitrites. On contact with crystals of the salts, the reagent gives a greenish yellow color with a blue border turning to orange-yellow upon addition of alcohol if nitrate is present, and with nitrite a dark blue color that changes to red upon solution in alcohol.

ALVAREZ REACTION FOR ACONITINE. If 1 mg. aconitine is heated on the steam bath with 8 drops bromine, then treated with 2 ml. fuming nitric acid, evaporated to dryness, treated with 1 ml. alcoholic potassium hydroxide, and evaporated again, a green color will result upon addition of 5 drops 10% cupric sulfate solution.

ALVAREZ REAGENT FOR COBALT, NICKEL, AND ZINC. A solution of 10 g. cobalt chloride in 100 ml. sulfurous acid, to which potassium cyanide solution is added to form the complex compound. It is used in analysis as a precipitant for cobalt, nickel, and zinc.

ALVAREZ REAGENT FOR NICKEL. A saturated solution of hydrogen chloride in ethyl ether. It precipitates nickel as its chloride, even in the presence of cobalt.

ALVAREZ REAGENT FOR ORGANIC ACIDS. A solution of 0.02 g. β-naphthol in 1 ml. concentrated sulfuric acid. It yields melts of characteristic colors when heated with certain organic acids, such as malic acid, tartaric acid, and citric acid.

ALVAREZ REAGENT FOR ORGANIC COMPOUNDS. A solution of 0.3 g. sodium peroxide in 5 ml. alcohol. Upon addition of chrysazolin, dioxyanthraquinone, rosolic acid, anthragallol and other organic compounds and dilution with water, characteristic colors are obtained.

ALVAREZ REAGENT FOR OSMIC ACID. A mixture of 2 ml. of a 1% aqueous solution of potassium iodide and 20 drops phosphoric acid. It gives a green color, soluble in ether, with osmic acid.

ALVAREZ REAGENT FOR POTASSIUM. A 5% aqueous solution of sodium amino-β-naphthol-sulfonate, which precipitates potassium.

ALVAREZ TEST FOR PYRUVIC ACID. Solutions of 5 g. α- or β-naphthol in 100 ml. concentrated sulfuric acid give characteristic colors with pyruvic acid. This test reaction is useful in the detection of pyruvic acid, with α- or β-naphthol and, conversely, in the detection of the naphthols, with pyruvic acid.

Am Symbol for the element americium.

AMADORI ARRANGEMENT. A shifting of an –O– linkage whereby an N-glucoside of an aldose sugar is converted into the amino derivative of the corresponding ketose.

AMAGAT UNITS. A system of units in which the unit of pressure is the atmosphere, and the unit of volume is the gram-molecular volume (22.4 liters at standard conditions).

AMALGAM. Any alloy containing mercury. The amalgams are formed by dissolving other metals in mercury, when combination takes place often with considerable evolution of heat. They are to be regarded as definite compounds of mercury with other metals, or as solutions of such compounds in mercury, and it has been shown that products which contain mercury and another metal in atomic proportions may be separated from amalgams.

AMALGAMATION. The process of forming an amalgam; applied in electrochemistry to the coating of electrodes with mercury, and in metallurgy to a process for separating silver and gold from other metals or rocky material.

AMANN SOLUTION. A solution of 2 g. sodium chloride, 2 g. mercuric chloride, and 4 g. succinic acid in 40 ml. water, 10 ml. glacial acetic acid, and 50 ml. ethyl alcohol. It is used as a test reagent for albumin.

AMBRIDGE TEST. A test of the permanence of paint films on the inner surfaces of steel vessels.

AMERICAN PETROLEUM INSTITUTE SCALE. An expression of the density of a liquid of the form:

$$\text{Degrees A.P.I.} = \frac{141.5}{s} - 131.5$$

in which s is the specific gravity of the liquid at 60° F., against water at 60° F.

AMERICAN PROCESS, ZINC OXIDE. A method of producing zinc oxide, in which oxidized ores are roasted with anthracite in intimate mixture, or in briquettes. Careful regulation of furnace temperature prevents mixing of the zinc oxide smoke with sulfur dioxide and other possible contaminants. Because the process starts from the ore, it is called the direct process. (See **French process, zinc oxide,** for the indirect method.)

AMERICIUM. Transuranic radioactive element. Symbol Am. Atomic number 95. Americium of mass number 241 has been produced by bombardment of plutonium with neutrons in the chain-reacting uranium-graphite structure. Plutonium 241 is first formed, and it yields americium 241 by beta decay. The nuclear reaction is:

$$\text{Pu}^{239}(n,\gamma)\text{Pu}^{240}(n,\gamma)\text{Pu}^{241} \xrightarrow{\beta^-} \text{Am}^{241}$$

This americium has been isolated, and has been found to have a half-period of 475 years. It is an α-emitter, yielding neptunium 237; in fact these two atomic species are members of the new fourth series of radioactive elements (the **Neptunium Series**) (q.v.). There are other isotopes of americium, of mass numbers 237, 238, 239, 240, 242, 243, and 244. Valences: 2, 3, 4, 6.

AMES DIAL. An apparatus for determining film thickness, especially of paints and similar coatings.

AMIC. Amido; for example, an amic acid is an amido-acid. As an illustration, amidosulfuric acid, $HO \cdot SO_2 \cdot NH_2$, is called sulfamic acid.

AMICI PRISM. A combination of **prisms** whereby a beam of light is dispersed into a spectrum without **mean deviation.**

AMICRON. A name applied by Zsigmondy to individual disperse particles invisible under the ultramicroscope whose size is about 10^{-7} cm. They act as nuclei for the formation of submicrons which are about five times as large.

AMIDATION. The formation of an **amide,** or any reaction by which it is effected.

AMIDE. A generic term for various organic compounds derived from ammonia by replacement of one or all of its three hydrogen atoms by radicals. The term is properly restricted to compounds that contain acyl residues; other substances should be referred to the class of amines but this strict classification is not always followed. (1) The acid amides are derived from ammonia by replacing hydrogen by acyl groups and are classified as primary, secondary, or tertiary, as one, two, or three hydrogen atoms are replaced, yielding compounds having the type-formulas NH_2OCR, $NH(OCR)_2$, or $N(OCR)_3$. Mixed amides may be formed by substituting, in primary or secondary amides, other acyl groups for the remaining ammoniacal hydrogen. (2) The **amino acids** (q.v.). (3) Cyclic amides. See **lactams.**

AMIDE, ALKYL. A compound in which one or both of the hydrogen atoms of a primary **amide** have been substituted by **alkyl** groups. The type formula is RCONHR′ or RCONR′R″.

AMIDE, HYDROXY (OR OXY). An **amide** containing a **hydroxy group.**

AMIDE, KETO. An **amide** containing a **keto group** on an α-carbon atom, as RCOCONH₂.

AMIDE, METAL. (Also called simply amide, or ammonobase.) A compound in which one of the hydrogen atoms of ammonia is replaced by a metal, as sodamide, $NaNH_2$, lead amide, $Pb(NH_2)_2$, etc.

AMIDINES. Derivatives of the **amides** in which the **carbonyl** oxygen is replaced by the **imide** group.

AMIDO-. The radical $-NH_2$, properly in acid groups only. However, some writers use the terms amido- and amino- synonymously, and even prefer to use the amido-form in naming aromatic compounds containing –NH$_2$, e.g., amidobenzene.

AMIDO ALDEHYDE. A compound containing both the **amino** and the **aldehyde** groups.

AMIDO KETONE. A compound containing both the **amino** and the **ketone** groups.

AMIDOGEN. An obsolete term for NH$_2^-$, especially in inorganic compounds.

AMIDOPHOSPHATE. The anion PO$_3$(NH$_2$)$^-$, or a compound containing it.

AMIDOSULFATE. See **sulfamate**.

AMIDOXALYL. See **oxamyl**.

AMIDOXIME. One of a group of compounds derived from the **amidines** by substitution of hydroxyl for an hydrogen atom of the **amido** or **imido** group, i.e., ethenylamidoxime,

$$CH_3 . C \overset{N . OH}{\underset{NH_2}{\diagup}} .$$

AMIDOXYL. The same as **hydroxylamino** (q.v.).

AMINATION. The formation of an **amine**, or the introduction of an **amino** group into a molecule.

AMINE. A generic term for various of organic compounds which may be formed by substituting **alkyl** or **aryl** groups for the hydrogen atoms of ammonia. They are classified (1) as primary, secondary, or tertiary according to the number (one, two, or three) of hydrogen atoms so replaced, (2) as simple or mixed, in the cases of secondary and tertiary amines, if the substituents are all of the same or of different kinds of alkyls or aryls. Thus, methylamine, CH$_3$NH$_2$, is a primary amine; dimethylamine, (CH$_3$)$_2$NH, a secondary amine; trimethylamine, (CH$_3$)$_3$N, a tertiary amine, and ethylmethylamine,

C$_2$H$_5$—NH—CH$_3$ is a mixed amine. Quaternary amines consist of four alkyl or aryl groups attached to a nitrogen atom; they are therefore substituted ammonium bases. Secondary amines are also called imines; and tertiary amines, nitriles. Diamines and triamines are compounds containing respectively, two or three NH$_2$ groups, or substituted NH$_2$ groups.

AMINE SEPARATION, HINSBERG METHOD OF. See **Hinsberg method of amine separation**.

AMINO-. The radical –NH$_2$.

AMINO ACID. One of a class of organic acids characterized by substitution of an **amino** group in the **alkyl** residue. This distinguishes them from the amides in which the amino group replaces hydroxyl in the carboxyl group. Amino acids are named from the parent acid and from the position of the amino group as alpha, beta, gamma, delta, etc., the Greek letter being prefixed to the name of the compound. The count is begun with the first carbon atom of the alkyl residue and proceeds away from the carboxyl group. Thus H$_2$NCH$_2$CH$_2$CH$_2$CH$_2$COOH is called δ-aminovaleric acid. Called also amido acids.

AMINO ACID SYNTHESIS. See **Strecker synthesis**.

AMINOKETONE. A compound of the type formula RNHCHO or the type formula RNHCOR′.

AMINOLYSIS. The conversion of **diazoamido** compounds into aminoazo compounds in the presence of a small amount of the hydrochloride of an aromatic base. Diazoaminobenzene (1,3-diphenyltriazene), C$_6$H$_5$N$_2$NH . C$_6$H$_5$, thus rearranges to p-aminoazobenzene, C$_6$H$_5$N$_2$C$_6$H$_4$NH$_2$. In this rearrangement the azo nitrogen preferably enters in the para position to the amino group, but, when this is occupied — as with the derivatives of p-toluidine — the azo nitrogen will sometimes combine in the ortho position to the amino group. The velocity of the aminolysis is a function of the strength of the acid present.

AMINOPHENOL. A **phenol** having an –NH₂ group attached to one of the carbon atoms of the benzene ring.

AMINOSULFATE. See **sulfamate.**

AMMER-SCHMITZ TEST REACTION. The presence of calcium, strontium, or barium, in dilute, slightly alkaline solution, is shown by a yellow-green color produced with tannic acid. The color changes rapidly to blue, and then fades to yellow again.

AMMETER. An electrical instrument used to measure the strength of **current.** It is usually a **galvanometer** provided with a scale that is graduated in amperes. The milliammeter is an ammeter of great sensitiveness and indicates the thousandth part of an ampere.

AMMINE. A metal-ammonium compound — e.g., the cobalt-ammino salts, cuprammonium salts, etc. — in which NH₃ molecules are combined with metallic salts. See **compound, coordination.**

AMMINO. A combining term indicating content of the –NH₂ group in inorganic combination.

AMMONATE. A compound containing ammonia of crystallization. It is analogous to a hydrate.

AMMONIA. A compound of nitrogen and hydrogen, NH₃, the simplest member of the class of **amines** and the prototype of the organic bases.

AMMONIA OXIDATION PROCESS. A process for the production of oxides of nitrogen, or nitric acid itself, by the catalytic atmospheric oxidation of ammonia. Commonly a mixture of about 10% NH₃ by volume with air is passed over the catalyst at temperatures from 700 to 900° C. The first stage in the oxidation yields nitric oxide (NO), which is subsequently oxidized to NO₂, which reacts with water to yield nitric acid.

AMMONIA-SODA PROCESS. See **Solvay process.**

AMMONIATE. Certain compounds of ammonia, as the **ammines** (q.v.), or compounds which are used as fertilizers.

AMMONIUM. The radical –NH₄, which forms salts analogous to those of the alkali metals.

AMMONO-SYSTEM. A dispersed system, commonly an **ionic solution,** in liquid ammonia.

AMMONOLYSIS. A process analogous to **hydrolysis** in which ammonia reacts with a compound to form an **amide** or **amine** and other products, commonly by the breaking of a valence bond in a compound, usually with the addition of an –NH₂ group to one fragment, and a hydrogen atom to the other. It is commonly regarded as a double **decomposition reaction** (q.v.) involving ammonia as reactant.

AMODEL REAGENT. A solution of 1 g. quinine sulfate in 40 ml. glycerol, to which is added a solution of 2 g. potassium iodide in 50 ml. water. This reagent gives an orange precipitate with an acidified solution prepared from the ignited residue from urine, if bismuth is present.

AMORPHOUS. Noncrystalline. Devoid of regular structure.

AMOXY. The radical CH₃(CH₂)₄O–.

AMPERE. The unit of electric **current.** One ampere delivers one coulomb in one second. The international ampere is defined as "the unvarying electric current which, when passed through a solution of nitrate of silver in water, deposits silver at the rate of 0.00111800 gram per second." The ampere is one-tenth of the **c.g.s. unit** of current.

AMPÈRE-HOUR. An electrical unit of quantity, being the amount of electricity represented by a current of one **ampere** flowing for one hour.

AMPÈRE RULE. To determine the direction in which the needle is deflected by a conductor carrying a current in a given direction.

Imagine yourself swimming in the wire

in the direction of the current and facing the magnetic needle; the north pole will then be deflected toward your left hand and the south pole in the opposite direction.

AMPÈRE THEOREM. The **magnetic field** due to an electric **current** flowing in any circuit is equivalent at external points to that due to a simple magnetic shell the bounding edge of which coincides with the conductor and the strength of which is equal to the strength of the current.

AMPHI-. Meaning literally, on both sides, or present in both forms, and used commonly to designate certain **isomers,** as amphi-naphthoquinone, in which the oxygen atoms occupy **amphi-positions.**

AMPHI-POSITION. The position of two substituent groups on atoms diagonally-opposite in β-positions on symmetrical fused rings, as the 2,6 or the 3,7 positions (which are identical) of a naphthalene ring.

AMPHICHROIC. A term applied to substances that exhibit two colors, or to indicators having two colors that are complementary.

AMPHIPROTIC SOLVENT. A **solvent** that acts to give **protons** as well as to accept them; in other words, it may behave as both an acidic and a basic solvent.

AMPHOLYTE. A substance capable of acting either as a **base** or **acid;** in other words, it acts either as a **proton** acceptor or a proton donor, and forms salts with acids and with bases.

AMPHOLYTOID. A **colloid** that is **amphoteric,** adsorbing either hydrogen or hydroxyl ions.

AMPHOTERIC. Capable of acting either as an **acid** or as a **base,** i.e., as a **proton** donor or acceptor, according to the nature of the environment. Thus, aluminic hydroxide dissolves in acids to form salts of aluminum, and it also dissolves in strong bases to form aluminates.

AMPLITUDE. The limiting, or greatest displacement, of a train of waves, or of **an** entity undergoing **vibratory motion.**

AMPOULE. A sealed glass container used for substances that must be kept out of contact with the atmosphere, such as very volatile liquids, small quantities of gases, and sterile solutions.

AMTHOR TEST REACTION. Caramel in alcoholic solution gives a brown precipitate when paraldehyde is added.

AMYL. The radical $CH_3(CH_2)_4-$.

AMYL (TERT.). The radical
$$(C_2H_5)(CH_3)_2C-.$$

AMYLIDENE. The radical
$$CH_3(CH_2)_3CH=.$$

AMYLOLYSIS. Conversion of starch into sugar. It is essentially a hydrolysis and splitting reaction, or series of reactions, and is usually effected by heating with dilute acids, or by **enzyme** action.

AMYLOLYTIC. Any agent capable of **hydrolyzing starches,** particularly the amylase enzymes.

ANA-POSITION. The position of two substituent groups on atoms diagonally opposite, in α-positions on symmetrical fused rings, as the 1,5 or the 4,8 positions (which are identical) of the naphthalene ring.

ANABOLISM. The assimilation of nutrient material by the living organism to build or restore its tissues and other living matter.

ANACONDA PACKED-CELL PROCESS. A modification of the **chamber process** for the production of sulfuric acid in which the chambers are replaced by packed towers, each divided into compartments by partitions. Cooling is effected by circulation of large amounts of dilute acid.

ANAEROBIC BACTERIA. Certain single-celled **microorganisms** that can maintain their vitality only in the absence of free oxygen.

ANALEPTIC. A drug that has a tonic effect upon the organism, i.e., one that restores health in a general and somewhat indefinite manner.

ANALGESIC. A drug that relieves pain either by its effect upon the sensory nerve fibers, or by direct action on the nerve centers.

ANALGIC. Without pain.

ANALOGUE. One of a group of chemical compounds that are similar in structure, but different in elementary composition.

ANALYSIS. The resolution of the compound or mixture into its elements or atomic groups, or the determination of the identity and proportion of its constituents or components. The correlative of synthesis. Various terms are applied to analytical processes employed for different purposes; they are described below.

ANALYSIS, ACTIVATION. See **activation analysis.**

ANALYSIS, ADSORPTION. Separation of substances by differential **adsorption.**

ANALYSIS, BIOCHEMICAL. The analysis of material derived from, or associated with, living organisms.

ANALYSIS, BLOWPIPE. Analysis by use of the blowpipe to produce various reactions of metals, metallic compounds, and ores on heating, with or without added substances.

ANALYSIS, COLORIMETRIC. A method of quantitative analysis based upon the measurement of the intensity of color of a solution of the substance to be determined which is present as a colored ion, colored molecule, or a colored derivative prepared for the purpose.

ANALYSIS, ELECTRO-. A process of analysis wherein the electric current is used to effect the separation of the elements, as copper, nickel, cadmium, zinc, silver, etc., or by indicating differences in potential or conductivity to determine the amount of substance present.

ANALYSIS, ELEMENTARY. See **analysis, ultimate.**

ANALYSIS, GAS. The process of analyzing a gaseous mixture, or of determining a substance by causing an evolution of gas through a chemical reaction with the substance in question and measuring the volume of the gas so evolved.

ANALYSIS, GRAVIMETRIC. See **analysis, quantitative.**

ANALYSIS, ISOTOPIC DILUTION. See **isotopic dilution analysis.**

ANALYSIS, MICRO. (1) Analysis on a very small scale, employing minute quantities of reagents and special apparatus; or, (2) the estimation of minute amounts of a substance; or, (3) analysis with use of the microscope, either to observe analytical processes or to study the microstructure of substances for purposes of identification.

ANALYSIS, NEPHELOMETRIC. The determination of the quantity of a substance, or of a component or constituent of it, by measure of the light **transmission** of a suspension. The essential determination is, in other words, one of turbidity.

ANALYSIS, ORGANIC. See **ultimate analysis.**

ANALYSIS, POWDER METHOD OF. See **powder method of analysis.**

ANALYSIS, PROXIMATE. The separation into and determination of the classes of **components** of a mixture. In this process no attempt is made to determine the elementary composition of the various components. Commonly the moisture, ash, alcohol extract, petroleum ether extract, water extract, hydrochloric acid extract, resins, starches, reducing sugars, protein, fat, free acids, esters, etc., are reported.

ANALYSIS, QUALITATIVE. The process of determining the nature of the various **elements** or simple **compounds** present in a mixture or compound without regard to the quantity of such elements present.

ANALYSIS, QUANTITATIVE. The process of determining the quantity of any or all **elements** present in a given **compound** or of the **components** of a mixture.

ANALYSIS, SPECTRUM. The qualitative or quantitative determination of elements or compounds (usually simpler compounds) by their characteristic radiations as observed by a **spectroscope,** or as recorded by a **spectrograph.**

ANALYSIS, ULTIMATE. A quantitative elementary analysis. This term is used commonly by the organic chemist to denote an analysis for the determination of the quantities of the **elements** in a chemical substance, in contrast with a **proximate analysis** (q.v.).

ANALYSIS, VOLUMETRIC. Analysis by **titration** with standard solutions.

ANALYTICAL CHEMISTRY. See **chemistry, analytical.**

ANALYTICAL GAP. In spectroscopy, the region between the two electrodes of the source in emission spectroscopic analysis; also called the electrode gap.

ANALYZER. (1) The **Nicol prism** situated in the eyepiece of a **polariscope.** (2) The first tower of the **Coffee still.** (3) An indicating device used in analytical control operations.

ANAMORPHISM. The process of modification of rocks and geological structures in general by physical processes.

ANAMORPHOSIS. An optical process which produces a distorted image.

ANAPHRODISIAC. A counter-aphrodisiac (see **aphrodisiac**).

ANAPHYLAXIS. A physiological reaction attributable to the effect upon an organism of repeated injection, ingestion, or assimilation by other means of a specific substance, commonly a protein, and characterized by marked increase in sensitiveness to subsequent doses. (Contrast **immunity.**)

-ANCE. A suffix meaning a property of a device or body; e.g., resistance, capacitance, transmittance, and absorbance.

ANCHORING. One of a number of processes resulting in the physical, or possibly chemical, attachment of organic molecules, as those in biochemical processes, in dyes or drugs, etc.

ANDERSON TEST REACTION FOR PAPAVERINE. A solution of papaverine in dilute nitric acid gives a dark red color and a yellow crystalline precipitate upon addition of concentrated nitric acid.

ANDERSON TEST REACTION FOR PYRIDINE BASES. Pyridine chloroplatinate, when boiled with water, forms a precipitate of golden leaflets.

ANDR-, ANDRO-. Prefix meaning relating to man or male, as in androsterone.

ANDRADE SOLUTION. A 0.5% aqueous solution of acid fuchsin made alkaline just past the color change with normal sodium hydroxide. This solution is an indicator used in the preparation of culture media.

ANDRÉ REAGENT FOR ALKALOIDS. An aqueous solution of potassium dichromate, which precipitates many alkaloids.

ANDRÉ TEST REACTION FOR QUININE. Upon treatment with chlorine and ammonia, a solution of quinine is colored green, changing to blue and then to red upon addition of acid.

ANDREASCH TEST REACTION. When ferric chloride and ammonia are added, a solution of cysteine hydrochloride becomes red-violet in color. This reaction is also used in testing for iron.

ANELECTRODE. The anode.

ANEMOMETER. An apparatus for measuring gas velocity, or sometimes pressure, especially that of air.

ANEROID BAROMETER. See **barometer, aneroid.**

ANESTHETIC. A drug that causes loss of sensation in a particular part of the body (local anesthetic), or which causes loss of consciousness (general anesthetic).

ANG-. This prefix denotes an angular displacement of the rings in the structure of a substance.

ANGELI-RIMINI REACTION. A reaction given by most **aldehydes.** Upon reacting with the sodium salt of nitrohydroxylamine, aldehydes give hydroxamic acids which, in turn, give purple colors with ferric chloride. This is the Angeli reaction. In the Rimini reaction, the aldehyde is heated with *N*-benzene sulfonylhydroxylamine to produce the hydroxamic acid.

ANGLE OF REPOSE. The maximum angle at which discrete solid material, such as sand, grain, ore, coal, etc., will hold its position without tending to slide.

ANGLE OF SLIP. The angle included between the direction of the applied force and the surface of **shear** during the **plastic flow** of a solid body.

ÅNGSTROM. (ANGSTROM.) A unit of length equal to $1/6438.4696$ of the wave length of the red line of Cd. This is almost, but not exactly, 10^{-8} cm. or 10^{-10} meter; the

$$RCHO + HON{=}NO_2Na \rightarrow RC\overset{\displaystyle OH}{{=}}NOH + NaNO_2.$$

$$RCHO + HONH{-}SO_2C_6H_5 \rightarrow RC\overset{\displaystyle OH}{{=}}NOH + C_6H_5SO_2H.$$

ANGELI TEST REACTION FOR HYDROXYLAMINE. On heating with sodium nitroprusside and sodium hydroxide solution, a solution of hydroxylamine gives a fuchsin-red color.

ANGELI TEST REACTION FOR INDOLE. On fusion in a glass tube with anhydrous oxalic acid, indole or its aliphatic homologues give a red melt that is soluble in acetic acid.

ANGELICO TEST REACTION FOR AROMATIC HYDROXYALDEHYDES. Various aldehydes in aqueous solution give a fuchsin-red color with concentrated sulfuric acid and *Atractylis* glucoside.

ANGER-WONG TEST. A spot test for phosgene, in which 1 drop of the solution to be tested is placed in a microcrucible, and a little phenylhydrazine cinnamate is added, followed after 5 minutes by 1 drop 1% cupric sulfate solution. A red-violet color indicates the presence of phosgene.

ANGLE OF DEVIATION. The angular change in direction of a ray of light, or other **electromagnetic radiation,** upon entering another medium.

difference is not significant in applied spectroscopy. (This unit may ultimately be based upon the green 5460 line of Hg^{198}.) Symbol Å or A.

ANHARMONICITY. (1) The term mechanical anharmonicity refers to a mechanical vibration in which the **restoring force** acting on the system does not vary linearly with the displacement of the system from its **equilibrium** position. (2) A phenomenon to which the term electrical anharmonicity is applied occurs in the calculation of the intensities of **infrared bands.** This phenomenon is a departure of the variation of **dipole moment** with internuclear distance from a strictly linear relationship.

ANHYDRIDE. A substance formed from another by the withdrawal of water, and from which the first substance may be reformed by the addition of water. (See **acid anhydride.**)

ANHYDRIDE, BASIC. An anhydride that forms a **base** upon reaction with water.

ANHYDRIDE, INNER. A substance formed by withdrawal of the elements of water from the same molecule, with the formation of a ring structure.

ANHYDRO-. This prefix denotes abstraction of water, as in anhydroglucose.

ANHYDROUS. Not containing water in substance. Dry. Said of exsiccated salts, e.g., burnt alum. It is to be noted that sugar and other substances which contain oxygen and hydrogen in the proportions to form water may yet be anhydrous.

ANILIDE. A compound formed from an aromatic **amine** by substitution of one or more **acyl groups,** or occasionally other groups, for hydrogen in the amino group. Referred especially to those compounds formed from aniline, as acetanilid, but the term may be extended to include all of such substances.

ANILINE THIOCYANATE REAGENT. A mixture of 20 ml. of a 5% aqueous solution of ammonium thiocyanate, with 18.6 g. aniline; 5 N hydrochloric acid is added until the emulsion clears, then water is added to make the volume 100 ml., and ethyl alcohol is added until the solution is again clear. This reagent gives a yellow-brown color with copper.

ANILINO. The radical C_6H_5NH-.

ANION. An ion which deposits on the anode. That portion of an electrolyte which carries the negative charge and travels against the conventional direction of the electric current in a cell. Within the catagory of anions are included all the nonmetallic ions and the acid radicals, as well as the hydroxyl ion. In electrochemical reactions they are designated by a minus sign placed above and behind the symbol, i.e., Cl^- or SO_4^-, the number of minus signs indicating the magnitude, in electrons, of the electrical charge carried by the anion.

ANIONIC CURRENT. That portion of the electric current carried by the anion.

ANIONOTROPHY. See **ionotropy.**

ANISAL. See **anisylidene.**

ANISIC. Related to anisic acid, p-CH_3O . C_6H_4 . $COOH$.

ANISOMERIC. Not **isomeric** (q.v.).

ANISOTONIC. Not **isotonic** (q.v.).

ANISOTROPIC. Nonisotropic, and thus having different optical or other physical properties in certain parts or directions.

ANISOTROPIC LIQUID. A liquid in the **mesomorphic** state, which is also called a liquid crystal. It possesses the properties of true liquids, such as the ability to flow, but it is doubly refracting and gives interference patterns in polarized light, as do anisotropic crystals. However, anisotropic liquids do not possess any of the usual crystalline properties, and hence the term liquid crystals is misleading.

ANISOTROPIC SUBSTANCE. A substance in which the measured values for optical or physical properties depend on the direction with respect to the crystal axes.

ANISOTROPY FACTOR. A factor that appears in an expression of the magnitude of the effect called **circular dichroism,** or differential absorption of right- and left-circularly polarized light by an optically-active medium. The relationship is:

$$g = (\kappa_l - \kappa_r)/\kappa$$

in which g is the anisotropy factor (also called the dissymmetry factor), κ_l and κ_r are the absorption indices for left- and right-circularly polarized light, and κ is the absorption index for ordinary light.

ANISOYL. The radical p-$CH_3OC_6H_4CO-$.

ANISYL. The radical $CH_3OC_6H_4-$, which is more commonly called methoxyphenyl. The term anisyl is sometimes used for **methoxybenzyl** (q.v.).

ANISYLIDENE. The radical

$$p\text{-}CH_3OC_6H_4\text{---}CH{=}\!=.$$

ANNEALING. A process for decreasing the hardness and brittleness of certain crystalline materials, such as alloys, glass, etc., by heating past certain definite temperatures and cooling them relatively slowly.

ANODE. The positive **electrode** of a cell; the electrode by which the current conventionally enters the cell; the electrode to which the anions travel and upon which they are deposited.

ANODIC OXIDATION. An electrochemical process in which articles are given a thin coating of oxide, usually to retard corrosion, by connecting them as anodes in an oxidizing electrolyte.

ANODIZE. To apply a process of **anodic oxidation** (q.v.), usually by connecting as an **anode** the object to be so processed, in an oxidizing **electrolyte.**

ANODYNE. A drug that reduces or overcomes the sensation of pain.

ANOLYTE. The liquid near the **anode** during **electrolysis.**

ANOMALOUS DISPERSION. A discontinuity or number of discontinuities in the relationship between the **refractive index** of a medium and the **wave length** of radiation passing through it, this relationship being normally an inverse proportionality. These discontinuities correspond to waves or bands in the absorption **spectrum** of the medium.

ANOMALOUS VALENCE. See **valence, anomalous.**

ANOMALY OF STRONG ELECTROLYTES. The **Arrhenius theory of ionization** (q.v.) is quite satisfactory for predicting the properties of dilute solutions of strong electrolytes, but it fails for their concentrated solutions. The **Debye-Hückel Theory** resolves this difficulty by recognizing that strong electrolytes are nearly completely ionized in water solution, and that there are practically no unionized molecules present. Instead, it is considered that the free ions become bound by acquiring an ionic atmosphere which reduces their **mobility.**

ANOMALY, OPTICAL. See **optical anomaly.**

ANOMER. An **isomeric compound,** generally of a sugar, which differs only in the

relative position of two atoms or groups, usually a hydrogen atom and a hydroxyl group.

ANSELMIER TEST. A test for curcuma in rhubarb, in which 0.1 g. of the powder is shaken for 1 minute with 20 drops olive oil, then placed in drops on white filter paper. A characteristic yellow ring is given by curcuma.

ANTACID. A drug which counteracts acidity or neutralizes acids.

ANTAGONISTIC DRUG. A drug that opposes, or partly or entirely counteracts, the physiological action of another drug.

ANTALKALINE DRUG. A drug that partly or entirely neutralizes alkalies.

ANTARTHRITIC. A drug that relieves arthritis.

ANTH-, ANTHO-. Relating to flowers, e.g., anthocyanin.

ANTHELMINTIC. A drug used to rid the intestinal tract of worms.

ANTHOCYAN. One of a class of flower pigments, commonly those of blue or red flowers.

ANTHOCYANIN. One of a class of **glucosides** of various **plant pigments** (q.v.); the anthocyans.

ANTHONY STAIN. A two-solution stain for capsules, consisting of (1) a 1% aqueous solution of crystal violet; and (2) a solution of 20 g. of cupric sulfate in 80 ml. of water.

ANTHOXANTHIN. One of a group of **glucosides** of various yellow **plant pigments** (q.v.).

ANTHR-, ANTHRA-. (1) Relating to coal, e.g., anthracite. (2) Relating to anthracene, e.g., anthraquinone.

ANTHRACOMETER. A gas-analysis apparatus for determining carbon dioxide.

ANTHRALENE. The radical $-C_{14}H_8-$, which is derived from anthracene and has 14 isomers.

ANTHRANOYL. The radical

$$o\text{-}NH_2 \cdot C_6H_4 \cdot CO-.$$

ANTHRAQUINONYL. The radical $C_{14}H_7O_2-$, which is derived from anthracene and has 2 isomers.

ANTHRYL. The radical $C_{14}H_9-$, which is derived from anthracene and has 3 isomers.

ANTI-. A prefix denoting opposite or opposed to, as *anti*-oxidant; specifically, it denotes one of two geometrical **isomers** in which certain atoms or groups are on opposite sides of a plane, as *anti*-benzaldoxime.

ANTIBACTERIAL. A drug or other substance that opposes or retards the growth of **bacteria**.

ANTIBIOTIC. An agent, or a chemical substance or product, generally or specifically destructive to living organisms, especially to **bacteria**. Most commerical antibiotics are derived from **molds,** as products of their metabolism.

ANTIBODY. A substance elaborated in animal organisms to overcome the effects of bacterial toxins and other foreign substances in the organism.

ANTICATALYST. See **catalyst, negative.**

ANTICATHODE. A metallic electrode or target placed in a **vacuum tube** in the path of the rays from the **cathode.**

ANTICHLOR. A substance which combines with, or neutralizes, the action of chlorine.

ANTICOAGULIN. A substance that prevents **coagulation.**

ANTIDIM. A substance that prevents the **condensation** of liquids on solid surfaces in the form of drops.

ANTIDOTE. Any substance or material used to counteract the noxious action of a **poison** when ingested into the animal organism. Antidotes may be mechanical, chemical, or physiological; mechanical when they cause emesis, chemical when they react with the poison to produce insoluble or harmless compounds, or physiological when they directly antagonize and neutralize the poison through the normal operation of the organism.

ANTIEMETIC. A drug that prevents vomiting.

ANTIENZYME. One of a group of substances analogous to the antitoxins which are produced by the organism following the injection of various **enzymes** into the blood. These antienzymes are able to inhibit the normal action of the enzymes from which they are formed to a remarkable extent and, like the antitoxins, are selective in their action. Antibodies for many enzymes have been prepared including the enzymes trypsin, pepsin, lipase, emulsin, urease, lactase, tyrosinase, thrombase, and rennin.

ANTIFREEZE. (1) A substance added to a material or to a system to prevent freezing. (2) Specifically, a water soluble substance, such as ethylene glycol, glycerol, or ethyl alcohol, added to the water in the radiator of an internal-combustion engine to prevent freezing at low external temperatures.

ANTIGALACTIC. A drug or other substance that reduces the secretion of milk.

ANTIGEN. An agent that brings about the formation of **antibodies** when injected into an organism.

ANTIHEMOLYTIC. An agent that prevents the destruction, or loss from the organism, of red blood corpuscles.

ANTIKNOCK. A substance commonly added to the fuel of an internal combustion engine to prevent premature excessively-rapid and irregular combustion of the fuel-air mixture. The "knocking" propensities of various fuels vary widely with their chemical structures and are expressed by their "octane rating" (q.v.).

ANTILYSIN. A substance elaborated by the animal organism to counteract the **lysins** produced by bacterial metabolism.

ANTIMER. One of a pair of substances having the same plane structural formula, but showing a difference in spatial configuration such that the space formula of one substance of the pair is the mirror image of the other. The chief difference in properties is optical — i.e., in the direction of rotation of the plane of polarized light.

ANTIMONATE (HYDROXO-). The anion $Sb(OH)_6{}^-$, or a compound containing it.

ANTIMONATE (META-). The anion $(SbO_3)_n{}^{n-}$, or a compound containing it.

ANTIMONATE (ORTHO-). The anion $SbO_4{}^{3-}$, or a compound containing it.

ANTIMONATE (PYRO-). The anion $Sb_2O_7{}^{4-}$ or $H_2Sb_2O_7{}^-$, or a compound containing one of these anions.

ANTIMONIC. (1) A compound of pentavalent antimony. (2) Relating to antimonic acid (ortho-), H_3SbO_4; to antimonic acid (meta-), $HSbO_3$; or to antimonic acid (pyro-), $H_4Sb_2O_7$.

ANTIMONITE. The anion $(SbO_2)_n{}^{n-}$ (meta), or a compound containing it.

ANTIMONO. The group $-Sb:Sb-$.

ANTIMONOUS. Containing trivalent antimony.

ANTIMONY. Metallic element. Symbol Sb (Stibium). Atomic number 51. Atomic weight 121.76. Density 6.68. Specific heat 0.0503. Melting point 630° C. Boiling point 1380° C. Valences 3, 4, and 5. Antimony forms three series of compounds. Its common ore is a sulfide, named stibnite. Antimony is frequently found in association with other metals.

ANTIMONY ELECTRODE. An electrode of metallic antimony that has sufficient antimony oxide (Sb_2O_3) on its surface to function as an oxide electrode for the measurement of **pH.**

ANTIMONYL. The radical SbO–.

ANTINEPHRITIC. A drug used to treat diseases of the kidneys.

ANTINEURALGIC. A drug used to treat neuralgia.

ANTINEURITIC. Preventing neuritis. This term is usually applied to thiamine, or its hydrochloride, named **vitamin B₁.** Deficiency of this vitamin causes the development of polyneuritis in experimental animals.

ANTINEUTRINO. An energy-carrying particle whose formation is postulated in the processes supposed to occur when a **positron** is emitted by an atomic nucleus. In this process a **proton** is transformed into a **neutron,** a positron, and a third particle of zero mass and charge which accounts for the energy distribution among the positrons and is called an antineutrino. The use of this term does not assert a difference between this particle and the **neutrino** (q.v.) which is postulated to accompany the conversion of a neutron into a proton.

ANTIOXIDANT. A substance used to retard the oxidation of another substance or group of substances. Antioxidants are widely used in formulating industrial products.

ANTIPHLOGISTIC. (1) A drug which retards the spread of inflammation. (2) Designating a theory proposed by Lavoisier directly contradicting the older **phlogiston** (q.v.) theory.

ANTIPODE. See **enantiomorph.**

ANTIPYRETIC. A drug used to reduce body temperature in fever.

ANTIPYROTIC. A drug used to treat burns.

ANTIPYROYL. The radical

$$\overline{CO} . N(C_6H_5) . N(CH_3) . C(CH_3):CCO-,$$

derived from antipyric acid.

ANTIPYRYL. The radical

$$\overline{CO} . N(C_6H_5) . N(CH_3) . C(CH_3):C-,$$

derived from antipyrine.

ANTIRACHITIC. A drug or substance used to prevent rickets.

ANTISCORBUTIC. A substance effective in the treatment of scurvy. Such substances have been shown to owe their action to their content of **vitamin C** (ascorbic acid).

ANTISCORCH. A substance used to retard the catalytic activity of rubber **accelerators** during processing.

ANTISEPTIC. A drug or other substance used to oppose **sepsis** by its action upon microorganisms.

ANTISERA. The blood sera which is drawn from animals that have been injected with organisms against which immunity is desired.

ANTISKINNING AGENT. A substance used to prevent the skinning of various **varnishes.** Antiskinning agents are usually phenolic compounds such as guaiacol and catechol.

ANTISPASMODIC. A drug used to decrease or prevent spasmodic or violent contractions of the voluntary muscles.

ANTI-STOKES LINES. Lines, in fluorescence or Raman **spectra** of molecules attributable to the emission of radiation of a shorter wave length, and hence higher energy, than the exciting radiation.

ANTISUDORIFIC. A drug that reduces perspiration.

ANTI-SYN ISOMERISM. See **isomerism, syn-anti.**

ANTITHROMBIN. A substance or group of substances in the blood that act to oppose its **coagulation.**

ANTITOXIN. A substance produced by the organism following the injection of, or elaboration of, **toxin,** derived from pathogenic bacteria, into the blood. These substances appear to combine with and neutralize the corresponding toxin and so immunize the organism against it, but they are inactive toward other toxins. Ehrlich considered this as due to an asymmetric configuration so that only those antitoxins which are constituted similarly to a certain toxin can unite with it. (See **Danysz effect.**)

ANTIZYMOTIC. A substance that prevents, inhibits, or retards **fermentation,** and is frequently used for that purpose in medicine, in food products, etc.

ANTONOFF RULE. The tension at the interface between two saturated liquid layers which are in **equilibrium** is equal to the difference between the individual **surface tensions** against air or vapor of the two saturated solutions.

ANTOZONE. (Obs.) Schönbein's term for a hypothetical form of active oxygen.

ANTOZONIDE. An oxide produced by "antozone," i.e., the peroxides of hydrogen, potassium, sodium, and others.

APERIENT. A drug or other substance that has mild purgative action upon the intestinal tract.

APHRODISIAC. A drug or other substance that stimulates sexual interest.

A.P.I. DEGREES. See **American Petroleum Institute Scale.**

APO-. A prefix denoting formation from, or relationship to, another compound, as apomorphine.

APOTHECARIES' SYSTEM. A system of weights and measures based upon a troy pound of 373.241 grams. The pound in this system contains 5760 grains, and the table of weights is as follows:

20 grains = 1 scruple (℈)
3 scruples = 1 dram (ℨ)
8 drams   = 1 ounce (℥)
12 ounces = 1 pound (lb.)

The table of measures is as follows:

60 minims (ɱ) = 1 fluid dram
8 fluid drams = 1 fluid ounce
16 fluid ounces = 1 pint (pt.)

The pint is equivalent to 473.16 cubic centimeters.

APPARATUS. The various equipment used in a laboratory or plant to carry out the various chemical reactions, synthetic operations, analytical tests, etc. The term covers in general all equipment, including that used to measure, control, and conduct, as well as simple containers.

APPARENT EQUILIBRIUM. When the velocity of a reaction is so small that it appears to remain unchanged with time, it is in a state of apparent, but not real, **equilibrium.** It differs from true equilibrium in that it is not re-established automatically after the system has been disturbed.

APPELIUS-SCHMIDT REAGENT. A mixture of 5 g. cinchonine in 100 ml. water, to which sulfuric acid is added until a clear solution is obtained, which is diluted with water to a volume of 1 l. The reagent is used in testing tanning extracts for sulfite-cellulose, which is indicated by the appearance of a dark-brown precipitate upon addition of the reagent to the sample, which has previously been treated with hydrochloric acid and boiled.

APPLICATOR. Any means, such as a device or apparatus, for the local application of a drug or medicinal preparation.

APROTIC SOLVENT. A solvent which is neither a **proton acceptor** nor a **proton donor.**

AQUA. Latin word for water.

AQUATE. The salt of an aquo acid.

AQUILINA SOLUTION. A solution of platinic chloride used in testing for alkali iodides. It is added to the solution to be tested, and a wine-red color indicates the presence of alkali iodides.

AQUOBASIC SALT. A basic **salt** formed by **hydrolysis.**

AQUO-ION. A complex ion containing one or more H_2O molecules.

AQUO-SYSTEM. A system **in which** water is the continuous **phase.**

AR-. A prefix meaning **aromatic.**

ARABITIC. Related to arabitic acid, $CH_2OH(CHOH)_3COOH$.

ARACHIDIC. Related to arachidic acid, $C_{19}H_{39}COOH$.

ARALKYL. An **alkyl group** containing a substituted **aryl group.**

ARBORESCENT. Tree-like.

ARBUSOW REARRANGEMENT. A method of formation of phosphonic acid esters, starting from trialkyl phosphites and alkyl halides.

$$P(OR')_3 + R''X \rightarrow R''PO(OR')_2 + R'X.$$

ARC. (1) A curved line. (2) A discharge of electricity between electrodes.

ARC FURNACE. A furnace heated by the electric arc.

ARC LAMP. An electric lamp consisting of two **electrodes,** by means of which an electric arc is maintained to yield light.

ARC, MERCURY. An electric arc that passes through mercury.

ARC PROCESS, BRADLEY. An old process for the **fixation** of atmospheric **nitrogen.** The air is passed rapidly through a number of small electric arcs, which heat it to a temperature at which nitric oxide is formed from some of the oxygen and nitrogen in the air. After rapid cooling of the reaction mixture, the nitric oxide in it is further oxidized to a mixture of oxides of nitrogen, which are absorbed in water to yield nitric acid. (See **Birkeland-Eyde process.**)

ARC SPECTRUM. See **spectrum, arc.**

ARC SPRAYING. A process for the spraying of metal that has been melted by the electric arc.

ARCHETTI TEST. A test for caffeine or uric acid, in which the material to be tested is added to a solution of potassium ferricyanide in nitric acid and heated to boiling. A precipitate of Prussian blue indicates the presence of caffeine or uric acid.

ARCHIMEDES PRINCIPLE. (1) On immersion in a liquid, a body will undergo an apparent loss of weight equal to that of the liquid displaced. Since the volume of liquid displaced is that of the body, this principle is applied in determining volumes and densities of bodies and of the substances of which they are composed. (2) The pressure exerted by gases on bodies immersed in them is transmitted equally in all directions.

ARENE. An aromatic **hydrocarbon,** i.e., any hydrocarbon in which at least one benzene ring is present. Examples: benzene, butylbenzene, naphthalene, dihydroanthracene, pyrene.

AREOMETRIC METHOD. The method of determining the **specific gravity** or **specific volume** of a liquid by suspending in it a solid of known weight arranged so that the solid can be weighed while floating in the liquid. From this weight, and its relationship to the weight of the solid in air, the weight of displaced liquid is determinable, and thus the specific gravity or specific volume of the liquid. The **Westphal balance** is commonly employed in this method.

ARGENTIC. Containing silver.

ARGENTIFEROUS. Containing silver.

ARGENTOCYANIDE. See **cyanoargentate (I).**

ARGENTOTHIOSULFATE. See **thiosulfatoargentate (I).**

ARGENTOUS. Containing monovalent silver (as of a compound).

ARGENTUM. Silver.

ARGINYL. The radical $H_2NC(:NH)NHCH_2CH_2CH_2CH(NH_2)CO-$.

ARGON. Gaseous element. Symbol A. Atomic number 18. Atomic weight 39.944. Density (g. per liter at S.T.P.) 1.784.

Specific heat 0.1233. Melting point $-189.2°$ C. Boiling point $-185.7°$C. Argon forms no known compounds. It is a component of the atmosphere of which it forms less than 1%.

ARMANI-BARBONI REACTION FOR GOLD AND SILVER. A solution of 2 parts formaldehyde and 1 part 20% potassium hydroxide solution precipitates the gold or silver in the deeply-colored colloidal form.

ARMANI-BARBONI TEST FOR CAFFEINE. Heat the material with potassium hydroxide solution; cool and add phosphomolybdic acid until a white precipitate forms, then add 50% potassium hydroxide solution until the precipitate dissolves. An intense blue color indicates the presence of caffeine.

ARMANI-RODANO TEST. A test for differentiating Vaseline from artificial Vaseline in which 1 g. of the material is dissolved in a mixture of 10 ml. benzene and 10 ml. absolute alcohol. Artificial Vaseline, only, gives a crystalline precipitate after standing for 24 hours at 20° C.

ARNDT-EISTERT SYNTHESIS. A series of reactions for converting an organic **acid** or its derivative to its next higher homologue or its derivative. The synthesis consists of three essential steps, as follows: (1) Formation of the acid chloride, followed by (2) its reaction with diazomethane to form a diazoketone

$$RCOCl + 2CH_2N_2 \rightarrow RCOCHN_2 + CH_3Cl + N_2,$$

and finally (3) rearrangement of the diazoketone, by reaction with water, an alcohol, or an amine, in the presence of catalysts (commonly certain colloidal metals). Step (3) with an alcohol, gives an ester

$$RCOCHN_2 + R'OH \rightarrow RCH_2CO_2R' + N_2.$$

Similarly, reactions with amines yield compounds of the type RCH_2CONHR', and with water, acids are obtained.

ARMSTRONG-BAEYER STRUCTURE OF BENZENE. See benzene, formulas.

ARNAUD-PADÉ REAGENT. The substance cinchonamine used as a reagent for nitrate. An insoluble precipitate is formed.

ARNDT TUBE. A glass laboratory apparatus used in the determination of hydrogen. It usually has four bulbs.

ARNOLD-MENTZEL REAGENT FOR HYDROGEN PEROXIDE. A solution of 1g. vanadic acid in 100 ml. dilute sulfuric acid, used in testing for hydrogen peroxide. A red color indicates the presence of hydrogen peroxide.

ARNOLD-MENTZEL REAGENT FOR OZONE. Paper impregnated with a saturated alcoholic benzidine solution is colored brown by ozone. Certain other oxidizing agents give colors, chiefly blue.

ARNOLD-MENTZEL REAGENT FOR OZONE IN WATER. A saturated solution of tetramethyl-p-diaminodiphenylmethane in methyl alcohol. One or two drops of this reagent are added to 1–2 ml. of a 2% silver nitrate or 10% manganese sulfate solution, and 25 ml. of the water to be tested is added. A blue color indicates the presence of ozone.

ARNOLD-MENTZEL REAGENTS FOR MILK. (1) A 2–3% alcoholic solution of p-diethyl-p-phenylenediamine. (2) A 2–3% alcoholic solution of p-diaminodiphenylamine hydrochloride. These reagents give red, and blue-green colors, respectively, with unboiled or unpasteurized milk, probably by reaction with peroxidase.

ARNOLD-MENTZEL TEST FOR FORMALDEHYDE. Add to 5 ml. of the sample, 0.03 g. phenylhydrazine hydrochloride, 4 drops ferric chloride solution, 10 drops concentrated sulfuric acid, and enough alcohol or sulfuric acid to clarify the solution. A red color indicates the presence of formaldehyde.

ARNOLD REACTIONS FOR ALKALOIDS. (1) On heating with syrupy phosphoric acid for about 10 minutes on the water bath, coniine produces a green to blue-green color, nicotine a yellow to orange-red color, and aconitine a violet color. (2) These alkaloids also give color reactions on warming with concentrated sulfuric acid, then adding an excess, by drops, of 30–40% potassium hydroxide solution. (3) On heating with a few drops of concentrated sulfuric acid and phenol, narceine or veratrine forms a cherry-red color, changing to dirty-yellow on the addition of water. Codeine gives a dirty red-violet to brown color.

ARNOLD SOLUTION. A mixture of one volume of a 1% aqueous solution of sodium nitrite, with two volumes of a 1% aqueous solution of p-aminoacetophenone hydrochloride. This is a reagent for acetoacetic acid in urine. A brownish-red color, in ammoniacal solution, indicates the presence of acetoacetic acid.

ARNOLD TEST REACTION FOR PROTEINS. Upon the addition to 1–2 ml. of the protein solution, of 2–4 drops of a 5% solution of sodium nitroprusside, and a few drops of ammonia, a purple-red color is formed.

ARNY-DIMLER TEST. To detect lactic acid in pharmaceuticals, the preparation is shaken with 20 ml. ethyl acetate, and the acetate extract is washed with water and dilute sulfuric acid. After filtration and evaporation, the residue is dissolved in 5 ml. 1% resorcinol solution and layered upon 5 ml. concentrated sulfuric acid. A red color indicates the presence of lactic acid.

ARNY SOLUTIONS. Several series of solutions — such as acidulated aqueous solutions of cobaltous chloride, cupric sulfate and ferric chloride; or solutions of potassium permanganate and potassium dichromate; and other series. The solutions of a given series are miscible in all proportions without precipitation, and they are used in the preparation of artificial color standards for a number of different colorimetric procedures.

AROMATIC COMPOUND. (Carbocyclic compound) A carbon **compound** derived from benzene, C_6H_6, and its derivatives, or other organic substances containing closed **rings,** such as naphthalene, anthracene, etc., as distinguished from the aliphatic compounds.

AROMATIZATION. A general term for the production of an **aromatic** organic compound by **ring** closure.

AROYL. A radical of the type-formula R·C(:O)–, in which R is an **aryl group.**

ARRAGON TEST REACTION. On shaking with nitric acid (sp. gr. 1.4) for some time, American petroleum becomes violet in color and the acid turns yellow; Russian and Austrian petroleums are colored yellow and the acid becomes brown.

ARREGUINE TEST REACTION FOR CITRIC ACID. The dilute solution to be tested is acidified with sulfuric acid and oxidized with a 4% acid potassium permanganate solution, then 0.1 g. resorcinol is added, and sulfuric acid until a red color develops. The solution is then extracted with ether, and water and a few drops of ammonia are added to the extract. An intense blue fluorescence indicates the presence of citric acid.

ARREGUINE TEST REACTION FOR GLYCEROL. The material is oxidized with bromine, an equal volume of concentrated sulfuric acid is then added, and a 1% alcoholic solution of veratrole is superimposed. An intense blue color in the zone of separation indicates the presence of glycerol.

ARREST POINT. A temperature at which a **system** of more than one **component** that is undergoing heating or cooling absorbs or yields heat without change in temperature, thus interrupting the heating or cooling process.

ARRHENIUS EQUATION. An equation for the variation of the rate of a chemical **reaction** with temperature. It is of the form:

$$\frac{d \ln k}{dT} = \frac{E}{RT^2}$$

in which the variation of the natural logarithm of the reaction velocity k, with variation in the absolute temperature, is equal to the energy of activation E divided by the product of the gas constant R and the square of the absolute temperature.

ARRHENIUS THEORY OF ACTIVATION. The theory which states that an **equilibrium** is reached between "normal" and "active" molecules in every system, and that only active molecules take part in reactions. "Active" molecules are considered to be those molecules which have acquired the requisite activation energy to enter chemical reactions.

ARRHENIUS THEORY OF ELECTROLYTIC DISSOCIATION. The theory proposed by Arrhenius, which states that when an electrolyte (an acid, base, or salt) is dissolved in water, a substantial portion of its molecules dissociate spontaneously into positive and negative ions, which, upon the application of an electrical potential difference to the solution, are attracted to the electrode of opposite sign and discharge, thus conducting current through the solution. This dissociation increases the number of particles in the solution, and thus changes the osmotic pressure, elevation of the boiling point, and depression of the freezing point to an extent determined by the degree of dissociation and concentration of the electrolyte. The degree of dissociation increases with dilution, becoming complete at "infinite dilution." Modern discoveries and interpretations have modified considerably this view of electrolytic dissociation.

ARSENATE (META-). The anion $(AsO_3)_n{}^{n-}$, or a compound containing it.

ARSENATE (ORTHO-). The anion $AsO_4{}^{3-}$, $HAsO_4{}^{=}$, or $H_2AsO_4{}^{-}$, or a compound containing one of these anions.

ARSENATE (PYRO-). The anion $As_2O_7{}^{4-}$, or a compound containing it.

ARSENIC. Element. Symbol As. Atomic number 33. Atomic weight 74.91. Exists in three allotropic forms: (1) Metallic arsenic (or gamma arsenic, the stable ordinary form), density 5.72. Sublimes on heating. (2) Gray or black arsenic (beta arsenic), density 4.64, at about 300° C. this form changes to ordinary metallic arsenic. (3) Yellow arsenic (alpha arsenic), density 3.7. Formed by rapid condensation of arsenic vapor. Changes to gray arsenic on exposure to light. Valences 3 and 5. Oxides As_2O_3 and As_2O_5.

The word arsenic is also used as an adjective to signify containing pentavalent arsenic, as, for example, arsenic chloride, $AsCl_5$; and the word arsenic is further used to denote relation to arsenic acid (ortho-), H_3AsO_4; to arsenic acid (meta-); $HAsO_3$; and to arsenic acid (pyro-), $H_4As_2O_7$.

ARSENITE (META-). The anion $(AsO_2)_n{}^{n-}$, or a compound containing it.

ARSENITE (ORTHO-). The anion $AsO_3{}^{3-}$, $HAsO_3{}^{-}$, or $H_2AsO_3{}^{-}$, or a compound containing one of these anions.

ARSENITE (PYRO-). The anion $As_2O_5{}^{4-}$, or a compound containing it.

ARSENITUNGSTATE. See **tungstoarsenate.**

ARSENO. The radical –As:As– in organic compounds.

ARSENOSO. The radical O:As– in organic compounds.

ARSENOUS. Containing trivalent arsenic.

ARSINE. The compound AsH_3, or one of its derivatives in which one or more organic radicals are substituted for hydrogen atoms.

ARSINE OXIDE. An arsenic-containing compound of the type $R'R''R'''AsO$, in which R', R'', and R''' are organic radicals.

ARSINIC ACID. (1) An arsenic-containing acid of the type-formula $RAsO_2H_2$, $R'R''AsO_2H$ or $R'R''R'''AsO$ in which R, R', etc., are organic radicals, and As is trivalent. (2) However, there is wide usage of the term arsinic acid to designate the dialkyl or diaryl **arsonic acids** (q.v.) which are derivatives of pentavalent arsenic.

ARSINICO. The radical $(HO)OAs=$ (pentavalent arsenic).

ARSINO. The radical H_2As-.

ARSO. The radical O_2As-.

ARSONATION. Treatment of an organic substance with arsenic acid, or other methods of producing partially or fully-substituted derivatives of o-arsenic acid, H_3AsO_4. Commonly, one or two of the three acidic hydroxyl groups are substituted by organic radicals.

ARSONIC ACID. (1) An arsenic-containing acid derived from orthoarsenic acid, $OAs(OH)_3$, of the type-formulas $RAsO(OH)_2$, $R'R''AsO_2OH$, and $R'R''R'''AsO_3$, in which R, R', etc., are organic radicals, and in which arsenic is pentavalent. (2) The term arsonic acid is commonly restricted to pentavalent arsenic acids of the type, $RAsO(OH)_2$, calling the $R'R''AsO_2OH$ types, **arsinic acids,** and the $R'R''R'''AsO_3$ types, **arsine oxides.**

ARSONIUM. The radical $-AsH_4$.

ARSONO. The radical $(HO)_2OAs-$.

ARSYL. The radical $-AsH_2$.

ARSYLENE. The radical $HAs=$.

ARTHAUD-BUTTE REAGENT. A solution of 20 g. of sodium thiosulfate, 40 g. of Rochelle salt, and 1.484 g. of cupric sulfate in 1 liter of water. This reagent is used as a precipitant for uric acid.

ARTIFICIAL RADIOACTIVITY. Radioactivity induced in stable **elements** by bombardment with **alpha particles, protons, deuterons, neutrons, gamma rays,** etc. Thus aluminum on alpha ray bombardment emits a neutron, forming radiophosphorus of mass 30

$$_{13}Al^{27} + {}_2He^4 \rightarrow {}_{15}P^{30} + {}_0n^1.$$

Radiophosphorus emits a positron to form silicon of mass 30, a stable isotope

$$_{15}P^{30} \rightarrow {}_{14}Si^{30} + {}_{+1}e^0,$$

this second process being an example of induced radioactivity. Other alpha ray bombardments, as well as bombardment with deuterons, neutrons, etc., may yield electron-emitting radioelements, as the process,

$$_{37}Rb^{85} + _{0}n^{1} \longrightarrow _{37}Rb^{84} + 2_{0}n^{1},$$

the radio-element rubidium of mass 84 is an electron-emitter,

$$_{37}Rb^{84} \longrightarrow _{38}Sr^{84} + _{-1}e^{0}.$$

There are also radioelements which decay by emission of alpha particles, by capturing one of their own K-electrons, etc.

ARTIFICIAL RESIN. A synthetic **resin** or a resin made by a chemical reaction conducted in industry, as distinguished from the large number of naturally-occurring resins.

ARYL. A **radical** derived from an aromatic **hydrocarbon** by the elimination of one atom of hydrogen, so producing a univalent unit. Examples are phenyl C_6H_5-, derived from benzene; tolyl (or benzyl) C_7H_7- derived from toluene, etc.

ARYLENE. A bivalent **radical** derived from an aromatic **hydrocarbon** by removal of a hydrogen atom from each of two carbon atoms of the nucleus. Examples: phenylene, naphthylene, biphenylene.

ARZBERGER TEST FOR OIL OF PEPPERMINT. One drop peppermint oil warmed with 5 ml. formaldehyde develops a pink color, which changes to red, red-violet, and dirty brown upon the addition of glacial acetic acid.

ARZBERGER TESTS FOR CURCUMA IN RHUBARB. (1) A strip of filter paper impregnated with the filtered chloroform extract of the substance gives a red color on moistening with a solution of boric acid in hydrochloric acid, if curcuma is present. (2) The powder to be tested is placed on filter paper and moistened with ether, after it dries, a solution of boric acid in hydrochloric acid is applied to the reverse side of the paper. A pink color, changed to blue (greenish-brown) by ammonia, indicates the presence of curcuma.

As (1) Symbol for the element **arsenic.** (2) The prefix, as-, is an abbreviation for **asymmetric,** as in as-trichlorobenzene.

ASARYL. The radical

$$2,4,5\text{-}(CH_3O)_3C_6H_2-.$$

ASEPSIS. The condition of absence of infection or means of infection. Modern surgical technique is directed to the maintenance, as far as possible, of aseptic conditions.

ASH. The residue left after a substance has undergone complete **combustion,** and when further heating in the presence of oxygen produces no further change in weight.

ASMACHER TEST REACTION. To test for a histamine salt, treat the solution with sodium hydroxide, then extract with hot chloroform, and add 0.2 g. anhydrous cupric sulfate. A dark blue color indicates the presence of histamine.

ASPARAGYL. The radical

$$H_2NCOCH_2CH(NH_2)CO-.$$

ASPARTIC. Related to aspartic acid,

$$NH_2 \cdot CH \cdot COOH.$$
$$| $$
$$CH_2 \cdot COOH$$

ASPARTYL. The radical

$$-COCH_2CH(NH_2)CO-.$$

ASPIRATOR. An apparatus which produces a movement of air or liquid by suction.

ASPIRATOR BOTTLE. Laboratory apparatus consisting of a closed glass container with tubes leading to its top and bottom, or with a top opening and an opening at the bottom of a side wall.

ASSAY. A form of **analysis** in which certain **constituents** of a substance or **components** only are determined, the others being usually neglected. Applied particularly to minerals and drugs.

ASSAY TON. A weight used in assaying ores containing precious metals in order to compensate the difference between the **avoirdupois system** (in which the ore is weighed) and the **troy system** (in which gold and silver are weighed). The avoirdupois ton contains 29,166 troy ounces and the assay ton is a weight of 29,166 milligrams, so that each milligram of metal found per assay ton equals one troy ounce per avoirdupois ton.

ASSAY VALUE. Strictly the content of precious metal found by analysis, expressed in **troy** ounces per ton of material processed.

ASSEMBLY. A collection of systems each consisting of the same number of molecules, each system in a container of the same shape, each system having the same total energy, but without any other restriction on the coordinates and momenta.

ASSEMBLY, MICROCANONICAL. A special case of the distribution of points in **gamma space** (q.v.) as a function of their energy, wherein all the systems have energies within the range E and $E + dE$. Over this range the density is taken as a constant, and the assembly is in statistical equilibrium.

ASSIMILATION. The transformation by a living organism of food into living matter.

ASSOCIATED COMPOUNDS. Compounds consisting of compound **molecules** formed by the combinations of two or more molecules of the same substance, as $(H_2O)_2$ and $(H_2O)_3$ are formed from H_2O, and N_2O_4 is formed from NO_2.

ASSOCIATION, CHEMICAL. The combination of molecules of the same substance to form larger aggregates consisting of two or more molecules. Liquid water, especially at lower temperatures, is believed to consist largely of $(H_2O)_2$, and to contain some $(H_2O)_3$.

ASSOCIATION THEORY. An attempt to explain the action of catalytic agents by assuming that the **catalyst** "associates" with one of the reagents, thus altering the

chemical **equilibrium** of the system in such a way that a reaction proceeds which would not occur in the absence of the catalyst.

ASTATIC GALVANOMETER. See **galvanometer, astatic.**

ASTATINE. Radioactive element. Symbol At. Atomic number 85. Isotopes with mass numbers 202–12 and 214–218 have been reported. Properties of some of them are: (1) Species of mass numbers **215** and **218**, which are members of the actinium and uranium series of radioactive elements, respectively, and which occur in Nature in minute amounts. (2) A species of mass number 211, which has a half-life of 7.5 hours, decaying by the emission of an α-particle and also by a K-electron capture. (3) A species of mass number **216**, which is an α-emitter, of half-life 0.02 seconds, which is a member of the neptunium series of radioactive elements.

ASTERISM. One of the characteristic effects sometimes observed in **x-ray spectrograms** (q.v.). It has, roughly, the shape of a star, and commonly indicates the presence of internal stress in the material under investigation.

ASTRINGENT. A drug used to produce contraction of tissues, especially to lessen secretions from mucous membranes and surfaces of wounds.

ASYMMETRIC TOP. A molecule which has no three-fold or higher-fold axis of symmetry, so that during rotation all three principal moments of inertia are in general different. Examples are the water molecule and the ethylene molecule.

ASYMMETRY. Lack of **symmetry.**

ASYMMETRY, INTRAMOLECULAR. Lack of symmetry in the spatial arrangement of the atoms and radicals within the molecule, especially of carbon compounds but also significant with other elements. See **atoms, isomerism.**

ASYMMETRY POTENTIAL. The **potential difference** between the outside and the inside surface of a hollow **electrode** (usually a glass electrode).

ASYMMETRY, RELATIVE AND ABSO-LUTE. Terms proposed by Baeyer to differentiate between the two forms of spacial **isomerism** known as optical and geometrical isomerism. Optical isomerism was considered absolute asymmetry, and geometrical, relative asymmetry.

At Symbol for the element **astatine.**

ATACK REAGENT FOR NICKEL. An alcoholic solution of α-benzildioxime, which gives a voluminous red precipitate with nickel salts in solution.

ATACK TEST FOR ALUMINUM. To 5 ml. of the solution to be tested, which has been made acid or neutral, add 1 ml. of a 0.1% filtered alizarin S solution, and then add ammonia until a purple color appears. Boil, cool, and acidify with acetic acid. A red color or precipitate indicates the presence of aluminum.

-ATION. A suffix meaning a process or result of a process. For example, calibration, excitation, ionization, and radiation (-ing, as in lighting, is also used to denote a process).

ATMOLYSIS. The separation of a mixture of gases by means of their relative **diffusibility** through a porous partition, as burned clay. The rates of **diffusion** are inversely proportional to the square roots of the densities of the gases. Hydrogen, thus, is the most diffusible gas.

ATMOMETER. An instrument for measuring **evaporation,** generally that of water into the atmosphere.

ATMOSPHERE. (1) A gaseous envelope surrounding a body, or a mass of gas occupying a region. (2) A standard unit of pressure equivalent to a column of mercury 760 mm. high at 0° C., under a gravitational acceleration of 980.665 c.g.s. units. One atmosphere is equal to 1.013×10^6 dynes/cm².

ATMOSPHERE, CONTROLLED. The use of a gas other than air, such as hydrogen, nitrogen, carbon dioxide, etc., in an apparatus or process which would react with atmospheric oxygen.

ATOM. The smallest particle of an **element** which can enter into chemical **combination.** All chemical compounds are formed of atoms, the difference between compounds being attributable to the nature, number, and arrangement of their constituent atoms.

ATOM, ACTIVATED. See **atom, excited.**

ATOM ANNIHILATION. The reverse of atom creation. In the most familiar case, a pair of positive and negative electrons disappear, and their equivalent energy appears as two γ-ray quanta.

ATOM, ASYMMETRIC. An atom whose **valences** are saturated by different atoms or groups so that the resulting compounds exhibit the phenomenon of **optical activity.** Asymmetric atoms must be at least trivalent according to the present view of stereochemical theory because the asymmetry is assumed to be due to the spatial arrangement of the atoms within the molecule in three dimensions. Carbon, nitrogen, silicon, tin, sulfur, and selenium have been found to possess this property.

ATOM, BOHR-SOMMERFELD. The **Bohr theory** of atomic **spectra** postulated an electron moving about the nucleus of its atom in a limited number of circular orbits, with energy changes due to abrupt transitions from one orbit to another accounting for the emission or absorption of radiation. To account for the fine structure of spectra, Sommerfeld also included elliptical orbits, with variations in the shape of the ellipse, to be formulated in terms of two quantum numbers (azimuthal and radical). Moreover, the ellipse of the electronic pathway "precesses" or moves through a series of positions.

ATOM BUILDING. The formation of atoms from their constituent parts (**electrons, protons,** etc.).

ATOM, CHARGED. An **ion;** in other words, an atom carrying an electric charge.

ATOM DISINTEGRATION. The **emission** by an atomic nucleus of a particle or particles, or larger fragments, and radiations, resulting in the formation of new atomic species, differing from the original in mass, atomic number, or energy or in more than one of those properties. Disintegration may occur naturally, as in the case of the radioactive **elements,** or artificially, by bombardment with particles or radiations.

ATOM, EXCITED. An atom which possesses more energy than a normal atom of that species. The additional energy commonly affects the electrons surrounding the atomic **nucleus,** raising them to higher energy levels.

ATOM, EXPLODING. An atom undergoing very rapid **disintegration.**

ATOM, IONIZED. An **ion,** which is an atom that has acquired an electric charge by gain or loss of **electrons** surrounding its **nucleus.**

ATOM, LABELED. A tracer atom which can easily be detected, and which is introduced into a system to study a chemical process or structure.

ATOM, LEWIS–LANGMUIR. A theory of **electron** arrangement in which it was postulated that the number of electrons surrounding the **nucleus** of an atom was equal to the **atomic number;** that the electrons are arranged in various shells, each consisting of electrons having the same orbital dimensions, but that the electrons in successive shells differ in the dimensions of their orbits; that if atoms were considered in order of increasing atomic number, the essential structure of their electron shells would be the same, with the numbers of electrons in completed shells being 2, 8, 8, 18, 18, and 32; that the inert nature of the rare gases was due to their possession of completed electron shells, that the chemical properties of other atoms depend upon the number of electrons in their partly-formed outer shells; that since elements whose outermost shells lack one electron of completion would tend strongly to acquire that electron, while elements having only one electron in their outermost shell would tend to lose it; that such processes in these and other atoms often result in compound

formation by such means, whereby the resulting atomic entities, or ions, are joined by the resulting electrostatic forces; and that many of the periodic properties of the elements are explicable by these postulates.

ATOM MODEL. A conception of the structure of the atom, in terms of its constituent parts and their arrangement; or a physical model based on such considerations.

ATOM, NEUTRAL. An atom which has no over-all, or resultant, electric charge.

ATOM, NORMAL. An atom which has no over-all electric charge, and in which all the electrons surrounding the nucleus are at their lowest **energy levels.**

ATOM, NUCLEAR. An atomic **nucleus** without surrounding electrons.

ATOM, RADIATING. An atom which is emitting **radiation** during the transition of one or more of its electrons from higher to lower energy states.

ATOM, RECOIL. An atom which undergoes a sudden change or reversal of its direction of motion as the result of the emission by it of a **particle** or **radiation.**

ATOM, RUTHERFORD. A theory of the structure of the atom, which embodied some conceptions still accepted. The **nucleus** of the atom contained practically all the mass, an equal number of positive and negative charges which balanced one another, and also a number of free positive charges equal to the **atomic number.** An equal number of electrons was considered to surround the nucleus. These ideas are still believed true, but Rutherford's conception of negative charges within the nucleus is no longer accepted.

ATOM, SCHRÖDINGER. See **Schrödinger concept.**

ATOM, STRIPPED. An atomic **nucleus** without surrounding electrons.

ATOMIC BOMB. See **plutonium.**

ATOMIC CHARGE. The electrical charge of an **ion** (charged atom) which is equal to the product of the number of electrons the atom has gained or lost in its **ionization,** by the charge on one electron. (See **charge, elementary.**)

ATOMIC CHARGE, EFFECTIVE. A quantity which enters into various mathematical expressions involving properties of atomic spectra. (See **spectrum, atomic.**)

ATOMIC DISTANCE. The average distance separating the centers of two atoms.

ATOMIC ENERGY. The constitutive internal **energy** of the **atom,** which would be absorbed when the atom is formed from its constituent particles, and released when it is broken up into them.

ATOMIC FREQUENCY. The vibrational frequency of an **atom,** used particularly with respect to the solid state.

ATOMIC HYDROGEN. See **hydrogen, atomic.**

ATOMIC HYPOTHESIS. The theory that all matter is composed of small indivisible particles, called atoms.

ATOMIC KERNEL. An atom which has lost the electrons in its outermost shell (the valency electrons).

ATOMIC MASS. The mass of an atom.

ATOMIC NUMBER. The number of free unit **positive charges** carried by the **nucleus** of the atom.

ATOMIC NUMBER, EFFECTIVE. The number of **electrons** in a stable coordination **compound** that are associated with the central atom.

ATOMIC ORBITAL. A quantum mechanical concept: the **wave function** characterizing the behavior of an **electron** in the field of a central **nucleus.**

ATOMIC PLANE. A plane passed through the atoms of a crystal **space lattice,** in accordance with certain rules relating its position to the **crystallographic axes.**

ATOMIC PROPERTIES. Properties of substances which are due to the nature of the constituent **atoms.**

ATOMIC RADIUS. In quantum mechanical concepts the atom has no definite radius. The atomic radius would be the effective radius of an atom as calculated from physical data such as **viscosity** or **cross-sections** (q.v.).

ATOMIC REFRACTION. See **refraction, atomic.**

ATOMIC SCATTERING FACTOR. The mean **amplitude** of a wave of **x-rays** scattered by atoms in a plane of a **crystal lattice structure.**

ATOMIC SPECIES. A distinctive type of atom. The basis of differentiation between atoms is (1) mass, (2) **atomic number,** or number of positive nuclear charges, (3) atomic energy. The reason for recognizing this third class is because certain atoms are known, chiefly among those obtained by artificial transmutation, which have the same atomic (isotopic) mass and atomic number, but differ in energetics. See **nuclear isotope.**

ATOMIC SPECTRUM. See **spectrum, atomic.**

ATOMIC STRUCTURE. According to current views an atom consists of a central **nucleus** possessing a fixed positive charge and of **electrons** held in the field of the nucleus. These electrons are described in quantum mechanical terminology by **wave functions** which characterize the extent to which the electron cloud is "smeared out" around the nucleus; from these functions one may determine the probability that an electron is in a certain fixed position relative to the nucleus. According to the theory of atomic structure the electrons can only be in certain discrete **energy levels;** transitions between these is accompanied by the emission or absorption of radiant energy of a monochromatic frequency.

ATOMIC SUSCEPTIBILITY. The change in **magnetic moment** of one gram-atom of a substance produced by the application of a magnetic field of unit strength.

ATOMIC CONSTANTS OF ELEMENTS

(This table is reproduced from Van Nostrand's *Scientific Encyclopedia*)

	Atomic Volume of Solid	Atomic Heat of Solid	Atomic Radius 10^{-8} cm. Neuburger	Atomic Compressibility at 20° C. $\times 10^7$
1. Hydrogen..............	13.21	....	0.37	
2. Helium				
3. Lithium...............	11.8	6.6 (50°)	1.50	9.0
4. Beryllium.............	5.3	4.5 (0–300°)	1.11	
5. Boron.................	4.5	5.5 (900°)	0.7	0.3
6. Carbon................	5.6 (graphite)	5.5 (900°) (graphite)	0.77	3.0 (graphite)
7. Nitrogen..............	13.6	....	0.53	
8. Oxygen................	11.2	....	0.60	
9. Fluorine..............	....	....	0.68	
10. Neon.................	....	....	1.60	
11. Sodium...............	22.9	6.8 (20°)	1.86	15.6
12. Magnesium............	14.0	6.0 (20°)	1.60	2.9
13. Aluminum.............	10.2	5.8 (20°)	1.48	1.47
14. Silicon..............	11.4	4.7 (14°)	1.17	0.32
15. Phosphorus...........	16.9 (yellow)	5.9 (90°) (yellow)	1.08	9.2 (yellow)
16. Sulfur...............	15.3 (rhombic)	5.7 (15–96°) (rhombic)	1.06	12.9 (rhombic)
17. Chlorine.............	....	....	0.97	
18. Argon................	....	....	1.91	
19. Potassium............	45.3	7.0 (14°)	2.27	31.7
20. Calcium..............	25.9	5.8 (0–20°)	1.97	5.7
21. Scandium.............	....	....	1.51	
22. Titanium.............	9.3	5.4 (0–100°)	1.45	
23. Vanadium.............	8.8	....	1.31	
24. Chromium.............	7.7	5.8 (18–100°)	1.25	0.9
25. Manganese............	7.4	6.6 (20–100°)	1.24	0.84
26. Iron.................	7.1	6.0 (20°)	1.24	0.63
27. Cobalt...............	6.8	5.9 (20°)	1.25	
28. Nickel...............	6.6	6.2 (20°)	1.24	0.40
29. Copper...............	7.1	5.9 (15–100°)	1.28	0.75
30. Zinc.................	9.2	6.2 (0–100°)	1.33	1.7
31. Gallium	11.8	....	1.22	2.09
32. Germanium............	13.6	....	1.22	
33. Arsenic..............	14.8	6.2 (0–100°)	1.25	4.5
34. Selenium.............	16.5	....	1.16	12.0
35. Bromine..............	....	....	1.13	
36. Krypton..............	....	....	2.0	
37. Rubidium.............	56.2	....	2.43	40.0
38. Strontium............	34.5	....	2.14	
39. Yttrium	19.5	....		
40. Zirconium	14.0	....	1.58	
41. Niobium (Columbium)...	12.7	....	1.43	
42. Molybdenum...........	10.7	....	1.36	0.46
43. Technetium				
44. Ruthenium............	8.3	....	1.32	

	Atomic Volume of Solid	Atomic Heat of Solid	Atomic Radius 10⁻⁸ cm. Neuburger	Atomic Compressibility at 20° C. × 10⁷
45. Rhodium...............	8.5	....	1.34	
46. Palladium..............	9.0	....	1.37	0.54
47. Silver.................	10.3	6.0 (20°)	1.44	1.01
48. Cadmium.............	13.0	6.2 (28°)	1.49	2.1
49. Indium................	15.1	....	1.57	
50. Tin....................	16.3	6.4 (18°)	1.51	1.9
51. Antimony..............	18.2	6.1 (20–100°)	1.44	2.4
52. Tellurium..............	20.4	....	1.44	
53. Iodine................	5.9	6.6 (20°)	1.35	13.0
54. Xenon.................	....	....	2.2	
55. Cesium...............	70.4	....	2.62	61.0
56. Barium...............	39.0	....	2.17	
57–71.				
72. Hafnium...............	13.4	....	1.59	
73. Tantalum..............	10.9	....	1.46	0.53
74. Tungsten (Wolfram).....	9.8	....	1.41	0.27
75. Rhenium..............	8.8	....	1.38	
76. Osmium...............	8.5	....	1.34	
77. Iridium...............	8.6	....	1.35	
78. Platinum..............	8.7	6.3 (20°)	1.38	0.38
79. Gold..................	10.2	6.2 (0–100°)	1.44	0.64
80. Mercury				
81. Thallium..............	17.2	....	1.71	2.3
82. Lead..................	18.2	6.3 (20°)	1.75	2.33
83. Bismuth...............	21.3	6.1 (20°)	1.82	3.0
84. Polonium				
85. Astatine				
86. Radon				
87. Francium				
88. Radium				
89. Actinium				
90. Thorium...............	19.2	....	1.82	
91. Protactinium				
92. Uranium...............	12.8			
93. Neptunium				
94. Plutonium				
95. Americium				
96. Curium				
97. Berkelium				
98. Californium				

ATOMIC THEORY. The assumption that matter is not infinitely divisible but is composed of ultimate particles called atoms. The hypothesis was enunciated by John Dalton in 1803, but the idea dates back to the Greek philosophers.

ATOMIC TRANSMUTATION. The changing of an **atom** into an atom of different **atomic number** or, in other words, into an atom of a different **element.** The process of transmutation occurs in Nature in the course of the disintegration of the various radioactive elements and may also be effected by artificial means, such as by bombardment with **neutrons, α-particles, γ-radiations,** etc.

ATOMIC VOLUME. A numerical result obtained by dividing the atomic weight of an element by its density. This quantity, when plotted against **atomic number,** exhibits a striking periodicity.

ATOMIC WEIGHT. The weight of an atom of any element, the weight of the oxygen atom being taken as 16. The atomic weight is also called the equivalent weight or the relative weight. Since many elements, as they commonly occur in Nature, are mixtures of isotopes, the accepted values of their atomic weights are in reality mean values of the isotopic atomic weights of the various isotopes present. The atomic weight, as defined above, is often called the "chemical atomic weight," taking as its basis a value of 16, for ordinary atmospheric oxygen. Since atmospheric oxygen consists of a mixture of 3 different isotopes, a "physical atomic weight" scale has been established which assigns to the lowest mass isotope the value 16.

ATOMICITY. (1) **Valence.** (2) **Basicity.** (3) The number of **atoms** in an elementary **molecule.**

ATOMIZATION. The process of breaking up a liquid into small droplets.

ATTENUATION. In general, reduction in concentration, density, or effectiveness, as the weakening of the toxicity of a culture of microorganisms (or rather of their metabolic products) by growth under certain conditions.

ATTRACTION, CAPILLARY. See **surface tension.**

ATTRACTION, ELECTRICAL. The force between electric charges of opposite sign, having a magnitude given by the **law of Coulomb** (q.v.).

ATTRACTION, GRAVITATIONAL. That force which attracts any mass of matter to all other masses of matter. It is illustrated in the solar system by the attraction exerted by the sun upon the planets and by the individual planets upon each other. It varies directly with the product of the attracted masses and inversely as the square of the distances between their centers of mass.

ATTRACTION, MAGNETIC. A force exerted by a magnetized body upon another capable of **magnetization,** as of an iron magnet upon a piece of iron. The force exerted is directly proportional to the degree of magnetization of the attracting body and inversely proportional to the square of the distance between the magnet and attracted body. When magnetic attraction becomes negative it is termed "repulsion."

ATTRACTION, MOLECULAR. See **molecular attraction.**

ATTRITION MILL. See **mill, attrition.**

Au Symbol for element **gold.**

AUBRY REAGENT. A mixture of (1) a solution of 1 g. of quinine sulfate in 20 ml. of water containing 4 drops of sulfuric acid, and (2) a solution of 2 g. of potassium iodide in 10 ml. of water; the mixture being then made up to 100 ml. It gives an orange color if bismuth is present in urine. The urine sample is evaporated and the residue dissolved in dilute nitric acid, before testing with the reagent.

AUCHÉ-DENIGÈS REAGENT. Two solutions used in testing for bile pigments in blood. The first solution is made by dissolving 1 g. zinc sulfate in 10 ml. water, adding ammonium hydroxide until the precipitate just dissolves, and then making

ATOMIC WEIGHTS

September 1951

	Symbol	Atomic Number	Atomic Weight *		Symbol	Atomic Number	Atomic Weight *
Actinium	Ac	89	227	Neodymium	Nd	60	144.27
Aluminium	Al	13	26.98	Neon	Ne	10	20.183
Americium	Am	95	[243]	Neptunium	Np	93	[237]
Antimony	Sb	51	121.76	Nickel	Ni	28	58.69
Argon	A	18	39.944	Niobium			
Arsenic	As	33	74.91	(Columbium)	Nb	41	92.91
Astatine	At	85	[210]	Nitrogen	N	7	14.008
Barium	Ba	56	137.36	Osmium	Os	76	190.2
Berkelium	Bk	97	[245]	Oxygen	O	8	16.0000
Beryllium	Be	4	9.013	Palladium	Pd	46	106.7
Bismuth	Bi	83	209.00	Phosphorus	P	15	30.975
Boron	B	5	10.82	Platinum	Pt	78	195.23
Bromine	Br	35	79.916	Plutonium	Pu	94	[242]
Cadmium	Cd	48	112.41	Polonium	Po	84	210
Calcium	Ca	20	40.08	Potassium	K	19	39.100
Californium	Cf	98	[246]	Praseodymium	Pr	59	140.92
Carbon	C	6	12.010	Promethium	Pm	61	[145]
Cerium	Ce	58	140.13	Protactinium	Pa	91	231
Cesium	Cs	55	132.91	Radium	Ra	88	226.05
Chlorine	Cl	17	35.457	Radon	Rn	86	222
Chromium	Cr	24	52.01	Rhenium	Re	75	186.31
Cobalt	Co	27	58.94	Rhodium	Rh	45	102.91
Copper	Cu	29	63.54	Rubidium	Rb	37	85.48
Curium	Cm	96	[243]	Ruthenium	Ru	44	101.7
Dysprosium	Dy	66	162.46	Samarium	Sm	62	150.43
Erbium	Er	68	167.2	Scandium	Sc	21	44.96
Europium	Eu	63	152.0	Selenium	Se	34	78.96
Fluorine	F	9	19.00	Silicon	Si	14	28.09
Francium	Fr	87	[223]	Silver	Ag	47	107.880
Gadolinium	Gd	64	156.9	Sodium	Na	11	22.997
Gallium	Ga	31	69.72	Strontium	Sr	38	87.63
Germanium	Ge	32	72.60	Sulfur	S	16	32.066 †
Gold	Au	79	197.2	Tantalum	Ta	73	180.88
Hafnium	Hf	72	178.6	Technetium	Tc	43	[99]
Helium	He	2	4.003	Tellurium	Te	52	127.61
Holmium	Ho	67	164.94	Terbium	Tb	65	159.2
Hydrogen	H	1	1.0080	Thallium	Tl	81	204.39
Indium	In	49	114.76	Thorium	Th	90	232.12
Iodine	I	53	126.91	Thulium	Tm	69	169.4
Iridium	Ir	77	193.1	Tin	Sn	50	118.70
Iron	Fe	26	55.85	Titanium	Ti	22	47.90
Krypton	Kr	36	83.80	Tungsten			
Lanthanum	La	57	138.92	(Wolfram)	W	74	183.92
Lead	Pb	82	207.21	Uranium	U	92	238.07
Lithium	Li	3	6.940	Vanadium	V	23	50.95
Lutetium	Lu	71	174.99	Xenon	Xe	54	131.3
Magnesium	Mg	12	24.32	Ytterbium	Yb	70	173.04
Manganese	Mn	25	54.93	Yttrium	Y	39	88.92
Mercury	Hg	80	200.61	Zinc	Zn	30	65.38
Molybdenum	Mo	42	95.95	Zirconium	Zr	40	91.22

* A value given in brackets denotes the mass number of the most stable known isotope.

† The Atomic Weights Commission recommends that a range of ±0.003 be attached to the official value of 32.066.

up to a volume of 50 ml. with a $1\frac{1}{2}\%$ solution of potassium cyanide. The other is a 1% solution of iodine in 2% potassium iodide solution. The two solutions yield a greenish fluorescence with blood in 5 ml. of alcoholic solution, containing 20 drops of ammonium hydroxide, if bile pigments are present.

AUDIFFREN TEST REACTION. This test is used for chrysanthemum-mono-carboxylic acid. To 1 ml. of a dilute solution of the acid, add 1 ml. acid mercuric sulfate solution, and underlay with 0.5 ml. concentrated sulfuric acid. On shaking, a red color, changing to violet, then green and, after standing for 24 hours, giving a yellow precipitate, indicates the presence of chrysanthemum-monocarboxylic acid.

AUERBACH METHOD. Ethylene dichloride is used to extract quaternary ammonium salts (used as preservatives) from foods. The intensity of color of the extract is measured with a colorimeter.

AUFRECHT TEST. Methanol is detected by oxidation with chromic acid. The distillate gives a blue color with dimethylaniline and sulfuric acid, followed by lead peroxide.

AUGUSTI MICROTEST FOR THE MANGANOUS ION. To 1 drop of the solution to be tested, add 1 drop of sodium hydroxide solution on a watch glass, let stand for 1 minute, evaporate to dryness and add 1–2 drops of a 1% solution of strychnine in sulfuric acid. A blue-violet color, changing to red, indicates the presence of manganous ion. Cobalt gives a similar test, and conflicts.

AUGUSTI MICROTEST FOR MERCUROUS ION. Evaporate 1 drop of the solution to be tested; add 1 drop of dilute ammonium thiocyanate solution, 1 drop of cobalt nitrate solution; let crystallize under cover; and examine microscopically (300 diameters). Blue crystals indicate the presence of mercurous ion.

AUGUSTI SOLUTION FOR COPPER AND IRON. A 3% alcoholic solution of p-aminophenol hydrochloride, used in testing for copper or iron. Blue-violet precipitates are obtained.

AULD-HANTZSCH TEST. In this test for aldehydes, a little sodium hydroxide solution is added to a few drops of 0.1 n mercuric chloride solution, followed by 2–3 ml. of the solution to be tested. A white precipitate is given by aldehydes.

AURANTIA SOLUTION. A solution of 1 g. of aurantia and 10 ml. of normal sodium carbonate solution, in 100 ml. of water. This is a test reagent for potassium, which yields an orange-red precipitate.

AURATE, HYDROXO-. The anion $Au(OH)_4^-$, or a compound containing it.

AURATE (META-). The anion AuO_2^-, or a compound containing it.

AURELJ TEST REACTION. A test for cocaine, in which 25 ml. of a 1% solution of the hydrochloride of the alkaloid are distilled with sulfuric acid. If cocaine is present, methanol will be found in the first portions of the distillate, and crystals of benzoic acid will be deposited in the condenser.

AURIBROMIC. Relating to auribromic acid $HAuBr_4 \cdot 5H_2O$.

AURIC. Containing or pertaining to trivalent gold.

AURICYANIDE. See **cyanoaurate (III)**.

AURIFEROUS. Containing **gold.**

AURIHALIDE. A compound containing the radical $[AuX_4]^-$, in which X is a **halogen.**

AURO. A combining term for monovalent gold.

AUROAURIC. The combining term for **aurous** and **auric** gold in the same compound.

AUROCYANIDE. See **cyanoaurate (I)**.

AUROUS. Containing or pertaining to trivalent gold.

AUROTHIOSULFATE. See **thiosulfato-aurate (I)**.

AURUM. Gold.

AUTOCATALYSIS. A name given by Ostwald to the condition which obtains when one of the products of a **reaction,** or one of the factors, acts as a **catalyst** and accelerates or retards the velocity of the reaction; e.g., in the **hydrolysis** of **esters** the acid products formed exert an influence to increase the velocity of the hydrolysis. Autocatalysis may be positive or negative according as the result of the catalytic action is acceleration or retardation.

AUTOCHEMICAL INDUCTION. See **induced reaction.**

AUTOCLAVE. A vessel in which substances may be heated under pressure.

AUTOLYSIS. Literally, self-solution; the solution of **cells** in their own sera (see **serum**).

AUTOOXIDATION. (1) An **oxidation reaction** (q.v.) which does not require a special oxidizing agent, other than atmospheric oxygen. (2) An oxidation reaction which occurs only in the presence of a substance entering into a simultaneous oxidation reaction.

AUTOPROTOLYSIS. The process whereby a molecule, or other chemical entity, yields a **proton,** or hydrogen ion, to another identical molecule. The process occurs in the ionization of water, whereby two H_2O molecules yield a hydronium ion and a hydroxyl ion.

$$2H_2O \rightleftharpoons H_3O^+ + OH^-.$$

AUTORACEMIZATION. The spontaneous racemization of an optically active substance. See **racemization.**

AUTENRIETH-HINSBERG TEST REACTION. A test for acetophenetidin based on the formation of its mononitro derivative on boiling with 10–12% nitric acid. The nitro derivative crystallizes from water in needles having a melting point of 103° C.

AUTENRIETH TEST FOR COLCHICINE. The substance to be tested is dissolved in 3 ml. concentrated hydrochloric acid, 2 drops ferric chloride solution are added, and the solution is boiled for 2–3 minutes. In the presence of colchicine, the solution darkens in color, becomes green on dilution, and yields a yellow-brown to garnet-red chloroform extract.

AUTENRIETH TEST FOR METHANOL. This test is based on the formation of the methyl ester of *p*-bromobenzoyl chloride by reaction of the latter substance with methanol in alkaline solution. The ester has an anise-like odor, and melts at 77–78° C.

AUWERS-SKITA RULE. A method of predicting which of the two possible **stereoisomers** will result in the catalytic **hydrogenation** of an unsaturated cyclic material from which stereoisomeric polymethylene products are possible, and where **labile** configurations do not result. The rule states that reduction in acid solution yields the *cis* configuration, and reduction in neutral or alkaline solution, the *trans* configuration.

AUWERS SYNTHESIS. A ring rearrangement of **halogen** (usually bromine) substituted **coumaranones,** brought about by the action of alkali, with the formation of **flavonols.**

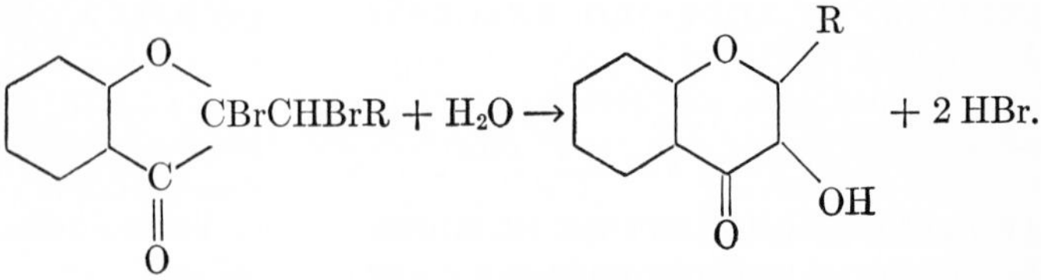

AUXOCHROME. A group which by its presence converts a molecule containing a chromophore group (q.v.) into a **dyestuff.** Auxochrome groups, of which NH_2- and OH– are examples, are considered to play a role in the interaction between dyestuff and fiber.

AUXOFLORE. An atom or group which by its substitution in a molecule tends to intensify its fluorescent **radiation** bands.

AUXOGLUC. A radical present in compounds which tends to intensify their sweet taste.

N, have been found by various methods, generally lying within a range of 1% about the value 6.02×10^{23}.

AVOGADRO HYPOTHESIS. (Avogadro rule.) Avogadro, in 1811, enunciated the rule that equal volumes of gases under like conditions of temperature and pressure contain equal numbers of molecules.

AVOIRDUPOIS SYSTEM. A system of weights and measures based upon an avoirdupois pound of 453.592 grams. The pound in this system contains 7,000 grains and the table of weights is as follows:

$437\frac{1}{2}$ grains (gr.)	= 1 ounce (oz.)
16 ounces	= 1 pound (lb.)
100 pounds	= 1 hundredweight (cwt.)
20 hundredweight	= 1 ton (T.) = 2000 (lbs.)
2240 pounds	= 1 long ton (used in mining)

AUXOMETER OR AUXIOMETER. An apparatus for measuring the **magnifying power** of a lens or any optical system.

AUZINGER TESTS FOR HONEY. A series of enzyme tests for differentiating unheated from heated or artificial honey, for detecting diastase in honey, and for detecting oxidase, peroxidase, and reductase in honey.

AVALANCHE. A term used in **counter** technology to describe the process in which an ion produces another ion by **collision,** and the new and original ions produce still others by further collisions, resulting finally in an "avalanche" of ions (or electrons). The terms "cumulative ionization" and "cascade" are also used to describe this process.

AVELLAR DE LOUREIRO REAGENT. A saturated solution of benzidine in petroleum benzine, used for detecting ozone in cod liver oil.

AVOGADRO CONSTANT OR NUMBER. The number of molecules contained in one **mole** or gram-molecular weight of a substance. A number of values of the Avogadro number, which is usually denoted by

AWENG MICROTEST FOR METHANOL. This test is made by oxidizing the methanol to formaldehyde and converting to hexamethylenetetramine with ammonia, then treating the hexamethylenetetramine with a solution of mercuric chloride or mercuric potassium iodide. Characteristic crystals are produced which are identified under the microscope.

AWENG TEST REACTION FOR PAPAVERINE. In 3 ml. acetic anhydride, dissolve 5 mg. of papaverine and heat to about 80° C. Then add 5 drops of sulfuric acid. A bright green fluorescence is produced.

AXENFELD REACTION FOR PROPEPTONE. Pyrogallol and propeptone, when mixed, form a precipitate which dissolves on warming.

AXENFELD REAGENT FOR ALBUMIN. A 0.1% solution of gold chloride used in testing for albumin in solution. The solution is acidulated with formic acid and the reagent added. A pink to purple-red color on heating indicates the presence of albumin.

AXIAL RATIOS, CRYSTALLOGRAPHIC. See **crystallographic axial ratios.**

AXIS. A line so situated that various parts of an object are symmetrically located in relation to it.

AXONOMETRY. Measurement of axes, especially in crystals.

AYMONIER SOLUTION. A solution of 1 g. of potassium dichromate and 1 ml. of nitric acid in 100 ml. of water. It is used as a test reagent for α-naphthol. A black precipitate indicates the presence of α-naphthol.

AZEOTROPE. One of two or more substances which, when mixed in certain proportions, have a **constant boiling point.**

AZEOTROPIC MIXTURE. A mixture of liquids which has a **constant boiling point** (q.v.).

AZEOTROPIC SOLUTION. See **constant boiling point.**

AZIDE. The anion N_3^-, or a compound containing it.

AZIDO-. In inorganic compounds, a prefix denoting the group N_3^-. In organic compounds, azido- means **triazo-** (q.v.).

AZIMETHYLENE GROUP. The group $N_2C=$ found in diazomethane, diazoacetic ester, etc.

AZIMUTHAL QUANTUM NUMBER. An integer obtained in quantizing the angular **momentum** of a particle, such as an electron, moving in an elliptical path. The total momentum is resolved into components, one directed radially and the other tangentially to the orbit. The latter has values given by the expression $\dfrac{hk}{2\pi}$, in which h is Planck's constant, and k is the azimuthal quantum number.

AZINE. A heterocyclic compound of six atoms in the **ring,** one or more of which is nitrogen, and a ring structure resembling benzene. Thus pyridine, C_6H_5N, is an azine.

AZINO. The group $=NN=$ in organic compounds.

AZLACTONE. An anhydride of an α-acyl-amino acid, of the type formula

$$R_2C—C=O$$
$$\quad\ \ | \quad\ |$$
$$\quad\ \ N \quad O$$
$$\quad\quad\ \backslash\!\!/$$
$$\quad\quad\ CR_1$$

These compounds contain the 5-oxazolone ring.

AZO. See **azo compounds.**

AZO COMPOUNDS. (1) (Obs.) Compounds which contain nitrogen. (2) Compounds which contain the azo group $-N=N-$ united on either side to a benzene nucleus; as, azobenzene,

$$C_6H_5N=N—C_6H_5$$

or to an aliphatic and an aromatic group, as benzene azomethane,

$$C_6H_5—N=N—CH_3.$$

When the two nuclei are the same the compound is called "symmetrical"; and, if one is **aromatic** and the other **aliphatic,** the compound is termed "mixed." Compounds which contain two or three azo groups are termed "disazo" and "trisazo."

AZOIMINO. The group $-N:N\cdot NH-$. It is found, for example, in compounds such as benzotriazole, $C_6H_4N_3H$, where the azo-imino group forms a five-membered ring with two adjacent carbon atoms of the benzene nucleus.

AZOLE. One of a group of heterocyclic, five-membered ring compounds, such as pyrrol, oxazole, the diazoles, etc.

AZOTIZE. To combine with nitrogen.

AZOTOMETER. See **nitrometer.**

AZOXY. The group $-N(O)N-$.

AZYLINE. A tetra-alkylic derivative of p-diaminoazobenzene.

AZZARELLO TEST FOR ALCOHOL IN ETHER, CHLOROFORM, AND VOLATILE OILS. (1) Shake 10 ml. of the ether with 2 drops of a solution of 0.2 g. cobalt nitrate and 0.4 g. ammonium thiocyanate in 30 ml. water. (2) Shake 15 ml. chloroform with 1 drop of a solution of 6 g. cobalt nitrate and 15 g. ammonium thiocyanate in 100 ml. water. (3) Shake 5 ml. of the volatile oil with 1 drop of the cobalt thiocyanate solution used in (2). The presence of alcohol is shown by a more or less deep blue color.

AZZOLLINI TEST. A test for epinephrine (adrenaline) in which 1–2 drops of hydrochloric acid are added to 4–5 ml. of the solution to be tested and shaken. Then 2–3 ml. of a mixture of 4 parts ammonia and 96 parts alcohol is superimposed. Epinephrine is indicated by a rose-red ring at the junction of acid and alcohol layers.

B. Symbol for the element boron (B). Symbol for a constant (b) in the **van der Waal equation** (q.v.). Abbreviation (b.) for "boils at." Symbol for density on the **Baumé scale** (° Bé.) (q.v.). Symbol for effective film thickness (B). Abbreviation for breadth (b or B). Symbol for brightness, or luminance (*B*). Wien displacement constant (*b*). Volume modulus of elasticity (*B*). Richardson equation factor (*b*). Susceptance (*B* or *b*). See also **beta.**

Ba Symbol for the element barium.

BABA TEST REACTION. With *p*-phenylenediamine, aqueous, ethereal, or benzene extracts of pine chips give deep red colors showing a characteristic spectrum.

BABCOCK APPARATUS. Various equipment, such as the Babcock bottle and the Babcock pipette, used in the analysis and testing of milk.

BABCOCK PIPETTE. See **pipette, Babcock.**

BABKIN TEST. A test for manganese in which 1–2 ml. of the solution is boiled with excess sodium hydroxide and 2–3 drops hydrogen peroxide, filtered, and the precipitate washed. The precipitate is boiled with lead dioxide and 2–3 ml. nitric acid. A violet color indicates the presence of manganese.

BACH REAGENT FOR COPPER AND NICKEL. A mixture of equal quantities of 20% formaldehyde and hydroxylamine hydrochloride. Add 0.5 ml. of this reagent and 0.5 ml. 15% potassium hydroxide solution to 15 ml. of the solution to be tested. A violet color is given by copper and an orange-yellow color by nickel.

BACH SOLUTION FOR HYDROGEN PEROXIDE. A solution of 0.03 g. of potassium dichromate and 5 drops of aniline in 1 liter of water. Five ml. of this solution, to which 2 drops of 5% oxalic acid solution have been added, give a violet color with 5 ml. of a solution in which hydrogen peroxide is present.

BACH TEST REACTION FOR SOLANINE. When solanine is added to a mixture of equal parts of sulfuric acid and alcohol, a red color is formed which persists for 5–6 hours.

BACHMEYER TEST REACTION. With a tannin solution, caustic alkalies and ammonia produce a red to reddish-brown color which, after a while, turns to a dirty green.

BACHSTEZ-CAVALLINI TEST REACTION. A reaction for differentiating ascorbic and isoascorbic acids. Add 2 drops 10% uranium acetate solution and a few drops concentrated sodium hydroxide solution to a 1% solution of the material to be tested, made faintly alkaline. Ascorbic acid produces a brownish color discharged by the alkali and then an amorphous precipitate of sodium uranate is formed. Isoascorbic acid produces a dark brownish red color and the solution remains clear.

BACK E.M.F. An electromotive force which acts in a direction opposite to the electromotive force originally applied. It is a counterelectromotive force.

BACK PROCESS. A method of **sulfonation** by dissolving a basic substance in glacial acetic acid and adding concentrated sulfuric acid. The acid sulfate is formed.

BACOVESCO REAGENT. A solution of 15 g. molybdic acid in 85 g. concentrated sulfuric acid. It forms a blue-violet ring with solutions containing alcohols or phenols.

BACTERIA. Microscopic organisms (*Schizomycetes*) of various shapes, constituting many of the most elemental forms of vegetable life.

BACTERICIDE. A substance having the power of destroying bacteria.

BACTERIOLOGY. The science of **bacteria,** covering their anatomy, growth, characteristics, culture, and identification.

BACTERIOLYSIS. The destruction of **bacteria** by a process of solution, commonly one due to a bacterial or biochemical agent.

BACTERIOPHAGE. A substance of biological origin which has a lytic (dissolving) action on **bacteria.** Little is known of the nature of bacteriophages; they are ultramicroscopic and pass through filters readily.

BADISCHE PROCESS. A **contact process** for the manufacture of sulfuric acid from sulfur or ores of sulfur, in which the burner gases are washed with dilute sulfuric acid, filtered through coke, converted to SO_3 by a platinized asbestos **catalyst,** and finally the absorption is effected by strong acid.

BAECCHI REAGENT FOR BLOOD. This reagent is alizarine blue S; used with hydrogen peroxide.

BAEMES SOLUTION. A solution of 20 g. sodium acetate and 10 g. sodium tungstate, in 100 ml. of water. It is used as a test reagent for tannin. A light yellow precipitate shows the presence of tannin.

BAEKELAND PROCESS. The **polymerization** of phenols and formaldehyde to yield **resins.** The reaction starts with the addition to the carbonyl group of formaldehyde. The hydrogen atoms in the ortho and para positions are reactive. One of these adds to the O atom and the rest of the phenol molecule adds to the C atom:

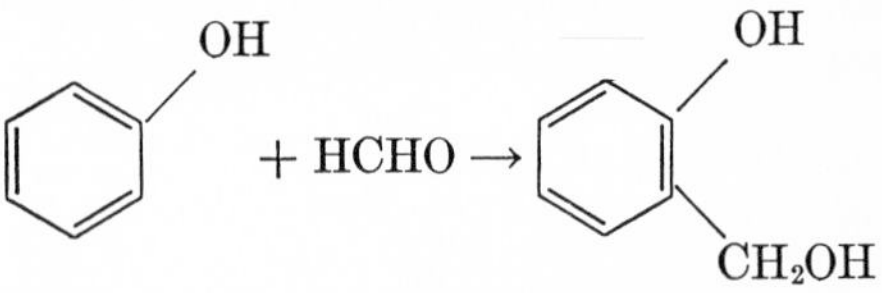

These molecules can condense with more phenol and more formaldehyde forming molecules with several reactive groups which continue to react until the final molecules are too complex to crystallize and so form resins.

BAERT TEST. A test for reducing sugars in raw sugars made by dissolving approximately 10 g. of the sugar in 50 ml. of water in a flask to which is added 1 ml. Fehling solution and 2 ml. of 1% methylene blue solution. A funnel is placed in the mouth of the flask and the mixture brought to a boil in $2\frac{1}{2}$ minutes and allowed to boil for another $2\frac{1}{2}$ minutes. The blue color is discharged if the sample contains more than 0.05% of invert sugar.

BAEYER-DREWSON INDIGO SYNTHESIS. Synthesis of indigo from *o*-nitrobenzaldehyde and acetone, acetaldehyde or related compounds.

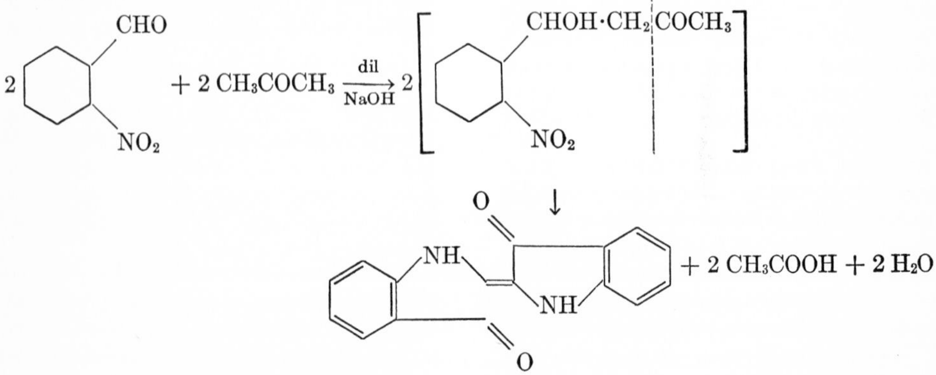

Two molecules of the intermediate compound undergo hydrolysis at the point indicated above, lose water, and condense to form indigo.

BAEYER-DREWSON TEST FOR ACETONE. Add some o-nitrobenzaldehyde to the solution containing acetone and heat the mixture to boiling, then add a few drops of sodium hydroxide or potassium hydroxide solution. If acetone is present, a blue color is produced. A number of modifications of this test have been developed.

BAEYER REACTION. A method of preparation of dihydroxy-diaryl alkanes by condensation of two molecules of a phenol with one of an aldehyde.

BAEYER TESTS FOR INDOLE. (1) Pine shavings are colored cherry-red in a solution of indole in alcohol acidulated with hydrochloric acid.

(2) If an indole solution is treated with nitric acid and sodium nitrite solution, the liquid becomes red and a red crystalline precipitate is formed.

BAEYER TEST REACTIONS FOR INDOXYL. (1) Sodium nitrite solution and hydrochloric acid, added to an aqueous solution of indoxyl, form yellow needles which, when heated with hydrochloric acid, are transformed into indigo.

(2) If diazobenzene chloride is added to an aqueous solution of indoxyl, a yellowish-red color to a red, crystalline precipitate is

See also **Baekeland process.**

BAEYER STRAIN THEORY. A theory dealing with **ring compounds** containing various numbers of atoms in the ring. This number determined the angles between the **valence bonds** on the atoms, and the angles for greatest stability were considered to be those in five- and six-membered carbon rings; more or less carbon atoms caused decreasing stability.

BAEYER TEST REACTION FOR EOSINE. When treated with sodium amalgam, an aqueous solution of eosine is decolorized. If 1 drop potassium permanganate solution is then added, a green fluorescence develops.

BAEYER TEST REACTION FOR GLUCOSE. (1) When a solution containing glucose is boiled with a solution of o-nitrophenylpropiolic acid in aqueous sodium carbonate, indigo precipitates.

(2) Alkaline potassium permanganate is reduced by glucose to produce a green color.

Several modifications of these reactions have been developed.

produced depending on the amount of indoxyl present.

(3) If sodium carbonate solution and isatin are added to an alcoholic solution of indoxyl, indirubin is produced in the form of red-brown needles with a metallic luster.

BAEYER TEST REACTION FOR PHENOL. When boiled with a mixture of concentrated sulfuric acid and a few drops of aldehyde, phenol produces a white, cement-like mass, soluble in sodium hydroxide solution to give a violet color. A number of modifications of this reaction have been developed.

BAEYER TEST REACTIONS FOR RESORCINOL. (1) Concentrated sulfuric acid gradually added to a mixture of resorcinol and benzaldehyde forms a red resinous substance which is soluble in alkalies to give a violet color.

(2) If resorcinol is heated with phthalic anhydride almost to the boiling point of the latter and the melt is dissolved in sodium hydroxide solution, a green fluorescence is produced.

BAEYER TEST REACTION FOR THIOPHENE. A blue solution is obtained when a solution of thiophene in benzene is mixed with concentrated sulfuric acid containing isatin.

BAEYER-VILLIGER TEST REACTION FOR ACETONE. While chilling with ice, add 10 ml. concentrated sulfuric acid to 3 ml. 3% hydrogen peroxide. When 1 drop of acetone is added to 1 ml. of this ice-cold reagent, an immediate crystalline precipitate of acetone peroxide is produced.

BAFFLE. A wall or other surface used to divert the flow of a fluid.

BAG FILTER. See **filter, bag.**

BAGINSKI SOLUTION. A solution formed by mixing 20 ml. of a $1\frac{1}{4}\%$ aqueous solution of silver nitrate, 30 ml. of a 2% aqueous solution of ammonium chromate, and 0.3 ml. concentrated ammonium hydroxide. This reagent gives a black precipitate with adrenaline, in neutral solution.

BAILEY TEST FOR CAMPHOR. Upon evaporation of the alcoholic solution on a slide, natural camphor shows colors under polarized light, whereas artificial camphor does not.

BAILEY TEST REACTION FOR SULFUR. When sulfur is fused with sodium carbonate, then dissolved in water, it gives a blood-red color upon addition of sodium nitroprusside solution.

BAINE REAGENT. A solution obtained by mixing 30 ml. 10% sodium hydroxide solution, 20 ml. glacial acetic acid, 1 ml. 0.25% sodium fluoresceinate solution and 50 ml. water. It is a test reagent for bromides, giving a characteristic pink color upon addition of 0.0001 N chlorine water, the color disappearing upon addition of an excess of the chlorine water.

BAKER-VENKATARAMAN TRANSFORMATION. The change of o-aroyloxyacetophenones into o-hydroxydiaroylmethanes.

BAKING. The general definition of baking is the drying or partial drying, of a material by the application of heat. In chemical technology, the term is usually associated with solids which, for example, may be produced on a surface by applying a liquid and then heating; or which may merely be heated to reduce their content of water or other liquids.

BALANCE. (1) A condition of partial or complete **equilibrium** or adjustment. (2) An instrument used for determining weight. In its usual form it employs the principle of the lever, either of the first or second classes. Coarse forms of the instrument which are used for large weights are known as scales, the term balance being restricted to those of great sensitiveness used in analytical operations.

BALANCE, CHAIN. A balance in which the smaller weights (commonly below 100 mg.) are applied by raising or lowering a chain attached to the beam, which is accomplished by moving the other end of the chain along a vertical scale.

BALANCE, CHAINOMATIC. See **balance, chain.**

BALANCE, CHAINWEIGHT. See **balance, chain.**

BALANCE, DAMPED. A balance equipped with means for damping the to-and-fro movements of the suspended system, so that the pointer comes to rest more rapidly. A magnetic system or a piston in a close-fitting cylinder are often used for the damping.

BALANCE, DIETARY SCALE. A balance with adjustable zero position, which can be set at zero when holding a dish or other empty container and the weight of the sample can be read directly.

BALANCE, JOLLY. A balance used for the determination of specific gravity of a substance by weighing it in air and in liquid. This balance consists of a spring from which the sample is suspended, with a scale for reading its position.

BALANCE, KEYBOARD. A balance in which all small weights (often up to 1 g.) are handled by a series of keys mounted on the outside of the case. The weights are not handled manually, and their total can be determined by adding the weight-values of the keys depressed in a given weighing.

BALANCE, MICRO. A balance for the precise weighing of small masses; the great sensitivity necessary is usually achieved by use of the torsion of a quartz fiber as a means of determination of weight.

BALANCE, MOHR. A balance designed, like the Westphal balance, for determining densities of solids by weighing them in air and when suspended in a liquid of known density; if the density of the solid is known, that of the liquid may be determined.

BALANCE, MOISTURE. A beam balance graduated directly in percentages of moisture and used for determination of moisture.

BALANCE, PER CENT. A balance which reads directly percentage change in weight, loss or gain. (See **balance, moisture.**)

BALANCE, PROJECTION. A balance in which the motion of the beam pointer is projected optically, for greater ease and accuracy of reading.

BALANCE, PULP. A balance for weighing ores, pulp, sugar, etc., where a heavy load (up to about 200 g.) may be encountered, and medium sensitivity (about $\frac{1}{2}$ mg.) is necessary.

BALANCE, SOLUTION. A rugged balance designed for weighing fairly large masses, usually up to 1 kg. The sensitivity commonly is from 0.1 to 1 g. This balance received its name from its use in preparing solutions, although, of course, it has other uses.

BALANCE, SPRING. A method of weighing in which a pan is suspended by a spring, calibrated so that a pointer attached to a point on the spring indicates weight directly by its position relative to a graduated scale.

BALANCE, TORSION. A balance in which the weight is determined by the twisting force necessary to turn a wire or band. In many types, the force of torsion works in opposition to the force of gravity.

BALANCE, TRIPLE BEAM. A rugged, single-pan beam balance, commonly used for dispensing chemicals, determining specific gravity, etc. The beam has three scales, carrying sliding weights or riders, and graduated in successively lower multiples of weight. For example, one scale may be graduated to 100 g. in 10 g. divisions, the second scale to 10 g. in 1 g. divisions, and the third beam to 1 g. in 0.1 g., and 0.01 g. divisions.

BALANCE, WESTPHAL. A balance designed for determining the densities of liquids or solids. It consists essentially of a plummet suspended from a beam, which is graduated and provided with riders. The densities of solids are determined by weighing them in air and in a liquid of known specific gravity; if the density of the solid is known, that of the liquid may be determined. Commonly, the riders on this balance have weight-ratios of 1, 1/10, 1/100, 1/1000, and the beam has nine divisions calibrated so that the specific gravity of the liquid can be read directly.

BALANCED REACTION. See **reaction, balanced.**

BALANCING, DETAILED. A principle of statistical mechanics which shows that the steady state of affairs at equilibrium is maintained by a direct balance between the rates of opposing processes.

BALAREFF TEST FOR METALS. The manganous, cobaltous, and ferrous ions give a dark brown or black color with silver oxide or an ammoniacal silver solution.

BALAREFF TESTS FOR PYROPHOS-PHATES. These tests show pyrophosphates in the presence of meta- or orthophosphates.

(1) The addition to the slightly alkaline solution of the sample, of 4–5 drops 5% copper sulfate solution gives a precipitate of pale gray crystals of cupric pyrophosphate.

(2) Upon addition of an excess of silver nitrate solution to the neutral solution of sample, followed by concentrated acetic acid, the silver pyrophosphate remains undissolved.

BALAVIONE TEST. To distinguish grape wine from cider, extract 25 ml. of the liquid with 10 ml. ether. Wash the ether extract, and to it add 2 ml. 0.5% ammonia and several crystals *p*-phenylenediamine hydrochloride. A cider extract is colored cherry red and a white grape wine extract becomes yellow.

BALBACH PROCESS. An electrolytic process for the separation of gold and silver, in which the metal to be separated forms the anode and is electrolyzed in a bath of silver nitrate, and the silver deposits on the cathode.

BALJET REAGENT. A freshly-prepared mixture of a 1% alcoholic solution of picric acid and an equal volume of a 10% sodium hydroxide solution free from carbonate. It gives a red to orange color with digitoxin, gitalin and *g*- or *k*-strophanthin.

BALL AND WINGHAM PROCESS. A metallurgical process for the desulfurization of molten metals, especially iron, by the action of an alkaline cyanide flux.

BALL MILL. See mill, ball.

BALL TEST REACTION FOR HYDROXYLAMINE. If a hydroxylamine solution is boiled with 1–2 drops yellow ammonium sulfide to incipient sulfur separation, and 3 ml. ammonia are added, followed by an equal volume of alcohol, a purple-red color is obtained.

BALL REAGENTS. Reagents for certain of the alkali metals. The reagent for rubidium and cesium is a solution of 50 g. sodium nitrite and 10 g. bismuth nitrate in dilute nitric acid. The reagent for sodium is a solution of 50 g. potassium nitrite and 10 g. bismuth nitrate in dilute nitric acid, to which 25 ml. 10% cesium nitrate solution is added.

The first reagent yields a yellow precipitate with solutions containing cesium or rubidium, and the second reagent gives a yellow precipitate with solutions containing sodium.

BALLING FURNACE. See furnace, balling.

BALLISTIC GALVANOMETER. See galvanometer, ballistic.

BALLOMETER. An apparatus for measuring electric charges upon droplets or particles.

BALLONI REAGENT. A 5% aqueous solution of ammonium molybdate, containing a few drops of acetic acid. This reagent gives a characteristic ring with urine containing acetic acid, if albumin is present.

BALMER SERIES. A group of lines in the visible spectrum of atomic **hydrogen** represented by the formula:

$$\bar{\nu} = R_H \left(\frac{1}{n_1{}^2} - \frac{1}{n_2{}^2} \right)$$

in which $\bar{\nu}$ is the **wave number**, R_H is the **Rydberg number**, and n_1 is 2, while n_2 has various integral values.

BALSAM. An **oleoresin** obtained by incising the trunk of a tree or naturally exuding from it. Balsams contain resins and **essential oils** in varying proportions among different members of the group. The best known are turpentine, balsam of Tolu, Peru balsam, and Canada balsam.

BALY TUBE. A pair of nested glass tubes used to hold liquids, in absorption spectroscopy.

BAMBERGER QUINOLINE TEST REACTION. On reduction with tin and hydrochloric acid, quinoline gives a red color with diazobenzenesulfonic acid. Isoquinoline does not.

BAMBERGER REAGENT FOR ALDEHYDES AND KETONES. Para-nitrophenylhydrazine is used as a reagent for aldehydes and ketones. Precipitates of characteristic crystalline form are obtained.

BAMBERGER-SEEBERGER TEST RE-ACTION. If dicyandiamide is boiled with dilute acetic acid for several hours, then the later addition of sodium hydroxide solution and a little cupric sulfate produces rose-colored crystals.

BAMBERGER TEST REACTION FOR ORTHO-DIKETONES. Addition of potassium hydroxide solution, in the absence of air, to a heated alcoholic solution of the *o*-diketone gives a dark red to black color, which disappears on shaking with air.

BAND SPECTRUM. See **spectrum, molecular.**

BANDONI TEST REACTION. Procaine and its derivatives give with sodium hypochlorite solution a red-yellow precipitate soluble in alcohol and chloroform.

BANFI TEST REACTION. Santonin gives a deep red fusion with potassium hydroxide, which decomposes on further heating.

BAR. A unit of pressure in the metric system equal to one million dynes per square centimeter. It is slightly less than one atmosphere.

BARAC TEST REACTION. Ascorbic acid in alkaline solution gives an orange color with diazotized sulfanilic acid.

BARBACHE REAGENT. A solution of 0.25 ml. phenol in 1 liter water, to which a few drops of a saturated solution of ferric chloride are added. It is used in testing for glycerin, which decolorizes this reagent.

BARBER REAGENT. Thiolacetomide is used as a reagent for arsonic acids. Thioarsenites with characteristic melting points are obtained.

BARBERIO REAGENT FOR INDICAN. A 0.05% aqueous solution of sodium nitrite used as a reagent for indican in urine. A blue color, which is obtained from urine strongly acidified with hydrochloric acid, indicates the presence of indican.

BARBET-JANDRIER REAGENT FOR FORMALDEHYDE. A solution of gallic acid in sulfuric acid, which is colored pink to red by formaldehyde.

BARBET-JANDRIER TEST. A solution containing 0.05 g. of phenol or of one of certain other aromatic hydroxy-compounds in 2 ml. alcohol, to which various aldehydes are added, gives ring-tests of characteristic color with concentrated sulfuric acid. The test is useful for detecting either the phenols or the aldehydes.

BARBIER TEST. To detect alcohol in volatile oils, distill off 10% of the volume of the oil, and add potassium acetate to the residue. The alcohol can be reclaimed and estimated by distillation from the separated layer.

BARBIER-WIELAND DEGRADATION. A method of elimination of one carbon atom at a time from an **aliphatic acid** type of side chain. The method consists essentially of the reaction of the ester of the acid with an aryl-magnesium halide and its removal by hydrolysis and oxidation of the compound at the resulting double bond.

$$RCH_2COOH + C_2H_5OH \xrightarrow{-H_2O} RCH_2COOC_2H_5$$

$$RCH_2COOC_2H_5 + 2C_6H_5MgX + 2HX \xrightarrow[-C_2H_5OH]{-2MgX_2} RCH_2C\overset{\displaystyle OH}{\underset{\displaystyle C_6H_5}{|}}C_6H_5$$

$$RCH_2C\overset{\displaystyle OH}{\underset{\displaystyle C_6H_5}{|}}C_6H_5 \xrightarrow{-H_2O} RCH{=}C\overset{\displaystyle C_6H_5}{\underset{\displaystyle C_6H_5}{}} \xrightarrow{O} RCOOH + C_6H_5COC_6H_5.$$

BARBITURIC. Related to barbituric acid,

$$
\begin{array}{c}
\text{NH---C=O} \\
\diagup \qquad \diagdown \\
\text{O=C} \qquad\qquad \text{CH}_2. \\
\diagdown \qquad \diagup \\
\text{NH---C=O}
\end{array}
$$

BARDACH TEST FOR PROTEINS. To 5 ml. of a fairly dilute solution of the material, add 3 drops 0.5% acetone solution, 0.1–0.2 ml. Lugol's iodine solution (an iodine-potassium iodide solution acidified with acetic acid) and 3 ml. ammonia. Yellow needles are given by proteins.

BARDHAN-SENGUPTA SYNTHESIS. Phosphorus pentoxide and other powerful dehydrating agents act upon 2-β phenethyl-l-cyclohexanol to form octahydrophenanthrene compounds.

BARFF PROCESS. A process for oxidizing the surface of metals, by the action of superheated steam, to increase their resistance to corrosion.

BARGELLINI REACTION. See **Kostanecki-Robinson reaction.**

BARGER-BERGEL-TODD TEST REACTION. A dilute solution of vitamin B_1, upon addition of a very dilute solution of potassium ferricyanide, followed by sodium hydroxide, gives a blue fluorescence.

BARIC. (Obs.) A salt containing barium as the basic radical.

BARISOL PROCESS. A process for **centrifugal dewaxing** (q.v.) of petroleum fractions, using a solvent that is a mixture of ethylene dichloride and benzene.

BARIUM. Metallic element. Symbol Ba. Atomic number 56. Atomic weight 137.36. Density 3.5. Specific heat 0.068. Melt-ing point 850° C. Boiling point 1140° C. Valence 2. Oxide BaO. Barium forms but one series of compounds. Its soluble salts are very poisonous. It is chiefly remarkable for the insolubility of its sulfate which requires 42,000 parts of water for solution. The color of barium is silver white.

BARIUM NUMBER. Absorption of barium hydroxide solution (commonly 0.25 N) by a textile sample, or the ratio of the amount absorbed by a given textile to that absorbed by a standard textile, such as untreated cotton.

BARKHAUSEN EFFECT. When the **magnetic field strength** applied to a ferric-magnetic material is changed, the magnetization changes discontinuously.

BARKOMETER. An hydrometer graduated so as to read directly in terms of percentage of tanning material in a given solution.

BARLOW AND POPE THEORY. Every **crystal** is a close-packed assemblage of atomic spheres which can be partitioned into small cells, all exactly similar and all marshaled in rows and columns, giving the symmetrical form to the crystal. These small cells are the chemical molecules and the atoms and molecules are assumed to be capable of a certain amount of distortion under the influence of the forces acting upon them.

BARLOW RULE. The volumes of space occupied by the various **atoms** in a given **molecule** are approximately proportional to the **valencies** of the atoms; whenever an element exhibits more than one kind of valency the lowest value is generally selected.

BARN. A unit nuclear **cross section** of the magnitude of 10^{-24} square centimeter per nucleus.

BARNARD REAGENT. A solution of 0.42 g. hydrazine in 1 liter water, to which has been added 7.5 ml. of a 2% acid fuchsin solution. This reagent gives a characteristic pink color with aldehydes.

BARNEBEY TEST. To detect cyanides in the presence of ferrocyanides, ferricyanides and thiocyanates, add ammonia to a dilute aqueous solution of cupric sulfide until the precipitate redissolves, then add a small quantity of hydrogen sulfide, precipitating a little cupric sulfide and follow with the solution being tested. If the precipitate of cupric sulfide dissolves, cyanide is present.

BAROGRAPH. A recording **barometer.**

BAROMETER. An instrument for measuring the pressure of the atmosphere. (1) The common mercury barometer consists of a column of mercury in an upright tube at least 80 cm. long from which the air has been exhausted; the upper end is sealed and the lower dips into a cup containing mercury which is open to the air. The height of the mercury column in the tube indicates the air pressure. The instrument was invented by Torricelli, of Florence, circa 1643. (2) The aneroid barometer consists of a thin disk of metal covering the aperture of a box from which the air base has been exhausted. Variation in atmospheric pressure causes a bulging of the disk which shifts a pointer over a scale and so indicates the pressures. It is less accurate than the mercury barometer but is more convenient to carry about.

BAROSCOPE. An indicating pressure gauge, consisting of a U-tube partly filled with liquid, having one end open to the atmosphere, and the other end connected to a system whose pressure is to be observed.

BARRAL SOLUTION. An aqueous solution of 20 g. o-phenolsulfonic acid in 100 ml. solution used to test for albumin and bile pigments in urine. The presence of the former is shown by the formation of a white ring between sample and reagent, and the presence of the latter by a green ring.

BARRAL TEST FOR ACETANILID. Phosphomolybdic acid gives a light yellow precipitate with acetanilid which, unlike that given by acetophenetidin, dissolves on warming.

BARRAL TESTS FOR ACETOPHENET-IDIN. (1) When acetophenetidin crystals are heated with bromine water, they are colored rose-red, the supernatant liquid becoming yellow-orange. A brown precipitate appears on cooling. (2) **Millon reagent** produces first a yellow and then a red color in the hot solution.

BARRAL TESTS FOR AMINOPYRINE. (1) Treatment of the aqueous solution with sodium peroxide and sulfuric acid gives colors changing from blue-violet to yellow.

(2) A drop of bromine water gives a violet color becoming pink and yellow.

(3) **Mandelin reagent** gives a brown color which becomes green.

(4) A solution of 2 g. potassium dichromate solution in 10 ml. water and 10 ml. sulfuric acid gives a brown color changing to olive green.

BARRAL TESTS FOR CRYOGENINE. (1) A solution of cryogenine in fuming nitric acid becomes red on the addition of water.

(2) Sodium peroxide gives a yellow color, becoming blood-red on addition of hydrochloric acid.

(3) Phosphomolybdic acid produces a blue color with a cryogenine solution, from which a brown precipitate is formed.

(4) On treatment with the **Marquis reagent** cryogenine gives a red-violet color with a green fluorescence.

BARRAL TESTS FOR HERMOPHENYL. (1) Hermophenyl colors warm sulfuric acid orange-yellow.

(2) Hermophenyl colors **Berg reagent** amethyst-red in the cold and orange on heating.

(3) Hermophenyl on warming with **Froehde reagent** gives a yellow color changing through orange and brown shades to amethyst-blue.

(4) Hermophenyl gives a deep-brown-red color on warming with formaldehyde-sulfuric acid.

BARRAL TESTS FOR PILOCARPINE. (1) On heating with sodium persulfate, pilocarpine forms a yellow color and gives an unpleasant odor suggestive of ammonia. The vapors blacken mercurous nitrate and turn litmus blue.

(2) Formaldehyde containing sulfuric acid colors pilocarpine yellow, changing to yellowish-brown and red.

(3) With a very dilute pilocarpine solution, **Mandelin reagent** gives a golden yellow color, changing to light green and then to light blue, which is stable.

BARRAL TESTS FOR SULFOSALICYLIC ACID. (1) **Mandelin reagent** gives an indigo blue color; with chlorinated soda solution, a brown color slowly develops. (2) **Millon reagent** on warming with sulfosalicylic acid becomes pink to fuchsin-red; salicylic acid is colored red-orange.

BARRESWIL TEST REACTION FOR CHROMATE. A solution containing chromic acid gives an intense blue color with a slightly acid 3% solution of hydrogen peroxide containing ether, the blue color passing into the ether layer on shaking.

BARRESWIL TEST REACTION FOR VANADIUM. Hydrogen peroxide, in limited amount, gives a red-brown to red color in acid vanadium solution.

BART REACTION. A method for the preparation of aromatic **arsonic acids** by reaction of a diazonium salt and a metal arsenite; or by reaction of a primary arylamine, nitrous acid and an arsenic trihalide, in the presence of a catalyst, such as a trace of a copper salt.

BARYE. The standard unit of pressure in the metric (c.g.s.) system. It is one dyne per square centimeter.

BARYTIC. Pertaining to, or containing, **barium.**

BASE. (1) A molecule, ion, or other entity that acts as a **proton** acceptor. (2) A substance which ionizes in solution to form **hydroxyl ions.** (3) Any substance which has the property of neutralizing **acids** to form salts and which will restore the color of reddened litmus. (4) Any substance which can replace the hydrogen of an acid, or which contains hydroxyl groups capable of uniting with the hydrogen of an acid to form water and a salt, or which contains trivalent nitrogen and

can add directly to an acid to produce a salt in which the nitrogen is pentavalent.

BASE, AMMONO. A substance that yields NH_2^- ions in liquid ammonia.

BASE, AQUO. A substance that yields OH^- ions in water.

BASE EXCHANGE. The exchange of one positive **ion** for another in an **adsorption** phase.

BASE, INORGANIC. A metallic **hydroxide.**

BASE, ORGANIC. An organic compound containing trivalent nitrogen.

BASE, PSEUDO. A substance that yields a base by a **tautomeric change.** Many such substances contain hydroxyl groups attached to carbon atoms that are adjacent to nitrogen atoms, and the base is formed by a shift of the hydroxyl group to the nitrogen atom.

BASE, SECONDARY. A secondary amine (see **amine**).

BASE, TERTIARY. A tertiary amine (see **amine**).

BASIC. Having the properties of a **base.**

BASIC ANHYDRIDE. A metallic **oxide.**

BASIC CAPACITY. The number of hydrogen ions yielded by complete **ionization** of a molecule.

BASIC DYE. One of a group of dyes that form soluble salts with mineral acids and certain organic acids, and that form insoluble compounds with acidic fibers.

BASIC OPEN HEARTH PROCESS. See **open hearth process, basic.**

BASIC SALT. A salt containing one or more **hydroxyl** radicals, or which yields one or more hydroxyl ions on complete **dissociation** in water.

BASIC SOLVENT. A solvent that accepts **protons** (hydrogen ions) from the solute.

BASICITY. The concentration of hydroxyl ions in a solution, or the normality of a base, or the number of total hydroxyl groups or ions in a molecule.

BASILEIOS TEST FOR IODATE. Add to 10 ml. of the 5% solution to be tested, 2 ml. chloroform, 1 ml. 0.001 N sodium thiosulfate, and 1 ml. N sulfuric acid. After standing for 1 minute, the solution is shaken. A blue color in the chloroform indicates the presence of iodate.

BASILEIOS TEST FOR IODIDE IN THE PRESENCE OF BROMATE, CHLORATE, AND IODATE. Shake 10 ml. of the neutral solution to be tested about 20 times with 2 ml. 0.5% iodine solution in chloroform. Add 3 drops 1% starch solution and turn the cylinder 4 times. If iodides are present the aqueous layer turns blue. Bromate gives a violet color.

BASOPHIL. Accepting, or being stained by, basic dyestuffs. This is one of the major means of bacteriological differentiation.

BASSETT-SNYDER REAGENT. A reagent prepared by mixing 3 parts glacial acetic acid, 4 parts nitric acid, and 16 parts water. It is used in metallography to etch lead and lead alloys.

BATE EQUATION. A relationship of the form:

$$\log_{10}\left(\frac{\Lambda\eta}{\Lambda_0\eta_0}\right)^2 \frac{C}{1 - \frac{\Lambda\eta}{\Lambda_0\eta_0}} = k + k'\left(\frac{C\Lambda\eta}{\Lambda_0\eta_0}\right)^h$$

$\frac{\eta}{\eta_0}$ = ratio of **viscosity** of a solution to that of water at the same temperature;

$\frac{\Lambda\eta}{\eta_0}$ = corrected equivalent conductance;

k, k', h, and Λ_0 are empirical constants; C is the concentration of the solution.

BATH. A limited region, usually filled with a specified medium, such as air, water, oil, etc. for controlling or modifying the temperature or other condition of objects or apparatus within, or partly within, the region.

BATHOCHROMIC GROUP. A group of atoms, or a radical, which by its introduction into an organic compound, displaces the absorption **spectrum** in the direction of increasing wave length, i.e., toward the red.

BATHOFLORE. An atom or radical which by its substitution in a molecule tends to shift its **fluorescent radiation** bands in the direction of longer wave length.

BATING OF SKINS. A process consisting of the treating of skins with a pancreatic enzymatic substance in an ammoniacal solution. It is used in the tanning industry.

BATTANDIER TEST REACTION FOR CHELIDONINE AND NARCEINE. If a little of either of these alkaloids is added to a mixture of 1 drop guaiacol and 0.5 ml. concentrated sulfuric acid, carmine-red striations appear. Tannin and sulfuric acid give a green color with each of these alkaloids.

BATTANDIER TEST REACTION FOR GLAUCINE. If a crystal of glaucine is treated in a porcelain dish with 10 ml. sulfuric acid and 4 drops mercuric nitrate, green streaks appear, changing to red.

BATTANDIER TEST REACTION FOR QUININE AND QUINIDINE. A weak acid solution to be tested is exposed to bromine vapors, then a cupric salt solution is added followed by ammonia (in drops). A peach color, becoming violet and green, and then on addition of acid, blue or violet, indicates the presence of quinine or quinidine.

BATTELLI-STERN SOLUTION. A solution prepared by mixing a 1% potassium iodide solution with twice its volume of a 3% starch solution, and acidifying with acetic acid. It is oxidized, giving the characteristic blue color of iodine-starch, by peroxidases in animal tissue.

BATTERY. A group of similar units operated together; this includes units for generating electricity, but here the term is also applied to a single **primary** or **secondary cell** (q.v.).

BAUBIGNY TEST. A filter paper that has been treated with a solution of fluorescein in 40–50% acetic acid and then dried, becomes rose colored when exposed to traces of bromine.

BAUDISCH REAGENT. A solution of the compound cupferron, the ammonium salt of nitrosophenylhydroxylamine, used in testing for copper and iron.

BAUDOUIN TEST FOR SESAME OIL. One g. of sugar is dissolved in 100 ml. hydrochloric acid (sp. gr. 1.18) and 10 ml. of the oil is treated with 5 ml. of the reagent. A deep red color indicates the presence of sesame oil. See also **Villavecchia Test.**

BAUER TEST REACTION FOR SOLANINE. A solution of telluric acid in dilute sulfuric acid gives a deep red color on warming with solanine.

BAUER TEST FOR MILK. One drop of a 0.25% aqueous solution of Nile blue sulfate is added to 3 ml. of the milk. Cows' milk becomes green-blue, human milk violet. On shaking with ether, cows' milk changes to blue, human milk becomes colorless.

BAUMANN BENZOYL CHLORIDE REACTION. When carbohydrates, diamines, and polyhydric alcohols in dilute aqueous solution are shaken with benzoyl chloride and sodium hydroxide, a precipitate of the benzoic acid esters forms.

BAUMANN TEST REACTION FOR AGAR-AGAR. Agar-agar is precipitated by a 5% solution of tannic acid.

BAUMANN TEST REACTION FOR IODIDE. Solutions of alkali iodides give a black precipitate with palladous chloride solution.

BAUMANN TEST FOR CORN STARCH IN WHEAT FLOUR. One-tenth g. of the flour is shaken for 2 minutes with 10 ml. potassium hydroxide solution (1.8%); then 4–5 drops 25% hydrochloric acid are added, and a microscopic examination is made. Corn starch is unchanged, but the wheat grains are completely swollen.

BAUMÉ. A **hydrometer** scale which is used for measuring the **specific gravity** of liquids, their relative weight as compared to the weight of an equal volume of a standard liquid. There are two Baumé scales: one for liquids which are heavier than water; the other for liquids which are lighter than water. For liquids heavier than water, the conversion formula is:

$$\text{Degrees Baumé (American)} = 145 - \frac{145}{\text{specific gravity } 60/60° \text{ F.}}$$

For liquids lighter than water, the conversion formula is:

$$\text{Degrees Baumé} = \frac{140}{\text{specific gravity } 60/60° \text{ F.}} - 130.$$

BAYER PROCESS. A process for the purification of alumina (chiefly for aluminum manufacture) by calcining and grinding the bauxite, treatment with sodium hydroxide solution to form sodium aluminate, settling and filtering, cooling and "seeding" to precipitate aluminum hydroxide, filtering, and calcining to alumina.

BAYER TEST REACTION FOR ADRENALINE. If 2 ml. adrenaline solution are mixed with 1 ml. sulfanilic acid solution, 2 ml. sodium bi-iodate solution, and 1 ml. 10% phosphoric acid, various colors are obtained ranging from red-yellow to yellow as concentration decreases.

BAYER TEST REACTION FOR GOLD. A drop of rubidium chloride solution and a drop of 0.1% silver nitrate solution, upon addition to a drop of gold chloride solution, give blood-red microscopic crystals.

Be Symbol for the element **beryllium.**

BEAD TEST. A test for the identification of various metals, made by fusing a small quantity of the sample with borax or other fluxing substance on a small loop of inert wire (usually platinum wire), to form a bead. The appearance of the bead — its color, transparency, etc. — is often characteristic of a particular metal, as well as of the **flux** used, and the kind of flame (oxidizing or reducing).

BÉCHAMP PROCESS. Reduction of aromatic nitro compounds to the amines by iron, or ferrous salts, and acids.

BÉCHAMP REACTION. A reaction for the preparation of aromatic **arsonic acids** by the interaction of arsenic acid with **phenols,** aromatic **amines,** or various derivatives of them.

$$C_6H_5OH + H_3AsO_4 \rightarrow OH \cdot C_6H_4 \cdot AsO(OH)_2(p) + H_2O.$$

BEALE REAGENT. A stain for certain animal tissues, prepared by dissolving 1 g. carmine in 30 ml. ethyl alcohol, and adding 110 ml. water, 80 ml. glycerol, and 5 ml. ammonium hydroxide.

BEATER. A machine used in the manufacture of paper. It is a tank in which the pulp-water mixture is agitated and cut by means of rotating blades, until the fibers have been separated and reduced in length to the degree desired before they pass to the fourdrinier (the actual sheet-forming apparatus).

BEATTIE AND BRIDGEMAN EQUATION. A form of the **equation of state,** relating the pressure, volume, and temperature of a gas, and the **gas constant.** The Beattie and Bridgeman Equation applies a correction for reduction of the effective number of molecules by molecular aggregation, due to various causes. It is of the form

$$P = \frac{RT(1 - \epsilon)}{V^2} (V + B) - \frac{A}{V^2}$$

in which P is the pressure, T is the absolute temperature, V is the volume, R is the gas constant and A, B and ϵ are constants defined in terms of five other empirical constants, A_0, B_0, a, b, and c by the following relationships:

$$A = A_0 \left(1 - \frac{a}{V} \right)$$

$$B = B_0 \left(1 - \frac{b}{V} \right)$$

$$\epsilon = \frac{c}{VT^3}$$

BÉCHAMP TEST FOR ALKALI SULFIDES. Alkali sulfides give a purple-red color with a 0.4% aqueous solution of sodium nitroprusside. For greater sensitivity, add sodium hydroxide to the solution to be tested.

BÉCHAMP TEST FOR NITROBENZENE IN OIL OF BITTER ALMOND. The oil is distilled with ferric acetate and chlorinated lime solution is added to the distillate. A blue color indicates the presence of nitrobenzene.

BECHER TEST REACTION FOR APOMORPHINE. A few drops of dilute sodium nitrite solution are added to 5–10 ml. of a very dilute aqueous solution of the alkaloid, then 1 drop hydrochloric acid is added. A blood-red color indicates the presence of apomorphine.

BECHHOLD FILTER. See **filter, Bechhold.**

BECHI-HEHNER SOLUTION. A solution of 1 g. silver nitrate in 250 ml. ethyl alcohol, with the addition of 53 ml. of ethyl ether and 0.1 ml. concentrated nitric acid. This reagent gives a dark red color with oily mixtures if cottonseed oil is present.

BECHI SOLUTION. A solution of 1 g. silver nitrate in 100 ml. 98% ethyl alcohol, used as a test reagent for cottonseed oil in olive oil. A dark color, obtained on heating the sample with the reagent and additional alcohol, indicates the presence of cottonseed oil.

BECK HYDROMETER. A **hydrometer** graduated for liquids lighter than water, in which the zero reading corresponds to the **specific gravity** of water (1.) and each degree corresponds to a decrease of 0.005 in specific gravity; thus 1° Beck = 0.995 specific gravity, 10° Beck = 0.950 specific gravity, etc.

BECKER OVEN. A type of coke oven used for the production of coke to be used in iron and steel manufacture. It consists essentially of a chamber of silica brick.

BECKMAN TEST REACTION FOR VERATRINE. When evaporated to dryness with fuming nitric acid on the steam bath, veratrine gives a yellow residue, which turns to orange-red with alcoholic potassium hydroxide.

BECKMAN TEST FOR AMYLODEX-TRIN IN HONEY. Dissolve 1 g. honey in 4 ml. water, add 3 ml. barium hydroxide solution and 17 ml. methanol. A flocculent precipitate indicates the presence of amylodextrin.

BECKMANN APPARATUS. Apparatus for the accurate determination of freezing-point lowering or boiling-point elevation, as in the determination of **molecular weights.**

BECKMANN MIXTURE. An oxidizing reagent consisting of 60 parts potassium dichromate, 80 parts concentrated sulfuric acid, and 270 parts water.

BECKMANN REARRANGEMENT. A rearrangement whereby **ketoximes** are converted into isomeric **amides,** usually effected by treatment with phosphorus pentachloride, but strong mineral acids may also be employed. The change occurs through entire rearrangement of the molecule: the hydroxyl group exchanges positions with the alkyl group in the *cis* position; then the hydroxyl hydrogen shifts to the nitrogen atom so that the double bond formerly between the nitrogen and carbonyl carbon is now found between the latter and the hydroxyl oxygen. It is represented by the following steps:

$$
\begin{array}{ccccc}
\text{R}'\!-\!\text{C}\!-\!\text{R} & & \text{HO}\!-\!\text{C}\!-\!\text{R} & & \text{O}\!=\!\text{C}\!-\!\text{R} \\
\| & \rightarrow & \| & \rightarrow & | \\
\text{HO}\!-\!\text{N} & & \text{R}'\!-\!\text{N} & & \text{R}'\text{NH} \\
\text{\small Ketoxime} & & & & \text{\small Amide}
\end{array}
$$

The reaction has been of particular service in determining the constitution of *syn-anti* isomers, for, from the acid formed by hydrolyzing the amide, one can determine the radical *anti* to the oxime hydroxyl group.

BECKMANN THERMOMETER. See **thermometer, Beckmann.**

BECKURT REAGENT. A 0.1 N aqueous solution of potassium permanganate, used in testing for alkaloids. Characteristic color reactions are obtained with individual alkaloids or groups of alkaloids, thus brucine, quinine, codeine, etc. give brown precipitates (MnO_2), while atropine, strychnine, etc. give a red color, etc.

BECQUEREL RAYS. See **rays, Becquerel.**

BEER LAW. See **law of Beer.**

BÉHAL TEST REACTION FOR ALCOHOLS. Cyanic acid is used to form, with the alcohol, the corresponding ester of allophanic acid.

BÉHAL REAGENT FOR ACETYLENE HYDROCARBONS. A saturated solution of silver nitrate in 95% alcohol.

BEHENIC. Related to behenic acid, $C_{21}H_{43}COOH$.

BEHRENS REAGENT FOR ALDE-HYDES AND KETONES. An aqueous solution of *p*-nitrophenylhydrazine hydrochloride, clarified by the addition of a few drops of acetic acid, and used in the microscopic detection of aldehydes and ketones.

BEHRENS SOLUTION FOR CELLU-LOSE. A solution of 8 g. potassium iodide, 25 g. zinc chloride, and an excess of iodine, in 8.5 ml. water. This reagent is used as a stain for cellulose in plant tissues.

BEIJERINCK REAGENT. The substance isatin hydrochloride, used in testing for indican in plant cells.

BEILSTEIN TEST. To detect halogens in organic compounds, dip a copper spiral in the organic substance to be tested, ignite, allow the substance to burn outside the flame, then place the spiral in the non-luminous portion of the flame. A green color indicates the presence of halogen.

BEISSENHIRTZ TEST REACTION. Aniline, when dissolved in concentrated sulfuric acid, gives a transitory blue color with 1–2 drops 5% potassium dichromate solution.

BELL PROCESS. A metallurgical process for the purification of iron by oxidation of phosphorus and other impurities by adding iron oxide to the charge.

BELL REAGENT FOR ALUM IN FLOUR. A freshly-prepared solution of 5 g. logwood in 100 ml. ethyl alcohol, which gives a lavender to blue color with flour and water, in the presence of ammonium carbonate solution, if alum is present in the flour.

BELL REAGENT FOR CURCUMA. A solution of 1 g. diphenylamine in 20 ml. ethyl alcohol and 25 ml. concentrated sulfuric acid, used in the detection of curcuma in compounded drugs.

BELLIER NUMBER. An expression of the temperature of crystallization of fatty acids from alcoholic solution upon cooling.

BELLIER TEST REACTION FOR DULCIN. Dissolve the material in 2 ml. sulfuric acid, add a few drops formaldehyde, and allow to stand for fifteen minutes. A white turbidity on the addition of 5 ml. water indicates the presence of dulcin.

BELLIER REAGENT FOR COCONUT OIL. A solution of 50 g. sodium sulfate and 21.85 g. cupric sulfate in 1 liter water, used in the detection of coconut oil.

BELLIER REAGENTS FOR WHEAT FLOUR. (1) A solution of 5 g. potassium hydroxide in 15 ml. glycerin and 85 ml. water. (2) A mixture of 100 ml. of (1) and 5 ml. glycerin. (3) A mixture of 1 part of (1) and 3 parts water. These reagents are used to differintiate starches from various sources by their swelling properties.

BELLIER TEST FOR PEANUT OIL. An old test for peanut oil in olive oil. Superseded by the **Evers-Bellier Test.**

BELLUCCI REAGENT. An alcoholic solution, commonly 1%, of β-nitroso-α-naphthol, used in testing for cobalt and for zirconium.

BELTZER REAGENT. An aqueous solution of ammonium ruthenium oxychloride, used in the differentiation of various natural and artificial fibers, which it stains different colors.

BENDA SOLUTION. A mixture of 4 parts of a 2% aqueous solution of osmic acid, 15 parts of a 1% aqueous solution of chromic acid, and a small amount of glacial acetic acid, used as a fixative.

BENDA STAIN. A mixture of 1 ml. of a saturated aqueous solution of alizarin red S and 80 ml. water, used as a biological stain.

BENEDICT ACETATE REAGENT. A solution prepared by saturating 20 ml. of a normal cobalt nitrate solution with hydrogen sulfide, and then adding about 25 drops of normal acetic acid. It is used in testing for acetate.

BENEDICT-BEHRE TEST REACTION FOR CREATININE. Creatinine gives a purple-red color with 3,5-dinitrobenzoic acid in alkaline solution.

BENEDICT-DENIS SULFUR REAGENT. A solution of 25 g. cupric nitrate, 10 g. ammonium nitrate, and 25 g. sodium chloride in 100 ml. water, used in the determination of sulfur.

BENEDICT-HOPKINS-COLE REAGENT. Add 250 ml. saturated oxalic acid solution, slowly and with cooling, to 10 g. magnesium powder. Filter, acidify with acetic acid, and dilute to 1 liter. This reagent is used to test for tryptophane or proteins yielding it. The substance to be tested is mixed with the reagent, and a ring-test is made with concentrated sulfuric acid. A red-violet ring indicates tryptophane.

BENEDICT REAGENT FOR BARIUM, STRONTIUM, AND CALCIUM. A saturated aqueous solution of potassium iodate.

BENEDICT SOLUTIONS. A well-known reagent for the determination of glucose and other reducing sugars. It comprises two solutions; one consisting of an aqueous solution of sodium carbonate and sodium or potassium citrate or tartrate; the second solution, which is mixed with the first just before using, is an aqueous solution of cupric sulfate. For accurate quantitative determinations, a small amount of a third solution (potassium thiocyanate) is sometimes added, and 2.5 to 5.0 g. anhydrous sodium carbonate is added for every 30 ml. of the mixed solutions.

Various modifications have been proposed. Fillinger developed a one-solution form of Benedict's solution containing 10.42 g. cupric sulfate, 250 g. potassium carbonate, 50 g. potassium thiocyanate per liter. The one-solution modifications are most widely used.

BENEDICT SULFUR REAGENT. A solution of 200 g. cupric sulfate and 50 g. sodium chlorate, in enough distilled water to make 1 liter of solution. This reagent is used for the determination of sulfur.

BENEDICT URIC ACID REAGENT. A solution of 100 g. of sodium tungstate and 30 g. arsenic pentoxide in 700 ml. water, which is then boiled with 50 ml. concentrated hydrochloric acid and made up to 1 liter. Another form of this solution is prepared from somewhat different amounts of these substances, plus phosphoric acid. This reagent gives a blue color with solutions containing uric acid, upon the addition of sodium carbonate solution.

BENOIST TEST. A test for ozone in air, in which a 0.0001% solution of fluorescein is shaken with the sample of air. If the dye loses its color, ozone is present. More concentrated solutions lose their fluorescence, but not their color.

BENTZEN TEST. A test for formaldehyde in paper in which the paper is boiled with fresh aniline-water in an apparatus designed to avoid direct contact with air. A turbidity indicates the presence of formaldehyde.

BENZ-, BENZO-. Relating to **benzene;** as benzoic; specifically, denoting presence of the benzene ring, as benzoquinoline.

BENZAL. See **benzylidene.**

BENZAL-ACETONE PROCESS. See **Govers process.**

BENZAMIDE REACTION. See **reaction, Von Braun's benzamide.**

BENZAMIDO. The radical C_6H_5CONH-.

BENZENE (BENZOL, BENZOLE). The parent **hydrocarbon** of the aromatic series: formula C_6H_6, molecular weight 78.05, melting point 5.42° C., boiling point 80.2° C. The chief characteristic of benzene is its cyclic structure. (See **benzene, formulas.**)

BENZENE OF CRYSTALLIZATION. Certain substances, particularly **hydrocarbons,** when crystallized from benzene retain a portion of the solvent in the same way that many salts crystallize from water with definite proportions of that solvent. Triphenylmethane crystallizes with one molecule of benzene.

BENZENE, FORMULAS. Many formulas have been advanced to represent the constitution of benzene and its derivatives but no one is free from objection. The more common formulas are presented below.

I. Plane formulas.
Kekulé (1865).

Claus. (Diagonal formula, 1867.)

Claus. (Prism formula, 1867.) Ladenburg (1869.)

```
        H
        C
       /|\
   HC__|__CH
    |   |  |
   HC__|__CH
       \|/
        C
        H
```

Centric formula. (Armstrong, 1887, Baeyer, 1892.)

```
        H
        C
       /|\
   HC   |   CH
    |>  X  <|
   HC   |   CH
       \|/
        C
        H
```

Thiele's "partial valency" formula. (1899.)

```
        H ..
        C·
      ..// \..
   HC·      ·CH
    |        ||
   HC        CH
      ··\   /··
         C·
        H··
```

II. Space formulas. Representing the six carbon atoms of benzene by six regular tetrahedrons arranged in various ways; spatial formulas have been advocated by Baeyer, Marsh, Vaubel, Sachse, and others. (Graebe, *Ber.* **35**, 526.)

III. Dynamic formulas. Kekulé advanced a dynamic hypothesis assuming an oscillation of the carbon atoms with shifting of the double bond from carbon 2 to carbon 6,

and simultaneous adjustment of the other atoms. Knoevenagel supposed each of the carbon atoms to rotate in an opposite direction to its neighbors, thus forming and breaking the double bond alternately.

Knorr assumed an oscillation of the hydrogen atoms, and Collie supposed that the carbon atoms not only change their relative positions but rotate as a whole.

The present-day conception of the structure of benzene is also a dynamic one, in which each pair of carbon atoms have a shared pair of electrons, constituting a single valence bond, and have also, for part of the time, another shared pair of electrons, which shifts constantly to other atoms in the ring.

BENZENE RING. (Benzene Nucleus) A regular hexagon conventionally adopted to represent the molecular structure of the six carbon atoms in benzene and to denote the presence and relations of that compound and its derivatives. It is represented and the carbon atoms are numbered thus:

BENZENE SUBSTITUTION PRODUCTS, NOMENCLATURE OF. All of the hydrogen atoms in benzene may be replaced by univalent atoms or groups forming mono-, di-, tri-, tetra-, penta-, or hexa-, derivatives according to the number of substituents. Two possibilities arise: (1) The substituents are all of one kind. Here we find but one modification of the mono-, penta-, and hexa-, derivatives and three of the di-, tri- and tetra-, derivatives. (a) The di-derivatives are named according to the relative positions which the substituents assume around the ring as ortho-, meta-, or para-; ortho- where adjacent carbon atoms are involved, meta- when an unsubstituted carbon rests between the two substituted carbons, and para- if two unsubstituted carbon atoms occur between the substituted carbons. Diagrammatically:

[o-dichlorobenzene   m-dichlorobenzene

p-dichlorobenzene

(b) The tri-derivatives are named adjacent (vicinal), unsymmetrical (asymmetrical), and symmetrical according as the groups take up the positions (1,2,3,) (1,2,4) or (1,3,5).

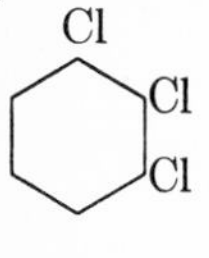

v-trichlorobenzene 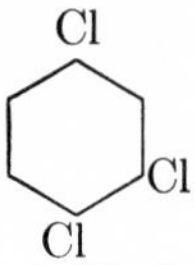   unsym-trichlorobenzene

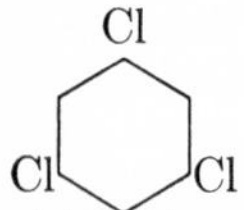

sym-trichlorobenzene

(c) The tetra- derivatives are named adjacent, symmetrical, or unsymmetrical according as the positions assumed by the substituents are (1,2,3,4), (1,2,4,5) or (1,2,3,5).

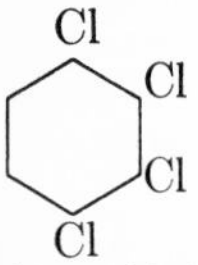

adjacent-tetrachlorobenzene 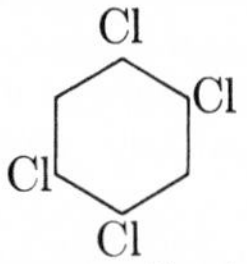   sym-tetrachlorobenzene

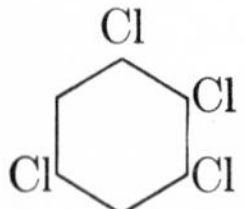

unsym-tetrachlorobenzene

(2) The substituents are of two or more kinds. Here the number of isomers is greatly multiplied. (a) The di-derivatives which contain two unlike substituents may be distinguished by the prefixes ortho-, meta-, and para-, as o-chloronitrobenzene, or the positions of the groups may be designated by number, as 1,2-chloronitrobenzene. (b) The system of numbering is usually followed in naming polysubstitution products of benzene, the compound being referred back to benzene or to another substance derived from benzene whose characteristic group is present. In this latter class the unnamed group is always regarded as assuming the 1 position; i.e. 3,6-bromonitrobenzoic acid is represented,

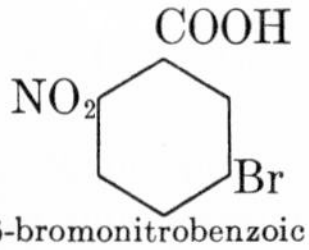

3, 6-bromonitrobenzoic acid

BENZENOID. Having the structure of benzene, particularly the Kekulé constitution, as distinguished from the "quinoid" form.

BENZENYL. See **benzylidyne**.

BENZHYDRYL (BENZOHYDRYL). The

radical
$$
\begin{array}{c}
C_6H_5 \\
\diagdown \\
CH-. \\
\diagup \\
C_6H_5
\end{array}
$$

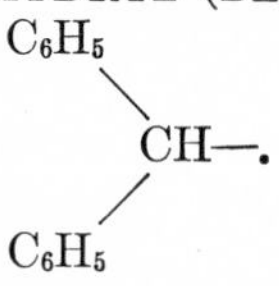

BENZIDINE REACTION. A test for blood (hemoglobin) made by acidifying the sample with glacial acetic acid, extracting with ether, and treating the ethereal extract with a solution of benzidine in glacial acetic acid, to which hydrogen peroxide has been added. In the absence of certain metals, a blue or green color, changing to deep blue or purple, indicates the presence of blood.

BENZIDINE REARRANGEMENT. See **rearrangement, benzidine**.

BENZIDINO. The radical

$$p\text{-}H_2NC_6H_4C_6H_4NH-$$

(from benzidine).

BENZILIC ACID REARRANGEMENT. See **rearrangement, benzilic acid**.

BENZILIDENE. The radical

$$C_6H_5-CH=;$$

preferably benzylidene.

BENZILOYL. The radical

$$(C_6H_5)_2C(OH)CO-.$$

BENZIMIDAZOLYL. The radical $C_7H_5N_2-$ (from benzimidazole).

BENZIMIDO. The radical $C_6H_5C(:NH)-$.

BENZINE. A product of petroleum boiling between 120° F. and 150° F. and composed of aliphatic **hydrocarbons**. Not to be confounded with benzene which is a chemical substance and an aromatic hydrocarbon.

BENZO-. A combining term for the radical C_6H_4=; specifically denoting the presence of the benzene ring.

BENZOFURYL. The radical C_8H_5O- (from benzofuran).

BENZOHYDRYL. The radical

$$(C_6H_5)_2CH-.$$

BENZOHYDRYLIDENE. The radical

$$(C_6H_5)_2C=.$$

BENZOIC. Related to benzoic acid, C_6H_5COOH.

BENZOIN CONDENSATION. See condensation, benzoin.

BENZOL. See benzene.

BENZOLATION. See reaction, benzolation.

BENZOPYRANYL. The radical C_9H_7O- (2-a-, etc.) (from benzopyran).

BENZOXY. The radical C_6H_5COO-.

BENZOYL. The radical C_6H_5CO-.

BENZOYLENE. The radical $-C_6H_4CO-$.

BENZYL. The radical $C_6H_5CH_2-$.

BENZYLATION. See reaction, benzylation.

BENZYLIDENE. The radical $C_6H_5CH=$.

BENZYLIDYNE. The radical $C_6H_5C\equiv$.

BERG REACTION FOR ALDEHYDE SUGARS. This reaction is based on the conversion of the aldose into a hydroxy acid by bromine water and then adding Berg reagent to produce an intense yellow color.

BERG REAGENT. A solution of 4 drops 60% ferric chloride solution and 2 drops concentrated hydrochloric acid in 100 ml. water.

BERG REAGENT FOR BISMUTH. An alcoholic solution of o-hydroxyquinoline.

BERG REAGENT FOR SEPARATING METALS. The substance 8-hydroxyquinoline, which from solutions containing tartrate alkalinized with sodium hydroxide, precipitates only copper, magnesium, cadmium, zinc, and ferrous iron.

BERG-TEITELBAUM TEST REACTION FOR SELENITE. To 2 ml. of the solution, add 1 ml. 5% ferric chloride solution and dilute to 10 ml. with phosphoric acid; then add 5–10 drops of 1% solution of pyrrole in alcohol. A deep blue color indicates the presence of selenite.

BERGÉ REAGENT FOR WOOD FIBER IN PAPER. A solution of 0.2 g. p-nitroaniline in 20 g. concentrated sulfuric acid and 80 ml. water. This reagent is used as a test reagent for wood fiber in paper. An orange color is given by wood fiber.

BERGELL REAGENT FOR PROTEINS. An ethereal solution of β-naphthalene sulfonechloride, used to investigate the degree of hydrolysis of meat proteins.

BERGER REAGENT FOR DIFFERENTIATING BENZENE FROM BENZINE. The substance dracorubin, which does not affect benzine but dissolves in benzene to form a red solution.

BERGIUS PROCESS. The best-known of various processes bearing the name of Bergius is that for the hydrogenation of coal to produce liquid hydrocarbons for use as fuels and lubricants.

BERGIUS-WILLSTATTER SACCHARIFICATION PROCESS. An industrial process for the production of sugars from wood by hydrolysis with strong (40–45%) hydrochloric acid. The product material is commonly used in a subsequent fermentation to yield alcohol.

BERGMANN AZLACTONE PEPTIDE SYNTHESIS. A method of synthesizing peptones from amino acids and the azlactones of acetylated amino acids.

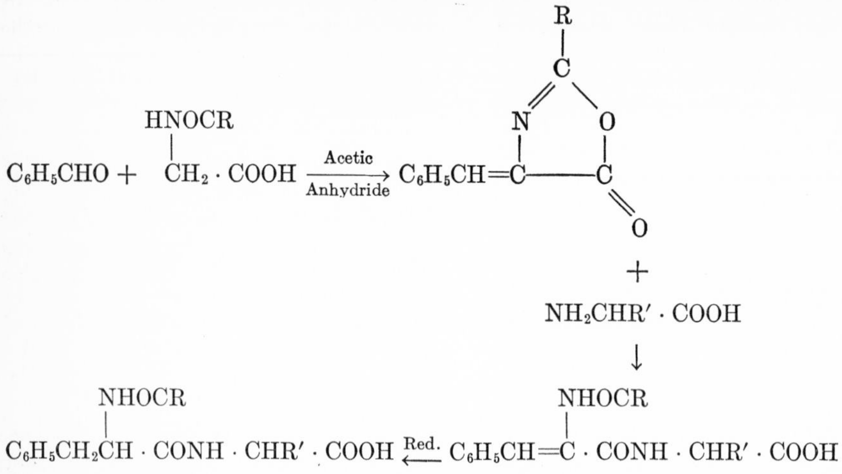

$$C_6H_5CHO + \begin{array}{c} HNOCR \\ | \\ CH_2 \cdot COOH \end{array} \xrightarrow[\text{Anhydride}]{\text{Acetic}} C_6H_5CH = C \underset{\overset{\displaystyle |}{\underset{O}{\|}}}{\overset{\overset{\displaystyle R}{\overset{\displaystyle |}{\underset{\displaystyle \|}{C}}}}{N \qquad O}} C$$

$$+$$

$$NH_2CHR' \cdot COOH$$

$$\downarrow$$

$$\begin{array}{c} NHOCR \\ | \\ C_6H_5CH_2CH \cdot CONH \cdot CHR' \cdot COOH \end{array} \xleftarrow{\text{Red.}} \begin{array}{c} NHOCR \\ | \\ C_6H_5CH = C \cdot CONH \cdot CHR' \cdot COOH \end{array}$$

BERGMANN DEGRADATION. A series of reactions for the mild degradation of **polypeptides** sidewise, so that the end amino acids can be determined. The reactions include condensation with phenyl isocyanate, followed by treatment with diazomethane, hydrazine, nitrous acid, and benzyl alcohol, with a final combined reduction and hydrolysis.

BERGMANN-ZERVAS CARBOBENZOXY METHOD. A method of protection of the **amino groups**, during a **peptide** synthesis, by blocking them by carbobenzoxy groups, which are later to be removed by reduction.

of chlorine disappears and a white precipitate is formed.

BERINGER TEST REACTION FOR SALOPHEN. Add 0.1 g. salophen to 2 ml. of 1:2 sodium hydroxide solution and boil for 1 minute, cool and add 5 ml. Javelle water. A brilliant green color, which changes to mahogany-brown after some time, is formed. If an excess of concentrated hydrochloric acid is then added, the color changes to scarlet and then gradually fades to orange-red.

BERKELIUM. Radioactive element of **actinide series.** Symbol Bk. Atomic number 97. Atomic species of mass num-

$$H_2N \cdot CHR \cdot COOCH_3 + C_6H_5 \cdot CH_2 \cdot O \cdot COCl \xrightarrow{HCl} C_6H_5CH_2 \cdot O \cdot CO \cdot NH \cdot CHR \cdot COOCH_3.$$

BERINGER TEST FOR ACETANILID IN ACETOPHENETIDIN. Add 0.1 g. acetophenetidin to 3 ml. of 50% sodium hydroxide solution and boil for 1 minute, cool and shake with 5 ml. chlorinated soda solution. The liquid is clear and yellow if the acetophenetidin is pure but if acetanilid is present, a red to brownish-red color or precipitate forms.

BERINGER TEST REACTIONS FOR ANTIPYRINE. (1) If antipyrine is boiled with Javelle water, the odor of chlorine disappears and is replaced by the odor of oil of bitter almonds. (2) When antipyrine is shaken with chlorine water, the odor

bers 243, 244, and 245 have been reported. The first has a half-period of 4.6 hours, for its chief decay process, which is by orbital electron capture. It also decays by α-emission. Valences 3, 4.

BERL PROCESS. A modification of the **chamber process** for the production of sulfuric acid, in which the chambers are operated under a pressure of about thirteen atmospheres. The reaction rate, and hence the yield per unit volume of chamber space, are greatly increased.

BERNARDI-TARTARINI TEST FOR VANILLIN AND PIPERONAL IN SUGAR SOLUTIONS. Boil the sugar solution with dimethylhydroresorcinol, cool and add a little aqueous ferric chloride. A yellow-brown color, produced on standing, indicates the presence of vanillin or piperonal.

BERNBECK TEST. A test for tarry substances in ammonia water in which the ammonia is superimposed on crude nitric acid. If tarry matter is present, a red ring is formed.

BERNEDÈ REAGENT. A solution of 12 g. phenol in 1/10 its volume of alcohol, to which 60 g. ether is then added. This reagent extracts certain dyes, such as fuchsin and gentian violet, from wine, and gives characteristic colors if they are present.

BERNOULLI THEOREM. When an incompressible liquid flows steadily (i.e., without turbulence), the total head is constant; in other words, the energy per unit volume is conserved. A form of this relationship is:

$$h_1 + \frac{V_1^2}{2g} + \frac{p_1}{\rho g} = \text{Constant}$$

where h_1 is the elevation head at any point in the system, V_1 is the velocity of the liquid at that point, p_1 is the pressure in the liquid at that point, g is the acceleration of gravity, ρ is the density of the liquid, and the total constant for the system is sometimes called Bernoulli's constant.

BERNSTEIN TEST. A test for boiled and unboiled milk in which 50 ml. of the sample is mixed with 4.5 ml. N acetic acid, filtered, and the clear filtrate heated. If the milk has not been heated or has been heated below 70° C. for a short time, a voluminous precipitation of lactalbumin is formed.

BERNTHSEN ACRIDINE SYNTHESIS. Condensation of **organic acids** and **diarylamines** to **acridines,** usually in the presence of zinc chloride.

BERTAGNINI TEST REACTION. A test reaction for aldehydes based on the formation of an aldehyde sulfite when the sample is shaken with sodium bisulfite solution.

BERTHELOT EQUATION. A form of the **equation of state,** relating the pressure, volume, and temperature of a gas, and the gas constant R. The Berthelot equation is derived from the **Clausius equation** and is of the form

$$PV = RT\left(1 + \frac{9PT_c}{128P_cT}\left[1 - 6\frac{T_c^2}{T^2}\right]\right)$$

in which P is the pressure, V is the volume, T is the absolute temperature, R is the gas constant, T_c is the critical temperature, and P_c the critical pressure.

BERTHELOT-MICHEL TEST REACTION FOR DIHYDROXYBENZENE (HYDROQUINONE, PYROCATECHOL, RESORCINOL). A cold saturated solution of 15 g. chloramine T in 85 ml. water is the reagent. If 1 ml. of this reagent is added to 4 ml. of a 10% aqueous solution of resorcinol, a green color is formed followed by a yellow color. An amethyst-red color is formed by pyrocatechol and a currant-red color changing rapidly to brownish-red is formed by hydroquinone.

BERTHELOT-MICHEL TEST REACTION FOR α- AND β-NAPHTHOL. A violet color is produced when a 1% α-naphthol solution is added to the chloramine T reagent (15 g. chloramine T in 85 ml. water). A brownish-red color is produced by the addition of β-naphthol and then warming.

BERTHELOT REAGENT FOR PEROXIDE IN ETHER. The substance lead ammonium iodide, which is colored yellow on contact with ether containing peroxide.

$$C_6H_5 \cdot NH \cdot C_6H_5 + RCOOH \xrightarrow{\Delta} \text{[acridine structure]} + 2 H_2O.$$

BERTHELOT TEST FOR ALCOHOL.
Add a few drops of benzoyl chloride to the
sample, shake well, and then add sodium
hydroxide solution until the odor of the
benzoyl chloride disappears. If the characteristic odor of ethyl benzoate develops,
alcohol is present.

**BERTHELOT TEST FOR CARBON
MONOXIDE.** Add ammonia drop by
drop to an aqueous solution of silver nitrate.
Continue until the precipitate formed just
dissolves. A brown color is formed with
this reagent in the cold and a black precipitate on heating, if carbon monoxide is
present.

**BERTHELOT TEST FOR ETHYL AL-
COHOL IN METHANOL.** If methanol
is treated with twice its volume of concentrated sulfuric acid, methyl ether is formed.
Ethyl alcohol forms ethylene under the
same conditions; this can be combined
with bromine and determined.

BERTHOLLET RULE. A means for
predicting whether a reaction will take
place. The rule states that if one of the
reaction products would leave the system
under the given conditions, as by precipitation, evolution (gaseous), or other means,
then the reaction will take place.

BERTRAND BLOOD REAGENT. A solution of 1 g. magnesium chloride in 1 g.
water, 20 g. glacial acetic acid, and 5 g.
glycerol. It is used in examining blood
stains. The appearance of characteristic,
microscopic crystals of hemin indicates the
presence of blood.

**BERTRAND-DESAINT-RAT REAGENT
FOR COPPER.** An 0.1% aqueous solution of urobilin, which gives a rose to
purple color with copper in neutral solution.

**BERTRAND-JAVILLIER TEST REAC-
TION FOR ZINC.** Add an excess of
ammonia and sufficient calcium hydroxide
to the sample. Then filter and heat the
filtrate to the boiling point. A crystalline
precipitate of calcium zincate indicates
the presence of zinc.

**BERTRAND MOLYBDENUM REA-
GENT.** A solution for the colorimetric
determination of molybdenum in steel,
prepared by adding to (1) a solution of
11.4 g. ammonium tungstate in 20 ml.
water and 20 ml. 20% sodium hydroxide
solution; (2) 70 ml. 30% tartaric acid solution and 5 ml. concentrated hydrochloric
acid, and (3) diluting with water to 500 ml.,
and then treating with hydrogen sulfide
and boiling.

**BERTRAND REAGENT FOR ALKA-
LOIDS.** An aqueous solution of silicotungstic acid which produces precipitates
with alkaloids.

BERTSCH TEST. A test for vinyl alcohol in ether in which the ether is shaken
with mercuric oxychloride. If a white
precipitate forms, vinyl alcohol is present.
Sodium hydroxide converts the precipitate
into a black, explosive powder.

BERYLLATE. The anion BeO_2^-, or a
compound containing it.

BERYLLATE (HYDROXO-). The anion
$Be(OH)_4^-$ or a compound containing it.

BERYLLIUM. Metallic element. Symbol Be. Atomic number 4. Atomic
weight 9.02. Density 1.85. Specific heat
0.475. Melting point 1350° C. Boiling
point 1530° C. Valence 2.

BESEMANN TEST. A test for differentiating chlorine and chloramines in solutions
which depends upon the decolorization of
methyl orange in acid solution by chlorine
only.

BESSEMER PROCESS. A method of
making steel by pouring the molten impure
iron (which has been obtained usually by
melting pig iron, or directly from a blast
furnace) into a converter and passing a
blast of air through the molten charge to
oxidize the carbon. The silicon and manganese are also oxidized and must be replaced to the extent desired in the finished
steel. This is done near the end of the
"blow" when the additional metals are
added, usually as ferro-alloys. The vanadium, used to remove nitrogen, is added

during the "pour." Since siliceous converter linings are widely used, the process does not materially reduce the sulfur and phosphorus content, and the process is not suitable for charges high in these elements. A "basic" Bessemer process, with a basic converter lining, has been used widely in Europe.

BEST CARMINE STAIN. A solution of 2 g. carmine, 1 g. potassium carbonate, and 5 g. potassium chloride in 60 ml. water. It is used as a stain for glycogen in tissue.

BETA (B OR β). The second letter of the Greek alphabet, used as a prefix to denote the carbon atom in a straight-chain compound next to the carbon atom to which the principal group is attached, or a derivative in which a substituted group is attached to that carbon atom (β-); in a polycyclic compound, a carbon atom separated by one ring carbon atom from any carbon atom shared by two rings, or a derivative in which a substituted group is attached to that carbon atom (β-); one of a group of isomers (β-); symbol for coefficient of volumetric expansion (β); symbol for angle (β); symbol for phase constant (β); relativity ratio (β). See also **beta-particle** and **beta-rays.**

BETA-PARTICLE. This term was originally applied to streams of negatively charged particles emitted from **radioactive** substances at high velocities. These beta-particles were later found to be **electrons.**

BETA-RAYS. Streams of **electrons.** The term was applied originally to one of the radiations from naturally-radioactive substances, which was found to consist of a stream of electrons having relatively great velocities.

BETAÏNES. Inner **anhydrides** of **amino-acid** derivatives containing a hydroxyl attached to the nitrogen atom which split out water with the carboxyl group, thus joining the nitrogen to the carboxyl carbon atom. They have the general constitution,

$$CH_2—C=O$$
$$| \qquad |$$
$$R_3N —O$$

BETATOPIC. Differing by, or pertaining to a difference by, unit atomic number. Thus, if one atom or element can be considered to form another atom or element, by ejection of an electron (beta-particle) from its nucleus, the two atoms are beta-topic.

BETATRON. An apparatus for accelerating **electrons** to high potential, by applying a potential to them by **electromagnetic induction** while they are already traveling in a suitably-directed magnetic field. The electrons may originate in various ways, as from a hot filament, and the magnetic force system is arranged to accelerate them while they move in a circular orbit.

BETT TEST. A test for manganese in which the sample is heated with sodium carbonate paste and potassium chlorate. A green color indicates the presence of manganese.

BETTEL TEST REACTION. A test for molybdenum in which a slightly ammoniacal solution of molybdic acid is colored red-brown by the addition of hydrogen peroxide.

BETTELLI TEST. A test for fusel oil in alcohol made by diluting 5 ml. of the sample with 35 ml. water, shaking with 15–20 drops chloroform, and then evaporating the chloroform. The odor of fusel oil is detected in the residue, if present in the sample.

BETTENDORFF-WINKLER REAGENT. A solution of 100 g. stannous chloride in concentrated hydrochloric acid, adjusted with the latter to a volume of 1 liter, and clarified by the addition of 1 g. of powdered glass. This reagent is used in testing for arsenic. A brown coloration on heating with a hydrochloric acid solution of the sample indicates the presence of arsenic.

BETTI REAGENT. The substance α-aminobenzyl-β-naphthol, which is used in differentiating between aldoses and ketoses. Crystalline compounds are formed with aldoses only.

BETTINK TEST REACTION FOR MANNITOL. In 1 ml. dilute sulfuric acid, dissolve 0.01 g. mannitol, add 3 drops 1:25 potassium dichromate solution, and boil for 1 minute. Make slightly alkaline with sodium hydroxide, filter and boil the filtrate with 1 ml. **Fehling's solution.** The Fehling's solution is reduced by *d*-mannose formed by the oxidation of the mannitol.

BETTINK TEST REACTION FOR SULFONAL. A garlic-like odor is detected on heating sulfonal with iron powder.

BETTS PROCESS. An electrolytic method of refining lead by using an electrolyte of lead fluosilicate with a little gelatin.

BEVATRON. A term proposed for a proton synchrotron to be built at Berkeley, California, which it is hoped will yield particles with energies of 6 billion electron volts, hence the name bevatron, although other such instruments are being built to produce particles with energies in the billions of electron volts. The term cosmotron has also been suggested for these high energy accelerators, especially for the proton accelerator at Brookhaven National Laboratory.

BEY REAGENT. A 5% ethereal solution of resorcinol, which gives a blue ring with cadmium chloride solutions, and a blue color with stannic tin solutions, under test conditions.

BEZSSONOV REAGENT. A solution of 44 g. sodium tungstate and 2.7 g. phosphomolybdic acid in 400 ml. water, 60 ml. 5 *N* sulfuric acid, and 5 ml. 85% phosphoric acid. It gives characteristic color reactions with many polyphenols and with antiscorbutic extracts.

Bi (1) Symbol for the element **bismuth.** (2) The prefix bi- means twice, two, or double; specifically: (a) in double proportion; as bicarbonate (no longer considered good usage); (b) denoting the doubling of an organic radical or molecule; as biphenyl, $C_6H_5C_6H_5$; 4,4'-bipyridine $C_6H_4N \cdot C_6H_4N$.

BIACID. A base able to neutralize two molecules of a monobasic acid or one of a dibasic acid; calcium hydroxide, $Ca(OH)_2$, is a biacid base.

BIAL REAGENT. A solution of 1 g. orcinol in 500 ml. 30% hydrochloric acid and 25 drops 10% ferric chloride solution. This reagent gives a characteristic green coloration with pentoses.

BIANCHI-NOLA TEST. A test for small amounts of nickel, an adaptation of the **Tschugaev test,** in which 1–2 drops of concentrated hydrochloric acid or nitric acid are placed on the substance to be tested. This solution is then taken up with a filter paper or transferred to a spot plate. It is made alkaline with ammonia, the paper exposed to ammonia fumes, acidified with 1 drop of acetic acid, and a few drops of a saturated alcoholic solution of dimethylglyoxime added. A red color is produced in the presence of nickel.

BICARBONATE. An **acid carbonate,** viz., $KHCO_3$, or any compound containing the radical $-HCO_3$.

BICHEROUX PROCESS. A process for the manufacture of plate glass, in which the formation of the molten glass into solid sheets between rollers, its cooling on a table, and its subsequent annealing, constitute a continuous operation.

BICHLORIDE. An **inorganic compound** that contains two atoms of chlorine.

BICHROMATE. See **dichromate.**

BICKEL-FRENCH TEST REACTION. A test reaction for alcohols in which they produce, with α-naphthylisocyanate, crystalline urethanes that can be identified by their melting points.

BICYCLIC. Having two rings, as of a compound, specifically designating certain bridged **compounds,** as bicyclo [3.1.1] heptane.

BICYCLO. See **bicyclic.**

BIEBER TEST. A test for the purity of almond oil. Carefully mix equal parts of water, concentrated sulfuric acid, and fuming red nitric acid and cool. Shake 5 parts of the almond oil with 1 part reagent. A faintly yellowish-white mixture is produced by pure almond oil, whereas other oils produce pronounced colorations.

BIEHRINGER-BUSCH TEST REAC-TION. A test reaction for *o*- and *p*-toluidines in which the hydrochloric acid solutions of the substances are boiled with ferric chloride solution. The ortho compound produces blue flocks and the para compound produces a Bordeaux red color.

BIEL TEST REACTION FOR COCAINE. In 1 ml. concentrated sulfuric acid, dissolve 0.03 g. cocaine, heat 1–2 minutes in boiling water, cool, and then carefully dilute with 3 ml. water. Within $\frac{1}{2}$ hour, crystals of benzoic acid separate, and the odor of methyl benzoate becomes evident.

BIEL TEST FOR PICRIC ACID IN IODOFORM. On shaking iodoform with water, a yellow coloration appears if picric acid is present. Confirm by filtering and adding potassium cyanide; a red-brown color on standing is given if picric acid is present.

BIELING REAGENT. A solution of 2 g. nitroanthraquinone in 100 ml. water. To one part of this reagent, 9 parts of physiological salt solution are added. The resulting solution gives a pink color with living tissue and is used to differentiate living from dead tissue.

BI-FUNCTIONAL REACTION. See **reaction, bi-functional.**

BIILMANN REAGENT FOR POTASSIUM. A solution of sodium cobaltic nitrate, consisting of 0.3 to 0.5 g. of the compound, prepared according to a special procedure, and dissolved in 2 to 3 ml. water.

BILI-. A prefix meaning relating to, or derived from, bile, as bilanic acid, biliverdine.

BILL TEST REACTION. A test reaction for cinchonine. When potassium ferrocyanide solution is added to solutions of neutral cinchonine salts, yellow crystalline precipitates are produced.

BILLON TEST REACTION. A test reaction for Ceylon cinnamon oil in which 1 drop of the oil is shaken in 10 ml. water,

filtered through a wet filter and a few drops of potassium arsenite solution added to the filtrate. A greenish-yellow color is obtained from Ceylon cinnamon oil.

BILTZ-MECKLENBURG TEST REACTION. A test reaction for zirconium. Add a few drops sodium phosphate solution to a zirconium solution which has been strongly acidified with hydrochloric or nitric acid and warm. A white hydrogel, containing zirconium and phosphoric acid, is formed.

BILTZ REAGENT FOR CARBONATE. A 5% aqueous solution of mercuric chloride, used in judging the amount of carbonate present in sodium bicarbonate. A reddish-brown turbidity indicates more than 4% carbonate.

BILTZ REAGENT FOR WATER. A test paper prepared by saturating filter paper with an acetone solution of potassium lead iodide, and then drying it. With water it gives a deep yellow color.

BIMOLECULAR REACTION. See **reaction, bimolecular.**

BINARY COMPOUND. See **compound, binary.**

BINDER. A material employed to hold solid substances together. For example, a binder is the nonvolatile portion of a paint vehicle.

BINDER TEST. A test for nitrate in water, in which a pinch of zinc dust is shaken in 30 ml. of the water, a few drops of dilute sulfuric acid added and shaken again. A little potassium iodide-starch paste is added. A blue color indicates the presence of nitrate or nitrite.

BINDER-WEINLAND REAGENT. An aqueous solution of ferrous ammonium sulfate (free from ferric salts) and pyrocatechol, alkalinized with sodium hydroxide. It gives a red color with free oxygen.

BINDING ELECTRON. See **electron, binding.**

BINDSCHEDLER TEST REACTION. A test reaction for resorcinol in which the material is warmed for a short time on the water bath with dilute sulfuric acid containing some sodium nitrite, water is added, and the solution is supersaturated with ammonia. The presence of resorcinol is indicated by the production of a red color which, when shaken with amyl alcohol, passes into it and forms a cinnabar-red fluorescence.

BINIODIDE. A salt of hydriodic acid that contains two atoms of iodine.

BINOXALATE. An acid oxalate.

BINOXIDE. A dioxide.

BIOASSAY OR BIOLOGICAL ASSAY. Determination of the **potency** or **activity** of drugs or, derivatively, the amount of active ingredient they contain, by observing their effects upon animals.

BIOCHEMICAL. See biochemistry.

BIOCHEMICAL RESOLUTION OF INACTIVE COMPOUNDS. The method of resolving optically inactive compounds, **racemes,** into active substances by employing bacteria, yeasts, and fungi to destroy one of the enantiomorphic forms present. Thus, Pasteur found that the *penicillium glaucum* assimilates and so destroys the dextro-ammonium tartrate. Other bacteria, etc., show different tastes, some attack dextro forms, others the laevo forms. None of these organisms attack both of the isomers, however, and a laevo-assimilating one would starve in the presence of unlimited dextro material. The phenomenon is known as selective assimilation.

BIOCHEMISTRY. That branch of chemistry which deals with the processes of living organisms and the products derived from them.

BIODYNE. A substance found in living cells, which influences their respiration.

BIOLYTIC. An agent that can destroy life.

BION. A general term denoting any living cell or other living organism or, hypothetically, the ultimate unit of life.

BIONDI-HEIDENHAIN MIXTURE. A mixture of 20 ml. of a saturated aqueous solution of orange G, 10 ml. of a saturated aqueous solution of methyl green, and 4 ml. of a saturated aqueous solution of fuchsin S. This reagent is used as a tissue stain.

BIOPHAGE. An organism or cell that eats living organisms or cells.

BIOSE. A monosaccharose that contains but two atoms of carbon. Glycolaldehyde is the only known member of the class.

BIPHENYLENE. The radical

$$-C_6H_4C_6H_4-.$$

BIPHENYLENEDISAZO. The radical

$$-N:NC_6H_4C_6H_4N:N-.$$

BIPHENYLYL. The radical (2-, 3-, or 4-) $C_6H_5C_6H_4-$ (from biphenyl).

BIPHENYLYLCARBONYL. The radical

$$C_6H_5C_6H_4CO-.$$

BIPHENYLYLOXY. The radical

$$C_6H_5C_6H_4O-.$$

BIRCH REDUCTION REACTION. The use of metallic sodium dissolved in liquid ammonia as a reducing agent for organic compounds.

BIREFRINGENCE. Double **refraction,** or the splitting of a ray of incident light into two components that travel at different velocities, and hence follow different paths, through the medium effecting the splitting.

BIRKELAND-EYDE PROCESS. A method of producing nitric acid by **fixation** of atmospheric **nitrogen.** Air is passed through an electric arc, the atmospheric oxygen and nitrogen combine to form NO, and the product gases are drawn away as rapidly as possible becuse the **equilibrium** $(O_2 + N_2 \rightleftarrows 2NO)$ is more to the right at lower temperatures, and it is therefore desirable to cool the gases as rapidly as possible to a temperature at which the reverse reaction rate is slow. The NO also reacts with atmospheric oxygen at lower temperatures to form NO_2, which is converted to nitric acid.

BIROTATION. Freshly prepared solutions of glucose show an abnormal **optical rotation** of 105.2 while, after standing for some time, the rotation sinks to one half the above value or 52.6. The phenomenon was termed birotation, but this has been discarded for the more comprehensive term **"mutarotation"** (q.v.).

BISCHLER-NAPIERALSKI REACTION. A method of formation of 3,4 dihydroisoquinoline derivatives by ring closure of β-phenethylamides.

BISHOP-KREIS TEST REACTION. A test reaction in which a fat or oil, believed to have been irradiated, is shaken with equal parts of unirradiated sesame oil and hydrochloric acid (sp. gr. 1.18). A green color indicates the presence of irradiated oil.

BISHOP TEST REACTION. A test reaction for sesame oil in which 8 ml. of the oil is shaken with 12 ml. hydrochloric acid and the mixture exposed to air and light. A green color, produced after standing a day, indicates the presence of sesame oil.

BISMUTH. Metallic element. Symbol Bi. Atomic number 83. Atomic weight 209.00. Density 9.78. Specific heat 0.0303. Melting point 271° C. Boiling point 1450° C. The principal valence of bismuth is three, but compounds are known in which the element has a valence of five. Oxides, Bi_2O_3, Bi_2O_5. Its normal salts react with water to form basic compounds, of which the basic carbonate and basic nitrates are pharmaceutically important.

BISMUTHATE (META-). The anion BiO_3^-, or a compound containing it.

BISMUTHIC. A combining term for pentavalent **bismuth.**

BISMUTHIDE. A binary compound of **bismuth.**

BISMUTHINE. One of a series of organic compounds of the type-formula, BiR_3, in which R represents **alkyl** or **aryl radicals.**

BISMUTHOUS. A combining term for trivalent **bismuth.**

BISMUTHYL. A name applied to the radical BiO– which occurs in certain basic salts of **bismuth.**

BISNOR-. Indicating removal of two carbon atoms (with accompanying hydrogen), as bisnorcholanic acid $C_{22}H_{36}O_2$ (cholanic acid is $C_{24}H_{40}O_2$).

BISULFATE. An acid **sulfate,** as $KHSO_4$, or any other compound containing the radical $-HSO_4$.

BISULFIDE. A binary compound which contains two atoms of **sulfur.**

BISULFITE. An acid **sulfite,** as $KHSO_3$, or any compound containing the radical $-HSO_3$.

BITARTRATE. An acid **tartrate,** as

$$KOOC-CHOH-CHOH-COOH,$$

or any compound containing the radical

BI-TRIFUNCTIONAL REACTION. See **reaction, bi-trifunctional.**

BITTER PRINCIPLE. A generic term applied to proximate principles of plants characterized by bitterness of taste and usually by medicinal value. The class includes the **glucosides, alkaloids,** and **resins** such as hop resins.

BIURET TEST. A test for the presence of peptides, proteins, amino acids, and albumin, which contain the –CONH– group. Potassium hydroxide solution and a few drops of cupric sulfate solution are added to the solution to be tested. A pinkish-violet color indicates the presence of compounds of the above types.

BIVALENT. (Divalent) Able to combine with or saturate two univalent radicals or their equivalent. (See **valence.**)

BIZZOZERO PICROCARMINE SOLUTION. A mixture of two solutions: (1) 1 g. carmine dissolved in 100 ml. water and 6 ml. ammonium hydroxide; and (2) 1 g. picric acid dissolved in 100 ml. water. This mixture is concentrated to 100 ml., and diluted with 20 ml. alcohol. It is a differential tissue stain.

BJERRUM THEORY. In the case of a monatomic gas, no energy is possessed other than that due to translational movement. As regards the rotation of the molecule as a whole, the potential energy of rotation is negligible compared with the kinetic energy. In regard to atomic vibra-

sium palmitate dissolved in glycerol and ethyl alcohol and used for the determination of hardness in water.

BLACK BODY. An entity or substance that absorbs all incident **radiant energy.**

BLACK REAGENT FOR BETA-HYDROXYBUTYRIC ACID. A solution of 5 g. ferric chloride and 0.4 g. ferrous chloride in 100 ml. water, used as a test reagent for β-hydroxybutyric acid in urine. A red color indicates the presence of β-hydroxybutyric acid.

BLAGDENS LAW. See **law of Blagden.**

BLAISE KETONE SYNTHESIS. A method of forming **ketones** from organic zinc derivatives and **acid halides.**

$$R'ZnCl + R''COCl \rightarrow R'COR'' + ZnCl_2$$

See also **Blaise-Maire reaction.**

BLAISE-MAIRE REACTION. A method of forming β-hydroxy **ketones,** or $\alpha\beta$ unsaturated ketones, from organic zinc derivatives and β-acetoxy acid halides.

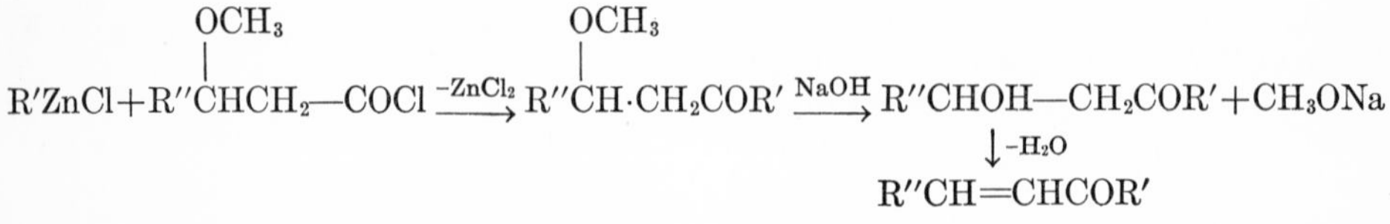

$$R'ZnCl+R''\overset{\overset{\displaystyle OCH_3}{|}}{CHCH_2}—COCl \xrightarrow{-ZnCl_2} R''\overset{\overset{\displaystyle OCH_3}{|}}{CH}\cdot CH_2COR' \xrightarrow{NaOH} R''CHOH—CH_2COR'+CH_3ONa$$
$$\downarrow -H_2O$$
$$R''CH=CHCOR'$$

tions the total vibrational energy is θRT where θ is a function of the temperature T and of the vibration frequency v.

Bk Symbol for the element **berkelium.**

BLACHER REAGENT FOR HARDNESS IN WATER. An 0.1 N solution of potas-

(See also **Blaise ketone synthesis.**)

BLAISE REACTION. A method of formation of β-ketoesters from α-bromoesters and nitriles. Zinc is used in the reaction, and intermediate compounds containing the metal are formed.

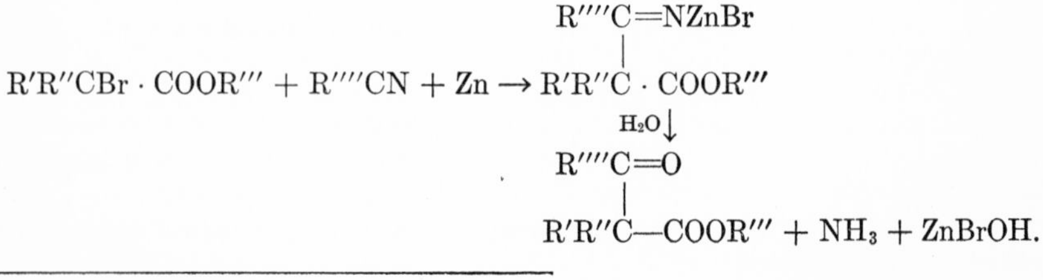

$$R'R''CBr \cdot COOR''' + R''''CN + Zn \rightarrow R'R''\overset{\overset{\displaystyle R''''C=NZnBr}{|}}{C} \cdot COOR'''$$
$$H_2O\downarrow$$
$$R'R''\overset{\overset{\displaystyle R''''C=O}{|}}{C}—COOR''' + NH_3 + ZnBrOH.$$

**BLANC CHLOROMETHYLATION RE-
ACTION.** A method of formation of
chloromethyl compounds by the action
upon aromatic hydrocarbons of formaldehyde and hydrochloric acid, in the presence
of zinc chloride.

$$C_6H_6 + HCHO + HCl \xrightarrow[-H_2O]{ZnCl_2} C_6H_5CH_2Cl.$$

BLANC REACTION. The method of
formation of cyclic **ketones** by heating
anhydrides of **dicarboxylic** acids. The
reaction yields ketones when adipic acid
(6 carbon atoms) and pimelic acid (7 carbon atoms) are heated with acetic anhydride, as expressed in Blanc's rule. On
the other hand, succinic acid (4 carbon
atoms) and glutaric acid (5 carbon acids)
yield cyclic **anhydrides.**

BLANC RULE. A generalization relating
to the behavior of **dicarboxylic acids** in **dehydration** reactions, whereby those acids
containing six or more carbon atoms are
stated to yield chiefly **ketones,** and those
with less than six carbon atoms yield the
corresponding **anhydrides.**

BLANCHETIÈRE REAGENT. Two solutions: (1) a solution of 100 g. uranium
acetate and 60 ml. glacial acetic acid in
water enough to make 1 liter; and (2) a solution of 333 g. magnesium acetate and 60
ml. glacial acetic acid in water enough to
make 1 liter. Equal volumes of the two
solutions are mixed to form the reagent,
which is used as a precipitant for sodium.

BLAREZ PEANUT OIL TEST. A test
for peanut oil in olive oil, in which 1 ml. of
the oil is saponified with 15 ml. 4–5%
alcoholic potassium hydroxide by heating
for 20 minutes. On cooling the reaction
mixture, a solid precipitate indicates more
than 5% peanut oil.

BLAREZ WINE TEST. A test for coal
tar dyes in wine, by heating 10 ml. of the
sample with 10 drops acetic acid to 100° C.,
and shaking with 0.2 g. powdered mercuric
acetate. The natural colors are precipitated, and the coal tar colors are present in
the filtrate.

BLAST. A sudden **detonation;** or a rapid
current of heated gases.

BLAST FURNACE. An apparatus for
the reduction of iron ore. It consists of a
tall cylindrical chamber with a charging
device at the top through which quantities
of coal or coke, lime and iron oxide are admitted; near the bottom is a ring of tubes,
called tuyères, through which hot air is
blown into the furnace; below is the hearth
with lateral openings for drawing off the
slag and the molten iron separately. The
ore is brought to a white heat near the top
of the furnace and as it descends is reduced
to molten metal when much of the phosphorus, sulfur, and silicon originally in the
ore combines with the lime to form the slag.
Blast furnaces are now fitted with checkerwork chambers of brick which are heated
by the waste gases from the furnace and
serve to preheat the air for the tuyères.
The product of the blast furnace is known
as pig iron.

BLAST LAMP. A laboratory burner for
producing somewhat higher temperatures
than those obtainable by the Bunsen
burner. Air for combustion is supplied
under pressure, or at any rate, in large
volume, and a corresponding volume of gas
is used.

BLAU TEST FOR FERROUS ION.
The formation with o-phenanthroline of
deep-red salts, relatively stable to acids
and ammonium sulfide, indicates the presence of the ferrous ion.

**BLAU TEST FOR p-PHENYLENEDI-
AMINE.** Solutions of this substance give,
on wood chips, a bright red color, which is
deepened by acids and destroyed by alkalies.

BLEACHING. The process of whitening
fibers or fabrics either by destroying the
coloring matter or by converting it into a
colorless substance. Two methods are in
use: (1) **Oxidation,** by far the more important and more generally employed, consists in decolorizing the coloring matter
with moist chlorine, hydrogen peroxide, or
other oxidizer. (2) **Reduction** consists of
converting the color into a colorless compound, as by the use of moist sulfur dioxide
or other reducing agent.

BLEACHING AGENT. A material that is used to lighten the color of materials, especially animal or vegetable fibers. Among the bleaching agents are: sodium bisulfite, sodium hyposulfite, hydrogen peroxide, and calcium hypochlorite.

BLEEKER PROCESS. An **electrolytic process** for the reduction of vanadium.

BLENDE. In general, a sulfide ore.

BLENDING. In general, the elimination of discontinuities in form and structure, or differences in appearance. Blending materials means mixing them to form a homogeneous mass. Blending colors means modifying their hues or shades so that their over-all pattern shows no sharp changes in hue or intensity.

BLENDING AGENT. A term applied in the petroleum industry to **hydrocarbons,** commonly those produced by **polymerization, alkylation,** and other processes, which have a high **antiknock** (q.v.) rating and which are mixed with gasoline to improve this property.

BLOM CARBAZOLE TEST. On solution in concentrated sulfuric acid, followed by the addition of a trace of nitric acid, carbazole and its derivatives give characteristic color reactions.

BLOM SOLUTIONS FOR HYDROXYL-AMINE. (1) A solution is prepared of 0.48 g. nickel sulfate heptahydrate in 100 ml. water; to 10 ml. of this solution is added 1 ml. of a solution of 1 g. diacetylmonoxime in 10 ml. ammonia (sp. gr. 0.90), followed by filtration. This reagent gives red colors or precipitates with neutral solutions containing hydroxylamine.
(2) (A) An alcoholic solution of 0.37 g. per liter *p*-bromonitrosobenzene; (B) an aqueous solution of 0.29/g. per liter α-naphthol (containing 5 drops hydrochloric acid per liter); (C) 0.5 N sodium hydroxide solution; and (D) a dilute solution of a magnesium salt. On mixing 3 ml. of (A) with 2 ml. of (B), and adding 2 ml. of this mixture to a mixture of 5 ml. of (C) and 20 ml. of the neutralized solution to be tested, an orange-red color appears, changing to red with a few drops of (D).

BLOMBERG TEST. Gitalin, in solution in glacial acetic acid containing ferric sulfate, gives a colored ring test with sulfuric acid.

BLOMSTRAND TEST. The cyanate ion is detected by a blue color or crystals produced by reaction of (potassium) cyanate solution with cobaltous acetate solution.

BLOOM. A **fluorescence** which characterizes certain organic compounds. Many petroleum distillates, especially of paraffin base petroleum, have a pronounced bloom. This term is also applied to a bluish cast which occasionally forms on the surfaces of dried lacquer or paint films.

BLOW MOLDING. See **molding, blow.**

BLOWN OIL. One of a group of fatty **oils** that have been oxidized by a stream of air blown through them. This treatment increases their specific gravities and viscosities. Cottonseed and rape oils are those most commonly "blown," but other fatty oils as peanut, olive, lard, and linseed are sometimes so treated.

BLOWPIPE. A curved tube of metal or earthenware through which air may be blown and used to deflect the flame of a lamp or gas burner in such a way that an object may be heated either in the **reducing** or **oxidizing flame.**

BLOWPIPE ANALYSIS. A systematic plan of qualitative **analysis** based upon the use of the blowpipe, and of various **bead tests** (q.v.), **flame tests** (q.v.), and **fusions,** with or without fluxing agents, on charcoal, tile, plaster of Paris, and other surfaces. These methods are used extensively in the assay of ores and other metal-containing materials. One of the more recently developed methods of differentiation is by examination of the beads and other fusion products under ultraviolet light.

BLOXAM REAGENTS FOR ALKALOIDS. The two Bloxam reagents are: (1) bromine water, which gives characteristic colors with many alkaloids; and (2) a weak aqueous solution of potassium chlorate, treated with enough concentrated hydrochloric acid to form a deep yellow color, and then diluted with water. This reagent also gives characteristic colors with many alkaloids (in boiling solution containing hydrochloric acid).

BLOXAM TEST FOR STRYCHNINE. A warm solution of strychnine in dilute nitric acid gives, with traces of potassium chlorate, an intense scarlet color changed to brown by ammonia, and then to green on drying.

BLUM REAGENT. A mixture of (1) a solution of 0.05 g. manganous chloride in dilute hydrochloric acid; and (2) a solution of 3 g. lead peroxide in 10 g. metaphosphoric acid and 95 ml. water. It is used in testing for albumin in urine. A turbidity is given by albumin.

BLUM TEST FOR FERROUS ION. Add a crystal of potassium nitrate and an excess of concentrated sulfuric acid to the solution to be tested. The appearance of red streaks about the crystal indicates the presence of ferrous ion, even if ferric ion is present.

BLUNCK TEST FOR POTATO STARCH. A microscopic test for potato starch in bread or flour, which depends upon the staining of the grains of potato starch yellow when its neutral suspension is treated on a slide with a saturated 30% alcoholic solution of metachrome red G, which has been diluted with one fourth its volume of water.

BLUNT TEST. Silver is detected in lead by dissolving the material in nitric acid, and adding a little saturated aqueous solution of lead chloride. A turbidity is given by silver.

BLUSHING. A term applied to a surface opacity or turbidity of varnish and lacquer films. The cause of this defect is commonly rapid evaporation of solvent, or improper formulation of the product.

BOAS HYDROCHLORIC ACID SOLUTIONS. Two solutions: (1) a solution of 0.1 g. tropaeoline 00 in 100 ml. alcohol; and (2) 10 g. resorcinol and 3 g. sucrose, in 100 ml. water and 3 ml. alcohol. These solutions are used in estimating free hydrochloric acid in gastric juice.

BOAS REAGENT FOR BLOOD. A solution of 25 g. potassium hydroxide and 1 g. thymolphthalein in 100 ml. water, which is heated with 10 g. zinc dust until decolorized. It is used in testing feces for blood.

BOAS TEST FOR ADRENALINE. Adrenaline gives a violet color with an excess of concentrated hydrochloric acid.

BOBIÈRRE TEST. A test for lead in tin in which a drop of glacial acetic acid is placed on the metal, which is then heated, and a drop of potassium iodide solution added. A yellow color indicates the presence of lead.

BOCHICHIO TEST. A test for salicylic acid in milk, in which 5 drops 10% sodium nitrite solution and 5 drops 10% cupric sulfate solution are added to a mixture of 5 ml. each of milk and distilled water, followed by heating on the water bath until the casein separates. A red color in the supernatant liquid indicates the presence of salicylic acid.

BODDE TEST. To distinguish resorcinol in solution from certain other phenolic compounds, add sodium hypochlorite solution. A violet color, changing to yellow, and becoming brown on warming, is given by resorcinol.

BODEKER TEST. A mixture of zinc sulfate solution with a little sodium nitroprusside solution gives a red to dark-red color in a neutral solution of a sulfite which has been neutralized with acetic acid or sodium bicarbonate. The sensitivity is increased by addition of potassium ferrocyanide solution.

BODROUX-CHICHIBABIN ALDEHYDE SYNTHESIS. A **Grignard reaction** with **orthoformates,** resulting in the formation of aldehydes.

$$R'MgX + HC(OR'')_3 \rightarrow R'CH(OR'')_2 + R''OMgX$$

$$R'CH(OR'')_2 \xrightarrow[H^+]{H_2O} R'CHO + 2R''OH.$$

BODY. In chemical technology, the consistency or strength of a substance. Thus an oil of relatively great consistency or viscosity is said to have great "body"; and a strong flavor or a color of high tintorial value is also said to have "body."

BODY COLOR. The dominant color of a **pigment,** in the pure, finely-ground state, as observed by reflected white light.

BOEHM-BODENDORF TEST. Isopropyl alcohol is detected in alcoholic preparations by decolorizing with charcoal or by distillation, and performing a ring test with a 1% solution of *m*-nitrobenzaldehyde in sulfuric acid. A carmine-red ring on warming in hot water for 1 minute indicates the presence of isopropyl alcohol.

BÖESEKEN REAGENT. A mixture of 2 g. phenylhydrazine in 20 ml. water, treated with sulfur dioxide until solution is complete. This reagent forms hydrazones with carbonyl compounds.

BOGERT-COOK SYNTHESIS. By the action of sulfuric acid, derivatives of 1-β-phenethyl-1-cyclohexanol yield octohydrophenanthrene derivatives

BOGOSLOVSKI-KRASNOVA TEST. A test for the cupric ion, based on its catalytic action, in the presence of sodium chloride, in producing a violet color, then a brown precipitate, with *p*-aminophenol hydrochloride.

BOHLIG REAGENT. Two solutions: (1) 3 g. of mercuric chloride in 90 ml. water; and (2) 2 g. potassium chloride in 100 ml. water. They are used in testing for ammonium compounds, which give white precipitates with them.

BÖHME SOLUTIONS. Two solutions: (1) 4 g. *p*-methylaminobenzaldehyde in 380 g. alcohol and 80 g. hydrochloric acid; and (2) a saturated aqueous solution of potassium persulfate. They are used in testing for indole. A red color is given by indole.

BÖHMER HEMATOXYLIN. A 10% alcoholic solution of hematoxylin used as a stain.

BÖHMER HEMATOXYLIN-ALUM. A solution of 1 g. hematoxylin in 10 ml. alcohol which is mixed with a solution of 10 g. potassium alum in 200 ml. water. This

In the course of this reaction, initial dehydration sometimes occurs; the cyclization of the resulting unsaturated compounds or similar substances is called the Bogert synthesis.

BOGERT SYNTHESIS. See **Bogert-Cook synthesis.**

solution is used as a stain for nuclei.

BOHN-SCHMIDT REACTION. A method of introducing hydroxyl groups, or additional hydroxyl groups, into anthraquinones by the action of sulfuric (or fuming sulfuric) and boric acids. Mercury is the preferred catalyst.

BOHR MAGNETON. See **magneton, Bohr.**

BOHR-SOMMERFELD ATOM. See atom, Bohr-Sommerfeld.

BOHR THEORY OF ATOMIC SPECTRA. The electrons surrounding the **nucleus** of an **atom** move in closed **orbits** about the nucleus; more than one such stable orbit, or **energy level,** is possible for a given electron: in fact, the number of such orbits is determined by the condition that the angular momentum of the electron be an integral multiple of $h/2\pi$ (where h is **Planck's constant**); emission of radiation results when an electron moves suddenly from one orbit to another in which it has less energy; and, conversely, absorption of radiation is attended by a jump of an electron from a lower energy level to a higher. Since there are numerous energy levels in each atom, there can be various transitions, and hence numerous spectral lines are possible.

BOHR-WHEELER THEORY. An analytical theory of the nature of nuclear **fission** and the conditions under which it might occur, based upon a liquid-drop analogy. One conclusion was that if the ratio Z^2/A exceeded 45, no additional energy would be necessary to cause fission to take place. ($Z =$ **atomic number;** $A =$ **mass number.**) An element having a Z^2/A ratio of 45 would have an atomic number of 120, according to the theory that elements of higher atomic number are not stable.

BOHRISCH TESTS FOR CAMPHOR. (1) A solution of 1 g. vanillin in 100 ml. 25% hydrochloric acid gives a rose-red color on heating with camphor. The color changes to blue-green at 75–100° C. (2) A mixture of the vanillin-hydrochloric acid solution in (1), with an equal volume of sulfuric acid, gives with natural camphor (not synthetic camphor) after $\frac{1}{2}$–1 hour a dirty green color, changing to green in 1 hour, and then to blue after 7–8 hours.

BOILED OIL. See **oil, boiled.**

BOILER. A closed or open vessel used for evaporating liquids.

BOILER COMPOUND. A mixture of substances added to boiler feed water to prevent formation of scale inside the boiler.

BOILING. The process of changing from the liquid state to the vapor state, the term being restricted usually to cases in which the vapor pressure of the liquid is equal to, or greater than, the atmospheric pressure above the liquid.

BOILING POINT. The temperature at which, under a given condition of pressure, a pure liquid and its vapor can coexist. In practice, boiling points are referred to the standard atmospheric pressure (760 mm.) and those determined at other pressures are qualified by an exponent which indicates the pressure, as 80° ^{14mm} (see below and **critical point**). The effect of pressure on the boiling point is to raise it proportionately to the increase in pressure or to lower it in proportion to the decrease in pressure. Thus the boiling point of water is lowered 0.37° by a decrease in pressure of 1 centimeter of the mercury barometer.

BOILING POINT, ABSOLUTE. The boiling point on the **absolute scale,** numerically equal to the boiling point in degrees centigrade plus 273.16°.

BOILING POINT, MAXIMUM. See **maximum boiling point.**

BOILING POINT, MINIMUM. See **minimum boiling point.**

BOILING POINT OF SOLUTIONS. The solution of a nonvolatile substance in a liquid lowers the **vapor tension** of the system and so raises the boiling point of the solvent. In dilute solutions the effect is proportional to the molecular ratio between the solvent and solute but in concentrated solutions deviations from this rule occur. (See **law of Raoult.**)

BOILING POINT, REGULARITIES OF. See **law of Kopp.**

BOILING RANGE. The range of temperature within which a liquid boils to dryness, or evaporates completely; technically, the range in which an industrial solvent or liquid distills.

BOLLENBACK REAGENT. An ammoniacal solution of ammonium persulfate used to precipitate lead and bismuth as their higher oxides, and thus to separate them from the other metals of the hydrogen sulfide group.

BOLLIGER TESTS FOR CREATININE. (1) Creatinine gives a purple color with a 10% solution of sodium 3,5-dinitrobenzoate in the presence of sodium hydroxide solution. (2) Creatinine gives a pink to brown color with an aqueous alcoholic solution of 1,3,5-trinitrobenzene and dilute sodium hydroxide solution.

BOLOMETER. An instrument for measuring minute quantities of **radiant energy.** This apparatus consists essentially of very thin, similar strips of blackened metal mounted side-by-side, and arranged in a **Wheatstone bridge** or other electrical circuit which measures accurately the small resistance changes due to temperature changes in certain of the strips.

BOLTZMANN CONSTANT. A molecular constant arising in thermodynamic calculation of the energy of a single molecule or oscillator. It is expressed most simply by the relationship $k = R/N$, in which R is the **gas constant** per mole and N is the **Avogadro number.** Its value is 1.380×10^{-16} erg per ° C.

BOLTZMANN LAW. See **Law of Boltzmann.**

BOMBARD. To subject to the impact of particles or radiations, as is used in the production of other particles or radiations, or in the **transmutation** of atoms.

BÖMER REAGENT FOR ALBUMOSES. A saturated aqueous solution of zinc sulfate, used as a precipitant for albumoses.

BONASTRE TEST. Myrrh is detected by (1) a violet color given by its alcoholic solution when warmed with nitric acid, (2) a red-violet color given by its ethereal solution when exposed to bromine vapor.

BOND. A symbol used to denote the number and attachments of the valences of an atom in constitutional formulas. The bond is represented by a dot ($\cdot$) or line (—) drawn between the atoms, as H $\cdot$ O $\cdot$ H or H—O—H. Double and triple bonds are used also and may express unsaturation, particularly when they join two atoms of the same element. Examples, $=C=O$, $H_2C=CH_2$, $Ca=O$, $HC\equiv CH$. The nature of the valence bond is considered to be electrical attraction attributable to various distributions of the electrons around the nuclei of the bonded atoms. Various arrangements of this kind, and their influence upon the properties of the resulting compounds, are discussed for the special types of bonds which follow.

BOND, ATOMIC. A **valence** linkage between atoms consisting of a pair of electrons, one of which has been contributed by each of the atoms bonded.

BOND, COORDINATE. A term applied to various types of **valence** bonds. The most common usage occurs probably in the case of the semicovalent bond formed between two atoms by a pair of electrons, both donated by one of the atoms, or in the special case of a coordination-type compound, in which the primary valences have already been satisfied, and in which the coordinate bond is formed later.

BOND, COVALENT. A type of linkage between atoms wherein each atom contributes one electron to a shared pair that constitutes an ordinary chemical bond.

BOND, DATIVE. A type of covalent bond (see **bond, covalent**) in which both electrons forming the bonding pair are supplied by one atom. An example is the forming of amine oxides between tertiary amines and oxygen, in which both electrons were donated by the nitrogen group. Such bonds exhibit some polarity and are frequently called semipolar bonds.

BOND, ELECTROSTATIC. A **valence** linkage in which two atoms are held together by **electrostatic forces** resulting from the transfer of one or more electrons from the outer shell of one atom to that of the other. In this process the atoms are converted into **ions** of opposite charge which attract each other. The transfer of electrons is commonly in the direction that gives completed, or more nearly completed, outer electron shells for both atoms.

BOND ENERGY. The energy characterizing a chemical bond between atoms, as measured by the energy required to disrupt it. See **heat of linkage.**

BOND, HETEROPOLAR. A **valence** linkage between two atoms consisting of a pair of electrons. This bond is characterized by an unequal distribution of **charge** due to a displacement of the electronic-pair so that the effect of the bond is to make one atom differ in polarity from the other.

BOND, HOMOPOLAR. A **valence** linkage between two atoms consisting of a pair of electrons that are held equally by both atoms, so that no difference in **polarity** exists between the atoms.

BOND, HYDROGEN. A **valence** linkage joining two electronegative atoms through a hydrogen atom. Since a stable hydrogen atom cannot be associated with more than two electrons, the hydrogen bond may be regarded as representing a **resonance** phenomenon, by which it is alternatively attached to one or the other of the two atoms. The ion HF_2^- may consist of two fluoride ions joined by a proton, through a hydrogen bond, whereas many associated molecules, such as those in water itself, may well owe their existence to the formation of hydrogen bonds. Intermolecular hydrogen bonds serve to explain the properties of certain **keto-esters** and other organic compounds.

BOND, HYDROXYL. A **valence** linkage in which a hydrogen atom serves to link two atoms of oxygen by a resonance phenomenon. (See **bond, hydrogen.**)

BOND, METALLIC. A special type of bond existing in metals, in which the **valence** electrons of the constituent atoms are free to move in the periodic lattice. This type of bonding accounts for the observed metallic properties.

BOND, MOLECULAR. A **valence** linkage between two atoms consisting of a pair of electrons, both of which have been furnished by one of the atoms.

BOND MOMENT. The electromagnetic **dipole moment** of a chemical bond between atoms.

BOND, ODD-ELECTRON. A **valence** linkage between two atoms which consists of one or three electrons. These bonds are so uncommon that definitions in the electronic theory of valence are usually discussed in terms of two-electron bonds. However, it is believed that one-electron bonds can exist in systems having two states with the same energy, as in the case of H_2^+, whereas the postulation of the existence of a three-electron bond would explain certain of the properties of nitric oxide.

BOND, SEMI-COVALENT OR BOND, POLARIZED IONIC. A **valence** linkage which is intermediate in character between a purely ionic and purely covalent **bond,** with intermediate properties. Such bonds arise quite often if the constituent atoms have unequal **electron affinities.**

BOND, SEMIPOLAR. See **bond, dative.**

BOND STRENGTH. The energy required to rupture a given valence **bond** in a given molecule.

BONDING ELECTRON. See **electron, bonding.**

BONDS, CUMULATED DOUBLE. Two double bonds on the same carbon atom.

BONGIOVANNI TEST. Thiocyanate ion is detected by the red color, becoming green on dilution, produced when its solution is treated with vanadium trichloride.

BONNES TEST. To detect formic and acetic acids, distill the sample with sulfuric acid. Neutralize with calcium carbonate, evaporate and distill the residue over a flame, into a little water. Then treat this solution with (1) fuchsin-bisulfate which gives a rose color if formic acid was present,

(2) alkaline sodium nitroprusside solution, which gives a yellow color becoming red with acetic acid, if acetic acid was present.

BONNET TEST FOR FORMALDE-HYDE. (1) Formaldehyde gives a pink to blue color to a solution of 0.35 g. morphine sulfate in 100 ml. concentrated sulfuric acid when the reagent is floated in a watch glass on the surface of a sample containing the formaldehyde. (2) The above reagent may be mixed directly with the sample, if the color of the latter does not interfere.

BONZ TEST FOR TELLURIUM IN BISMUTH. A solution of 1 g. of a bismuth salt in 2.5 ml. hydrochloric acid gives a black color with 2.5 ml. **Bettendorf-Winkler solution** (q.v.) if tellurium is present. With twice as much reagent, the color is light green.

BOORD SYNTHESIS. A system of synthesis of pure **olefins**, applied with notable success to the production of all twenty-seven possible structural isomers of heptene, C_7H_{14}. The synthesis depends on the following successive reactions: (1) The treating of an aldehyde with an alcohol and hydrochloric acid to form an α-chloroether. (2) The reaction of the chloroether with bromine. (3) The reaction of a Grignard reagent with the resultant α, β-dibromoether to replace the α-bromine with an alkyl group. (4) The removal of the bromine and alkoxyl group by the interaction of the β-bromoether and zinc. The product is an olefin.

BORACIC. See **boric.**

BORATE. The anions $(BO_2)_n{}^{n-}$ or $H_2B_5O_{10}{}^{3-}$ (meta); $BO_3{}^{3-}$ (ortho); or $B_4O_7{}^{=}$ (tetra or pyro); or a compound containing one of them. For other borates, see **borate (hypo)** and **borate (per).**

BORATE (BI-). An acid borate, commonly a compound in which one or two of the hydrogen atoms of H_3BO_3 have been replaced.

BORATE (HYPO). The anion BO^-, or a compound containing it.

BORATE (META-). The anion $(BO_2)_n{}^{n-}$ or $H_2B_5O_{10}{}^{3-}$, or a compound containing one of these anions.

BORATE (ORTHO-). The anion $BO_3{}^{3-}$, or a compound containing it.

BORATE (PER). The anion $BO_3{}^-$, or a compound containing it. Addition compounds of metaborates with hydrogen peroxide, such as $NaBO_2 \cdot H_2O_2 \cdot 3H_2O$, are also called perborates (see **borate (peroxy)**).

BORATE (PEROXY). (1) An addition compound of a metaborate with hydrogen peroxide, for example,

$$NaBO_2 \cdot H_2O_2 \cdot 3H_2O.$$

(2) A perborate, for example, $NaBO_3$.

BORATE (PYRO-). See **borate (tetra-).**

BORATE (TETRA-). The anion $B_4O_7{}^=$, or a compound containing it.

BORCHER PROCESS. A process for the electrorefining of a silver, in which the impure silver is the anode and the pure silver is deposited on the cathode of an electrolytic cell having an electrolyte consisting of an aqueous solution of silver nitrate and nitric acid.

BORCHERS FURNACE. A furnace for roasting bismuth ores, which is gas-fired and is divided into six compartments that contain crucibles with ore charges in various stages of treatment (each pair of compartments becoming in turn a **preheating chamber,** a **combustion chamber,** and a **cooling chamber**).

BORDE REAGENTS. Three standard reagents used for the determination of iodine number. They are: (1) a solution of 18.8 g. antipyrine in 1 liter alcohol; (2) a solution of 5 g. iodine in 100 ml. alcohol; and (3) a solution of 6 g. mercuric chloride in 100 ml. alcohol. The alcohol used should be somewhat weaker than the usual 95%.

BORDET TEST. An agglutination test for blood, applied in differentiating animal and human blood.

BORGHESIO TEST. A test for alum in flour in which a 10% water extract of the flour, after precipitation of the proteins with tannin, gives a carmine-red color with cochineal tincture (2 drops) if alum is present. A 1% alcoholic solution of alizarin gives an orange-red color if alum is present.

BORGMANN TEST FOR ORGANIC HALOGENS. To test for bromine and iodine in organic combination, add the solution to be tested to 2–3 ml. dilute hydrochloric acid containing a few drops 30% hydrogen peroxide, and shake with chloroform, which gives a violet color for iodine. It shows yellow to brown for bromine if warmed before extracting.

BORGMANN TEST FOR β-NAPH-THOL. A solution containing β-naphthol gives, with sodium hypochlorite solution and hydrochloric acid, a yellow precipitate, which forms a dark violet solution with ammonia.

BORIC. Relating to boric or boracic acid, H_3BO_3; to boric acid (meta-), HBO_2; to boric acid (per-), HBO_3; or to boric acid (pyro-), $H_2B_4O_7$.

BORIDE. A binary compound of **boron.**

BORINSKI REAGENT. A solution of 0.85 g. guaiac resin in 85 g. 70% alcohol, to which are then added 10 ml. liquid phenol and 5 ml. 3% hydrogen peroxide. This reagent is used for detecting peroxidases in milk. A blue color indicates the presence of peroxidases.

BORN-HABER CYCLE. A cycle of changes, chemical and physical, applied to a chemical substance, commonly a crystalline metallic halide, to calculate the **electron affinities** of certain atoms. The stages include the **dissociation** of the molecules of the crystal into gaseous ions, the **neutralization** of these ions by transfer of electrons from the negative ions to the positive ones, the **condensation** of the gaseous atoms to form solid molecules of the two substances (e.g., **metal** and **halogen**), and the recombination of the solid molecules to reform the original crystalline compound. From this cycle, it is possible to derive the equation:

$$E = Q + S + \frac{D}{2} + I - U_{MX}$$

in which E is the electron affinity of the halogen atoms, Q is the **heat of formation** of the compound, S is the **heat of sublimation** of the metal, D is the **heat of dissociation** of the molecular halogen, I is the **ionization potential** of the metal, and U_{MX} is the **lattice energy** of the crystal.

BORNEMANN REACTION. A modification of **Étard reaction** for the oxidation (to carbonyl groups) of heterocyclic bound methyl groups. Bornemann used proportions of slightly less than 2 moles of chromyl chloride to one of the substance, both dissolved in carbon disulfide.

BORNET REAGENT. A freshly-prepared, neutral, saturated solution of cryogenine used to give color reactions with heavy metals.

BÖRNSTEIN TEST. Saccharin gives with resorcinol and sulfuric acid a yellow color, changing to red and to dark green, and yielding a red solution with green fluorescence with water and alkali.

BORNTRÄGER TEST FOR ALOES. A 10% aqueous solution of aloes after boiling, cooling, and filtering, on shaking with ether and 5% ammonia, gives a red color. This reaction varies with aloes from different sources.

BORNTRÄGER TEST FOR AMYL ALCOHOL. Amyl alcohol is detected in ethyl alcohol by the production of a raspberry-red color with 3 drops concentrated hydrochloric acid and 10 drops colorless aniline.

BORNTRÄGER TEST FOR FERROUS ION. Potassium hydroxyquinoline sulfate gives with ferrous ion in alkaline solution a green-black color, disappearing on addition of acid.

BORNTRÄGER TEST FOR RESORCI-NOL AND THYMOL. Mix equal parts gypsum, sodium nitrite, and sodium bisulfate, moisten with water, heat, and add the solution to be tested. Chrome-green indicates resorcinol; chrome-red, thymol.

BORNTRÄGER TEST FOR SENNA. The material is boiled with 10% alcoholic potassium hydroxide, diluted with water, filtered and acidified with hydrochloric acid. If an ethereal extract turns yellow-red with ammonia, senna is present.

BORNYL. The radical

$$CH_2 \cdot CH \cdot CH_2 \cdot CH_2 \cdot C(CH_3) \cdot CH— \text{ (from borneol).}$$

with a $C(CH_3)_2$ bridge connecting the first and last carbons.

BOROFLUORIDE. See **fluoborate.**

BORON. Nonmetallic element. Symbol B. Atomic number 5. Atomic weight 10.82. Exists in two modifications: (1) a crystalline form, density 2.54, hardness 9.5, which has a variation sometimes called the adamantine form (density 2.50); and (2) an amorphous form, having a density of 2.45. Melting point 2300° C. Boiling point 2550° C. Valence 3. Oxide B_2O_3. Occurs naturally as boric acid and as borates of which the sodium salt, borax, is the most important.

BOROTUNGSTIC. Related to borotungstic acid, $(WO_3)_9B_2O_3 \cdot 24H_2O$.

BOROWOLFRAMIC. See **borotungstic.**

BORSCHE-DRECHSEL SYNTHESIS. Ring closure of aryl **hydrazones** of alicyclic **ketones,** yielding hydrogenated **carbazoles.**

BORYL. The radical O:B–.

BOSCH-MEISER UREA PROCESS. An industrial method of producing urea from carbon dioxide and ammonia. High temperatures and pressures favor the reaction.

$$2NH_3 + CO_2 \rightarrow H_2N \cdot CO \cdot NH_2 + H_2O.$$

BOSCH PROCESS. A catalytic process for producing hydrogen from carbon monoxide and steam by the reaction

$$CO + H_2O \rightarrow H_2 + CO_2.$$

By means of this process it is possible to increase the yield of hydrogen from the familiar **water-gas** reaction (steam + carbon → hydrogen + carbon monoxide). The carbon dioxide is easily separated by dissolving it in water under pressure.

BOSE-EINSTEIN STATISTICS. A form of **quantum statistics,** applicable to radiations, or to systems of particles such as atoms or molecules, if they contain an even number of particles (protons, neutrons, and electrons), in which it is assumed that the **eigenfunction** of the system is symmetric and, in consequence, that interchange of the coordinates of any two particles will not change the sign of the eigenfunction. (Contrast **Fermi-Dirac statistics.**)

BOSE-NICHOLSON TEST. To test for nitro-compounds, dissolve 0.1 g. of the substance in 10 ml. acetone, and add 3 ml. 5% sodium hydroxide. A purple-blue color shows dinitro-compounds, and a blood-red color, trinitro-compounds. Mononitro-compounds give no color.

BOSE TEST FOR NITRO-GROUP IN ORGANIC COMPOUNDS. Heat 0.01–0.05 g. of the substance for 1–2 minutes with 1 ml. of a solution of 10 g. potassium hydroxide in 6 ml. water. Cool rapidly, add 1 ml. water, acidify with 50% acetic acid. A rose-red color with **Griess-Ilosvay Reagent** (q.v.) indicates the presence of the nitro-group.

BOSE TEST FOR POLYHYDROXY PHENOLS. Certain polyhydroxy phenols in alkaline solution reduce a 1% solution of o-dinitrobenzene to the deep violet quinoid form.

BOSE TEST FOR REDUCING SUGARS. A mixture of 2 ml. 25% sodium carbonate solution with 1 drop 1% solution of o-dinitrobenzene is heated for somewhat less than 1 minute, then the solution to be tested is added. A violet color is given by reducing sugars.

BOSWELL FLUORESCEIN REACTION. On heating 0.1 g. of various naphthalene derivatives to 160° C. for 3 minutes with 0.1 g. resorcinol and 1 drop sulfuric acid, then cooling, neutralizing and diluting, characteristic colors are obtained.

BÖTTCHER TEST. The presence of cinnamic acid in benzoic acid is detected by oxidation to benzaldehyde with potassium permanganate or other oxidizing agents.

BÖTTGER SOLUTION FOR NITRITE. A solution of 1 g. starch in 200 ml. water containing 1 g. hydrochloric acid. To this solution is then added 10 g. calcium carbonate, 10 g. sodium chloride, and 0.5 g. cadmium chloride. It is then diluted to 250 ml. This reagent is used in the detection of nitrites. A blue color is given by nitrites.

BÖTTGER TEST FOR ALCOHOL IN VOLATILE OILS. Shake 5 ml. of the oil with 5 ml. of glycerin in a graduated cylinder. Presence of alcohol causes an increase in volume of the glycerin.

BÖTTGER TEST FOR CARBON MONOXIDE. Palladous chloride paper is blackened by carbon monoxide. Several modifications of this test have been proposed.

BÖTTGER TEST FOR CHLORATE. Chlorate solutions become blue on the addition of anilene sulfate and concentrated sulfuric acid.

BÖTTGER TEST FOR ERGOT IN FLOUR. The flour is mixed with oxalic acid and warmed with ether. A red colored solution indicates the presence of ergot alkaloids.

BÖTTGER TEST FOR HYDROGEN PEROXIDE. An ammoniacal solution of silver nitrate is reduced to metallic silver on warming with hydrogen peroxide.

BÖTTGER TEST FOR NICKEL. Nickel in solution gives a yellow color or precipitate with an aqueous solution of potassium xanthogenate; the color is stable on addition of a little ammonia.

BÖTTGER TEST FOR OZONE. Filter paper treated with acid-free gold chloride is colored violet by ozone.

BÖTTINGER TEST FOR GLYOXALIC ACID. Glyoxalic acid condenses with urea in the presence of hydrochloric acid to form allantoin.

BÖTTINGER TEST FOR PYROCATECHOL. Pyrocatechol gives a precipitate when its solution in water is added to an ammoniacal calcium chloride solution. This test differentiates pyrocatechol from resorcinol and hydroquinone.

BÖTTINGER TEST FOR TANNIN AND GALLIC ACID. On heating the substance with twice its weight of phenylhydrazine to 100° C. for a few minutes, and adding a little water and heating to boiling, followed by transferring 1–2 drops of the liquid to a large volume of very dilute sodium hydroxide solution, a blue color changing to yellow indicates the presence of tannin, and a yellow to orange color indicates gallic acid.

BOTTLE. A small container for liquids or divided solids. Bottles are made, most commonly of glass (although stoneware, rubber, paraffin, and other materials are also used), with a neck designed for convenient closure by an easily removed and replaced device, such as a cap or stopper.

BOTTLE, ASPIRATOR. See **bottle, washing.**

BOTTLE, DOUBLE-CHAMBER. A bottle constructed in two parts — an outer glass container, and a hollow-tapering inner glass vessel with a ground-glass collar at its line of junction with the outer container. This bottle is used for two liquids that are employed in the same work, such as a microscope immersion oil and its solvent.

BOTTLE, DROPPING. A bottle containing a removable hollow glass tube or a rod for dispensing liquids by drops.

BOTTLE, GAS. A bottle with the necessary connections for use in a train of apparatus, and used for washing, measuring, or generating gases.

BOTTLE, GRETHEN. A weighing bottle having a glass stopcock integral with a ground-in glass stopper.

BOTTLE, LE CHATELIER. A specific gravity bottle with long neck, having two series of graduations with a small bulb between.

BOTTLE, LUNGE. A weighing bottle with a ground-in glass stopper that has integral with it two glass stopcocks separated by a small chamber.

BOTTLE, MICROSCOPE IMMERSION OIL. A bottle with a screw-cap or other tight-fitting closure, to prevent evaporation and gumming of the oil.

BOTTLE, MILK-TESTING. See **Babcock bottle.**

BOTTLE, MILLIGAN. A bottle, for scrubbing gases, that contains a glass spiral which increases the length and time of travel of gas bubbles through the apparatus, and thus increases efficiency.

BOTTLE, NICOL TUBE. A glass container made integral with two capillary tubes, one drawn to a point. Used in specific gravity determinations.

BOTTLE, OIL SAMPLE. A relatively tall, cylindrical bottle made to a standard size to enable one to compare the appearance of different samples.

BOTTLE, PRESSURE. A bottle designed to withstand pressure. A common form has thick walls, a rounded bottom, and a clamped stopper.

BOTTLE, REAGENT. A bottle with the name of a reagent formed in the glass or fused or etched on it.

BOTTLE, SERUM AND VACCINE. A bottle, usually made of low-alkali glass, designed to hold serums or vaccines. A rubber stopper drawn over its neck is perforated near the top to permit the insertion of a hypodermic needle.

BOTTLE, SPECIFIC GRAVITY. A small bottle designed to hold an accurately-measured volume of liquid. This bottle is, therefore, provided with (1) a relatively long, narrow neck that bears a calibration mark; or (2) a ground glass stopper having a capillary. This bottle is used for determining specific gravity by weighing empty, then when filled with water, and finally, when filled with a liquid whose specific gravity is to be determined.

BOTTLE, VOLUMETER. A bottle having a glass measuring tube and reservoir attached to its stopper. It is used for determining the volume of a solid by the measurement of the volume of liquid displaced.

BOTTLE, WASHING. A bottle used as a handy source for small quantities of water in the laboratory, especially for washing precipitates, etc. It is commonly provided with two tubes, through one of which water may be expelled by air blown in by mouth or by an aspirator bulb; the other tube having a constricted end attached by rubber tubing to allow water to be directed wherever required.

BOTTLE, WEIGHING. A small bottle with a light, ground-glass full-diameter stopper. This bottle is used for weighing materials on the analytical balance.

BOTTLE, WOULFF. A special type of bottle, with several necks, used in gas washing or generation, or for reactions requiring mechanical stirring and addition of reagents.

BOUCHARDAT REAGENT. A solution of 2 g. iodine and 4 g. potassium iodide in 100 ml. water. This solution is used as a test reagent for alkaloids, which give brown precipitates with it.

BOUGAULT ARSENIC REAGENT. A solution of 20 g. sodium hypophosphite, in 20 ml. water, to which 200 ml. concentrated hydrochloric acid is then added. This reagent is a reducing agent, used in the determination of arsenic.

BOUGAULT SODIUM REAGENT. A solution of 1 g. antimony trichloride in 10 ml. 33% potassium carbonate solution and 45 ml. 3% hydrogen peroxide solution. This reagent is a precipitant for sodium.

BOUREAU REAGENT. A solution of 2 g. sulfosalicylic acid and 6 g. phenolsulfonic acid in 40 ml. water, used in testing urine for albumin. A white precipitate indicates the presence of albumin.

BOUSSINGAULT TEST. Nitrate is detected by its decolorization of indigo in sulfuric acid solution.

BOUVEAULT ALDEHYDE SYNTHESIS. A **Grignard** method of formation of aldehydes by use of dialkylformamides.

$$HCONR_2 + R'MgCl \rightarrow R'CHOMgClNR_2$$
$$\downarrow HCl$$
$$R'CHO + R_2NH + MgCl_2.$$

BOUGE TEST FOR CHLORINE IN IODINE. Mix 2.0 g. of sample and 25 ml. benzene; after 15 minutes shake with 5 ml. water; extract the iodine from the aqueous layer by repeated washing with 5 ml. benzene. Heat the aqueous extract with potassium permanganate and sulfuric acid, distilling its vapor into sodium hydroxide solution, which will give a blue color with carbolated aniline water if chlorine is present.

BOUMAN REAGENT. A solution of 0.02 g. isatin in 1 liter dilute hydrochloric acid, used as a test reagent for indican in urine.

BOUND OXYGEN. In autooxidation, that part of the oxygen that unites with the substance undergoing oxidation.

BOURCET TEST. The presence of antipyrine in aminopyrine is shown by heating 0.02 g. of the material in 4 ml. water with 2 drops sulfuric acid and a little sodium nitrite. A blue-green color is given by antipyrine; do not confuse with a fugitive blue-violet color.

BOURDIER TESTS FOR VERBENALIN. (1) On treatment with emulsin, sulfuric acid or other hydrolyzing agents, verbenalin gives d-glucose and a phenolic compound. (2) Salts of hydroxylamine and phenylhydrazine give crystalline precipitates with verbenalin.

BOUVEAULT AND BLANC REDUCTION OF ESTERS. Reduction of **esters** to **alcohols** by metallic sodium and absolute alcohol. The general form of this reaction is:

$$R \cdot COO \cdot C_2H_5 \xrightarrow{2H_2} R \cdot CH_2OH + C_2H_5OH.$$

BOUVEAULT REAGENT FOR FATTY ACIDS. Tetrachlorohydroquinone.

BOWER-BARFF PROCESS. A process for producing a corrosion-resistant film on the surface of a metal, chiefly iron, by oxidation with superheated steam, followed by treatment with hot linseed oil.

BOYD, SCHUBERT AND ADAMSON EQUATION. An **ion-exchange** equation of the form:

$$X_A = \frac{kb_1a_A}{1 + b_1a_Ab_2a_B}$$

where X_A = amount of A adsorbed per gram, a_A and a_B are the cation activities in equilibrium solution, k = total **exchange capacity,** and b_1 and b_2 are constants.

BOYLE, LAW OF. See **law of Boyle.**

BOYLE TEMPERATURE. The temperature, for a given gas, at which Boyle's law (see **Law of Boyle**) is most closely obeyed in the lower pressure range. At this temperature the minimum point (of inflection) in the pV-T curve falls on the pV axis.

Br Symbol for the element **bromine.**

BRABENDER FARINOGRAPH. A twin-bladed, water-jacketed mixer directly coupled to an electric motor which is supported so it is free to turn in a vertical plane and to the housing of which is connected a pen that can write on a clock-work-driven band of ruled paper. This instrument is used to test flour, by recording the varying resistance of the dough to a given mixing operation.

BRACKETT SERIES. A group of lines in the **infrared spectrum** of atomic hydrogen represented by the formula:

$$\bar{\nu} = R_H \left(\frac{1}{n_1{}^2} - \frac{1}{n_2{}^2} \right)$$

in which $\bar{\nu}$ is the **wave number,** R_H is the Rydberg number, n_1 is 4, and n_2 has various integral values.

BRADLEY ARC PROCESS. See **arc process, Bradley.**

BRADLEY TEST. Copper salts in solution give a blue color with hematoxylin.

BRAGG EQUATION. The basic relationship used in calculating the distance between the **atomic planes** of a crystal by the **Bragg method** of crystal analysis, or of the wave length of x-rays, if that distance is known. The relationship is of the form

$$n\lambda = 2d \sin \theta$$

in which n is the number of wave lengths, and λ is the wave length of the x-rays, d is the distance between the lattice planes of the crystal, and θ is the glancing angle.

BRAGG METHOD OF CRYSTAL ANALYSIS. A beam of **x-rays** is directed against a **crystal,** and its atoms, because of their **lattice** arrangement, reflect the rays as would a series of plane surfaces. The measurements of the **diffraction patterns** formed by the reflected radiations furnish a means of calculating the spacings between the **atomic planes,** if the wave length of the x-rays is known.

BRALEY-HOBART TEST. Cobalt gives a brown solution with dimethylglyoxime which, unlike other metal glyoximes, is stable to mineral acids.

BRAMLEY MILL. See **mill, Bramley.**

BRANCHING RATIO. In cases where a **radioactive** element may undergo more than one radioactive disintegration, the ratio of the quantities of the element entering into the various types of disintegrations is called the branching ratio.

BRANDERHORST TEST. To detect paraffin in spermaceti, saponify the latter by boiling 1 g. of it with 20 ml. alcoholic potassium hydroxide for 5 minutes, then add 10–15 ml. water. A turbidity indicates the presence of paraffin.

BRANDES TEST. Tartrates in neutral solution give a black precipitate with platinic chloride solution on heating.

BRANT REAGENT. A solution of 3 g. sodium selenate in 80 ml. water and 60 ml. sulfuric acid. This reagent is used as a test reagent for solanine and solanidine, which give a red color with it.

BRAU REAGENT FOR COPPER. The compound 2,7-diaminodibenzofuran, which gives a blue to violet precipitate with cupric ion in the presence of cyanides or cyanates.

BRAUER TEST REACTION FOR ORGANIC ACIDS. Concentrated sulfuric acid and resorcinol give a violet color with oxalic acid, and a red color with tartaric acid. Dilute sulfuric acid and resorcinol give a red color with lactic acid.

BRAUER TEST FOR PHENOLS. On treatment with phosphomolybdic acid, then with ammonia, characteristic colors are produced by a number of the polyhydric phenols.

BRAUER TEST REACTIONS FOR RESINS. A series of tests used to differentiate between many resins, including both natural and synthetic resins. Five colors are observed as follows: (1) the color with sulfuric acid and ammonium molybdate; (2) the color of (1) on neutralization with ammonia; (3) the color with sulfuric acid; (4) the color of (3) after 10 minutes, and (5) the color with diazosulfanilic acid in potassium hydroxide solution.

BRAUN TEST FOR CYANIDE. An aqueous solution of picric acid gives a red color on heating with a solution of alkali cyanide.

BRAUN TEST FOR MANGANESE. On fusion of a substance with sodium pyrophosphate in the oxidizing flame (a bead test) and moistening with nitric acid, a violet color indicates manganese.

BRAUN TEST REACTIONS FOR MOLYBDIC ACID. An aqueous solution of molybdic acid gives: (1) a carmine-red color with a little zinc and potassium thiocyanate solution on the addition of hydrochloric acid by drops; (2) a blood-red color and brown-black crystalline precipitate when boiled for some time with ammonia and ammonium sulfide.

BRAUN TEST FOR NAPHTHENIC ACIDS. Ammonium salts of naphthenic acids give a green color with an aqueous solution of cupric sulfate and petroleum benzine.

BRAUN TEST FOR NICKEL. A rose-red color with an aqueous solution of potassium sulfocarbonate indicates the presence of nickel.

BRAUN TEST FOR PICRIC ACID. An alkaline solution of picric acid gives a red color on heating with glucose.

BRAUN TEST FOR PYROPHOSPHATE. Fairly dilute solutions of alkali pyrophosphates give a pale red-yellow precipitate with a concentrated aqueous solution of cobaltic chloride hexammine.

BRAUN TEST FOR TARTARIC ACID. On heating to boiling an aqueous solution of tartaric acid with a solution of 1 g. cobaltic chloride hexammine in 12 ml. water, and adding sodium hydroxide solution, a green color changing to blue-violet is obtained.

BRAÜTIGAM-EDELMANN TEST. To detect horse meat, boil 50 g. of the chopped meat in 200 ml. water, cool, and add 1:1 nitric acid, filter, and superimpose a saturated aqueous solution of iodine on the filtrate. A burgundy red to violet ring is given by glycogen, present in horse meat.

BREDT RULE. The existence (and thus the formation) of a carbon-carbon or carbon-nitrogen double bond at a bridgehead position in a **polycylic compound** is not possible unless the rings are large enough to stand the strain introduced by the distortion of the bond angles and/or distances.

BREH-GEABLER REAGENT. A filtered mixture of 2 ml. 40% silver nitrate solution and 20 ml. 15% sodium cobaltinitrite solution, used as a reagent for potassium.

BREIT-WIGNER FORMULA. An expression for the **nuclear cross section** of a reaction $X(a, b)Y$:

$$\sigma = \frac{\lambda^2}{4\pi} \cdot \frac{\Gamma_a \Gamma_b}{(E - E_r)^2 + \frac{1}{4}\Gamma^2}$$

in which σ is the nuclear cross section, λ is the equivalent wave length of the incident particle as derived from its mass and velocity by the **de Broglie equation,** Γ_a and Γ_b are the **level widths** (q.v.) representing the probability of emission of particles a and b, by the compound nucleus in a specific quantum state, Γ is the total level width, E is the total energy of the incident particle, and E_r is the energy value which would give exact **resonance** with the specified quantum level of the compound nucleus.

BREMSSTRAHLUNG. A German word, meaning literally "braking radiation," applied to radiations, usually radiation bands, produced during deceleration of charged particles.

BREWSTER ANGLE. The **angle of incidence,** for a given material, at which a beam of plane-polarized light is shifted in phase by 90°.

BREWSTER PROCESS. A process for the concentration of dilute acetic acid by extraction with solvents, such as isopropyl ether, which are subsequently recovered by distillation.

BRIDGE, ATOMIC OR STRUCTURAL.
One or more atoms so linked by **valences** in a **ring-structure** chemical compound that the valences of the atom or atoms form a connection within the ring, linking two of its atoms to produce a **bridge** inside it.

BRIEGER TEST REACTION. Choline gives a precipitate with phosphotungstic acid but not with tannic acid; neurine gives a precipitate with tannic acid but not with phosphotungstic acid.

BRILLOUIN EFFECT. Upon the scattering of monochromatic radiation by certain liquids, a doublet is produced, in which the frequency of each of the two lines differs from the frequency of the original line by the same amount, one line having a higher frequency, and the other a lower frequency.

BRIN PROCESS. A method for separating oxygen from air by use of barium oxide as an absorbing medium. When barium oxide is heated to about 500° C., barium peroxide is formed, which on heating to a higher temperature, such as 1000° C., dissociates to yield oxygen and the original barium oxide.

BRINELL HARDNESS. See **hardness, Brinell.**

BRINGHETTI TEST. To detect nitrate in solution, add to the evaporated residue of the solution a little salicin and concentrated sulfuric acid. A blood-red color, changing to violet on dilution with water, indicates the presence of nitrate.

BRITISH THERMAL UNIT. (B.T.U.) The quantity of heat required to raise the temperature of one pound of water through one degree Fahrenheit, specified for the most accurate work as from 39° F. to 40° F. The mean B.T.U. is 1/180 of the heat required to raise the temperature of one pound of water from 32° F. to 212° F.

BRIX SCALE. A **hydrometer** scale widely used in the sugar industry, based upon the relationship (at 20° C. or at 15.6° C.):

The number of Brix degrees is identical (at 15.6° C.) with the sucrose content of the solution in grams per hundred milliliters.

BROCKMANN-CHEN REAGENT. A saturated solution of 25 g. antimony trichloride in chloroform used in the colorimetric determination of vitamin D. An orange-yellow color is obtained.

BROMATE. The anion BrO_3^-, or a compound containing it.

BROMATO. A prefix indicating the presence of the bromate group $-BrO_3$.

BROMIC. (1) Related to bromic acid, $HBrO_3$. (2) Containing pentavalent bromine.

BROMIDE. The ion Br^-, or a compound containing it.

BROMIDE (TRI-). The anion Br_3^-, or a compound containing it.

BROMINATION. The addition of bromine to a substance either directly or through replacement.

BROMINE. Nonmetallic element. Symbol Br. Atomic number 35. Atomic weight 79.916. Molecular weight 159.83 (Br_2). Density 3.19. Specific heat 0.107. Melting point $-7.3°$ C. Boiling point 58.78° C. Valences 1, 3, 4, 5, and 7. Bromine is a reddish liquid at ordinary temperatures.

BROMINE ABSORPTION NUMBER. Fatty oils add bromine directly and the amount of the bromine so absorbed is used as an analytical test for the purity of the oil. This bromine number may be converted into the "iodine number" by multiplying it by 1.5875.

BROMO. A prefix designating the presence of the bromine atom $-Br$.

BROMOACETIC. Related to bromoacetic acid, $CH_2Br \cdot COOH$.

$$\text{Specific Gravity of Solution} = \frac{400}{400 + \text{Degrees Brix}}$$

BROMOANTIMONATE (III). The anion $SbBr_4^-$, $SbBr_5^-$, or $SbBr_6^{3-}$, or a compound containing one of these anions.

BROMOANTIMONATE (V). The anion $SbBr_6^-$, or a compound containing it.

BROMOAURATE (III). The anion $AuBr_4^-$, or a compound containing it.

BROMOCHLOROIODATE (I). The anion $IBrCl^-$, or a compound containing it.

BROMOCUPRATE (I). The anion $CuBr_2^-$, $CuBr_3^-$, or $Cu_2Br_6^{4-}$, or a compound containing one of these anions.

BROMOCUPRATE (II). The anion $CuBr_3^-$ or $CuBr_4^{2-}$, or a compound containing one of these anions.

BROMOHYPOIODITE. See **bromoiodate (I).**

BROMOIODATE (I). The anion IBr_2^-, or a compound containing it.

BROMOIODIDE. See **bromoiodate (I).**

BROMOIRIDATE (III). The anion $IrBr_6^{3-}$, or a compound containing it.

BROMOIRIDATE (IV). The anion $IrBr_6^-$, or a compound containing it.

BROMOIRIDITE. See **bromoiridate (III).**

BROMOMETRY. Chemical analysis, usually **titrimetric,** by determination of the amount of bromine which is absorbed or which, in general, enters into a chemical reaction.

BROMOÖSMATE (III). The anion $OsBr_6^{3-}$, or a compound containing it.

BROMOÖSMATE (IV). The anion $OsBr_6^-$, or a compound containing it.

BROMOPALLADATE (II). The anion $PdBr_4^-$, or a compound containing it.

BROMOPALLADATE (IV). The anion $PdBr_6^-$, or a compound containing it.

BROMOPLATINATE (II). The anion $PtBr_4^-$, or a compound containing it.

BROMOPLATINATE (IV). The anion $PtBr_6^-$, or a compound containing it.

BROMOPLATINIC. Related to bromoplatinic acid, $H_2PtBr_6 \cdot 9H_2O$.

BROMOPLATINITE. See **bromoplatinate (II).**

BROMORHENATE (IV). The anion $ReBr_6^-$, or a compound containing it.

BROMORHODATE (III). The anion $RhBr_6^{3-}$, or a compound containing it.

BROMOSELENITE. The anion $SeO_2Br_2^-$ or $SeBr_6^-$, or a compound containing one of these anions.

BROMOSTANNATE (II). The anion $SnBr_3^-$ or $SnBr_4^-$, or a compound containing one of these anions.

BROMOSTANNATE (IV). The anion $SnBr_6^-$, or a compound containing it.

BROMOTELLURITE. The anion $TeBr_6^-$, or a compound containing it.

BROMOTITANATE. The anion $TiBr_6^-$, or a compound containing it.

BROMOTUNGSTATE (V). The anion $WOBr_4^-$ or $WOBr_5^-$, or a compound containing one of these anions.

BROMOTUNGSTATE (VI). The anion $WO_2Br_4^-$, or a compound containing it.

BROMOUS. (1) Related to bromous acid, $HBrO_2$. (2) Containing trivalent bromine.

BROMOZINCATE. The anion $ZnBr_3^-$, $ZnBr_4^-$, or $ZnBr_5^{3-}$ or a compound containing one of these anions.

BRÖNSTED-LOWRY THEORY. A broad, generalized conception of the nature of **acids** and **bases,** by which an acid is defined as any substance, molecular or ionic, that can yield a **proton** (hydrogen ion) to another substance; whereas a base is any substance which can combine with a proton. Substances such as the H_2O molecule, which can yield a proton to form OH^- ions, or combine with a proton to form H_3O^+ complexes, are both acids and bases. Every acid has a base which differs from it by a proton, and vice versa, and such acids and bases are said to be conjugate to one another. An acid may react with a base not conjugate to it, however, producing their respective conjugate base and conjugate acid. Since free protons do not exist to any extent in solution, the acidic or basic properties of a substance cannot be evident unless the solvent itself has basic or acidic properties, that is, unless its molecules can accept or give protons.

BRÖNSTED RELATIONSHIP. A relationship between the **dissociation constant** of an acid and its catalytic activity, of the form:

$$k = Gk_\alpha{}^x$$

in which k is the **catalytic coefficient** of the acid, k_α is its dissociation constant, and G and x are constants for the reaction.

BRÖNSTED TEST. To test for tartaric acid, add calcium acetate solution to a 0.1% aqueous solution of the acid. A precipitate of calcium tartrate forms after standing for hours; however a precipitate of calcium racemate appears immediately if 1 drop of an l-tartrate solution is added.

BROWN ALCOHOL TEST. To test ethyl alcohol for the presence of other alcohols, dissolve 0.1 g. vanillin in 10 ml. of the alcohol, and pour 1 ml. concentrated sulfuric acid down the side of the tube. Characteristic colors are obtained in the interface and the liquid layers.

BROWN-LUM TEST REACTION. To differentiate dextrose and levulose, dissolve 0.05 g. of the sugar in 1 ml. water, and add ferric chloride solution by drops to a permanent yellow color, then warm. With dextrose the yellow color disappears; with levulose it deepens, and becomes violet with 1 drop of a 2% solution of diphenylamine in sulfuric acid.

BROWN RULE. A means of predicting positions upon the benzene ring taken by substituent atoms or groups, proposed by Crum Brown. It states that **meta** substitution occurs wherever the replaced hydrogen atom can be oxidized directly to a hydroxyl group. Otherwise, the **ortho** or **para** position is substituted.

BROWNIAN MOVEMENT. A phenomenon described by R. Brown in 1827. When particles less than 0.01 mm. in diameter are suspended in a medium that offers no impediment to their free motion, they may be observed (under the microscope) to move about in irregular paths. The motion appears to be capable of indefinite prolongation, and the behavior of the particles is exactly what the kinetic theory indicates would be the behavior of molecules of the same size. It is believed to be due to the bombardment of the particles by the molecules of the medium, in the course of their normal movement.

BROWNING-PALMER TEST. To test for the ferrocyanide, ferricyanide, and thiocyanate ions in solution, acidulate the solution and add thorium nitrate solution, which precipitates the ferrocyanide. Ferricyanide is precipitated from the filtrate with cadmium nitrate. Filter again, and add ferric chloride solution to the filtrate, obtaining a deep red color if thiocyanate is present.

BRÜCKE REAGENT FOR PROTEINS. A 10% solution of potassium iodide that is saturated with mercuric iodide. It is used as a reagent to precipitate proteins from acid solution.

BRÜCKE REAGENTS FOR PEPTONES. Phosphomolybdic acid or potassium mercuric iodide solution, which gives precipitates in acid solutions of peptones.

BRÜCKNER SOLUTION FOR GLYCOGEN. A 10% solution of potassium iodide that is saturated with mercuric iodide, and to which a little potassium iodide is then added. It is used as a reagent for glycogen.

BRÜCKNER TEST FOR ERGOSTEROL. Add to a solution of the sample in 2 ml.

chloroform, 1 ml. acetic anhydride, 0.5 ml. acetone, a crystal of copper acetate, and 0.5–1.0 g. anhydrous zinc chloride. A blue-violet color with red fluorescence is given by ergosterol.

BRUEHL RECEIVER. A closed chamber containing a number of receivers for liquids, so arranged that the liquid flowing from a condenser can be diverted readily into any of the receivers.

BRUGEAS TEST. To detect aconitine and aconite alkaloids, dissolve 0.01 of the sample by heating in 1 ml. sulfuric acid. Add a crystal of resorcinol and heat 20 minutes longer on the steam bath; cool and neutralize with sodium carbonate. A colorless solution with blue fluorescence is positive for aconitine; a purple solution with green fluorescence indicates the aconite alkaloids.

BRUNAUER-EMMETT-TELLER THEORY. A theory relating the quantity of gas adsorbed physically on a solid surface to the gas pressure with which the solid is in equilibrium. The theory also furnishes information on the heats of adsorption accompanying the process and on the magnitude of the surface area.

BRUNI-TORNANI TEST. To detect the propenyl group in the presence of the allyl group, treat an alcoholic or ethereal solution of the substance with picric acid. A colored crystalline precipitate indicates the presence of the propenyl group.

BRUNNER REAGENTS. Two solutions: (1) 0.5 g. of p-aminoacetophenone dissolved in 1 liter of water and 50 ml. hydrochloric acid; and (2) 1 g. of sodium nitrite dissolved in 200 ml. water. These solutions are used in determining typhoid fever by examination of urine. A red color is positive.

BRUNNER TEST FOR ATROPINE. On warming with a few crystals of chromic acid until they become green, atropine gives a characteristic flowery odor.

BRUNNER TEST FOR FUCHSIN. Wine containing fuchsin becomes violet on heating with stearic acid. The color deepens if the stearic acid is allowed to solidify.

BRUNNER TEST FOR GLUCOSIDES. Add, to the solution to be tested, an aqueous solution of bile, then add sulfuric acid and heat to 70° C. A red color is given by glucosides. Similar tests are given by digatalin, salicin, and other compounds.

BRUNNER TEST FOR SULFUR. Add a little strong potassium hydroxide solution and a few drops alcohol and nitrobenzene to the material to be tested. A red color on standing indicates the presence of sulfur.

BRUNSWICK REAGENT FOR PHYTOSTEROL. A 0.5% solution of digitonin in 85% alcohol, which gives microscopically-distinguishable crystals with phytosterol.

BRUNSWICK TESTS FOR CYANIDE IN PLANTS. (1) A 1% solution of silver nitrate, faintly colored by methylene blue gives blue crystals. (2) A solution of benzidine and cupric acetate gives blue needles.

BRUNTON FURNACE. A furnace for roasting arsenic ore, in which a rotating hearth and stationary rabbles volatilize the arsenius oxide, which is then condensed in arsenic kitchens.

BRUYÈRE TEST. On trituration with a drop of concentrated sulfuric acid and a little guaiacol, various carbohydrates give characteristic colors.

Bu Abbreviation for **butyl** or **bushel.**

BUBBLE. A small volume of gas in a liquid or solid.

BUBBLE COUNTER. Any apparatus for counting bubbles by indicating their passage, either mechanically or electrically, through an apparatus.

BUBBLE GAUGE. A small liquid-containing trap, installed in a gas line, which permits the rate of gas flow to be determined by counting the number of gas bubbles, as they move through the liquid.

BUBBLE TOWER. See **tower, bubble.**

BUCHER PROCESS. A process for the production of sodium cyanide by **fixation**

of atmospheric nitrogen. A charge of sodium carbonate and powdered coal is heated with atmospheric nitrogen in the presence of an iron catalyst.

BUCHERER CARBAZOLE SYNTHESIS. A synthesis of **carbazoles** from **naphthols** (or **naphthylamines**) and aryl hydrazines, in the presence of sodium bisulfite.

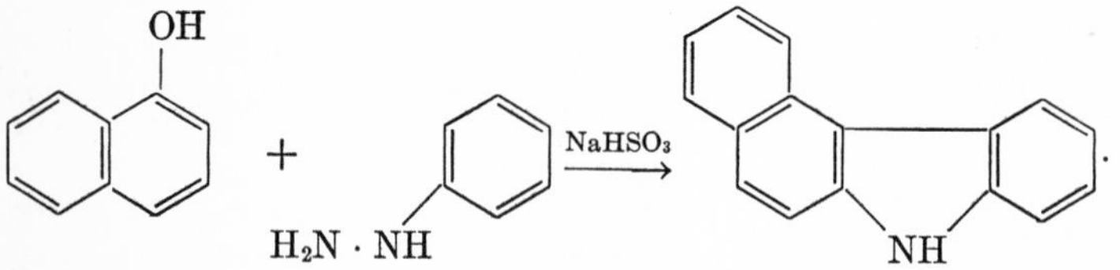

BUCHERER HYDANTOIN SYNTHE-SIS. The synthesis of substituted **hydantoins** from **ketones** or **aldehydes**, HCN or alkali cyanides, and ammonium carbonate.

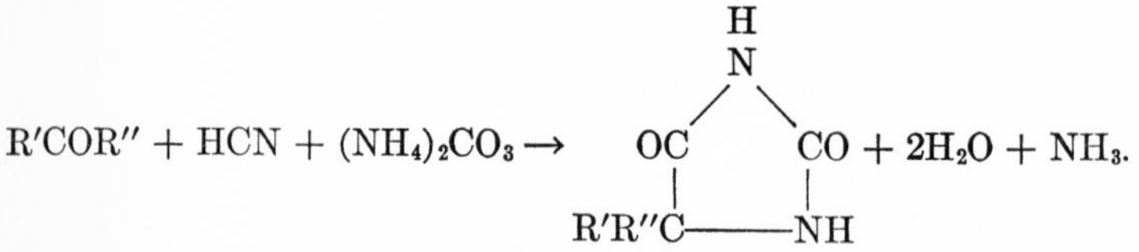

BUCHERER REACTION. The conversion of a **naphthylamine** to a **naphthol** (or other polynuclear amino compound to its hydroxy derivative) in the presence of an aqueous solution of a bisulfite or a sulfite. The reverse reaction, whereby a naphthol is converted to a naphthylamine by a solution of ammonium sulfite or bisulfite, is also used extensively, and is also designated by the name of Bucherer reaction.

BUCHNER-CURTIUS-SCHLOTTER-BECK REACTION. The direct addition, with loss of nitrogen, of **diazo compounds** and **aldehydes** to form **ketones.**

$$R'CHN_2 + R''CHO \rightarrow R'CH_2COR'' + N_2.$$

(R' should be aliphatic.)

BÜCHNER FILTER. A funnel, usually of porcelain, with an integral perforated plate, which serves to support a filter paper or other filtering medium.

BÜCHNER TEST OF BEESWAX. To test for paraffin or ceresin, boil with a 25% alcoholic solution of potassium hydroxide. On standing on the hot water bath, an oily layer separates if paraffin or ceresin is present.

BÜCHNER TEST FOR GALLIC ACID AND TANNIN. On treatment with lead acetate and sodium hydroxide solution, aqueous solutions of tannin give a red color. Gallic acid gives a red precipitate with lead acetate, which forms a raspberry-red solution with sodium hydroxide.

BUCHWALD-TREML TEST. Flour bleached with nitrogen peroxide gives a red color on treatment with the **Griess-Ilosvay reagent** for nitrites (q.v.).

BUCKLEY GAUGE. An extremely sensitive pressure gauge, based on measurement of the amount of ionization produced in the gas by a specified current.

BUDDE EFFECT. The increase in volume of halogens, especially chlorine and bromine vapor, on exposure to light. It is a thermal effect, due to the heat from recombination of atoms.

BUEB PROCESS. A process for the manufacture of ferrous ferrocyanide from ammonia, iron sulfate, and hydrocyanic acid.

BUELL TEST FOR URANIUM. Dissolve the sample in nitric acid and add zinc shavings; a yellow deposit on the zinc indicates the presence of uranium.

BUF, BUFO-. A prefix meaning derived from the toad, as bufagin.

BUFFER. A substance that enables a system or entity to resist changes in conditions, mechanical shocks, addition of foreign substances, etc. As the term is most commonly used in chemistry, a buffer is a substance which, upon addition to a system, renders the hydrogen ion concentration resistant to, or less sensitive to, additions of acidic or alkaline substances. There are other chemical buffers, however, such as the oxidation-reduction buffer, which tends, in the same way, to stabilize the **oxidation-reduction potential** of a system.

BUFFER CAPACITY. The amount (in **moles** or millimoles) of hydrogen ions neutralized by unit volume of solution. Cf. **buffer index.**

BUFFER INDEX. The amount (in **moles** or millimoles) of a standard solution of acid or base necessary to produce a given change in the hydrogen ion **concentration** of a solution or other system.

BUFFER SOLUTION. A solution whose **pH** is changed only a relatively small amount by the addition, within limits, of acids and bases — even strong ones if the amount added is small. Solutions of weak acids or bases or their salts, such as phosphates, borates, etc., are buffer solutions.

BUFFER, UNIVERSAL. A **buffer** (q.v.) that is effective over a wide **pH** range.

BUFFER VALUE. The same as **buffer index** (q.v.).

BUHR MILL. See **mill, buhr.**

BUJWID TEST. A test for nitrite in which a few drops of hydrochloric acid and a few drops of a 1:5000 alcoholic solution of indole that has been diluted with water are added to 10 ml. of the solution to be tested, which is then heated to 70–80° C. A red color indicates the presence of nitrite. Various modifications of this test have been developed.

BULB. A spherical, or round and tapering apparatus or part, most commonly of glass.

BULK. A term used in the broadest sense to express mass per unit volume, or variations in a volume or volume-mass relationship. Thus, the bulk of a substance is the relation to mass of volume, or any dimension; the bulk of a solution is the increase in volume due to addition of the dissolved substance; and the **bulking value** (q.v.) expresses the increase in volume by addition of a solid to a liquid.

BULKING VALUE. The volume which a solid adds to that of a liquid in which it is ground. In the paint industry, it is often expressed in the number of gallons added to a liquid by grinding in it 100 pounds of solid. The bulking value is an important criterion of pigments.

BULLING TEST FOR PHENYLPROPIOLIC ACID. (1) Alkalinize the solution to be tested with ammonia; add it to ammoniacal silver nitrate. A white precipitate soluble in dilute sulfuric acid with odor of phenylacetylene is given by phenylpropiolic acid.
(2) Dissolve the material in nitric acid, then add one drop of this solution to 2 ml. water and alkalinize with sodium hydroxide; a yellow-red color and odor of benzaldehyde is given by phenylpropiolic acid.

BÜLOW TEST FOR PHENYLHYDRAZIDES. Phenylhydrazides dissolved in concentrated sulfuric acid give a deep red to blue-violet color on addition of ferric chloride or potassium dichromate.

BUMPING. The formation of large bubbles in boiling, due to local **superheating,** and the consequent violent effect of their passage through the liquid.

BUNSEN BURNER. See **burner, Bunsen.**

BUNSEN COEFFICIENT. (Absorption coefficient) The volume of gas under **standard conditions** of temperature and pressure (S.T.P.) which is absorbed by a unit volume of gas solution.

BUNSEN REACTION FOR ACETATE. On heating an alkali acetate with arsenic trioxide, the characteristic odor of *poisonous* cacodyl appears.

BUNSEN-ROSCOE LAW. See **law of Bunsen-Roscoe.**

BUNTING TEST. Tin is detected in alloys by boiling with hydrochloric acid and adding a drop of chloroplatinic acid. Tin gives a red color.

BUOYANCY. The supporting force exerted upon a body by the surrounding medium or media which it displaces.

BURCHARD-LIEBERMAN REACTION. See **reaction, Burchard-Lieberman.**

BURCHARD TEST REACTION. Cholesterol, when dissolved in chloroform, chlorobenzene, or other chlorine-containing organic substances, gives a red to violet color and green fluorescence on addition of acetic anhydride and a few drops of sulfuric acid.

BUREAU OF MINES PROCESS. See **U. S. Bureau of Mines process.**

BURETTE. A laboratory apparatus which consists of a glass cylinder of uniform bore provided with a stopcock for delivering any desired volume of liquid or solution. It has graduations for determining the volume and is used extensively in analytical titrations.

BURETTE, AUTOMATIC. A burette arranged to fill only to a predetermined level, as by provision of an overflow tube and an attachment to a reservoir.

BURETTE, CALIBRATING. A burette, usually constructed with a large central bulb to act as a reservoir, designed for calibrating volumetric apparatus in terms other than the true metric liter. A 500 ml. burette of this type may have a lower stem graduated at close intervals (such as 1 millimeter).

BURETTE, CHAMBER. A burette having an integral upper chamber and lower graduated portion. The purpose of this design is to minimize drainage errors.

BURETTE CLAMP. A pinch-clamp that closes a rubber tube attached to a burette or other container.

BURETTE, DISPENSING. A large capacity burette (250 to 1000 ml.) used for dispensing solutions in clinical and industrial laboratories.

BURETTE FLOAT. A small floating object, usually of glass, used in burettes to facilitate precise reading of the liquid level.

BURETTE, GAS. A burette used to measure gas volumes, rather than volumes of liquids.

BURETTE HOLDER. A clamp or device used to hold burettes.

BURETTE READER. An attachment to facilitate accurate reading of burettes.

BURETTE, SCHELLBACH. A burette having a backing of milk-glass with a central blue line, to facilitate accurate sighting of the meniscus against the scale.

BURETTE, WEIGHING. A short burette, with a ground-glass end that fits into a small bottle and with lugs for suspension from balance stirrups.

BURGESS REAGENT FOR AROMATIC COMPOUNDS. A solution of 10 g. mercuric sulfate in enough 25% sulfuric acid to make a volume of 100 ml. This is a general reagent for aromatic compounds, many of which give characteristic color reactions.

BURGESS-KAMM TEST. A modified cobaltinitrite test in which 10 ml. of a solution are tested for potassium by adding 1 drop 25% sodium cobaltinitrite solution and a little $0.01N$ silver nitrate solution. A yellow to orange precipitate indicates the presence of potassium.

BURIAN TEST FOR XANTHINE BASES. Adenine, guanine, and other xanthine bases, in alkaline solution, give a red color with diazobenzenesulfonic acid.

BURN. To oxidize so rapidly that the products of the oxidation are rendered incandescent.

BURNER. (1) An apparatus for conducting the combustion of gases, liquids, or solids. (2) An apparatus used to supply controlled or directed heat or flames, by combustion of gas or liquid, as in the laboratory.

BURNER, BARTHEL. A burner for alcohol or other liquids.

BURNER, BLAST. A burner to which air is supplied under pressure.

BURNER, BLOWTORCH. A double-tube burner, having two connections for inlet gases, with a mixing space and nozzle, suitable for burning a combustible gas with compressed air or oxygen.

BURNER, BOYCE. A burner for gasoline vapor, as well as gas.

BURNER, BUNSEN. A type of laboratory gas burner with an air supply that can be regulated.

BURNER, CHADDOCK. A burner constructed of refractory material, shaped like a blast furnace.

BURNER, COMBUSTION TUBE. A series of burners, with wing-tops to spread their flames, used to heat combustion tubes uniformly.

BURNER, CROSS-FIRE. A multiple-flame burner designed primarily for use in laboratory glass-blowing.

BURNER, EVAPORATING. A round disc with numerous holes, for producing many small flames.

BURNER, FLETCHER. A round, hollow, cast-iron ring with openings for heating large vessels.

BURNER, JANSEN. A burner with means for accurate and rapid adjustment of gas supply and air blast, provided by separate controls.

BURNER, MEKER. A gas burner of the Bunsen type (see **burner, Bunsen**). A distinctive feature of the Meker burner is its heavy wire grid that provides a uniform and steady flame.

BURNER, MICRO. A small-size burner designed for heating microapparatus. It has means of accurate flame control, such as needle-valves and interchangeable tips.

BURNER, ROSE. A burner with a metal attachment, with holes around its edge, and often rose-shaped, suitable for producing very small flames.

BURNER, SARGENT. A burner with means for adjustment of both the gas feed and the air supply.

BURNER, SCIMATCO. A high temperature gas burner.

BURNER, SPECTRUM. A burner provided with containers for solid substances, in order to produce a flame coloration of reasonable duration, for use in spectroscopic work.

BURNER, UNIVERSAL. A burner with a number of nozzles and tips. It is usually designed not only to produce a variety of flame sizes and intensities with air and manufactured gas, but also to operate on oxygen, natural gas, cylinder gases, in various combinations of fuel and oxidant.

BURY THEORY. A modification of the **Langmuir theory** of electronic arrangement around the nucleus. Bury suggested that the maximum number of electrons in the outermost shell of any atom is limited to 8, and that a new layer must commence to form in the case of the next element. The formation of the fourth shell would commence, for example, when the third shell contains 8 electrons, even though the ultimate capacity of the third shell is 18 electrons, and this number is undoubtedly present in higher elements. The Bury modification is supported by much evidence, including the properties of the rare earths.

BUSCH REAGENT. A solution of 10 g. **nitron** in 90 g. 5% acetic acid. This solution is used as a test reagent for nitrate. The solution to be tested is acidified with dilute sulfuric acid and a few drops of reagent added. A white precipitate indicates the presence of nitrate.

BUSCH-BLUME TEST. If picric acid is present in solution, a precipitate of nitron picrate is obtained by adding a solution made by dissolving 10 g. **nitron** in 90 ml. 5% acetic acid.

BUSCHI TEST. Mercuric cyanide, on heating its solution with a few drops potassium nitrite solution and then adding hydrochloric acid, gives a red color.

BUSSOLINI TEST. Copper salts, even in traces, give a red color when treated with a solution of potassium ferrocyanide diluted until nearly colorless.

BURTON PROCESS. The first commercially-successful petroleum **cracking process** in the United States. It was a batch process, in which the petroleum was heated to a temperature of about 400° C., under a pressure of 75–100 pounds per square inch.

1-BUTENYL. The radical

$$CH_3CH_2CH:CH-.$$

2-BUTENYL. The radical

$$CH_3CH:CHCH_2-.$$

3-BUTENYL. The radical

$$CH_2:CH(CH_2)_2-.$$

BUTOXY. The radical $CH_3(CH_2)_3O-$.

BUTYL. The radical $CH_3(CH_2)_3-$.

BUTYL, ISO. See **isobutyl.**

BUTYL, NORMAL. See **butyl.**

sec-BUTYL. The radical

$$(C_2H_5)(CH_3)CH-.$$

tert-BUTYL. The radical $(CH_3)_3C-$.

BUTYLENE (1,4). See **tetramethylene.**

BUTYLIC FERMENTATION. A **fermentation** yielding butyl alcohol, especially the fermentation process developed by Weizmann and Fernback which produces 30% acetone and 60% of *n*-butyl alcohol, and small amounts of ethanol, hydrogen, and carbon dioxide.

BUTYLIDENE. The radical

$$CH_3(CH_2)_2CH=.$$

BUTYRATE. A compound containing the radical

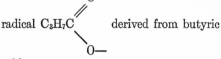

derived from butyric acid.

BUTYRIC. Related to butyric acid, $C_3H_7 \cdot COOH$.

BUTYROMETER. An apparatus used to determine butterfat.

BUTYRYL. The radical $CH_3(CH_2)_2CO-$.

BUZNEA-CERNATESCO TEST. Nitric acid is detected by a red color produced with a freshly-prepared solution of diaminophenol hydrochloride in concentrated sulfuric acid.

BY-PRODUCT. A secondary product of a reaction or of manufacture obtained in addition to the primary product.

BYERS PROCESS. A process for the production of wrought iron with a minimum of hand labor, as distinguished from the old manual-working process. The molten metal passes through several stages in desulfurization and other operations in purification, including a "cold-slag" treatment.

Bz Abbreviation for **benzoyl** or **benzene.**

C. Symbol for the element **carbon** (C). Symbol for **centigrade temperature** (° C). Symbol for **normality** (C). Symbol for the velocity of light (*c*). Symbol for concentration (*C* or *c*). Symbol for **compliance** (*C*). Symbol for **heat capacity**, total (*C*), per unit mass — specific heat (*c*), per mole (*c*, *C* or C_M), per atom or molecule (*c* or c_m). Symbol for **specific** heat at constant volume (c_v). Symbol for specific heat at constant pressure (c_p). Symbol for **molecular heat** at constant volume (C_v). Symbol for molecular heat at constant pressure (C_p). Symbol for hydrogen ion concentration (c_H). Symbol for **discharge coefficient** (c). Symbol for **resistance coefficient** (C). Symbol for thermal conductance (C). Symbol for **capacitance** or permittance (C). Symbol for partial capacitance (c). Symbol for Planck radiation law constants (c_1, c_2). See also **chi.**

Ca Symbol for the element **calcium.**

CACODYL. The radical $(CH_3)_2As-$.

CACODYLATE. A compound containing

the radical $(CH_3)_2As$

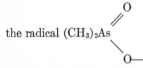

CADET TEST. Arsenic trioxide is detected by the odor of cacodyl (poisonous) on heating with sodium acetate.

CADMATE. The anion $CdO_2^=$, or a compound containing it.

CADMATE, HYDROXO-. The anion $Cd(OH)_4^=$ or $Cd(OH)_6^{4-}$, or a compound containing one of these anions.

CADMICYANIDE. See **cyanocadmate.**

CADMIUM. Metallic element. Symbol Cd. Atomic number 48. Atomic weight 112.41. Density 8.65. Specific heat 0.0549. Melting point 320.9° C. Boiling point 767° C. Valence 2 (cadmous salts, in which the metal apparently is univalent, have been prepared). Cadmium is found in many zinc ores. Oxide CdO. The gas molecule of cadmium is monatomic.

CADMIUM CELL. A standard or "normal" cell usually constructed in the "H" form. The cathode is an amalgam of $12\frac{1}{2}$ parts of cadmium and $87\frac{1}{2}$ parts of mercury by weight. The anode may be made of highly purified mercury or of amalgamated platinum. The electrolyte is a saturated solution of cadmium sulfate in water. The cathode is surrounded by undissolved cadmium sulfate crystals, and the anode is covered with a paste made of mercurous

sulfate and cadmium sulfate solution. The cell is sealed to prevent evaporation. At the ordinary temperature (20°) the cadmium cell furnishes an electromotive force of 1.0186 volts, and this varies only 0.00007 volt per degree change of temperature.

CADMOUS. Containing monovalent cadmium.

CAGE MILL. See **mill, cage.**

CAGLIOTI TEST REACTION. Microchemical tests for beryllium made (1) by mixing a drop of uranium acetate solution containing a trace of sodium, with a drop of the solution tested, and allowing it to evaporate; pale yellow rhombohedral crystals indicate the presence of beryllium; (2) by acidifying the solution tested with acetic acid and treating with acetylacetone. Monoclinic tablets or thin prisms on slow evaporation indicate the presence of beryllium.

CAILLE-VIEL SOLUTION. A solution of 2 g. antipyrine and 4 g. potassium iodide in 60 ml. water. This solution is used as a test reagent for bismuth and antimony in biological fluids.

CAILLETET AND MATHIAS LAW. See **law of Cailletet and Mathias.**

CALCAREOUS. Containing **calcium.**

CALCIC. A salt that contains **calcium.**

CALCIFICATION. The process of formation of hard, relatively-insoluble deposits of **calcium** salts, most commonly in tissues.

CALCIMETER. A laboratory apparatus used for the determination of carbon dioxide by absorption in a suitable medium, such as calcium hydroxide. Commonly the apparatus also contains a chamber for liberating the carbon dioxide from a carbonate sample by treatment with acid.

CALCINATION. Heating at a high temperature in order to render a mass friable, or to drive off a volatile or oxidizable substance, as the calcination of limestone to produce lime.

CALCIUM. Metallic element. Symbol Ca. Atomic number 20. Atomic weight 40.08. Density 1.54. Specific heat 0.157. Melting point 810° C. Boiling point 1240° C. Valence 2. Calcium forms but one series of compounds. Oxide (lime) CaO. Calcium is very abundant and widely distributed over the earth's surface.

CALCIUM CHLORIDE TUBE. A U-tube often provided with two ground-glass stoppers, and with side tubes, for outlet and inlet of gases, used for drying gases and for the determination of the quantity of water present. The absorbing medium used is commonly anhydrous calcium chloride, although phosphorus pentoxide and other solids which absorb water may also be used.

CALEFACIENT. Heat-producing. This term is used in medicine to denote a substance that warms or heats when externally applied.

CALENDERING. Smoothing between rollers, a process used extensively in the paper industry, and to a lesser degree in processing textiles, rubber, and other materials.

CALEOMETER. An electrical instrument used to measure the heat loss from a calibrated wire and useful in making a number of determinations, such as that of the variation of the concentration of one of the components of the gas surrounding the wire.

CALEY REAGENT FOR SODIUM. Two solutions: (1) 4 g. uranyl acetate, 3 g. glacial acetic acid and enough water to make a volume of 50 ml.; and (2) 20 g. cobaltous acetate, 3 g. glacial acetic acid and enough water to make a volume of 50 ml. The two solutions are mixed and used in testing for sodium. A yellow precipitate is given by sodium-containing solutions.

CALEY TEST FOR CALCIUM. To detect calcium in the presence of strontium and barium, ignite at 900° C. the alkaline earth group precipitated as carbonates, leach with 25 ml. water, evaporate the solution to 5 ml., acidify with hydrochloric acid, heat to boiling, dissolve 1 g. potassium iodide and then 0.1 g. yellow mercuric oxide. A white turbidity indicates the presence of calcium.

CALEY TEST FOR LITHIUM. Treat the precipitated alkali chlorides by digestion with amyl alcohol, and add a solution of 1.5–2.0% stearic acid in ether which has been treated with ammonia gas to form the ammonium stearate. Lithium chloride, if present, produces a turbidity.

CALEY TEST FOR OXALIC ACID. Dissolve 0.1 g. of the material in 2.0 ml. water and shake for 1–2 minutes with 1 ml. 6 N sodium hydroxide solution. A white crystalline precipitate shows oxalate.

CALIBRATION. Determination or checking of the absolute values of the readings of any apparatus, measuring device, or method of determination of quantitative values of properties or compositions.

CALIFORNIUM. Radioactive element of actinide series. Symbol Cf. Atomic number 98. Atomic species have been reported of mass numbers 244 and 246. They are α-emitters with half periods of 45 minutes and 35.7 hours, respectively. Valence 3.

CALIPERS. A device for measuring small distances, especially outside and inside diameters of small pipes and tubing.

CALKING COMPOUND. A mixture of substances used to fill cracks and keep them liquid-tight and, in some cases, gas-tight. Ideally, calking compounds should bond with various surfaces and retain their elasticity.

CALLAN-HENDERSON REAGENT. Sodium diethyldithiocarbamate, which produces a brown-yellow color with copper salts.

CALMBERG TEST FOR CODEINE. Add 1 drop of ferric chloride solution to a heated solution of codeine in sulfuric acid. A blue color is formed after foaming.

CALOMEL ELECTRODE. See **electrode, calomel.**

CALORIE. A unit for the measurement of the quantity of heat. As originally defined, it was the amount of heat required to raise the temperature of one gram of water through one degree Centigrade. As thermal measurements increased in precision, this definition was not sufficiently exact and many different kinds of calories were used, considerable confusion resulting. After 1930 an artificial, conventional calorie was defined by the relation 1 calorie = 4.1833 international joules and, in 1948, it was redefined as 1 calorie = 4.1840 absolute joules. This definition is now generally accepted by chemists in the United States. The large calorie (Cal. or Kcal.) is 1,000 times as large. Another artificial calorie, used in engineering steam tables, is the International Table calorie: 1 I.T. calorie = 1/860 international watt-hour = 0.00116298 absolute watt-hour. Conversion to other energy units gives:

1 cal. = 0.00396573 B.T.U.
1 cal. = 0.0412917 liter-atmosphere
1 cal. = 0.999346 I.T. cal.

CALORIFACIENT. A drug or other substance that produces heat within the organism.

CALORIFIC INTENSITY. The maximum temperature attainable by combustion of a given fuel with atmospheric oxygen under atmospheric pressure.

CALORIFIC VALUE. The number of units of heat obtained by complete combustion of unit mass of a substance. Determinations of calorific value are very commonly made in the evaluation of fuels, the study of foods, etc.

CALORIFIC VALUE, GROSS. The quantity of heat produced by the combustion of a unit mass of a substance with oxygen under pressure, as in a bomb calorimeter. If this value is corrected for the **latent heat of evaporation** of the water present, then the net calorific value is obtained.

CALORIGENIC. Heat-generating.

CALORIMETER. An apparatus for measuring the conversion of mechanical energy into heat or for determining the heat produced in a chemical reaction. In its usual form it consists of a metallic vessel, surrounded by water which is warmed by the heat evolved from the reaction or combustion taking place in the metallic vessel. From the temperature change of the water and its weight and after application of necessary corrections, the heat units evolved may be calculated. Berthollet's bomb, modified by several investigators, is a common type of calorimeter.

CALORIMETER, ADIABATIC. A calorimeter so well insulated from its surroundings that reactions or processes involving heat transfer can be studied without having any heat exchange occurring with the outside.

CALORIMETER, EMERSON. A calorimeter used especially for fuels.

CALORIMETER, GAS. An apparatus used in the analysis of combustible gases, primarily to determine calorific value and, incidentally, to determine moisture content and to test for the presence of other materials.

CALORIMETER, OXYGEN-BOMB. A calorimeter in which a weighed sample of solid or liquid material is ignited by an electrically-heated wire and burned by oxygen under pressure. The heat evolved is determined, usually by absorption in a water jacket surrounding the combustion chamber (oxygen-bomb).

CALORIMETER, SODIUM PEROXIDE. A calorimeter in which a weighed sample of solid or liquid is burned by oxygen derived from sodium peroxide, usually when an accelerator such as potassium perchlorate or benzoic acid is added to aid combustion.

CALORIMETRY. The quantitative determination of heat exchange.

CALORIZATOR. An apparatus used in the diffusion process for extraction of beets, consisting of steam-jacketed brass pipes through which the juice flows from one digester to another. It is arranged to maintain a temperature of 60° C. in the extracting liquid. It is also called "juice warmer."

CALORIZING. A process for impregnating or coating a surface of iron, steel, etc., with aluminum by heating it with aluminum, alumina, and ammonium chloride in an atmosphere of hydrogen. Articles so treated are in many cases highly resistant to corrosive materials, and at high temperatures are resistant to oxidation.

CALZOLARI TEST REACTION. A test for methenamine and for formaldehyde. Methenamine in 0.1% solution gives a yellow crystalline precipitate with equal volumes of a saturated magnesium sulfate solution and a saturated potassium ferricyanide solution. To test for formaldehyde by this reaction, first evaporate 1 ml. of the solution to dryness with 20% ammonia, then proceed with the test for methenamine.

CAMERER-ARNSTEIN TEST. Xanthine bases in ammoniacal solutions give amorphous precipitates with silver nitrate solution.

CAMILLA-PERTUSI TEST FOR SACCHARIN AND DULCIN. To detect saccharin and dulcin, heat 25–30 g. of the finely powdered material for 10 minutes with an excess of baryta water (if a liquid, concentrate and add barium hydroxide solution). Filter and wash with water. Acidify 50 ml. of the filtrate with sulfuric or phosphoric acid, extract with 200 ml. ether-petroleum benzine, and distill off the solvent. The sweetener crystallizes.

CAMILLA-PERTUSI TEST FOR XANTHINE BASES. Add a few drops strong potassium hydroxide solution to the material, then a saturated potassium permanganate solution. Xanthine bases reduce the permanganate, giving a carbylamine-like odor.

CAMPBELL-STARK TEST REACTION. To detect hydrogen peroxide, float an equal amount of ether on the sample liquid, add a few drops of 10% chromic acid, and shake. A blue color is a positive test for hydrogen peroxide.

CAMPBELL TEST. A test for dihydroxyacetone by the formation of a blue solution with phosphomolybdic acid.

CAMPHANYL. The radical $C_{10}H_{17}-$ having three isomers and derived from camphane

$$
\begin{array}{ccc}
& CH_3 & \\
& | & \\
CH_2\!-\!\!\!\!&C&\!\!\!\!-\!CH_2 \\
| & & | \\
& H_3C\!-\!C\!-\!CH_3 & \\
| & & | \\
CH_2\!-\!\!\!\!&CH&\!\!\!\!-\!CH_2
\end{array}
$$

by loss of a hydrogen atom.

CAMPHOR. Camphor is a hydrocarbon containing a carbonyl group, of the formula $C_{10}H_{16}O$. The term camphor is also applied to an ill-defined classification of vegetable principles usually associated with, or derived from, the volatile oils. They are solids, strongly odorous, very volatile, many of them are derivatives of terpenes.

CAMPHOROYL. The radical $C_{10}H_{14}O_2=$

$$
\begin{array}{c}
CH_3 \\
/ \\
CH_2\!-\!C\!-\!CO\!- \\
| \qquad \backslash \\
\qquad C(CH_3)_2 \\
| \qquad / \\
CH_2\!-\!C\!-\!CO\!- \\
\backslash \\
H
\end{array}
$$

derived from camphoric acid.

CAMPHORYL. The radical $C_{10}H_{15}O-$, derived, by loss of a hydrogen atom, from camphor

$$
\begin{array}{ccc}
& CH_3 & \\
& | & \\
CH_2\!-\!\!\!\!&C&\!\!\!\!-\!CO \\
| & & | \\
& H_3C\!-\!C\!-\!CH_3 & \quad . \\
| & & | \\
CH_2\!-\!\!\!\!&CH&\!\!\!\!-\!CH_2
\end{array}
$$

CAMPHORYLIDENE. The radical $C_{10}H_{14}O=$ derived, by loss of two hydrogen atoms, from camphor.

CAMPO-CERDAN TEST REACTION. Zinc is detected in weakly-ammoniacal solution by the formation of a blue color (characteristic absorption spectrum) with alcoholic resorcinol solution.

CAMPS QUINOLINE SYNTHESIS. A method of formation of substituted hydroxyquinolines by ring closure of *o*-acylaminoacetophenones and related compounds.

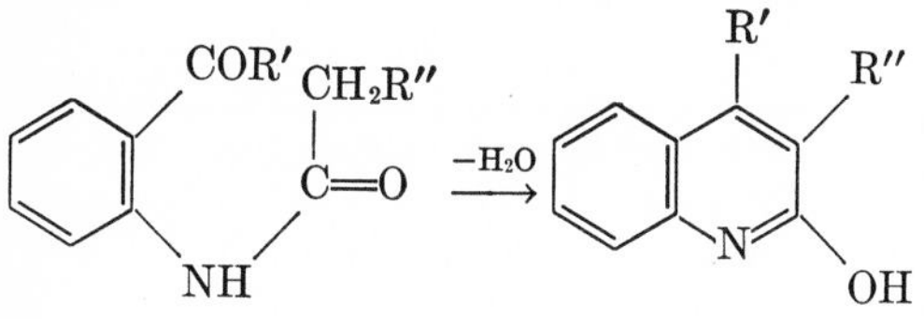

CANADIAN LEAD NUMBER. See **lead number.**

CANAL RAYS. Rays originally discovered in early investigations with discharge-tubes by making holes in the **cathode,** or using a perforated cathode. Since the rays in question streamed out through these openings, they were called canal rays. They are streams of positively charged particles, which are, in fact, ionized atoms.

CANDLE POWER. A unit of **luminous intensity** based upon the light produced by the standard candle.

CANDLE, STANDARD. A candle of carefully defined weight and material, which is used as the basis of photometric measurement, producing a light of fixed and definite brightness, burning two grains of sperm wax per minute, and weighing one-sixth of a pound.

CANDUSSIO REAGENT FOR PHENOLIC COMPOUNDS. A 1% solution of potassium ferricyanide with 10–20% of ammonia added. It gives characteristic colors, or successions of colors, or precipitates with many phenolic compounds.

CANFIELD REAGENT. A solution of 6 g. ferric chloride, 5 g. nickel nitrate, and 1.5 g. cupric chloride, dissolved in 12 ml. of hot water, to which is then added 150 ml. of methyl alcohol and 1 ml. of nitric acid.

This reagent is used to find phosphorus segregation in steel.

CANNIZZARO REACTION. The formation of **acids** and **alcohols** by the simultaneous oxidation and reduction (a process called **dismutation**) of a pair of **aldehyde** molecules, most commonly one that has no alpha carbon atom, or no hydrogen atoms on an alpha carbon atom. Thus, benzaldehyde yields benzyl alcohol and benzoic acid, and formaldehyde gives methyl alcohol and formic acid. Mixed aldehydes may be used.

$$2C_6H_5 \cdot CHO \xrightarrow{+H_2O} C_6H_5 \cdot CH_2OH + C_6H_5 \cdot COOH$$

$$2HCHO \xrightarrow{+H_2O} CH_3OH + HCOOH.$$

CAPACITY. (1) Extent of space; specifically cubic content or volume. (2) Power of receiving or absorbing, as exemplified by thermal capacity, electric capacity, capacity for moisture. (3) Maximum output. (4) Power, as exemplified by the carrying capacity of a stream.

CAPACITY, ELECTROSTATIC. The quantity of electricity required to raise a body or system by unit potential.

CAPACITY, HEAT. Quantity of heat required to raise the temperature of a body by a given amount, such as one degree Centigrade.

CAPACITY, SPECIFIC INDUCTIVE. The **dielectric constant** (q.v.).

CAPILLARITY. A phenomenon exhibited by small tubes of capillary size, in which the level of liquid inside, may, under the action of surface tension, differ from that on the outside.

CAPILLARY. A cylindrical space of very small radius, or a tube containing such space.

CAPILLARY CONSTANT. A quantity used in the petroleum industry to express a property of liquids that is essentially reciprocal surface tension. The capillary constant is determined by immersing a rectangular frame of wire in the liquid, partially withdrawing it, and determining the force that must be exerted upon the frame to restrain it from being drawn into the liquid. The capillary constant is defined by the expression $F/2L$ where F is the restraining force and $2L$ is the width of the film.

CAPILLARY CORRECTION. A correction applied to mercury thermometers to correct readings for the effect of the capillarity of mercury.

CAPILLARY PIPETTE. A narrow bore or small pipette, usually with a capacity of less than one cubic centimeter.

CAPILLARY PRESSURE. The pressure developed through capillary action. The use of wooden wedges in rock crevices represents an example of this process. When the wedge is wetted the swelling is generally sufficient to split the rock.

CAPILLARY TUBING. Glass tubing of small bore, usually less than one millimeter.

CAPRANICA TEST REACTION. Guanine, in warm concentrated solution, gives an orange-yellow crystalline precipitate with a saturated picric acid solution, and an orange-red precipitate with potassium chromate (on cooling).

CAPRIC. Related to capric acid,

$$C_9H_{19}COOH.$$

CAPROIC. Related to caproic acid, $C_5H_{11} \cdot COOH.$

CAPROYL. The radical $CH_3(CH_2)_4CO-$.

CAPRYL. The radical $CH_3(CH_2)_8CO-$.

CAPRYLIC. Related to caprylic acid, $C_7H_{15} \cdot COOH.$

CAPRYLYL. The aliphatic radical $CH_3(CH_2)_6CO-$.

CAPTURE REACTION. See **reaction, capture.**

CARAT. A unit of mass of 205 milligrams (in England, 205.31 milligrams). The carat is used widely to express weights of gems and precious metals, and this has given rise to another usage of the term carat, i.e., as a standard of purity of gold.

CARBAMATE. The anion H_2NCOO^-, or a compound containing it.

CARBAMIC. The radical

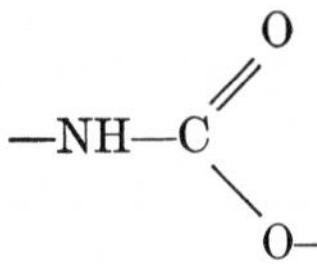

(from carbamic acid, $NH_2 \cdot COOH$).

CARBAMIDO. The radical $H_2NCONH-$, preferably termed ureido.

CARBAMYL. The radical H_2NCO-.

CARBANILINO. The radical

$$C_6H_5NHCO-,$$

preferably termed phenylcarbonyl.

CARBAZIDE. A compound of the typeformula $RNH-NH-CO-NH-NHR'$.

CARBAZOLYL. The radical $C_{12}H_8N-$, which has 5 isomers and is derived by loss of a hydrogen atom, from carbazole

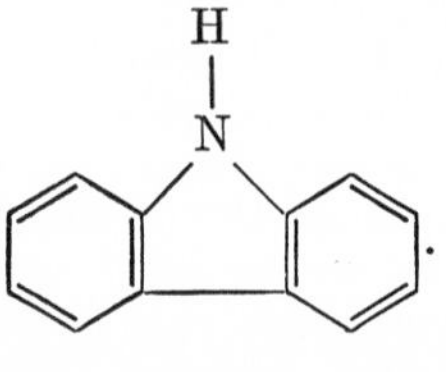

CARBAZONE. A compound of the typeformula $R-N=N-CO-NH-NHR'$.

CARBETHOXY. The radical C_2H_5OOC-.

CARBIDE. A binary compound of carbon.

CARBINOL. Either a primary **alcohol,** of type-formula RCH_2OH; or the primary alcohol radical, $-CH_2OH$; or the first of the primary alcohols, methanol, CH_3OH; or acetyl methyl carbinol.

CARBOCYCLIC. Pertaining to an organic compound containing in its formula one or more **ring-structures** in which all the ring-atoms are carbon atoms.

CARBODIAZONE. A compound of the type-formula $R-N=N-CO-N=N-R'$.

CARBODITHIOIC. The radical

$$-C(:S)SH.$$

CARBOHYDRATE(S). A large and important group of compounds which contain carbon, hydrogen, and oxygen, the last two elements — in most cases — in the proportions to form water. They form the largest proportion of the solid constituents of all plants. The crystalline, sweet members are usually called sugars; the amorphous, tasteless compounds are called starches and cellulose.

The carbohydrates are classified into (1) monosaccharides (or monosaccharoses or monoses), which are simple sugars that cannot be hydrolyzed to simpler molecules and that usually contain the grouping $-CHOHCHO$ or $-COCH_2OH$ or their equivalent, and are designated accordingly as aldoses or ketoses (even though the aldehyde or ketone group does not usually exist free); the monosaccharides are also designated according to the number of carbon atoms they contain as pentoses (5 carbon atoms), hexoses (6 carbon atoms), decoses (10 carbon atoms); and (2) the polysaccharides (or polysaccharoses or polyoses or holosides) are substances which give only simple sugars on hydrolysis. They include sweet, water-soluble substances like sucrose and comparatively insoluble substances such as the starches and celluloses. Some of them may be classified according to the number of molecules of monosaccharide yielded per molecule of polysaccharide, as disaccharides (such as sucrose and lactose), trisaccharides (such as raffinose and melezitose), and tetrasaccharides (such as lupeose and

stachyose). Other polysaccharides are the dextrins, the starches, and the celluloses. Conjugated saccharides contain a nonsugar group in combination with a sugar. Gums, glucosides, and tannins are members of this group.

CARBOHYDRATE NOMENCLATURE. The following rules for carbohydrate nomenclature were proposed by the ACS Committee in 1953, with the recommendation that they be adopted by the American Chemical Society after being tentative for one year. (*Chemical and Engineering News* **31,** April 27, 1953.)

Rule 1. Carbohydrate nomenclature should follow the general principles of established organic nomenclature.

Rule 2. As few changes as possible will be made in terminology universally adopted.

Comment. This is Rule 1 of the Definitive Report of the Commission on the Reform of Nomenclature of Organic Chemistry (1930), published in *J. Am. Chem. Soc.,* **55,** 3905–3925 (1933), as supplemented in Comptes Rendus de la Quinzième Conférence (Amsterdam, 1949), Union Internationale de Chimie Pure et Appliquée, and in Comptes Rendus de la Seizième Conférence (New York and Washington, 1951), Union Internationale de Chimie Pure et Appliquée. The rules of these reports will hereinafter be referred to as I.U.P.A.C. Rules (International Union of Pure and Applied Chemistry Rules).

Rule 3. The names "aldose" or "ketose" will be used in a generic sense to denote the respective character of the reducing, or potentially reducing, group of the monosaccharide or derivative thereof. In an aldose, the carbon atom of the aldehyde function is atom number one; and, in a ketose, the carbonyl carbon atom has the lowest possible number.

For indicating the number of carbon atoms in the chain, the appropriate one of the following names will be used: triose, tetrose, pentose, hexose, heptose, octose, nonose, etc.

Rule 4. Configurational relationships shall be denoted by the capital letters D and L which in print should preferably be small capital Roman letters and which are pronounced "dee" and "ell" (not "dextro" and "levo"). Such symbols will be placed immediately before the sugar stem name (see, however, Rules 23 and 28, examples c), and be employed only with compounds which have been definitively related to the reference-standard glyceraldehyde (see Rule 5). In a definitive name, the configurational symbol should not be omitted.

If the optical rotational sign under specified conditions is to be indicated, this may be done by adding (*dextro*) or (*levo*), which are italicized in print, or by adding (+) or (−). Racemic modifications may be indicated by the prefixes DL, or (±), or *inactive*, the last being italicized in print.

Examples:

D-glucose or D(*dextro*)-glucose or D(+)-glucose

D-fructose or D(*levo*)-fructose or D(−)-fructose

DL-glucose, or (±)-glucose, or *inactive*-glucose

Rule 5. Carbohydrates having the same configuration of the highest numbered asymmetric carbon atom as that of D(*dextro*)-glyceraldehyde will belong to the D-configurational series; those having the opposite configuration will belong to the L-series.

D(*dextro*)-Glyceraldehyde, the configurational reference standard, is written as follows:

$$
\begin{array}{c}
\text{CHO} \\
\text{H}\!\!\diamond\!\!\text{OH} \\
\text{CH}_2\text{OH}
\end{array}
$$

Comment. For the conventions employed in the two-dimensional representations of carbohydrate configurations, see *Chem. Eng. News* **26**, 1623 (1948). When more than one configurational center is involved, the formulas may be written horizontally, in which case the top orienting group (carbon one) lies to the extreme right and the Fischer conventions are thus altered. In making a configurational interpretation of formulas so written it is necessary to rotate the plane of depiction so that carbon one is at the top.

$$
\begin{array}{ccc}
\text{CHO} & & \text{COOH} \\
|1 & & |1 \\
\text{HCOH} & & \text{HOCH} \\
|2 & & |2 \\
\text{HOCH} & & \text{HOCH} \\
|3 & & |3 \\
\text{HCOH} & & \text{HCOH} \\
|4 & & |4 \\
\text{CH}_2\text{OH} & & \text{CH}_2\text{OH} \\
5 & & 5 \\
\text{D} & & \text{D}
\end{array}
$$

$$
\begin{array}{ccc}
\text{CH}_2\text{OH} & & \text{CH}_2\text{OH} \\
|1 & & |1 \\
\text{CO} & & \text{C(SC}_2\text{H}_5)_2 \\
|2 & & |2 \\
\text{HOCH} & & \text{HOCH} \\
|3 & & |3 \\
\text{HCOH} & & \text{HCOH} \\
|4 & & |4 \\
\text{HOCH} & & \text{HOCH} \\
|5 & & |5 \\
\text{CH}_2\text{OH} & & \text{CH}_2\text{OH} \\
6 & & 6 \\
\text{L} & & \text{L}
\end{array}
$$

$$
\text{HOCH}_2 \underset{6}{} - \overset{\text{H}}{\underset{\text{OH}}{\text{C}}} \underset{5}{} - \overset{\text{H}}{\underset{\text{OH}}{\text{C}}} \underset{4}{} - \overset{\text{OH}}{\underset{\text{H}}{\text{C}}} \underset{3}{} - \overset{\text{H}}{\underset{\text{OH}}{\text{C}}} \underset{2}{} - \text{CHO} \, \underset{1}{}
$$

D-glucose

Rule 6. The configuration of a group of consecutive and adjacent asymmetric carbons, such as ⟍CHOH, ⟍CHOCH₃, ⟍CHOAc, or ⟍CHNH₂, containing one to four asymmetric carbons is designated by the appropriate one of these prefixes:

NUMBER OF ASYMMETRIC CARBONS

One	*glycero*
Two	*threo, erythro*
Three	*arabino (arabo), ribo, xylo, lyxo*
Four	*gluco, manno, gulo, ido, galacto (gala), talo, allo, altro*

Each is D or L, as D-*talo* or L-*manno*.
The prefix, which is derived by omitting the last two letters from the name of the aldose having the same configuration as the group to which it refers, is to be uncapitalized, italicized (in print), and at-

tached by hyphens to the name to which it refers. Examples:

In each formula below, the principal function is placed at Y.

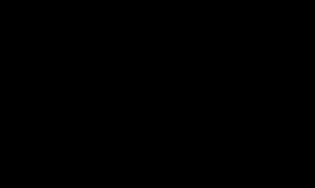

$$
\begin{array}{c}
\text{H \ \ H} \\
\text{X—C—C—Y} \\
\text{OH OH} \\
\textit{D-erythro-}
\end{array}
$$

$$
\begin{array}{cc}
\begin{array}{c}
\text{OH H \ \ OH} \\
\text{X—C—C—C—Y} \\
\text{H \ \ H \ \ H} \\
\textit{L-erythro-}
\end{array}
&
\begin{array}{c}
\text{OH OH} \\
\text{X—C—C—Y} \\
\text{H \ \ H} \\
\end{array}
\end{array}
$$

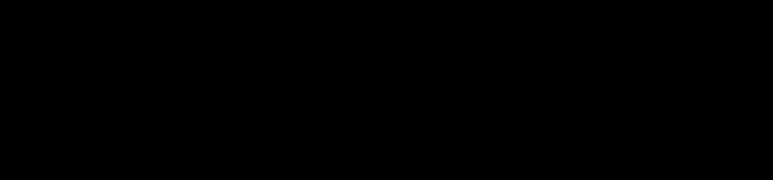

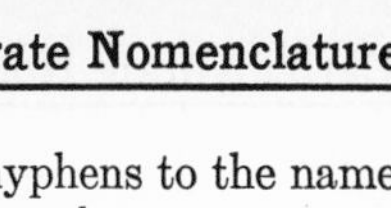

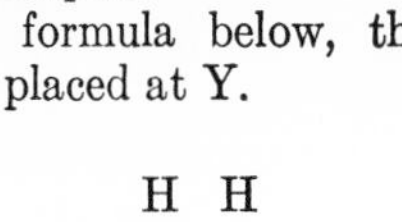

$$
\begin{array}{cc}
\begin{array}{c}
\text{H \ \ OH} \\
\text{X—C—C—Y} \\
\text{OH H} \\
\textit{D-threo-}
\end{array}
&
\begin{array}{c}
\text{OH H} \\
\text{X—C—C—Y} \\
\text{H \ \ OH} \\
\textit{L-threo-}
\end{array}
\end{array}
$$

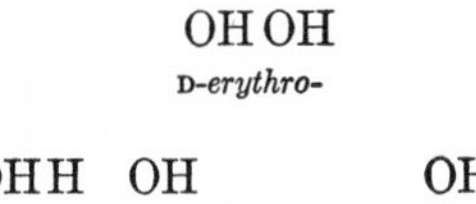

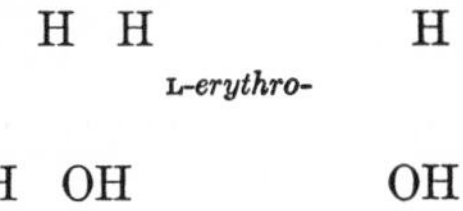

$$
\begin{array}{c}
\text{H \ \ OH H} \\
\text{X—C—C—C—Y} \\
\text{OH H \ \ OH} \\
\textit{D-xylo-}
\end{array}
$$

$$
\begin{array}{c}
\text{H \ \ H \ \ OH} \\
\text{X—C—C—C—Y} \\
\text{OH OH H} \\
\textit{D-arabo-} \\
\textit{D-arabino-}
\end{array}
$$

$$
\begin{array}{c}
\text{H \ \ H \ \ OH H} \\
\text{X—C—C—C—C—Y} \\
\text{OH OH H \ \ OH} \\
\textit{D-gluco-}
\end{array}
$$

$$
\begin{array}{c}
\text{H \ \ OH OH H} \\
\text{X—C—C—C—C—Y} \\
\text{OH H \ \ H \ \ OH} \\
\textit{D-galacto-(D-gala-)}
\end{array}
$$

$$
\begin{array}{c}
\text{H \ \ H \ \ OH H} \\
\text{HOCH}_2\text{—C—C—C—C—} \\
\text{OH OH H \ \ OH} \\
\textit{D-gluco-}\text{pentahydroxypentyl}
\end{array}
$$

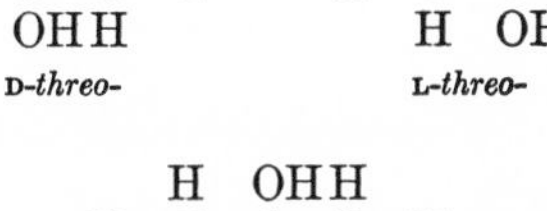

Rule 7. Ketoses having the carbonyl group at carbon atom number two will be named by means of the suffix "-ulose"; before this will be a prefix denoting the number of carbon atoms in the chain, which, in turn, will be preceded by the prefix denoting the configuration of the group of asymmetric centers present (see Rule 6).

Ketoses having the carbonyl group at a carbon atom other than number two will be named by inserting the appropriate numeral immediately before the prefix denoting the number of carbon atoms in the chain.

Comment. Trivial names for the hexuloses, established by usage, are: D-fructose, D-psicose, D-sorbose, D-tagatose, and the corresponding names for the L forms.

Examples:

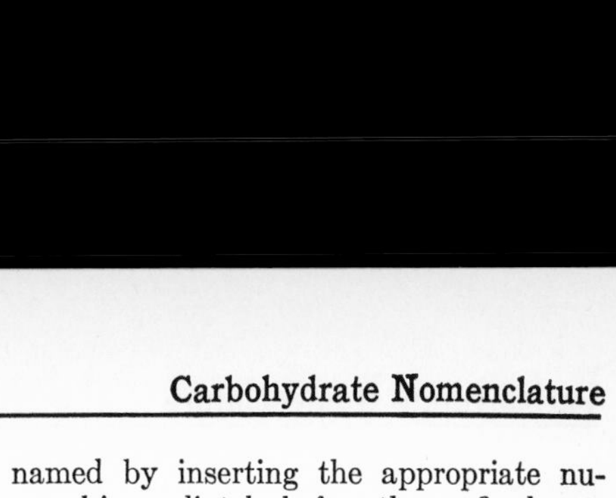

$$
\begin{array}{ccc}
&
&
\begin{array}{c}
\text{CH}_2\text{OH} \\
\vert
\end{array}
\\
&
\begin{array}{c}
\text{CH}_2\text{OH} \\
\vert
\end{array}
&
\begin{array}{c}
\text{C=O} \\
\vert
\end{array}
\\
\begin{array}{c}
\text{CH}_2\text{OH} \\
\vert
\end{array}
&
\begin{array}{c}
\text{HOCH} \\
\vert
\end{array}
&
\begin{array}{c}
\text{HOCH} \\
\vert
\end{array}
\\
\begin{array}{c}
\text{C=O} \\
\vert
\end{array}
&
\begin{array}{c}
\text{C=O} \\
\vert
\end{array}
&
\begin{array}{c}
\text{HCOH} \\
\vert
\end{array}
\\
\begin{array}{c}
\text{HCOH} \\
\vert
\end{array}
&
\begin{array}{c}
\text{HCOH} \\
\vert
\end{array}
&
\begin{array}{c}
\text{HOCH} \\
\vert
\end{array}
\\
\begin{array}{c}
\text{HCOH} \\
\vert
\end{array}
&
\begin{array}{c}
\text{HCOH} \\
\vert
\end{array}
&
\begin{array}{c}
\text{HOCH} \\
\vert
\end{array}
\\
\text{CH}_2\text{OH}
&
\text{CH}_2\text{OH}
&
\text{CH}_2\text{OH}
\\
\begin{array}{c}
\textit{D-erythro-} \\
\text{pentulose}
\end{array}
&
\begin{array}{c}
\textit{D-arabo-} \\
\text{3-hexulose}
\end{array}
&
\begin{array}{c}
\textit{L-gluco-} \\
\text{heptulose}
\end{array}
\end{array}
$$

Rule 8. When an alcoholic hydroxyl group of a monosaccharide is replaced by a hydrogen atom, the compound will be named by attaching by a hyphen, before the sugar name, the appropriate numeral (indicating position), a hyphen, and the prefix "deoxy." The configuration of the sugar will be designated, when necessary, as given in Rule 6. This deoxy moiety can be further substituted.

Comment. Trivial names, established by usage, include:

L-rhamnose (6-deoxy-L-mannose);
D-fucose (6-deoxy-D-galactose); and
D-epirhamnose (6-deoxy-D-glucose).

Examples:

2-deoxy-*aldehydo*-L-*xylo*-hexose
4-deoxy-α-D-*glycero*-pentulofuranose   (see Rule 18)
2,6-dideoxy-3-O-methyl-β-D-*lyxo*-hexopyranose (see Rule 18)
6-deoxy-α-L-idofuranose
2-deoxy-D-*erythro*-pentose (2-deoxy-D-arabinose or, as commonly termed, 2-deoxy-D-ribose)
6-deoxy-6-iodo-α-D-galactopyranose
2-chloro-2-deoxy-α-D-glucopyranose

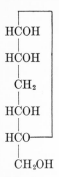

$$HCOH$$
$$HCOH$$
$$CH_2$$
$$HCOH$$
$$HCO$$
$$CH_2OH$$

3-deoxy-α-D-*ribo*-hexopyranose

3-amino-3-deoxy-β-L-galactofuranose

2-amino-2-deoxy-α-D-glucopyranose (common names: D-glucosamine, chitosamine)

2-amino-2-deoxy-α-D-galactopyranose (common names: D-galactosamine, chondrosamine)

1-amino-1-deoxy-α-D-fructofuranose (common name: isoglucosamine)

2-acetamido-2-deoxy-α-D-glucopyranose

Rule 9. When the hydrogen atom of an alcoholic hydroxyl group of a carbohydrate is substituted, an italic capital letter *O* (for oxygen) will be attached by a hyphen directly before the substituting prefix. The *O* prefix need not be repeated for multiple substitutions by one group. Similar principles apply where necessary to substitution on nitrogen (prefix, *N*). (The prefix *C* may be used to indicate substitution on carbon to avoid possible ambiguity.)

Examples:

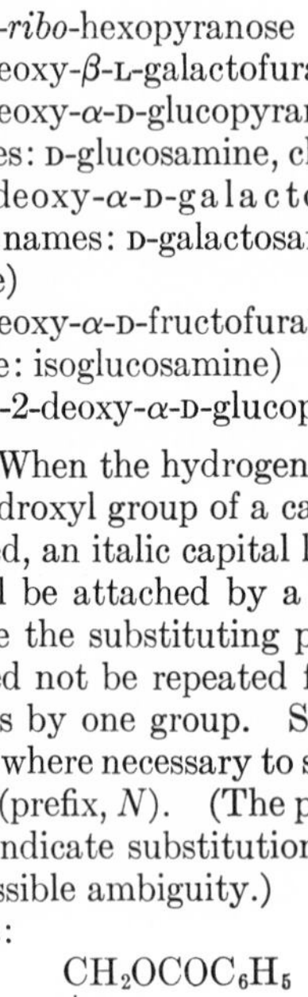

$$CH_2OCOC_6H_5$$
$$HCOH$$
$$HOCH$$
$$HOCH$$
$$HCOH$$
$$CH_2OCOC_6H_5$$

1,6-di-*O*-benzoyldulcitol

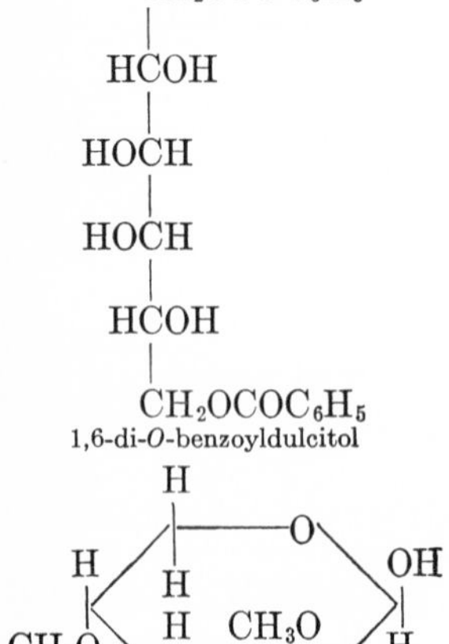

2,3,4-tri-*O*-methyl-β-D-arabinose

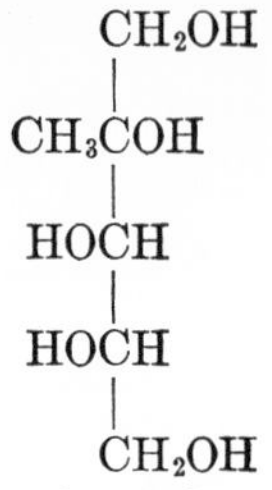

$$CH_2OH$$
$$CH_3COH$$
$$HOCH$$
$$HOCH$$
$$CH_2OH$$

2-methyl-L-arabitol

$$HCO$$
$$HOCH$$
$$HCOH$$
$$CH_3CH_2COH$$
$$HOCH$$
$$CH_2OH$$

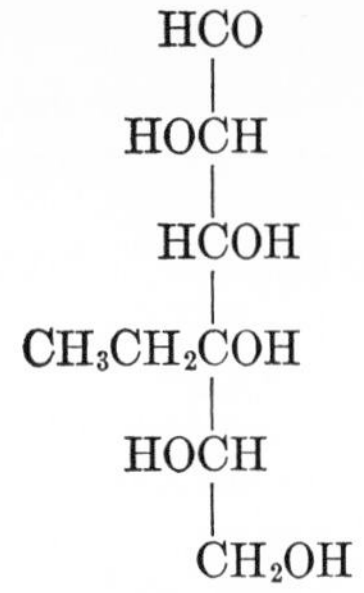

4-eth-L-*aldehydo*-L-galactose

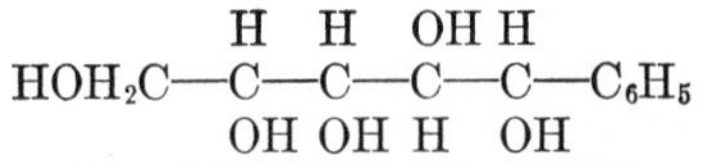

$$HOH_2C\!-\!\underset{OH}{\overset{H}{C}}\!-\!\underset{OH}{\overset{H}{C}}\!-\!\underset{H}{\overset{OH}{C}}\!-\!\underset{OH}{\overset{H}{C}}\!-\!C_6H_5$$

5-*O*-methyl-1-phenyl-D-*gluco*-pentitol

2-deoxy-2-*N*-methylacetamido-α-L-glucopyranose

2-*O*-methyl-3,4-dimethyl-α-D-glucose

Rule 10. When a hydrogen atom of an alcoholic hydroxyl group of a carbohydrate (see Rule 9) is substituted by another atom or group, the name of the parent compound may be retained as the root for the substituted compound. In such names, the prefix (denoting the substituent) is to be attached directly to the root and not spaced from it.

Comment. See Rule 6.

Examples:
2,3,4,6-tetramethyl-α-D-glucose
hexa-*O*-acetyldulcitol
2-*O*-methyl-β-D-glucose
penta-*O*-propionyl-β-D-galactopyranose

Rule 11. An ester formed from a sugar or sugar derivative by reaction with one or more of its alcoholic hydroxyl groups will be named by placing, after the sugar name and separated therefrom by a space, the appropriate numeral (indicating position) and a hyphen as prefix to the name of the group derived from an acid.

Examples:
α-D-glucopyranose 3-acetate
methyl β-D-talofuranoside 2-benzoate
Comment. Naming of *O*-acyl derivatives of carbohydrates may follow this terminology or Rule 9.

Examples:
(a) *Esters of monobasic carboxylic acids*
1. glycerol triacetate; tri-*O*-acetylglycerol
2. glycerol 1,3-dipropionate; 1,3-di-*O*-propionylglycerol
3. α-D-glucopyranose pentaacetate; penta-*O*-acetyl-α-D-glucopyranose
4. β-L-mannofuranuronic acid 2-benzoate; 2-*O*-benzoyl-β-L-mannofuranuronic acid
(b) *Esters of sulfonic acids*
1. methyl β-D-galactoside 2,3,4-triacetate 6-methanesulfonate or methyl 2,3,4-tri-*O*-acetyl-6-*O*-methylsulfonyl-β-D-galactoside
2. methyl α-D-glucopyranoside 6-*p*-toluenesulfonate or methyl 6-*O*-*p*-tolylsulfonyl-α-D-glucopyranoside
(c) *Esters of nitric acid* are usually named by Rule 11.
1. methyl β-D-galactopyranoside 6-nitrate
2. D-mannitol 1,6-dinitrate
3. methyl 4,6-*O*-ethylidene-β-D-glucoside 2,3-dinitrate
(d) *Esters of polybasic acids* are usually named by Rule 11 (see Rule 25)
1. β-D-glucopyranose 6-(dihydrogen phosphate)
2. α-D-glucofuranose 6-(disodium phosphate)

Rule 12. Class terms (excepting amine) such as acetal, alcohol, anhydride, ether, glycoside, ketone, sulfide, xyloside, and the like, which, when used singly, represent no definite unsubstituted compound, are used as separate words.
Comment. This is in conformity with established usage for such examples as methyl ether and ethyl methyl ketone.

Examples:
β-D-idose 2,3,4,6-tetramethyl ether
methyl α-D-mannopyranoside
ethyl β-L-xylopyranoside
di-D-fructopyranose 2,1′:2′,1-dianhydride (see Rule 34)

Rule 13. When ethers of polyols (glycols, glycerol, polyhydric phenols, carbohydrates, and the like) are named as ethers, the name of the polyol (a one-word name) shall be the first word, "ether" the last word, and the name of the appropriate radical (or radicals) shall be the middle word (or words).
Comment. The term ether does not apply to compounds derived by substitution of the hydrogen of the hemiacetal hydroxyl of the reducing or glycosidic carbon.

Names of bivalent and trivalent radicals derived by removal of two or three hydrogen atoms from the *same* carbon atom are sanctioned in the I.U.P.A.C. nomenclature (namely propylidene, propylidyne, I.U.P.A.C. Rule 56.1).

Except for a few established names, however, I.U.P.A.C. Rules 21, 33, and 62 show avoidance of distinctive names for multivalent radicals derived by removal of hydrogen atoms from *different* carbon atoms. The illustrations given below (with glycerol and D-glucose as first names) are in conformity with this decision. Names such as "glyceryl α-monomethyl ether" and "glyceryl α,γ-dimethyl ether" are being used in the trade. Here "glyceryl" is used incorrectly to denote two different radicals. In "glyceryl trimethyl ether" a third "glyceryl" radical would appear. It is obvious that a ruling should be made against the use of multivalent radicals in the naming of polyhydroxy derivatives.

Examples:

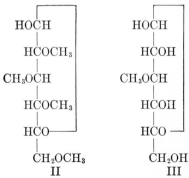

I. Glycerol 1,3-diethyl ether (synonyms: 1,3-diethoxy-2-propanol and 1,3-di-*O*-ethylglycerol)

II. β-D-glucose 2,3,4,6-tetramethyl ether or β-D-glucopyranose tetramethyl ether (synonym: 2,3,4,6-tetra-O-methyl-β-D-glucose)

III. β-D-glucopyranose 3-methyl ether (synonym: 3-O-methyl-β-D-glucopyranose)

Rule 14. When a prefix is attached to one of the words in a two- or three-word name, it modifies only the word to which it is attached and does not modify the remaining words in the name. But if a preceding word in this name is the name of a compound, numerals to indicate position of substitution in it may be placed before the following word, and, if necessary, parentheses should be used to avoid ambiguity.

Unless otherwise specified (Rules 15 and 17), prefixes take an alphabetical order, regardless of the numerical prefix of each; a compound radical name is treated as a unit.

Thus, triacetyl and diacetyl are to be listed under acetyl. Anhydro and deoxy are subject to alphabeting under "a" and "d," respectively.

Comment. This is in conformity with established usage; for example, CH_3OCH_2-CO_2CH_3: methyl methoxyacetate.

Examples:

$$\begin{array}{cccccc} & H & H & OMe & H & H \\ MeOCH_2 & C & C & C & C & C \\ & O & OMe & H & OMe & OMe \end{array}$$

methyl 2,3,4,6-tetra-O-methyl-α-D-glucoside

$$\begin{array}{cccccc} & H & H & OH & H & H \\ C_6H_5COOCH_2 & C & C & C & C & C \\ & O & OH & H & OH & OMe \end{array}$$

methyl 6-O-benzoyl-α-D-glucopyranoside
ethyl 2,3,4-tri-O-acetyl-6-O-(phenylsulfonyl)-α-D-glucoside
methyl 3-O-(2-chloroethyl)-β-D-glucopyranoside

Rule 15. The anomeric prefix (α- or β-), which can be used only in conjunction with a configurational prefix (D or L), will immediately precede the latter. The configurational prefix will directly precede the stem name (see Rule 6).

Comment. In some accepted trivial names (see last example below) the configurational prefix is understood and may be omitted.

Examples:
α-D-*gluco*-heptulopyranose
ethyl β-D-galactofuranoside
methyl α-D-glucopyranoside
methyl β-cellobioside

Rule 16. In conformity with established practice, hyphens shall be used in names to connect letters or numerals to syllables, or to separate different kinds of characters such as Roman letters from Greek letters or letters from numerals.

The preferred style is to connect syllables directly (no hyphens). Hyphens may be inserted, however, for the sake of clarity.

Examples:
α-D-glucose
3-O-methyl-β-L-mannose
penta-O-acetyl-α-D-glucopyranose
methyl tri-O-acetyl-α-D-glucopyranoside
1,3:4,6-di-O-methylenedulcitol (see Rule 30)
2-O-methyl-3,4-dimethyl-D-glucose

Rule 17. The acyclic nature of a sugar or derivative containing an unmodified CHO or CO group as the primary function will be indicated by inserting the italicized prefix *aldehydo* or *keto*, respectively, immediately before the configurational prefix and stem name.

Examples:
aldehydo-D-glucose pentaacetate
3,6-anhydro-*aldehydo*-D-galactose
keto-D-fructose pentabenzoate

Rule 18. The size of the ring in the heterocyclic forms of monosaccharides (aldoses and ketoses) may be indicated by replacing, in the sugar name, the letters "se" by "pyranose" for the 6-atom ring; "furanose" for the 5-atom ring; and "septanose" for the 7-atom ring. Likewise, for the glycosides (aldosides and ketosides), the size of the ring may be revealed by replacing the syllable "-side" by "pyranoside," "furanoside," or "septanoside."

Examples:
α-L-iodofuranose
methyl β-D-*altro*-heptulopyranoside

Rule 19. The root "glyc" in glycose or glycoside shall be used in a generic sense to denote any simple sugar or derivative thereof, rather than some specified sugar.

Examples:

glycose } generic
methyl glycoside
β-L-glucose
methyl α-D-glucopyranoside } specific
ethyl β-D-altropyranoside
methyl β-L-fructofuranoside

Rule 20. A glycoside is a mixed acetal resulting from the exchange of an organic radical for the hydrogen of the hemiacetal hydroxyl group of a cyclic form of an aldose or ketose. It is named by substituting "ide" as a suffix in place of the terminal "e" of the corresponding sugar name and placing before this word, separated by a space, the name of the organic substituent.

Examples:

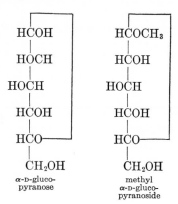

α-D-gluco-
pyranose

methyl
α-D-gluco-
pyranoside

methyl 2-amino-2-deoxy-α-D-glucopyrano-side (common name: methyl α-D-glucos-aminide)

Rule 21. If the hemiacetal hydroxyl is detached from a cyclic modification of an aldose or ketose, the residue is a glycosyl glycopyranosyl, glycofuranosyl, glycosep-tanosyl) radical. It is named by substi-tuting "yl" as a suffix in place of the terminal "e" of the corresponding sugar name.

Comment. A glycosyloxy radical is iden-tical with a glycoside radical (see Rule 20).

Examples:

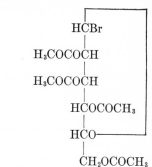

tetra-O-acetyl-α-D-mannopyranosyl bromide

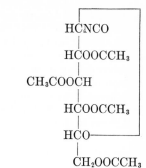

tetra-O-acetyl-α-D-glucopyranosyl isocyanate

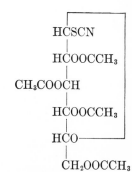

tetra-O-acetyl-α-D-glucopyranosyl thiocyanate

N-methyl-6-O-methyl-β-L-talofuranosyl-amine
N-n-butyl-α-D-glucopyranosylamine

N-phenyl-α-D-glucopyranosylamine (common name: D-glucose anilide)

N-hydroxy-α-D-glucopyranosylamine or N-α-D-glucopyranosylhydroxylamine (common name: D-glucose oxime)

9-β-D-ribofuranosyladenine (common name: adenosine)

9-(2,3,5-tri-O-acetyl-β-D-ribosyl)adenine

Rule 22. A monosaccharide containing more than four configurational asymmetric carbon atoms will be named by adding two or more prefixes indicating the configurations of those asymmetric carbon atoms to a root indicating the number of carbon atoms in the chain and ending with the suffix "-ose" for aldoses and "-ulose" for ketoses.

The configurational prefixes employed are given in Rule 6. The sequence of asymmetric carbon atoms will be divided into units, commencing, with a four-carbon unit, at the asymmetric carbon atom (or atoms) next to the functional group (see below). The order of citation of these prefixes will commence at the end farthest from carbon atom number one, and proceed along the carbon chain to the asymmetric carbon atom nearest to carbon atom number one. In designating anomeric ring forms of aldoses and 2-ketoses the anomeric prefix here (see Rule 15) will immediately precede the configurational prefix nearest to the root name.

Number of asymmetric carbons in the sequence	Prefixes to be used
5	one 4-carbon + one 1-carbon
6	one 4-carbon + one 2-carbon
7	one 4-carbon + one 3-carbon
8	two 4-carbon
9	two 4-carbon + one 1-carbon
10	two 4-carbon + one 2-carbon
11, etc.	two 4-carbon + one 3-carbon, etc.

Examples:

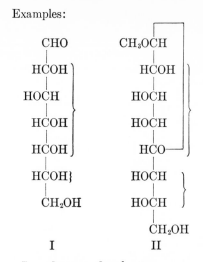

I. D-*glycero*-D-*gluco*-heptose

II. methyl L-*erythro*-β-D-*galacto*-octopyranoside

For oxygen-ring forms of ketoses other than 2-ketoses, the ending (furanose, furanoside, etc.) will, when necessary, be immediately preceded by a pair of numerals identifying the two carbon atoms to which the oxygen ring is attached, the potential ketone group being cited first. When the potential ketone group of an oxygen-ring form is in the middle of the chain, the numeral identifying the position of the original hydroxyl group will be the higher of the two possibilities (see example VI).

Examples:

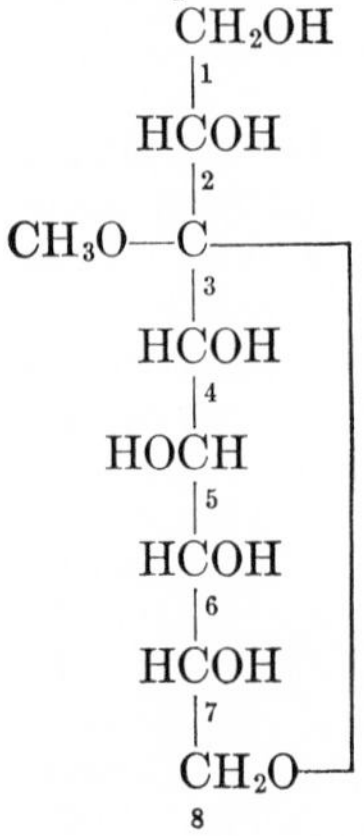

$$
\begin{array}{l}
\text{CH}_2\text{OH} \quad |1 \\
\text{HCOH} \quad |2 \\
\text{CH}_3\text{O—C} \quad |3 \\
\text{HCOH} \quad |4 \\
\text{HOCH} \quad |5 \\
\text{HCOH} \quad |6 \\
\text{HCOH} \quad |7 \\
\text{CH}_2\text{O} \quad 8
\end{array}
$$

III

$$
\begin{array}{l}
\text{CH}_2\text{OH} \quad |1 \\
\text{HCOH} \quad |2 \\
\text{HCOH} \quad |3 \\
\text{CH}_3\text{O—C} \quad |4 \\
\text{HOCH} \quad |5 \\
\text{HOCH} \quad |6 \\
\text{HCO} \quad |7 \\
\text{HCOH} \quad |8 \\
\text{CH}_2\text{OH} \quad 9
\end{array}
$$

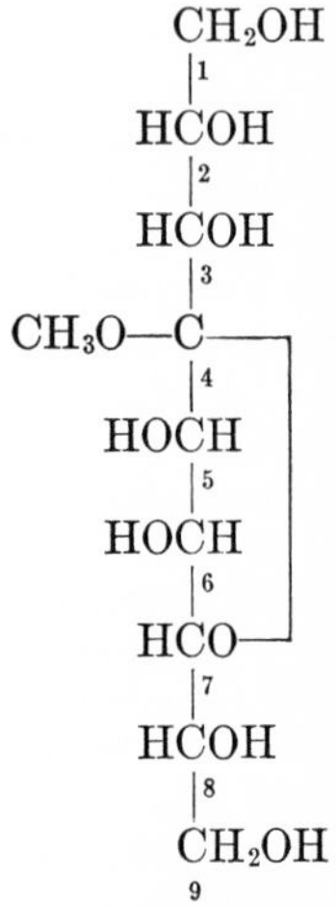

IV

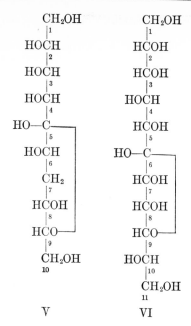

V   VI

III. methyl   D-*gluco*-D-*glycero*-3-octulo-septanoside

IV. methyl D-*manno*-D-*erythro*-4-nonulo-4,7-furanoside

V. 7-deoxy-D-*arabo*-L-*ribo*-5-deculo-5,9-pyranose

VI. L-*talo*-D-*gulo*-6-undeculo-6,9-furanose

Comment. Methods for naming, as well as representing correctly, the configuration of the anomeric forms of these ketoses can be devised when such compounds are prepared and their configurations determined.

Rule 23. Names for the polyhydric alcohols may be derived from the names of the corresponding aldose sugars by changing the suffix "ose" to "itol," using for non-meso compounds the same family-determining asymmetric carbon as that characterizing the name of the sugar.

Examples and comments.

(a) Permissible names established by usage:

     glycerol for glyceritol
     adonitol for ribitol
     arabitol for arabinitol
     sorbitol for D-glucitol
     dulcitol for galactitol
     perseitol
     volemitol

(b) Names requiring D or L:
     threitol, mannitol, glucitol, iditol, talitol, rhamnitol

(c) Names used without D or L:
     glycerol, erythritol, xylitol, ribitol, sorbitol, allitol, dulcitol, lactitol, cellobiitol, melibiitol

     The names of meso forms can be used advantageously with D or L in naming derivatives which have become optically active by substitution.

     Examples:
       2,3-*O*-isopropylidene-D-xylitol or
       D(2,3-*O*-isopropylidenexylitol)
       1-*O*-methyl-L-glycerol or
       L(1-*O*-methylglyceritol)

(d) Equivalent names:
     D-arabitol and D-lyxitol
     D-talitol and D-altritol
     D-glucitol and L-gulitol

(e)

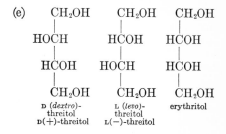

Rule 24. "Aldityl and alditylidene" (under further discussion).

Rule 25. Aldonic acids, formed from aldoses by oxidation of only the hemiacetal or aldehydic carbon atom to $-CO_2H$, may be named by substituting "onic acid" as a suffix in place of "ose" of the corresponding aldose. Esters, salts, acid chlorides, lactones (see *comment*, Rule 27), amides, nitriles, and the like, are named in the conventional manner.

Comment. Glyceric acid, arabonic acid, and lactobionic acid will be considered acceptable names in view of their general usage.

Examples:
cellobionic acid
barium D-gluconate
penta-*O*-acetyl-D-gluconic acid or D-gluconic acid pentaacetate
penta-*O*-acetyl-D-galactonic acid monohydrate or D-galactonic acid pentaacetate monohydrate

methyl   tetra-*O*-acetyl-L-arabonate   or
methyl L-arabonate tetraacetate

D-glucono-γ-lactone or D-glucono-1,4-lactone

D-gluconic 1,4-lactone or D-gluconic γ-lactone

D-glucono-δ-lactone or D-glucono-1,5-lactone

D-gluconic 1,5-lactone or D-gluconic δ-lactone

2,3,4,6-tetra-*O*-methyl-L-altronolactone or
2,3,4,6-tetra-*O*-methyl-L-altronic lactone

2-amino-2-deoxy-D-gluconic acid (common
name: D-glucosaminic acid)

Examples illustrating combination of
Rules 11 and 25:

barium D-gluconate 6-(dihydrogen phosphate)

barium D-gluconate 6-(sodium hydrogen
phosphate)

barium D-gluconate 6-(disodium phosphate)

barium D-gluconate 6-(barium phosphate)

Rule 26. Uronic acids, formed from
aldoses having a terminal –CH₂OH group
by oxidation only of this group to –CO₂H,
may be named by substituting "uronic
acid" as a suffix in place of "ose" of the
corresponding aldose name. The hemiacetal or aldehydic carbon atom is carbon
number one, and the syllable "ur" has the
significance of "ω."

Esters, salts, acid chlorides, lactones (see
comment, Rule 27), amides, nitriles, and
the like, are named in the conventional
manner.

Examples:

α-D-mannopyranuronic acid

tetra-*O*-acetyl-β-D-talopyranuronic acid (or
β-D-talopyranuronic acid tetraacetate)

methyl β-L-galactopyranuronate

barium α-L-glucofuranuronate

ethyl tetra-*O*-benzoyl-α-D-idofuranuronate

3-*O*-methyl-α-D-ribofuranurono-5,2-lactone

α-D-mannopyranurono-6,2-lactone

2-*O*-ethyl-β-L-glucopyranurono-γ-lactone

Rule 27. If the glycoside radical (see
Rule 20) of an aldose glycoside possesses a
terminal –CH₂OH group, and if this group
of the glycoside is oxidized to a carboxyl
group, the product may be named by substituting "uronic acid" as a suffix in place
of the terminal "e" of the parent glycoside

name. The glycoside hemiacetal carbon
atom is carbon number one.

Esters, salts, acid chlorides, lactones,
amides, nitriles, and the like, may then be
named in the conventional manner.

Comment. Parentheses are suitably inserted where it is necessary to distinguish
between an ester alkyl group and the hemiacetal alkyl group of a glycoside of a uronic
acid. In numbering lactones, the first
number refers to the position of the carbonyl carbon.

Examples:

methyl α-D-mannopyranosiduronic acid

ethyl tri-*O*-benzoyl-α-D-idofuranosiduronic
acid

methyl α-D-glucopyranosidurono-γ-lactone
(or 6,3-lactone)

ethyl 3-*O*-ethyl-β-L-glucopyranosiduronoδ-lactone (or 6,2-lactone)

ethyl (methyl β-L-galactopyranosid)uronate

barium (bornyl α-D-glucofuranosid)uronate

butyl (propyl tri-*O*-acetyl-β-D-talopyranosid)uronate

methyl (ethyl 2,3,4-tri-*O*-methyl-α-D-galactosid)uronate

Rule 28. α,ω-Dicarboxylic sugar acids
(aldaric or glycaric acids), formed by the
oxidation of aldoses at both terminal carbon
atoms, may be named by substituting "aric
acid" as a suffix in place of "ose" of the
corresponding aldose name.

Examples:
(a) Permissible names established by
usage:

tartronic acid	for glyceraric acid
dextro-tartaric acid	for L-threaric acid
meso-tartaric acid	for erythraric acid
saccharic acid	for D-glucaric acid
idosaccharic acid	for idaric acid
mannosaccharic acid	for mannaric acid
mucic acid	for galactaric acid
allomucic acid	for allaric acid
talomucic acid	for talaric acid

(b) Names requiring D or L:
threaric acid
arabinaric (arabaric) acid
glucaric acid
talaric acid
idaric acid
mannaric acid

(c) Names used without D or L:

glyceraric acid
erythraric acid
ribaric acid
xylaric acid
allaric acid
galactaric acid

The names of meso forms can be used advantageously with D or L in naming derivatives which have become optically active by substitution (see Rule 23c).

(d) Equivalent names:

lyxaric acid and arabinaric acid
talaric acid and altraric acid
L-gularic acid and D-glucaric acid

Rule 29. The "glycosides of ortho ester structure" may be named as the ortho esters with the carbohydrate group given as the first term in the name.

Comment. This is in conformity with established usage for such compounds as:

$$CH_3C(OC_2H_5)_3$$

ethyl orthoacetate

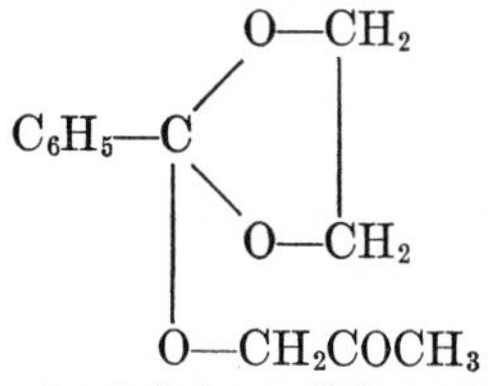

$$O—CH_2COCH_3$$

acetonyl ethylene orthobenzoate

Examples:

(a)

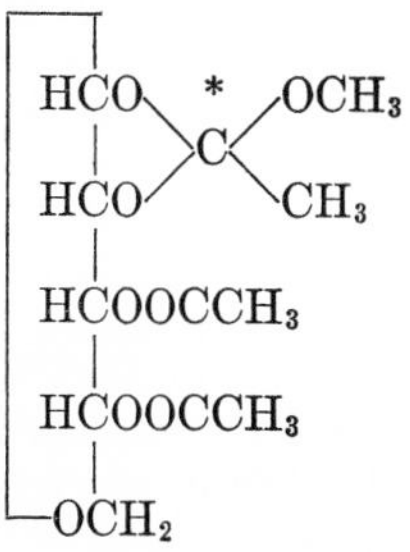

D-ribose 1,2-(methyl orthoacetate) 3,4-diacetate

It is to be noted that this compound may also be named according to Rule 30 as 3,4-di-O-acetyl-1,2-O-(1-methoxyethylidene)-D-ribose. This latter system appears to be the best one for assigning an accurate name to the following:

(b)

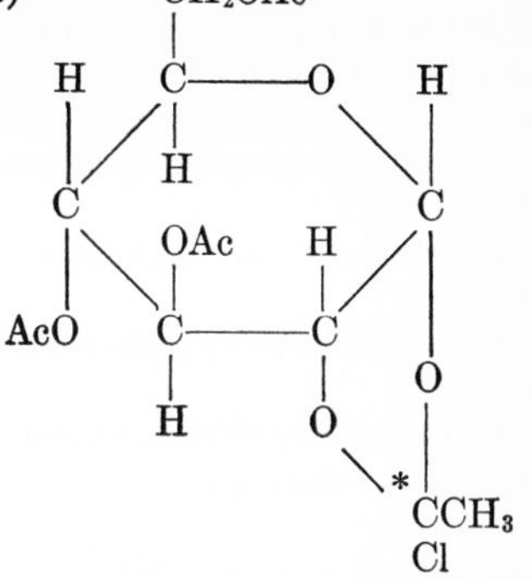

3,4,6-tri-O-acetyl-1,2-O-(1-chloroethylidene)-α-D-glucose

Comment. These two examples contain an asymmetric carbon atom (marked with *) and two forms are possible. No recommendations are made at present for their differentiation.

Rule 30. Cyclic acetals which are formed by the reaction of carbohydrates with aldehydes or ketones may be named with bivalent radicals as prefixes in accordance with Rule 7, such radicals to follow the nomenclature set forth in I.U.P.A.C. Rule 56.1. In representing more than one cyclic acetal grouping, the numeral pairs are separated typographically when the exact placement of the acetal groups is known.

Examples:

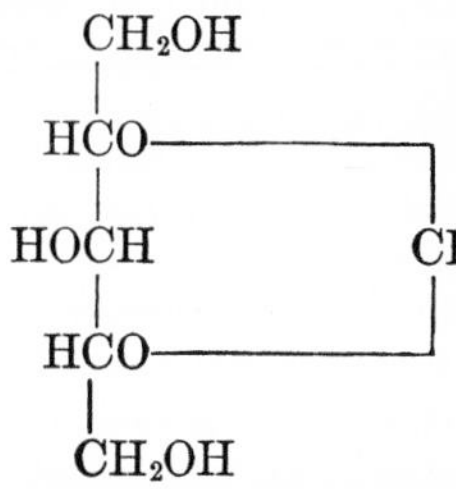

2,4-O-methylenexylitol

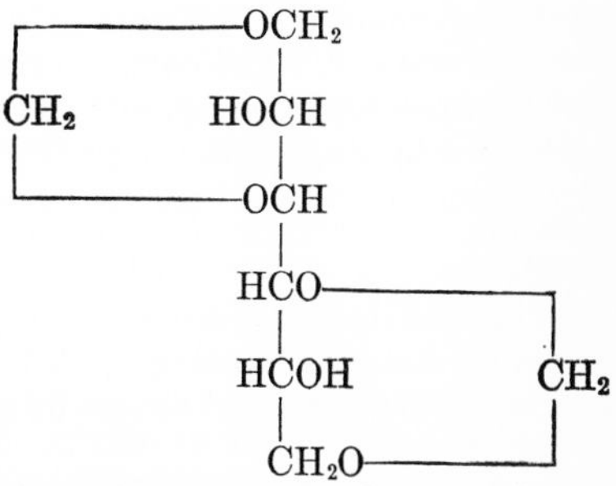

1,3:4,6-di-O-methylene-D-mannitol

I. 1,2-*O*-isopropylidene-D-glucofuranose
II. 1,2:4,5-di-*O*-isopropylidene-D-fructo-pyranose
III. 4,6-*O*-ethylidene-D-glucose
IV. 1,2:3,4-bis-*O*-(1-methylpropylidene)-D-xylose
V. methyl 4,6-*O*-benzylidene-α-D-gluco-side
VI. 1,2-*O*-(2-chloroethylidene)-α-D-gluco-furanose
VII. 1,2-*O*-(1-chloroethylidene)-α-D-gluco-pyranose triacetate

Comment. It is to be noted that in examples III to VII, inclusive, new asymmetric centers are introduced in the carbonyl carbon of the aldehyde or ketone that has reacted with the sugar. In IV two such new centers have been introduced. A differentiating nomenclature for such isomers is not attempted.

Rule 31. "Acetals (acyclic)" (under further discussion).

Rule 32. "Acyclic derivatives" (under further discussion).

Rule 33. An intramolecular anhydride, formed by the elimination of the elements of water from two hydroxyl groups of a monosaccharide molecule (aldose or ketose), is named by attaching by a hyphen before the sugar name the prefix "anhydro"; this, in turn, is preceded by a pair of numerals identifying the two hydroxyl groups involved. Anhydrides of sugar acids, lactones, alcohols, and the like, are named similarly.
Comment. The substances usually known as sugar anhydrides, glycose anhydrides, or glycosans (whose formation involves the reducing group), as well as the anhydro sugars (whose formation does not involve the reducing group) are not here differentiated in treatment. The name "levoglucosan" (for 1,6-anhydro-β-D-glucopyranose) is established by usage, but, except for this, names of glucosan type should not be used.

Examples:

3,6-anhydro-*aldehydo*-D-glucose
3,6-anhydro-β-D-glucofuranose
2,3-anhydro-4-*O*-methyl-α-D-**manno**-pyranose
2,7-anhydro-β-D-*altro*-heptulopyranose

1,6:3,4-dianhydro-β-D-talopyranose
methyl 4,6-di-*O*-acetyl-2,3-anhydro-α-D-alloside
2,5-anhydro-D-gluconic acid
3,6-anhydro-D-gluconic 1,4-lactone
1,4:3,6-dianhydro-D-glucitol, or 1,4:3,6-dianhydro-L-gulitol (See Rule 23)

Rule 34. An intermolecular anhydride, formed by condensation of two monosaccharide molecules with the elimination of the elements of two molecules of water, will be named by the word "dianhydride" placed after the names of the two parent sugars. The position of each anhydride link is indicated by a pair of numerals showing the positions of the two hydroxyl groups involved; the numerals relating to one sugar (in a mixed dianhydride, the second sugar named) will be primed. Both pairs of numerals will immediately precede the word "dianhydride."

Examples:

di-D-fructopyranose 2,1':2',1-dianhydride
di-β-D-fructofuranose 2,3':2',1-dianhydride
β-D-fructofuranose β-D-*threo*-pentulofuranose 2,1':2',1-dianhydride

Rule 35. An oligosaccharide is a compound which, on complete hydrolysis, gives monosaccharide units only, in relatively small number per molecule (in contrast to the high-polymeric polysaccharides).
Comment. Most of the naturally occurring oligosaccharides have well-established and useful common names (sucrose, lactose, maltose, cellobiose, melezitose, raffinose, stachyose) which were assigned before their complete structures were known. Rational names may now be assigned as follows.
Disaccharides. A reducing disaccharide may be named as a glycosylaldose (glycosyl-ketose), and a non-reducing disaccharide as a glycosyl aldoside (glycosyl ketoside), from its component parts.

Examples:
(a) *Reducing*
α-lactose: 4-*O*-β-D-galactopyranosyl-α-D-glucopyranose
(b) *Non-reducing*
sucrose: β-D-fructofuranosyl α-D-glucopyranoside, or α-D-glucopyranosyl β-D-fructofuranoside

(c) *Glycosides of reducing disaccharides*
    methyl α-lactoside: methyl 4-*O*-β-D-galactopyranosyl-α-D-glucopyranoside

Tri and Higher Oligo-saccharides

(a) *Reducing.* Beginning with the first non-reducing component, and following Rule 20, the first glycosyl portion with its configurational prefixes is delineated. This is followed by two numbers, separated by an arrow, in parentheses inserted into the name by hyphens. This numeral pair indicates the respective positions involved in the first glycosidic union, the first number giving the position on the terminal non-reducing component and the second referring to the position on the other component concerned. The next disaccharide linkage is treated similarly (and so on), and the last portion of the name delineates the reducing sugar unit.

Examples:

α-cellotriose:

Reducing, branched. By inserting one glycosyl substituent in brackets, it is distinguished from the second glycosyl substituent.

O - α - D - glucopyranosyl - (1 → 4) - *O* - [α-D - glucopyranosyl - (1 → 6)] - α - D - glucopyranose

synonym: 4,6-di-*O*-α-D-glucopyranosyl-α-D-glucopyranose

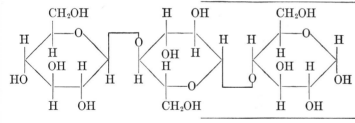

O - β - D - glucopyranosyl - (1 → 4) - *O* - β-D - glucopyranosyl - (1 → 4) - α - D - glucopyranose

α - maltotriose: *O* - α - D - glucopyranosyl-(1 → 4)-*O*-α-D-glucopyranosyl-(1 → 4)-α-D-glucopyranose

O - α - D - glucopyranosyl - (1 → 6) - *O* - α - D-glucopyranosyl-(1 → 4)-α-D-glucopyranose

(b) *Non-reducing*

raffinose: *O*-α-D-galactopyranosyl-(1 → 6)-*O*-α-D-glucopyranosyl-(1 → 2) β-D-fructofuranoside or *O*-β-D-fructofuranosyl-(2 → 1)-*O*-α-D-glucopyranosyl-(6 → 1) α-D-galactopyranoside

gentianose: *O*-β-D-glucopyranosyl-(1 → 6)-*O*-α-D-glucopyranosyl-(1 → 2) β-D-fructofuranoside

CARBOHYDROXAMAMIDE. The radical –C(:NOH)NH₂.

CARBOHYDROXAMIC. The radical –C(:NOH)OH.

CARBOLFUCHSIN. A staining solution, containing phenol and fuchsin dissolved in dilute alcohol.

CARBOMETER. (1) An instrument for determining the carbon content of steel by measuring magnetic properties of the steel induced by a **field** of known **intensity.** (2) An instrument for measuring the amount of carbon dioxide in the air.

CARBOMETHOXY. The radical

$$CH_3OOC-.$$

CARBOMETHYL VIOLET. A staining solution containing phenol and methyl violet dissolved in dilute alcohol.

CARBON. Nonmetallic element. Symbol C. Atomic number 6. Atomic weight 12.010. Exists in three allotropic forms: (1) Diamond. Density 3.51. Specific heat 0.079. (2) Graphite. Density 2.26 at 20° C. Specific heat 0.160. (3) Amorphous. Density 1.75 to 2.10. Melting point 3527° C. Sublimation point 4200° C. (atmospheric pressure). Carbon occurs in combination in all organic matter, animal and vegetable, in inorganic carbonates in many minerals, in the air as carbon dioxide, in coal as elementary carbon, in petroleum, usually in combination with hydrogen, etc. Valence, principal 4, subordinate 2 and 3. Oxides, CO, CO_2, C_3O_2.

CARBON APPARATUS. Analytical apparatus for determining total carbon, especially in fuels.

CARBON CELL. A voltaic cell having

tains one or more asymmetric carbon atoms. (See **isomerism, optical.**)

CARBON CYCLE. The cycle of processes by which living things utilize the carbon of the carbon dioxide of the atmosphere in their **metabolism.** The cycle includes **photosynthesis** of **carbohydrates** by plants from carbon dioxide and water in the presence of chlorophyll, with the aid of sunshine, the transformation of plant carbohydrates by animals into substances required in their structure and processes, the decay of animal bodies and excreta, aided by bacterial action, to return carbon dioxide to the atmosphere.

CARBON, NEUTRALITY OF. The element carbon is neither strongly positive nor negative in chemical behavior, and the character of the other elements in carbon compounds, as well as their relative positions, usually determines the positive or negative properties of the compound or radical.

CARBON RESIDUE. The amount of carbon residue left, after combustion of oils (usually lubricating oil), under controlled conditions.

CARBONACEOUS. Containing carbon.

CARBONATATION (CARBONATION). (1) In beet sugar refining, the process of precipitating, with a stream of carbon dioxide, the lime which has been added to the juice to neutralize the free acids and precipitate the albuminoids. (2) The reduction of carbon compounds to carbon. (3) Saturation with carbon dioxide. (4) The introduction of a carboxy group (–COOH) into an organic compound (in other words, the preparation of an organic acid) by the action of carbon dioxide on certain organic compounds, especially alkylmagnesium halides. For example:

$$(CH_3)_3CMgCl + CO_2 \rightarrow (CH_3)_3CC(O)OMgCl \xrightarrow[H_2O]{\Delta} (CH_3)_3CCOOH + MgClOH.$$

a carbon anode, a zinc cathode, and an electrolyte solution of sodium hydroxide.

CARBON COMPOUND, UNSYMMETRICAL. An organic substance which con-

CARBONATE (or METACARBONATE). The anion CO_3^- or $(HCO_3)n^{n-}$, or a compound containing one of these anions. (The anion HCO_3^- is known as the **bicarbonate** ion.)

CARBONATE (ORTHO-). See **ortho-carbonate.**

CARBONATING TOWER. An apparatus used in the treatment or saturation of a solution with carbon dioxide, as in the processes for its separation from flue gases, in which a sodium carbonate solution is the absorbing medium. The term is also applied specifically to apparatus used for the saturation of brine with carbon dioxide.

CARBONATO-. The radical O_3C⟨

CARBONIC. (1) Containing quadrivalent carbon. (2) Related to carbonic acid, $HO \cdot COOH$ or H_2CO_3.

CARBONIUM. A compound in which carbon is believed to have, temporarily, the exceptional valences two or three, or, stated otherwise, a carbon atom having temporarily four or six valence electrons. For example, the tertiary-butyl carbonium ion offers a clear understanding of the probable course of the conversion of isobutylene to its dimers and trimers.

$$(CH_3)_2C{=}CH_2 + H^+ \rightleftarrows (CH_3)_3C^+$$

$$(CH_3)_3C^+ + (CH_3)_2C{=}CH_2 \rightleftarrows (CH_3)_2\overset{+}{C}{-}CH_2C(CH_3)_3$$

The larger carbonium ion thus formed cannot continue to exist, but may depolymerize, unite with the catalyst, or stabilize itself by the attraction of an electron pair from a carbon atom adjacent to the electronically deficient carbon (C^+) with its proton. This establishes a double bond involving the formerly deficient atom. Thus a proton is expelled to the catalyst or attracted to the catalyst. If this takes place with one of the methyl groups, the product is $CH_2{=}C{-}CH_2C(CH_3)_3$. If the

$$|$$
$$CH_3$$

methylene group is involved, the product is $(CH_3)_2C{=}CHC(CH_3)_3$.

CARBONIZE. (1) To convert into carbon. (2) To cause combination with, or addition of, carbon, as in the cementation process for making steel. (3) To cleanse

wood of vegetable matter by soaking it in a bath of aluminum chloride (or dilute sulfuric acid) ridding it of excess moisture, and placing it in heated chambers where the aluminum chloride is decomposed. The hydrochloric acid thus formed attacks the foreign matter and renders it so friable that it is easily removed in a beating machine. (4) To distill coal.

CARBONOMETER. An instrument for measuring the amount of carbon or carbon dioxide present in a substance. The term is usually applied to an instrument designed for an approximate determination of the amount of carbon dioxide in a gas by precipitation of calcium carbonate from lime water.

CARBONYL. (1) The group $={=}C{=}O$. (2) A compound formed by the union of carbon monoxide with a metal. Nickel carbonyl $Ni(CO)_4$, a colorless volatile liquid, iron carbonyl $Fe(CO)_5$, cobalt carbonyl, $Co(CO)_4$ are important compounds of this type.

CARBONYLIDIOXY. The radical $-OCOO-$.

CARBOTHIOLIC. The radical $-C(:O)SH$.

CARBOTHIONIC. The radical $-C(:S)OH$.

CARBOXAMIDE. The radical $-CONH_2$.

CARBOXAMIDINE. The radical $-C(:NH)NH_2$.

CARBOXAMIDOXINE. The radical $-C(:NOH)NH_2$.

CARBOXIDE. (1) A metallic **carbonyl** (q.v.) derivative. (2) The keto group ⟩$C{=}O$.

CARBOXIMIDIC. The radical $C(:NH)OH$.

CARBOXY (CARBOXYL). The radical HOOC– characteristic of organic acids. Unless otherwise qualified, the addition of the suffix "acid" to a carbon compound indicates the presence of the carboxyl group. Exceptions are carbolic acid and picric acid.

CARBOXYLIC. Pertaining to the carboxyl group, HOOC–, characteristic of organic acids.

CARBOY. A large glass bottle or flask enclosed in a box or wickerwork for protection, used for shipments of acids, ammonia, and other liquids.

CARBURETOR. (1) An apparatus employed in the manufacture of illuminating gas from water gas in order to supply the illuminants that water gas lacks. It consists of a chamber rigged with a checkerwork which is heated by waste gases. When it is at the proper temperature, the waste gas is shut off and water gas is allowed to pass through while a stream of oil is admitted through the top of the chamber. The oil furnishes **hydrocarbons** such as acetylene, ethane, ethylene, and benzene to the gas. The process is known as carbureting.

(2) An element of an internal combustion engine operating on volatile fuel or gas. This element consists of a small chamber for mixing fuel and air in controlled proportions, and also for volatilizing the fuel (if it is liquid).

CARBURETTED. Combined with carbon, as "carburetted hydrogen," an obsolete name for **acetylene.**

CARBURIZATION. Addition of carbon to molten or heated metals, resulting in the formation of compounds or solutions with different properties.

CARBURIZER. A substance used in the surface heat-treatment of certain metals to increase the carbon content, and hence the hardness, of the portion of the metal at or near the surface. This process is known as **case hardening** (q.v.).

CARBYL. The radical –C–.

CARBYLAMINE. An isocyanide, i.e., a compound containing the radical –NC.

CARBYLIC ACID. Any organic acid which contains carbon in its acid radical. All carboxylic acids are included, as well as other organic acids, in this group.

CARCANO REACTION FOR MORPHINE DERIVATIVES. By using the **Ehrlich reagent** (q.v.) in the presence of ammonia, characteristic colors are obtained with various alkaloids, such as heroin and morphine, and with dionin in codeine.

CARCINOGEN. A cancer-producing substance.

CAREY-FOSTER BRIDGE. A circuit for the measurement of **electrical resistance,** consisting of three bridge wires, four sets of coils, and two shunts.

CARINTHIAN PROCESS. A metallurgical process for the recovery of lead by low-temperature roasting and volatilization.

CARIUS METHOD. The use of nitric acid in the sealed-tube decomposition, at about 300° C., of organic compounds, in such a manner that the sulfur is converted to sulfate and the halogen to ionic halide.

CARLETTI SOLUTIONS FOR MINERAL ACIDS. Two solutions: (1) 1 g. furfural dissolved in 100 ml. 95% ethyl alcohol; and (2) 5 g. aniline dissolved in 20 ml. glacial acetic acid and 75 ml. water. These solutions are used in testing for mineral acids in wine and other liquids used as foods. The liquid to be tested is first decolorized with charcoal; five drops of the test solutions are then added successively and form a pink color in the presence of mineral acids.

CARLETTI TEST FOR MENTHOL, EUCALYPTOL, AND THYMOL. Treat 0.01 g. of the sample with 1 ml. concentrated sulfuric acid. Add 1 ml. of a solution of 1 g. vanillin or piperonal in 100 ml. sulfuric acid, mix, and add 1 ml. water or alcohol. A violet color indicates the presence of menthol or eucalyptol; a red color is formed in the presence of thymol.

CARLETTI TEST FOR α-NAPHTHOL.
α-naphthol in β-naphthol is detected by adding, to 2 ml. of the solution, 2 ml. saturated sodium carbonate solution, 0.5 ml. 10% potassium cyanide solution, and 1 ml. 1% cupric sulfate solution. A red-violet color indicates the presence of α-naphthol.

CARLETTI TEST REACTION FOR PYROGALLOL. Pyrogallol, when added to an alcoholic tartaric acid solution containing sulfuric acid, forms a violet color that disappears when the solution is diluted.

CARMINATIVE. Any drug that promotes the expulsion of gas from the gastrointestinal tract.

CARNAUBIC. Related to carnaubic acid, $C_{23}H_{47}COOH$.

CARNEY REAGENT. A solution of 2.5 g. tetramethyldiaminodiphenylmethane and 5 g. citric acid in 500 ml. water. When added to gold in solution the reagent forms a purple to blue color.

CARNOT CYCLE. An ideal cycle of four reversible changes in the physical condition of a substance, useful in thermodynamic theory. Starting with specified values of the variable temperature, **specific volume,** and pressure, the substance undergoes in succession (1) an **isothermal** (constant temperature) expansion, (2) an adiabatic expansion (see **adiabatic processes**), and (3) an isothermal compression to such a point that (4) a further adiabatic compression will return the substance to its original condition. These changes are represented on the volume-pressure diagram respectively by *ab*, *bc*, *cd*, and *da* in the accompanying figure. Or the cycle may be reversed: *a d c b a.*

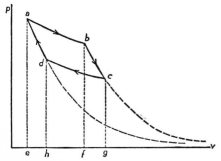

In the former (clockwise) case, heat is taken in from a hot source and work is done by the hot substance during the high-temperature expansion *ab*; also additional work is done at the expense of the thermal energy of the substance during the further expansion *bc*. Then a less amount of work is done on the cooled substance, and a less amount of heat discharged to the cool surroundings, during the low-temperature compression *cd*; and finally, by the further application of work during the compression *da*, the substance is raised to its original high temperature. The net result of all this is that a quantity of heat has been taken from a hot source and a portion of it imparted to something colder (a "sink"), while the balance is transformed into mechanical work represented by the area *abcd*. If the cycle takes place in the counterclockwise direction, heat is transferred from the colder to the warmer surroundings at the expense of the net amount of energy which must be supplied during the process (also represented by area *abcd*).

CARNOT REACTION FOR POTASSIUM. Add an aqueous solution of sodium thiosulfate to an aqueous solution of bismuth subnitrate. Filter off the precipitated double salt and dissolve it in ethyl alcohol. This reagent precipitates potassium quantitatively as yellow crystals.

CARNOT TEST FOR COBALT. An ammoniacal solution of cobalt is warmed with hydrogen peroxide, acidified with acetic acid, and then precipitated by ammonium molybdate.

CARNOY HARDENING SOLUTION. A solution of 2 g. chromic acid, 0.6 g. osmic acid, and 6 g. acetic acid in 130 ml. water, used in hardening biological preparations for microscopical examination.

CARNOY-LE BRUN FLUID. A mixture of equal parts of alcohol, acetic acid, and chloroform, saturated with mercuric chloride, and used as a fixative.

CARO REAGENT. A saturated solution of potassium persulfate in concentrated sulfuric acid, used as an oxidizing agent.

CARO TEST FOR PERSULFATE ION.
A 2% aqueous solution of aniline is added
to the persulfate solution. A brown or
orange brown color or a precipitate is
formed on standing or heating. The precipitate can be treated with benzene, resulting in the extraction of a substance which
is soluble in hydrochloric acid. A yellow
solution, turning violet on boiling, is obtained.

CARO TEST FOR SULFIDE. Mix the
solution to be tested with 2% of its volume
of fuming hydrochloric acid, add several
particles of *p*-aminodimethylaniline sulfate,
and then add 1–2 drops ferric chloride solution. A deep blue color on standing indicates sulfide.

**CAROBBIO TEST FOR ZINC OR
RESORCINOL.** A saturated solution of
zinc chloride in ammonia water gives a
yellow ring, changing to green and to blue,
with a layer of ether containing resorcinol.
This reaction can be used to test for zinc or
for resorcinol.

**CARON-RAQUET TEST FOR MAN-
GANESE.** To 10 ml. of the solution to be
tested, add 2 ml. of a saturated aqueous
potassium oxalate solution, 1 ml. glacial
acetic acid, and a few drops potassium
hypochlorite solution. A red color indicates manganese. Various simplifications
have been proposed.

CARON SOLUTION. A solution of
0.005 g. diphenylamine in 100 ml. concentrated sulfuric acid, which is then diluted
with 40 ml. water and a little dilute hydrochloric acid. It is used as a test reagent
for nitrates, giving a blue color in their
presence.

CAROTENOID. One of a group of **lipo-
chromes** found in plants and animal tissues
(derived by animals from plant food).
Carotenoids include various chemical compounds, which closely resemble carotene
in their structures.

CARPENÉ SOLUTION. A solution of
20 g. zinc acetate in 80 ml. water, to which
is then added 12 ml. of a solution made by
neutralizing acetic acid with ammonium
hydroxide. Finally, add 8 ml. ammonium
hydroxide. This reagent is used in precipitating tannin from wine and other food
products.

CARR-PRICE REAGENT. A 30% solution of antimony trichloride in chloroform
used in the colorimetric determination of
vitamin A in foods.

CARR-PRICE TESTS FOR VITAMIN A.
(1) On adding 2 ml. of the **Carr-Price reagent** to 0.2 ml. of the oil to be tested a blue
color indicates the presence of vitamin A.
(2) Stannic chloride, dissolved in chloroform, gives with Vitamin A a deep blue
color changing to purple. (3) Anhydrous
ferric chloride, on addition to an oil containing Vitamin A, dissolved in chloroform, gives a fluorescent red-violet color.
(4) Powdered anhydrous aluminum chloride gives with an oil containing Vitamin A,
a red-violet color fading to brown.

CARRARA TEST. If carbazole is heated
on the steam bath with half its molecular-
weight ratio of salicylaldehyde and twice as
much sulfuric acid, a violet-red compound,
soluble in water or alcohol, is formed.

CARREL-DAKIN SOLUTION. An isotonic solution of sodium hypochlorite, used
as an antiseptic in surgical treatments. It
is prepared by dissolving 15.4 g. chlorinated
lime (U.S.P.), 6.4 g. sodium bicarbonate,
and 7.7 g. sodium carbonate in 1 liter of
water.

CARREZ REAGENT. A solution of 180 g.
lactic acid in 200 ml. potassium hydroxide
solution (sp. gr. 1.332) and 200 ml. water;
after boiling, and neutralization with acid
or alkali, as required, it is mixed with a
solution of 34.65 g. cupric sulfate crystals
in 250 ml. water, and diluted to 1 liter.

CARRIER METAL. A metal serving as
the base for supporting a second metal,
especially as applied in **photoelectric cells**,
where extremely thin films of the active
metal are used.

CARRIER, SPECTROSCOPIC. A material added to a sample to facilitate its
vaporization into an **excitation** source.

The carrier may serve to sweep the entire sample rapidly into the source or it may be limited in its action to assisting in the fractional distillation of the sample.

CARVACRYL. The radical

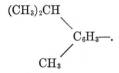

CASALE PROCESS. A process for the production of ammonia by the direct combination of nitrogen and hydrogen. Pressures of seven hundred atmospheres are used, the hydrogen is usually obtained by electrolysis of water, and part of the ammonia is recirculated to hold down temperatures in the catalyzer.

CASANOVA TEST REACTION. Lecithin is detected by shaking its solution in ether with a 10% aqueous solution of ammonium molybdate and floating the mixture on concentrated sulfuric acid. A reddish ring, changing to green and to deep blue, represents a positive test.

CASARES TEST. Citric acid is detected by evaporating to dryness 0.1 ml. of its solution on a water bath, cooling, and adding 0.5 ml. acetic anhydride and 2.5 ml. pyridine. A rose color on standing for 5 minutes indicates the presence of citric acid.

CASE HARDENING. A process for increasing the carbon content in the outer portion of a ferrous metal part. The object of case hardening is to produce hardening and resistance to wear on the surface, whereas the bulk of the metal has the toughness and resistance to shock of low carbon iron or steel. The process is carried out by heating the part in contact with readily reducible materials such as cyanides and other organic substances.

The term is also applied to denote a drying process of paints and varnishes in which the surface hardens, but the bulk of the material remains soft.

CASENEUVE TEST REACTIONS. Resorcinol is detected by adding a few drops of its solution to 3 ml. of a mixture of 10 ml.

ammonia, 5 ml. saturated aqueous sodium acetate solution, and 10 ml. 10% aqueous sodium nitroprusside solution. A green or blue-green color represents a positive test.

Nitroprusside is detected by the same color reaction, using a 10% resorcinol solution in ammonia.

Ammonia or amines are detected by the same color reaction using a solution of resorcinol and sodium nitroprusside.

CASOLORI REACTIONS FOR PEROXIDASE. Various dyes in their leucoforms indicate the presence of fresh milk, blood, rancidity in fats and similar hydrogen-acceptors. Instead of using leucoforms of dyes, the test may be performed by using as reagents substances which react to form the leuco-base, such as dimethylaniline, glacial acetic acid, and water.

CASOLORI SOLUTION FOR THIOSULFATE. A solution of 5 g. sodium nitroprusside in 95 ml. water, which is allowed to oxidize by exposure to air, used as a reagent for thiosulfate. A blue color represents a positive test.

CASPARIS REAGENT. A solution of cobalt thiocyanate diluted until a certain color (between violet-red and violet) is reached. This solution is used as a stain for plant tissues.

CASSAL-GORRAUS TEST REACTION. A test for borate, in which the solution tested is evaporated with curcumin and oxalic acid. The formation of a red-colored substance, soluble in alcohol and ether, indicates the presence of borate.

CAST. (1) To form a metallic shape or object by permitting molten metal to solidify in a mold. (2) A small, physiological product, found in urine, usually spherical in shape, or of roughly circular section, sometimes indicative of pathological conditions.

CASTELLANA TEST FOR BORATES. Vapors, formed on heating a substance in a test tube with excess potassium ethyl sulfate, burn with a green-edged flame if borates are present.

CASTELLANI TEST FOR SUCROSE IN MILK. To 1 ml. of the milk add 2 ml. of a 20% alcoholic solution of vanillin and 10 ml. concentrated hydrochloric acid, and maintain at 50° C. for 5 minutes. A red color indicates the presence of sucrose.

CASTETS TEST REACTION. Picric acid is detected by adding 1 drop of bromine water to 10 ml. of the aqueous solution to be tested, heating to boiling, and extracting with ether. The ethereal extract gives: (1) a red color if its evaporated residue is treated with ammonia gas, (2) a red color if its dried residue on paper is treated with ammonia, and (3) a red color (on drying) if 1% potassium cyanide solution is applied to the paper.

CASTIGLIONI TEST FOR PEROXIDE IN ETHER. The evaporated residue of the ether gives a bright red color on addition of 1 drop each of alcohol, benzaldehyde, and concentrated sulfuric acid.

CASTIGLIONI TEST FOR PYRIDINE. Paper moistened with a 1% quinoline solution, then with a solution containing pyridine, gives a golden-yellow color on exposure to ultraviolet light.

CASTIGLIONI TEST REACTIONS FOR NITRITE. (1) A solution containing nitrite gives a cherry red color when heated to boiling with a little sozoiodol (diiodo-p-phenolsulfonic acid).

(2) Alkaline nitrite solutions give a wine-red color when boiled with pyrocatechol.

(3) Aqueous solutions of nitrite give, with resorcinol or its alcoholic solution, a yellow color, changing to orange-red on heating.

CASTING. (1) A solid object made by the solidification of molten material in a mold. (2) The process, or art, of making castings.

CASTNER-KELLNER CELL. An industrial electrolytic cell, of multicompartment type, for the production of sodium hydroxide, chlorine, and hydrogen from sodium chloride. The electrolysis takes place in compartments, in which the sodium ions discharge upon an anode of metallic mercury with which the sodium amalgamates. Since the mercury anode is contained in the bottom of the cell, it is readily shifted, through openings at the base of the partitions, into other compartments, in which water is added to form sodium hydroxide and hydrogen by reacting with the sodium amalgam and liberating the mercury.

CASTNER PROCESS. A method of preparing metallic sodium by the electrolysis of fused sodium hydroxide to yield sodium and hydrogen at the cathode and oxygen at the anode.

CATABOLISM. The destruction of living matter by physiological processes within the living **organism,** with the formation of waste materials that are eliminated. (See **metabolism.**)

CATALYSIS. The process of changing the **velocity** of a chemical reaction by the presence of a substance that remains apparently chemically unaffected throughout the reaction. Berzelius (1836) applied this term to those reactions that do not progress unless a catalyst is present in the mixture. "Contact actions" (Mitscherlich) and "cyclic actions" (Brodie) have been suggested as names for the phenomenon. In general, the following rules hold true for all catalytic processes: The catalyst has the same composition at the beginning as at the end of the reaction. A small quantity of the catalyst is capable of effecting the transformation of an indefinitely large quantity of the reacting substance. No catalytic agent has power to start a chemical reaction; it may merely modify the velocity of that reaction. The catalyst has no effect upon the final state of equilibrium of the forward reaction with any opposing reactions. The velocity of two inverse reactions is affected in the same degree by a catalyst. Catalytic phenomena are classified according to two systems:

Ostwald Classification

I. Crystallization from supersaturated solutions.

II. Catalyses in homogeneous systems.

III. Catalyses in heterogeneous systems.

IV. Action of the enzymes.

Henri and Larguier des Bancels' Classification

I. Reactions induced by one catalytic agent.
  (i) Simple contact action.
  (ii) Formation of intermediate compounds.
II. Reactions which take place in the presence of two catalysts.
  (i) The two catalysts produce the same final products.
    (1) Simple contact action.
      (a) Catalysts have no action on one another.
      (b) Catalysts mutually influence each other's action.
    (2) Formation of intermediate compounds.
  (ii) The two catalysts produce different reactions.
  (iii) Two consecutive reactions are produced by the two catalysts.

Instances of catalysis may be found in the hydrolysis of esters by dilute acids; in the "contact process" for the manufacture of sulfuric acid; in the hydrogenation (1) of nitrogen to produce ammonia, (2) of carbon monoxide to produce methyl alcohol, or synthetic fuels, (3) of coal to produce oils, and (4) of liquid fats to produce solid fats; in the cracking, isomerization or alkylization of petroleum to produce improved fuels; the action of enzymes, although these catalysts do not appear capable of inducing the transformation of indefinitely large quantities of material; and in the retardation of the oxidation of sulfites by free oxygen in the presence of alcohol. Catalysis may be positive, as when the reaction velocity is accelerated; or negative, as when the catalyst retards the reaction.

CATALYSIS, DUAL THEORY OF. A concept of catalytic activity occurring in solution which recognized the existence of a catalytic effect exhibited by acids and their **dissociation** products, especially hydrogen ion. More recent investigations have revealed that a large number of other ions also possess this property.

CATALYSIS, PSEUDO-. A term used to denote a catalytic process in which the catalyst takes part in the reaction but is ultimately transformed back into its original form. The process is frequently described as a "cyclic action."

CATALYST. A substance that influences the rate of a chemical reaction but remains apparently chemically unchanged throughout the reaction (see **catalysis**).

CATALYST, NEGATIVE. A substance that retards the rate of a chemical reaction but remains apparently chemically unchanged throughout the reaction.

CATALYSTS, JOINT EFFECT OF TWO. If two **catalysts** which influence the same reaction are added to the **reaction** mixture, the net effect differs from that produced when either component is used by itself in the mixture. For example, the observed rate may be greater than that calculated by adding the rates obtained individually with the two constituents. Alternately, the reaction might be retarded by use of two catalysts. An example of the former case is given by naphthalene which is oxidized by sulfuric acid in the presence of a mixture of cupric and mercuric sulfates. The oxidation process with this mixture is much faster than the sum of the oxidation rates obtained with cupric and mercuric sulfates separately.

CATALYTIC COEFFICIENT. The velocity constant of a catalytic reaction.

CATALYTIC POISON. A material that reduces or nullifies the effect of a **catalyst**, such as by changing its chemical composition or physical condition, by coating its surface, by being adsorbed upon it, or by other means.

CATALYTIC POLYMERIZATION PROCESS. A process for the polymerization of hydrocarbon gases, usually consisting chiefly of paraffins and olefins, by catalytic action, to yield gasolines and other liquid products.

CATAPHORESIS. The migration of a sol through its medium toward anode or cathode under the influence of an electric charge. It is due to the establishment of potential differences at the interface between liquid and solid which results in displacement of one phase against the other when electricity is passed through the system or it is electrified. Positive sols (metallic hydroxides, etc.) migrate to the **cathode,** and negative sols (metals, etc.) migrate to the **anode.** Called also **electroendosmosis.**

CATELECTRODE. The **cathode** (q.v.).

CATHARTIC. A drug that causes action of the bowels to eliminate feces.

CATHODE. The negative pole of a battery, cell, discharge tube, or other electrical system.

CATHODE RAY (CATHODE STREAM). A stream of **electrons** discharged from the **cathode** of a **vacuum tube.** The emitted electrons are capable of causing phosphorescence, chemical changes, mechanical effects; they can raise the temperature of bodies which are subjected to their bombardment, penetrate solids, cause mechanical effects, and give rise to **x-rays.**

CATHOLYTE. The liquid found in the immediate neighborhood of the **cathode** during **electrolysis.**

CATHOTOMETER. (Kathetometer) An instrument for accurate measurement of differences in height. It consists of a horizontal telescope mounted upon an adjustable standard which is graduated. The telescope is focused on the lower edge of the object to be measured and a reading is taken; it is then elevated to the upper edge end and a second reading taken. The difference between the readings is the distance between the heights. The instrument gives very accurate results.

CATION. A positively-charged **ion.** Cations are those ions that carry the positive current in a cell and are deposited on the cathode; or the positively-charged ions of a gas. They travel in the nominal direction of the current. In electrochemical reactions they are designated by a dot or a plus sign placed above and behind the atomic symbol, as H $\cdot$ or H$^+$, the number of dots or plus signs indicating the **valence** of the ion. (See **cell, ion, anion.**)

CATIONIC CURRENT. That portion of the total current which is carried by the cations.

CATIONOTROPHY. An ionization of certain **tautomeric** organic compounds, whereby one of their equilibrium forms dissociates into a simple **cation** (such as H$^+$) and a complex **anion.**

CATTELAIN TEST REACTION. Phenols give an orange-red color when a little benzoylacrylic acid is added to their sulfuric acid solutions. (Diphenols require warming to give this color.)

CAUCHY FORMULA. An expression of the relationship between the **index of refraction** of a medium and the **wave length** of the light for which it is determined. It is of the form:

$$n = A + \frac{B}{\lambda^2} + \frac{C}{\lambda^4} + \cdots$$

where n is the index of refraction, λ is the wave length, and $A, B, C, \ldots$ are constants.

CAUSTIC. A term which has the general meaning of corrosive and is applied to the water-soluble hydroxides of the light metals to distinguish them from their carbonates. It is also used in medicine to designate substances that destroy body tissues; thus lunar caustic is silver nitrate.

CAUSTIC EMBRITTLEMENT. The development of brittleness in metals such as steel or ferrous alloys upon prolonged exposure to alkaline substances, like caustic soda, in solution. Failures and explosions in boilers and evaporators have been caused by this action.

CAVALLI SOLUTION. A solution of 2 g. resorcinol in 15 ml. sulfuric acid and 20 ml. water, used to detect cottonseed oil in olive oil. A characteristic series of color changes is obtained if the test is positive.

CAVITATION. A method of producing a vapor-liquid **emulsion** by reduction of the hydrodynamic pressure within the liquid to a value below the vapor pressure.

CAZENEUVE-DÉFOURNEL TEST. A modified **Kersting test** for nitrite in water. The evaporated residue is treated with 0.05 g. brucine and 20 ml. water and evaporated again. On addition to the residue of a few drops of formic acid, water, and a little hydrogen peroxide, a pink color after standing for 15 minutes indicates the presence of nitrite.

CAZENEUVE REAGENT FOR METALS. Diphenylcarbazide, which gives characteristic colors with many metal ions and is used in quantitative determinations for several of them.

CAZENEUVE SOLUTION FOR OXYGEN. A solution of 1 g. m-phenylenediamine in 100 g. alcohol.

Cb Symbol for the element columbium, which is now named **niobium** (q.v.).

Cd Symbol for the element **cadmium** (q.v.).

Ce Symbol for the element **cerium** (q.v.).

Cel. (From "celeritas.") A unit of **velocity** defined as the velocity given to one gram by a force of one **dyne** acting for one second; in other words, as one centimeter per second.

CELL. (Electrochemical) An apparatus for the transformation of chemical into electrical energy or the reverse. The essential parts of the cell are the containing vessel, the electrodes, and the **electrolyte** solution. The electrodes are usually plates of metal or carbon immersed in the electrolyte solution; the electrode by which the current leaves the cell is termed the cathode, and that through which the current enters is called the anode. The mechanism of the generation of electrical energy is this: the electrolyte is ionized, the anions migrate toward the anode while the cations travel to the cathode. At the anode the anions are discharged, and either combine with the metal or are deposited upon it, the cations simultaneously pick up electrons from the cathode in amount sufficient to neutralize their own charge, and deposit upon it. The charges of the ions are thus

communicated to the electrodes and appear in the outside circuit. The heat ordinarily evolved by the reaction does not appear in the cell inasmuch as the chemical energy having been converted into electrical energy, the heat change is small.

(Biological) The structural unit composing living matter, consisting of a nucleus and body, each containing various specialized units and composed of a dynamic protoplasmic system.

(Technical) A container or apparatus containing an absorbing substance.

CELL, ALKALI. An evacuated or gas cell with alkali metal electrodes, used in **photoelectric** (q.v.) measurements.

CELL, ALLEN-MOORE. See **Allen-Moore cell.**

CELL, CADMIUM. See **cadmium cell.**

CELL, CASTNER-KELLNER. See **Castner-Kellner cell.**

CELL, CHROMATOPHORE. A biological cell containing colored substances.

CELL, CLARKE'S. See **Clarke cell.**

CELL, COMBINATION. An **electrolytic** cell in which one electrode is composed of an active metal (such as zinc) and the other electrode of an active nonmetal (such as chlorine) and current is produced in an external circuit by the formation of ions at the electrodes (zinc ions at the zinc electrode and chlorine ions at the chlorine electrode). It is called a combination cell because the cell reaction is the same as the combination reaction between the metal and nonmetal.

CELL, CONCENTRATION. An electrical cell in which an e.m.f. is obtained by using two solutions of the same electrolyte at different concentrations. The electrodes are commonly of the same element. For example, a cell consisting of two chambers connected by a salt bridge, one containing N copper sulfate solution and the other 0.01 N copper sulfate solution, and each chamber having a copper electrode, would constitute a concentration cell.

The term is sometimes applied to a cell having electrodes containing the same active substance, but differing in its concentration because of varying dilution by another substance.

CELL, CONDUCTIVITY. See **conductivity cell.**

CELL CONSTANT. The ratio of the distance between two electrodes in a conductivity cell to the area of each electrode. It can be measured directly or determined by using a solution of known specific conductance.

CELL, DANIELL. See **Daniell cell.**

CELL, DAUGHTER. A biological cell produced directly from another cell, as by division.

CELL, DIFFUSION. A chamber used for the extraction of soluble materials from mixtures with insoluble solids. The process is slow, because of the time required for diffusion from the interior of the mass, and, therefore, countercurrent flow is usually employed and sufficient capacity provided to give ample time for the process to be completed.

CELL, DISPLACEMENT. An electrolytic cell in which the essential chemical reaction is the **ionization** and entry into solution of atoms of one element, and the **discharge** and deposition from solution of the ions of another. A well-known displacement cell is the Daniell cell, in which metallic zinc dissolves in a zinc sulfate solution, yielding zinc ions, while copper ions are discharged and deposited from a copper sulfate solution, with accompanying flow of electricity in an external circuit.

CELL, DOWNS. See **Downs cell.**

CELL, ECHELON. A hollow glass vessel of triangular horizontal cross-section used in absorption **spectrography,** because of its convenience in adjusting the thickness of the layer of the absorbing liquid to any value up to that represented by the altitude of the triangle constituting the section of the cell.

CELL, GAS. See **gas cell.**

CELL, GIANT. A biological cell so much larger than the mean size of its type that it may be regarded as abnormal.

CELL, GRAVITY. A primary cell in which the separation between the two ionic solutions is maintained by means of gravity. An example is the **Daniell cell** in which a cupric sulfate solution in contact with a copper electrode is below a zinc sulfate solution in contact with a zinc electrode. The difference in specific gravity of the solutions prevents, or at least retards, mixing.

CELL, GROVE. See **Grove cell.**

CELL, HALL-HÉROULT. See **Hall-Héroult cell.**

CELL, HARGREAVES-BIRD. See **Hargreaves-Bird cell.**

CELL, LECLANCHÉ. See **Leclanché cell.**

CELL, OXIDATION AND REDUCTION. A cell in which the electric energy is produced by the interaction of a reducing and an oxidizing substance in separate solutions, each bathing an electrode.

CELL, PHOTOELECTRIC. See **photoelectric cell.**

CELL, PRIMARY. A system in which electrical energy is obtained as the result of a chemical reaction or reactions. Although the reactions are usually reversible, the primary cell is not arranged to operate reversibly, cells so constructed being called secondary cells. Primary cells consist commonly of an electrode of a metal or other substance in contact with a solution containing its ions, and the solution being electrolytically connected, in a manner that will avoid mixing, with another solution in contact with another electrode. To complete the circuit, electrical contact is made between the electrodes, commonly through an external circuit which consumes the electrical energy produced by the cell.

CELL, SECONDARY. An electrolytic cell in which the interacting substances may be restored to their original chemical form by sending a direct current of electricity through the cell in reverse direction to that of the discharge. Secondary cells are commonly used to store and furnish electricity.

CELL, SODERBERG. See **Soderberg cell.**

CELL, STANDARD. An electrochemical cell designed to furnish a known, standard voltage.

CELL, TRANSITION. (1) In electrochemistry, a voltaic cell containing an electrolyte which undergoes a chemical transition that is accompanied by a corresponding electromotive force, and that usually occurs at a definite temperature. (2) In biology, a living cell with characteristics between two other types of cells, into which it may change, under suitable conditions.

CELL, VORCE. See **Vorce cell.**

CELLULOSE NUMBER. A cellulose solubility number; the amount or proportion by weight of a cellulose-containing material that dissolves in a sodium hydroxide solution of a specified concentration at a specified temperature. These test conditions are such that cellulose itself does not dissolve.

CELS. Celsius. Used occasionally instead of the abbreviation "C" for Centigrade.

CELSI REACTION FOR GALLIC AND TANNIC ACIDS. A cherry red color is obtained on heating either of these acids with glacial acetic acid and a few drops of formaldehyde and hydrochloric acid.

CELSI REACTION FOR MALIC ACID. Add 2 ml. concentrated sulfuric acid containing orcin to 2 or 3 drops of the solution to be tested, heat for 5 minutes on the water bath, cool, and add 10 ml. water. On cooling and adding concentrated ammonium hydroxide, a fluorescence indicates the presence of malic acid.

CELSI REAGENT FOR POTASSIUM. Two solutions: (1) 7 g. of cobalt nitrate dissolved in 50 ml. 80% methyl alcohol; and (2) 19 g. sodium thiosulfate dissolved in 50 ml. water. These solutions are used in testing for potassium. A blue precipitate represents a positive test for potassium.

CELSIUS. Equivalent to **Centigrade.**

CEMENT. Any material that can be prepared in plastic form and that hardens to bond together various solid surfaces or entities; or Portland cement, a complex mixture of calcium silicates and aluminates, obtained by roasting a mixture of clays and calcareous substances and grinding the product.

CEMENTATION. The process of surrounding a solid body with a powder of some substance with which it is desired to combine it and heating the whole to some temperature below fusion. The solid combines with the powder and the resulting compound gradually diffuses through the object being cemented. Thus wrought iron is converted into steel by heating with powdered charcoal.

CENTER OF GRAVITY. See **center of mass.**

CENTER OF MASS. A more accurate term for the point commonly called the center of gravity. If a body is regarded as composed of infinitesimal elements of mass, and if each of these elements is acted upon in the same direction, chosen at random, by a force proportional to its mass, the resultant of this set of parallel forces always passes through a certain point, which is the center of mass of the body. Since the weight of the particles of a small body constitutes approximately such a series of forces, it has become customary to call this point the center of gravity, although it is in general not strictly correct to do so.

CENTIGRADE (CELSIUS). Abbreviated C. or Cels. A **thermometric scale** based on the fusion point of water under standard pressure for 0°, and the boiling point of water under standard pressure for 100°.

CENTIGRAM. One one-hundredth of a gram.

CENTILITER. One one-hundredth of a liter.

CENTIMETER. One one-hundredth of a meter.

CENTIMETER CUBE. Any solid figure whose length, breadth, and thickness are each one centimeter. The volume of such a solid is one cubic centimeter. The distinction is made because a cubic centimeter is not restricted to any definite shape and, in certain measurements, especially electrochemical, the dimensions of the cubic centimeter become highly important.

CENTINORMAL. One one-hundredth normal.

CENTIPOISE. The standard unit of viscosity. Water at 20° C. has a viscosity of one centipoise, or 0.01 poise.

CENTRAL FORCES. Forces between interacting systems which depend only on the distance between their centers.

CENTRIFUGAL. Moving outward or directed outward, in the sense of away from a center.

CENTRIFUGE. An apparatus for the separation of substances by the application of centrifugal force.

CENTRIPETAL. Moving inward, or directed inward, in the sense of toward a center.

CENTRON. A term proposed to designate the atomic **nucleus.**

CERAMICS. The art and science of producing articles from clay, especially when the process requires firing or baking.

CERATE. A product made from lard, or from oil with waxes or resins; or a compound containing the cerotic radical

$$C_{25}H_{51}C \overset{\displaystyle O}{\underset{\displaystyle O-}{\big\|}} \quad .$$

CERBELAND TESTS OF HAIR-DYEING SUBSTANCES. On adding 5 drops of Javelle water and 1 drop 1:10 hydrochloric acid to 5 ml. of an alcoholic solution of a hair dye diluted if necessary, colors are obtained, characteristic of the various amino and phenolic compounds used as ingredients. Variations of these colors may be obtained by adding hydrochloric acid to the above tests, or by treating the dye solution with sodium nitrite and then with hydrochloric acid, or by treating it with ferric chloride.

CERDEIRAS SOLUTION. A solution of 0.5 g. vanillin in 5 ml. alcohol, which is then made up to 100 ml. with hydrochloric acid. This reagent gives characteristic colors with certain volatile oils.

CEREBRAL DEPRESSANT. A drug that has a specific depressive (i.e. sedative) action upon the central nervous system.

CEREBRAL STIMULANT. A drug that has a specific stimulating action upon the central nervous system.

CERENKOV COUNTER. An apparatus for detecting the Cerenkov radiation (see **radiation, Cerenkov**) and determining its directional characteristics.

CERENKOV RADIATION. See **radiation, Cerenkov.**

CERIC. (1) A salt of cerium in which the metal is quadrivalent. (2) A product from wax.

CERIOMETRY. **Titrimetric** analysis using ceric sulfate as a standard oxidizing solution.

CERIUM. Rare earth metallic element. Atomic number 58. Atomic weight 140.13. Density 6.9. Specific heat 0.0448. Melting point 640° C. Boiling point 1400° C. Valence 3 and 4. Cerium forms ceric and cerous compounds.

CEROTIC. Related to cerotic acid,

$$C_{26}H_{53}COOH.$$

CEROUS. Containing trivalent **cerium.**

CERYL. The aliphatic hydrocarbon radical $C_{26}H_{53}-$.

CESIUM. Metallic element. Symbol Cs. Atomic number 55. Atomic weight 132.91. Density 1.87. Specific heat 0.04817. Melting point 28.5° C. Boiling point 670° C. Valence 1.

CETANE RATING. A system of rating oils for use in Diesel engines, defined as the percentage of cetane in a mixture with α-methyl naphthalene, which gives the same ignition performance as the fuel tested. The criterion of ignition performance is the direct **ignition lag.**

CETYL. The radical $CH_3(CH_2)_{14}CH_2-$, preferably called hexadecyl.

Cf Symbol for the element **californium.**

C.G.S. SYSTEM. See **metric system.**

CHADWICK-GOLDHABER EFFECT. A term applied to nuclear reactions (see **reaction, nuclear**) brought about by bombardment with **gamma radiations.**

CHAIN. A series of **atoms** connected by **bonds,** forming the skeleton of a number of derivatives. The carbon chains are the most important.

CHAIN, BRANCHED. A chain of **atoms** which forks or branches off from another chain when the compound is designated by a structural formula.

CHAIN, CLOSED. When the terminal **atoms** of a chain mutually combine, the series forms a ring and the chain is said to be "closed." Such closed chains, or rings, are of great importance in organic chemistry.

CHAIN, FORKED. A chain which divides at some point, producing two new chains attached to the parent chain. Isopentane,

$$CH_3CH_2CH \begin{array}{c} \diagup CH_3 \\ \diagdown CH_3 \end{array}$$

contains a forked chain.

CHAIN, LATERAL OR SIDE. A chain of atoms combined with a longer chain, which may be either open or ring-shaped.

$$CH_3CH_2CH_2CH-CH_2CH_3$$
$$|$$
$$CH_2$$
$$|$$
$$CH_2$$
$$|$$
$$CH_3$$

or $CH_2CH_2CH_3$

In either case the propyl group is the lateral or side chain.

CHAIN REACTION. A series of self-perpetuating successive reactions. The concept was first postulated in regard to the photochemical combination of hydrogen and chlorine. In this process, the two reactions:

$$Cl + H_2 \rightarrow HCl + H$$
$$H + Cl_2 \rightarrow HCl + Cl$$

occur rapidly to regenerate the chlorine and hydrogen atoms, which can then bring about further combination of hydrogen and chlorine to yield hydrogen chloride. Thus, the initial presence of a few hydrogen or chlorine atoms can start the chain reaction, which continues until one or both of the reactants are consumed, or until removal of the hydrogen or chlorine atoms from the system breaks the chain.

The concept of chain reactions applies to many other thermal and photochemical reactions.

CHAINOMATIC. Pertaining to a method of weighing by means of a chain, one end of which is attached to one arm of a **balance** and the other end to a vertical slider. The amount of weight applied by the chain is adjusted by varying the position of the slider, which moves over a vertical scale. The use of small-size weights or of riders is eliminated in this method of weighing.

CHAKRAVARTI-ROY TEST REACTION. A microtest for procaine or primary amines. If a small quantity of such substances, or their solutions, are mixed on a microscope slide with a drop of 4 g. *p*-dimethylaminobenzaldehyde solution in 480 ml. alcohol and 80 ml. concentrated hydrochloric acid, a greenish-yellow color is positive indication for the presence of procaine or primary amines.

CHALMOT TEST. Furfural or methylfurfural solutions in alcohol, when mixed with a 1% alcoholic solution of aniline, give a red color on addition of acetic acid. The color disappears in sunlight; returns with hydrochloric acid.

CHAMBER ACID. The direct product of the lead chambers in the manufacture of sulfuric acid. It is a dilute acid that contains 62 to 70% of sulfuric acid.

CHAMBER, CLOUD. See **cloud chamber.**

CHAMBER, IONIZATION. See **ionization chamber.**

CHAMBER PROCESS. A process for the manufacture of sulfuric acid by the reaction of sulfur dioxide, air, and steam, in lead chambers, in the presence of oxides of nitrogen. The various substances react to form an intermediate compound, or compounds, containing nitrogen, which are subsequently hydrolyzed by the water to yield sulfuric acid and to release the oxides of nitrogen.

CHAMPY FIXATIVE. A mixture of **7** parts of a 1% aqueous solution of chromic acid, 7 parts of a 3% aqueous solution of potassium dichromate, and 4 parts of a 2% aqueous solution of osmic acid, used as a fixative for animal materials.

CHANCE-CLAUS PROCESS. An old process for the recovery of sulfur from alkali wastes of the **Leblanc Process** (q.v.) that are burned to yield sulfur dioxide.

CHANCEL TEST. Secondary alcohols are detected by warming 1 ml. of the alcohol with 1 ml. nitric acid (sp. gr. 1.35), diluting with water, and extracting with ether. The evaporated residue of this extract on

solution in alcohol, and treatment with alcoholic potassium hydroxide, yields yellow prisms if the alcohol tested was a secondary alcohol.

CHANG-KAO REAGENT. The compound 2,4,6-trinitrobenzoyl chloride, used as a reagent for alcohols.

CHANGE OF STATE. Transformation from one to another of the three states of matter — gaseous, liquid, or solid.

CHANNEL POINT. The pour point of a lubricant, usually determined by aeration and chilling.

CHAPMAN EQUATION. An equation expressing the **viscosity** of a gas in terms of certain molecular constants. This relationship has been simplified to the expression:

$$\eta = \frac{5m\bar{c}}{\sqrt{2}\pi\sigma^2(1 + c/T)}$$

in which η is the viscosity, m is the mass of a molecule, $\bar{c}$ is its average speed, σ is the collision diameter of the molecule, c is **Sutherland's constant,** and T is the absolute temperature.

CHAPMAN REARRANGEMENT. The transformation of imido esters (alkyl or aryl) into substituted amides by heating.

$$R'C\substack{OR'' \\ \shortparallel}=NR''' \xrightarrow{\Delta} R'CO \cdot NR''R'''.$$

CHAPMAN TEST FOR ISOMERIC ALLYL AND PROPENYL PHENOLS. A solution (1:5) of the phenol in acetic anhydride gives characteristic colors on addition of 1 drop concentrated sulfuric acid, and gives other colors on the addition of a particle of zinc chloride.

CHAR. (1) To carbonize. (2) To burn slightly. (3) Charcoal, especially animal charcoal which is also called "animal or bone char."

CHARACTERISTIC CURVE, COUNTER. See **counter characteristic curve.**

CHARACTERISTIC X-RAYS. See **x-rays, characteristic.**

CHARACTERIZATION FACTOR. A relationship between the **boiling point** and **specific gravity** of a liquid, widely used in the petroleum industry as an aid in the investigation of oils. It is of the form:

$$K = \frac{\sqrt[3]{T}}{S}$$

where T is the average boiling point in degrees Rankine ($°$ F. $+ 460$), S is the specific gravity at $60°$ F., and K is the characterization factor.

CHARAUX TEST REACTIONS. Chlorogenic acid in aqueous solution gives a green color with ferric chloride solution, changing to blue on addition of sodium hydroxide solution. If only sodium hydroxide is added to the chlorogenic acid solution, a rose-red color, changing to yellow with acids, is obtained.

CHARDONNET NITROCELLULOSE PROCESS. A process for the manufacture of a rayon fiber by nitrating cellulose with nitric and sulfuric acids, dissolving the product in ether and alcohol, forcing the solution through very fine openings into a stream of warm air; the nitrocellulose thread formed is then denitrated in an alkaline sulfide bath.

CHARGE. A more or less definite quantity of matter or energy, as a quantity of electricity on a given body or in a given region, or the quantity of material in a reacting chamber or processing vessel.

CHARGE, ATOMIC. See **atomic charge.**

CHARGE, ELEMENTARY. The unit charge of electricity, the charge on the electron, approximately 4.8022×10^{-10} electrostatic units or 1.6019×10^{-19} coulombs.

CHARLES' LAW. See **law of Charles.**

CHARPY TEST. An impact-fracture test for metals, which gives a value representative of the **impact strength** of the metal.

CHASER. A mill used for a wide variety of grinding operations throughout the process industries. It consists of a shallow pan in which stone rollers turn about a central axis.

CHATILLON FURNACE. A furnace for production of antimony trioxide in which the stibnite ore is charged upon a liquating shelf from which the molten sulfide drops upon incandescent material on the upper grates. In falling, it is largely oxidized by the oxygen-bearing gases from the lower and upper grates.

CHAULMOOGROYL. The radical

$$\begin{array}{c} CH=CH \\ | \qquad \diagdown \\ \qquad\qquad CH(CH_2)_{12}CO- \\ | \qquad \diagup \\ CH_2-CH_2 \end{array}$$

(from chaulmoogric acid).

CHAULMOOGRYL. The radical

$$\begin{array}{c} CH=CH \\ | \qquad \diagdown \\ \qquad\qquad CH(CH_2)_{12}CH_2- \\ | \qquad \diagup \\ CH_2-CH_2 \end{array}$$

(from chaulmoogryl alcohol).

CHAVASTELON TEST REACTION. Acetylene combines with silver nitrate in alcoholic or aqueous solution to give the addition product acetylene-silver.

CHELATE COMPOUND. A compound containing a **chelate ring** (q.v.).

CHELATE RING. A ring structure formed by hydrogen bonding (see **bond, hydrogen**). For example, the lack of **association** indicated by the high volatility of the enol form of acetoacetic ester is attributed to the formation of a chelate ring;

$$\begin{array}{c} H-C-C-OC_2H_5 \\ \diagup\diagup \qquad\quad \diagdown\diagdown \\ CH_3C \qquad\qquad\quad O \\ \diagdown \qquad\qquad \diagup \\ O-H \end{array}$$

The hydrogen bond links the hydrogen atom of the hydroxyl group and the carbonyl oxygen atom.

CHELLE TEST REACTION. Alanine and glycocoll are converted to the hydroxyacids by nitrous acid, which are identified by **Denigés' reactions** for lactic and glycolic acids.

CHEMICAL ACTION. A chemical reaction, or a change in the chemical composition of a substance or system.

CHEMICAL ASSOCIATION. See **association, chemical.**

CHEMICAL COMBINATION. See **reaction, combination.**

CHEMICAL COMPOUND. See **compound.**

CHEMICAL DISPLACEMENT. See **reaction, displacement.**

CHEMICAL DISSOCIATION. See **reaction, dissociation.**

CHEMICAL ENERGY. See **energy, chemical.**

CHEMICAL ENTITY. One of the elementary particles or groups involved in chemical reactions as **electrons, atoms, ions, radicals, molecules,** or associated molecules.

CHEMICAL EQUATION. An expression, in symbols, of the substances that enter into a chemical **reaction,** and those that result from it, with numerical coefficients to indicate the proportionate number of **moles** of each substance that enters into the reaction, or the proportionate number of **gram-atomic weights** of each atom or ion. Thus the equation

$$2HCl + Na_2CO_3 = 2NaCl + H_2O + CO_2 \uparrow$$

indicates that hydrochloric acid reacts with sodium carbonate to produce sodium chloride, water, and carbon dioxide. The proportions in which these substances enter the reaction are 2 moles of hydrochloric acid (one mole of hydrochloric acid is $1.008 + 35.457 = 36.465$ grams — see table of **atomic weights** for figures), one mole of sodium carbonate (106.0 grams) to yield 2 moles of sodium chloride (one mole

of sodium chloride is 58.457 grams), one mole of water (18.016 grams), and one mole of carbon dioxide (44.0 grams). The symbol $\uparrow$ is sometimes used to indicate a gas that may escape, or partly escape, from the system; the symbol $\downarrow$, to designate a precipitate. Also, the symbol for equality ($=$) is usually replaced by the symbol $\rightarrow$, particularly when a reaction is irreversible, while the symbol $\rightleftarrows$ is used for reversible reactions.

CHEMICAL EQUILIBRIUM. See **equilibrium, chemical.**

CHEMICAL EQUILIBRIUM, LAW OF. See **law of chemical equilibrium.**

CHEMICAL NOMENCLATURE AND PRONUNCIATION. Based on the "Report of the Commission on the Reform of the Nomenclature of Organic Chemistry," from the translation published in the *Journal of the American Chemical Society,* Vol. 55, No. 10, p. 3905, October, 1933.

The subject is treated under the following general headings: I. General. II. Hydrocarbons. 1. Saturated Hydrocarbons. 2. Unsaturated Hydrocarbons. 3. Cyclic Hydrocarbons. III. Fundamental Heterocyclic Compounds. IV. Simple Functions. V. Complex Functions. VI. Radicals. VII. Numbering.

I. General

1. As few changes as possible will be made in terminology universally adopted.

2. For the present, only the nomenclature of compounds of known constitution will be dealt with; the question of substances of imperfectly known constitution is postponed.

3. The precise form of words, endings, etc., prescribed in the rules should be adapted to the genius of each language by the subcommittees.

II. Hydrocarbons

4. The ending *ane* is adopted for saturated hydrocarbons. Open-chain hydrocarbons will have the generic name *alkanes.*

The name "alkane" is better and shorter than "paraffin," especially since the latter term is now so commonly applied to a solid mixture.

5. The present names of the first four normal saturated hydrocarbons (methane, ethane, propane, butane) are retained. Names derived from the Greek or Latin numerals will be used for those having more than four atoms of carbon.

6. Branched-chain hydrocarbons are regarded as derivatives of the normal hydrocarbons; their names will be referred to the longest normal chain present in the formula by adding to it the designations of the side chains. In case of ambiguity, or if a simpler name would result, that chain which admits of the maximum of substitutions will be selected as the fundamental chain.

If there are two or more choices for the longest chain, then that one should be chosen in which there is the greatest number of substitutions (the reason being that the substituting radicals, while more numerous, will be of simpler structure). Example:

$$CH_3CH_2CH_2CH_2CHCH_2CH_2CH_2CH_3$$
$$|$$
$$CH(CH_3)CH(CH_3)CH_3$$

By the principle of the "longest chain" the name would be 5-(1,2-dimethylpropyl)-nonane; but according to the rule the name 4-butyl-2,3-dimethyloctane (which avoids a branched side chain) is the one to be chosen if it seems simpler.

7. In case there are several side chains, the order in which such chains are named will correspond to the order of their complexity. The chain having the greatest number of secondary and tertiary atoms will be considered the most complex. The alphabetic order may also be followed in such cases.

8. In the names of open-chain unsaturated hydrocarbons having one double bond the ending *ane* of the corresponding saturated hydrocarbon will be replaced by the ending *ene;* if there are two double bonds, the ending will be *diene,* etc. These hydrocarbons will bear the generic names *alkenes, alkadienes, alkatrienes,* etc. Examples: propene, hexene, etc.

9. The names of triple-bond hydrocarbons will end in *yne, diyne,* etc. They will bear the generic name *alkynes.* Examples: propyne, heptyne, etc.

10. If there are both double and triple bonds in the fundamental chain the endings *enyne, dienyne,* etc., will be used. The generic names of these hydrocarbons will be *alkenynes, alkadienynes,* etc.

11. Saturated monocyclic hydrocarbons will take the names of the corresponding open-chain saturated hydrocarbons, preceded by the prefix *cyclo.* They will bear the generic name *cycloalkanes.*

12. When they are unsaturated, rules 8–10 will be applied. However, in the case of partially saturated polycyclic aromatic compounds the prefix *hydro,* preceded by *di-, tetra-,* etc., will be used. Example: dihydroanthracene.

13. Aromatic hydrocarbons will be denoted by the ending *ene* and will otherwise retain their customary names. However, the name *phene* may be used instead of *benzene.*

III. Fundamental Heterocyclic Compounds

14. The endings of customary names, endings which do not correspond to the function of the substance, will undergo the following modifications, so far as they are in accord with the genius of each language: (a) The ending *ol* will be changed to *ole.* Example: pyrrole. (b) The ending *ane* will be changed to *an.* Example: pyran.

The change from -*ol* to -*ole* is obviously for the purpose of reserving -ol as an ending for the names of alcohols and phenols; similarly, the change from -*ane* to -*an* is made in order to reserve -ane for saturated parent compounds.

15. When nitrogenous heterocycles not having the ending *ine* give basic compounds on progressive hydrogenation, such derivation will be indicated by the successive endings *ine, idine.* Examples: pyrrole, pyrroline, pyrrolidine; oxazole, oxazoline.

16. The ending *a* is adopted for hetero atoms occurring in a ring. Oxygen will accordingly be indicated by *oxa,* sulfur by *thia,* nitrogen by *aza,* etc. The letter *a* may be elided before a vowel. Examples: thiadiazole, oxadiazole, thiazine, oxazine.

While the universally accepted names of heterocyclic compounds are retained, the names of other heterocyclic compounds are derived from that of the corresponding homocyclic compound by adding to it the names of the hetero atoms ending in *a*. Example: 2,7,9-triazaphenanthrene.

IV. Simple Functions

17. Substances of simple function are defined as those containing a function of one kind only, which may be repeated several times in the same molecule.

That is to say, a compound which is an acid, an alcohol or an aldehyde and only that, is defined as a substance of simple function, while one which is at the same time an alcohol and an acid, or an acid and an aldehyde, is said to be a substance of complex function.

18. When there is only one functional group, the fundamental chain will be selected so as to contain this group. When there are several functional groups the fundamental chain will be selected so as to contain the maximum number of these groups.

19. Halogen derivatives will be designated by the name of the hydrocarbon from which they are derived, preceded by a prefix indicating the nature and number of the halogen atoms.

20. Alcohols and phenols will be given the name of the hydrocarbon from which they are derived, followed by the suffix *ol*. In accordance with rule 1 names universally adopted will be retained, as: phenol, cresol, naphthol, etc.

This nomenclature may also be applied to heterocyclics. Example: quinolinol.

21. In naming polyhydric alcohols or phenols, one of the forms *di*, *tri*, *tetra*, etc., will be inserted between the name of the parent hydrocarbon and the suffix *ol*. Example: CH_2OHCH_2OH, 1,2-ethanediol.

22. The name *mercaptan* as a suffix is abandoned; this function will be denoted by the suffix *thiol*. Examples: CH_3SH,

methanethiol; C_6H_5SH,   benzenethiol; CH_2SHCH_2SH, 1,2-ethanedithiol.

23. Ethers are considered as hydrocarbons in which one or several hydrogen atoms are replaced by alkoxy groups. However, for symmetrical ethers the present nomenclature may be retained. Examples: $CH_3OC_2H_5$,   methoxyethane; CH_3OCH_3, methoxymethane or methyl ether.

24. Oxygen linked, in a chain of carbon atoms, to two of these atoms will be denoted by the prefix *epoxy* in all cases where it would be unprofitable to name the substance as a cyclic compound. Examples: ethylene oxide = epoxyethane; epichlorohydrin = 3-chloro-1,2-epoxypropane; tetramethylene oxide = 1,4-epoxybutane.

25. Sulfides, disulfides, sulfoxides and sulfones will be named like the ethers, *oxy* being replaced by *thio*, *dithio*, *sulfinyl* and *sulfonyl*, respectively. Examples: CH_3SO_2-C_2H_5 methysulfonylethane; $CH_3SC_3H_7$, methylthiopropane;

$$CH_3CH_2CH_2SOCH_2CH_2CH_2CH_3,$$

1-(propylsulfinyl) butane.

26. Aldehydes are characterized by the suffix *al* added to the name of the hydrocarbon from which they are derived; thioaldehydes, by the suffix *thial*. Acetals will be named as 1,1-dialkoxyalkanes.

27. Ketones will receive the ending *one*. Diketones, triketones, thioketones will be designated by the suffixes *dione*, *trione*, *thione*.

28. The name *ketene* is retained.

"Ketene" (or, as spelled by some, "keten") is accordingly recognized as a name for the parent compound $CH_2=CO$.

29. For acids the rule of the Geneva nomenclature is retained. However, in cases where the use of that nomenclature would not be convenient the carboxyl group will be considered as a substituting group and the name of the acid will be formed by adding to the name of the hydrocarbon the suffix *carbonique* or *carboxylic*, according to the language.

30. Acids in which an atom of sulfur replaces an atom of oxygen will be named according to the Geneva nomenclature. Example: ethanethioic, -thiolic, -thionic, -thionothiolic. If the carboxyl is con-

sidered as a substituent the compounds will be named *carbothioic* acids. The suffix *carbothiolic* will be used if it is certain that the oxygen of the OH group is replaced by sulfur; the suffix *carbothionic* if it is the oxygen of the CO group; the suffix *carbodithioic* will be used if both oxygen atoms are replaced. Examples of the two systems of names: CH_3COSH or CH_3CSOH (either one), ethanethiolic acid, methanecarbothiolic acid; CH_3CSOH, ethanethionic acid, methanecarbothionic acid, CH_3CSSH, ethanethionothiolic acid, methanecarbodithioic acid.

31. The existing conventions will be retained for salts and esters. Examples: Sodium butanoate or sodium salt of butanoic acid; diethyl, 1,2-ethanedicarboxylate or diethyl ester of 1,2-ethanedicarboxylic acid; sodium acetate; methyl succinate.

32. Acid anhydrides will retain their present mode of designation according to the names of the corresponding acids. For names formed in accordance with the Geneva nomenclature, the amides, amidoximes, amidines, imides and nitriles will be named like the acids by adding to the name of the corresponding hydrocarbon the endings *amide*, *amidine*, *amidoxime*, *imide* and *nitrile*, respectively, while the halides will be named by combining *chloride*, etc., with the name of the radical. Examples: C_3H_7COCl, butanoyl chloride; $C_3H_7CONH_2$, butanamide; etc.

If the carboxyl is considered as a substituent the endings *carbonamide*, *carbonamidine*, *carbonamidoxime*, *carbonimide*, *carbonitrile* will be used. Examples: C_3H_7COCl, propanecarbonyl chloride; $C_3H_7CONH_2$, propanecarbonamide; etc.

33. The ending *ime* is reserved exclusively for nitrogenous bases. The present nomenclature of monoamines is retained. For polyamines, the name of the hydrocarbon will be followed by the suffixes *diamine*, *triamine*, etc.

For aliphatic compounds containing quinquivalent nitrogen the ending *ine* will be changed to *onium*. For cyclic substances containing quinquivalent nitrogen in the ring the ending *ine* will be changed to *inium;* for those with the ending *ole*, this will be changed to *olium*. Examples: pyridine, pyridinium; imidazole, imidazolium.

In accordance with the first sentence of this rule the spelling of names of non-bases ending in -ine should be changed; thus glycerine becomes glycerol, dextrine becomes dextrin, propine becomes propyne (see rule 9). Examples of names of amines: CH_3NH_2, methylamine; $(CH_3)_2NH$, dimethylamine; $(CH_3)_3N$, trimethylamine; $H_2NCH_2CH_2NH_2$, 1,2-ethanediamine; $C_6H_4(NH_2)_2$, benzenediamine.

34. The nomenclature of the derivatives of phosphorus, arsenic, antimony and bismuth, being very complicated, requires special consideration.

35. Oximes will be named by adding the suffix *oxime* to the name of the corresponding aldehyde, ketone or quinone. Examples: $C_2H_5ONH_2$, ethoxyamine; C_2H_5NHOH, ethylhydroxylamine.

36. The generic term *urea* is retained; it will be used as a suffix for the alkyl and acyl derivatives of urea. Examples: butylurea, $C_4H_9NHCONH_2$; butyrylurea, $C_3H_7CONHCONH_2$. The bivalent radical $-NHCONH-$ will be named *ureylene*.

37. The generic name *guanidine* is retained.

38. The name *carbylamine* is retained.

39. Isocyanic and isothiocyanic esters (RNCO, RNCS) will be named *isocyanates* and *isothiocyanates*.

40. The name *cyanate* is reserved for true esters which on saponification yield cyanic acid or its hydration products. The name *sulfocyanate* will be replaced by *thiocyanate*.

41. Nitro derivatives: no change in the present nomenclature. That is, the group NO_2 is always indicated by the prefix *nitro*, never by a suffix. Nitroso compounds are treated similarly (see rule 52). Examples: nitrosobenzene, 2,4,6-trinitrophenol.

42. Azo derivatives: the forms *azo, azoxy* are retained.

43. (a) Diazonium compounds, RN_2X, are named by addition of the suffix *diazonium* to the name of the parent substance (benzenediazonium chloride).

(b) Compounds having the same empirical formula but containing trivalent nitrogen will be named by replacing diazonium with *diazo* (benzenediazohydroxide).

(c) Substances of the type RN_2OM will be named *diazoates*.

(d) Compounds in which the two nitrogen atoms are united to a single carbon atom will be designated by the prefix *diazo* (diazomethane, diazoacetic acid).

44. Hydrazines are designated by the name of the alkyl radicals from which they are derived, followed by the suffix *hydrazine*. In cases where the amino group, of carbonamides is replaced by the hydrazino group, the suffix *hydrazide* will be used. Hydrazo derivatives are regarded as derivatives of hydrazine. Examples: CH_3NHNH_2, methylhydrazine; $C_2H_5NHNHC_3H_7$, 1-ethyl-2-propylhydrazine; $C_3H_7CONHNH_2$, butyrohydrazide or propanecarbohydrazide.

45. Hydrazones and semicarbazones are named like the oximes. The term *osazone* is retained.

46. The name *quinone* is retained.

47. Sulfonic and sulfinic acids will be designated by adding the suffixes *sulfonic* and *sulfinic* to the name of the hydrocarbon.

The analogous acids of selenium and tellurium will bear the names *alkaneselenonic* and *-seleninic* acids; *alkanetelluronic* and *-tellurinic* acids. Examples: $C_2H_5SO_3H$, ethanesulfonic acid; $C_{10}H_6(SO_2H)_2$, naphthalenedisulfinic acid.

48. Organometallic compounds will be designated by the names of the organic radicals united to the metal which they contain, followed by the name of the metal. Examples: dimethylzinc, tetraethyllead, methylmagnesium chloride.

However, if the metal is united in a complex manner it may be considered as a substituent. Example: $ClHgC_6H_4CO_2H$, chloromercuribenzoic acid.

49. The nomenclature of cyclic derivatives having side chains requires special consideration.

50. If it is necessary to avoid ambiguity, the names of complex radicals will be placed in parentheses. Examples: (dimethylphenyl)amine = $(CH_3)_2C_6H_3NH_2$; dimethylphenylamine = $C_6H_5N(CH_3)_2$.

V. Complex Functions

51. For compounds of complex function, that is to say, for compounds possessing different functions, only one kind of function (the principal function) will be expressed by the ending of the name. The other functions will be designated by appropriate prefixes.

52. The following prefixes and suffixes will be used for designating the functions.

Function	Prefix	Suffix
Acid and derivatives.	carboxy	carbonylic, carbonyl, carbonamide, etc., or oic, oyl, etc.
Alcohol............	hydroxy	ol
Aldehyde..........	oxo, aldo (for aldehyde O) or formyl (for CHO)	al
Amine.............	amino	amine
Azo derivative.....	azo	....
Azoxy derivative...	azoxy	....
Carbonitrile (nitrile)	cyano	carbonitrile or nitrile
Double bond.......	....	ene
Ether.............	alkoxy	....
Ethylene oxid, etc. .	epoxy	....
Halide............	halogeno [halo]	....
Hydrazine.........	hydrazino	hydrazine
Ketone............	oxo or keto	one
Mercaptan........	mercapto	thiol
Nitro derivative....	nitro	....
Nitroso derivative..	nitroso	....
Quinquivalent nitrogen.........	....	onium, inium [olium]
Sulfide............	alkylthio	....
Sulfinic derivative ..	sulfino	sulfinic
Sulfone............	sulfonyl	....
Sulfonic derivative..	sulfo	sulfonic
Sulfoxide..........	sulfinyl	....
Triple bond........	....	yne
Urea..............	ureido	urea

For the order used in the *Chemical Abstracts* indexes, see Patterson and Curran, *Journal of the American Chemical Society*, **39**, 1624 (1917).

53. The names of derivatives of fundamental heterocyclic substances will be formed according to the preceding rules. Example: Hydroxyquinolinecarbonamide, not quinolinolcarbonamide.

VI. Radicals

54. Univalent radicals derived from saturated aliphatic hydrocarbons by removal of one atom of hydrogen will be named by replacing the ending *ane* of the hydrocarbon by the ending *yl*.

Examples: methyl, ethyl, pentyl (or anyl), etc. Since isopropylidene is recognized (rule 56) it was no doubt the intention of the Committee to recognize isopropyl similarly.

55. The names of univalent radicals derived from unsaturated aliphatic hydrocarbons will have the endings *enyl*, *ynyl*, *dienyl*, etc., the positions of the double or triple bonds being indicated by numerals or letters where necessary. Examples: $CH_2=CH—$, ethenyl (or vinyl); $CH\equiv C—$, ethynyl; $CH_2-CH=CH-CH_2-$, 2-butenyl; $CH_2=CH-CH=CH—$, 1,3-butadienyl.

56. Bivalent or trivalent radicals derived from saturated hydrocarbons by removal of 2 or 3 hydrogen atoms from the same carbon atom will be named by replacing the ending *ane* of the hydrocarbon by the endings *ylidene* or *ylidyne*. For radicals derived from unsaturated hydrocarbons, these endings will be added to the name of the hydrocarbon. The names isopropylidene and methylene are retained.

57. The names of bivalent radicals derived from aliphatic hydrocarbons by removal of a hydrogen atom from each of the two terminal carbon atoms of the chain will be ethylene, trimethylene, tetramethylene, etc.

Only saturated radicals are provided for: $-CH_2CH_2-$, ethylene; $-CH_2CH_2CH_2-$, trimethylene, etc.

58. Radicals derived from acids by removal of OH will be named by changing the ending carboxylic to *carbonyl* or, if the Geneva nomenclature is used, oic to oyl. Examples: CH_3CO, ethanoyl or methanecarbonyl (or acetyl).

59. Univalent radicals derived from aromatic hydrocarbons by removal of a hydrogen atom from the ring will in principle be named by changing the ending *ene* to *yl*. However, the radicals C_6H_5 and $C_6H_5CH_2$ will continue provisionally to be named phenyl and benzyl, respectively. Moreover, certain abbreviations sanctioned by usage are authorized, as *naphthyl* instead of *naphthalyl*. Examples: $CH_3C_6H_4-$, tolyl (instead of toluyl), anthryl (instead of anthracyl), phenanthryl, fluoryl.

60. Univalent radicals derived from heterocyclic compounds by removal of hydrogen from the ring will be named by changing their endings to *yl*. In cases where this would give rise to ambiguity, merely the final *e* will be changed to *yl*. Examples: pyridine, pyridyl; indole, indoyl; pyrroline, pyrrolinyl; triazole, triazolyl; triazine, triazinyl.

61. Radicals formed by removal of a hydrogen atom from a side chain of a cyclic compound will be regarded as substituted aliphatic radicals. Examples: $C_6H_5CH_2CH_2-$, (2-phenylethyl); $C_6H_5CH=CHCH_2-$, (3-phenyl-2-propenyl).

62. In general, special names will not be given to multivalent radicals, derived from cyclic compounds by removal of several hydrogen atoms from the ring. In this case prefixes or suffixes will be used. Examples: triaminobenzene or benzenetriamine; dihydroxypyrrole or pyrrolediol.

63. The order in which prefixes or radicals are stated (alphabetic order or conventional order) remains optional.

VII. Numbering

64. In aliphatic compounds the carbon atoms of the fundamental chain will be numbered from one end to the other with the use of arabic numerals. In case of ambiguity the lowest numbers will be given (1) to the principal function, (2) to double bonds, (3) to triple bonds, (4) to atoms or radicals designated by prefixes. The expression "lowest numbers" signifies those that include the lowest individual number or numbers. Thus, 1,3,5 is lower than 2,4,6; 1,5,5 lower than 2,6,6; 1,2,5 lower than 1,4,5; 1,1,3,4 lower than 1,2,2,4. The Committee has left full latitude on the position of numbers.

65. Positions in a side chain will be designated by numerals or letters, starting from the point of attachment. The numerals or letters will be in parentheses with the name of the chain. Examples: $(CH_3)_2CH-$, (1-methylethyl) or isopropyl; $CH_3CHClCH_2-$, (2-chloropropyl). The rule equally permits Greek letters, ordinary letters, primed numbers $(1', 2)$, numbers with indices $(4, 4^2)$ or other designations.

66. In case of ambiguity in the numbering of atoms or radicals designated by prefixes, the order will be that chosen for the prefixes before the name of the fundamental compound or side chain of which they are substituents.

67. The prefixes, *di*, *tri*, *tetra*, etc., will be used before simple expressions (for example, **diethylbutanetriol**) and the pre-

fixes *bis, tris, tetrakis,* etc., before complex expressions. Examples: bis(methylamino)-propane: $CH_3NH(CH_2)_3NHCH_3$; bis(dimethylamino)ethane, $(CH_3)_2NCH_2CH_2$-$N(CH_3)_2$. The prefix *bi* will be used only to denote the doubling of a radical or compound; for example, biphenyl.

CHEMICAL PASSIVITY. See **passivity, chemical.**

CHEMICAL REACTION. See **reaction.**

CHEMICAL REPLACEMENT. See **reaction, replacement.**

CHEMICAL SUBSTITUTION. See **reaction, substitution.**

CHEMICAL THEORY OF DYEING. See **dyeing.**

CHEMICAL THEORY OF TANNING. See **tanning.**

CHEMICALLY PURE (C.P.). An expression used in specifying the purity of chemicals. Chemicals are rarely, if ever, so pure that other substances cannot be detected in them by sufficiently refined methods. Thus the term nowadays refers merely to chemicals of a high degree of purity.

CHEMICO CONTACT PROCESS. A **contact process** (q.v.) for the manufacture of sulfuric acid, in which the gas purification problems are simplified by the use of silica gel catalyst, usually a vanadium catalyst. This process is widely used where the SO_2 is obtained from brimstone, and also where it is obtained in the form of smelter gases.

CHEMICO PROCESS FOR ALUMINA. A process in which high-alumina clay is digested in molten ammonium bisulfate, yielding ammonium sulfate (which is reconverted to ammonium bisulfate and reused) and aluminum sulfate, which is treated with ammonia to precipitate aluminum hydroxide, from which the alumina is obtained.

CHEMILUMINESCENCE. The direct transformation of chemical energy into radiant energy without liberation of heat. The luminosity of phosphorus, of the fire-fly, and the phosphorescence sometimes observed on decaying wood or herring brine, is due to this phenomenon.

CHEMISORPTION. See **activated adsorption.**

CHEMISTRY. That branch of natural science which investigates the composition of all matter, and the transformations which it exhibits upon subjection to energy change.

CHEMISTRY, AGRICULTURAL. That branch of chemistry which applies chemical facts and principles to the problems encountered in farming, including plant processes in their relation to the growth of crops, plant nutrition, and a host of pertinent subjects.

CHEMISTRY, ANALYTICAL. That branch of chemistry dealing with the determination of qualitative or quantitative composition of substances and materials.

CHEMISTRY, BIOLOGICAL (PHYSIOLOGICAL). A division of chemistry that investigates the chemical mechanism of the living organism and the chemical processes of **metabolism.** Also called biochemistry.

CHEMISTRY, COLLOID. Colloidal chemistry may be described as the study of systems comprising a **dispersion medium** and a **dispersed phase,** and having certain characteristic properties. Colloidal sols differ from each other, and from solutions of **crystalloids** (such as sugar, salt, etc.) principally in their degree of heterogeneity. Colloidal sols exhibit the **Brownian movement** (q.v.) and exhibit a relatively slow rate of passage through a parchment (or other semipermeable membrane with a small aperture). Colloids are further characterized by a slow rate of **diffusion** and by the fact that a path of light is illuminated on passage through a colloidal solution. The particles are for the most part of greater than molecular size in solution and are intermediate between molecular or ionic solutions and coarse suspensions, although the lines of demarcation are somewhat indefinite.

CHEMISTRY, ELECTRO. That branch of chemistry concerned with **electrolysis,** and other phenomena which relate to the passage of a current through an electrolyte or are concerned with the behavior of **ions** in ionizing solvents. However, wider significance has been given to the term so that it includes all branches of science concerned with chemical reactions induced by electricity in any form, or which are accompanied by electrical phenomena.

CHEMISTRY, FERMENTATION. That branch of chemistry dealing with the reactions involving **enzymes** and **ferments,** and their various products.

CHEMISTRY, FORENSIC. The application of chemical knowledge to the solution of legal problems.

CHEMISTRY, GEO-. That branch of chemistry dealing with geological processes and substances.

CHEMISTRY, INDUSTRIAL. That branch of chemistry which is concerned with the application of chemical facts and principles in the production in industry of chemical, or nonchemical materials.

CHEMISTRY, INORGANIC. That branch of chemistry dealing with salts, acids, and bases, and in general with all compounds not containing carbon. Sometimes, however, it is convenient to extend this branch of chemistry to cover certain simple carbon compounds, such as the oxides of carbon, the metallic carbides, etc.

CHEMISTRY, MICRO. That branch of chemistry devoted to processes of chemical analysis for the investigation of small traces of compounds. These investigations are conducted either with a microscope, as by drop reactions on its slide, or by use of very small-scale apparatus.

CHEMISTRY, ORGANIC. The branch of chemistry which deals exclusively with the compounds of carbon. The distinction between inorganic and organic chemistry was made at the time when it was the general belief among chemists that the processes of the organism and their products differed in an essential degree from processes not associated with life and their products. This idea has long since been discarded, but the distinction has been retained because of the enormous number of the carbon compounds and certain peculiarities which arise from the ability of carbon to combine with itself. Because carbon compounds have their own characteristic properties, it is convenient to study them separately.

CHEMISTRY, PATHOLOGICAL. That branch of chemistry dealing with the study of the tissues, products, processes, and other chemical aspects of the body and its parts during disease.

CHEMISTRY, PHARMACEUTICAL. A branch of applied chemistry that deals with the composition and preparation of medicinal materials.

CHEMISTRY, PHOTO-. That division of chemistry which investigates the phenomena associated with the mutual transformations of **radiant energy** and chemical energy. Photography and other chemical phenomena produced by light fall under this head.

CHEMISTRY, PHYSICAL. The subject covers physical properties of chemicals and the relations between **energy** and **chemical change.**

CHEMISTRY, PHYSIOLOGICAL. See **chemistry, biological.**

CHEMISTRY, PHYTO. That branch of chemistry which deals with the substances found in plants, and their reactions.

CHEMISTRY, PURE. As originally used, this term was loosely applied to those portions of chemical science that dealt with principles and relationships rather than experimental data. More recently, pure chemistry has come to mean the facts and principles of the science as contrasted with their applications in industry or other sciences.

CHEMISTRY, STEREO. That branch of chemistry which is concerned with the structure of molecules, especially with those differences in chemical or physical properties of substances which are due to differences in spatial arrangement between compounds that are similar in composition.

CHEMISTRY, STOICHIOMETRIC. That branch of chemistry which deals with the quantitative relations of chemical substances undergoing reactions.

CHEMISTRY, STRUCTURAL. That branch of chemistry which deals with the grouping and linkages of atoms within the molecule.

CHEMISTRY, SYNTHETIC. That branch of chemistry which is concerned with the preparation or production of relatively complex substances from simpler ones.

CHEMISTRY, THEORETICAL. The branch of chemistry dealing with the deduction of mathematical laws to explain quantitatively the observed experimental facts.

CHEMISTRY, THERMO. That branch of chemistry dealing with the heat changes that accompany chemical reactions and processes, the heat produced by them, and the influence of temperature and other thermal quantities upon them.

CHEMOCEPTER. A structural or chemical group or portion of the **protoplasm** of a **cell** which takes part in reactions with drugs by uniting with a portion of the drug molecule.

CHEMOKINESIS. The process by which a chemical substance increases the activity of an organism.

CHEMOLYSIS. (Obs.) The decomposition of organic substances by chemical reagents outside the organism.

CHEMOSMOSIS. The phenomenon of chemical action taking place through an intervening **membrane.**

CHEMOTAXIS. (Chemotropism) A phenomenon shown by living **cells** and **microorganisms** that move toward or away from some point at which the chemical composition, concentration, or equilibrium is different from that of their initial location. If

the cells are attracted by the chemical stimulus, the phenomenon is known as positive chemotaxis; if they are repelled, it is termed negative chemotaxis. In animal organisms, the phenomenon is believed to be the cause of the accumulation of leucocytes at points of infection.

CHEMOTHERAPY. In general, the specific treatment of disease by chemical agents, involving the relationship between chemical structure and pharmacological action, especially in regard to effects upon **protoplasm.**

CHEMOTROPISM. See **chemotaxis.**

CHEMURGY. The employment of the methods of chemistry, and the resources of chemical knowledge, to increase the number of uses of agricultural products and thereby to build a broader farm-factory economy.

CHEN REAGENT. p-Nitrobenzohydrazide, used to identify aldehydes and ketones by identification of the p-nitrobenzohydrazones formed.

CHEN-SAK REAGENT. β-Naphthylhydrazine, used to identify aldehydes and ketones by identification of the β-naphthylhydrazones formed.

CHEN-SHIK REAGENT. p-Bromophenacyl bromide, used to identify acids.

CHENG TEST. Methenamine, on treatment with sulfuric acid, and addition of the mixture to salicylic acid, gives a pinkish color, destroyed by water.

CHENOT PROCESS. A process for the direct production of finely-divided iron, by heating iron ore with powdered coke or coal.

CHEVALLIER-CHORON TEST. Vitamin A in blood is detected by mixing 3 ml. blood with 20 g. anhydrous sodium sulfate. After drying, 20 ml. anhydrous alcohol are added. Upon standing for one hour the mixture is irradiated with ultraviolet light. The existence of an absorption band at a wave length of 3250 Å represents a positive test for vitamin A.

CHI (**X** or χ). The twenty-second letter in the Greek alphabet, used to denote the twenty-second carbon atom in a straight-chain compound, or a derivative in which the substituent group is attached to that carbon atom. (χ-) Symbol for specific **magnetic susceptibility** (χ).

CHIAROTTINO'S REAGENT. An alcoholic solution of benzidine and dimethylglyoxime used in testing for cobalt. An orange-red color is given by cobalt solutions with this reagent.

CHICHIBABIN PYRIDINE SYNTHESIS. A condensation of **carbonyl** compounds with ammonia (or amines) to form **pyridine** derivatives.

CHLOPIN TEST REAGENT FOR OZONE. Filter paper impregnated with Ursol D or J, which is colored blue by ozone.

CHLORACID. An acid, commonly organic, that contains **chlorine.**

CHLORATE. The anion ClO_3^-, or a compound containing it.

CHLORIDE. The anion Cl^-, or a compound containing it; in general, a binary compound of chlorine.

CHLORIDOMETER. Apparatus for determining chlorine.

CHLORIMETRY. (1) The process of determining the "available chlorine" in

$$4CH_3CHO + NH_3 \xrightarrow{\Delta} \quad \begin{array}{c} C_2H_5 \\ \text{(pyridine ring)} \\ CH_3 \end{array} \quad + 4H_2O.$$

CHICHIBABIN REACTION. The formation of amino derivatives of **heterocyclic** bases by the action of sodamide (and other metal amides).

bleaching powder. The term may be extended to include any analysis to determine chlorine. (2) A **titrimetric** system of analysis in which standard hypochlorite solu-

$$\text{(quinoline)} + NaNH_2 \rightarrow \text{(quinoline-NHNa)} + H_2.$$

CHIEN-SHIH SOLUTION. A 0.2% solution of resorcylaldoxime in 5% alcohol, used in testing for ferric iron, which gives a purple color in slightly acidic solution.

CHIZYNSKI TEST. Calcium is detected in the presence of magnesium by evaporating the chloride solution, and digesting in the cold with sulfuric acid. In the presence of calcium a turbidity or precipitate is formed.

CHLOPIN TEST REACTION FOR IRIDIUM. Benzidine gives a sky-blue color or flocculent precipitate with tetravalent iridium ions.

tions are used as in the approximate determination of arsenic and antimony. Other standard solutions containing "available chlorine" may also be used.

CHLORINATE. To combine with **chlorine.** Specifically, the process of adding chlorine to or substituting chlorine, especially for hydrogen, in a compound.

CHLORINATION. The process of chlorinating.

CHLORINATION, EXHAUSTIVE. The prolongation of chlorination until all the replaceable hydrogen (or other element) has been substituted by chlorine. Thus hexachlorobenzene C_6Cl_6 is formed by the exhaustive chlorination of many benzene derivatives.

CHLORINE. Nonmetallic element. Symbol Cl. Atomic number 17. Atomic weight 35.457. Gaseous at ordinary temperature. Molecular weight 70.914. Density 1.557 (liq.). Specific heat 0.226. Melting point $-102°$ C. Boiling point $-33.7°$ C. Valences 1,3,4,5, and 7. Oxides Cl_2O, $ClO_2(Cl_2O_4)$, and Cl_2O_7. Acids: hydrochloric HCl; hypochlorous, HClO; chlorous, $HClO_2$ (unknown in free state); chloric $HClO_3$; and perchloric, $HClO_4$.

CHLORINOLYSIS. A replacement or decomposition reaction brought about by the action of chlorine. This term, chlorinolysis, usually connotes the action of the chlorine in combining with an atom or group displaced from the compound reacted upon, as well as the combination with it of one or more chlorine atoms. Replacement of hydrogen atoms in organic substances by chlorine atoms, with the formation of hydrogen chloride, is the most common type of chlorinolysis.

CHLORITE. The anion ClO_2^-, or a compound containing it.

CHLORO- or **CHLOR-.** The radical Cl–.

CHLOROACETYL. The radical

$$Cl-CH_2-C\overset{\displaystyle O}{\underset{\displaystyle O}{\diagup}}\;\;.$$

CHLOROANTIMONATE (III). The anion $SbCl_4^-$, $SbCl_5^=$, or $SbCl_6^{3-}$, or a compound containing one of these anions.

CHLOROANTIMONATE (V). The anion $SbCl_6^-$, or a compound containing it.

CHLOROARGENTATE. The anion chloroargentate (I) $AgCl_2^-$, or a compound containing it.

CHLOROARGENTATE(I)AURATE (III). The anion, $AgAuCl_6^=$, or a compound containing it.

CHLOROAURATE (I). The anion $AuCl_2^-$, or a compound containing it.

CHLOROAURATE (I, III). The anion $Au^IAu^{III}Cl_6^=$, or a compound containing it.

CHLOROAURATE (III). The anion $AuCl_4^-$, or a compound containing it.

CHLOROBROMATE. The anion $BrCl_2^-$, or a compound containing it.

CHLOROBROMIDE. See **chlorobromate.**

CHLOROCADMATE. The anion $CdCl_4^=$, or a compound containing it.

CHLOROCHROMATE (II). The anion $CrO_2Cl_2^{4-}$, or a compound containing it.

CHLOROCHROMATE (III). The anion $CrCl_6^{3-}$, or a compound containing it.

CHLOROCHROMATE (VI). The anion CrO_3Cl^-, or a compound containing it.

CHLOROCUPRATE (I). The anion $CuCl_2^-$, $CuCl_3^=$, or $Cu_2Cl_6^{4-}$, or a compound containing one of these anions.

CHLOROCUPRATE (II). The anion $CuCl_3^-$ or $CuCl_4^=$, or a compound containing one of these anions.

CHLOROIODATE (I). The anion ICl_2^-, or a compound containing it.

CHLOROIODATE (III). The anion ICl_4^-, or a compound containing it.

CHLOROIODIDE. See **chloroiodate (I)** and **(III).**

CHLOROIRIDATE (III). The anion $IrCl_6^{3-}$, or a compound containing it.

CHLOROMANGANATE (IV). The anion $MnCl_6^=$, or a compound containing it.

CHLOROMERCURATE (II). The anion $(HgCl_4)_n^{2n-}$, or a compound containing it.

CHLOROMERCURI. The radical ClHg–.

CHLOROMOLYBDATE (VI). The anion $MoO_2Cl_4^=$, or a compound containing it.

CHLORONIOBATE (II). The anion $NbCl_4^-$, or a compound containing it.

CHLORONIOBATE (V). The anion $NbOCl_5^-$, or a compound containing it.

CHLOROÖSMATE (III). The anion $OsCl_6^{3-}$, or a compound containing it.

CHLOROÖSMATE (IV). The anion $OsCl_6^-$, or a compound containing it.

CHLOROÖSMATE (VI). The anion $OsO_2Cl_4^-$, or a compound containing it.

CHLOROPALLADATE (II). The anion $PdCl_4^-$, or a compound containing it.

CHLOROPALLADATE (IV). The anion $PdCl_6^-$, or a compound containing it.

CHLOROPHOSPHATE. The anion $PO_2Cl_2^-$, PO_3Cl^-, or PCl_6^-, or a compound containing one of these anions.

CHLOROPHYLL. See **plant pigments.**

CHLOROPLASTS. See **plant pigments.**

CHLOROPLATINATE (II). The anion $PtCl_4^-$, or a compound containing it.

CHLOROPLATINATE (IV). The anion $PtCl_6^-$, or a compound containing it.

CHLOROPLATINATE, HYDROXO-. The anion $Pt(OH)_4Cl_2^-$, $Pt(OH)_2Cl_4^-$, etc., or a compound containing one of these anions.

CHLOROPLATINITE. See **chloroplatinate (II).**

CHLOROPLUMBATE (IV). The anion $PbCl_6^-$, or a compound containing it.

CHLORORHENATE (III). The anion $ReCl_4^-$, $ReCl_5^-$, or $ReCl_6^{3-}$, or a compound containing one of these anions.

CHLORORHENATE (IV). The anion $ReCl_6^-$, or a compound containing it.

CHLORORHENATE (V). The anion $ReOCl_5^-$, or a compound containing it.

CHLORORHODATE (III). The anion $RhCl_6^{3-}$, or a compound containing it.

CHLORORUTHENATE (IV). The anion $RuCl_6^-$, or a compound containing it.

CHLOROSELENITE. The anion $SeO_2Cl_2^-$ or $SeCl_6^-$ or a compound containing one of these anions.

CHLOROSIS. (1) Technological or agricultural processes using **chlorine.** (2) A pathological condition in animals caused by a deficiency of hemoglobin.

CHLOROSTANNATE (II). The anion $SnCl_3^-$ or $SnCl_4^-$, or a compound containing one of these anions.

CHLOROSTANNATE (IV). The anion $SnCl_6^-$, or a compound containing it.

CHLOROSULFONATE. The anion SO_3Cl^-, or a compound containing it.

CHLOROSULFONIC. Related to chlorosulfonic acid, $HO(Cl)SO_2$.

CHLOROSULFURIC. Related to chlorosulfuric acid, Cl_2SO_2, which is commonly called sulfuryl chloride.

CHLOROTELLURITE. The anion $TeCl_6^-$, or a compound containing it.

CHLOROTHALLATE. The anion $Tl_2Cl_9^{3-}$, or a compound containing it.

CHLOROTITANATE (IV). The anion $TiCl_6^-$, or a compound containing it.

CHLOROTUNGSTATE (III). The anion $W_2Cl_9^{3-}$, or a compound containing it.

CHLOROTUNGSTATE (V). The anion $WOCl_4^-$ or $WOCl_5^-$, or a compound containing one of these anions.

CHLOROUS. (1) Related to chlorous acid ($HClO_2$). (2) Containing trivalent chlorine.

CHLOROX PROCESS. A process for the refining of lubricating oil, involving extraction with "chlorox," or dichloroethyl ether, $(CH_2ClCH_2)_2O$.

CHLOROZINCATE. The anion $ZnCl_3^-$ or $ZnCl_4^=$, or a compound containing one of these anions.

CHLOROZIRCONATE. The anion $ZrCl_6^=$, or a compound containing it.

CHLORYL. The hypochlorite radical $ClO-$.

CHODAT TEST REACTION. Solutions containing polypeptides or amino acids give with tyrosinase and p-cresol a red color changing to blue with a red dichroism. Proteins give only the red color.

CHOL-, CHOLE-, CHOLO-. (Greek) Relating to, or derived from, bile; as cholesterol, cholocyanin, choline.

CHOLAGOGUE. A substance or drug that increases the flow of bile.

CHRISTEL REACTIONS. Tests for picric acid. The presence of picric acid gives (1) a reddish precipitate with lead acetate solution, but only after addition of ammonia (a green precipitate with cupric sulfate and ammonia); (2) with methyl green aqueous solution, a green precipitate sparingly soluble in water (blue solution); (3) a red color with ammonium sulfide or alkaline stannous chloride solutions; (4) a red-yellow liquid with zinc and dilute sulfuric acid, which gives color changes with alcohol.

CHRISTENSEN PROCESS. A process for producing alumina from kaolin by roasting the clay, grinding, treating with boiling hydrochloric acid, filtering, evaporating to 172 g. per liter alumina, crystallizing the aluminum chloride hexahydrate, calcining at 750° C. to obtain alumina and to recover the hydrogen chloride.

CHRISTENSEN REAGENT FOR QUININE. A solution of 1 g. iodine in a mixture of 1 g. 50% hydriodic acid, 0.8 g. sulfuric acid, and 50 g. 70% ethyl alcohol. This solution is used as a test reagent for quinine. Characteristic crystals are obtained.

CHRISTENSEN TEST REACTION FOR HORMONES AND VITAMINS. Hormones and vitamins produce a red-brown to black color with phosphorus pentoxide.

CHROMA. The concentration of a color, or its degree of saturation.

CHROMATE. The anion $CrO_4^=$, or a compound containing it.

CHROMATE, BI- or DI-. See **dichromate**.

CHROMATE, TETRA-. See **tetrachromate**.

CHROMATE, TRI-. See **trichromate**.

CHROMATIC. Pertaining to color and colors.

CHROMATIC ABERRATION. See **aberration, chromatic**.

CHROMATOFUGE. A term proposed for an apparatus in which **chromatographic adsorption** takes place on the radial flow of a solution through a disc or cylinder from the axis to the perimeter, in which the process may be assisted by centrifugal forces to give greater speed and clearer zone definition. The process is adapted to the recovery of products on a laboratory or even a small plant scale.

CHROMATOGRAPHIC ANALYSIS. Analysis of mixtures by passage of their solutions through an **adsorbent** column. The different constituents adsorb at different rates, and advantage is taken of this property to separate the components in different sections of the column. Quantitative as well as qualitative methods have been developed.

CHROME. Pertaining to chromium, or chromic oxide or lead chromate.

CHROME TANNING. See **tanning process, chrome**.

CHROMIC. Containing or pertaining to trivalent **chromium**.

CHROMICYANIDE. See **cyanochromate (III).**

CHROMIOXALATE. See **oxalatochromate (III).**

CHROMITE. The anion CrO_2^- or CrO_3^{3-}, or a compound containing one of these anions; a combination of chromic oxide with another metallic oxide, especially ferrous oxide. Salts of chromous acid are also termed chromites.

CHROMITE, HYDROXO-. The anion $Cr(OH)_6^{3-}$, or a compound containing it.

CHROMIUM. Metallic element. Symbol Cr. Atomic number 24. Atomic weight 52.01. Density 6.92. Specific heat 0.0793. Melting point 1615° C. Boiling point 2200° C. Chromium forms three series of compounds, chromous, chromic, and chromates. Valence 2, 3, and 6. Oxides CrO, CrO_2, Cr_2O_3, and CrO_3. Chromium may be substituted for aluminum in the alums.

CHROMO-. (Greek) Chroma, color, colored; as chromophore, chromoprotein, chromoisomer (a colored isomer of a colorless compound).

CHROMOCYANIDE. See **cyanochromate (II).**

CHROMOGEN. Any substance which yields a colored compound on oxidation. According to a theory proposed by **Witt**, chromogens are parent substances of dyestuffs. They are formed by the substitution of a chromophore group in a hydrocarbon, and further substitution of an auxochromic group converts the chromogens into true dyestuffs. (See **chromophore, auxochrome.**)

CHROMOISOMERISM. Isomerism in which the isomers exhibit different colors.

CHROMOPHORE. An atom or group of atoms or electrons in a molecule which is chiefly responsible for an absorption band. When the band is in the visible spectrum, the compound is colored. Among chromophore groups are the **nitro, azo,** and **quinoid**

(q.v.) groups. Such groups do not confer dyeing properties upon the compounds which contain them; dyes are formed when the substance is further substituted by a salt-forming or **auxochrome** group.

CHROMOPHORIC ELECTRONS. Electrons in the double bonds of the chromophoric groups. Such electrons are not bound as tightly as those of single bonds and can thus be transferred into higher energy levels with less expenditure of energy. Their electronic spectra appear at frequencies in the visible or near ultraviolet region of the spectrum.

CHROMOPROTEINS. A class of **protein** substances characterized by being colored. The **prosthetic group** (q.v.) is a colored compound in such cases. Hemoglobin and hemocyanin are the best known examples of this class of proteins.

CHROMOSCOPE. An apparatus for measuring color values and intensities.

CHROMOSOME. A biological entity, in some species of microscope size, formed during **mitosis** from the chromatin of the nucleus.

CHROMOTROPISM. A process of isomeric change in which a change of color is involved.

CHROMOUS. Containing or pertaining to divalent **chromium.**

CHROMYL. The radical CrO_2^-.

CHRONOGRAPH. An instrument for measuring time, as a clock. The term is generally reserved for an instrument which keeps time accurately.

CHRONOMETER. An instrument for measuring time, as a clock. The term is generally reserved for an instrument that keeps time accurately.

CHRONOSCOPE. An instrument for measuring time.

CHRYS-, CHRYSO-. (Greek) Gold, golden yellow, yellow; as chrysophanic acid, chrysazin.

CHRYSENYL. The radical $C_{18}H_{11}-$ derived from chrysene

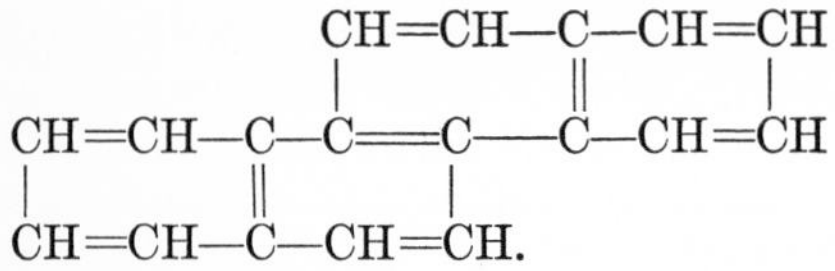

$$\begin{array}{c} \text{CH}{=}\text{CH}{-}\text{C}{-}\text{CH}{=}\text{CH} \\ | \quad \| \quad | \\ \text{CH}{=}\text{CH}{-}\text{C}{=}\text{C}{-}\text{C}{-}\text{CH}{=}\text{CH} \\ | \quad \| \quad | \\ \text{CH}{=}\text{CH}{-}\text{C}{-}\text{CH}{=}\text{CH}. \end{array}$$

CHUGAEV METHOD. A method of preparation of **olefins** from **alcohols** through the intermediate formation of methyl **xanthates.**

$$RCH_2 \cdot CH_2OH + CS_2 + NaOH \rightarrow RCH_2CH_2 \cdot O \cdot CS \cdot SNa + H_2O$$

$$RCH_2CH_2 \cdot O \cdot CS \cdot SNa + CH_3I \rightarrow RCH_2CH_2 \cdot O \cdot CS \cdot SCH_3 + NaI$$

$$RCH_2CH_2 \cdot O \cdot CS \cdot SCH_3 \xrightarrow{\Delta} RCH{=}CH_2 + CH_3SH + COS.$$

CIAMICIAN-DENNSTEDT REARRANGEMENT. A method of formation of **pyridines** from **pyrroles.**

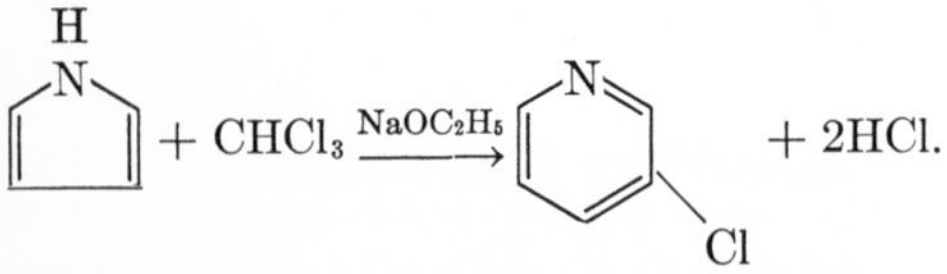

CIAMICIAN-MAGNANINI TEST. Skatol gives a purple-red color on warming with concentrated sulfuric acid.

CIMMINO REAGENT. A modified **Kopp reagent** consisting of diphenylamine and sulfuric acid dissolved in 5% hydrochloric acid. It is used in testing for nitrate, which gives a blue color with the reagent and sulfuric acid.

CINCHO-, CINCH-. Relating to cinchona or cinchonine; as cinchomeronic, cinchene.

CINNAMAL. See **cinnamylidene.**

CINNAMATE. An ester of cinnamic acid,

$$(C_6H_5{-}CH{=}CH{-}COOH).$$

CINNAMENYL. See **styryl.**

CINNAMIC. (1) The radical

$$C_6H_5CH{:}CH{-}.$$

(2) Derived from cinnamic acid,

$$C_6H_5CH{:}CHCOOH.$$

CINNAMOYL. The radical

$$C_6H_5CH{:}CHCO{-}.$$

CINNAMYL. The radical

$$C_6H_5CH{:}CHCH_2{-}.$$

CINNAMYLIDENE. The radical

$$C_6H_5CH{:}CHCH{=}.$$

CIRCULAR DICHROISM. See **Cotton effect.**

CIS-. (Latin) On this side. Indicating one of two geometrical isomers in which certain atoms or groups are on the same side of a plane; as, *cis*-cinnamic acid,

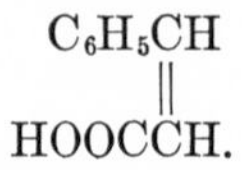

$$\begin{array}{c} C_6H_5CH \\ \| \\ HOOCCH. \end{array}$$

CIS-TRANS ISOMERISM. See **isomerism, cis-trans.**

CITRATE. An ester or salt of citric acid,

$$HOOC(HO)C(CH_2COOH)_2.$$

CITRIC. Related to citric acid,

$$HOOC(HO)C(CH_2COOH)_2.$$

CIUSA TEST REACTION. Pyrrol in ethereal solution gives a wine-red color with chloranil.

Cl Symbol for the element **chlorine.**

CLAISEN CONDENSATION. The condensation of **esters,** or esters and **ketones,** to form β-dicarbonyl type compounds; or the condensation of arylaldehydes and acyl-

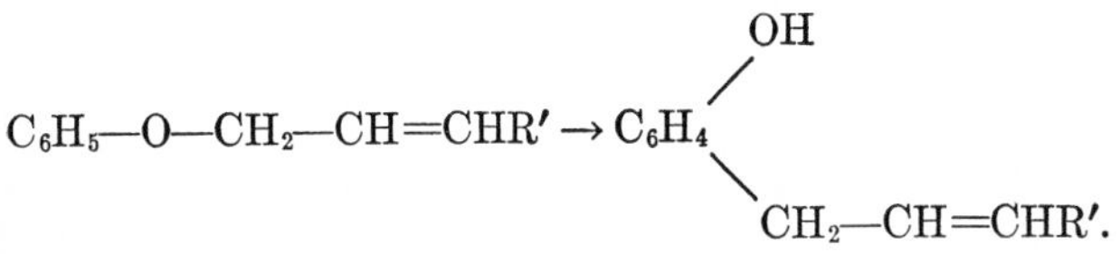

The allyl group commonly shifts to the *ortho* position, or, if that is substituted, to the *para* position.

CLAISEN-SCHMIDT CONDENSATION. A form of the **Claisen condensation** used for the preparation of unsaturated aldehydes or ketones by the condensation of aromatic aldehydes with aliphatic aldehydes or ketones.

$$C_6H_5CHO + CH_3CHO \xrightarrow{\text{NaOH}} C_6H_5CH{=}CHCHO + H_2O.$$

phenones with esters or ketones (in the presence of sodium and alcohol or sodium alcoholate) to form unsaturated esters.

CLAISEN TEST FOR THIOPHENE IN BENZENE. Add a few drops of isoamyl nitrite and some concentrated

$$CH_3COOR + CH_3COOR \xrightarrow[\text{Alc}]{\text{Na}} CH_3COCH_2COOR + ROH$$

$$C_6H_5CHO + CH_3COOR \xrightarrow[\text{Cold}]{\text{Na}} C_6H_5CH{=}CHCOOR + H_2O$$

$$C_6H_5CHO + CH_3COCH_3 \xrightarrow[\text{Cold}]{\text{Na}} C_6H_5CH{=}CHCOCH_3 + H_2O$$

Other related reactions involving condensation of active methylene groups with carbonyl groups include the **aldol condensation,** the **acetoacetic ester synthesis,** the **Claisen-Schmidt condensation,** and the **Perkin reaction** (q.v.).

CLAISEN REACTION FOR PHENYLGLYOXYLIC ACID. A solution in benzene of phenylglyoxylic acid gives with sulfuric acid a deep red color, becoming blue-violet and changing to red on addition of water.

CLAISEN REARRANGEMENT. A rearrangement of allyl ethers of certain typecompounds, such as phenols or enols, whereby an allyl group attached to the oxygen atom of the ether shifts to an adjacent carbon atom, leaving a hydroxy or carbonyl group instead of the ether linkage.

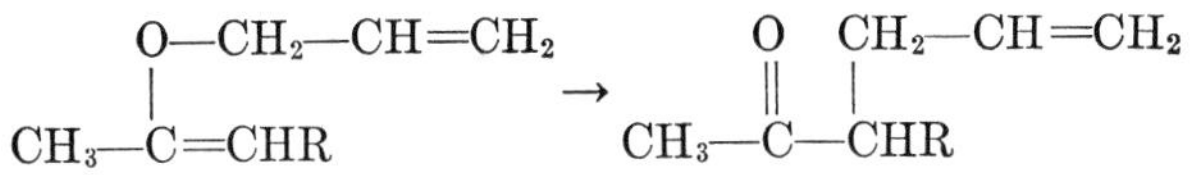

sulfuric acid to 10 ml. of the benzene. A brown-red color produced on shaking, later becoming violet, indicates the presence of thiophene.

CLAPEYRON-CLAUSIUS EQUATION. A fundamental relationship between the temperature at which an inter-phase transition occurs, the change in **heat content** and the change in volume, of the form:

$$\frac{dp}{dT} = \frac{\Delta H}{T\,\Delta V},$$

in which p is the pressure, T the temperature, dp/dT is the rate of change of pressure with temperature, ΔH the change in heat content and ΔV the change in volume.

$$
\begin{array}{ccc}
\text{O---CH}_2\text{---CH=CH}_2 & & \text{O} \quad \text{CH}_2\text{---CH=CH}_2 \\
| & \rightarrow & \| \quad | \\
\text{CH}_3\text{---C=CHR} & & \text{CH}_3\text{---C---CHR}
\end{array}
$$

or the group involved in the shift may be an aryl group (or a substituted aryl group)

$$C_6H_5{-}O{-}CH_2{-}CH{=}CHR' \rightarrow C_6H_4 \begin{array}{l} {}^{\textstyle OH} \\ {} \\ CH_2{-}CH{=}CHR'. \end{array}$$

When applied specifically to the evaporation of liquids, this equation becomes

$$\frac{dp}{dT} = \frac{L}{T(V_2 - V_1)},$$

in which dp/dT is the rate of change of vapor pressure with temperature, L is the molar heat of evaporation, T is the temperature, and V_2 and V_1 are the molar volumes of vapor and liquid, respectively.

CLARIFICATION. The removal of suspended solids from a liquid or solution by means of mechanical processes, such as filtration, sedimentation, or centrifuging. The suspended solids are generally first treated with **fining agents** (q.v.), substances which absorb or adsorb the foreign particles, by chemical action, generally precipitation reactions.

CLARK-WILLIT TEST. Potassium is detected in solution by precipitation with one-third its volume of a 2% solution of naphthol yellow S.

CLARKE CELL. A standard **cell** designed by Latimer Clarke in 1872. The **anode,** consisting of a zinc rod, is immersed in a saturated zinc sulfate solution. The mercury **cathode** is covered with a paste of mercurous sulfate. The cell must be kept below the **transition temperature** (at 39° C.) of $ZnSO_4 \cdot 7H_2O$ into $ZnSO_4 \cdot 6H_2O$ to prevent serious changes in the electromotive force. At 20° C. the Clarke cell furnishes an emf of 1.4267 volts; the emf values are very sensitive to small changes in temperature.

CLARKE-JONES · TEST REACTION. Copper is detected in neutral cupric sulfate solutions by addition of 1 drop 1:3 sulfuric acid, and dilution to 100 ml. with water, followed by the addition of 1 g. ammonium persulfate, 1 ml. saturated aqueous solution of dimethylglyoxime, 0.5 ml. 0.5% aqueous silver nitrate solution, and 2 ml. 10% aqueous pyridine solution. A reddish-violet color on shaking indicates the presence of copper.

CLASSIFICATION. Arrangement in accordance with a system or the magnitude of a property; the term extends to the arrangement of chemical compounds or types of compounds, atoms, molecules or any other group of entities. It also applies to the sorting of particles by size, specific gravity, or other property.

CLASSIFICATION, HYDRAULIC. Free **settling** in water or other liquids, used commonly to obtain a preliminary coarse separation of particles.

CLASSIFIER, DORR. An inclined settling box in which a stream of water, or other fluid carrying particles, enters at the shallow end and overflows at the deep end, while mechanically operated rakes push the settled solids up the incline to overflow at a point past the point of entry of the feed.

CLAUDE PROCESS. Synthesis of ammonia from nitrogen and hydrogen at about 900 atmospheres pressure and 600° C. The term Claude process is also applied to a method of liquefaction of air by a series of operations, including cooling by expansion through an orifice, and cooling by expansion against external pressure in a piston engine.

CLAUDIUS SOLUTION. A solution of 2 g. trichloracetic acid, 0.5 g. tannic acid, and 0.1 g. acid fuchsin, in 100 ml. water. This solution is used as a test reagent for albumin.

CLAUS STRUCTURE OF BENZENE. See **benzene, formulas.**

CLAUS-RISLER BENZIDINE TESTS FOR CHLORINE AND BROMINE. (1) An aqueous solution of benzidine hydrochloride gives a blue color with chlorine water, becoming green and then yielding a red precipitate as more reagent is added.

(2) Benzidine dissolved in chloroform or ether gives a dark blue precipitate with bromine vapor.

(3) Very dilute bromine water, on addition to a carbon disulfide solution of benzidine, becomes blue, then green, then colorless, while the carbon disulfide layer becomes dark red.

CLAUS TEST FOR ANTHRAQUINONE.
Sodium amalgam is added to an alcoholic solution of anthraquinone. A dark violet zone is formed about the amalgam with moss-green clouds rising from it. The mixture becomes moss-green on heating.

CLAUS TEST FOR WATER IN ALCOHOL. An alcoholic solution of anthraquinone gives with sodium amalgam a red zone if water is present in the alcohol. The red color fades on shaking with air, but reappears on standing. (Cf. **Claus test for anthraquinone.**)

CLAUSIUS. A unit of **entropy,** the calorie per degree.

CLAUSIUS-CLAPEYRON EQUATION. See **Clapeyron-Clausius equation.**

CLAUSIUS EQUATION. A form of the **equation of state,** relating the pressure, volume, and temperature of a gas, and the gas constant. The Clausius equation applies a correction to the **van der Waals equation** to correct the pressure-correction term a for its variation with temperature. The Clausius equation takes the form

$$\left[P + \frac{a}{T(V + c)^2} \right] (V - b) = RT$$

in which P is the pressure of the gas, T is the absolute temperature, V is the volume, R is the **gas constant,** a and b are the van der Waals' constants, and c is a constant which is a function of a, b, and R.

CLAUSIUS LAW. See **law, Clausius.**

CLAUSIUS-MOSOTTI EQUATION. See **Mosotti-Clausius equation.**

CLAY PROCESS FOR ROSIN REFINING. A process for the decolorization of crude wood rosin involving its solution in warm naphtha (or other inexpensive solvent) and its passage through towers containing such adsorbents as fuller's earth and magnesium silicate. The naphtha is then separated from the purified rosin by distillation.

CLEANING COMPOUND. (1) A mixture of substances such as borax, sodium carbonate, sodium peroxide, soap, surface active agents, etc., which is used for cleaning and washing materials. (2) A **detergent** (q.v.).

CLEANING SOLUTION. A solution used to clean chemical glassware, which may be prepared by dissolving 10 or 15 g. of sodium dichromate in the minimum volume of water, and adding 500 ml. of concentrated sulfuric acid.

CLEARING FLUID. A liquid which increases the light **transmission** through solid objects immersed in it. Clearing fluids are commonly used in microscopy.

CLEAVAGE. (1) A property of crystals by virtue of which they split more readily in certain directions than in others, leaving nearly smooth faces. It is due to the fact that there is a minimum of cohesion between the atoms in the direction of cleavage. (2) The splitting of organic compounds by reactions with various reagents.

CLEMMENSEN REACTION. Reduction of the $\overset{\diagdown}{C}O$ (**carbonyl**) group to a $\overset{\diagdown}{C}H_2$ (methylene) group in **aldehydes** and **ketones** by means of zinc and hydrochloric acid.

CLERGET METHOD. A double dilution method for correcting the error in determining sugars, where **clarifying agents** are used, which error is due to the volume of the precipitate formed by the clarifier. If the volume of precipitate is greater than 1 ml. from 26 g. of material, the Clerget method is used to correct this volume error. The Clerget method as usually conducted involves the determination of the sucrose at two dilutions by polarization before and after inversion with hydrochloric acid.

CLERICI SOLUTION. A solution of thallium malonate and thallium formate in molar concentration, used in the determination of densities of minerals.

CLEVELAND FLASH POINT TESTER. An open-cup apparatus used to determine the **flash point** and "**fire point**" of an oil.

CLOUD CHAMBER. See **cloud-track apparatus.**

CLOUD CHAMBER APPARATUS. Apparatus for the detection of electrically charged particles or **radiation.** The particles are allowed to move at high velocities through a low pressure chamber which is supersaturated with respect to water vapor. The water vapor condenses on those ionized particles which are created by impact of the incident (primary) radiation or particles with the molecules of the chamber. These impacts occur continually along the path of the primary particles. The resulting foggy streak traces the path of the incident particles or radiation through the chamber. The apparatus is used extensively in the detection and investigation of radiations and electrified particles.

CLOUD POINT. The temperature at which a solution becomes cloudy as it is cooled at a specified rate. The cloud point is an important property in the specification of lacquers, oils, and other important solutions.

CLUSTER. A group of closely-related or interacting molecules which has an independent existence within a larger molecular domain; the postulation of such clusters leads to quite satisfactory treatments of certain properties of liquids, such as **condensation** and the **critical state.**

Cm Symbol for the element **curium.**

Co Symbol for the element **cobalt.**

COACERVATION. The production, by **coagulation** of a **hydrophilic sol,** of a liquid phase, which often appears as viscous drops, instead of forming a continuous liquid phase.

COAGEL. A gel formed by **precipitation** or **coagulation,** as distinguished from gel formed by swelling of a solid colloid.

COAGULATION. (1) The process of complete or partial solidification of a sol to a gelatinous mass; or of the separation from a liquid system of a gelatinous mass. It involves the separation of the disperse from the **continuous phase** which fact distinguishes it from "gelation." (2) The result of an alteration of a **disperse phase** or of a dissolved solid which causes the separation of the system into a liquid phase and an insoluble mass, as the coagulation of egg albumin. (3) The separation of a gelatinous mass from a liquid system, as the clotting of blood. Derived terms: coagulate; coagulator; coagulum.

COAGULATION VALUE. The concentration of a coagulant which effects a given amount of coagulation of a colloidal, or other dispersed system.

COBALT. Metallic element. Symbol Co. Atomic number 27. Atomic weight 58.94. Density 8.9. Specific heat 0.0827. Melting point 1480° C. Boiling point 2900° C. Valence 2 and 3. Oxides CoO, Co_2O_3 and Co_3O_4. The cobaltous compounds are the more stable; when hydrated they are pink in color, and they become green when rendered anhydrous.

COBALTAMMINE. One of a number of **coordination compounds** formed with ammonia by certain cobalt salts.

COBALTATE (II). The anion $Co(OH)_4^-$ or $Co(OH)_6^{4-}$, or a compound containing one of these anions.

COBALTIC. Containing or pertaining to trivalent **cobalt.**

COBALTICYANIDE. The anion

$$Co(CN)_6^{3-},$$

or a compound containing it.

COBALTINITRITE. The anion

$$Co(NO_2)_6^{3-},$$

or a compound containing it.

COBALTIOXALATE. See **oxalatocobaltate (III).**

COBALTOCYANIDE. The anion $Co(CN)_5^{3-}$ or $Co(CN)_6^{4-}$, or a compound containing one of these anions.

COBALTONITRITE. The anion $Co(NO_2)_6^{4-}$, or a compound containing it.

COBALTOTHIOCYANATE. See **thiocyanatocobaltate (II)**.

COBALTOUS. Containing or pertaining to divalent **cobalt**.

COCCUS. A **bacterium** that is spherical in shape.

COEFFICIENT, ACTIVITY. See **activity coefficient**.

COEFFICIENT, COMPRESSIBILITY. See **compressibility coefficient**.

COEFFICIENT, CONDUCTIVITY. See **conductivity coefficient**.

COEFFICIENT, CRITICAL. See **critical coefficient**.

COEFFICIENT, DIFFUSION. See **law of diffusion, Fick's**.

COEFFICIENT, DISTRIBUTION. See **distribution coefficient**.

COEFFICIENT, EVASION. See **evasion coefficient**.

COEFFICIENT, INVASION. See **invasion coefficient**.

COEFFICIENT OF DISCHARGE. A constant quantity that appears in various expressions for the rate of flow of fluids in pipes containing constrictions, such as those expressions giving the relationship between rate of flow, fluid head, and the various cross-sectional area of the pipe.

COEFFICIENT OF EXPANSION. The increment in volume per unit mass per degree rise in temperature. For **isotropic** solids, the expansion with temperature is the same in all directions; for such solids a coefficient of linear expansion along one axis can also be defined.

COEFFICIENT OF HEAT TRANSFER. See **heat transfer, coefficient of**.

COEFFICIENT OF PURITY. (Quotient of Purity.) An approximate factor used in the sugar industry obtained by multiplying the **polarization** of the juice by 100 and dividing the product by the reading it gives with the **Brix hydrometer**. It furnishes an approximation of the quantity of pure sucrose present.

COEFFICIENT, OSMOTIC. See **osmotic coefficient**.

COEFFICIENT, PARTITION. See **distribution coefficient**.

COEFFICIENT OF SLIP. See **slip, coefficient of**.

COEFFICIENT, VELOCITY. (Velocity constant. Specific speed of reaction.) The rate of transformation of unit mass of a substance in a chemical reaction.

COENZYME. The separable portion or **prosthetic group** (q.v.), generally a low molecular weight organic substance, as opposed to the protein portion of an **enzyme**, capable of supplementing a specific protein to form the active enzyme; as cozymase or diphosphopyridine nucleotide being the coenzyme of zymase.

COERCIVE FORCE. The **magnetic force** necessary to demagnetize a body previously magnetized.

COEXISTENCE OF REACTIONS, PRINCIPLE OF. When a number of reactions are taking place simultaneously in any system, each obeys the **law of mass action,** and each proceeds as if it were independent of the others; the total change is the sum of all the independent changes.

COFERMENT. Any substance that increases or makes possible the action of an **enzyme**. Thus phosphates and a complex organic phosphate have been shown to increase the activity of the yeast ferment and blood does not clot in the absence of calcium salts, apparently because calcium salts are necessary for the conversion of the blood zymogen into thrombase, the clotting ferment. (See also **coenzyme**.)

COFERMENTATION. A condition of fermentation in which the principal **enzyme** is unable to carry on its specific reaction in the absence of a coferment. (See coferment.)

COHEN TEST REACTION. Rosin dissolved in chloroform gives a violet-red color with a 20% solution of chlorosulfonic acid in chloroform.

COHESION. Molecular attraction between the particles of any given mass by virtue of which the mass tends to resist physical disintegration. It differs from adhesion which refers to surface attractions.

COHESION PRESSURE. The addition term a/V^2 used in the **van der Waals equation** to correct the pressure by adding the attractive force of the molecules. V is the volume of the gas, and a is approximately constant for a given gas.

COHOBATION. A process of **distilling** in which the distillate or a portion of the distillate is repeatedly returned to the still.

COINCIDENCE COUNTING. A technique for counting **particles** or **radiations** wherein several **counters** are connected so that they must discharge simultaneously or within an assignable time interval of each other. This arrangement makes it possible to determine the direction in which a particle is traveling by the use of two or more counters connected in coincidence and arranged in line. Multiple coincidences permit analysis of complex ionizing events encountered in such work as the analysis of cosmic radiation, in which an ionizing ray may be followed as it traverses matter and generates secondary particles.

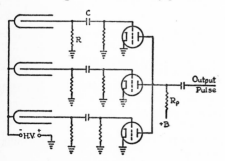

There are a number of coincidence circuits. A simple example is the Rossi circuit (shown connected for triple coincidences, and for resistance-quenched, nonselfquenching counters), which has as its essential feature the direct connection of the plates of all the tubes, which are then connected to the B supply through a common resistor. The grids of all the tubes are connected to the cathodes so that the tubes are conducting.

COLASANTI TEST REACTION FOR THIOCYANATES. Solutions of thiocyanates give (1) a persistent green color with cupric sulfate solution; (2) an intense violet color with a 0.1% gold chloride solution alkalinized weakly with sodium carbonate.

COLASANTI TEST REACTION FOR THIOCYANATES AND MUSTARD OILS. Dilute solutions of mustard oils or thiocyanates, when added to a 20% alcoholic α-naphthol solution, give an emerald-green ring test with twice the volume of concentrated sulfuric acid. On shaking, the mixture becomes violet.

COLATURE. A liquid that has been strained.

COLBURN PROCESS. A continuous process for the manufacture of sheet glass by means of a machine that is supplied directly from a fused glass tank.

COLD PROCESS. (1) A method of low temperature saponification once used widely in the soap industry. The fat is melted, emulsified with sodium hydroxide solution or other alkali, and allowed to stand until saponification is complete or, rather, until saponification has progressed to the desired extent. (2) A low temperature **polymerization** (q.v.) method used in the synthetic rubber industry.

COLD SETTLING PROCESS. A simple process for the **dewaxing** (q.v.) of petroleum, consisting chiefly of mixing it with gasoline or naphtha, cooling, and standing, whereupon the wax settles. Later the gasoline or naphtha is separated by distillation.

COLE MICROCHEMICAL REAGENT FOR ALKALOIDS. Potassium ferrocyanide, which gives yellow, crystalline precipitates with the hydrochlorides of many alkaloids.

COLE REAGENT FOR GOLD. A reagent used to impregnate viscose silk to prepare a test medium for gold. The reagent consists of a solution of 10 g. stannous chloride in 95 ml. water and 5 ml. hydrochloric acid, to which 10 g. pyrogallol is then added. The impregnated fibers acquire a red to violet color in solutions containing gold.

COLLATERAL SERIES. See **element, radioactive series.**

COLLECTOR. An auxiliary **flotation** agent or **promotor,** which increases the yield of flotation apparatus.

COLLIGATIVE PROPERTY. A property, of a substance or system, which is determined by the number of particles present in the system but independent of the properties of the particles themselves.

COLLIMATOR. The objective tube of a **spectroscope** or other optical apparatus. It is equipped with a convex lens and a slit and serves to align in parallel direction the rays emitted by the volatilized element under observation and to direct the rays into the prism. The tube containing the eyepiece is known as the telescope.

COLLISION DIAMETER OF MOLECULES. The distance of closest approach between the centers of any two molecules in a collision.

COLLISION, ELASTIC. A collision between particles in which only kinetic energy, and not internal energy, is exchanged.

COLLISION NUMBER. A term used in reaction rate theory to denote the number of collisions between molecules occurring per second per unit of concentration.

COLLISION THEORY OF REACTION RATES. The hypothesis that a reaction takes place on every collision between two molecules having sufficient **energy of activation.** This hypothesis fails in many instances and offers at best an incomplete explanation of the factors involved.

COLLOID. Noncrystalloid. Substances that form two-phase systems with **solvents** which exhibit the gross properties of solutions, or modifications of crystalline substances which are capable of forming such systems. The former view that the colloid is essentially different from substances which form true solutions is giving way to the consideration that the colloidal state is merely a condition into which all, or nearly all, substances can be brought by suitable means. Colloidal "solutions" do not obey the solution laws: the alterations of the boiling and freezing points are inappreciable, and the osmotic pressures very small. A colloidal solution is, in reality, a disperse system, and such measures as separate disperse systems will usually cause the **coagulation** and **precipitation** of colloids. Ostwald distinguished between two classes of colloidal liquids, one in which the suspended colloid does not sensibly affect the properties of the dispersive medium such as suspensions of metals, metallic sulfides or clay; and the class in which the reverse is true as in the case of gelatin solutions which "set" to gels below a certain temperature.

COLLOID CHEMISTRY. See **chemistry, colloid.**

COLLOID, EMULSION. A colloidal system in which both the continuous phase and the dispersed phase are liquids.

COLLOID, EU-. See **eucolloid.**

COLLOID, HEMI-. See **hemicolloid.**

COLLOID, HETEROPOLAR. A colloidal system in which the dispersed particles are **polar compounds** (q.v.).

COLLOID, HOMOPOLAR. A colloidal system in which the dispersed particles are **nonpolar compounds** (q.v.).

COLLOID, LYOPHILIC. See **lyophilic system.**

COLLOID, LYOPHOBIC. See **lyophobic system.**

COLLOID, MESO-. See **mesocolloid.**

COLLOID, MOLECULAR. A large molecule, which has a length as great as that of some colloidal particles.

COLLOID, PROTECTIVE. A substance added to a colloidal system to augment its stability.

COLLOID, REVERSIBLE AND IRREVERSIBLE. (1) A distinction based on the fact that certain substances immediately assume the colloidal state on contact with pure water. These are termed reversible colloids. Others remain insoluble when once separated from the disperse system. There is no real theoretical distinction between the classes, for the phenomenon depends upon the velocity with which the disperse particles form grains of precipitable size, and all such "reversible" colloids eventually become irreversible. (2) Colloids which, like agar agar or gelatin, form both solutions and two phase systems with water according to temperature are termed reversible.

COLLOIDAL. Existing in the colloid state. (See **colloid.**)

COLLOIDAL ELECTROLYTE. A compound having a long **hydrocarbon** chain terminating in a group that can ionize. Colloidal electrolytes resemble nonelectrolytes in some of their properties and **electrolytes** in others. Thus, the alkaline salts of the fatty acids, for example, have the osmotic properties of a nonelectrolyte, but they show a marked electrical conductance and other properties of weak electrolytes.

COLLOIDAL EQUIVALENT. A term applied to the **dispersed phase** of a colloidal system, denoting the number of molecules per unit electric charge.

COLLOIDAL STATE. A system of particles in a dispersing medium, in which the mean size of the particles lies between molecular size and a size great enough to be visible to the eye or in the optical microscope. Colloidal systems are associated with distinctive properties and behavior.

COLLOIDAL SUSPENSION. See **suspension, colloidal.**

COLOR BASE. A colorless, or slightly colored, substance that yields a **dye** upon **oxidation,** or by some other simple reaction, usually involving a minor rearrangement of the molecule.

COLOR, COMPLEMENTARY. A color of light that combines to produce white light with the given color of light.

COLOR FILTER. A layer, film, or plate of a substance or material that absorbs certain **frequencies** of **transmitted light.**

COLOR, GROUND. See **ground color.**

COLOR REACTION. See **reaction, color.**

COLOR SCALE TEMPERATURE. See **temperature, color scale.**

COLOR SCREEN. A color filter used to exclude certain **frequencies** of light from a reaction system in order to control or modify a photo-process, physical or chemical.

COLOR THEORY. An explanation of the color of substances on the basis of their chemical structure and physical condition.

COLORIMETER. An instrument for measuring the percentage **transmission** of monochromatic light through a colored liquid. Usually these values are compared to values obtained under identical conditions with colored solutions of known concentration. Such instruments are of service in the quantitative estimation of substances that are colored or that develop colors during certain reactions.

COLORIMETRIC ANALYSIS. See **analysis, colorimetric.**

COLUMBATE. Now called **niobate** (q.v.).

COLUMBIC. Now called **niobic** (q.v.).

COLUMBIUM. Formerly the name of the element **niobium** (q.v.).

COLUMBOUS. Now called **niobous** (q.v.).

COMBES QUINOLINE SYNTHESIS. A method of formation of **quinolines** from β-diketones and aromatic amines, followed by dehydration of the intermediate compounds.

$$CH_3COCH_2COCH_3 + C_6H_5NH_2 \xrightarrow{-H_2O} CH_3COCH_2C(=NC_6H_5)CH_3.$$

$$H_2SO_4 \downarrow -H_2O$$

COMBINATION. A term indicating the operation of a chemical process by which two or more individual substances or two or more molecules of a single substance condense to form a new chemical individual.

COMBINATION CELL. See **cell, combination.**

COMBINATION, CHEMICAL. In general, the union of two or more substances to form a new substance, which cannot be resolved into the parent substances by ordinary mechanical or ordinary physical means.

COMBINATION PRINCIPLE. A method of calculating the **frequencies** of lines in **atomic spectra.** These frequencies are related to the separation of those two terms which represent the two energy levels of the electron emitting the radiation. (See **Ritz combination principle.**)

COMBINATION PROCESS. The name applied to a number of petroleum treating processes which combine two or more operations including cracking. For example, the Gasoline Products Company's combination process combines in one unit crude stripping, viscosity breaking of the residual product, and reforming of naphtha. This process has been modified to yield the unicoil injection system, which combines viscosity breaking and high temperature cracking, and is characterized by the injection of the preheated feed into the partially cracked stream of high-temperature clean gas oil passing through the heater.

COMBINATION TANNING. A process of tanning hides which depends upon the use of two tanning agents, such as gambier and alum, rather than one.

COMBINING WEIGHT. A property of elementary substances that determines their proportions by weight in compounds. Numerically the combining weight is equal to the **atomic weight** of the element divided by the **valence** which the element exhibits in the particular compound. Also known as **equivalent weight.**

COMBINING WEIGHTS, LAW OF. See **law of combining weights.**

COMBUSTION. (1) The combination of oxidizable substance with an **oxidizing agent,** or any chemical change attended by the production of heat and light.
(2) The term combustion is also used in a more restricted sense to donate a rapid oxidation process, attended usually by a considerable production of heat and light.

COMBUSTION BOAT. A small, shallow, open container used to hold the sample to be burned in a combustion apparatus.

COMBUSTION CRUCIBLE. A crucible used to hold the coal or oil to be burned in a calorific determination.

COMBUSTION, FRACTIONAL. A method of separating and determining gaseous mixtures by burning one component (usually hydrogen) under conditions such that other combustible components are unaffected.

COMBUSTION FURNACE. A laboratory furnace used as part of the combustion train in making an ultimate **analysis.**

COMBUSTION TRAIN. An arrangement of laboratory apparatus for the complete **oxidation** (combustion) of a compound or mixture, and for the collection, identification, or, more commonly, the quantitative determination of the products of the oxidation. The apparatus is used extensively in the ultimate **analysis** of organic substances to determine the amounts of the various elements contained.

COMBUSTION TUBE. A tube of refractory glass or ceramic material, in which complete **oxidation** of substances is carried out, as in an ultimate **analysis.**

COMMANDUCCI TEST REACTION. Formic acid in solution gives a yellow-red color on warming with 15 drops of a 50% sodium bisulfite solution.

COMMINUTION. Reduction in size. The term is commonly used in reference to processes such as **grinding, crushing, shredding,** etc., of materials.

COMMON ION EFFECT. The reversal of **ionization** which occurs when a compound is added to a solution of a second compound with which it has a common ion, the volume being kept constant. The degree of ionization of the second compound then is lowered, i.e., it retrogresses.

COMMUNAL ENTROPY. A differential entropy for a liquid, $R = S_g - S_s$, where R is the communal entropy, S_s is the entropy derived from that value of the **work function,** which is related to the **partition function** as for a solid (each molecule confined to its cell), and S_g is the entropy derived from that value of the work function, which is related to the partition function on the assumption that there is

enough freedom of the molecules of the liquid so that any molecule may occupy any part of the entire free volume of the liquid.

The communal entropy is interpreted physically as that contribution to the entropy of a system due to the disorder arising when the molecules become sufficiently free to change places with each other.

COMPARISON SPECTROSCOPE. See **spectroscope, comparison.**

COMPARISON SPECTRUM. See **spectrum, comparison.**

COMPARISON TUBES. Tubes of uniform material and diameter, which are used in colorimeters for matching or comparing colors.

COMPATIBILITY. The property of two or more drugs, or therapeutic agents, by which they can be administered together without impairment of the action of any of them, and without injurious results to the patient as the result of their joint physiological action.

COMPENSATION, EXTERNAL. A term used to denote a racemic condition of optical isomers. (See **isomerism, optical.**)

COMPENSATION, INTERNAL. The condition in which the **optical activity** of a substance that contains an even number of **asymmetric carbon atoms** is not exhibited, through opposing activities of the asymmetric atoms which neutralize each other. Thus, half the asymmetric carbon atoms may rotate the plane of polarized light in one direction, while the remainder act in the opposite direction. Therefore, there is no net change in the plane of the incident polarized light.

COMPENSATION METHOD, POGGENDORFF. See **Poggendorff compensation method.**

COMPENSATOR. A device used in **saccharimeters** for measuring the **rotation** of the sugar solution instead of employing the usual rotating analyzer. It consists of two wedges of dextrorotatory and a block of levorotatory quartz. The wedges are fixed so that one may be shifted to change the thickness of the quartz layer through which the light must pass. The zero point is read when the combined thickness of the two dextro wedges equals that of the levo block. On inserting a tube of dextrorotatory sugar solution into the instrument, the quartz wedge must be shifted to bring less dextro quartz into the line of vision until the whole is just neutral again. The amount of displacement measures the rotatory power of the sugar solution.

COMPIN TEST REACTION. Cobalt in neutral or slightly acid solution gives a green precipitate with potassium xanthate.

COMPLEMENT. In addition to its general meaning of a supplementary part, this term is used specifically to denote a **thermolabile substance** having a **haptophore** and a **zymophore group** (q.v.), the latter having a destructive action on the cell.

COMPLEX ACID. A compound containing two or more acid radicals.

COMPLEX, AUTO. See **auto-complex.**

COMPLEX COMPOUND. See **compound, complex.**

COMPLEX ION. A complex electrically charged **radical** or group of atoms such as $Cu(NH_3)_2^{++}$, which may be formed by the addition of an electrically neutral radical or molecule to an ion.

COMPLEX SALT, INNER. A complex salt which has a cyclic structural formula. A great many compounds of this type are formed by the **coordination** with metals of compounds, usually organic, having an acid radical and a neutral group.

COMPONENT. In its most general usage, one of the ingredients of a mixture, or one of the distinct molecular or atomic species composing a mixture. In physical chemistry, one among the smallest number of chemical substances which need to be specified in order to reproduce a given chemical **system.**

COMPONENT, ACTIVE. See **enantiomorph.**

COMPOSITION, CRITICAL. See **critical composition.**

COMPOUND. A homogeneous, pure substance composed of two or more essentially different chemical elements, which are present in definite proportions; compounds usually possess properties differing from those of the constituent elements.

COMPOUND, ACTIVE. A compound which exhibits **optical activity,** i.e., rotates the plane of **polarized light.**

COMPOUND, ADDITION. A compound that is formed by the junction or union of two simpler compounds.

COMPOUND, ADDITIVE. An organic compound formed by an addition **reaction,** as by the **saturation** or partial saturation of a double or a triple bond or bonds.

COMPOUND, ALIPHATIC. An organic compound without ring structures, i.e., with straight chain arrangement of carbon and, possibly other, atoms. In the narrower sense, an aliphatic compound is a member of the **paraffin series** of hydrocarbons, or one of their derivatives.

COMPOUND, AROMATIC. An organic compound containing a **ring** of carbon atoms, usually unsaturated, such as a **benzene, naphthalene, anthracene, acenaphthene,** etc., ring.

COMPOUND, ASSOCIATED. A compound formed by the union of two or more molecules, usually of the same or similar chemical composition, to form a single complex molecule.

COMPOUND, ASYMMETRIC. A compound containing an **asymmetric carbon atom** (q.v.).

COMPOUND, BINARY. A compound made up of only two elements, in one definite molecular ratio.

COMPOUND, COMPLEX. A compound which is made up structurally of two or more compounds or ions.

COMPOUND, CONDENSATION. A compound formed by a combination reaction between molecules, usually organic molecules, and usually by a reaction which results in the elimination of the elements of water or ethyl alcohol or their equivalent.

COMPOUND, COORDINATION. One of a number of types of complex compounds, usually derived by addition from simpler inorganic substances. Coordination compounds are essentially compounds to which atoms or groups have been added beyond the number possible on the basis of electrovalent linkages or the usual covalent linkages, to which each of the two atoms linked donates one electron to form the duplet. The coordinated groups are linked to the atoms of the compound usually by semipolar covalences, in which both the electrons in the bond are furnished by the linked atom of the coordinated group. The ammines and complex cyanides are representative coordination compounds.

COMPOUND, COVALENT. A compound formed by the sharing of electrons, between atoms; as distinguished from electrovalent compounds, in which there occurs a transfer of electrons.

COMPOUND, CYCLIC. An organic compound containing a ring of carbon atoms.

COMPOUND, ENDOTHERMIC. A compound whose formation is accompanied by a positive change in heat content, i.e., by the absorption of heat.

COMPOUND, EPOXY. A compound containing an oxygen bridge, as

$$\overset{\displaystyle O}{\overbrace{CH_2—CH_2—CH_2—CH_2,}}$$

which is 1,4 epoxy butane.

COMPOUND, EXOTHERMIC. A compound whose formation is accompanied by a negative change in heat content, i.e., with the liberation of heat.

COMPOUND, HETEROCYCLIC. A compound that contains a ring-shaped nucleus composed of dissimilar elements. A few inorganic substances fall into this classification, but by far the majority of them are carbon compounds. In organic chemistry substances of cyclic structure, as acid anhydrides, lactides, lactams, lactones, cyclic ethers, and cyclic derivatives of dicarboxylic acids which are formed by the elimination of water from aliphatic compounds, are not considered among the heterocyclic substances. Derivatives of pyridine, quinoline, thiophene, thiazole, pyrone, etc., which contain heterocyclic rings that persist in the compound through chemical reactions, are considered the true members of this class. Heterocyclic rings are known that contain nitrogen, sulfur, and oxygen members. The noncarbon members of the ring are termed "heteroatoms," and their number is indicated by the prefixes mono, di, tri, tetra, etc. The number of members in the ring may reach as high as sixteen, as in tetrasalicylide.

COMPOUND, HOMOCYCLIC. An organic compound containing a homocyclic ring, i.e., a ring containing carbon atoms only.

COMPOUND, HOMOLOGOUS. A member of an homologous series (q.v.).

COMPOUND, INACTIVE. A compound that does not affect the plane of polarized light. Such compounds may contain asymmetric carbon atoms that are rendered inactive by internal or external compensation.

COMPOUND, INNER. Compounds in which an additional valence bond has been formed between two atoms of an already existing structure, usually by loss of the elements of water or other simple substance. Inner compound formation commonly results in the formation of a ring. The inner esters, inner anhydrides, and inner coordination compounds are well known classes of inner compounds.

COMPOUND, INORGANIC. In general, a compound that does not contain carbon atoms. Some very simple carbon compounds, such as carbon monoxide and dioxide, binary metallic carbon compounds (carbides) and carbonates, are usually also included in the group of inorganic compounds.

COMPOUND, INTERMETALLIC. A compound consisting of metallic atoms only, which are joined by **metallic bonds** (q.v.).

COMPOUND, INTERSTITIAL. A compound of a metal or metals and certain **metalloid** elements, in which the metalloid atoms occupy the interstices between the atoms of the metal lattice. Compounds of this type are, for example, TaC, TiC, ZrC, NbC, and similar compounds of carbon, nitrogen, boron, and hydrogen with metals.

COMPOUND, IONIC. One of a class of compounds which **ionize** readily in aqueous solution, and which are formed when atoms combine to produce molecules having stable **configurations** by the transfer of one or more electrons within the molecule. This type of combination is illustrated by the combination of sodium atoms and chlorine atoms to form sodium chloride. The sodium atom loses the single electron in its outer shell, and thus is left with the stable configuration of eight electrons; the chlorine atom acquires an electron to increase the number of electrons in its outer shell from seven to eight; as a result of the loss and gain of the electrons, the atoms have acquired positive and negative charges, respectively, which constitute an electrovalent bond, that is disrupted in water and other polar solvents to yield sodium and chloride ions.

COMPOUND, ISOCYCLIC. (Homocyclic) A compound that contains a ring-shaped **nucleus** composed of the same element throughout, as benzene, naphthalene, and their derivatives. Cf. **heterocyclic compounds.**

COMPOUND, MOLECULAR. A compound formed by the union of two or more already saturated molecules apparently in defiance of the laws of **valence.** The class includes double salts, salts with water of **crystallization,** and metal ammonium derivatives. These salts are usually formed by **van der Waal's** attraction between the constituent molecules. They do not differ in any characteristic manner from compounds formed in strict accordance with the concept of valence. They are also called addition **compounds.**

COMPOUND, NONPOLAR. A compound in which the centers of positive and negative charge almost coincide so that no permanent **dipole moments** are produced. The term nonpolar also applies to compounds in which the effect of oppositely directed dipole moments cancel. Nonpolar compounds may contain polar bonds, if their effect is canceled by opposing bonds, as may occur in a perfectly symmetrical molecule. Nonpolar compounds do not ionize or conduct electricity. Most organic compounds are to be classed as nonpolar compounds.

COMPOUND, ORGANIC. One of the great number of compounds consisting of carbon linked in chains or rings; such compounds usually also contain hydrogen and may contain elements such as oxygen, nitrogen, sulfur, chlorine, etc. Some of the simpler carbon compounds are classified as inorganic compounds. (See **compound, inorganic.**)

COMPOUND, ORGANO-METALLIC. An organic compound in which one or more hydrogen atoms have been replaced by a metallic atom or atoms, usually with the establishment of a **valence bond** between the metal atom and a carbon atom. A metallic salt of an organic acid, in which the hydrogen atom of a $-COOH$ group is replaced by a metal atom, is not classified as an organo-metallic compound.

COMPOUND, POLAR. In general, a compound that exhibits **polarity,** or local differences in electrical properties, and has a **dipole moment** associated with one more of its interatomic **valence bonds.** Polar compounds have relatively high **dielectric constants,** associate readily in most cases, and include the substances that exhibit **tautomerism.** In the most general use of the term, polar compounds include all **electrolytes,** most inorganic substances, and many organic ones. Specifically, the term polar compound is frequently applied to the extreme type of polarity which arises in the presence of an **electrovalent bond** (q.v.) or in wave-mechanical terms, to cases in which one ionic term dominates in the orbital function of the molecule. Such compounds are exemplified by the inorganic acids, bases, and salts which possess, to a greater or lesser degree, the power to conduct electricity, associate, form double molecules and complex ions, etc.

COMPOUND, QUATERNARY. Either a compound containing an ammonium radical in which all hydrogen atoms are substituted, or a compound containing four different atomic species or radicals.

COMPOUND, RACEMIC. See isomerism, optical.

COMPOUND, SATURATED. A compound in which the **valence** of all the atoms is completely satisfied without linking any two atoms by more than one valence bond. (Cf. compound, unsaturated.)

COMPOUND, SPIRO-. A compound containing two ring structures having one common carbon atom.

COMPOUND, TRACER. A compound which by its ease of detection enables a reaction or process to be studied conveniently. Wide use has been made of **isotopes,** including radioactive isotopes of common elements, which are added in small quantities, in the form of the proper compound, to follow the course of an atom or a compound through a complicated series of reactions; or conversely to determine the properties of a tracer — that is available only in quantities too small to handle alone — by adding it to a system containing chemically related elements, and then following its course throughout a given series of reactions. Considerable use of tracer compounds is made in the study of physiological reactions.

COMPOUND, UNSATURATED. A term specifically applied to a carbon compound containing one or more **double bonds or triple bonds.** One consequence of the presence of these double bonds or triple

bonds, from which a broader concept of unsaturation stems, is the relative ease with which such bonds are split, and other constituents linked to them.

COMPOUNDS, PARTIALLY RACEMIC. Optically active compounds may crystallize together in double salts even though they are of different structure. When the two compounds are of opposite **rotatory power** the double salt is said to be a partially racemic compound. As an example, Pasteur obtained a double salt of ammonium d-tartrate and acid ammonium l-malate.

COMPRESSIBILITY COEFFICIENT. The deviation of a gas from **Boyle's law,** $pV =$ constant (at constant temperature).

COMPTON EFFECT. A change of **wave length** of **x-rays** which occurs when they are scattered upon impact with atoms or molecules. The effect is most pronounced when the scattering substance is of low atomic weight.

COMPTON METER. An **ionization chamber** especially useful for cosmic ray measurements. It is of the compensating type, using a balance chamber with a uranium source which is adjusted until it balances out the normal cosmic radiation. Variations in this radiation are shown on the collecting system, which is connected to an **electrometer.**

COMPTON RULE. An empirical relationship between thermal properties of elements, of the form:

$$\frac{(\text{At. Wt.})(L_f)}{T_f} = 2,$$

in which At. Wt. is the atomic weight, L_f is the **heat of fusion,** and T_f is the fusing point (in degrees absolute).

COMSTOCK AND WESCOTT PROCESS. A process for the recovery of sulfur from sulfide ores by treatment with chlorine, which frees sulfur according to the reaction:

$$FeS + Cl_2 \rightarrow FeCl_2 + S.$$

The chlorine is regenerated by oxidation of the chloride.

CONALBUMIN. A coagulable, noncrystalline, nitrogenous substance obtained during the purification of egg albumen.

CONCENTRATION. Either the process of increasing the quantity of a substance or form of energy or other entity that exists in a volume of space, as in increasing by evaporation the amount of solute contained in unit volume in a solution, or as in gathering heat, light, electricity, or other energy or form of energy; or the quantity itself of matter or other entity that exists in a unit volume, as the strength of a solution in mass of solute per unit mass of solution, or in the number of moles, hydrogen ions, etc., contained per unit volume or per unit mass.

CONCENTRATION, ABSOLUTE. The quantity of a substance, or form of energy or other entity that exists in a unit volume, expressed in mass per unit volume (ergs per cubic centimeter), or number of particles (as of atoms, hydrogen-ions, etc.) per unit volume.

CONCENTRATION CELL. See **cell, concentration.**

CONCENTRATION, CRITICAL. When two immiscible liquids are heated in contact with each other their mutual solubility is usually increased until, at the **critical solution point,** they become **consolute** (q.v.). The composition of the two solutions immediately before they become consolute is termed the critical concentration.

CONCENTRATION, IONIC. The number of **gram-ions** (calculated from the atomic weight of the substance or substances composing the ion) contained in unit volume of solution.

CONCENTRATION, MOLAL. See **molal concentration.**

CONCENTRATION, MOLAR. See **molar concentration.**

CONCENTRATION, NORMAL. See **normal concentration.**

CONCRETE. (1) A material or mass formed by the aggregation, spontaneous union, or coalescence of separate particles. (2) A solid construction material formed by mixing cement and water, commonly with sand and gravel or other aggregates. (3) A waxy essence of flowers or other plant material obtained by extraction and evaporation. (4) Crude sugar obtained in compact masses by boiling sugar cane juice or other solutions of sugar.

CONDAMINE REAGENT. A solution of 5 g. cuprous chloride and 10 g. β-naphthol, in a mixture of 95 g. concentrated sulfuric acid and 5 g. water. This reagent is used to absorb carbon monoxide.

CONDENSATION. A term having a number of uses in physics and chemistry, all connoting conversion to a more concentrated or compact form. Thus, it is used in physics to express the transformation of a substance from the gaseous state to the liquid state, the focusing of divergent radiations or the accumulation of electrons. In chemistry, it is applied to certain cases of combination of molecules, as in instances where the molecules are similar, or in classes of reactions between organic molecules or parts of the same molecule in which water, hydrochloric acid, ammonia, alcohol, or similar substance is eliminated and a new bond between carbon atoms is formed, or such union without elimination as in the aldol condensation. The process is usually not reversible. Esterification, alkylation, acylation, and the formation of compounds in which the union takes place through an oxygen or nitrogen atom are not regarded as condensations. See specific examples below, and those listed throughout this book under the name or names of the men to whom they are commonly accredited.

CONDENSATION, ACETOACETIC ESTER. A class of reactions occasioned by the dehydrating power of metallic sodium or sodium ethoxide on the ethyl esters of monobasic aliphatic acids and a few other esters. It is best known in the formation of acetoacetic ester:

$$2CH_3 \cdot COOC_2H_5 + 2CH_3 \cdot COOC_2H_5 + 2Na \rightarrow 2CH_3 \cdot C(ONa):CH \cdot COOC_2H_5 + 2C_2H_5OH + H_2$$

The actual course of the reaction is still a subject of controversy. By the action of acids the sodium may be eliminated from the first product of the reaction and the free ester obtained. This may exist in the tautomeric enol and keto forms. On boiling the ester with acids or alkalies it will split in two ways, the circumstances determining the nature of the main product. Thus, if moderately strong acid or weak alkali is employed, acetone is formed with very little acetic acid (ketone splitting). In the presence of strong alkalies however, very little acetone and much acetic acid result (acid splitting). Derivatives of ace-

Weak alkalies and acids are employed to effect the condensation. (Cf. **condensation, benzoin; condensation, crotonaldehyde; Claisen condensation;** and **condensation, pinacone.**)

CONDENSATION, AROMATIC. The formation of cyclic compounds by the condensation of aliphatic substances. (Cf. **polymerization, aromatic.**)

CONDENSATION, BENZOIN. A condensation of two molecules of aromatic aldehydes effected by potassium cyanide. For example, benzaldehyde condenses with itself to form benzoin,

toacetic ester may be decomposed in the same fashion, and this fact is responsible for the great utility of this condensation in organic synthesis. See also **synthesis, acetoacetic ester;** and **Claisen condensation.**

CONDENSATION, ACYLOIN. Reduc-

CONDENSATION, CROTONALDEHYDE. A condensation of aldehydes with elimination of water. The first step is the aldol condensation. (See **condensation, aldol.**) Water is split out from the product to yield an unsaturated aldehyde, viz.,

$$CH_3 \cdot CHOH \cdot CH_2 \cdot CHO \rightarrow CH_3 \cdot CH:CH \cdot CHO + H_2O.$$
$$\text{Aldol} \qquad\qquad\qquad \text{Crotonaldehyde}$$

tion of esters by the action of metallic sodium to yield aliphatic α-hydroxy ketones.

$$2R'COOR'' \xrightarrow{\text{Na}} R'C(ONa):(ONa)CR' + 2NaOR''.$$
$$\downarrow \text{H}_2\text{O}$$
$$R'CO \cdot CHOH \cdot R' + 2 NaOH$$

CONDENSATION, DIFFERENTIAL. A partial condensation in which the conden-

CONDENSATION, ALDOL. A reaction between **aldehydes** or aldehydes and **ketones** which occurs without the elimination of any secondary product, and yields β-hydroxycarbonyl compounds. It is distinguished from polymerization by the facts that it occurs between aldehydes and ketones and is not generally reversible. In its simplest form it may be represented by the condensation of two molecules of acetaldehyde to aldol:

sate is continually removed from the system as soon as it is formed.

CONDENSATION, EQUILIBRIUM. A partial condensation in which the condensate is kept in contact and in equilibrium with the residual vapor.

CONDENSATION, EXTERNAL. (Intermolecular condensation) Condensation in which two or more molecules combine, as distinguished from internal condensation.

$$CH_3 \cdot CHO + CH_3 \cdot CHO \rightarrow CH_3 \cdot CHOH \cdot CH_2 \cdot CHO.$$

CONDENSATION, FRACTIONAL. A process for the separation of substances in the vapor phase by partial condensation, thus obtaining a condensate richer in one component. The degree of the separation can be extended by repeated applications of the process.

CONDENSATION, HYDROLYTIC. The condensation of one or more molecules of aliphatic compounds with the elimination of water, if ring compounds are formed. Such condensations might more properly be termed hydrosynthetic condensations. An example is the condensation of three molecules of acetone to form one molecule of trimethylbenzene and three molecules of water.

CONDENSATION, INTERMOLECULAR. See **condensation, external.**

CONDENSATION, INTERNAL. (Intramolecular condensation) Condensation in which combination takes place between carbon atoms in the same molecule as the condensation of phenylpropionyl chloride to form hydrindone, viz.,

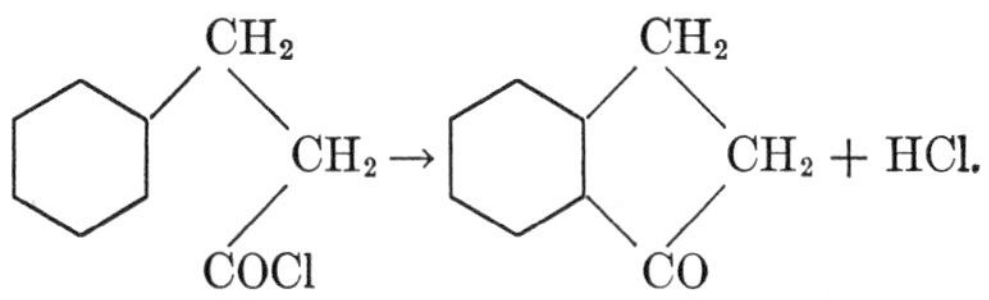

CONDENSATION, INTRAMOLECULAR. See **condensation, internal.**

CONDENSATION, MAGNESIUM-ALKYL. A condensation reaction using metallic magnesium. A halogen derivative of one of the reagents, RX, is dissolved in ether. Magnesium is then added to this mixture to form an intermediate compound with the following probable structure:

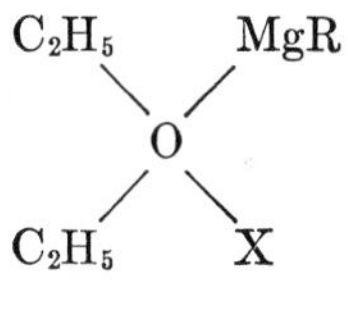

If a second reagent is now added, such as

an aldehyde, R′—C(=O)—H, a further reaction with the RMgX fragment occurs in which

$$R-\underset{\underset{R'}{|}}{\overset{\overset{H}{|}}{C}}-OMgX$$ is formed. Addition of

water then yields $R-\underset{\underset{R'}{|}}{\overset{\overset{H}{|}}{C}}-OH$. Similarly

with ketones and esters, the reaction yields alcohols; with cyanogen, cyanides, and amides it yields ketones; with carbon dioxide and subsequent hydrolysis it yields acids; with dialkylformamides (RR′N · CHO) it yields aldehydes; numerous other types of reactions have been discovered. (See also **Grignard reaction.**)

CONDENSATION, ORGANO-METALLIC. See **condensation, zinc-alkyl; condensation, magnesium-alkyl; Grignard reaction;** and **Frankland reaction.**

CONDENSATION, PARTIAL. The enrichment of a mixture of two (or more) vapors in a more volatile component by cooling it enough to separate as liquid a part richer in a less volatile component.

CONDENSATION, PINACONE. A condensation accompanying the reduction of aldehydes and ketones especially in neutral and alkaline solutions, in which the carbonyl carbon atoms are linked together and two atoms of hydrogen are added, viz.,

$$2CH_3 \cdot CO \cdot CH_3 + H_2 \rightarrow$$

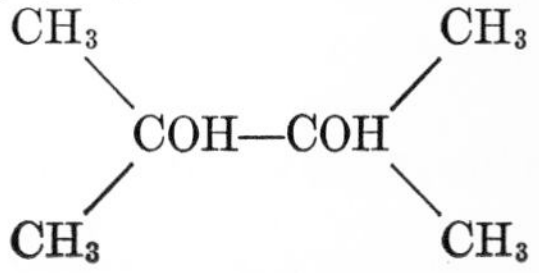

and

$$2C_6H_5 \cdot CHO + H_2 \rightarrow$$
$$C_6H_5 \cdot CHOH{-}CHOH \cdot C_6H_5.$$

CONDENSATION POLYMERIZATION. See **polymerization, condensation.**

CONDENSATION, PYRO. Condensation effected by the agency of high temperature, as methane, when conducted through red hot tubes, yields benzene. Note, the formation of benzene from acetylene under similar circumstances is not condensation, but **polymerization** (q.v.).

CONDENSATION THEORY OF CATALYSIS. Theory proposed by Faraday to explain the phenomenon of catalysis. Faraday postulated that near the catalyst surface the concentration of reactants is greater than in the gas phase. The reacting substances are thus in closer contact and consequently the reaction takes place with greater velocity near the catalyst.

CONDENSATION, ZINC-ALKYL. Condensation in which zinc-alkyl compounds are employed to introduce hydrocarbon residues into organic substances, the zinc being eliminated as a hydrate or halide, as for example

$$Zn(CH_3)_2 + 2R_3CI \rightarrow 2R_3C{-}CH_3 + ZnI_2.$$

The zinc-alkyls react with water:

$$Zn(CH_3)_2 + 2H_2O \rightarrow 2CH_4 + Zn(OH)_2.$$

CONDENSED SURFACE FILM. See **surface film, condensed.**

CONDENSER. Any apparatus used to effect a **condensation** (q.v.) of either physical or chemical nature.

CONDENSER, ALLIHN. A jacketed condensing tube incorporating bulbs which increase the condensing surface and lessen the resistance to the passage of vapors.

CONDENSER, COILED TUBE. A jacketed condenser, with its inner tube coiled to provide a larger condensing surface.

CONDENSER, EASTMAN. A vertical condenser in which the cooling water is supplied to an inner tube, while the vapor is fed from the top to an annular space between inner and outer tubes. This condenser is used especially for removal of solvent from extracts to be concentrated.

CONDENSER, ELECTRICAL. An apparatus for storing or accumulating electricity, consisting of alternate layers of insulating and readily-charged material, the latter being usually a metallic substance in which electrons move freely.

CONDENSER, HOPKINS. A vertical condenser in which a sealed inner chamber is cooled by water conducted to its bottom by a glass tube. The vapor to be condensed is conducted to an annular outer chamber. This condenser thus consists of three concentric glass tubes.

CONDENSER, JET. An apparatus used to remove noncondensable gas from a system by means of an aspirator.

CONDENSER, KJELDAHL. A tubular, glass water-cooled condenser used for condensing the distillate during the **Kjeldahl analysis** for nitrogen.

CONDENSER, LIEBIG. A simple type of laboratory condenser, consisting essentially of two glass tubes, one inside the other, with the necessary outlets and inlets. The cooling medium occupies the annular space between the tubes while the vapor to be condensed passes through the inner one.

CONDENSER, SURFACE. A condenser in which the cooling water or other medium is kept separate from the condensing vapor by a *surface* through which the heat passes.

CONDENSING AGENT. A substance that brings about a **condensation** reaction between other substances.

CONDITION OF A GAS, EQUATION OF. The equation $PV = RT$ where P represents pressure; V, volume; T, the absolute temperature; and R, the gas constant. The expression states that the product of the pressure into the volume is proportional to the absolute temperature times a constant. This relationship is also known as the **equation of state** of a **gas** (q.v.).

CONDUCTANCE. The capacity to conduct, as applied particularly to heat or electricity; or the quantity of electricity which flows through a unit volume (unit cube) under unit difference of electrical potential per unit time. It is the reciprocal of resistance.

CONDUCTANCE, DISPERSION OF. See Debye-Falkenhagen effect.

CONDUCTANCE, EQUIVALENT. The electrical conductance of a solution containing one gram-equivalent weight of solute at a specified concentration. It is equal to the specific conductance multiplied by the volume of solution containing one gram-equivalent weight of solute.

CONDUCTANCE, IONIC. The amount contributed by each characteristic ion to the total equivalent conductance at infinite dilution. Thus, in the mathematical expression of the law of independent migration of ions:

$$\Lambda_0 = \lambda_+ + \lambda_-$$

in which λ_+ and λ_- are the ionic conductances of cation and anion, respectively, and Λ_0 is the total conductance of the electrolyte.

CONDUCTANCE, MOLAR. The conductance of a solution which contains one mole of solute measured when placed between electrodes which are one centimeter apart. It is equal to the product of the specific conductance, and the volume (in cubic centimeters) of solution containing one mole of electrolyte.

CONDUCTANCE, MOLECULAR. See conductance, molar.

CONDUCTANCE RATIO. The ratio of the equivalent conductance of a given ionic (electrolytic) solution to its equivalent conductance at infinite dilution.

CONDUCTANCE, SPECIFIC. The electrical conductance of a centimeter cube of a substance or a solution. It is measured in mhos (reciprocal ohms). For solutions, the specific conductance varies with the concentration.

CONDUCTION. The transmission of energy (heat, sound, electricity) by means of a medium without movement of the medium itself, as distinguished from convection, in which such movement occurs, or from radiation in which the energy quanta pass *through* the medium and so the transmission does not occur *by means of the medium.*

CONDUCTIVITY. In general chemical use, the same as **conductance** (q.v.), although this term is often used to mean specific conductance. (See **conductance, specific.**) It is the reciprocal of resistivity.

CONDUCTIVITY APPARATUS. An apparatus for determining the conductivity (conductance) of a liquid or solution. It consists of a conductivity cell, with all the accessory equipment for measuring resistance, and for measuring and controlling temperature.

CONDUCTIVITY CELL. A cell for determining the conductivity of a solution (or fused solid), consisting of a chamber containing two electrodes.

CONDUCTIVITY COEFFICIENT. The amount of energy, i.e., heat or electricity, passing through a unit length of a medium in a unit time, under a unit difference of **temperature** or **potential.**

CONDUCTIVITY, SUPER. The anomalous conductivity of substances at temperatures near absolute zero, which increases very rapidly with small reductions in temperature.

CONDUCTOMETRIC TITRATION. See titration, conductometric.

CONDUCTOR. A substance that conducts **energy** relatively well, especially electricity or heat.

CONE-CADY REAGENT. Two solutions — a $\frac{1}{2}\%$ aqueous solution of potassium ferricyanide, and a 1% glacial acetic acid solution of diphenylamine — used in testing for zinc. A brown, green, or purple precipitate indicates the presence of zinc.

CONE, FILTER. See filter cone.

CONES, PYROMETRIC. See pyrometric cones.

CONFIGURATION, ATOMIC. The arrangement in space of the atoms of a molecule.

CONFIGURATION, AXIALLY SYMMETRIC. (Centrally symmetric configuration) The spacial arrangement of the atoms in the trans or fumaroid form of a stereoisomer. (See **isomerism, stereo.**)

CONFIGURATION, PLANE SYMMETRIC. The spacial arrangement of the atoms in the cis or malenoid form of a stereoisomer. (See **isomerism, stereo.**)

CONGEAL. To solidify.

CONGO RED SOLUTION. An aqueous solution of sodium tetrazodiphenylnaphthionate, used as an indicator of hydrogen-ion concentration. The color changes from blue to red in the **pH** range of 3.5 to 5.

CONGRUENT MELTING POINT. See **melting point, congruent.**

CONJUGATE ACID AND BASE. An acid and a base which are so related that the acid molecule is formed by the addition to the base of a hydrogen ion (**proton**) and the base molecule is formed by dissociation of a hydrogen ion (proton) from the acid. Thus, in the **equilibrium,**

$$A \rightleftarrows H^+ + B^-,$$

A and B are conjugate acid and base.

CONJUGATE SOLUTIONS. A system in **equilibrium** consisting of two liquid phases and two components; if the components of such a two-component system are designated as A and B, then one phase is a solution of component A in component B, and the other phase is a solution of component B in component A. Such liquids are spoken of as "partially miscible."

CONJUGATED DOUBLE BONDS. A system of double bonds in a chain of at least four atoms in which the double linkings occur between alternate atoms, as atoms 1 and 2, 3 and 4, etc.,

$$-W{=}X{-}Y{=}Z{-}.$$

CONJUGATION. Formation of certain so-called conjugated molecules, as are found among the complex proteins; or formation of **conjugate double bonds** (q.v.) or compounds containing them.

CONN STAIN. A solution of 1 g. rose bengal dye and 0.001 g. calcium chloride in 100 ml. of a 5% aqueous solution of phenol. This stain is used in testing for bacteria in soil.

CONNATE SALTS. See **salts, connate.**

CONRAD-LIMPACH SYNTHESIS. A method of formation of 4-hydroxyquinolines, by condensing β-keto-esters and aromatic amines followed by ring closure of the intermediate compounds.

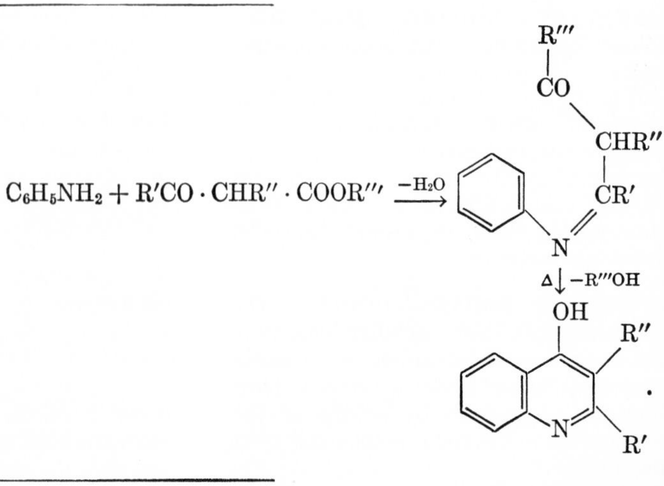

$$C_6H_5NH_2 + R'CO \cdot CHR'' \cdot COOR''' \xrightarrow{-H_2O}$$

CONSECUTIVE REACTION. See reaction, consecutive.

CONSERVATION OF ENERGY. See law of conservation of energy.

CONSERVATION OF MATTER. See law of conservation of matter.

CONSISTENCY. (1) The degree of **viscosity** or **fluidity** of a liquid, or the degree of **firmness** or **plasticity** of a solid. (2) The relative amount of solid material in a mixture.

CONSISTOMETER. A testing apparatus for measuring the **hardness** (consistency) of materials. Its essential element is a pointed plunger which is dropped from a fixed height on the material being tested; the depth of penetration is a measure of the relative hardness of the material.

CONSOLUTE. Completely miscible. Term applied to liquids when they are miscible in all proportions, i.e., mutually completely soluble, under some given conditions. Not usually applied to gases which are all miscible.

CONSOLUTE TEMPERATURE. See critical composition.

CONSTANT. A magnitude which suffers no change during a specific operation.

CONSTANT, AVOGADRO. See Avogadro constant.

CONSTANT BOILING MIXTURES. Liquids consisting of two or more **components** which boil at constant temperature and distill without change in composition. Commonly, there is only one composition at which two particular liquids form a constant boiling mixture. (The proportions vary, of course, with the pressure.) Constant boiling liquid systems are also called **azeotropic** mixtures.

CONSTANT BOILING POINT. The temperature at which a **solution** boils without a change in composition, at a definite concentration and under a constant pressure; the proportion by weight of the **components** in the vapor is the same as in the liquid.

CONSTANT, BOLTZMANN. See Boltzmann constant.

CONSTANT, DIELECTRIC. (Specific inductive capacity) A measure of that property of a medium by virtue of which it modifies the mutual interaction of electrified bodies immersed in it or separated by it. The dielectric constant of a vacuum is taken as a reference standard and assigned the value unity, and the constants for several gases and vapors (at less than 3 cycles per second) are: air, 1.000567 (0° C.); benzene, 1.0028 (100° C.); ethane, 1.0015 (0° C.); hydrogen chloride, 1.0046 (0° C.); and steam, 1.00785 (at 140° C.).

The dielectric constants of several liquids (at audio frequency, 20–20,000 cycles per second) are: amyl alcohol, 15.8 (20° C.); benzene, 2.283 (20° C.); chlorine, 2.0 (0° C.); ethyl acetate, 6.4 (20° C.); sulfur dioxide, 15.6 (0° C.); water (at 10^8 cycles and 20° C.), 80; and, sulfur 3.42 (400° C.).

The dielectric constants of several solids (at audio frequencies) are: calcite, 8.5 (20° C.); potassium chloride 5.03 (20° C.); quartz 4.34 (20° C.); ice, 40 (−22° C. and 40×10^8 cycles); sulfur 4.0 (20° C.); wood, oak 2.4–4.2 (20° C.).

CONSTANT, DISSOCIATION. See ionization constant.

CONSTANT, EQUILIBRIUM. The quantity obtained, in the case of a homogeneous reversible **reaction** which has reached **equilibrium,** by dividing the product of the **concentration** of the substances produced by the reaction by the product of the concentration of the reacting substances. This quantity, in accordance with the **Law of Mass Action,** is constant for a given temperature. Thus for the reversible homogeneous gas reaction

$$mA + nB \cdots \rightleftarrows pC + qD \cdots$$

the equilibrium constant is given by the expression

$$K = \frac{c_C^p \, c_D^q \cdots}{c_A^m \, c_B^n \cdots}$$

in which c_A^m, c_B^n, c_C^p and c_D^q are the molar concentrations of the reacting substances, and K is the equilibrium constant. Since the Law of Mass Action applies strictly to activities and not to concentrations, the above form of the law applies strictly to ideal systems; and for nonideal systems it should be written in terms of activities, as follows:

$$K = \left(\frac{\gamma_C^p \, \gamma_D^q \cdots}{\gamma_A^m \, \gamma_B^n \cdots}\right)\left(\frac{c_C^p \, c_D^q \cdots}{c_A^m \, c_B^n \cdots}\right).$$

CONSTANT, GAS. Since for an **ideal gas,** by the **law of Boyle,** the product of its volume and pressure is constant at a given temperature, and since by the **law of Gay-Lussac,** the ratio of volume to temperature is constant at a given pressure, the combination of the two gives the relationship:

$$PV = (\text{Constant}) \, T.$$

Assuming the **law of Avogadro,** that all gases contain the same number of molecules under the same conditions, then the above constant is the same for all gases, if they are assumed to behave ideally. Its value for one mole of gas is 0.08205 liter-atmosphere per degree Centigrade per mole, using the stated units for volume, pressure, temperature, and quantity. It is usually denoted by the letter R and is also called the molar gas constant.

CONSTANT, MADELUNG. See **Madelung constant.**

CONSTANT, PLANCK. See **quantum theory.**

CONSTANT, RYDBERG. See **Rydberg constant.**

CONSTANT, STEFAN-BOLTZMANN. The figure 1.36×10^{-12} calories per second per square centimeter which is the numerical value of constant σ in the **Stefan-Boltzmann equation** (q.v.).

CONSTANT, SUTHERLAND. See **Sutherland constant.**

CONSTANT, TRANSFORMATION. A constant that expresses the rate of decay of a radio-element. This constant is the fraction of the total mass of the radio-element which disintegrates per second.

CONSTANT, VELOCITY. See **coefficient, velocity.**

CONSTANT, VERDET. See **Verdet constant.**

CONSTANTINESCU TEST REACTIONS. The various silver proteins (Argyrol, Collargol, Protargol, etc.) give characteristic precipitates and solution colors when 2 ml. of their solutions are treated with 1 ml. 10% sodium iodide solution, 5 ml. water, and 10 drops 10% ammonium molybdate solution containing nitric acid.

CONSTITUENT. In general, one of the elements or parts of a compound; in physical chemistry, one of the distinctive elements or compounds, which are present in a system, and which are formed from its **components** (q.v.).

CONSTITUTION. (1) The arrangement of the atoms in the molecule. (2) A diagram designed to show the relative positions of atoms and groups in two dimensions. When the arrangement is considered in three dimensions, so as to show spacial relationships, it is called a configuration.

CONSTITUTIVE PROPERTY. A property of a substance or system which depends for the most part on the arrangement of the atoms in the molecule, and to a lesser extent on their number and nature.

CONTACT ANGLE. The angle formed by a liquid resting upon the surface of a solid at the gas-solid-liquid interface. The angle is measured in the liquid, being the angle included between the surface of the solid, and a plane (or line) normal to the surface of the liquid at the gas-solid-liquid interface.

CONTACT POTENTIAL. See **potential, contact.**

CONTACT PROCESS. A process for the manufacture of sulfuric acid. The sulfur or sulfides are burned in an excess of air to form sulfur dioxide. The gases are then passed over a catalyst of platinum supported upon asbestos or other medium, or of a suitable complex vanadium compound, whereupon the sulfur dioxide combines with oxygen, which is available from the excess amount of air used in the initial combustion. The sulfur trioxide thus formed is absorbed in sulfuric acid, which is then diluted with water to reduce it to its original strength, and thus in effect, to add the equivalent H_2O for combination with the sulfur trioxide absorbed. Acid of any desired concentration can be produced by the contact process, although it offers the greatest advantages over the chamber process at high concentrations, since the most effective strength of acid for the absorption of sulfur trioxide is 98%.

CONTINUITY, EQUATION OF. See **equation of continuity.**

CONTINUITY OF STATE. Transition between the gaseous and liquid states, in either direction, without discontinuity, or abrupt change in physical properties. Although this transition is not realizable in practice by mere pressure-volume change, it can be accomplished by some processes, as by a sequence of temperature changes in one direction at constant volume, followed by temperature changes in the other direction at constant pressure, or vice versa.

CONTINUOUS SPECTRUM. See **spectrum, continuous.**

CONTRACTION. In general, any process of shortening, or reduction of length, area, or volume. A specific use of the term in chemistry is its application to molecules which have a smaller molecular volume than the sum of the volumes of the constituent atoms. This effect is caused by strong electrical interaction between the atomic constituents.

CONTRAVALENCE. (Obs.) A subordinate valency. Abegg and Bodlander assumed that each atom possessed eight valencies distributed as positive and negative. The type of valence in excess was termed the normal valence and determined the positive or negative character of the atom; the subordinate valence was termed the contravalency. See **covalence.**

CONTROL. A comparison analysis or test, usually run in parallel with another test to determine the effect of variable conditions, the interference of competing reactions, or the corrections to be applied for errors arising from various sources.

CONVECTION. (1) The transference of heat by the bodily movement of heated particles of matter, as the heating of buildings by steam or hot air, or hot water. (2) The transfer of mass by streaming motion.

CONVERSION. (1) A change in numerical value of a quantity resulting from the use of a different unit in the same or a different system of measurement. (2) An intramolecular **rearrangement** of organic substances in which the relative positions of the **radicals** are modified. The **Beckmann rearrangement** is a case in point. Radicals may be transferred from carbon, oxygen, or nitrogen to carbon; from carbon or oxygen to nitrogen; from side chains to nucleus, etc. See specific examples below, and also under the names of individual investigators.

CONVERSION, BENZIDINE. (Benzidine rearrangement) The intramolecular rearrangement of hydrazobenzene and its derivatives to benzidine and benzidine derivatives on boiling with mineral acids. A typical example of this conversion is:

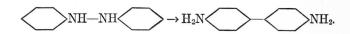

which have a smaller molecular volume than the sum of the volumes of the constituent atoms. This effect is caused by strong electrical interaction between the atomic constituents.

A small amount of diphenyline base

is produced simultaneously. If the para-position in one of the hydrazobenzene rings is occupied, the benzidine conversion can take place only if the substituent is eliminated. Cf. **rearrangement, semidine.**

CONVERSION, DIAZOAMINO-AMINAZO. (Diazoamino-aminazo rearrangement) The intramolecular rearrangement of diazoamino into aminazo compounds in the presence of a small amount of the hydrochloride of an aromatic base (such as *p*-toluidine hydrochloride). The reaction may be represented by the equation:

$$R—N=N—NH—R' \rightarrow R—N=N—R'—NH_2$$

in which R and R' are aryl radicals. The —NH₂ group enters the para-position; or if that is occupied, the ortho-position (more slowly).

CONVERSION FACTOR. A number used to multiply a quantity or magnitude (as a dimensional quantity, or the result of analytical determination) in order to express it in other units.

CONVERSION OF OXIMES. The conversion of **syn** to **anti** and anti to syn forms of **oximes** by chemical treatment.

CONVERSION, PINACOL-PINACO-LONE (or Pinacone Rearrangement). An intramolecular change in which a methyl group is transferred from one carbon atom to another. The reverse change is also included in the term. Viz.,

COOLING CURVE. A graphical representation of the temperature of a substance plotted against time, such as is obtained for a molten alloy cooling through its solidification temperature or range of temperatures.

COOLING, LAW OF. See **law of Newton for heat loss.**

COOPER-HEWITT LAMP. A mercury vapor lamp (it is evacuated, and contains a little mercury vapor) which emits a relatively high proportion of its radiation in the violet and ultraviolet region, and is therefore especially effective for photographic use.

COOPER REAGENT. A solution of 10 g. 2,4-dihydroxyacetophenone in 100 ml. alcohol, which gives a red color with ferric ion.

COOPERATIVE PHENOMENON. Any process for whose occurrence the simultaneous interaction between several molecules or systems is required.

Pinacol or "Pinacone"   Pinacolone

CONVULSANT. A drug that induces convulsions.

COOK FORMULA. A relationship for calculating the **acetyl number** of an organic substance from the **saponification** titers before and after acetylation. It is equal to their difference, divided by a correction factor that approaches unity as the initial saponification value decreases.

COOLIDGE TUBE. A type of **x-ray tube** or **cathode tube** having an electrically heated cathode. In the original Coolidge x-ray tube the cathode consisted of a tungsten spiral in a molybdenum tube; a nickel window permitted passage of high-speed electrons.

COORDINATE BOND. See **bond, coordinate.**

COORDINATE COVALENCE. See **coordinate valence.**

COORDINATE VALENCE. A valence **bond** between two atoms in which both the electrons constituting the shared pair have been furnished by one of the two atoms. This linkage is also called a semipolar bond, a dative bond, a dative covalence, and a coordinate link. It occurs extensively in coordination compounds.

COORDINATION COMPOUND. See **compound, coordination.**

COORDINATION LINKAGE. The valence **bond** by which a molecule or ion is joined, in a coordination compound, to a central metallic atom. The nature of this bond is considered to be a pair of electrons donated by the coordinating group, which exert an electrostatic bonding force upon the group and upon the central metallic atom. This linkage is, therefore, a dative, or semipolar linkage.

COORDINATION NUMBER. The number of molecules or ions coordinated with a central metallic atom.

COORDINATION THEORY. See **Werner theory.**

COPOLYMERIZATION. See **polymerization, co-.**

COPPER. Metallic element. Symbol Cu. Atomic number 29. Atomic weight 63.54. Density 8.94. Specific heat 0.0788. Melting point 1083° C. Boiling point 2310° C. Valence 1 and 2. Oxides, Cu_2O, CuO, CuO_2. Ores, native copper, copper oxide, malachite, azurite, copper glance. Copper forms two series of compounds, cuprous and cupric.

COPPER NUMBER. An expression of the quantity of a reducing **carbohydrate,** in terms of the number of milligrams of metallic copper required for reduction of that quantity of **Fehling's solution** (q.v.), which is reduced by one gram of the sample.

COPPER STRIP TEST (COPPER CORROSION TEST). A test made simply by prolonged immersion of a strip of metallic copper in a liquid. This test is used extensively in the petroleum industry, where it shows the presence of certain impurities, such as sulfur compounds, certain acids, etc.

COPRO-. (Greek) Derived from, or relating to, dung or excrement, as coprosterol.

COPSON, WALTHALL, AND HIGNETT PROCESS. A process for the purification of alumina (chiefly for aluminum manufacture) consisting of the following steps; a finely ground mixture of clay and limestone is heated to 1390° C. to form the simple silicates of calcium and aluminum; it is then cooled and leached. The filtered leach liquor is treated with carbon dioxide to precipitate aluminum hydroxide, filtered (to recover sodium carbonate from the filtrate), and calcined to convert aluminum hydroxide to alumina.

CORDIRIE PROCESS. A process for the purification of molten lead by passing steam through it.

CORONA. (1) A crownlike part or structure. (2) A luminous circle around one of the heavenly bodies, specifically the irregular, radial streams of light seen around the sun during a total eclipse. (3) The pattern of light and other **radiation** produced at **electrodes** during an electrical discharge at high voltage.

CORRESPONDENCE PRINCIPLE. The assertion that in the limit of high **quantum numbers** the predictions of quantum theory agree with those of classical physics.

CORRESPONDING STATES. If any two or more substances are at the same **reduced pressure** (q.v.), or the same fraction or multiple of their respective critical pressures, and are at equal **reduced temperatures** (q.v.) or the same fraction or multiple of their respective critical temperatures, their **reduced volumes** (q.v.) should be equal. These substances are said to be in corresponding states, and the above statement is the law of corresponding states.

CORRIGENT. A corrective drug, i.e., a drug that modifies the action of another drug in a desired direction.

CORROSION. Gradual destruction of a material, an entity, or substance, usually by solution or other means attributable to a chemical process.

CORROSIVE. Ability to dissolve or destroy. Substances which corrode living tissues are termed escharotics. Corrosion of metals is often a process of simple oxidation.

CORSO SOLUTION. A solution of 1 g. ammonium molybdate and 4 g. tartaric acid in 20 ml. water, used in testing for albumin in urine. The formation of a precipitate, which does not dissolve on heating, represents a positive test.

COSMETIC. A material, generally a mixture of substances, used to enhance or preserve beauty, by application to the face, hair, hands, and other parts of the body.

COSMIC RAYS. Radiations of the shortest wave length (greatest frequency) known in the electromagnetic spectrum. Cosmic rays and their reaction products (even the "primary" cosmic rays entering our atmosphere are almost entirely composed of positive-charged atomic nuclei) are found in the atmosphere (in fact, everywhere on earth). Since their intensity increases in the upper atmosphere, they are believed to reach the earth from space, arriving from all directions.

COSMOTRON. A particle accelerator capable of accelerating particles to energies of billions of electron volts (see **bevatron**); specifically the proton accelerator at Brookhaven National Laboratory, Long Island, N. Y.

COTTON EFFECT. Certain optical phenomena discovered by Cotton, relating to the **optical activity** of certain solutions within their absorption bands. The optical rotation increased to a maximum near the absorption band, decreased to zero within the band, and then increased to a second maximum. Another phenomenon observed is called **circular dichroism,** wherein right-circularly polarized light is absorbed to a different extent than left-circularly polarized light so that a linear polarized ray within an absorption band is converted into an elliptically polarized one on passage through the material.

COTTON TEST REACTION FOR BRUCINE. Brucine in dilute nitric acid solution, warmed to 40–50° C., gives a violet color changing to green, with a concentrated solution of sodium hydrosulfide.

COTTRELL PRECIPITATOR. An apparatus for the removal of particles suspended in the air or in a gas. It consists of an electrically charged wire, usually maintained at a high potential, from a direct current source; and a pipe, chimney, or other boundary surface which surrounds the charged wire, and through which the gas passes. Since the pipe is grounded, or is maintained at a lower potential than the wire, the particles in the gas become electrified and move to the boundary surface where they collect.

COULOMB. A unit of quantity of electricity: the quantity of electricity delivered by a current of one **ampere** flowing for one second. There is a difference between the coulomb (absolute) and the coulomb (International).

1 coulomb absolute = 1.000165 International coulombs.
1 faraday = 96,500 coulombs (absolute).
1 faraday = 96,507 coulombs (International).

COULOMB ELECTROMAGNETIC LAW. See law of Coulomb, electromagnetic.

COULOMB ELECTROSTATIC LAW. See law of Coulomb, electrostatic.

COULOMETER. (Voltameter. Coulombmeter.) An instrument designed to measure the quantity of electric **current** which passes through a circuit. The common types depend upon measuring the volume of a gas evolved by the current or on weighing the amount of a metal deposited by the current.

COUNTER (ELECTRON AND NUCLEAR). An instrument used to detect and measure emanations, especially those of a radioactive nature. These electron and nuclear counters, also called Geiger-Mueller counters, are used not only in the enumeration of charged particles and radiations — **x-rays, gamma rays,** and **cosmic rays** — but also in the counting of **neutrons,** even to the extent of distinguishing between fast and slow neutrons. A common form of this apparatus consists of an **ionization chamber** in which the charge on the wall is of an opposite sign to the charge upon the central wire.

COUNTER CHARACTERISTIC CURVE. The curve of the counting rate against voltage, all pulses counted being greater than a certain minimum size, determined by the sensitivity of the receiving circuit.

COUNTER DEAD TIME. The time interval, after recording a count, that the counter is completely insensitive and does not detect other ionizing events occurring inside it.

COUNTER EFFICIENCY. The efficiency of a counter is defined as the probability that a count will take place when the entity to be detected enters the counter.

COUNTER GAS AMPLIFICATION. The number of additional **ions** produced by each electron produced in the **primary ionizing event** as it travels to the central wire.

COUNTER LIFE (TIME). The life or lifetime of a counter is the number of counts which that counter is capable of detecting before becoming useless due to internal failure for any reason (e.g., gas decomposition or wire pitting, etc.). The life is not a time but a measure of the amount of use.

COUNTER OPERATING VOLTAGE. The voltage across the counter, when operating, measured between the anode and the cathode.

COUNTER OVERSHOOTING. A counter is said to overshoot if the change in potential of the wire is greater than the **overvoltage.**

COUNTER OVERVOLTAGE. The difference in voltage between the **operating potential** and the **threshold** for **Geiger counting action.**

COUNTER, PROPORTIONAL. A counter designed to operate in the **proportional region** (q.v.).

COUNTER RECOVERY TIME. The time interval, after recording a count, before the pulses produced by the next **ionizing event** in the counter are of full size.

COUNTER RESOLVING TIME. The minimum time interval between counts

that can be detected. The word may refer to an electronic circuit, to a mechanical recording device, or to a counter.

COUNTER SPURIOUS COUNTS. A spurious count is one that is caused by any agency whatsoever other than the entity to be detected, or the normal contamination or cosmic-ray background.

COUNTER STARTING POTENTIAL. The voltage which must be applied to a counter to cause it to count, with the particular recording circuit which may be attached. The potential is not necessarily the same as, and generally is not equal to, the **Geiger threshold** (q.v.) although there is some usage of the term "threshold" to denote starting potential.

COUNTER TIME LAG (STATISTICAL). The time between the occurrence of the **primary ionizing event** and the occurrence of the count in the counter.

COUNTERCURRENT PRINCIPLE. In a continuous process, where possible, the current of material to be acted upon should run in a direction opposite to that of the processing agent so that the fresh material may first come in contact with the most worn-out agent and the fresh, most active agent may first come in contact with and exert its power upon the most modified material. In this way the issuing agent will be more thoroughly used and the issuing material more modified, other factors being equal, than in any other. Processes such as percolation, diffusion batteries, the absorption of gases in towers where the fresh gas enters at the bottom and issues from the top, while the fresh absorbent enters at the top and the solution issues at the bottom, represent examples of the above principle.

COUNTERIRRITANT. A drug causing superficial irritation, which is applied to overcome the effect of abnormal processes.

COUNTING CHAMBER. A microscope slide used for counting particles. It is marked with rulings at regular, known intervals, and is recessed to a known depth, so it will contain a known volume of liquid.

COUNTING, COINCIDENCE. See **coincidence counting.**

COUPLE. (1) This term is used as a verb to denote the act of joining or condensing two or more molecules in a **coupling** reaction. (2) The word couple is also used in science to denote a point or area of contact between two dissimilar substances, especially metals, which gives rise to an electrical difference of potential.

COUPLING. Reactions for the formation of chemical compounds usually by establishing a valence **bond** between a carbon atom and a nitrogen atom, as in the following example.

Phenols and other substances are also said "to couple."

COUQUET MICROCHEMICAL REAGENT. A solution of chromic acid in concentrated sulfuric acid, used in detecting yttrium, erbium, neodymium, and praseodymium.

COVALENCE. Covalence is a chemical **linkage** in which the sharing of electrons occurs in pairs, each pair being equivalent to one conventional chemical bond, and in the union there is a tendency for each atom to acquire an outermost layer of eight electrons. In most cases, each of the atoms joined by the bond furnishes one electron of the pair, although there are many exceptions (see **covalence, dative**). The term covalence is opposed to **electrovalence,** in which the atoms or radicals are joined by electrostatic forces due to the actual transfer of electrons from the field of one atom to that of the other. These differences in structure are accompanied by resulting differences in properties.

COVALENCE, COORDINATE. See **coordinate covalence.**

COVALENCE, DATIVE. A valence linkage between two atoms in which both the electrons forming a covalent bond are furnished by one of the atoms.

COVALENCE, SEMI-POLAR. See **covalence, dative.**

COVELLI TEST FOR ARSENITE. To detect arsenite in the presence of arsenate, alkalinize the sample solution strongly with potassium hydroxide; place in a U-tube with 2 platinum electrodes connected to **Grove cells** (q.v.). A strip of ammoniacal silver nitrate paper, placed in the cathode arm of the tube, turns brown in one hour if arsenite is present.

COVELLI TEST FOR CHLORAL. Place a fragment of antimony trichloride in 1 ml. of warm castor oil. When the resulting resinous mass is warmed with a trace of chloral hydrate, a blue-green spot appears.

COVERING POWER. The amount of surface that can be covered by a unit mass or volume of a covering agent such as paint. This term is a loose one, because the paint must be applied to the particular surface so that it will yield a strong, continuous film upon drying, which will have the required opacity (hiding power) and will spread evenly (spreading power). Any or all of these properties may determine the covering power.

COVOLUME. The correction term applied in certain **equations of state,** as in that of **van der Waals,** to correct the volume of the gas for *the effect of* the volume of the molecules. This term is not the molecular volume itself.

COWLES PROCESS. A process for the manufacture of aluminum alloys by reduction of alumina, or an aluminum ore (usually bauxite) with carbon and the alloying element or elements.

Cr Symbol for the element **chromium.**

CRACKING OF PETROLEUM. A process for producing **hydrocarbons** of lower molecular weight, such as gasoline, from other hydrocarbons by heating, by the action of catalysts, or both.

CRAIG METHOD. A method of replacement of the amino group in α-amino-pyridines with halogens, in the presence of the concentrated halogen halide, and sodium nitrite.

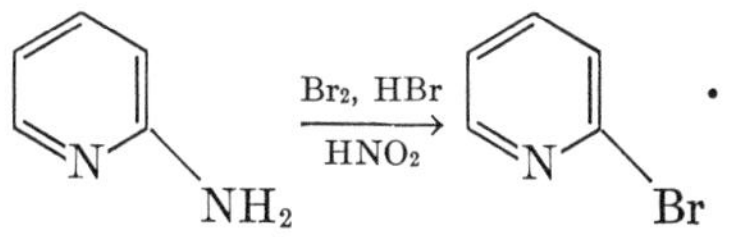

CRAMER SOLUTION. A solution in 1 liter water of 60 g. potassium iodide, and 4 g. mercuric oxide. The alkalinity of this solution is adjusted, and it is used as a test reagent for reducing sugars. A black precipitate indicates the presence of such sugars.

CRAVEN TEST REACTION. Many quinones when treated with 2–3 drops of ethyl cyanoacetate and 3 ml. of a mixture of equal parts absolute alcohol and concentrated ammonia give a blue-violet color, changing to blue, green, and red-brown.

CREEPING. Elongation of a metal, or metallic part, under heating and tension; or the tendency of particles of a precipitate

to "move up" the wet walls of a beaker or other container above the level of liquid.

CREIGHTON PROCESS. A method for the reduction of sugars electrolytically, such as that for the formation of sorbitol from glucose, involving the reduction of the –CHO terminal group to CH_2OH.

CREMER TEST REACTIONS FOR PHLORIDZIN. Phloridzin gives (1) an amorphous, difficultly-soluble material when treated with benzoyl chloride and sodium hydroxide solution; (2) when in sodium carbonate solution, a red dye with diazobenzene chloride solution; (3) a red color with vanillin and hydrochloric acid.

CRESOTYL. The radical

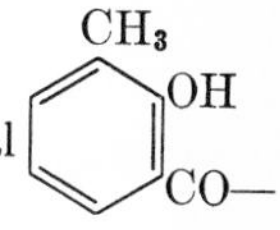

(from cresotic acid). In the structure given, the 2,3-form of the radical is shown.

CRESOXY. See **toloxy.**

CRESTI TEST. Copper in solution forms a black deposit on the platinum wire of a zinc-platinum couple; when the coated platinum wire is washed, and exposed to bromine and hydrobromic acid vapors, a violet color appears.

CRESYL. See **ar-hydroxytolyl** or **tolyl.**

CRESYLENE. See **tolylene.**

CRIEGEE REACTION. The splitting of a glycol compound between the carbon atoms attached to the hydroxyl groups of the glycol. The reagent is lead tetraacetate.

CRISMER TEST REACTION. Chloroform or chloral hydrate solutions, when heated to boiling with an alcoholic solution of resorcinol and sodium hydroxide, give a violet-red to yellow-red color.

CRISMER TEST REACTION FOR HYDROGEN PEROXIDE. A modified **Deniges reaction,** in which 3–4 ml. 10% ammonium molybdate solution and a few drops of citric acid solution are added to the solution to be tested. A yellow color shows the presence of hydrogen peroxide.

CRISMER TEST FOR WATER IN ALCOHOL, CHLOROFORM, AND ETHER. Addition of liquid paraffin to the test solutions of alcohol, chloroform, or ether causes turbidity if water is present in proportions greater than 1:500.

CRISWELL REAGENT. A solution of 35 g. cupric sulfate in 100 ml. of water and 200 g. of glycerol, to which 450 ml. 20% sodium hydroxide solution is then added, followed by boiling for 15 minutes, and dilution to 1 liter. This reagent is used in testing for glucose, which causes reduction of the solution and appearance of cuprous oxide.

CRITH. A unit of mass equal to the weight in grams of one liter of hydrogen at standard temperature and pressure, 0.0906 g.

CRITICAL ANGLE. The maximum **angle of incidence,** for a given medium, at which light or other radiation will be transmitted directly through the medium. At greater angles the radiation will be reflected from the inner face of a surface of the medium, and therefore undergo a major change in direction. Mathematically, the critical angle is the angle of incidence for a given medium for which the angle of emergence of the radiation is 90°.

CRITICAL COEFFICIENT. An additive property of substances which is also a measure of the space actually occupied by the molecules and is proportional to the **critical volume.** It is expressed as the ratio between the critical temperature T_c and the critical pressure P_c, or

$$k = \frac{T_c}{P_c}.$$

(Some writers define the critical coefficient as the product: $RT \dfrac{T_c}{P_c}.$)

CRITICAL COMPOSITION. Systems, consisting of two liquid layers that are formed by the equilibrium between two partly-miscible liquids, frequently have a **consolute temperature** or a critical solution temperature, beyond* which the two liquids are miscible to all proportions. At this temperature, the phase boundary disappears, and the two liquid layers merge into one. The composition of the mixture at that point is called the critical composition.

CRITICAL CONDITION. The **critical pressure** (q.v.) or the **critical temperature** (q.v.).

CRITICAL DENSITY. The density of a substance which is at its critical temperature and critical pressure.

CRITICAL HUMIDITY. The point at which the water vapor pressure of a solution or substance is equal to that of the water vapor in the atmosphere.

CRITICAL OPALESCENCE. The phenomenon produced when a homogeneous solution of two liquids at its **critical composition** (q.v.) is cooled from a temperature above its consolute temperature to one below that value. This phenomenon consists of a bluish haze which is believed to be due to the scattering of light brought about by local variations of density within the liquid.

CRITICAL PHENOMENA. The critical temperature, pressure, and volume.

CRITICAL POINT. A point where two **phases,** which are continually approximating each other, become identical and form but one phase. With a liquid in equi-

* There are, in some cases, lower consolute temperatures as well as upper consolute temperatures.

librium with its vapor, the critical point is such a combination of temperature and pressure that the specific volumes of the liquid and its vapor are identical, and there is no distinction between the two states. The critical solution point is such a combination of temperature and pressure that two otherwise partially miscible liquids become **consolute.**

CRITICAL POINT, TERNARY. The point where, upon adding a mutual solvent to two partially miscible liquids (as adding alcohol to ether and water), the two solutions become consolute and one phase results.

CRITICAL POTENTIAL. The potential required to raise one of the electrons surrounding an atomic **nucleus** from a lower to a higher **energy level,** the highest level being that in which the electron is totally removed, and the atom becomes an ion. Since the charge on the electron is constant, the magnitude of the critical potential is a direct measure of the energy expended in the change.

CRITICAL PRESSURE. The pressure of a vapor at its critical point, the temperature above which the vapor can exist only in the form of a gas.

In fluid dynamics, the term critical pressure is used to denote a value of the final pressure of a fluid flowing through an orifice or nozzle, above which the volume of flow depends on the final pressure.

CRITICAL SOLUTION POINT. See critical point.

CRITICAL SOLUTION TEMPERATURE. See **critical composition.**

CRITICAL SPEED. A rotation speed of shafts and other bodies at which vibrations due to unbalanced forces reach a maximum. Above this speed, the vibrations decrease, but often attain other maxima at higher speeds, called second, third, and higher critical speeds. These maxima are considered to correspond to the natural period of vibration of the system, or some integral multiple of it.

CRITICAL TEMPERATURE. The maximum temperature at which a gas or vapor can be liquefied (by application of the critical pressure). Above this temperature the substance exists only as a gas.

CRITICAL VOLUME. The volume occupied by unit mass, commonly one mole, of a substance at its **critical temperature** and **critical pressure.**

CROCKER TESTS FOR ALDEHYDES. (1) Add to 5 ml. of the solution tested 2 drops 1% resorcinol solution and 15 ml. 80% sulfuric acid. Aldehydes give a color on shaking and standing.

(2) Add to 10 ml. of the solution tested, 1 drop 1% phloroglucinol solution, and 10 ml. concentrated hydrochloric acid. Shake. Aldehydes produce colors: higher cyclic aldehydes deep red; and aliphatic aldehydes a turbidity.

(3) Follow (1) above, using guaiacol instead of resorcinol solution.

(4) 1 g. aniline dissolved in 100 3 N hydrochloric acid gives yellow colors with aldehydes.

CROLAS-DUCKER TEST REACTION. Uranium salts give a green color with a cochineal tincture containing alum.

CRONER-CRONHEIM TEST. Lactic acid solutions, after boiling with potassium hydroxide solution, give an odor of isonitrile on addition of a reagent consisting of 2 g. potassium iodide and 1 g. iodine in 50 ml. water and 5 g. aniline.

CROOKE'S DARK SPACE. A region in a low pressure electric discharge tube near the **cathode** that remains dark even though it is conducting current.

CROOKE'S RADIOMETER. An apparatus for detecting small quantities of **radiant energy,** chiefly in the visible and infrared region of the **electromagnetic spectrum.** It consists of four arms, each terminating in a metallic disc, silvered on one side and blackened on the other, mounted on a shaft in an evacuated glass bulb. Upon incidence of radiation the assembly begins to rotate about the shaft.

CROOKE'S TUBE. A highly evacuated tube, commonly used for the production of x-rays.

CROSS-BEVAN PROCESS. (Viscose process) A method of production of a synthetic fiber by treatment of cellulose with carbon disulfide and alkali to obtain cellulose xanthate, and regenerating the cellulose as a fiber by forcing the solution through spinnerets into an acid bath.

CROSS-BEVAN REAGENT FOR CELLULOSE. A 30% solution of zinc chloride in concentrated hydrochloric acid (specific gravity 1.19), used as a solvent for cellulose.

CROSS-BEVAN SOLUTION. A solution of 21 g. zinc chloride in 42 ml. concentrated hydrochloric acid. This solution is used as a solvent for cellulose.

CROSS-BEVAN TEST FOR JUTE. Jute, when treated with a mixture of 0.1 N ferric chloride solution and 0.1 N potassium ferricyanide solution, gives a blue color.

CROSS BOMBARDMENT. A method of determination of the **atomic number** of a **radio-element,** by producing it by a number of different nuclear reactions. As an illustration, in order to determine the atomic number of a 47-day, β-activity **isotope** of iron produced by deuteron bombardment, cobalt oxide was treated with neutrons of medium energy. It was observed that a 47-day, β-activity developed, and that the isotope having this activity could be extracted by chemical methods for iron. It was evident, therefore, that deuteron bombardment of a stable isotope of iron, and neutron bombardment of a stable isotope of cobalt, produced the same radioisotope of iron.

CROSS PROCESS. A process for the simultaneous cracking and distilling of crude oil (or a fraction distilled therefrom) by the application of heat and pressure. The oil is preheated and is circulated through heated steel tubes under a pressure of 600 pounds per square inch. The charge flows continuously into a chamber in which the vapor separates from the remaining liquid and carbon.

CROSS SECTION. The cross section of an atom or molecule, usually expressed as an area in square centimeters, is the area obscured by that particle. The cross section of a process (e.g., a collision cross section or capture cross section) is a measure of the probability that that process will occur. The term is usually used in referring to interactions which may occur when one entity moves through a space containing others. Thus, if an electron advances through a gas, the collision cross section of an atom of the gas for such electronic collisions is the number of collisions per atom that the electron will make in a 1-cm advance. Symbol σ. If there are L atoms per cc, the electron mentioned will make $L\sigma$ collisions per cm. advance.

CROTONYL. The radical

$$CH_3CH:CHCO-$$

CROTYL. See **2-butenyl.**

CROWAK PROCESS. A method of coating zinc by dipping it in an aqueous solution of sodium dichromate and sulfuric acid that deposits a protective film of basic chromium chromate.

CROWE PROCESS. A method for removing occluded or dissolved air from gold-bearing cyanide solutions. The solution is sucked into a drum under high vacuum and flows down over a series of perforated trays which break it up into a finely-divided spray.

CRUCIBLE. A vessel of sand, porcelain, nickel, platinum, or other refractory substance used in the melting or calcination of materials or reaction mixtures at high temperatures.

CRUCIBLE, ALUNDUM FILTER. A filtering crucible of alundum which uses the pores in its own structure for separation of liquids from solids.

CRUCIBLE, ASSAY. A small glazed-porcelain crucible used primarily for combustion of filter-paper containing precipitates, in quantitative analysis.

CRUCIBLE, FRITTED GLASS. Fritted glass is made by heating powdered glass to incipient fusion so that the particles partially fuse together and, in crucible work, leave pores of controllable size useful in filtration.

CRUCIBLE FURNACE. A high-temperature, small-capacity furnace, used for laboratory purposes such as heating crucibles.

CRUCIBLE, GOOCH. A crucible having a perforated base used in the laboratory for filtering precipitates upon a prepared bed of asbestos or other fibers.

CRUCIBLE, HESSIAN. A large clay crucible, used in work with alloys.

CRUCIBLE, MELTING. A refractory fire-clay crucible used for fusing glass, metals, enamels, and similar materials.

CRUCIBLE, MONROE. A crucible containing a filtering-medium of spongy platinum, on a porous support.

CRUCIBLE, SKIDMORE. An iron crucible with clamped cover, inlet and outlet tubes, suitable for use as a gas generator, a retort, or an open crucible.

CRUCIBLE (SULFUR), PENNOCK AND MARTIN. A nickel crucible used for determining sulfur in solid fuels, and having a small opening in its cover through which an ignition wire is introduced.

CRUM-BROWN AND GIBSON RULE. A rule used to predict the location of a second substituent, introduced into a mono-substituted **benzene** ring, with respect to the first substituent. If the latter, with hydrogen, forms a compound which can be converted by direct oxidation into the corresponding hydroxyl compound, the new substituent will enter the *meta*-position; otherwise it will enter the *ortho*- and/or *para*-positions.

CRUM BROWN-WALKER REACTION. The method of formation of diesters by electrolysis of salts of acid esters of dibasic acids.

$$2ROOC \cdot CH_2 \cdot COO^- \rightarrow ROOC \cdot CH_2 \cdot CH_2 \cdot COOR + 2CO_2.$$

CRUCIBLE PROCESS. A process for the manufacture of special steels, such as tool steel, by fusing a pure low-carbon steel in a graphite crucible with charcoal or cast-iron in sufficient amount to yield a steel containing from 0.75% to 1.50% carbon. If necessary, alloying elements are also added to the charge, usually, in the form of their ferro-alloys. The process has been partly superseded by the **electric-furnace process.**

CRUCIBLE, ROSE. A crucible provided with a lid through which a tube passes, to permit heating of small samples in a current of a gas.

CRUCIBLE, SILLIMANITE. Sillimanite is a rhombic aluminum silicate which is used for the manufacture of high quality porcelain crucibles. These are highly resistant to shock and to rapid change in temperature.

See also **Kolbe reaction,** and **Hofer-Moest reaction.**

CRUM TEST FOR MANGANESE. Heat to near boiling a mixture of equal volumes of nitric acid and of water containing a little lead dioxide, then add the dilute solution to be tested (free from chloride ion). A purple-red color shows manganese. Many modifications of this test have been developed.

CRUSHER. A device used to break up solids into small pieces or into coarse material. There are various types of crushers, such as jaw crushers, rotary crushers, and various types of roller crushers.

CRUSHER, GYRATORY. A crushing mill consisting of a fixed conical surface, or frame surrounding a gyrating conical surface, or head. The head is driven by a conical shaft which moves it up and down, causing it to approach and recede continuously from the frame. At the same time, an eccentric on the drive shaft causes a gyratory movement about the axis, which increases the crushing action.

CRUSHER, JAW. A crushing mill in which the material is broken by the motion of a moving surface, or jaw, toward a fixed jaw. One of the jaws is oblique, so that the distance between jaws is widest at the top, where the material enters, and least at the bottom, where it is discharged.

CRUSHER, ROLL. A crushing mill consisting of two heavy rollers moving in opposite directions (toward each other). The material to be crushed is passed between the rollers, which are often grooved.

CRUSHER, ROTARY. A mill consisting of a corrugated metal cone moving against corrugated side plates.

CRUTCHER. A mixing machine used in the manufacture of soap. The liquid soap is pumped from the boiling vats into the crutcher and stirred thoroughly while perfume, fillers, or other ingredients are added and mixed in. When the mixing has been completed the contents of the crutcher are run into frames.

CRYOHYDRATE. An **eutectic** system consisting of a salt and water, having a concentration at which complete fusion or solidification occurs at a definite temperature (eutectic temperature) as if only one substance were present.

CRYOHYDRIC POINT. The point on the composition-temperature diagram, or the particular concentration and temperature, at which a given salt-water system melts and freezes without change in composition.

At this point, the solution is in equilibrium with ice and the solid salt; therefore, consideration should be given to the possibility that the salt may be one of those which have more than one crystalline form.

CRYOMETER. A low-temperature thermometer.

CRYOSCOPE. An instrument for measuring the freezing or solidification point. The Hortvet cryoscope is used for the estimation of added water in milk from the lowering of the freezing point.

CRYOSCOPIC CONSTANT. A quantity calculated to represent the molal depression of the freezing point of a solution, by the relationship

$$K = \frac{R T_0^2}{1000 l_f}$$

in which K is the cryoscopic constant, R is the **gas constant,** T_0 is the freezing point of the pure solvent, and l_f is the **latent heat of fusion** per gram. The product of the cryoscopic constant and the **molality** of the solution gives the actual depression of the freezing point for the range of values for which this relationship applies. Unfortunately, this range is limited to very dilute solutions, usually up to molalities of $\frac{1}{100}$.

CRYOSCOPIC METHOD. (1) A method for determining the molecular weight of a substance by observing the depression of the freezing point when a definite quantity of the substance is dissolved in a solvent. (2) A method for detecting adulteration, as in the instance of determining the change in the freezing point of milk attributable to the addition of water.

CRYOSTAT. A low-temperature thermostat.

CRYPTOCRYSTALLINE. Substances whose crystalline form is "hidden" and difficult to recognize, so that they appear to be amorphous, e.g., flint, jasper.

CRYPTOVALENCY. An old term for a rare or anomalous **valency,** or one encountered only in one or a few compounds of a substance.

CRYSTAL. (1) A homogeneous solid body of definite geometrical form bounded by plane surfaces, formed when certain liquid or gaseous substances pass into the solid state (or crystallize). Most compounds possess a definite crystal form in the solid condition and are said to be crystalline. Substances which crystallize in two, three, or more forms are termed di-, tri-, or polymorphous. Cf. **isomorphism.** (2) Certain uniaxial and anisotropic liquids; see **crystal, liquid.**

CRYSTAL, AEOLOTROPIC. See **crystal, liquid.**

CRYSTAL ALCOHOL. Alcohol of crystallization.

CRYSTAL ANALYSIS, BRAGG METHOD OF. See **Bragg method of crystal analysis.**

CRYSTAL ANGLES. The characteristic constant angles between the faces of any given crystal form.

CRYSTAL, ANISOTROPIC. See **crystal, liquid.**

CRYSTAL, BIAXIAL. A doubly refracting crystal which has two **optic axes.** There are two directions parallel to which light travels with one definite velocity. Crystals of the **rhombic, monoclinic,** and **triclinic** systems are biaxial.

CRYSTAL CHLOROFORM. Chloroform of crystallization.

CRYSTAL CLASSES. Also known as point groups, or classes of crystal symmetry. One of the thirty-two different symmetry groups which characterize the degree of symmetry of a crystallographic system.

CRYSTAL, DOUBLE. A twin crystal.

CRYSTAL ELEMENTS. The angles, plus the **axial ratios** or **intercept ratios,** in terms of which the position of any crystal face may be described.

CRYSTAL HABIT. The external shape of a crystal, which depends on the relative development of the different faces, as well as upon the interfacial angles characteristic of the crystal.

CRYSTAL, HEMIHEDRAL. A crystal that has half of its faces developed.

CRYSTAL, HOLOHEDRAL. A crystal that has all of its faces developed.

CRYSTAL INDICES, MILLER. Three indices used to represent any crystal face in terms of the **crystallographic axes** and the **axial ratios.** These integers give the ratio of the intercepts of the unit plane to those of the particular face.

CRYSTAL INTERCEPTS. See **crystallographic parameters.**

CRYSTAL, ISOMORPHOUS. One of two or more crystals which are similar in crystalline form and in chemical properties and are related in chemical composition in that one or more of the atoms and radicals in one are of similar chemical type to the corresponding atoms or radicals in the other. Usually, one or more of their other atoms or radicals are identical.

CRYSTAL, ISOTROPIC. See **isotropic crystals and isotropism.**

CRYSTAL LATTICE. See **space lattice.**

CRYSTAL, LIQUID. A liquid having the optical properties of a crystal. Such liquid crystals are **uniaxial, anisotropic** (q.v.), and cloudy, and have a definite temperature (melting point) at which the crystalline optical properties and cloudiness disappear.

CRYSTAL, MIXED. A crystal consisting of two or more chemical compounds, which may have the same positive radical or the same negative radical, and which, in their pure form, are isomorphous, i.e., have the same crystal form.

CRYSTAL, MOLECULAR. See **molecular crystal.**

CRYSTAL POINT GROUPS. The same as **crystal classes** (q.v.).

CRYSTAL, SEED. A crystal which is added to a **saturated solution** or **supersaturated solution** to act as a nucleus for crystallization, as in the refining of sugar, the manufacture of sodium glutamate, etc.

CRYSTAL STRUCTURE. The internal structure of a particular crystal or type of crystal. Its present-day method of elucidation is by **X-ray diffraction** photographs, called crystallograms, from which the arrangement of the individual atoms within the crystal can be deduced. Since these atoms are arranged in a definite order (the space lattice), they act as a diffraction grating for the x-rays.

CRYSTAL SYSTEM. See **crystallographic system.**

CRYSTAL, TWIN. Two crystals of the same substance having one common face.

CRYSTAL, UNIAXIAL. A doubly refracting crystal which has but one optic axis and which shows characteristic **interference** figures, as Iceland spar, quartz, and tourmaline.

CRYSTAL WATER. Water of crystallization.

CRYSTALLINE. (1) Occurring in a crystal form. (2) Clear, not cloudy. See **crystal.**

CRYSTALLIZATION. To assume the crystal state by transformation from another state, which is commonly that of a solute in solution, although it may also be the state of a liquid, a non-crystalline solid, or (less commonly) a gas.

CRYSTALLIZATION, FRACTIONAL. A process for the separation of a mixture in solution by arranging conditions so that one component may crystallize alone or with but small admixture of another component.

CRYSTALLIZATION, NUCLEI OF. Small solid particles placed in solutions upon which crystals may form. Crystals of the dissolved substance or of other substances which are **isomorphous** with it, grains of dust, etc., may serve as nuclei.

CRYSTALLIZATION, WATER OF. See **water of crystallization.**

CRYSTALLIZE. To assume definite geometric shape. See **crystal.**

CRYSTALLOGRAM. A photograph of x-rays diffracted by a crystal. From the crystallogram, the arrangement and spacing of the **lattice-planes** in the crystal may be calculated, giving in turn the arrangement of the atoms, radicals and other structural elements.

CRYSTALLOGRAPHIC AXES. The crystallographic axes are usually three, sometimes four, lines meeting at a point which are so chosen as to bear a definite relationship to the characteristic features of the crystallographic symmetry. They may, for example, be normal to the plane of symmetry, or parallel to, or coincident with, the edge between principal faces or the axes of symmetry. Although the choice of axes is to some extent arbitrary, some sets produce a simpler representation than others. Whenever possible, the three axes are chosen to be at right angles to each other.

CRYSTALLOGRAPHIC AXIAL RATIOS. The ratios of the crystal intercepts, i.e., the ratios of distances from the origin of the crystallographic axes to the points where they are intercepted by the faces of the unit cell.

CRYSTALLOGRAPHIC PARAMETERS. The crystal intercepts, which are the distances from the origin of the crystallographic axes to the points where they are cut by the faces bounding the unit cell of the crystal.

CRYSTALLOGRAPHIC SYSTEM. One of the seven divisions to which all crystals are assigned; the crystals in each of the seven systems have the same or related axial angles and ratios. The seven systems are the cubic or regular, the tetragonal, the orthorhombic or rhombic, the monoclinic, the triclinic or anorthic, the hexagonal and the trigonal or rhombohedral.

CRYSTALLOGRAPHY. The study of crystals, both from the standpoint of their external shape and properties, and from the point of view of their structure and the relationship of the atoms, radicals, and molecules of which they are composed.

CRYSTALLOID. (Dispersoid) A term used by Graham to distinguish the crystalline substances, which are soluble in water and dialyze readily, from colloidal compounds, which dialyze not at all or only very slowly. This distinction now has little fundamental meaning. Moreover, there are some substances, including some proteins, that crystallize but do not dialyze.

CRYSTALLOIDAL SOLUTION. A solution of a crystalline substance or substances, or a true solution as distinguished from a colloidal solution.

Cs Symbol for the element **cesium** (q.v.).

Cu Symbol for the element **copper** (q.v.).

CUBIC CENTIMETER. A unit of volume in the metric system. It is defined as the volume of a cube whose edge is one centimeter, but the form of the volume need not of necessity be that of a cube. Cf. **centimeter cube.**

1 cubic centimeter = 0.061 cubic inch
16.38 cubic centimeters = 1.00 cubic inch
1.000027 cubic centi-
    meters   = 1.00 milliliter
1 cubic centimeter of pure water at 4° C. weighs 0.99996 gram.

CUBIC SYSTEM. See **crystallographic system.**

CULTURE. To grow or breed **microorganisms,** or their growth or breeding, as for the diagnosis or investigation of disease; the preparation of certain industrial chemicals by microbiological reactions, etc.

CULTURE APPARATUS. An apparatus for growing cultures of **microorganisms** in atmospheres other than air. It is used extensively in work with anaerobic organisms.

CULTURE MEDIUM. A substance in which, or on which, the **bacteria** are grown; or that part, or element, of a food on which bacteria grow.

CUMAL. See **cuminylidene.**

CUMIDINO. The radical

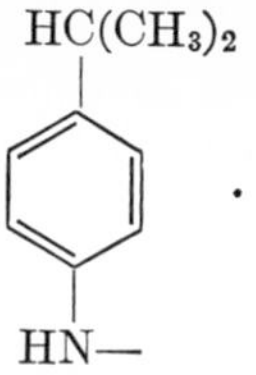

HC(CH₃)₂

HN—

CUMINAL. See **cuminylidene.**

CUMINYL. The radical

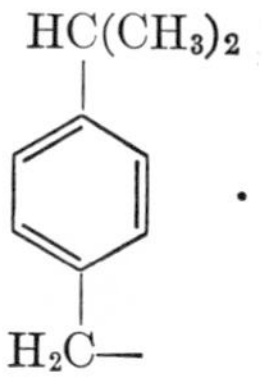

HC(CH₃)₂

H₂C—

CUMOYL. The radical

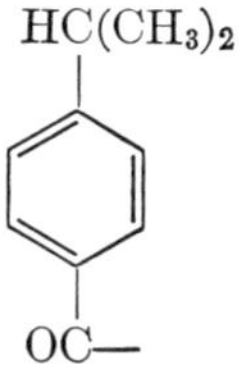

HC(CH₃)₂

OC—

(from cumic acid).

CUMULATED DOUBLE BONDS. Two double bonds on one atom, as in compounds of carbon, silicon, etc.

CUMYL. The radical

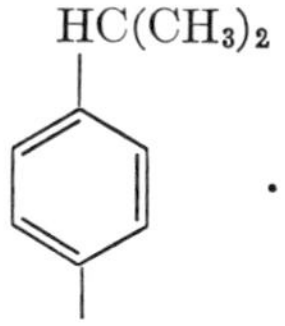

HC(CH₃)₂

CUNIASSE SOLUTION. A solution used in testing for *m*- and *p*-phenylenediamine. It consists of 1 ml. acetaldehyde in 100 ml. 50% alcohol, acidified with acetic acid. It gives a yellow color with green fluorescence, on cooling, after warming with an aqueous solution of *m*-phenylenediamine hydrochloride. *p*-Phenylenediamine gives an orange-red color without fluorescence.

CUNY-POIROT TEST. Bismuth solutions, to which an aqueous solution of gum acacia has been added, give an orange-red color with a solution of potassium iodide and quinine sulfate.

CUPEL. A shallow porous vessel usually made of bone ashes used in cupellation; or to submit to the process of **cupellation** (q.v.).

CUPELLATION. A metallurgical process for refining **noble metals** especially for purposes of **assay.** The sample of unrefined metal mixed with lead is placed in a cupel and heated in a **muffle furnace.** The base metals are oxidized, part of them being volatilized at the temperature of the muffle and the rest being absorbed by the cupel. A "button" of noble metal is left behind. Cupellation during crucible or **scorification** assay for the precious metals eliminates the lead which is generally used to separate the noble metals from the ore samples.

CUPFERRON. The ammoniacal salt of _N_-nitrosophenyl-hydroxylamine, $C_6H_5 \cdot N(NO) \cdot ONH_4$, used as a reagent in quantitative inorganic analysis. Under suitable conditions, it precipitates quantitatively from solution, iron, vanadium, titanium, etc.

CUPFERRON SOLUTION. An aqueous solution of ammonium nitrosophenylhydroxylamine, used as a test reagent for metals.

CUPOLA. A furnace used in foundries for melting large quantities of metals, especially pig iron.

CUPRATE (II) (HYDROXY). The anion $Cu(OH)_4^-$ or $Cu(OH)_6^{4-}$, or a compound containing one of them.

CUPRIC. Containing or pertaining to divalent **copper.**

CUPROCYANIDE. See **cyanocuprate (I).**

CUPRON SOLUTION. An alcoholic solution of _α_-benzoinoxime, used as a test reagent for copper and other metals.

CUPROUS. Containing or pertaining to monovalent **copper.**

CURCUMIN SOLUTION. An alcoholic solution of curcumin, used as a hydrogen-ion indicator and also as a test reagent for beryllium.

CURD. (1) A precipitate produced by the coagulation of milk. (2) A precipitate similar in appearance to that produced by the coagulation of milk.

CURIE. This unit of **radioactivity** was originally defined as the amount of emanation (radon) from or in equilibrium with one gram of pure radium. Because of experimental uncertainties, the unit has been redefined and is now generally understood to mean the amount of any radioactive material which decays at the rate of 3.7×10^{10} disintegrations per second. Smaller units are the millicurie and the microcurie.

CURIE LAW. See **law of Curie.**

CURIE POINT. The critical temperature above which ferromagnetic substances (iron, cobalt, and their alloys) become paramagnetic compounds whose magnetic susceptibility is nearly inversely proportional to the absolute temperature.

CURIUM. Transuranic radioactive element. Symbol Cm. Atomic number 96. Its isotope of mass number 242 was produced by the (α, n) reaction in the bombardment of plutonium 239 by α-particles having resonance energies. It is also produced by the reaction Am^{241} (n, γ) Am^{242}, the Am^{242}, yielding Cm^{242} by beta decay. It is itself an α-particle emitter, with a half-period of 162.5 days. Its investigation by tracer methods shows it to be trivalent in aqueous solution. Other curium isotopes have been reported with mass numbers of 238, 239, 240, 241, 243, and 244. Valence 3.

CURRAN-KNOWLES PROCESS. A relative low temperature carbonization process, in which the coal is placed in a coke oven laid horizontally, and heated only from the bottom.

CURRENT DENSITY. The electric current per square centimeter of conductor or of electrode immersed in a solution of an electrolyte.

CURRENT STRENGTH. The amperage of an electric current. See **ampere.**

CURTIUS-FRAZEN TEST REACTION. Formic acid when treated with concentrated sulfuric acid gives carbon monoxide (detected with palladous chloride solution).

CURTIUS REACTION. A chemical change resulting in the formation of a primary **amine** (RNH_2) or a **urethane** ($RCOONH_2$) from an acid **azide.** The process may be carried out by heating an acid chloride with sodium azide (NaN_3) in toluene, or by treating an ester successively with hydrazine and nitrous acid, and hydrolyzing the acid azide by heating with HCl. The isocyanate is an intermediate product.

$$RCOCl + NaN_3 \rightarrow RCON_3 + NaCl$$
$$RCON_3 \rightarrow RNCO + N_2$$
$$RNCO + H_2O \rightarrow RNH_2 + CO_2.$$

CURTMAN-PLECHNER TEST. Reducing substances are detected by adding to 5 ml. of their neutral solution, 0.5 ml. 3 N sulfuric acid, and 2 drops of 0.1 N potassium permanganate. If decolorization occurs, the presence of 1 mg. or more of arsenite, sulfite, iodide and other strongly-reducing substances is indicated. If decolorization does not occur, heat. If bleaching then occurs, the presence of 10 mg. or more of oxalate, tartrate, cyanide or other less strongly-reducing substances is indicated.

CURTMAN REAGENT FOR POTASSIUM, CESIUM, RUBIDIUM, AND AMMONIUM. A modified **Erdmann reagent** (q.v.) made by dissolving cobalt nitrite in a saturated aqueous solution of sodium nitrite, and acidifying with acetic acid. Yellow precipitates are given with the four ions listed.

CURTMAN SOLUTION FOR NITRITE. A solution of 1 g. antipyrine in 100 g. 10% acetic acid solution. This reagent is used in testing for nitrite. A green color indicates the presence of nitrite.

CUSSON TEST. Carbon disulfide is detected in oils by mixing 200 ml. of the sample with 50 g. 90% alcohol, then distilling and collecting the distillate in alcoholic potassium hydroxide. The mixture is acidified with acetic acid and a few drops of cupric acetate are added. A yellow color, precipitating on standing, indicates the presence of carbon disulfide.

CUTOLO REAGENT. A solution of 1 g. gelatin in 10–15 ml. 65% nitric acid, which is then made up to 100 ml. with nitric acid. This solution is used as a test reagent for other oils in cottonseed oil. Various colors are obtained, depending upon the particular oils present.

CUTTING OIL. See **oil, cutting.**

CYANACETIC. Related to cyanacetic acid, $NC \cdot CH_2 \cdot COOH$.

CYANAMIDE. The anion CN_2^-, or a compound containing it.

CYANARGENTATE (I). The anion $Ag(CN)_2^-$, $Ag(CN)_3^-$, or $Ag(CN)_4^{3-}$, or a compound containing one of these anions.

CYANATE. The anion OCN^-, or a compound containing it.

CYANIC. Related to cyanic acid, $HCNO$.

CYANIC REARRANGEMENT. See **rearrangement, cyanic** or **thiocyanic.**

CYANIDE. (1) The anion CN^- or a compound containing it. (2) Thus a salt of hydrocyanic acid. (3) An organic compound containing the radical $-CN$, although organic cyanides are preferably termed **nitriles** (q.v.).

CYANINE DYE. See **dye, cyanine.**

CYANO. The radical $NC-$.

CYANOAURATE (I). The anion $Au(CN)_2^-$, or a compound containing it.

CYANOAURATE (III). The anion $Au(CN)_4^-$, or a compound containing it.

CYANOCADMATE. The anion $Cd(CN)_3^-$ or $Cd(CN)_4^{2-}$, or a compound containing one of these anions.

CYANOCHROMATE (II). The anion $Cr(CN)_6^{4-}$, or a compound containing it.

CYANOCHROMATE (III). The anion $Cr(CN)_6^{3-}$, or a compound containing it.

CYANOCOBALTATE (II). See **cobaltocyanide.**

CYANOCOBALTATE (III). See **cobalticyanide.**

CYANOCUPRATE (I). The anion $Cu_2(CN)_3^-$, $Cu(CN)_2^-$, $Cu(CN)_3^-$, or $Cu(CN)_4^{3-}$, or a compound containing one of these anions.

CYANOFERRATE (II). See **ferrocyanide.**

CYANOFERRATE (III). See **ferricyanide.**

CYANOHYDRIN SYNTHESIS. See **Kiliani synthesis.**

CYANOIRIDATE (III). The anion $Ir(CN)_6^{3-}$, or a compound containing it.

CYANOMANGANATE (I). The anion $Mn(CN)_3^-$ or $Mn(CN)_6^{5-}$, or a compound containing one of these anions.

CYANOMANGANATE (II). The anion $Mn(CN)_3^-$, $MnMn(CN)_6^-$, or $Mn(CN)_6^{4-}$ or a compound containing one of these anions.

CYANOMANGANATE (III). The anion $Mn(CN)_6^{3-}$, or a compound containing it.

CYANOMERCURATE (II). The anion $Hg(CN)_3^-$ or $Hg(CN)_4^-$, or a compound containing one of these anions.

CYANOMOLYBDATE (IV). The anion $Mo(CN)_8^{4-}$, or a compound containing it.

CYANOMOLYBDATE (V). The anion $Mo(CN)_8^{3-}$, or a compound containing it.

CYANONICKELATE (O). The anion $Ni(CN)_4^{4-}$, or a compound containing it.

CYANONICKELATE (I). The anion $Ni(CN)_3^-$, or a compound containing it.

CYANONICKELATE (II). The anion $Ni(CN)_4^-$, or a compound containing it.

CYANOÖSMATE. The anion $Os(CN)_6^{4-}$, or a compound containing it.

CYANOPALLADATE (O). The anion $Pd(CN)_4^{4-}$, or a compound containing it.

CYANOPALLADATE (II). The anion $Pd(CN)_4^-$, or a compound containing it.

CYANOPLATINATE (II). The anion $Pt(CN)_4^-$, or a compound containing it.

CYANOPLATINATE (IV). The anion $Pt(CN)_6^-$, or a compound containing it.

CYANORHODATE (II). The anion $Rh(CN)_6^{4-}$, or a compound containing it.

CYANORHODATE (III). The anion $Rh(CN)_6^{3-}$, or a compound containing it.

CYANORUTHENATE (II). The anion $Ru(CN)_6^{4-}$, or a compound containing it.

CYANOTUNGSTATE (IV). The anion $W(CN)_8^{4-}$, or a compound containing it.

CYANOTUNGSTATE (V). The anion $W(CN)_8^{3-}$, or a compound containing it.

CYANOVANADATE (II). The anion $V(CN)_6^{4-}$, or a compound containing it.

CYANOZINCATE. The anion $Zn(CN)_3^-$, or $Zn(CN)_4^-$, or a compound containing one of these anions.

CYBOTACTATES. Associated molecules exhibiting orientation, as described for the term **cybotaxis** (q.v.).

CYBOTACTIC. Exhibiting the phenomenon of **cybotaxis** (q.v.).

CYBOTAXIS. The three-dimensional arrangement of molecules of a substance; in general, the term is applied to liquid, non-crystalline substances. Two of the most common arrangements are the end-to-end $(AB \cdots BA)$ and the side-by-side $\left(\begin{array}{c}AB\\ \vdots \\ AB\end{array}\right)$ forms, with **coordinate bonds** (q.v.) existing between certain contiguous atoms or radicals, as indicated by the dotted lines.

CYCLE. (1) A period of time, at the end of which a sequence of events repeats. (2) A series of events which repeats. (3) A closed pathway or ring, especially in compound words, as heterocycle.

CYCLIC COMPOUND. A compound in which some or all of the atoms are arranged in a ring structure. Compounds in which the ring is composed solely of carbon atoms are known as "carbocyclic."

CYCLIZATION. The process of establishing a **ring** structure within a molecule by intramolecular **bond** linkage.

CYCLO-. (Greek) *Kyklos*, circle. Ring structure, cyclic; as cyclohexane.

CYCLOALKANE. The generic name for a saturated monocyclic **hydrocarbon.**

CYCLOBUTYL. The radical C_4H_7-. Its structural formula is

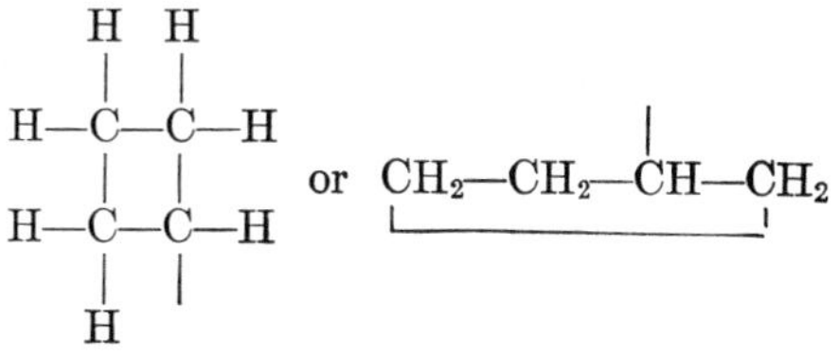

or $CH_2-CH_2-CH-CH_2$

CYCLODIOLEFIN. An unsaturated **hydrocarbon** with cyclic structure which contains two double bonds, as cyclopentadiene,

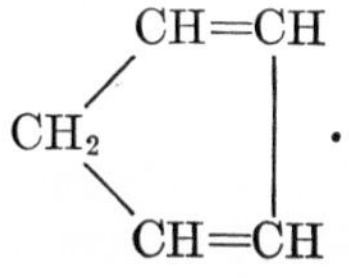

CYCLOHEXADIENYL. The radical

$CH_2 \cdot CH : CH \cdot CH : CH \cdot CH-$

or

$CH : CH \cdot CH_2 \cdot CH : CH \cdot CH-$.

CYCLOHEXADIENYLIDENE. The radical

$CH_2 \cdot CH : CH \cdot CH : CH \cdot C =$

or

$CH : CH \cdot CH_2 \cdot CH : CH \cdot C =$.

CYCLOHEXASILANYL. The radical

$$SiH_2-SiH_2-SiH-$$
$$SiH_2-SiH_2-SiH-.$$

CYCLOHEXENYL. The radical C_6H_9- (from cyclohexane, 3, isomers).

CYCLOHEXENYLIDENE. The radical $CH_2 \cdot CH_2 \cdot CH_2 \cdot CH : CH \cdot C =$. More than one structural form of this radical is known. The 2-ene form is shown.

CYCLOHEXYL. The radical $C_6H_{11}-$ (from cyclohexane).

CYCLOHEXYLIDENE. The radical

$CH_2 \cdot CH_2 \cdot CH_2 \cdot CH_2 \cdot CH_2 \cdot C =$.

CYCLOOLEFIN. An unsaturated **hydrocarbon** with cyclic structure which contains one double bond, as cyclopentene,

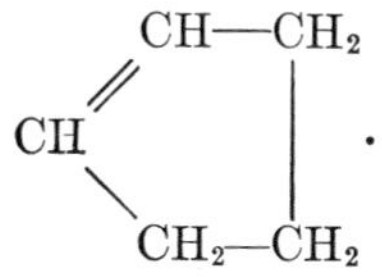

CYCLOPARAFFIN. A saturated **hydrocarbon** with a cyclic or ring structure, as cyclopentane,

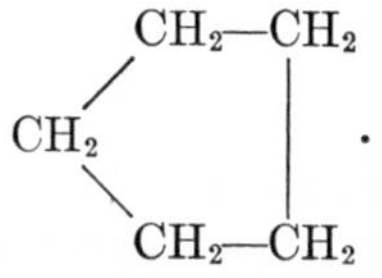

CYCLOPENTENYL. The radical C_5H_7- (from cyclopentene).

CYCLOPENTYL. The radical C_5H_9- (from cyclopentane).

CYCLOPROPYL. The radical C_3H_5- (from cyclopropane).

CYCLOSILANES. Cyclic silicon compounds having the general formula $(SiH_2)_n$, which are called cyclotrisilane, cyclotetrasilane, etc., according to the number of members in the ring; they have the generic name *cyclosilanes*.

CYCLOSILAZANES. Cyclic compounds having the general formula $(SiH_2NH)_n$ which are called cyclodisilazane, cyclotrisilazine, etc., according to the number of silicon atoms in the ring; they have the generic name *cyclosilazanes*. Example: cyclotrisilazane,

$$\overline{HN-SiH_2-NH-SiH_2-NH-SiH_2}.$$

CYCLOSILOXANES. Cyclic compounds having the general formula $(SiH_2O)_n$, which are called cyclodisiloxane, cyclotrisiloxane, etc., according to the number of silicon atoms in the ring; they have the generic name *cyclosiloxanes*. Example: cyclotrisiloxane,

$$\overline{O-SiH_2-O-SiH_2-O-SiH_2}.$$

CYCLOSILTHIANES. Cyclic compounds having the general formula $(SiH_2S)_n$ which are called cyclodisilthiane, cyclotrisilthiane, etc., according to the number of silicon atoms in the ring; they have the generic name *cyclosilthianes*. Example: cyclotrisilthiane,

$$\overline{S-SiH_2-S-SiH_2-S-SiH_2}.$$

CYCLOTRIOLEFIN. An unsaturated hydrocarbon which contains a cyclic structure and three double bonds.

CYCLOTRON. An apparatus used to produce high-speed particles for nuclear bombardments and similar investigations. It consists essentially of a circular apparatus in which the particles travel along a spiral pathway that passes many times around the apparatus. Twice during each trip around the apparatus, the particles are accelerated by a powerful magnetic field between two huge electrodes, on which the electric charge vibrates in resonance with the rotation of the particles. In its form, this apparatus consists of 2 "dees," $\mathbb{C}\,D$; the particles receive their acceleration while traveling from one "dee" to the other across the gap and they follow circular paths within the domain bounded by the "dees," being constrained to move in such circular paths by a magnetic field permeating the region. The over-all path traversed by a particle consists of a spiral extending from the center to the periphery. The electric field applied between the "dees" changes periodically in direction to keep in step with the particle as the latter executes one semicircular path through one "dee" region.

CYCLOVERSION PROCESS. A petroleum cracking process using a bauxite catalyst operating on preformed cracked naphtha fractions. Temperatures of about $600°$ F., and pressures around 100 pounds per square inch are used.

CYLINDER, GRADUATED. A glass cylinder provided with a scale to determine the volume of liquids placed into it. The cylinder is frequently provided with a shaped lip to facilitate pouring.

CYMYL. The radical $C_{10}H_{13}-$ (from cymene).

2-p-CYMYL. See **carvacryl.**

3-p-CYMYL. See **thymyl.**

CYSTYL. The radical $-COCH(NH_2)CH_2SSCH_2CH(NH_2)CO-$.

CYTOCHEMISTRY. The branch of chemical science dealing with the chemical composition of living cells and with the nature, properties, and reactions of the substances of which they are composed.

CZAPEK TESTS. Various phenols, naphthols, and aromatic amines in alcoholic or aqueous solution, give distinctive colors to wood fibers or lignin in the presence of hydrochloric acid.

CZERNOTZKY TEST. This test is used to differentiate pentathionate solutions from those of other thionates. The test is based on the fact that pentathionate, which decomposes to tetrathionate and sulfur in the presence of hydroxyl ion, does not so react in the presence of sulfite. If formaldehyde is first added, however, the sulfur deposition from pentathionate solutions can be obtained.

CZOKOR ALUM-COCHINEAL. A solution of 1 g. cochineal in 100 ml. of a 1% aqueous solution of potassium alum, which is then reduced to half its volume by boiling. This solution is a stain for the nuclei of cells.

CZUMPLITZ TEST REACTION. Many alkaloids give characteristic colors on moistening with a few drops of a solution of 1 g. zinc chloride in 30 ml. water and 30 ml.

ferred). Abbreviation for density of electric flux (D). **Coefficient of diffusion** (fluid) (D). Abbreviation for angular **dispersion** (D). Abbreviation for **electric displacement** and displacement flux density (D). Symbol for grating space between corresponding points (d). See also **delta.**

DADDI SOLUTION. A solution of 0.1 g. potassium p-nitrodiazobenzene in 100 ml. water. This reagent is used in testing for bilirubin, which, when in acetic acid solution, gives a red color.

DAHLMANN TEST. Lignin in paper is colored yellow by a 0.1% solution of sodium gold chloride; sulfite or soda cellulose is colored red-brown.

DAKIN REACTION. A method for the replacement by hydroxyl of an **aldehyde** group, or an aceto group in phenolic aldehydes or ketones by the action of warm hydrogen peroxide and sodium hydroxide.

$$HO \cdot C_6H_4 \cdot CHO + H_2O_2 \xrightarrow{\text{NaOH}} HO \cdot C_6H_4 \cdot OH + HCOOH.$$

hydrochloric acid, followed by drying on the steam bath.

CZYHLARZ-FURTH TEST. Peroxidases liberate iodine from a solution of potassium iodide slightly acidified with acetic acid, in the presence of hydrogen peroxide.

D. Symbol for deuterium (D). Abbreviation for diameter (D or d). The characteristic line of sodium (D). Abbreviation for dextro- or for **dextrorotary** (d or d). The mathematical symbol for differential (d, followed by another letter or letters). Symbol for distillate rate (D). Symbol for

DAKIN REAGENT FOR ALDEHYDES AND KETONES. A modified **Fischer reagent** (q.v.) consisting of a solution of 1 part p-nitrophenylhydrazine in 30 parts 40% acetic acid. It gives the corresponding nitrophenylhydrazones with aldehydes and ketones.

DAKIN SOLUTION. An aqueous solution containing 0.5% sodium hypochlorite, in which the pH has been carefully adjusted, and which is used to sterilize cuts and wounds.

DAKIN-WEST REACTION. A method of formation of α-acylamino ketones from α-amino acids and acid anhydrides or acyl fluorides.

$$R \cdot CHNH_2 \cdot COOH + (CH_3CO)_2O \rightarrow R \cdot CH(NHCOCH_3) \cdot CO \cdot CH_3 + H_2O + CO_2.$$

diffusivity of vapor (D_v). Symbol for spacing of Bragg planes in a **crystal** (d).

Symbol for current **displacement** $\left(D, \dfrac{D}{4\pi}\right)$.

Symbol for density $\left(= \dfrac{m}{V}\right)$ (D, but ρ is pre-

DALTON LAW. See law of Dalton.

DAMIENS REAGENT. A solution of 5 g. cuprous oxide in 100 ml. sulfuric acid, of a density of 66° **Baumé** (q.v.) (approximately 93%). This solution is used in gas analysis to absorb carbon monoxide.

DAMPING TIME. The time taken by an excited electron to emit radiation and "jump back" to an orbit of lower energy.

DANCHAKOFF FLUID. A solution of 25 g. potassium dichromate, 50 g. mercuric chloride and 10 g. sodium sulfate, in 1000 g. water, to which formaldehyde solution is then added. This reagent is used as a fixative for plant tissues.

DANÉ TEST REACTION FOR FORM-ALDEHYDE. α-Naphthol dissolved in a little sodium hydroxide solution, on the addition of a little formaldehyde solution gives a green color, changing to dark blue on warming. This reaction is used conversely to test for α-naphthol.

DANHEISER SOLUTION. A solution prepared by mixing 0.1 g. dimethyglyoxime, dissolved in 10 ml. ethyl alcohol, with 5 g. citric acid, dissolved in 90 ml. ammonium hydroxide solution (sp. gr. 0.90). This reagent is used as a test agent for solutions of nickel, which give with it a red color or precipitate.

DANIELL CELL. See **cell, Daniell.**

on a water bath. Tryptophane liberates free iodine.

DANTEC TEST REACTION. To test for antipyrine, add to 0.1 g. of sample, 1 ml. of a 10% solution of xanthydrol in acetic acid, and then 2 ml. glacial acetic acid, and heat to boiling. A red color indicates the presence of antipyrine.

DANZIGER TEST REACTION. Cobalt is detected by acidifying 5 ml. of a very dilute solution with hydrochloric acid, adding solid ammonium thiocyanate and a few drops of stannous chloride solution, and shaking with amyl alcohol; the solution becomes blue in the presence of cobalt.

D'ARSONVAL GALVANOMETER. See **galvanometer, d'Arsonval.**

DARZENS-CLAISEN REACTION. See **Darzens condensation.**

DARZENS CONDENSATION. A method of forming glycidic esters by condensation of aldehydes or ketones with esters of α-halogen acids. The glycidic esters yield on saponification the corresponding carboxylic acids of the ethylene oxide series, which on loss of CO_2 yield aldehydes or ketones.

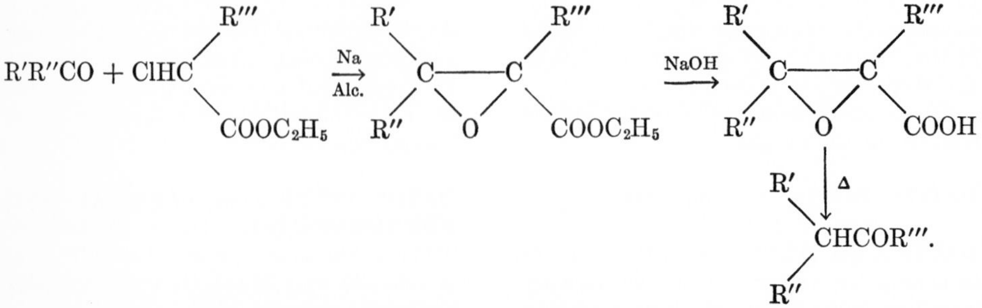

$$R'R''CO + ClHC \overset{R'''}{\underset{COOC_2H_5}{<}} \xrightarrow[\text{Alc.}]{\text{Na}} \overset{R'}{\underset{R''}{>}}C\overset{}{\underset{O}{-}}C\overset{R'''}{\underset{COOC_2H_5}{<}} \xrightarrow{\text{NaOH}} \overset{R'}{\underset{R''}{>}}C\overset{}{\underset{O}{-}}C\overset{R'''}{\underset{COOH}{<}}$$

$$\overset{R'}{\underset{R''}{>}}CHCOR'''.$$

See also **Darzens synthesis.**

DANILA TEST REACTION. Tryptophane is detected by adding 0.1 ml. of a 1:200 aqueous solution of the substance to a 1:250 solution of iodic acid, and heating

DARZENS SYNTHESIS OF TETRALIN DERIVATIVES. A method of formation of tetralin derivatives by ring closure of benzylallylacetic acid and related compounds.

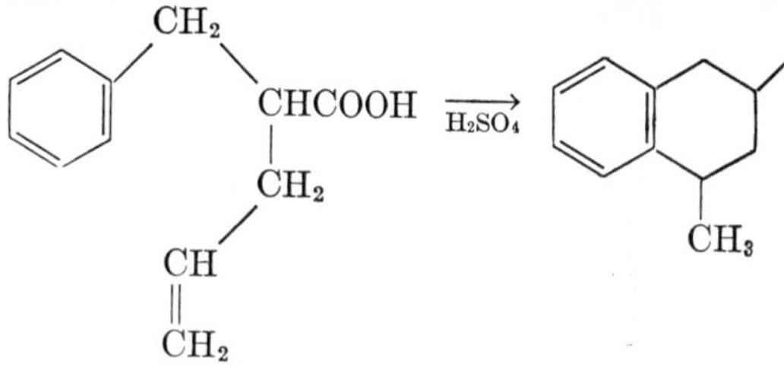

DARZENS SYNTHESIS OF UNSATURATED KETONES. A method of formation of unsaturated ketones by reaction of the corresponding unsaturated hydrocarbon with an acid chloride, then removing the hydrochloric acid.

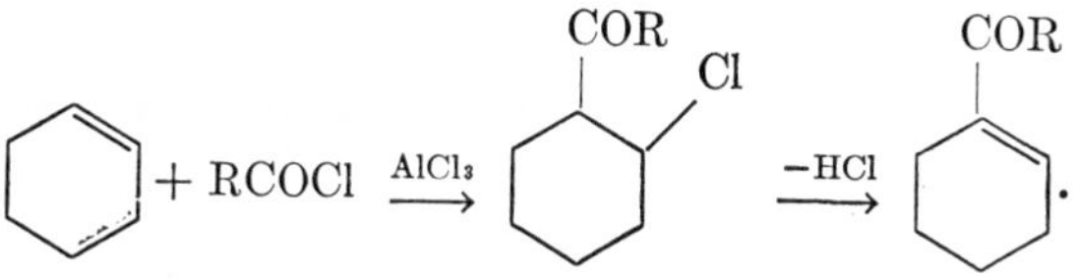

DA SILVA REACTION FOR COCAINE. Evaporate the material with fuming nitric acid on the steam bath, and add 1–2 drops of a concentrated alcoholic solution of potassium hydroxide. An odor suggestive of peppermint indicates the presence of cocaine.

DASYMETER. (1) An instrument used to determine the density of a gas. It consists of a thin glass globe which is weighed in the (unknown) gas or mixture of gases and then in a gas of known density.

(2) An instrument used to determine the composition of flue gas.

DATIVE BOND. See bond, dative.

DAUTRICHE TEST. A method of determining the velocity of an explosion by installing, in the tube in which the explosion takes place, two detonators connected to explosive fuses. The point of inflection of the deformation produced by the two secondary explosions gives the rate of travel of the primary explosion from one detonator to the other.

DAUVÉ TEST REACTION. Gold is detected by suspending in its solution a small piece of aluminum, which colors the solution red-purple if viewed by transmitted light, or yellow if viewed by reflected light.

DÁVID REAGENT FOR OPIUM ALKALOIDS. Basic magnesium hypochlorite is used in glacial acetic acid solution to test for opium alkaloids. To 3 ml. of this solution and 3 ml. of sulfuric acid, add 0.005 g. of the alkaloid; characteristic colors are obtained.

DÁVID TEST FOR ALCOHOL IN ESSENTIAL OILS. Extract the oil with a little water, and superimpose the water on a solution of 2 g. molybdic acid in 100 ml. concentrated sulfuric acid. A blue ring indicates alcohol. If the sample contains an aldehyde, it must be removed from the sample of oil with petroleum ether before making the test.

DÁVID TESTS FOR BARBITAL AND PHENOBARBITAL. To a solution of 0.02 g. of the substance in 1.5 ml. 10% ammonia, add 3 ml. of a mixture of 5 ml. 30% hydrogen peroxide with 10 ml. water. Heat on the hot water bath. A color of wine-must indicates the presence of phenobarbital. To a solution of 0.02–0.03 g. of the substance in 1 ml. alcohol, add 2 ml. water, 1 ml. N sodium nitrite solution, and 1 ml. concentrated sulfuric acid; an orange-yellow color indicates the presence of barbital; a lemon-yellow color, the presence of phenobarbital.

DAVIS CONCENTRATOR. A nitric acid concentrator, consisting of a short, packed tower; dilute nitric acid or a mixture of this acid with weak sulfuric acid enters at the top. Steam from a boiler enters at the bottom and boils off strong nitric acid (90–96%), which is condensed externally.

DAVY REAGENT. A solution of 5 g. molybdic acid in 100 g. concentrated sulfuric acid, used as a test reagent for various phenols, especially phenol itself. The latter gives a yellow color, changing to purplered, except in dilute solution, where a green color, changing to blue, is obtained.

DE-, DES-. (Latin) Indicating removal of something from the molecule; as desoxybenzoin, $C_6H_5CH_2COC_6H_5$ (benzoin with oxygen atom removed).

DEACIDIFICATION. Removing or neutralizing an acid in a system.

DEACON PROCESS. An older process for the production of chlorine from hydrochloric acid. The hydrochloric acid vapors are mixed with air, heated to about 400° C., and passed over a catalyst, commonly pumice impregnated with cuprous chloride. This process is now practically obsolete.

DEACON TEST REACTION FOR AMYGDALIN. With a little concentrated sulfuric acid, amygdalin gives a carmine-red color which disappears on dilution.

DEACTIVATION. A special use of this term occurs in the **flotation process,** where a deactivator is used to modify selectively the action of an activator, reducing its effect upon an undesired substance.

DEAD SPACE. (1) The volume of a vessel not occupied by a porous solid (as in **adsorption**) or to that portion of the volume of a vessel through which no discharge takes place (in **discharge tubes**), etc. (2) When

the **surface tension** of a system increases as chemical action proceeds, **capillarity** will tend to stop the action. If any part of the system is then subjected to capillary action, as in a capillary tube, no reaction takes place. This is called "dead space" of the reaction.

DEAMIDIZATION. (Desamidization, disamidization) Any process for removing the amino group from an amide, e.g.,

$$CH_3CONH_2 + HCl + H_2O = CH_3COOH + NH_4Cl.$$

DEAMINATION. (Desamination) Any process for removing an amino group from a compound, e.g., by diazotization and subsequent boiling with alcohol.

DE BOER TEST REACTIONS. Both zirconium and hafnium give a violet color with alizarinsulfonic acid which is not discharged by hydrochloric acid, but which is changed to yellow by a trace of fluoride.

DEBRAY REAGENT. An aqueous solution of phosphomolybdic acid, which is used to test for salts of cesium, potassium, rubidium, and thallium, giving yellow precipitates with those ions.

DE BROGLIE MATTER WAVES. A concept arising from the dual nature of small quantities of matter, which may be regarded as possessing both **particle** and **wave** characteristics. According to the theory a particle of mass m and velocity v can be associated with a matter wave of length $\lambda = \dfrac{h}{mv}$, where h is **Planck's constant.** From a consideration of these matter waves, statistical inferences concerning the behavior of small particles may be made.

DEBYE-FALKENHAGEN EFFECT. The variation of the **conductance** of an electrolytic solution with **frequency.** This effect, which is noted at high frequencies, is also called the dispersion of conductance.

DEBYE-HÜCKEL LIMITING LAW. The mean activity coefficient of the ions in a dilute solution is proportional to the product of the valences of the ions and the square root of the ionic strength of the solution. Therefore, the departure from ideal behavior is independent of the chemical nature of the electrolyte, being determined solely by ionic valences and ionic strength.

DEBYE-HÜCKEL THEORY OF CONDUCTIVITY. The underlying idea of the Debye-Hückel Theory of Conductivity is that there are, on an average, more ions of unlike than of like charge in the neighborhood of any ion as a consequence of electrical attractions between different charges. Thus each ion is surrounded by an atmosphere of ions of opposite charge. This ionic atmosphere has central symmetry as long as the system is stationary. In the presence of an external field this symmetry is destroyed, since the central atom moves in one direction while ions of opposite charge go in the opposite direction. The over-all conductivity is affected by four different factors: the direct effect of the applied field in moving the ions to the electrodes of opposite charge; the opposing frictional force attributable to viscosity of solvent; the dissymmetry in ionic field surrounding a moving ion, and thus opposing the motion; and the effect of collisions between solvent molecules and moving ions.

DEBYE UNIT. A unit of electrical moment equal to 10^{-18} electrostatic unit of moment.

DECAGRAM. Ten grams.

DECALESCENCE. Absorption of heat, usually by an alloy without rise of temperature, due to an **allotropic transformation.**

DECALITER. Ten **liters.**

DECAMETER. Ten **meters.**

DECANT. To pour off the clear liquid above a settled or partly-settled suspension, or, in general, to pour off the supernatant phase.

DECARBONIZE. To remove carbon from any system which contains it. The substitution of oxygen for carbon dioxide in the blood in the lungs is termed decarbonization, as is also the burning out of a portion of the carbon in cast iron to make steel.

DECARBOXYLATION. Elimination of one or more **carboxyl** groups from the molecule of an organic acid, or related compound, by elimination of the group as carbon dioxide.

DECAY. A general term for **decomposition,** usually restricted to the breaking down of organic substances by natural processes, or to the decrease in activity of **radioactive substances** as more and more of their atoms disintegrate.

DECAY, PERIOD OF HALF. See **period of half decay.**

DE CHANCOURTOIS SCREW (TELLURIC SCREW). An arrangement of the **elements** around a cylinder at an angle of 45° in order of their **atomic weight,** whereby the elements which make up Döbereiner's triads were found to fall beneath each other.

DECIGRAM. One-tenth of a **gram.**

DECILITER. One-tenth of a **liter.**

DECIMETER. One-tenth of a **meter.**

DECIMOLAR. Containing one-tenth of a mole (gram-molecular weight).

DECINORMAL. One-tenth **normal.**

DECKERT REAGENT FOR ZINC. One ml. of a solution of dithizone in $0.01 N$ sodium hydroxide is diluted with 90 ml. zinc-free water. The mixture is then added to the test solution which has previously been adjusted to the same pH. The formation of a red color is indicative of the presence of zinc.

DECKERT TEST FOR ETHYLENE OXIDE IN AIR. Pass 50 ml. of the air through 1–2 ml. of a 40% solution of potassium thiocyanate containing 1 drop 0.1% alcoholic phenolphthalein. The test is negative for ethylene oxide if no red color appears in 2 minutes.

DECOCTION. A solution that is made by boiling a solid material to dissolve one or more of its **component** substances.

DECOLORIZE. To remove the color from; to bleach. Decolorization may be carried out in a variety of ways: (1) by **adsorption,** in which the coloring matter is removed from solution by placing it in contact with charcoal, activated carbon, alumina, etc.; (2) by **precipitation;** many coloring matters form insoluble compounds with aluminum, lead, and other heavy metals; (3) by destruction, e.g., oxidation or reduction. The agent in the process is termed a decolorizer. Cf. **bleaching.**

DECOMPOSITION. The division of a molecule by any chemical process so as to furnish two or more new molecules. Complete decomposition refers to such a condition of the products that they are not readily decomposed further, e.g., such decomposition products as ammonia and carbon dioxide. **Degradation** (q.v.) refers to gradual decomposition in which the molecule is diminished in size in small steps.

DECOMPOSITION, CHEMICAL. The breaking down of a substance into two or more other substances which differ from one another and from the original material in their properties.

DECOMPOSITION, DOUBLE. A term used to express the interaction of molecules which exchange one or more of their constituent atoms or radicals.

DECOMPOSITION, SENSITIZED. A chemical decomposition that is brought about by the presence of a second substance which absorbs an **exciting radiation.** The essential mechanism of the reaction is the excitation of particles of the second substance by the radiation, followed by collisions between these excited particles and molecules to be decomposed. The process proceeds most effectively if the energy difference between the **ground state** and excited state of the sensitizer is nearly equal to the energy of the decomposition reaction.

DECOMPOSITION VOLTAGE. The minimum **electromotive force** which must be applied to a given solution and given electrodes to produce steady **electrolysis.** The value of the decomposition voltage is not known precisely because the rise in the current-voltage curve does not begin at a sharply defined point. Instead the curve at first rises very slowly with increasing applied voltage; in the neighborhood of the decomposition voltage there is an abrupt change in slope (a sharp bend) and thereafter the curve rises rapidly with applied electromotive force.

DE CONINCK TEST FOR SUCCINIC AND MALIC ACIDS. A saturated aqueous solution of succinic acid gives a permanent rose-red color on boiling with an aqueous suspension of calcium salicylate. With a saturated solution of malic acid the red color disappears on boiling gently for 15–20 minutes.

DECREPITATION. The emission of a crackling sound, commonly by **crystals** on shattering under the internal stresses resulting from heating.

DECYL. The radical $CH_3(CH_2)_9-$.

DEE. See **cyclotron.**

DEER REACTION FOR CODEINE, DIONINE, MORPHINE, AND PAPAVERINE. To about 0.3 g. of the alkaloid add a little lead peroxide, 5 ml. water, and a few drops glacial acetic acid. Heat to boiling, filter, and to 1–2 drops of the filtrate add 5 ml. concentrated sulfuric acid. Codeine and dionine give a blue-violet color; morphine, a yellow-brown color; and papaverine, a cherry-red color.

DE FAZI TEST REACTION. Aromatic aldehydes are detected by adding a few drops of the substance under test, in chloroform solution, to 3 drops of a 1% chloroform solution of acenaphthene, then add 1 ml. concentrated sulfuric acid. A green ring changing to red-violet indicates the presence of aromatic aldehydes.

DEFECATION. (1) A process used in sugar manufacture to clarify sugar solutions. (2) In general, the procedure of clarifying solutions by precipitation reactions.

DEFERVESCENCE. Cessation or discontinuance of boiling or of effervescence.

DEFINITE PROPORTIONS, LAW OF. See **law of definite proportions.**

DEFLAGRATION. An **exothermic** reaction, commonly between a solid and a gas, and usually accompanied by noise and flame.

DEFLEURAGE. Removal of exhausted flowers from an **enfleurage** (q.v.) medium.

DEFLOCCULATION. The reverse process of **flocculation** (q.v.), or the process of preventing flocculation.

DE FLOREZ PROCESS. A process for the **distillation** and cracking of crude oil (or a fraction distilled therefrom) by the application of heat and pressure. The preheated oil passes into a huge pipe still, externally heated, from which the vapor is conducted to a tower. By changing the pressures at which the tower and still are operated it is possible to vary yields of oil

DE GIACOMO REAGENTS. A number of solutions used in preparing diazobenzene-sulfonic acid when required. This substance is used in testing plant tissues for guanine. A red color indicates the presence of guanine.

DEGRADATION. (1) A gradual decomposition occurring in stages with well marked intermediate products. For example, the maltose chain loses one carbon atom under certain conditions to produce a sugar with eleven carbon atoms in its skeleton. (2) Degradation of energy; see **law of degradation of energy.**

DEGRADATION OF ACIDS (KRAFT METHOD). A method of reducing the number of carbon atoms in the molecule of an acid, especially a **fatty acid** by the decomposition of its calcium or barium salt in the presence of a salt of acetic acid, followed by oxidation of the resulting methyl ketone.

$$(R \cdot CH_2 \cdot COO)_2Ca + (CH_3 \cdot COO)_2Ca \rightarrow 2R \cdot CH_2 \cdot CO \cdot CH_3 + 2CaCO_3$$
$$\downarrow CrO_3$$
$$2RCOOH + 2CH_3COOH.$$

and gasoline as well as to change the antiknock value of the gasoline.

DEFOAMING AGENT. A substance or material used to reduce **foaming** in a liquid system.

DEFROTHER. An agent which prevents **frothing.**

DEGASIFICATION. Removal of gas, as applied particularly to the removal of the last traces of gas from wires used in vacuum tubes, from metals to be plated, and from substances to be used in other specialized applications.

DEGENERATE. (1) This expression was used in the kinetic theory of gases to describe a gas which did not obey the ideal gas laws, in other words, any real gas. The greater the deviation of the real gas from ideality, the greater its degeneracy.

(2) In quantum mechanics the term applies to any system for which two or more states correspond to the same eigenvalue.

DEGREASING AGENT. A solvent used to remove grease, either a fat or oil or a mixture of both, as from a metal in a plating operation.

DEGREE. (1) A division or interval marked on a scale, as a thermometric degree. For comparison of degrees, see **thermometric scales.** (2) Condition in terms of some unit or in relation to some standard, as degree of acidity.

DEGREE A.P.I. See **American Petroleum Institute Scale.**

DEGREE OF FREEDOM. In the statement of the **phase rule** (q.v.) a degree of freedom is one of that number of variable factors such as pressure, temperature, or concentration, which must be fixed to define completely the state of a system. In terms of the energy of a system the number of degrees of freedom is the number of independent squared terms of the type $\frac{1}{2}mv_x^2$ or $\frac{1}{2}Ir^2$ or $\frac{1}{2}kx^2$, which must be specified in order to determine uniquely the energy of the system.

DEGREE OF IONIZATION. See ionization, degree of.

DE HAAS TEST FOR β-NAPHTHOL. One ml. of an aqueous solution of the substance is added to 5 ml. acetic acid, and the solution is floated on 5 ml. concentrated sulfuric acid. A colored ring at the interface, and fluorescence on shaking, indicate the presence of β-naphthol.

DEHN-SCOTT TEST REACTION FOR ALKALOIDS. Many alkaloids are detected by adding 5 mg. of a substance to be tested to 5 ml. of alcohol, and treating this solution with 2–3 drops sodium hypobromite solution. Many alkaloids produce characteristic colors, and others give characteristic odors.

DEHN-SCOTT TEST REACTION FOR AROMATIC AMINES. A 0.1% alcoholic solution of the substance is treated with 1–2 drops of ammonia and 2–3 drops sodium hypobromite solution. Characteristic colors are obtained with many aromatic amines.

DEHN-SCOTT TEST REACTION FOR PHENOLIC COMPOUNDS. A 0.1% alcoholic solution of the substance is treated with 2–3 drops sodium hypobromite solution. Characteristic colors are obtained for many phenolic compounds. If 1 drop ammonia is added before the hypobromite, other colors are obtained in several instances.

DEHUMIDIFICATION. A process used in air-conditioning in which air partially saturated with water is cooled to below the **dew point,** so that part of the water vapor is condensed.

DEHYDRATE. To remove water, or to render anhydrous.

DEHYDRATION. Removal of water from a substance or system or chemical compound, or removal of the elements of water, in correct proportion, from a chemical compound or compounds.

DEHYDRO-. Denoting (a) removal of hydrogen; as, dehydrocholic acid; (b) sometimes, removal of water; as dehydromucic acid.

DEHYDROFREEZING. A method of food processing combining dehydration and freezing.

DEHYDROGENATE. To reduce the content of hydrogen in a substance. Oxidation with removal of hydrogen is dehydrogenation, but simple addition of oxygen, complete combustion, or the substitution of halogen for hydrogen is not considered to be dehydrogenation.

DEKALITER. Ten liters.

DEKAMETER. Ten meters.

DE KONINCK ETHER TEST. Sulfur compounds and hydrogen peroxide in ether are detected by shaking the ether with a drop of mercury, which becomes black and powdery if those substances are present.

DE KONINCK TEST FOR MANGANESE. A solution of a manganese compound in fuming hydrochloric acid, on addition of a few drops concentrated nitric acid, and heating, gives a greenish-black color which disappears on dilution or further heating.

DE KONINCK TEST REACTION FOR THIOSULFATE. Metallic aluminum and sodium hydroxide solution reduce thiosulfate to sulfide.

DEL BOCA-REMAZZANO TEST. The acetyl group is detected by adding to 1–2 ml. of the solution containing it, 4–5 drops 5% lanthanum nitrate solution, then enough 0.02 N iodine to color the solution light brown, and then ammonia by drops until a faint turbidity appears. A blue or violet color or precipitate indicates the presence of the acetyl group.

DELÉPINE REACTION. A method of obtaining **amines** from **organic halides** by forming the hexamethylenetetramine addition product, and treating it with hydrochloric acid and alcohol. See **Sommelet reaction.**

DELÈPINE TEST FOR FENCHONE.
Fenchone is separated from camphor by treating the material in alcoholic potassium hydroxide solution with hydroxylamine hydrochloride. The β-fenchone oxime is less soluble than the camphor oxime, and crystallizes.

DELÈPINE TEST FOR METHYLAMINE. Methylamine in aqueous solution gives a yellow precipitate with **Nessler's solution** (q.v.). This precipitate is insoluble in excess reagent or in water. On the other hand, dimethylamine or trimethylamine give white precipitates soluble in excess reagent or water.

DELFF REAGENTS FOR ALKALOIDS.
Aqueous solutions of potassium platinocyanide and potassium mercuric iodide, used as test reagents for alkaloids.

DELFF TEST FOR FUMARIC ACID.
An aqueous solution of fumaric acid gives a precipitate, on warming with cadmium sulfate, of characteristic leaflets, if the fumaric acid solution is not too dilute.

DELIQUESCENCE. Dissolution of a substance, commonly a salt, by absorption of water from the air. This phenomenon is observed in the case of substances readily soluble in water, which form solutions having a lower vapor pressure than that of the water vapor in the air.

DELIQUESCENCE, WATER OF. Water extracted from air by a substance which exhibits the phenomenon of **deliquescence** (q.v.).

DELIVERY FLASK. See **flask, delivery.**

DELTA (Δ, δ or ∂). The fourth letter of the Greek alphabet, used to denote the fourth carbon atom in a straight-chain compound or a derivative in which a substituted group is attached to that carbon atom (δ). Symbol for a **double bond** (Δ). Symbol for a finite difference (Δ or δ). Symbol for a partial derivative (∂, followed by distinguishing letters). Symbol for the application of heat in the course of a chemical reaction (Δ). Symbol for the **angle of deviation** (δ). Symbol for **deviation** (δ). Symbol for difference in **phase** (δ). Symbol for **total elongation** (deflection) (δ). Symbol for optical length (Δ).

DELUSTRANT. A substance used to reduce the **luster** of a synthetic fiber, in order to enhance the appearance of the finished textile.

DEMAL SOLUTION. A solution which contains one **gram-equivalent** of solute per cubic decimeter of solution. It is slightly weaker than a normal solution, in the ratio of the magnitude of the liter to the cubic decimeter. The unit *demal* is used in conductivity measurements.

DEMARCAY REACTION FOR RHODIUM. A neutral or weakly-acid solution of rhodium ammonium chloride gives a yellow precipitate with a slight excess of sodium hypochlorite solution. The precipitate dissolves in 1:5 acetic acid solution to give an orange-yellow color, which fades to give a gray precipitate, then a sky-blue color.

DEMJANOV REARRANGEMENT. Rearrangement of structure that accompanies the treatment of certain primary **aliphatic amines** with nitrous acid; change in size of the ring frequently occurs.

DEMULCENT. A drug used to reduce the irritation of inflamed tissues or other surfaces, commonly a drug which owes its action to its ability to form an adherent coating over the affected areas.

DENATURANT. A substance added to render another substance unfit for certain uses, as to render ethyl alcohol unsuitable for use as a beverage by addition of small quantities of methyl alcohol.

DENATURED SUBSTANCE. A product which has been rendered unfit for human consumption by the addition of harmful, odorous, or inert substances.

DENIGÈS ARSENIC MIRROR REAGENT. A solution of 10 g. ammonium molybdate and 25 g. ammonium nitrate in 100 ml. water, to which 100 ml. concentrated nitric acid is then added. This reagent is used in differentiating arsenic and antimony test deposits. The deposit is dissolved in nitric acid and treated with the reagent. A yellow precipitate indicates the presence of arsenic.

DENIGÈS BENZOYL REAGENT. A solution of 2 ml. 37% formaldehyde in 100 ml. concentrated sulfuric acid used in testing for the presence of the benzoyl group. A brown-red color, obtained on heating at 120°C., indicates the presence of the benzoyl group.

DENIGÈS-CHELLE REAGENT FOR HALOGENS. A solution of 0.01 g. fuchsin in 10 ml. of water, decolorized by the addition of 100 ml. of a 5% aqueous solution of sulfur dioxide, and acidified by the addition of 50 ml. glacial acetic acid and 2 ml. concentrated sulfuric acid per 50 ml. of decolorized solution. This reagent gives a violet-red color with free bromine, and a yellow color with free chlorine.

DENIGÈS-CHELLE TEST FOR BROMINE. This test is a modification of the Guareschi Test, and is used to detect bromine in the presence of nitrites. Five ml. of the test solution, containing less than 1 g. per liter bromine, are mixed with 4 drops concentrated hydrochloric acid, 4 drops 10% potassium dichromate solution, and 1 ml. concentrated sulfuric acid. The test tube containing this mixture is then placed for 5 minutes in water at 15° C., followed by the addition of 1 ml. of a 0.01% fuchsin solution which has been decolorized with sulfur dioxide, and 1 ml. chloroform. The mixture is shaken for one minute. A pink color on standing indicates the presence of bromine.

DENIGÈS HYDROSTRYCHNINE SOLUTION. A preparation made by adding 5 ml. hydrochloric acid and 5 g. amalgamated zinc to 5 ml. of a 1% aqueous solution of strychnine. This reagent is used in testing for bromine. A purple-red color indicates the presence of bromine.

DENIGÈS-LEBAT TEST REACTIONS FOR ARSPHENAMINE. (1) Five ml. of a 0.1% solution of arsphenamine give with 0.5 ml. hydrogen peroxide, 0.5 ml. ammonia and 1 drop 4% cupric sulfate solution, a deep blue-green color, changing to red with hydrochloric acid.

(2) One drop ferric chloride solution gives a red-violet color with an arsphenamine solution. This color is unchanged by acids.

DENIGÈS MERCURIC SULFATE REAGENT. A solution of 5 g. mercuric chloride in a mixture of 20 ml. concentrated sulfuric acid and water to make 100 ml. This solution is used as a test reagent for a number of organic radicals and substances, including citrates, isothiocyanates, acetone, carbon disulfide, and thiophene.

DENIGÈS METHYLGLYOXAL REAGENT. Twenty g. 5% glycerin solution are heated with 0.6 ml. bromine and 100 ml. water for 20 minutes on the water bath, boiled for 5 minutes, and evaporated to 100 ml. On cooling, 20 ml. sulfuric acid is added, and the mixture distilled, the first 50 ml. of distillate being used as the test reagent. It gives characteristic colors with many substances upon the addition of sulfuric acid.

DENIGÈS MICRO-REACTION FOR COCAINE. The mixture of cocaine hydrochloride with an equal volume of 5% sodium perchlorate solution results in a characteristic turbidity or a deposit of crystals.

DENIGÈS MICRO-REACTION FOR SALOL. A tiny crystal of salol is mixed with a drop of chloroform on a slide and allowed to evaporate. It is treated with concentrated sulfuric acid and the center of the drop is touched with a glass rod wet with formaldehyde. A white cloudiness is observed, then a red color.

DENIGÈS MICRO-REACTION FOR STRYCHNINE. A small drop of 0.1% strychnine solution is dried on a slide. On the addition of a small drop 1.0 N sodium hydroxide solution, characteristic prismatic crystals appear under the microscope.

DENIGÈS MICRO-REAGENT. Sodium perchlorate, which gives characteristic crystals with many substances.

DENIGÈS MICRO-REAGENT FOR ALKALINE EARTHS. A 10% aqueous solution of iodic acid which gives characteristic micro-crystals with calcium, strontium, and barium.

DENIGÈS MICRO-REAGENT FOR BARIUM. A 1% aqueous solution of sodium tungstate, which gives characteristic crystals with barium.

DENIGÈS MICRO-TEST FOR "NOVOCAINE." Less than 1 mg. Novocaine is dissolved in a drop of water on a slide. A little 5% sodium perchlorate solution is added to the center of the drop by a platinum wire. Spherical refractive bodies, distinct from the crystals of Novocaine perchlorate, can be seen under the microscope.

DENIGÈS PHOSPHATE-ARSENATE REAGENT. A volume of 50 ml. 10% aqueous ammonium molybdate solution, to which 50 ml. concentrated sulfuric acid is added. This reagent is used, with stannous chloride solution, in testing for phosphate and arsenate. A blue color indicates the presence of phosphate or arsenate.

DENIGÈS SELENATE AND TELLURATE REAGENT. A solution of 10 g. mercurous nitrate and 10 ml. nitric acid in 100 ml. water. This solution is used as a test reagent for tellurates, selenates, and selenites. A white precipitate is given with the reagent by solutions containing these ions.

DENIGÈS SOLUTION FOR BUTYRIC ACID. A solution of 5 g. ferrous ammonium sulfate in 10 ml. 1:10 sulfuric acid, diluted with water to 100 ml. It is used in testing for butyric acid.

DENIGÈS SUGAR REAGENT. A solution is prepared of 10 g. sodium acetate, 5 ml. glacial acetic acid, and 100 ml. water, and to 20 ml. of this solution, there are added 3 ml. glacial acetic acid, 1 ml. phenylhydrazine, and 1 ml. 10% sodium bisulfite solution. This solution is used as a test reagent for aldoses and ketoses.

DENIGÈS TEST FOR ACETOACETIC ACID. A solution of acetoacetic acid gives a ruby-red color with sodium nitroprusside solution.

DENIGÈS TEST FOR ALLYL ALCOHOL. To 0.1 ml. of the alcohol, add bromine water to a light yellow, heat to boiling and cool. To 0.4 ml. of this solution add 0.1 ml. of a 5% alcoholic solution of codeine, resorcinol, thymol or β-naphthol, then add 2 ml. sulfuric acid, and heat on the steam bath. Allyl alcohol gives a violet-red color with codeine or thymol, a wine-red color with resorcinol, and a yellow color (green fluorescence) with β-naphthol.

DENIGÈS TEST FOR ANILIDES. Many anilides, on boiling with alcoholic sodium hyprobromite solution, give a yellow-red precipitate and an odor of methyl cyanide.

DENIGÈS TEST FOR BENZOIC ACID. An aqueous solution of benzoic acid, on heating with ferric chloride solution, acetic acid, and hydrogen peroxide, gives a violet color.

DENIGÈS TEST FOR CHLORATE. A solution of resorcinol in an aqueous solution of sulfuric acid gives a green color with chlorate.

DENIGÈS TEST FOR CHLOROBUTANOL. On boiling 5 ml. of a 5% alcoholic solution of chlorobutanol with 1–2 ml. sodium hydroxide, acetone is produced.

DENIGÈS TEST FOR CHROMATE. A neutral chromate solution is treated with hydrogen peroxide, then acidified with acetic acid. It gives a brown color, becoming red, and then red-violet, changed to blue by adding an equal volume of glacial acetic acid.

DENIGÈS TESTS FOR CINCHONA ALKALOIDS. Various cinchona alkaloids, when dissolved in glacial acetic acid, fluoresce on addition of concentrated sulfuric acid, and exhibit other fluorescent effects on further addition of formaldehyde.

DENIGÈS TEST FOR CINNAMIC ACID. On boiling a solution of cinnamic acid with a few drops of hydrogen peroxide and ferric chloride solution, benzaldehyde is evolved.

DENIGÈS TEST FOR CYCLIC ALDE-HYDES. The addition of 0.02 g. α- or β-naphthol, dissolved in 1 ml. ethanol to a 1% alcoholic solution of many cyclic aldehydes, followed by the addition of 2 ml. concentrated sulfuric acid, yields intense colors or fluorescence.

DENIGÈS TEST FOR ETHANOL IN METHANOL. Add 5 ml. of 0.6% (by volume) bromine water to 0.2 ml. of the methanol. Heat in boiling water until decolorized (not more than 6 minutes). Cool and add fuchsin-sulfurous acid. A red to violet color, appearing in 5–8 minutes, shows the presence of ethanol.

DENIGÈS TEST FOR FERRIC ION. A solution of 0.1 g. alloxantin in 10 ml. 1 N sodium hydroxide gives a blue color with ferric ions.

DENIGÈS TEST FOR FORMIC ACID. Add 1–2 drops of the acid to be tested to 5 ml. water, then add 5 drops of a 0.02% solution of methylene blue, boil and add at once 5 drops saturated sodium bisulfite solution. The disappearance of the blue color on shaking shows formic acid.

DENIGÈS TEST FOR GLYCERIN. Oxidize the glycerin to dihydroxyacetone with bromine water; the addition of guaiacol, salicylic acid, or similar substances results in the formation of colored compounds.

DENIGÈS TEST FOR HIPPURIC ACID. A brown precipitate appears on boiling hippuric acid solutions with sodium hydroxide solution and bromine. Benzoic acid solutions do not give this reaction.

DENIGÈS TEST FOR INDOLE. Treat 5 ml. of an alcoholic solution of the material with 5 ml. 0.2% alcoholic solution of vanillin and 3 ml. concentrated hydrochloric acid. A garnet-red color, with characteristic absorption bands in the green and blue, indicates the presence of indole.

DENIGÈS TEST FOR INOSITOL. On evaporation with fuming nitric acid, and addition of sodium hydroxide solution, the presence of inositol is indicated by a yellow color, changing to blue on addition of sodium nitroprusside and acetic acid.

DENIGÈS TEST FOR ISOTHIOCY-ANATES. Prepare a solution of 5 g. mercuric oxide in 20 ml. sulfuric acid and water to make 100 ml. On shaking this reagent with one-half its volume of the liquid to be tested, filtering and boiling, precipitation of characteristic crystals of dithiomercuric sulfate indicates the presence of isothiocyanates.

DENIGÈS TEST FOR MERCAPTANS. If an alcoholic solution of a mercaptan is added to a few ml. of a solution of 1g. isatin in 100 ml. concentrated sulfuric acid, to which several volumes of concentrated sulfuric acid have been added, a green color is obtained.

DENIGÈS TEST FOR METALDE-HYDE. On solution in 1 drop of concentrated sulfuric acid, metaldehyde gives a blood-red color with a small crystal of guaiacol.

DENIGÈS TEST FOR NITRITE. A few ml. of the solution to be tested are boiled with several ml. of a solution of 2 ml. aniline in 40 ml. glacial acetic acid and 60 ml. water. In the presence of nitrite a yellow color is obtained.

DENIGÈS TEST FOR PHOSPHATE AND ARSENATE. A mixture of 10% ammonium molybdate solution and concentrated sulfuric acid in equal volumes, when added in amounts of 1–10 drops to 5 ml. of a phosphate or arsenate solution, to which 1–2 drops stannous chloride solution are then added, produces a blue color.

DENIGÈS TEST FOR SALICYLATE. Denigès methylglyoxal reagent (q.v.) gives a violet color with salicylate; after addition of potassium bromide solution and sulfuric acid a violet color appears which changes to red upon addition of methylsalicylate.

DENIGÈS TEST FOR SELENIUM. The dry material is treated in a porcelain dish with a drop of 5% thiourea solution, then 1 drop 1 N hydrochloric acid is added. Selenite ion gives a red precipitate at once; selenate only after several minutes.

DENIGÈS TEST FOR SULFATE ION IN INSOLUBLE SUBSTANCES. Dissolve 10 g. mercuric nitrate in 100 ml. water and 1 ml. concentrated nitric acid. With 0.02–0.03 mg. of calcium or lead sulfate, 2–3 ml. of this solution gives a yellow color at once; with strontium sulfate the coloration appears only after some time; in the presence of barium sulfate it is necessary to heat the solution.

DENIGÈS TEST FOR SULFANILIDES. Several mg. of the substance are heated in a glass tube for 20–30 seconds with 0.02–0.03 g. potassium ferrocyanide (powdered). An odor of mercaptan indicates the presence of sulfanilides.

DENIGÈS TEST FOR TARTRATE. The substance is heated to just under boiling with 1 ml. of a solution of 2 g. resorcinol in 100 ml. water and 0.5 ml. concentrated sulfuric acid. A red color indicates the presence of tartrate. Any oxidizing substances present must first be reduced with zinc and hydrochloric acid.

DENIGÈS TEST FOR THIOPHENE IN BENZENE. Five g. of mercuric oxide are dissolved in 20 ml. concentrated sulfuric acid and diluted with water to 100 ml. Then 10 ml. of this solution is mixed with 30 ml. methanol (acetone-free). One ml. of the benzene to be tested is added to 10 ml. of the reagent. A precipitate or turbidity appearing in a few seconds indicates the presence of more than 0.001% thiophene.

DENIGÈS TEST REACTION FOR BISMUTH. A dilute, hydrochloric acid solution of bismuth gives with a 5% solution of methenamine, microscopic, rhombic, colorless crystals.

DENIGÈS TEST REACTION FOR CADMIUM. Add enough ammonia to 5 ml. of the solution to form the complex ion, and boil with 0.5–1.0 ml. of 5% thiourea solution. A yellow precipitate indicates the presence of cadmium.

DENIGÈS TEST REACTION FOR CARBON DISULFIDE. Prepare a solution of 5 g. mercuric oxide (or mercuric chloride or nitrate) in 20 ml. concentrated sulfuric acid and 100 ml. water. Carbon disulfide gives characteristic crystals when heated with this reagent.

DENIGÈS TEST REACTION FOR COPPER. A test using as reagent a solution of 1 drop 50% potassium bromide solution in 4 ml. glacial acetic acid. This reagent gives, with 1–2 drops 1% cupric sulfate solution, a green color, changing to sepia and red-violet on further additions of reagent.

DENIGÈS TEST REACTION FOR CRESOLS. A mixture of 4 ml. glacial acetic acid, 2–3 ml. formaldehyde, and 1 ml. sulfuric acid gives characteristic colors differentiating o-, m-, and p-cresol. Ammonium hydroxide and chlorine water are also used to differentiate the cresols.

DENIGÈS TEST REACTION FOR CUPREINE. On the addition to 10 ml. 0.2% cupreine solution of 1 ml. each of ammonia and 1% hydrogen peroxide, shaking and adding 0.1 ml. 3% cupric sulfate solution, a green color appears, which is changed to yellow-red by excess sulfuric acid.

DENIGÈS TEST REACTION FOR GLYCOCOLL. On heating 0.05 g. glycocoll with 0.1 g. benzamide to boiling, a red color appears, changing to blue, and odors of ammonia, benzoic acid, hydrocyanic acid, and benzonitrile are evolved.

DENIGÈS TEST REACTION FOR GLYCOL. On oxidation with potassium permanganate and treatment with resorcinol-sulfuric acid, a wine-red color indicates the presence of glycol.

DENIGÈS TEST REACTION FOR HYDROGEN PEROXIDE. Mix 2 ml. 5% tartaric acid solution with 2 drops 5% ferrous ammonium sulfate solution. Add 1–2 drops of the solution to be tested, then 5–6 drops sodium hydroxide solution and shake. A violet color shows the presence of hydrogen peroxide.

DENIGÈS TEST REACTION FOR MALIC ACID. A malic acid solution gives a white precipitate on addition of acetic acid and mercuric acetate solution, heating to boiling, and adding a few drops potassium permanganate solution.

DENIGÈS TEST REACTIONS FOR MANGANESE. (1) In very dilute solution, manganese gives with sodium hypobromite solution, a brown-black precipitate, and a red supernatant liquor on boiling.

(2) Ten ml. of a very dilute manganese solution give, on addition of 1 drop each of 5% copper sulfate solution and sodium hypochlorite solution, then boiling and filtering, a rose color.

DENIGÈS TEST REACTION FOR α- and β-NAPHTHOL. Heat small pieces of titanium dioxide in concentrated sulfuric acid nearly to boiling; cool, decant the clear liquid, which gives a green color with α-naphthol and a blood-red with β-naphthol; the addition of glacial acetic acid changes the α-naphthol color, only, to violet-red.

DENIGÈS TEST REACTION FOR NICKEL. With 1–2 ml. concentrated hydriodic acid, a drop of 4% nickel solution gives a blood-red color which disappears on dilution with water.

DENIGÈS TEST REACTION FOR PEPTIDES AND α-AMINO ACIDS. To 10 ml. of the solution to be tested, add 0.2 ml. aqueous solution of triketohydrinene hydrate, and boil for 1 minute. A characteristic blue-violet color indicates the presence of peptides or α-amino acids. Ten ml. of this blue-violet solution is mixed with 2 drops glacial acetic acid, and shaken with 2 ml. chloroform. The aqueous layer is discolored, and the chloroform is colored orange.

DENIGÈS TEST REACTION FOR SKATOL. On adding 0.3 ml. 0.5% alcoholic vanillin solution and 3 ml. concentrated hydrochloric acid to 5 ml. of an alcoholic skatol solution, a yellow-pink color appears, changing to violet in a few hours, and to pink or red on addition of 5 ml. hydrochloric acid.

DENIGÈS TEST REACTION FOR SUCCINATE. To 0.2–0.4 g. of a succinate in a hard glass tube, 2 ml. concentrated sulfuric acid are added, followed by 4 drops sodium hypobromite solution. The solution is heated to boiling, the flame is removed, and the bromine remaining in the tube is blown out. Then the solution is again heated to boiling, cooled for 1 minute, and 1 drop 2% resorcinol solution acidified with sulfuric acid is added. The liquid becomes wine-red on shaking if succinate is present.

DENIGÈS TEST REACTION FOR TIN OR STANNOUS SALTS. A solution of 0.1 g. brucine in 1 ml. nitric acid and 50 ml. water, which has been heated to boiling for 15 minutes, gives a red-violet color with tin or stannous salts.

DENIGÈS TEST REACTIONS FOR THIOUREA. (1) With ferric perchlorate, an aqueous solution of thiourea produces a yellow color, giving colloidal sulfur on boiling.

(2) A little thiourea heated to boiling with 2 drops sodium hydroxide solution, gives a purple color on addition of 2 ml. water and 2 drops sodium nitroprusside solution.

(3) Ammoniacal silver nitrate, the **Nessler reagent,** and sodium plumbite solution give black precipitates with thiourea.

(4) An aqueous thiourea solution gives a red precipitate with a solution of sodium selenite.

DENIGÈS TEST REAGENT FOR ACETYLENE. An aqueous solution of 50 g. ammonium chloride, 25 g. cupric sulfate, and 0.5 ml. hydrochloric acid is diluted with water to a volume of 250 ml. of solution. In testing, 4–5 ml. of this solution are boiled with 0.3 g. copper turnings until colorless. The colorless liquid is diluted with 1 ml. water and cooled with ice. Paper moistened with it turns red if acetylene is present.

DENIGÈS TEST REAGENT FOR COBALT, COPPER, NICKEL, AND MANGANESE. A solution of 3 g. trioxymethylene, 7 g. hydroxylamine chloride, and 15 ml. water is boiled until clear. One drop of this reagent and 2 drops 1.0 N solution of sodium hydroxide give characteristic colors with 10 ml. of aqueous solutions containing various metallic ions.

DENIGÈS TEST REAGENT FOR CYANIDE. A mixture of 2 ml. 10% ammonia, 1 drop 5% potassium iodide solution, 20 ml. water, and 1 drop 2% silver nitrate solution. The sulfides in the sample are precipitated with mercuric chloride, and the filtrate is treated with zinc and sulfuric acid, the gas evolved being absorbed in sodium hydroxide solution, which is then added to the opalescent reagent. The presence of cyanide causes the opalescence to disappear.

DENIGÈS TEST REAGENT FOR FERROUS, CADMIUM, COBALT, MAGNESIUM, ZINC, AND OTHER METAL SALTS. A mixture of 2 g. uric acid with 2 ml. nitric acid (sp. gr. 1.14) to which is then added 2 ml. water and, after heating, water to dilute the solution to 100 ml. This reagent gives characteristic colors with many metallic ions, and color changes on subsequent addition of sodium hydroxide solution.

DENIGÈS TEST REAGENT FOR LACTIC AND GLYCOLIC ACID. A 5% alcoholic solution of codeine. If 1–2 drops of it are added to 0.2 ml. of a solution of lactic acid which has been oxidized with 2 ml. concentrated sulfuric acid to acetaldehyde, a dichromate-red color appears. Using a guaiacol solution, a fuchsin-red color is produced. If the codeine solution is added to a solution of glycolic acid which has been oxidized to formaldehyde by sulfuric acid, a yellow color, changing to violet, appears.

DENIGÈS TEST REAGENT FOR MERCURY SALTS. A solution of 0.1 g. alloxan in 10 ml. 1 N solution of sodium hydroxide, which is boiled with a little zinc for 5 minutes. This orange-yellow reagent gives a peach-red color with neutral mercury salts.

DENIGÈS TEST REAGENT FOR PHENOLIC ALKALOIDS. A solution of titanium oxide in sulfuric or hydrochloric acid, which gives characteristic colors with many of the alkaloids.

DENIGÈS TEST REAGENT FOR PHOSPHATE. A solution of 0.5 g. strychnine sulfate in 50 ml. water, to which 10 ml. nitric acid and 10 ml. nitro-ammonium molybdate solution are added, the mixture then being made up to 100 ml. with water.

DENITRATION. (To denitrate or denitrify. Denitrification) (1) Any process for removing or altering the **nitro group** in an organic compound. The nitro group may be altered by reduction, being converted into the amino group and then the nitrogen may be wholly removed from the compound by **diazotizing** this reduction product and boiling with water or alcohol. (2) Bacterial decomposition of nitrates with production of gaseous nitrogen. The bacteria which effect the change are termed denitrifiers.

DENNIS-BROWNE TEST REACTION. Hydrazoic acid gives a characteristic red color with ferric chloride. One drop 2 N hydrochloric acid decolorizes the test solution.

DENSIMETER. Any instrument used to determine density.

DENSITY. (1) The mass of a substance per unit volume. A mass of one gram occupying a volume of one cubic centimeter has unit density. (Cf. **specific volume.**) (2) The degree of blackening of a photographic plate or film.

DENSITY, ABSOLUTE. Mass per unit volume, understood to be expressed in grams per cubic centimeter when no units are specified.

DENSITY, CURRENT. The strength of an electric current per unit cross-section of the conductor; the units are expressed for example as amperes per square centimeter.

DENSITY, MODULUS OF. See **law of moduli, Valson.**

DENSITY, NORMAL. The weight of one liter of a gas under standard conditions (temperature at 0° C., pressure at 760 millimeters of mercury, at sea level, and at 45° latitude).

DENSITY OF GASES. The weight of a unit volume at 0° C., at 760 millimeters of mercury pressure, at sea level, and at 45° latitude.

DENSITY OF WATER. In contradistinction to most other liquids, water has a maximum density at 4° C. Below and above this temperature the density of water decreases. The relationship between density and temperature of water is shown by the following table:

Temperature	Density (in grams per milliliter)
0° C.	0.999868
3° C.	0.999992
5° C.	0.999992
6° C.	0.999986
100° C.	0.95838
150° C.	*0.9173
250° C.	*0.794
300° C.	*0.70

* At temperatures above 100° C., the water is in equilibrium with steam at pressures greater than atmospheric pressure.

DENSITY, PHOTOMETRIC. The light-absorption of a film or medium, as measured by **photometric** (q.v.) methods.

DENSITY, RELATIVE. The ratio of the mass of a given volume of a substance to that of the same volume of another substance chosen as a standard.

DENUDING. The treatment of a liquid by a gas or vapor in order to remove a volatile component.

DEODORANT. A substance used to remove an objectionable odor. Deodorants range in application from substances used in hospitals, toilets, and other places where undesirable odors occur, to cosmetics used on the human body. They range in manner of functioning from substances which mask the objectionable odor with another odor to substances intended to prevent the cause, as certain body deodorants that contain substances to prevent formation of ill-smelling compounds from compounds present in perspiration, or substances to combine with these compounds when they do form.

DEOXIDIZE. To remove oxygen from a molecule or system; or to reduce. The process is termed deoxidation.

DEOXIDIZER. A substance capable of removing oxygen from a compound or system.

DE PAOLINI TEST. Aromatic amines, when added to an alcoholic suspension of benzoyl peroxide and warmed slightly, give a reddish-brown to violet color.

DEPHLEGMATION. A process for increasing the efficiency of fractional **distillation** by forcing the vapors from the still to bubble through shallow layers of condensate in a column or "dephlegmator," whereby the amount of low-boiling component in the vapor is increased and a substantial portion of the higher-boiling components is retained in the condensate.

DEPHLEGMATOR. Any apparatus used in increasing the efficiency of fractional **distillation** by **dephlegmation** (q.v.).

DEPILATORY. A substance used to remove hair from hides or skin.

DEPOLARIZATION. The process of removing polarization. See **polarization, electrical** and **polarization, optical** for descriptions of polarization of electrochemical systems and light, respectively.

DEPOLARIZATION IN METAL DEPOSITION. The deposition of a metal by electrolytic processes at the cathode at higher potentials than normal, by virtue of the ability of the metal to form a **solid solution** or a compound with the cathode.

DEPOLARIZER. An agent or means for the prevention or removal of **polarization.** Thus, an electrical depolarizer is a substance added to a "dry" battery (a cell used to generate on electricity by a chemical reaction) to prevent the accumulation of reaction products that interfere with the functioning of the cell. The term electrical depolarizer is also applied to a diaphragm placed in an electrolytic cell to prevent mixing of the reaction products. An optical depolarizer is a device for the **resolution** of **polarized light.**

DEPOLYMERIZATION. The breaking down of a **polymer** into its monomeric components by heating or other means.

DEPOSITION, ELECTRICAL. (1) Electroplating. (2) The deposition of elements from solutions of their compounds upon an electrode in an **electrolytic cell.** One **faraday** is required for the deposition of one gram-equivalent of any substance.

DEPRESSANT. (1) A narcotic or sedative drug that acts upon the cerebrospinal nervous system. (2) A term occurring in the flotation process, where a depressant is used to reduce the concentration of undesired substances in the air-solution interface; and consequently, to reduce the amount of these undesired substances appearing in the product.

DEPRESSO-MOTOR. A drug that diminishes motor nerve activity.

DEPRESSOR. A substance that reduces the acidity of a solution indirectly (by

buffer action); or reduces the activity of a **catalyst;** or reduces the action of a wetting agent (in its undesired effect upon nonmetallic particles).

DEPURANT. A drug used to effect purification of the system by stimulating excretion.

DE RADA TEST. To detect sodium or potassium, add a few drops of a 1% solution of the salt to be tested to a solution of lithium ferricyanide in 73% alcohol to which magnesium chloride has been added until a precipitate no longer forms. Then add a few drops cupric sulfate solution. Sodium gives a dark precipitate, and potassium forms a turbid yellow solution with a voluminous rose-colored precipitate.

DERIVATIVE. A term used in organic chemistry to express the relation between certain known or hypothetical substances and the compounds formed from them by simple chemical processes in which the **nucleus** or skeleton of the parent substance exists. Thus phenol, aniline, and toluene are derivatives of benzene, and many of the terpenes are derivatives of cymene.

DERIVE. To obtain one compound from another either by actual or theoretical chemical process.

DERMIC. A drug used in the treatment of skin disease.

DESATURATION. The reverse process of **saturation,** as applied to an organic compound, whereby a saturated compound becomes unsaturated, as a hydrocarbon by catalytic dehydrogenation.

DESBASSINS DE RICHEMONT TEST. To detect nitrate and nitrite, dissolve 1 part ferrous sulfate in a mixture of 1 part water and 1 part 15% sulfuric acid. Superimpose this reagent upon the substance to be tested, mixed with sulfuric acid. A brown ring indicates the presence of nitrate or nitrite. Many modifications of this test have been developed.

DE SCHEPPER PROCESS. A process for drying latex on a finely-divided solid by spraying it on a heated drum or other surface, in the presence of suitable agents.

DESENSITIZATION. (1) The action of rendering less subject to reactions brought about by light, as, e.g., in the case of a photographic emulsion. (2) The action of destroying or inactivating immune bodies.

DESICCANT. A substance which removes moisture from substances or systems.

DESICCATE. To render practically **anhydrous;** to dehydrate.

DESICCATOR. A closed vessel in which **desiccation** may be carried out at either atmospheric or reduced pressures or in *vacuo.* Water-absorbing substances like sulfuric acid, fused calcium chloride, or fused caustic potash are used to remove the moisture from the air of the vessel and from the substance to be dried. Desiccators are used also to preserve material in a dry state.

DESMOTROPISM. See **isomerism, dynamic.**

DESORPTION. The reverse of absorption or adsorption, as in the release of one substance which has been "taken into" another by a physical process, or the release of a substance which has been held in concentrated form upon a surface.

DESOXY COMPOUND. A compound which has lost oxygen, commonly by replacement of a hydroxyl group by a hydrogen atom.

DESTRUCTIVE DISTILLATION. See **distillation, destructive.**

DESVERGNES TEST REACTION. Diphenylamine in alcoholic solution gives, with chlorine water, a green color changing to violet. Ethereal solutions give only green solutions.

DESYL. The radical $(C_6H_5)COCH(C_6H_5)-$.

DETAILED BALANCING. See **balancing, detailed.**

DETECTABILITY. The lowest detectable amount of a substance in a given analytical procedure, expressed either as a mass or as a concentration.

DETECTION. The identification of an element or compound in a substance or a material.

DETERGENT. (1) A substance used for its cleansing action. (2) A particular type of cleansing agent that does not precipitate insoluble sludge. Such detergents often contain organic **sulfonates.**

DETERMINATION. In general, a method for obtaining numerical data, or the performance of such a method; more specifically, a method for obtaining numerical data on the quantitative chemical composition of a material, or a substance or substances, or the performance of such a method.

DETONATION. A reaction which proceeds with increasing velocity and temperature until it finally reaches explosive violence with production of a report.

DETONATION WAVE. (Explosion wave) The specific value for the rate at which an explosive combustion spreads throughout a body of gas when it is once started at any point. It is much faster than the velocity of sound in the same gas, e.g., for $2H_2 + O_2$ it is 2810 meters per second, and for $C_2H_2 + 2O_2$, 2195 meters per second.

DETONATOR. A substance used to set off **explosives** by means of a reaction producing an energy-wave that initiates the explosive reaction.

DEUTERIUM. See **hydrogen, isotopes.**

DEUTERON. The nucleus of the **deuterium** atom (the atom of the hydrogen isotope of mass number 2).

DE VATHAIRE PROCESS. A metallurgical process for the desulfurization of impure molten iron by treatment with alkaline earth cyanides and carbon.

DEVELOPER. A reducing agent used in the **development** (q.v.) of films and other materials containing photosensitive substances which have been exposed to the action of light.

DEVELOPMENT. In general, development is the growth and differentiation in the structure of an entity, such as a crystal or an organism, and the acquisition of new characteristics.

In photography, development is a process whereby the exposed light-sensitive film or other material is treated with a chemical agent to reduce or otherwise change enough of the **photosensitive** substance (such as silver bromide to free silver) in order to produce a visible (reverse) image of the object photographed. This step is necessary because the initial exposure merely transforms enough of the photosensitive substance to serve as a starting point (probably as a system of nuclei) for the development.

DEVILLE-PÉCHINEY PROCESS. A process for the purification of alumina (chiefly for aluminum manufacture) by calcining the bauxite with soda ash at 1000° C. to form sodium aluminate, leaching with hot water, gassing with carbon dioxide to precipitate aluminum hydroxide, filtering, calcining the aluminum hydroxide to alumina, and recovering the sodium carbonate from the filtrate.

DEVITRIFICATION. The crystallization of glass, detected by the appearance of opaque areas.

DEVOLUTION OF ELEMENTS. See **elements, devolution of.**

DE VRIJ SOLUTION. An alcoholic solution of quinodine iodide, used in testing for quinine. A red-brown precipitate is given by quinine in sulfuric acid solution.

DEW POINT. The temperature at which the actual content of water vapor in the atmosphere is sufficient to saturate the air with water vapor. If the atmosphere contains much water vapor the dew point is higher than in the case of drier air, so that the dew point is an indication of the humidity of the atmosphere.

DEWAR FLASK. A cylindrical vessel with a double wall, in which the annular region between the walls has been evacuated, and in which the walls bordering this space have been silvered. With this construction the region within the inner cylinder is very well insulated from the outside. The vessel is commonly used for storage of liquefied gases.

DEWAXING. Removal by refrigeration, solvent action, or other methods or combinations of methods, of the various waxy components (probably chiefly paraffins or isoparaffins) from naphtha, oil, and other petroleum fractions.

DEXTRO-. (Latin) *dexter*, right. To the right, as in dextrorotation; rotating the plane of polarization to the right, as dextropinene. Abbreviation, d; as d-valine.

DEXTROROTATORY SUBSTANCE. A substance which has the property of rotating the plane of polarized light to the right, or clockwise. See **isomerism, optical.**

DIACIDIC BASE. A **base** which, for its complete **neutralization,** requires two molecules of a monobasic acid.

DIACTINIC. Having the property of transmitting actinic (chemically active) radiation.

DIACTINISM. The property of transmitting chemically active radiation.

DIAD. An atom or radical that is **divalent.**

DIAGONAL FORMULA. The Claus formula for **benzene** (q.v.).

DIALYSIS. The process of separating compounds or materials by the difference in their rates of diffusion through a colloidal semipermeable **membrane.** Thus, sodium chloride diffuses eleven times as fast as tannin and twenty-one times as fast as albumin. See **dialyzer.**

DIALYSIS, ELECTRO. Dialysis (q.v.) which is accelerated or otherwise modified by placing the semipermeable **membrane** between electrodes to which a direct-current potential is applied.

DIALYZATE. The solution of a dialyzed substance.

DIALYZER. An apparatus for carrying out a **dialysis,** usually consisting of two chambers separated by a semipermeable **membrane** of parchment paper latex, animal tissue, or other colloid. In one chamber the solution is placed, and in the other, the pure solvent. Crystalline substances diffuse from the solution through the membrane and into the solvent much more rapidly than amorphous substances, colloids or large molecules.

DIAMAGNETIC. (1) Being repelled by a magnet. (2) Having a negative **magnetic susceptibility.**

DIAMIDE. (1) An organic compound that contains two **amido groups.** (2) Oxamide $(CONH_2)_2$.

DIAMIDOPHOSPHATE. The anion $PN_2O_2^{5-}$, or a compound containing it.

DIAMINE. (1) A compound that contains two **amino groups,** e.g., ethylenediamine.

$$CH_2NH_2$$
$$|$$
$$CH_2NH_2$$

(2) Hydrazine $H_2N—NH_2$.

DIAPHANOMETER. An instrument used to measure the degree of transparency of solids, liquids, or gases.

DIAPHORETIC. A drug that stimulates the secretion of perspiration.

DIAPHRAGM. In general, a separating wall which transmits or passes substances or stresses selectively. Thus, a diaphragm with many small openings is used in electrolytic cells to permit passage of ions and yet to segregate reaction products. Diaphragms with a single opening, that may be adjustable in size, are used to control flow of substances or radiations, as in the camera.

DIASTASIC ACTION. See **diastatic action.**

DIASTATIC ACTION. The **enzymatic** process whereby diastase converts starch into water-soluble substances.

DIATHERMATOUS. Transparent, or largely transparent to thermal radiation.

DIAZINE. A cyclic compound having two nitrogen atoms in the ring. In many cases, the six-membered ring-diazine compounds have individual names, thus

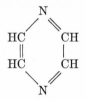

is pyrazine (*p*-diazine). Similarly, *m*-diazine is called pyrimidine, and *o*-diazine is called pyridazine.

DIAZO. The radical $-N:N-$ or $N:N=$.

DIAZO REACTION (GRIESS). A method of diazotization by the action of nitrogen trioxide on primary aromatic amines in acid solution, as represented by the equation:

$$2ArNH_2 + N_2O_3 + H_2O + 2HNO_3 \rightarrow 2ArN_2NO_3 + 4H_2O.$$

(See **reaction, diazo.**) The name of Griess is also used to denote the diazotization reaction itself, not being limited to the specific reaction above in which nitrogen trioxide is used.

DIAZO REACTION (KNOEVENAGEL). A method of diazotization (see **reaction, diazo**) in which the aromatic amines are treated with an alkyl nitrite or nitrosyl chloride.

$$ArNH_2 + RONO + HX \rightarrow ArN_2X + ROH + H_2O.$$

DIAZO REACTION (WITT). A method of diazotization (see **reaction, diazo**) in which the aromatic amines are dissolved in nitric acid, to which is added a reducing agent to form the nitrous acid for the diazotization.

$$2ArNH_2 + 4HNO_3 + Na_2S_2O_5 \rightarrow 2ArN_2NO_3 + Na_2S_2O_7 + 4H_2O.$$

DIAZOAMINO. The radical $-N:NNH-$.

DIAZOATE. A substance of the general formula $R-N=N-OM$, in which R is an organic (usually aryl) radical and M is a metal atom, ammonium radical, etc.

DIAZONIUM COMPOUNDS. Derivatives of the diazonium hydrates

$$N\equiv N\begin{smallmatrix} \diagup R \\ \diagdown OH \end{smallmatrix}$$

in which the hydroxyl group is replaced by an acid radical.

DIAZOTIZE. To introduce the diazo group into a compound, usually effected by treating an amine with any compound of nitrogen capable of releasing nitrogen oxides, as from nitriles or nitrous acid. The amino group is converted into the diazo group, thus

$$RNH_2 + HONO + HCl \rightarrow RN_2Cl + 2H_2O.$$

DIBASIC COMPOUND. An acid which furnishes two protons per molecule, and which forms salts with two atoms of a univalent or one atom of a divalent metal; or a dihydroxy alcohol.

DICARBOXIMIDO. The radical

$$-CO \cdot NH \cdot CO-.$$

DICHERT REAGENT. A mixture of 10 ml. 30% hydrogen peroxide and 75 ml. 25% sodium hydroxide solution, used in oxidizing the sulfur in illuminating gas.

DICHROISM. The property of exhibiting two colors, especially of exhibiting one color when viewed in reflected light and another when viewed in transmitted light, as in the case of solutions of chlorophyll. Substances which have this property are termed dichroic.

DICHROISM, CIRCULAR. See **Cotton effect.**

DICHROMATE. The anion $Cr_2O_7^=$, or a compound containing it.

DICKENSON REAGENT. A solution of 3 g. cupric chloride, 40 g. ferric chloride, and 40 ml. hydrochloric acid, in 500 ml. water, used for etching steels.

DICROSCOPIC EYEPIECE. An eyepiece for a **polariscope** or polarizing microscope which gives a comparison view of the same object or field under illumination by the two complementary rays of polarized light.

DIDYMIUM. A name given to a mixture of **praseodymium** and **neodymium** which was originally thought to be an element in the rare earth series.

DIECKMANN SYNTHESIS. A method of effecting ring closure between an ester group and a δ- or ε-methylene group, by heating with sodium and alcohol, as, for example,

$$\begin{smallmatrix} CH_2-COOR' \\ CH_2 \quad COOR \\ CH_2-CH_2 \end{smallmatrix} \xrightarrow{NaOEt} \begin{smallmatrix} CHCOOR' \\ CH_2 \quad CO \\ CH_2-CH_2 \end{smallmatrix} + ROH.$$

DIELECTRIC. An insulator or non-conductor of electricity.

DIELECTRIC CONSTANT. See **constant, dielectric.**

DIELECTRIC STRENGTH. The maximum difference of potential per centimeter thickness which an **insulator** can support without rupture.

DIELS-ALDER REACTION. A synthesis which takes place by addition to the 1,4 position of a compound containing two conjugated double bonds, of another unsaturated compound, commonly an anhydride of an unsaturated acid, although other unsaturated compounds may be used. Thus the reaction with maleic anhydride may be formulated as follows:

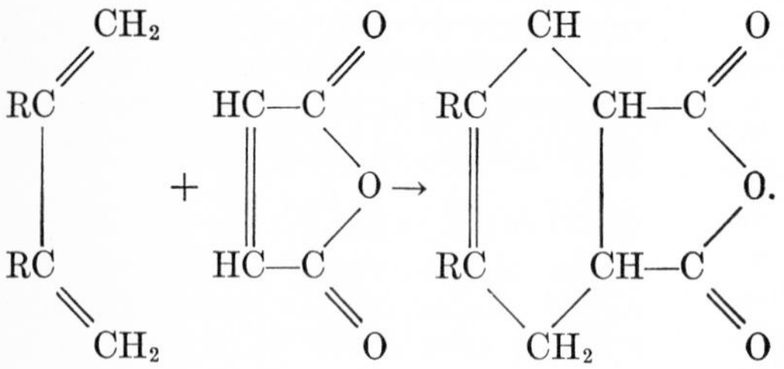

The general reaction is as follows:

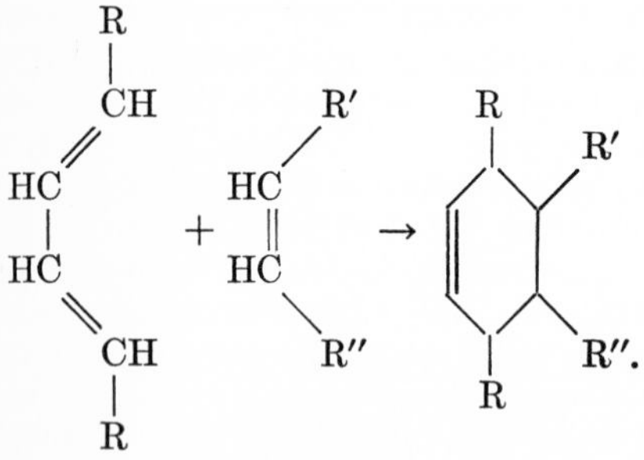

DIETERICH TEST REACTION FOR URIC ACID. Uric acid gives a rose-red color with sodium hypochlorite solution containing bromine.

DIETERICI EQUATION. A form of the **equation of state,** relating pressure, volume, and temperature of gas, and the gas constant. The Dieterici equation applies a correction to the **van der Waals equation** to allow for variation in density throughout a gas, due to the higher potential energies of molecules on or near the boundaries. One form of this equation is

$$P = \frac{RT}{V - b} e^{-a/RTV}$$

in which P is the pressure of the gas, T is the absolute temperature, V is the volume, R is the gas constant, e is the natural log base 2.718 . . . , and a and b are the van der Waals constants.

DIETRICH FLUID. A mixture of 10–12 ml. formaldehyde, 2 ml. glacial acetic acid, 30 ml. ethyl alcohol, and 60 ml. distilled water. It is used as a fixative.

DIETZE TEST. Hydrogen peroxide in ether is detected by a modified **Rogai test** (q.v.), in which 5 ml. of the ether are shaken with 1 ml. of 0.1 N ammonium thiocyanate solution, with 2 drops of an acidified 10% solution of ferrous ammonium sulfate added (made from oxygen-free water and free from ferric ions). A red color indicates the presence of hydrogen peroxide.

DIFFERENTIAL ABSORPTION. See absorption, differential.

DIFFERENTIAL CONDENSATION. See condensation, differential.

DIFFERENTIAL HEAT OF DILUTION. See **heat of dilution, differential.**

DIFFRACTION. A class of phenomena arising from the encounter between a **wave train** and a new medium, resulting in a change of direction of the wave train and/or the production of interference patterns. Thus, sound waves are diffracted in passing the edge or angle of a solid body; **x-rays** are diffracted by **crystals**; radio waves are diffracted by screens of wires. Light waves are diffracted on encountering an edge or a small aperture of an opaque obstacle. As a result of such encounters patterns of alternating dark and light fringes are observed which result from the interference of all secondary wave trains which arise in the encounter.

DIFFRACTION GRATING. A surface on which a large number of parallel lines have been ruled and which, by means of the interference effect discussed above (see **diffraction**), produces a series of **spectra** from white light (or other polychromatic light) incident upon it.

DIFFRACTION, X-RAY. See **x-ray, diffraction.**

DIFFUSATE. (Dialyzate) The solution of the diffused substance produced in a **dialyzer** (q.v.).

DIFFUSE SERIES. A series of lines in the **spectra** produced by many atoms which, either in their **normal state** or as the result of an **ionization,** possess one, two, or three electrons in the outer shell. The diffuse series differs from the other series for such elements in having a somewhat distinctive physical appearance, and in having a characteristic formula,

$$\nu_D = L - \frac{R}{(m + c)^2},$$

where ν_D is the wave number of a line in the diffuse series, L and c are constants for the diffuse series, m is a variable integer, whose values give the various lines in the diffuse series and R is the Rydberg constant. Atoms possessing but a single electron, such as hydrogen, singly ionized helium, doubly ionized lithium, etc., do not give rise to such a series.

DIFFUSER. A passage so shaped that it will change the characteristics of a fluid flow from a certain pressure and velocity to a lower velocity and a higher pressure. The diffusion must be carried out in a well-streamlined passage having smooth interior surfaces, and sides not diverging at so great an angle as to cause the fluid to leave the sides of the diffusing chamber. By reducing the velocity through increasing the cross-sectional area of flow, the pressure may be built up as the velocity head is diminished. Diffusers are applied to centrifugal fans, centrifugal pumps, jet pumps, wind tunnels, and other equipment where it is required to conserve energy by efficiently converting velocity head into pressure.

DIFFUSION. The process by which two or more initially separate species of atoms or molecules intermingle as a result of their random atomic or molecular motion. Diffusion may occur in the gaseous, liquid, or even solid phases. Frequently, the fact that different species diffuse at different rates is used to separate the species. The rates at which gases diffuse are inversely proportional to the square roots of their molecular weights. Both gases and liquids exhibit selective diffusion through suitable porous partitions and membranes; such partitions may be designed to allow passage of the smaller, but not of the larger, species.

DIFFUSION ANALYSIS. The determination of the relative size or molecular weight of particles by comparing their diffusion rates, or by separating them by differential diffusion methods.

DIFFUSION BATTERY. A series of extraction vessels, each of which consists essentially of a closed chamber in which material to be extracted is supported upon a grillwork or other base, and each of which has inlet and outlet piping through which solvents are introduced to extract components of the charge by differential diffusion. The various extraction vessels in the series are usually arranged for counter-current flow of solvent, so that the fresh solvent acts upon the nearly-exhausted material.

DIFFUSION COEFFICIENT. See **law of diffusion, Fick.**

DIFFUSION CURRENT. The limiting current which is reached by electrolytic **migration** of the ions in a solution under the application of a **potential difference** to the electrodes. As the potential difference is increased the ion current to the electrodes increases rapidly at first but soon reaches a limiting value (the diffusion current value) as the potential difference is increased. If the potential difference is increased still further, a point is ultimately reached at which a new ion species begins to discharge.

DIFFUSION LAW. See **law of Graham** or **law of diffusion, Fick.**

DIFFUSION LAYER. A layer of solution, actually a double layer, that is in immediate contact with an electrode during electrolysis. The apparent thicknesses of diffusion layers depend on factors influencing the rate of diffusion. (See **diffusion potential**.)

DIFFUSION OF GASES, LAW OF. See **law of Graham**.

DIFFUSION POTENTIAL. When liquid junctions exist where two **electrolytic solutions** are in contact, as in the case of two solutions of different concentrations of the same electrolyte, diffusion of ions occurs between the solutions, and the differences in rates of diffusion of different ions set up an electrical double layer, having a difference of potential, known as the diffusion potential or liquid junction potential.

DIFFUSIVE SUBSTANCES. Substances that readily dialyze through colloidal septa, viz., crystalloids.

DIFFUSIVITY. Diffusion coefficient; a constant, relating the rate of change of **concentration** of material at any point in space to the **gradient** of the concentration at that point along a given direction.

DIGESTER. See **autoclave**.

DIHYDROXYACETIC. See **glyoxalic**.

DIHYDROXYSUCCINIC. See **tartaric**.

DILATANCY. The property of certain **colloidal solutions** of becoming solid, or setting, under pressure. Dilatancy is one of the gel-sol transformations known under the general term of **thixotropy**.

DILATION NUMBER. Ratio of the volume of a liquid to the volume of a solid of the same composition at the same temperature.

DILATOMETER. An instrument used to measure small increments in the volume of liquids, as a solid phase separates.

DILLE-KOPPANYI TEST. Barbiturates are detected by dissolving the material in water, acidifying with hydrochloric acid, and extracting with chloroform. Two ml. of the extract are treated with 0.1 ml. of a

1% solution of cobalt acetate in anhydrous methanol and 0.6 ml. of a solution of isopropylamine in anhydrous methanol. A red-violet color indicates the presence of barbiturates.

DILUENT. An inert substance used to increase the volume of some other substance or solution.

DILUTE. Not concentrated. A solution in which the solvent is in great excess. A relative term of inexact nature unless qualified by a statement of the actual concentration.

DILUTE SOLUTIONS, THEORY OF. Van't Hoff's theory that substances in dilute solution obey the same laws that apply to gases.

DILUTION. (1) The act of increasing the proportion of solvent to solute in any solution, e.g., by the addition of the same or another (miscible) solvent. (2) Improperly used in the same sense as concentration, to express the amount of solute per unit volume of solution.

DILUTION, HEAT OF. See **heat of dilution, integral** and **heat of dilution, differential**.

DILUTION, INTEGRAL HEAT OF. See **heat of dilution, integral**.

DILUTION LAW. See **law of dilution**.

DILUTION RATIO. The ratio of the maximum volume of a liquid which can be added to a solution, without causing precipitation, to the total volume of solution.

DIMER. A compound consisting of a combination of two of the same molecules.

N,N'-DIMETHYLPHOSPHORODIAMIDIMIDIC. Related to N,N'-dimethylphosphorodiamidimidic acid,

$$(HO)(CH_3HN)_2P(NH).$$

N,N''-DIMETHYLPHOSPHORODIAMIDIMIDIC. Related to N,N''-dimethylphosphorodiamidimidic acid,

$$(HO)(CH_3HN)(H_2N)P(NCH_3).$$

DIMINOFLORE. An atom or group which, by its substitution in a molecule, tends to reduce the intensity of the **fluorescent radiation** bands of that molecule.

DIMORPHIC. See polymorphic.

DINEUTRON. A combination of two **neutrons,** considered to have a transitory existence in **nuclear reactions** produced by **tritons** which result in the formation of a proton and nucleus having the same atomic number as, but a mass number two units greater than, the target nucleus.

DIPHOSPHORUS, TRIOXY. See pyrophosphoryl.

DIPHOSPHORUS, TRISULFO. See thiopyrophosphoryl.

DIPHOSPHORYL. See pyrophosphoryl.

DIPOLE. A collection of two electrically or magnetically charged particles of opposite sign which are separated by a very small distance.

DIPOLE ASSOCIATION. The combination, connection, or correlation of dipoles.

DIPOLE MOMENT. A mathematical entity: the product of one of the charges of a dipole unit with the distance separating the two dipolar charges.

DIRECT DYES. See dyes, substantive.

DIRECT ILLUMINATION. See illumination, direct.

DIRECT PROCESS (ZINC OXIDE). See American process (zinc oxide).

DIRECTING EFFECT. The effect of substituent groups already present in benzene and other aromatic derivatives which forces new substituent groups, about to enter the molecule, into definite positions relative to the original groups.

DISACIDIFY. To neutralize the acid in, or to remove it from, any mixture.

DISASSOCIATION. The breaking up of an entity, or a system of like entities, into parts. In molecular disassociation, for example, a compound molecule splits into two or more smaller, and commonly similar, molecules of which it is composed.

DISC FILTER. See **filter, disc.**

DISCHARGE. (1) The effluent from a plant, process, apparatus, etc.; or (2) the action by which it is expelled. The latter meaning has a common connotation of suddenness, from its use for electric spark discharges. (3) Passage of electric current between electrodes through a gas.

DISCHARGE, COEFFICIENT OF. See coefficient of discharge.

DISCHARGE POTENTIAL. See **potential, discharge.**

DISCHARGE TUBE. A glass tube, having two **electrodes** to which a potential is applied sufficient to produce a discharge of electricity through the gas contained in the tube.

DISCHARGING AGENT. A substance which removes, or otherwise permanently decolorizes, a dye that has been applied to, or within, the fibers of a fabric.

DISCHE CARBAZOLE SOLUTION. A 0.5% solution of carbazole in ethyl alcohol, used as a test reagent for lactic acid, methylglyoxal, and carbohydrates. Characteristic color reactions are obtained.

DISILANOXY. The radical

$$H_3Si—SiH_2—O—.$$

DISILANYL. The radical

$$H_3Si—SiH_2—.$$

DISILANYLAMINO. The radical

$$H_3Si—SiH_2—NH—.$$

DISILANYLENE. The radical

$$—SiH_2—SiH_2—.$$

DISILANYLTHIO. The radical

$$H_3Si—SiH_2—S—.$$

DISILAZANOXY. The radical

$H_3Si—NH—SiH_2—O—$.

DISILAZANYL. The radical

$H_3Si—NH—SiH_2—$.

DISILAZANYLAMINO. The radical

$H_3Si—NH—SiH_2—NH—$.

DISILOXANOXY. The radical

$H_3Si—O—SiH_2—O—$.

DISILOXANYL. The radical

$H_3Si—O—SiH_2—$.

DISILOXANYLAMINO. The radical

$H_3Si—O—SiH_2—NH—$.

DISILOXANYLTHIO. The radical

$H_3Si—O—SiH_2—S—$.

DISILTHIANOXY. The radical

$H_3Si—S—SiH_2—O—$.

DISILTHIANYL. The radical

$H_3Si—S—SiH_2—$.

DISILTHIANYLTHIO. The radical

$H_3Si—S—SiH_2—S—$.

DISINFECTANT. A substance that acts to prevent infection by destroying many classes of microorganisms.

DISINFESTANT. A substance that acts to destroy insects, worms, rats, mice, and other animal pests. (See **rodenticide, insecticide,** etc.)

DISINTEGRATION. (1) Loss of form or powdering. (2) The passage of a metal into colloidal solution when it is made an electrode under certain conditions. (3) Transformations of radioactive elements are sometimes termed disintegrations, when they result from **radioactivity,** (q.v.).

DISINTEGRATION, URANIUM. See **radioactivity.**

DISINTEGRATOR. An apparatus used for grinding materials. It consists of two steel cages which rotate in opposite directions.

DISMUTATION. A mutation, or change, which yields two products from one, as in the **Cannizzaro reaction** (q.v.).

DISOXIDATION. (Disoxygenation) De-oxidation, reduction.

DISPERSE MEDIUM. (Dispersive or dispersion medium, continuous phase) The medium in which a **colloid** is dispersed, in a manner analogous to that of the solvent in a true solution.

DISPERSE PARTICLES. (Disperse phase) The particles of **colloid** in a colloidal system.

DISPERSE PHASE. The distributed phase in a **colloidal system,** i.e., the phase which is composed of the distributed particles.

DISPERSE SYSTEM. A **colloidal system,** consisting of two phases: the disperse phase (the one forming particles) and the dispersion medium (the medium in which the particles are distributed).

DISPERSING AGENT. A substance which promotes the formation of a **colloidal solution** of solid particles in a liquid medium.

DISPERSIODIOLOGY. Colloid chemistry.

DISPERSION. (1) The process of preparing a **colloidal solution** of a substance. (2) The separation of light into its components, producing a **spectrum** from polychromatic light.

DISPERSION, CATHODE. See **dispersion, electrical.**

DISPERSION EFFECT. The attraction between electrically neutral molecules arising from the tendency of their temporary **dipoles** to align themselves in a manner so as to produce a net attractive force. The temporary dipoles arise from various instantaneous dipolar configurations, in which the electron cloud is spread unsymmetrically about the nucleus.

DISPERSION, ELECTRICAL. The preparation of **colloidal solutions** by means of the electric current. Two methods are commonly employed: (1) cathode dispersion, in which the cathode is made of the material which is to form the disperse phase, the anode is of platinum or other inert metal, and a high potential is used; (2) electric arc formation between wires of various metals under water. Many metals (platinum, silver, iridium, cadmium, etc.) give metal sols by method 2; other metals (thallium, zinc, iron, aluminum, etc.) give hydroxide sols only. Metals which are above hydrogen in the **electromotive force series** (q.v.) are not likely to yield metal sols in water.

DISPERSION, EPIPOLIC. Fluorescence.

DISPERSION, LINEAR. The derivative $dx/d\lambda$, where x is distance along the **spectrum** and λ is the **wave length**. Linear dispersion is usually expressed as millimeters per Ångstrom.

DISPERSION MEDIUM. See **disperse medium.**

DISPERSION OF CONDUCTANCE. See **Debye-Falkenhagen effect.**

DISPERSION, RECIPROCAL LINEAR. The derivative $d\lambda/dx$, where λ is **wave length** and x is the distance along the **spectrum.** The reciprocal linear dispersion is usually expressed in Ångstroms per millimeter.

DISPERSITY. The degree of dispersion of a **colloid,** i.e., the extent to which the dimensions of the individual particles have been reduced. Expressed numerically in terms of **specific surface.**

DISPERSIVE MEDIUM. See **disperse medium.**

DISPERSIVE POWER. The ratio of the difference in dispersion of light of two different **wave lengths** relative to the dispersion for light whose wave length is an average of the two. Thus, if D_A, D_B are the deviations for light of wave length $\lambda = A$ and $\lambda = B$ and if D_C is that for light of some intermediate wave length $\lambda = C = \frac{1}{2}(A + B)$, then the dispersive power is given by

$$d = \frac{D_A - D_B}{D_C}.$$

DISPERSIVITY. Differential **refractivity.** The difference in refractivity of the same medium for various wave lengths of radiant energy.

DISPERSIVITY. MOLAR. The difference between the molar **refractions** of a compound for two stated wave lengths of light.

DISPERSIVITY, MOLECULAR. See **dispersivity, molar.**

DISPERSIVITY, SPECIFIC. The difference between the specific **refractions** of two wave lengths of radiant energy.

DISPERSOID. A **colloidal system** in which the dispersity is relatively great, as in **emulsoids** and **suspensoids.**

DISPERSOID SOLUTION. (Dispersoid system) **Colloidal solution.**

DISPLACEMENT. A chemical reaction in which one molecule, atom, or radical is replaced by another, as, for example, in the reaction $Zn + CuCl_2 \rightarrow Cu + ZnCl_2$, in which molecular zinc replaces copper atoms (ions) in the compound cupric chloride, forming zinc atoms (ions) and metallic copper.

DISPLACEMENT CELL. An electrical **cell** which consists of two electrodes which are made of two different metals, or otherwise differ in composition, and are commonly in contact with solutions containing their ions, so that in the operation of the cell, one electrode dissolves to form ions, and the ions of the other electrode-material deposit upon the latter. Since the net effect of this process is to displace in solution ions of one electrode-material by those of the other, the cell is called a displacement cell.

DISPLACEMENT, CHEMICAL. See displacement.

DISPLACEMENT LAW, GROUP. See law of group displacement.

DISPLACEMENT OF EQUILIBRIUM. The upsetting of a condition of **equilibrium** by the interference of some external influence (e.g., change of temperature) resulting in the ultimate formation of a new condition of equilibrium. See **law of Le Chatelier.**

DISPLACEMENT REACTION. See **displacement.**

DISPLACEMENT SERIES. See **electromotive force series.**

DISSIMULATION OF A RADICAL. See **radical, dissimulated.**

DISSIPATION. The interaction between matter and energy incident on it, such that the portion of energy used up in the interaction is no longer available for conversion into useful work.

DISSOCIATION. The process of breaking up into simpler entities, commonly restricted in chemistry to the agency of heat or other physical means, as distinguished from dissociation resulting from definite chemical reactions.

DISSOCIATION CATALYSIS. The use of a **catalyst** to decompose one of the reactants in a reaction so that one of the decomposition products may react with the second reactant.

DISSOCIATION, CHEMICAL. A special type of chemical **decomposition** in which the dissociation products are capable of reforming the original compound upon suitable alteration of conditions. Thus chemical dissociation is a reversible decomposition.

DISSOCIATION CONSTANT. See **ionization constant.**

DISSOCIATION, DEGREE OF. See **ionization, degree of.**

DISSOCIATION, ELECTROLYTIC. Ionization (q.v.).

DISSOCIATION, HEAT OF. See **ionization, heat of.**

DISSOCIATION PRESSURE. At any given temperature that pressure at which a solid and the gas formed from the solid by chemical dissociation (See **dissociation, chemical**) are in equilibrium.

DISSOCIATION, THERMAL. Dissociation by application of heat.

DISSOCIATIVE. Showing a tendency to dissociate.

DISSOLUBLE. (Obs.) Soluble.

DISSOLUTION. The process of **solution.**

DISSOLVE. To enter into **solution.**

DISSOLVENT. (Dissolver). The **solvent.**

DISSYMMETRY FACTOR OR ANISOTROPY FACTOR. A quantity used to express conveniently the magnitude of circular dichromism (refer to the **Cotton effect**). It is defined by the following formula:

$$g = \frac{(\kappa_l - \kappa_r)}{\kappa}$$

where g is the dissymmetry factor, κ_l and κ_r are the absorption indices for the left- and right-circularly polarized light, and κ is the absorption index for ordinary light of the same wave length.

DISSYMMETRY, INVERSE. Optical isomerism.

DISSYMMETRY, MOLECULAR. The exhibition of differences in optical properties by **isomeric** molecules.

DISTILLATE. That product of **distillation** obtained by the condensation of vaporized compounds.

DISTILLATION. The **unit operation in** which a liquid, a solution, or any mixture containing a liquid or a fusible substance is heated to the boiling point of the mixture corresponding to the external pressure maintained on the system. During the process some of the liquid is transformed into vapor; in the case of **solutions** the vapor will be richer in the more volatile **components** than the liquid phase. The vapors obtained in this manner are subsequently led away, recondensed, and recovered. The object of the operation may be to purify solvents, to separate liquid from solid components of a system, or to obtain separation of volatile liquid components, or to identify substances by their boiling point or range, or to determine their percentage composition, etc.

DISTILLATION, COMPRESSION. A **distillation** process in which the vapors from the still are subjected to compression. The vapors heated in this manner are then used to furnish heat to other units of equipment.

DISTILLATION, DESTRUCTIVE. The **distillation** of organic substances under such conditions as to produce simultaneously chemical **decomposition.**

DISTILLATION, DRY. Distillation of dry material, as in the case of sublimation or of destructive distillation.

DISTILLATION, FRACTIONAL. A method for the separation of several volatile **components** or fractions of different boiling points, conducted by distilling the mixture at the lowest possible boiling point and collecting the distillate as one fraction until the temperature of the vapor rises showing that a higher boiling component or mixture is beginning to distill. The receiver with fraction No. 1 is disconnected at this point from the condenser and a new receiver substituted for it which collects fraction No. 2, the next higher boiling fraction desired. When the temperature again rises a third receiver is substituted to collect fraction No. 3, and this method is continued until the highest boiling fraction has been distilled. For solutions whose **boiling** point changes continually with changes in composition, fractional distillation is also achieved in stages. The original solution is distilled until a certain fraction of the liquid has been vaporized; the distillate is then separately redistilled until a certain fraction of it is volatilized, and this process is kept up through several stages. If the process is repeated long enough or if the "cuts" have been made appropriately, then the different fractions will each be rich in one particular component of the original solution. In many industrial operations especially designed **fractionation columns** are used which permit fractional distillation to be carried out continuously **in** one stage.

DISTILLATION, STEAM. A simultaneous **distillation** of a substance immiscible with water and of water at a temperature such that the combined **vapor pressure** of the substance and of the water is equal to the external (usually atmospheric) pressure. Volatilization of high boiling substances or of substances which would decompose at their normal boiling points is readily effected in this manner.

DISTILLATION, VACUUM. A **distillation** conducted under reduced pressure so as to lower the boiling point of a volatile substance, usually resorted to in order to avoid the **decomposition** or other alteration of the substance which might occur at high temperature, or to reduce a very high boiling point to a temperature that is more reasonably accessible in the laboratory.

DISTILLATION VALUE. An expression relating the **concentration** of a **component** in the **vapor phase** to its concentration in the liquid in the still. This value is important in steam distillations.

DISTRIBUTION. In its most general sense, the arrangement, occurrence, or presence of a substance in a defined space or area. Specifically, the types of distribution important in chemistry include (1) the amount or concentration of a substance in two or more **phases** of a multiphase **system,** (2) the occurrence of a substance in the earth's crust, (3) the scattering and local concentration of a food or drug throughout the animal organism, (4) the **relative**

amount of an acid which reacts with two bases present in a reacting system, or of a base with two acids, etc.

DISTRIBUTION COEFFICIENT. The ratio between the concentrations of a solute in two immiscible solvents which are in contact. (See **law of distribution**.) Called also, partition coefficient.

DISTRIBUTION LAW. See **law of distribution**.

DISTRIBUTION LAW OF MAXWELL. See **law of Maxwell, distribution**.

DISTRIBUTION RATIO. See **law of distribution**.

DISULFAMATE. See **imidodisulfate**.

DISULFATE. See **pyrosulfate**.

DITHIONATE. The anion $S_2O_6^-$, or a compound containing it.

DITHIONATE PROCESS FOR MANGANESE. A U. S. Bureau of Mines process in which sulfur dioxide is passed through an aqueous suspension of finely-divided ore in the presence of calcium dithionate solution. The dissolved manganese is precipitated with slaked lime and, after filtering, the product is nodulized or sintered.

DITHIONIC. Related to dithionic acid, $H_2S_2O_5$; its salts are often called hyposulfates. See also **thioacid**.

DITHIONITE. The anion $S_2O_4^-$, or a compound containing it.

DITHIONOUS. Related to dithionous acid, $H_2S_2O_4$; its salts are often called thiosulfates.

DITMAR REAGENTS. A hydrochloric acid solution of sodium nitrite and potassium iodide, and a chlorinated aqueous solution of iodine; used in testing for alkaloids. Yellow or brown precipitates are given by alkaloids with these reagents.

DITZ TEST REACTIONS. Various aromatic hydrocarbons give characteristic

colors with formaldehyde, in the presence of concentrated sulfuric acid; naphthalene gives a blue color, phenanthrine, blue-green, chrysene, red-violet, etc. All these colors, except that with anthracene, disappear on dilution with water, methanol, or ethanol, and reappear with sulfuric acid.

DIURETIC. A drug that increases the secretion of urine. It may act by stimulating the functional activity of the kidneys, by raising the osmotic pressure of the blood, or by increasing blood pressure. Among the most common diuretics are the acetate and citrate of potassium, digitalis, buchu, uva ursi, and caffeine.

DIVALENT. (1) Pertaining to an element forming compounds in which it has two valences, due to its having two states of oxidation. (2) A substance which in its combined state has a valence of two.

DIVERS LIQUID. A concentrated solution of ammonium nitrate in liquid ammonia. This solution is known for its solvent action, especially upon metals, metallic oxides, and metallic hydroxides.

DOBBIN REAGENT. A reagent prepared by adding a 5% aqueous solution of mercuric chloride to a 2% aqueous solution of potassium iodide until the precipitate no longer redissolves, then adding a little ammonium chloride and, finally, alkalinizing with sodium hydroxide solution until a precipitate just forms. Water is added to bring the volume to 200 ml. This reagent is used in detecting alkali hydroxides in carbonates and other salts. A yellow color indicates the presence of an alkali hydroxide.

DOBELL SOLUTION. An aqueous solution of 1.5% sodium borate, 1.5% sodium bicarbonate, phenol, and glycerol. It is used as an antiseptic, commonly for the throat, by gargling a dilute solution.

DÖBNER REAGENT. A solution of 0.5 g. guaiaconic acid in 100 ml. alcohol and 100 ml. water. It is used to detect cyanides, hydrogen peroxide, or blood, each of which gives a blue color with this solution. With blood in feces, the color with this reagent may be green instead of blue.

DOBROLYUBSKII TEST. Titanium is detected by dissolving the material to be tested in 6 N hydrochloric acid, and adding 3–4 drops 0.025% methylene blue solution and a piece of zinc. Decolorization within 4 minutes indicates the presence of titanium.

DOCTOR SOLUTION. A sodium plumbite solution used in the petroleum refining industry to detect or remove certain sulfur compounds.

DOCTOR TEST. A method for detecting the presence of sulfur and some of its compounds in petroleum. Sodium plumbite, added to the petroleum distillates, is

of (2), shake and underlay with 1 ml. of (1). A purple ring indicates the presence of formaldehyde.

DOEBNER-MILLER SYNTHESIS. A method of formation of quinoline derivatives from aromatic **amines** and two molecules of an **aldehyde** (or one molecule of an aldehyde and one of a ketone) in the presence of HCl or certain other mineral acids.

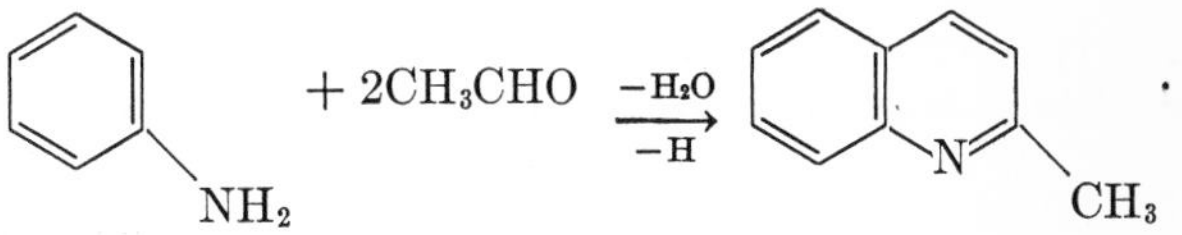

DOEBNER SYNTHESIS. A method of formation of substituted cinchoninic acids by condensation of aromatic **amines, aldehydes,** and pyruvic acids.

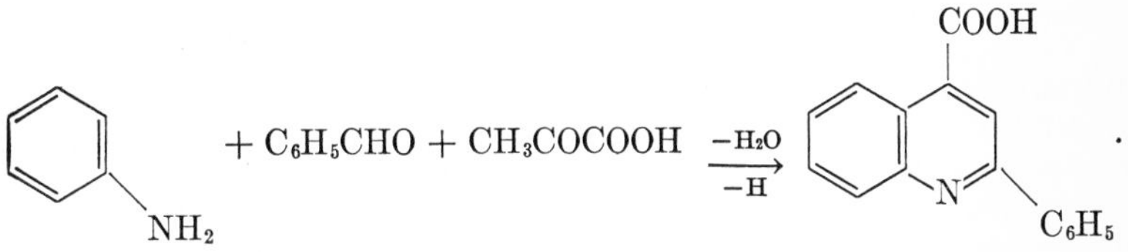

darkened if sulfur is present.

DODD TEST. To test for borate, add to 10 ml. of the aqueous solution, a few drops of methyl red and neutralize with sodium hydroxide solution. Boil, filter, and cool. Acidify with sulfuric acid, then add 0.1 N sodium hydroxide solution until the pink color just disappears. Shake with 0.5 g. mannitol. A reddish pink color indicates the presence of borate.

DODECYL. The radical

$$CH_3(CH_2)_{10}CH_2-.$$

DODSWORTH-LYONS REAGENTS. (1) A solution of 0.03 g. ferrous ammonium sulfate in 1 ml. distilled water, which is added to 100 ml. concentrated sulfuric acid. (2) A solution of 0.1 g. dried egg albumin in 10 ml. water. To test for formaldehyde in alcohol, add to 10 ml. of the latter, 0.33 ml.

DOHMÉE REAGENT. An aqueous solution of trichloracetic acid and picric acid, plus acetic acid or citric acid, used as a precipitant for albumin.

DOMINIKIEWCZ TEST. Reducing sugars are detected in alkaline solution by treatment with 3,6-dinitro-2,7-dihydroxyfluorane, which gives a cerise color, changed on acidification to an orange fluorescence.

DONALDSON REAGENT. A solution of 4 g. cupric sulfate, 6 g. potassium bitartrate, 5 g. sodium carbonate, and 5 g. potassium hydroxide, in 32 ml. of water. It is used in testing for glucose in body fluids. Reduction of the solution, shown by the formation of cuprous oxide, indicates the presence of glucose.

DONATH TEST REACTION FOR COBALT. A few drops of a cobalt solution gives a deep blue color with a 30%

sodium hydroxide solution. The color darkens on heating.

DONATH TEST REACTION FOR QUINOLINE. Quinoline solutions give with mercuric potassium iodide a yellow-white amorphous precipitate, changed by hydrochloric acid to amber-yellow needles.

DONAU TEST REACTION. Gold is detected in solution by soaking in it an asbestos thread, which on heating to redness gains a permanent purple color.

DONNAN EQUILIBRIUM. If a solution containing a nondiffusible substance with or without **diffusible** ions is separated from a solution containing diffusible ions by a semipermeable **membrane,** then an electrostatic difference of **potential** and a difference in **osmotic pressure** will be established at **equilibrium.**

DORÉE-GARDNER TEST REACTION. Cholesterol is detected by converting it to its benzoate (m.p., 145° C.), on reaction with dry pyridine and benzoyl chloride. The liquid cholesterol remains turbid up to 180° C. On cooling, it gives a color reaction.

DORN EFFECT. The development of a difference in potential by the motion of particles through water. The **potential difference** is established between the particles and the water.

DORR CLASSIFIER. A **classifier** (q.v.), i.e., a mechanical apparatus designed to separate suspended particles according to their sizes or weights. The Dorr classifier is a reciprocating rake machine.

DORR THICKENER. An apparatus used for the concentration of **slurries,** consisting essentially of a large, cylindrical tank with conical bottom and a slowly revolving agitator. The feed enters at the top center, the effluent overflows at the top periphery, and the concentrated solids are discharged at the bottom center.

DORRONSORO-FERNANDEZ TEST. Oxalic acid is detected in solution by heating 5 ml. of the solution with a crystal of

resorcinol, and floating it on 5 ml. sulfuric acid. A blue ring indicates oxalic acid. If no ring appears, the liquids are mixed and the mixture floated on another 5 ml. sulfuric acid, and heated. A dark green ring indicates oxalic acid.

DOUBLE BOND. See **bond.**

DOUBLE BOND(S), CONJUGATED. Two double **bonds** in positions connecting alternate pairs of carbon atoms. For example, the compound

$$CH_2{=}CH{-}CH{=}CH_2$$

has conjugated double bonds. In addition reactions, the conjugated double bond system commonly changes to a single double bond between the second and third carbon atoms, accompanied by the addition of atoms or groups to the first and fourth carbon atoms.

DOUBLE BOND, CUMULATED. Two double **bonds** linked to the same carbon atom as in $R_2C{=}C{=}CR_2$.

DOUBLE BOND(S), ISOLATED. Double **bonds** which are neither cumulated nor conjugated.

DOUBLE BOND SHIFT. The shift of a double **bond** within a chemical compound as in

$$RCH{=}CH{-}CH_2 \rightarrow RCH_2{-}CH{=}CH.$$

DOUBLE LAYER POTENTIAL. See **zeta potential.**

DOUBLE SALTS. See **salts, double.**

DOUBLET. Two electrons which are shared by two atoms so as to form a nonpolar valence bond. (See **bond, non-polar.**)

DOW PROCESS. A metallurgical process for the production of metallic magnesium by electrolysis of its fused chloride.

DOW PROCESS FOR MAGNESIUM. The method of magnesium production in which magnesium in sea water is precipitated as hydroxide by addition of calcium hydroxide. The magnesium hydroxide is dissolved in hydrochloric acid (with a little sulfuric acid to precipitate the calcium); finally the magnesium chloride so obtained is electrolyzed.

DOWELL PROCESS. A method for opening blocked oil wells by use of hydrochloric acid, commonly containing corrosion inhibitors to protect the casing as much as possible.

DOWNS CELL. An electric cell used to produce metallic sodium by the electrolysis of molten sodium chloride containing sodium carbonate.

DRAG EFFECT. The effect of interionic attraction in reducing the freedom of an ion to move in an electrical field, because of the interference of the ions of opposite charge by which a given ion is surrounded. The drag effect is an essential part of the explanation of the **Debye-Hückel theory** of the anomalous properties of concentrated solutions of strong electrolytes.

DRAGENDORFF ALKALOID REAGENT. A reagent prepared by adding to a solution of 22.7 g. potassium iodide in 25 ml. water, a solution of 8 ml. bismuth subnitrate in 20 ml. concentrated nitric acid, and adding water to obtain a total volume of 100 ml. This reagent yields a characteristic red-yellow precipitate with many alkaloids.

DRAGENDORFF-BRASCHE TEST REACTION. Physostigmine, on treatment with baryta water and evaporation with ammonia, gives a blue substance forming a solution in alcohol with characteristic absorption spectrum.

DRAGENDORFF HELLEBOREIN REAGENT. A mixture of 0.1 ml. of a 10% aqueous solution of potassium iodide, 10 ml. concentrated sulfuric acid, and 7 ml. alcohol. This is a reagent for helleborein, yielding a deep pink color.

DRAGENDORFF-HUSEMANN TEST REACTION. Narcotine, when its solution in 20% sulfuric acid is slowly evaporated, becomes orange-red, blue-violet, and then red-violet at the boiling point.

DRAGENDORFF TEST FOR BENZENE IN PETROLEUM BENZINE. On oxidation of the sample with fuming nitric acid, nitrobenzene is formed.

DRAGENDORFF TEST REACTION FOR AMYGDALIN. Amygdalin forms, with sulfuric acid, a red solution, changing to cherry-red on addition of potassium dichromate.

DRAGENDORFF TEST REACTIONS FOR VARIOUS SUBSTANCES. Brucine gives a raspberry-red color changing to orange shades on treatment with 10% sulfuric acid and very little dilute potassium dichromate solution.

Cinchonamine gives a green color when dissolved in seleno-sulfuric acid.

Covallomarine dissolves in sulfuric acid to give a yellow-brown solution, changing to violet, then to blue-violet on contact with moist air.

Cotoin gives a lemon-yellow solution in sulfuric acid.

Cupreine gives a brown color with chlorine water, and a white precipitate, soluble in excess reagent, with potassium thiocyanate.

Curarine gives a red color on evaporation, at 40° C., of its solution in 2% sulfuric acid.

Digitalin dissolves in sulfuric acid to give a green-yellow color, changing to yellow and to red. Addition of a little nitrite or ferric chloride gives a blue-violet color.

Digitonin dissolves in sulfuric acid to give a pale red color, changing to red violet.

Ditaine dissolves in sulfuric acid with a red color, becoming purple-red in several hours. Ditaine dissolved in nitrous ether is colored red by sulfuric acid.

Ditamine forms a red solution in sulfuric acid, which becomes violet-red on warming. Ditamine forms a yellow solution in nitric acid, changing to dark green and orange-red.

Eseridine dissolved in ammonia gives, on evaporation, a green residue soluble in alcohol.

Helleborein dissolves in alcoholic sulfuric acid (10:7) containing a little potassium iodide, to form a dark pink color in 15 minutes.

Hesperidine dissolves in sulfuric acid with an orange-red color; in **Fröhde solution** (q.v.) it gives a red-brown color, changing to blue, then green with hydrochloric acid.

Leukotine dissolves in sulfuric acid with a yellow color, which gives, with ferric chloride, a white precipitate; with more ferric chloride, a dark red color appears.

Ononine dissolves with a red color in sulfuric acid containing ferric chloride; ononine dissolves in hydrochloric or nitric acids with a green color.

Osthrutine dissolves in sulfuric acid with a pale yellow color, changing to blue-red with a blue fluorescence.

Peucedanine dissolves in sulfuric acid with a green-yellow color and blue-green fluorescence. Addition of manganese dioxide gives a green color.

Phloridzin dissolves in sulfuric acid with a yellow color changing to red and to brown; in nitric acid, it dissolves with a deep green color changing to dark brown.

Picropodophylline dissolves in sulfuric acid with a red color changing to brown, and in alcoholic sulfuric acid with a violet color.

Podophyllotoxin dissolves in sulfuric acid with a brown color, and in nitric acid with a red color, changing to red-brown and to yellow.

Thymol gives a pale red color on warming with concentrated sulfuric acid and glacial acetic acid; thymol in alcoholic solution gives a red color with concentrated sulfuric acid and a trace of sugar.

DRAM (or DRACHM). A unit of weight in the **avoirdupois** and **apothecaries'** systems. The liquid unit, fluid dram, is often abbreviated "dram."

1 apothecaries' dram	= 60 grains
1 apothecaries' dram	= $\frac{1}{8}$ apothecaries' ounce
1 apothecaries' dram	= 3.8879 grams
1 avoirdupois dram	= $\frac{1}{16}$ avoirdupois ounce
1 avoirdupois dram	= 27.344 grains
1 avoirdupois dram	= 1.7718 grams
1 gram	= 0.56438 avoirdupois dram
1 gram	= 0.25720 apothecaries' dram

DRAPER EFFECT. An increase of volume at constant temperature which sets in at the start of a gaseous **combination;** the phenomenon was discovered in the reaction between hydrogen and chlorine.

DRESCHEL REAGENT. Silicotungstic acid, prepared by precipitation by ether from sulfuric acid solution, and used in testing for alkaloids.

DREWSEN TEST REACTION. To detect acetone, add *o*-nitrobenzaldehyde to the liquid tested, warm, cool, then add sodium hydroxide solution. A blue color indicates the presence of acetone.

DRIER. (Sometimes dryer) Either a mechanical device used to remove water from a substance or system, or a substance used for the same purpose, such as calcium chloride or phosphorus pentoxide. The term drier is also used in some industries to denote substances used to accelerate solidification, as in the paint industry where driers are substances added to the paint to hasten its hardening, which they do by oxidizing or catalyzing the oxidation of the drying oil.

DRIER, DRUM. A type of drier in which a liquid, with or without suspended solids, is applied to the surface of a drum which is heated and revolved, allowing the moisture to evaporate. The thin film of dried material is then generally scraped off.

DRIER, PAINT. A substance added to paint or varnish to hasten its drying, commonly consisting of oxides of lead, manganese, zinc, or various other metals, or of compounds of such metals with certain organic acid radicals.

DRIER, ROTARY. A rotating drum in which material to be dried is brought into contact with circulated hot air, or other source of heat. The motion of the drum turns the material, constantly exposing new surfaces to be dried.

DRIER, SPRAY. A system in which a solution or suspension is sprayed from a nozzle or nozzles into ascending hot air or other gases, so that the liquid is vaporized almost instantaneously, and the dry solid falls into a collecting chamber. Instead of nozzles, high-speed rotating wheels are also used, the liquid spinning off the wheels in the form of droplets and then falling through the hot air.

DRIER, VACUUM. In general, any apparatus in which the drying of a substance is accelerated by the application of vacuum. Specifically, a closed compartment, in which material is placed in trays on shelves which are commonly steam-jacketed. The entire enclosure is attached to a vacuum pump and is of heavy construction to withstand atmospheric pressure. The apparatus is also called a vacuum shelf drier or, for certain types, a tunnel drier.

DROP-RATIO METHOD FOR pH. A method of determining the pH of a solution by comparing the color produced in it by a given indicator with the color of a series of comparison tubes which are arranged in pairs. To each *pair* is added the same number of drops of indicator, but the distribution of these drops between the twin tubes differs for each pair. Acid and alkali are then added to bring out the acid or the basic color of the indicator.

DROPPING BOTTLE. A glass bottle equipped with constricted tube, rod, or other means for delivering its contents drop by drop.

DROPPING FUNNEL. A separatory funnel with a glass stopcock and a long stem.

DROSS. Oxidized metallic residues, or other metallic waste-products, such as the scum-material which forms on the surface of molten metals during refining or casting.

DRUDE EQUATION. A relationship between the specific **rotation** of an **optically-active** substance and the wave length of the light, of the form:

$$[\alpha] = \frac{k}{\lambda^2 - \lambda_0^2}$$

where $[\alpha]$ is the specific rotation, λ the wave length, and k and λ_0^2 are constants, known as the rotation constant and the dispersion constant.

DRUG. A medicinal agent or a substance used internally for the treatment of disease.

DRUM FILTER. See **filter, drum.**

DRY CELL. A small electric battery widely used to supply small electric currents at low voltages, for radio sets, bell circuits, and various alarm systems and control devices. It consists of a central carbon **anode,** and of a zinc cup acting as **cathode,** and container for the cell. The **electrolyte** is a wet paste of ammonium chloride, with some zinc chloride, and manganese dioxide (**depolarizer**).

DRY PAN. An apparatus used in **grinding,** chiefly of clays in the ceramic industries. It consists of a rotating pan which moves the material to be ground under heavy rollers, or "mullers." After crushing, the fines fall through holes in the pan, while the coarse particles are redistributed on the pan, by scrapers, for the next pass under the rollers.

DRYER. See **drier.**

DRYING. (1) Removal of water from solids, liquids, or gases by evaporation or by chemical agents. (2) The process whereby a liquid, such as linseed oil, is oxidized or otherwise transformed into a solid film.

DRYING AGENTS. Substances used to absorb moisture, especially in a desiccator and in towers through which moist gases are passed. The principal laboratory drying agents are sulfuric acid, fused calcium chloride, solid sodium hydroxide, calcium oxide, and phosphorus pentoxide.

DRYING OIL. An oil which absorbs oxygen or **polymerizes** in the presence of oxygen to form a solid mass. Drying oils contain unsaturated compounds and have many uses, as in paints to form hard, adherent films.

DRYING TUBE. A U-shaped or other conveniently shaped glass tube that is filled with a drying agent, and is used for drying gases or vapors.

DRYING TUNNEL. A chamber provided with heat sources and with fans, suction pumps, or other apparatus for withdrawal of gases and vapors. The tunnel, which is used for drying solids, is equipped with roads or tracks so that cars or trucks carrying the material to be dried can be moved easily in and out.

DUAL THEORY OF CATALYSIS. The postulate that both **hydrogen ions** and undissociated molecules of an acid are able to act catalytically. This view has been extended to include **hydroxyl ions**, undissociated molecules of bases, and even **cations** of weak bases and **anions** of weak acids.

DUANE-HUNT, LAW OF. See **law of Duane-Hunt.**

DUBAQUIÉ TEST REACTION. Benzoic acid is detected by treating it with cupric sulfate and hydrogen peroxide, producing salicylic acid, which reacts on addition of ferric chloride to produce a violet color.

DUBBS PROCESS. A process for the simultaneous **cracking** and **distilling** of crude oil (or a fraction distilled therefrom) by the application of heat and pressure. The oil is preheated to about 400° C. and is circulated through steel tubes heated to about 450° C., under a pressure of 350 pounds per square inch. The charge passes continuously into a chamber in which the vapor separates from the remaining liquid and carbon.

DUBLANC TEST REACTION. Iodide ion is detected by formation in alkaline solution of a red or green-yellow color or precipitate with platinic chloride or mercurous nitrate solution.

DUBSKY-HRDLIČKA REAGENT. A micro-reagent for aluminum, consisting of the soluble potassium salt of 1-aminoanthraquinone-2-carboxylic acid. It gives a red precipitate with aluminum (also with zinc and magnesium).

DUBSKY-KRAMETZ TEST REACTION. Beryllium is detected by adding to a few drops of its solution, a few drops of a mixture of 6 parts 0.05% alcoholic quinalizarin solution, and 1 part 10% ethylenediamine solution. A color change from blue to violet indicates the presence of beryllium.

DUBSKY-KURAS TEST REACTION. Ferrous ion is detected by adding 5 ml. of its dilute solution to 1 ml. 1% alcoholic diisonitrosoacetone solution, which is then neutralized with ammonium acetate solution. An intense blue color indicates the presence of ferrous ion.

DUBSKY-LANGER-STONAD REAGENTS. Two reagents which give characteristic colored precipitates with many metal ions. They are saturated solutions of (1) ethylenebiguanide; and (2) o-phenylenebiguanide.

DUBSKY-OKAC TEST REACTION FOR BISMUTH. A solution of 0.7 g. dimercaptothiodiazole in 35 ml. 0.1 N potassium hydroxide, used in testing for bismuth, which gives a red precipitate in acid solution. Many other metal ions also give precipitates.

DUBSKY-OKAC TEST REACTION FOR MAGNESIUM. A solution of o,p-dihydroxy-benzeneazo-p-nitrobenzene gives a blue color with salts of magnesium in alkaline solution. Nickel and cobalt also give blue colors.

DUBSKY-WAGNER TEST FOR ALUMINUM. To 5 ml. of the solution tested, add 2 ml. 0.05% solution of alkannin in alcohol, or 0.03% naphthazarin solution, then add with agitation ammonia until the color changes to blue, then an additional 3 ml. ammonia. A dark violet precipitate indicates the presence of aluminum.

DUBSKY-WAGNER TESTS FOR MAGNESIUM. (1) To 50 ml. of the solution tested add 5 drops 0.05% solution of alizarin in alcohol, or 0.03% naphthazarin solution, then add a slight excess of 2.5 N sodium hydroxide. A blue precipitate (on warming if necessary) indicates magnesium. (2) With 0.03% naphthazarin and 10% ethylenediamine solutions in 5:1 proportions, magnesium gives a blue color also.

DUCKERT TEST REACTION FOR ANTIMONY. A saturated alcoholic solution of 2,3,7-trihydroxy-9-methyl-6-fluorone gives a bright red precipitate with antimony at pH 4.

DUCTILITY. A property of solids, whereby they are capable of being drawn, or reduced in area, by tensile force.

DUCTLESS GLAND. One of a number of **glands** of man and certain animals which elaborate **hormones,** chemicals of marked physiological activity, and discharge them directly into the blood.

DUDLEY PIPETTE. See **pipette, Dudley.**

DUDLEY SOLUTION FOR GLUCOSE. A solution of bismuth subnitrate in nitric acid to which an equal volume of acetic acid and 10 volumes of water are added. It is a test reagent for glucose. A black or gray color, obtained on heating in alkaline solution, indicates the presence of glucose.

DUDLEY TEST REACTION FOR GALLIC ACID. A dilute aqueous solution of picric acid, to which an excess of ammonia has been added, gives with gallic acid a red color changing to green.

DUFF REACTION. A reaction of phenols or dialkylanilines with hexamethylenetetramine, yielding orthoformyl phenols or *p*-dialkylaminobenzaldehydes.

DUFLOS TEST REACTION FOR ANILINE. A solution of aniline in dilute sulfuric acid gives a green color with lead peroxide.

DUFOUR EFFECT. Abnormal **Zeeman effect.** Individual lines show Zeeman effect in band spectra, if observed in a direction parallel to field and if circular vibrations are converted into plane ones with a quarter-wave plate, through Nicol prism.

DULONG AND PETIT, LAW OF. See **law of Dulong and Petit.**

DUMAS METHOD FOR NITROGEN. In this method for the determination of nitrogen in organic substances, the nitrogen is freed by **combustion** of the substance and is determined volumetrically as in the gas phase.

DUOSOL PROCESS. A process for the refining of lubricating oil, involving extraction with liquid propane and cresol base.

DUPASQUIER REAGENT. An aqueous solution of gold chloride, used in testing water for organic matter. A blue-violet color, obtained on boiling, indicates the presence of organic matter.

DUPLET. A pair of electrons that is shared by two atoms and that corresponds to a single valence **bond.**

DUNAJEWA TEST. Sulfite is detected by placing its solution upon the **Bettendorff-Winkler reagent** (q.v.). A yellow-brown ring indicates the presence of sulfite.

DUNLOP TEST REACTION FOR FERRIC ION. Ferric salts in very dilute solution impart a yellow color to glycerin.

DUPOUY TEST FOR HALOFORMS. When 0.5 ml. of an alcoholic thymol solution is heated to boiling for 0.5 minute with a little dry potassium carbonate and one drop of chloroform, a red-yellow color develops, which is changed to violet by addition of 1 ml. sulfuric acid and further boiling. On dilution with acetic acid and water, the solution is blue. Characteristic absorption bands are shown. Bromoform and iodoform give the same reaction.

DUPPA-PERKIN TEST REACTIONS. Glyoxylic acid is detected by: (1) the light orange-yellow precipitate obtained by treating an aqueous solution of calcium glyoxylate with aniline oxalate, filtering, and allowing the filtrate to stand. (2) The production of oxalic acid on boiling glyoxylic acid with lime.

DURRANT TEST REACTION. Cobalt is detected by adding to its dilute solution an excess of sodium bicarbonate and then some hydrogen peroxide or chlorine or bromine, with the development of an apple-green color.

DURYL. The radical 2,3,5,6-(CH₃)₄C₆H–.

DURYLENE. The radical

DUST. Finely-divided waste material, or wind-blown earth.

DUST CHAMBER. A large enclosed space, commonly provided with baffles, and used to remove solid particles from industrial gases, such as those produced by combustion, etc.

DUST, INDUSTRIAL. Finely-divided waste material produced by factories, and by industrial operations generally. If combustible, it may constitute an explosion hazard within the plant, and whether combustible or not, it is a potential health hazard inside or outside the plant.

DUTCH PROCESS FOR WHITE LEAD. Sheet lead, in "buckles," is placed on a shelf in an earthenware pot 5 inches in diameter and 8 inches high, the bottom of which contains 3% to 5% acetic acid. Carbon dioxide derived from the fermentation of spent tan bark in which several such pots are stacked fills the air spaces, while the heat from the fermentation vaporizes the acetic acid and this attacks the lead. The basic lead acetate so formed is decomposed by the moist carbon dioxide present and white lead is produced.

DUYK SOLUTION FOR GLUCOSE. A mixture of 25 ml. of a 20% aqueous solution of nickel sulfate, 20 ml. of a 25% aqueous solution of sodium hydroxide, and 50 ml. of a 6% aqueous solution of tartaric acid. This reagent gives a characteristic color change (green to dark brown) when heated or boiled with a solution containing glucose.

DUYK TEST FOR DIFFERENTIATING FIBERS. (1) Natural silk gives, on burning, an odor of burnt horn; artificial silk does not.

(2) Natural silk dissolves in a solution of 1 g. nickel carbonate in 6 ml. water and 6 ml. ammonia; artificial silk does not.

DVI-. (Sanskrit, two, twice) Designating, provisionally, an element of the same family, in the second place beyond the one to whose name it is prefixed, as dvi-manganese (**rhenium**).

DWIGHT-LLOYD MACHINE. A sintering machine consisting of a heavy frame supporting two heavy sprockets and a steel track or guide. Grate bars carry the charge along the track, while wind-boxes below are connected to a down-draft fan discharging to a baghouse or Cottrell precipitators.

DWIGHT-LLOYD PROCESS. A method of roasting ore by passage of hot combustion gases down through the ore bed in a furnace.

DWYER-MURPHY REAGENT. Add 1 ml. of 50% ammonium thiocyanate solution to 1 ml. aniline; then add 2 N hydrochloric acid until the emulsion clears, dilute to 5 ml. and clear with drops of alcohol. This reagent gives a yellow-brown precipitate with a solution containing copper.

DWYER REAGENT FOR CADMIUM. A solution of p-nitrodiazoaminoazobenzene prepared by dissolving 0.02 g. of the reagent in 100 ml. of 0.02 N alcoholic potassium hydroxide solution. This solution is used in making spot tests for cadmium. A pink spot, shading into violet at the edges, indicates the presence of cadmium.

DWYER REAGENTS FOR MAGNESIUM. p,p'-Dinitrodiazoamino compounds and related substances give very sensitive absorption colors with magnesium oxide and hydroxide.

DWYER TEST FOR COBALT. Add potassium permanganate solution to 5–10 ml. of the hot test solution until the pink color remains. Decolorize with sulfurous acid, and add 5–10 drops excess; add 5–10 ml. potassium thiocyanate solution and boil until decolorized, then add 0.05% methylene blue solution and excess 1% sodium sulfite in $2N$ sodium cyanide. If cobalt is present, the blue color fades, but reappears on shaking.

DWYER TEST FOR MAGNESIUM AND CADMIUM. The test reagent for magnesium is a 0.01% solution of 4-nitronaphthalene diazobenzene-4'-azobenzene in 0.01% alcoholic potassium hydroxide solution. Five to 10 drops of it are added to 10 ml. of the solution tested, which has been acidified with acetic acid. On alkalinizing with $2N$ potassium hydroxide, a blue absorption precipitate or a blue-green color indicates magnesium.

To test for cadmium, add 0.25 g. potassium sodium tartrate to the solution to be tested, followed by several drops of the reagent and then $2N$ potassium hydroxide. A pink color indicates cadmium.

Dy Symbol for the element **dysprosium.**

DYAD. (1) An atom or radical that is **divalent.** (2) In an older usage, a class of substances having two closely-related forms, such as the cyanides XCN and the isocyanides XNC.

DYE. (Dyestuff) Any substance capable of being absorbed from solution by fibers or of combining with them when **mordanted** to impart a color to textiles and similar materials. Dyes are classified as direct, mordant, substantive, adjective, monogenetic, polygenetic, natural, synthetic, mineral, etc., according to their **origin** and mode of application.

DYE, ACID. A dyestuff that dyes animal fibers directly from an acid bath. Acid dyes are of little use for application to vegetable fibers, e.g., nitro and azo dyes.

DYE, ACID MORDANT. An acid dye which requires a **mordant** for achieving best results on animal fibers.

DYE, ACRIDINE. A dyestuff derived from acridine,

DYE, ADJECTIVE. (Mordant dye) A dyestuff that requires a **mordant,** as alizarin.

DYE, ARTIFICIAL. A synthetic dyestuff, as distinguished from natural products. The most important synthetic dyestuffs are the coal-tar colors, including azo dyes and phthaleins.

DYE, AZINE. A dyestuff having the chromophore group,

DYE, AZO. A dyestuff which has as its **chromophore** the azo group, $—N=N—$.

DYE, BASIC. A salt of a colorless base, e.g., auramine, malachite green, methyl violet.

DYE, CYANINE. One of a group of dyes derived from the compound cyanine,

in which the $C_5H_{11}-$ groups are **isoamyl** groups. An important special use of the cyanine dyes is as sensitizers in photographic emulsions.

DYE, DIRECT. A **substantive dye** (see **dye, substantive**).

DYE, INGRAIN. A dyestuff produced in the fiber by successive treatment with the components of the dye or with the dye in its leuco (reduced and soluble) form, followed by oxidation.

DYE, MINERAL. An inorganic compound used in dyeing, as ferric hydrate, chromic hydrate, lead chromate, Prussian blue.

DYE, MONOGENETIC. A dyestuff that produces only one color on the fiber. Cf. **dye, polygenetic.**

DYE, MORDANT. An **adjective dye** (see **dye, adjective**).

DYE, NATURAL. A dyestuff extracted from animal and vegetable tissues in which they are preformed or exist in combination, as indigo, alizarin, logwood, carmine.

DYE, NITRO. A dyestuff whose **chromophore** is the nitro group ($-NO_2$).

DYE, NITROSO. A dyestuff containing the **chromophore group** $-NO$.

DYE, OXYAZINE. A dyestuff containing

the **chromophore group,** R ⟨O⟩ R.

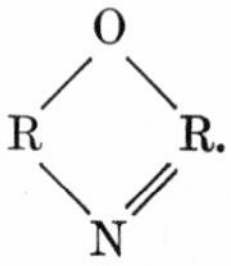

DYE, OXYAZO. A dyestuff having as its **chromophore** the **azo group** ($-N=N-$), and also containing an **oxy group.**

DYE, OXYKETONE. A dyestuff containing as its **chromophore,** the **quinone group,**

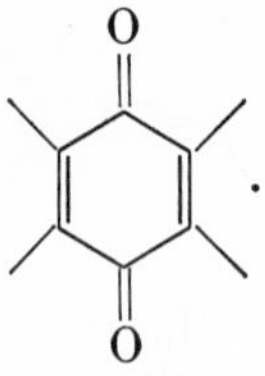

DYE, POLYGENETIC. A dyestuff which yields different colors on the fiber according to the mordant used, e.g., alizarin.

DYE, PYRONINE. A dyestuff having

the **chromophore group,** R ⟨O⟩ R.

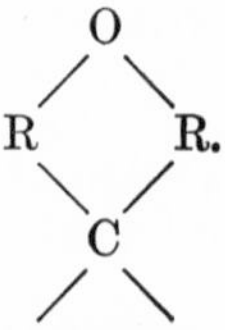

DYE, SUBSTANTIVE. (Direct dye) **A** dyestuff which yields colors directly to the fiber without the use of a mordant.

DYE, SULFIDE. A dyestuff which dyes vegetable fiber from a bath of sodium sulfide, followed by oxidation.

DYE, THIAZINE. A sulfur-containing dyestuff having the chromophore group,

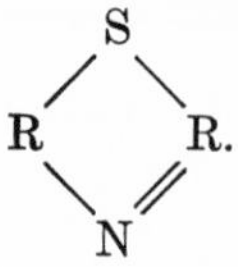

DYE, TRIPHENYLMETHANE. A dyestuff derived from $(C_6H_5)_3CH$, having the **chromophore group,**

$$
\begin{array}{c}
C=C \\
\diagup \qquad \diagdown \\
=C \qquad\qquad C= \\
\diagdown \qquad \diagup \\
C=C
\end{array}
$$

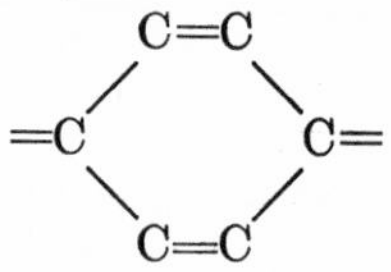

e.g., crystal violet, *p*-rosaniline, and methyl green.

DYE, VAT. A dyestuff which is applied to the fiber in the form of its **leuco compound,** the color being later developed by oxidation.

DYEING. The process of coloring fibers by means of dyestuffs.

DYEING, ABSORPTION THEORY OF. An hypothesis that dyestuffs are adsorbed out of colloidal solution by fibers and that dyeing follows the laws of adsorption.

DYEING, CHEMICAL THEORY OF. An hypothesis which postulates a chemical combination between dyestuff and fibers.

DYEING, MECHANICAL THEORY OF. An hypothesis which assumes that dyestuffs are absorbed within the pores of the fiber.

DYEING, SOLID SOLUTION THEORY OF. An hypothesis which states that the dyestuff or **mordants** (when one is used) form a solid solution in the fibers.

DYNAMIC ALLOTROPY. See **allotropy, dynamic.**

DYNAMIC ISOMERS AND ISOMERISM. See **isomerism, dynamic.**

DYNAMIC STRUCTURE OF BENZENE. See **benzene, formulas.**

DYNE. The unit of force in the c.g.s. system, defined as the force which acting upon unit mass (one gram) for one second produces unit velocity (one centimeter per second).

DYS-. (Greek) Hard, difficult, bad; as dyslysin, dysprosium. See **eu-.**

DYSPROSIUM. Rare earth metallic element. Symbol Dy. Atomic number 66. Atomic weight 162.46. Valence 3. Oxide Dy_2O_3. Dysprosium occurs in gadolinite and other minerals. Its salts are green or yellow.

DYSTECTIC MIXTURE. A mixture of two or more substances in such proportions as to yield the maximum melting point, so that upon altering the proportions the melting point is lowered. Correlative of **eutectic mixture.**

E. Symbol for an **electron,** or its electrical charge (e). Symbol for the natural logarithmic base, $2.718 \ldots (e)$. Symbol for **electromotive force** (E). Symbol for electrode potential (E). Symbol for **electroaffinity** (E_o). Symbol for the **einstein,** a unit of energy (E). Symbol for energy (E). Symbol for **entrainment ratio** (E). Symbol for evaporation (E). Symbol for electronic charge $(-e)$. Symbol for kinetic energy (E_k); for vibrational energy (E_v); for potential energy (E_p); for total energy (E). Symbol for **electric field strength** (E). Symbol for **illuminance** (E). Symbol for modulus of **elasticity,** Young's (E). Coefficient of **resilience** or restitution (e). See also **epsilon** and **eta.**

EARTH, ALKALINE. A term applied to the oxides of **calcium, barium, strontium,** usually **magnesium,** i.e., to oxides of the metals of the alkaline earth group.

EARTH, RARE. An oxide of one of the fifteen elements having atomic numbers 57 (lanthanum) to 71 (lutecium), inclusive. The elements themselves constitute the **rare earth metals** (q.v.) possessing very similar chemical properties.

EBER SOLUTION. A mixture of 10 g. hydrochloric acid, 10 g. ether, and 30 g.

alcohol used in testing for spoiled meat. A fume is formed by the ammonia in spoiled meat.

EBER TEST REACTION FOR PHYSOSTIGMINE. On bringing a drop of physostigmine into contact with a drop of 5% sodium hydroxide solution, a red color appears at the interface. It darkens on standing, is orange-yellow after evaporation, and dissolves in water to give a red solution.

EBOLI TEST REACTION. Many alkaloids give characteristic colors when 1–2 mg. of them are treated on a watch glass with 5–6 drops of a 1:1 sulfuric acid solution, followed by addition of a small piece of potassium dichromate.

EBULLIOSCOPE. Any instrument that measures a property by a deviation from a normal known **boiling point.** Thus this term is applied to an apparatus in which the percentage of alcohol in a mixture is estimated by an observation of the boiling point. **Beckmann's apparatus** for molecular weight determination is an ebullioscope.

EBULLIOSCOPIC CONSTANT. A quantity calculated to represent the molal elevation of the boiling point of a solution, by the relationship:

$$K = \frac{RT_o^2}{1000 l_e}$$

in which K is the ebullioscopic constant, R is the **gas constant,** T_o is the boiling point of the pure solvent, and l_e is the **latent heat of evaporation** per gram. The product of the ebullioscopic constant and the **molality** of the solution give the actual elevation of the boiling point for the range of values for which this relationship applies. Unfortunately, this range is limited to very dilute solutions, not extending to solutions of unit molality.

EBULLITION. The phenomenon of bubble formation such as that accompanying boiling.

–ECANE. A suffix indicating a 10-membered ring.

ECHELON CELL. See **cell, echelon.**

–ECIN, –ECINE. A suffix indicating a 10-membered ring.

EDELEANU PROCESS. A process for the removal of sulfur compounds from petroleum fractions by extraction with liquid sulfur dioxide.

EDDY-DE EDS TEST. Phenothiazine is detected by treatment with saturated bromine water, which forms a red compound, useful in colorimetric determination of phenothiazine.

EDLBACHER TEST REACTION. Many proteins, after shaking with sodium hydroxide solution and dimethyl sulfate, give a blue-red ring test with concentrated sulfuric acid.

EDLEFSEN TEST REACTION FOR RESORCINOL. A resorcinol solution, when treated with an aqueous solution of β-naphthoquinone after the addition of ammonia, is colored blue-green, changing to red with nitric acid. This test may also be used for β-naphthoquinone.

EEGRIWE MICRO-TEST FOR PHENOL. A drop of the solution tested is added to a little m-nitrobenzaldehyde in a test tube; after addition of 2 ml. 63% sulfuric acid, the mixture is heated to 65° C. A pink color indicates the presence of phenol.

EEGRIWE REAGENT FOR SILICA AND FLUORINE. A 20% aqueous solution of ammonium molybdate, which is used to moisten filter paper, that is then turned yellow by silicon tetrafluoride.

EEGRIWE REAGENT FOR TIN. A solution of 0.01 g. diazine green S in 100 ml. water to which hydrochloric acid is added until the solution is blue. The solution to be tested is reduced with iron and hydrochloric acid, then the test reagent is superimposed on it. A violet ring, becoming red, indicates the presence of tin.

EEGRIWE REAGENTS FOR ZINC. (1) A solution of 5–10 mg. metanil yellow or orange IV in 100 ml. water. One drop of it, mixed with 3 drops 2% aqueous potassium ferricyanide solution, and acidified to a red color with hydrochloric acid, becomes colorless in 5 minutes on addition of 1 drop of a weakly-acidic zinc solution.
(2) A mixture of 0.25 ml. 2% aqueous potassium ferricyanide solution and 0.3 ml. of an 0.25% diethylaniline (which must be free from monoethylaniline) solution in 50% phosphoric acid. (The diethylaniline solution is added to the ferrocyanide.) One drop of a weakly-acid zinc solution gives a brown-yellow to brown-red color with this reagent.

EEGRIWE TEST FOR ANTIMONY AND TUNGSTEN. Dissolve 0.05 g. rhodamine B in 500 ml. water. Add to 5 ml. of this reagent, 1 drop of the solution to be tested. A violet to blue-violet color indicates the presence of pentavalent antimony or tungsten (the latter in dilute hydrochloric acid solution).

EEGRIWE TESTS FOR COBALT. Add to 1 drop of the neutral solution tested, 5–10 drops of 0.02% solution of Eriochrome blue-black B and 1 drop of a 3.5% sodium nitrite solution and acidify with 0.5 N acetic acid. A violet color indicates the presence of cobalt (brown-violet if nickel is also present).

EEGRIWE TEST FOR FREE CHLORINE. Fuchsin S solution, dried on filter paper, is colored yellow by free chlorine.

EEGRIWE TEST FOR GLYCOLIC ACID. On heating with a sulfuric acid solution of 2,7-dihydroxynaphthalene, glycolic acid gives a violet-red color.

EEGRIWE TEST FOR LACTIC ACID. One drop of the solution tested is heated with 1 ml. sulfuric acid for 2 minutes at 85° C., cooled to 25° C., and mixed with a little solid p-hydroxydiphenyl. A violet color on standing indicates the presence of lactic acid.

EEGRIWE TEST FOR MAGNESIUM. The neutralized solution to be tested is treated by a 0.1% solution of benzoazurine G, followed by 1 ml. concentrated ammonia. A blue precipitate indicates the presence of magnesium.

EEGRIWE TEST FOR MALIC ACID. On heating on the steam bath for several minutes with sulfuric acid containing α- or β-naphthol, malic acid gives a blue fluorescence after cooling.

EEGRIWE TEST FOR NITRITE AND NITRATE. Treat 1 ml. of the solution tested with 1 drop of a solution of 0.03 g. Safranine T in 100 ml. water, and acidify with dilute sulfuric acid. A blue color indicates the presence of nitrite.

Concentrate the solution to be tested, and add 3 drops of the Safranine T solution, some magnesium powder and a few drops 2 N sulfuric acid, followed by a few more drops of the sulfuric acid after gas evolution is over. A violet to blue color indicates the presence of nitrate.

EEGRIWE TEST FOR ORCINOL. A drop of the solution tested, some solid 2,4-dihydroxybenzaldehyde, and 1–2 drops concentrated hydrochloric acid are heated to boiling. On cooling and alkalization with 2 N sodium hydroxide, a green fluorescence indicates the presence of orcinol.

EEGRIWE TEST FOR SULFITE. After precipitating sulfide and hydroxyl ions with cadmium carbonate, pass in carbon dioxide until phenolphthalein is no longer pink in the solution, then add, with shaking, 0.01% True Blue R Solution. A sulfur dioxide concentration of 0.01 mg. per ml. decolorizes 8 drops of the reagent.

EEGRIWE TEST FOR SULFUR DIOXIDE. Sulfur dioxide in air is detected by a rod dipped in zinc nitroprusside solution and then held over ammonia; it is then colored red by air containing sulfur dioxide.

EEGRIWE TESTS FOR TARTRATE. (1) On heating with sulfuric acid containing β, β'-binaphthol, a green fluorescence shows the presence of tartrate. (2) On heating with sulfuric acid containing tannic acid, a blue, blue-green, or green-yellow color shows the presence of tartrate.

EFFECTIVE ATOMIC CHARGE. See atomic charge, effective.

EFFECTIVE ATOMIC NUMBER. See atomic number, effective.

EFFECTIVE MOBILITY OF IONS. The average velocity of an ion due to electric force taken over a long time and including the periods of rest, i.e., when the ion is neutralized; or the average velocity of all the ions including those neutralized at the time.

EFFERVESCENCE. A frothing of a cold or hot liquid as a result of the formation within it and subsequent discharge of a large number of gas bubbles. It occurs during fermentation, during the action of acids upon carbonates, etc. Boiling is not regarded as effervescence, nor is the frothing produced in such actions as that of concentrated sulfuric acid upon sugar.

EFFICIENCY. The general significance of this term as applied to a machine or device may be expressed as the ratio of output to input of energy or power. The concept may be extended to other than purely mechanical systems. For example, the efficiency of an electric lamp may be expressed in candles or lumens of luminous flux (output) per watt of electric power (input).

EFFLORESCENCE. The phenomenon which occurs when an hydrated solid substance, especially a crystal, parts with its solvent of **crystallization** or hydration and becomes an anhydrous powder. The term is also used to describe an outgrowth of saline matter upon walls and similar surfaces.

EFFLUENT. As used in chemistry, effluent means either emergent, as of particles or radiations, or the waste product discharged from a system or an industrial plant.

EFFUSIOMETER. Any instrument measuring rates of effusion of material from an orifice.

EFFUSION. A general term denoting a process of discharge, that is also used specifically to denote the passage of gas under pressure through a small orifice.

EHRLICH ACID HEMATOXYLIN. A solution of 2 g. hematoxylin in 100 ml. absolute alcohol and 10 ml. glacial acetic acid, to which is added 100 ml. glycerol, and 100 ml. water; the solution being then saturated with alum, and used as a stain.

EHRLICH BACTERIA STAIN. A solution of 3 g. methylene blue in 100 ml. water, used as a bacteriological stain.

EHRLICH-BERTEIM TEST REACTION. Arsphenamine gives an orange color or precipitate on addition of a solution of p-dimethylaminobenzaldehyde in dilute hydrochloric acid.

EHRLICH BILIRUBIN SOLUTION. Two solutions — (1) a solution of 2.5 g. sulfanilic acid and 25 ml. hydrochloric acid in 100 ml. water; and (2) a solution of 0.5 g. sodium nitrite in 100 ml. water. One ml. of solution (2) and 49 ml. of solution (1) are mixed and acidified with acetic acid for use in testing for bilirubin. A violet or blue color indicates the presence of bilirubin.

EHRLICH-BIONDI TRIACID STAIN. An aqueous solution of ruby S, orange G, and methyl green OO, used as a tissue stain.

EHRLICH DIAZO REAGENT. A reagent prepared by the mixing of 1 ml. of a 0.5% aqueous solution of sodium nitrite and 50 ml. of a solution of 5 ml. sulfanilic acid and 50 ml. hydrochloric acid in water to make 1 l. This reagent is used in testing urine, determining urea, phenols, etc.

EHRLICH INDICAN SOLUTION. A solution of 0.33 g. dimethylaminobenzaldehyde in 50 ml. water and 50 ml. hydrochloric acid, used in testing for indican in urine. A red color in ammoniacal solution indicates the presence of indican.

EHRLICH NEUTRAL RED STAIN. A solution of 1 g. neutral red in 100 ml. of a dilute aqueous solution of sodium chloride, used as a bacteriological stain.

EHRLICH REACTION FOR INDOLE. Dissolve the substance tested in 10 ml. benzene, add 2 ml. alcoholic solution of p-dimethylaminobenzaldehyde, and shake with 0.5 ml. hydrochloric acid. Indole imparts a violet-red color to the aqueous layer.

EHRLICH-SACHS REACTION. A condensation of aromatic nitroso compounds with compounds containing active methylene groups; anils usually result.

$$RCH_2X + C_6H_5NO \rightarrow RC \overset{X}{=} NC_6H_5 + H_2O.$$

Nitrones (compounds containing the group $(:C:NO-)$) may also be formed.

EHRLICH THEORY. A theory by which the mechanism of **immunity** from disease is explained in chemical terms. The process is explained in terms of two great classes of substances (each in turn composed of many subclasses), present in the organism — the **antigens** and the **antibodies**.

Antibodies are present in the body as a result of action to counteract antigens which are really extraneous to the body, such as foreign proteins produced by bacteria or injected, etc. They may or may not be toxic. Thus diphtheria or tetanus toxoid are nontoxic foreign proteins which cause the body to develop diphtheria or tetanus antitoxin (antibody).

To affect the **cells,** the antigens must enter into a chemical combination with the **protoplasm,** probably by means of side chains which couple together. The side chains may, according to Ehrlich, break away from the protoplasm, and circulate in the blood where they can combine with the antigens of the disease before the latter can reach the protoplasm. Thus, these broken-off side chains are the antibodies which render the organism immune to the disease.

EHRLICH TRIACID STAIN. A stain prepared by mixing 125 ml. of a saturated aqueous solution of orange G, 80–165 ml. of a saturated aqueous solution of acid fuchsin, 125 ml. of a saturated aqueous solution of methylene green, 300 ml. water, 200 ml. absolute alcohol, and 100 ml. glycerol.

EHRLICH TUBERCLE STAIN. An alcohol-water solution of aniline, fuchsin, methyl violet, and gentian violet, used as a tubercle stain. It must be freshly prepared from solutions of the various component substances.

EICHLER AMINE REAGENT. A solution of 2 g. resorufin and 2 g. sodium carbonate in 1 liter of water, used as a test reagent for diazonium salts. The formation of a brown dye indicates their presence. This solution is called an amine reagent because it can be used in testing for primary amines, after first diazotizing them.

EICHLER NITRATE REAGENT. A solution of 0.1 g. magadala red in 100 ml. of formic or acetic acid, used as a reagent for nitrite in the presence of nitrate. Nitrites cause the disappearance of the fluorescence of this reagent and the appearance of a blue color.

EICHLER RESORCINOL SOLUTION. A solution of 0.5 g. resorcinol in 100 g. sulfuric acid, used in testing for nitrate, nitrite, and related inorganic radicals. A violet color, resulting from alkalinizing the residue obtained by evaporating the sample with the reagent, indicates the presence of the nitrate, nitrite, or other inorganic radicals.

EICHLER TEST FOR NITROBENZENE. Heat the material with sulfuric acid and resorcinol until a violet color appears or sulfur trioxide is evolved. Cool, dilute, and neutralize with sodium carbonate. A violet color indicates nitrobenzene. The test can be used conversely to detect resorcinol (or phenol).

EIGENFUNCTION. A mathematical function, or one of a group of functions, which are satisfactory solutions of a generalized differential equation. An important class of eigenfunctions are the satisfactory solutions of the Schrödinger wave equation (which are, therefore, also called wave functions) for definite values — eigenvalues or characteristic values — of the total energy.

EIJKMAN TEST REACTION FOR PHENOL. A dilute phenol solution, to which a few drops of an alcoholic solution of ethyl nitrite has been added, gives a red ring test with concentrated sulfuric acid. On mixing, the entire solution becomes red.

EIKONOMETER. A scale, attached to the eyepiece of a microscope, which is seen superimposed on the image, and is used to measure the dimensions of the objects viewed.

EILOART TEST REACTION FOR QUININE. An aqueous solution of quinine gives a red color on addition of bromine water, mercuric cyanide solution, and calcium carbonate.

EIMBRODT REAGENT FOR AMMONIUM ION. A solution of mercuric chloride slightly alkalinized with sodium carbonate. It gives a white turbidity or precipitate with ammonium ion.

EINSTEIN. A photochemical unit quantity defined under the heading **Stark-Einstein equation.**

EINSTEIN DIFFUSION EQUATION. An equation for the displacement, due to Brownian movement, of spherical colloidal particles, which may be expressed in the form:

$$\frac{x^2}{2\tau} = \frac{RT}{6\pi r\eta N}$$

in which x is the mean displacement, along a given axis, of a particle in time τ, R is the **gas constant,** T is the absolute temperature, r is the radius of the particle, η is the viscosity of the gas, and N is **Avogadro's constant.**

EINSTEIN EQUATION FOR HEAT CAPACITY. A **quantum** relationship for the heat capacity at constant volume of an element of the form:

$$Cv = 3R\left(\frac{h\nu}{kT}\right)^2\left(\frac{e^{h\nu/kT}}{(e^{h\nu/kT} - 1)^2}\right)$$

in which Cv is the **heat capacity** at constant volume for one gram-atom of an element, R is the **gas constant,** h is **Planck's constant,** k is the **Boltzmann constant,** ν is the **characteristic frequency** of oscillation of the atoms of the element, T is the absolute temperature, and e is the natural logarithmic base.

EINSTEIN LAW. See **law of the photochemical equivalent.**

EINTHOVEN GALVANOMETER. See galvanometer, Einthoven.

EISENLOHR TEST REACTION. A 5% alcoholic solution of alkannin, to which 1 drop 2 N ammonium carbonate has been added, gives a blue-violet color with 1 drop neutral magnesium sulfate solution. With 1–2 drops 2 N hydrochloric acid, the color becomes light-red, and the blue-violet color is then reproduced by addition of 3–4 drops of 2 N ammonium carbonate.

EKA-. A prefix used in tables of elements and elsewhere to designate an element of the same family, in the first place beyond the one to whose name it is prefixed, as eka-manganese, element #43, now called technetium.

EKKERT TEST REACTIONS FOR ADRENALINE AND EPHEDRINE. With salicyl aldehyde and sulfuric acid, adrenaline gives a yellow to flesh color, and ephedrine a deep red; and other color reactions are given by potassium hydroxide solution, by a mixture of sulfanilic acid, hydrochloric acid and sodium nitrite solution, and by other reagents.

EKKERT TEST REACTION FOR ALCOHOL. Two ml. of alcohol containing 0.01 g. resorcinol gives a pale pink red ring-test with 1 ml. sulfuric acid. With more acid and less alcohol, a deepening red color is obtained on heating.

EKKERT TEST REACTION FOR ALKALOIDS. Three or four drops of a reagent, consisting of 1 g. of a 1% aqueous solution of furfural and 10 g. concentrated sulfuric acid, added to 0.02 g. of various alkaloids produce characteristic colors.

EKKERT TEST REACTION FOR BARBITAL, PHENOBARBITAL, CINCHOPHEN, AND NEOCINCHOPHEN. On heating with a solution of 0.2 g. selenious acid in 1 ml. sulfuric acid, 0.2 g. of barbital gives an emerald-green color and a red precipitate on dilution; phenobarbital a wine-red color and yellow flocks on dilution; cinchophen a yellow color and neocinchophen a red color.

EKKERT TEST REACTIONS FOR BARBITURATES. (1) On addition to ten times its weight of fused potassium hydroxide, barbital gives a rancid odor; phenobarbital a honey-like odor becoming pungent; and propanal an aromatic odor becoming pungent.

(2) On solution of 0.01–0.02 g. of the substance in 1–2 ml. alcohol containing 1 drop salicylaldehyde, all three of the above barbiturates give a deep red ring-test with concentrated sulfuric acid.

(3) With 0.5–1 ml. 3–12% formaldehyde and 4 ml. concentrated sulfuric acid, and heating, 0.01–0.02 g. barbital or propanal give a yellowish color; phenobarbital a rose color, changing to wine-red.

EKKERT TEST REACTION FOR BENZOCAINE. On addition to 0.01 g. benzocaine dissolved in 2 ml. water of a few drops of a solution of chlorinated lime, a brick-red precipitate appears, changing to green with phenol, and then to blue with ammonia.

EKKERT TEST REACTION FOR BETAINE. The reagent consists of a few milligrams of potassium guaiacolsulfonate or 10 mg. resorcinol dissolved in 3 ml. concentrated sulfuric acid. About 0.1 g. of the substance to be tested are evaporated with 2 ml. 1 N potassium hydroxide to a volume of 0.2–0.3 ml.; on cooling 5 drops 5 N sulfuric acid are added, then, after cooling, the reagent is added. A characteristic color, depending on which of the two test substances were used, is obtained on warming, if betaine is present.

EKKERT TEST REACTIONS FOR COCAINE, EUCAINE, AND SIMILAR SUBSTANCES. (1) Ten mg. of the test substance are dissolved in 1 ml. water and 1 ml. 1% aqueous solution of chloramine T added. Characteristic colors are obtained.

(2) To one-tenth gram of the test substance is added 1 drop 10% formaldehyde and 1 ml. sulfuric acid. On heating on the water bath, characteristic colors are obtained.

EKKERT TEST REACTION FOR ETHYL URETHANE. On addition of 0.1 g. of ethyl urethane to a mixture of

0.02 g. resorcinol and 1.5 ml. sulfuric acid, carbon dioxide is evolved on warming, and a rose-red color appears.

EKKERT TEST REACTION FOR GLYCERIN. A mixture of glycerin, sulfuric acid, and codeine becomes deep blue on heating. If codeine is replaced by resorcinol, the color is deep-red.

EKKERT TEST REACTION FOR LACTIC ACID. When a lactic acid solution is floated on a 1% solution of pyrocatechol in sulfuric acid, a blood-red ring test is obtained.

EKKERT TEST REACTION FOR LEVULOSE (FRUCTOSE). Add to 10–30 mg. levulose, 3–5 drops 3 N sodium hydroxide and 0.5–1.0 g. solid sodium hydroxide. A red zone appears around the sodium hydroxide, and the mixture becomes blood-red in color.

EKKERT TEST REACTIONS FOR NITRATE AND NITRITE. Add 0.1 g. sodium nitrite to 5 ml. 33% hydrochloric acid containing 0.02–0.03 g. resorcinol. A saffron-yellow color appears, changing to brown-red and then to dark mulberry-red. After 20–25 minutes, add enough 0.2 N sodium hydroxide to produce a dark green liquid. This liquid colors methyl acetate violet-red, ethyl acetate rose to eosin-red; and it turns violet red and then green with red fluorescence on dilution.

To 0.01 g. potassium nitrate add 5 ml. 33% hydrochloric acid containing 0.02–0.03 g. resorcinol. A pale yellow color forms after 5 minutes, turning yellow, peach-red, and mulberry-red on heating in a boiling water bath. The addition of 0.2 N sodium hydroxide produces a green liquid, which colors methyl acetate violet-red or lilac with a red fluorescence on dilution.

EKKERT TEST REACTION FOR PAPAVERINE. On heating a mixture of 0.01 g. papaverine, 0.02 g. zinc chloride, and 5 drops benzoyl chloride, a rose to blood-red color is obtained, changing to yellow with green fluorescence, and becoming greenish-yellow on cooling and addition of 1–2 drops alcohol.

EKKERT TEST REACTION FOR PHENACAINE (HOLOCAINE). On heating a mixture of 0.01 g. phenacaine, 0.01 g. resorcinol, and 0.5–1 ml. concentrated sulfuric acid, a wine-red to raspberry red color is obtained.

EKKERT REACTION FOR PHENOLIC COMPOUNDS. Phenol, hydroquinone, thymol, and α- and β-naphthol give characteristic colors when 0.03–0.05 g. of any of these substances is dissolved in 0.05 ml. water, and treated with 0.02 g. sodium nitroprusside dissolved in 4 ml. concentrated sulfuric acid. Two layers form, with various colors in the interfacial region, in the upper layer and on mixing.

EKKERT TEST REACTION FOR PILOCARPINE. Add 1 ml. 2% sodium nitroprusside solution and 1 ml. 1 N sodium hydroxide to 1 ml. of a 1% solution of pilocarpine hydrochloride, and then in a few minutes add some dilute hydrochloric acid. A red solution is formed, which turns green with 10% sodium thiosulfate solution and carmine-red with hydrogen peroxide.

EKKERT TEST REACTION FOR SACCHARIN. On shaking 1–2 ml. water with 0.2 g. saccharin and adding 3–6 drops 30% hydrogen peroxide and 0.02–0.04 g. sodium nitrite, a yellow color is produced, changing to brown-red with ammonia.

EKKERT TEST REACTION FOR SALICYLATE. A solution of 0.01–0.02 g. salicylate and 0.002 g. sodium nitrite in 0.5 ml. water gives with 1 ml. sulfuric acid a red ring, a red mixture on shaking, changing to green with excess sodium hydroxide solution. With salol a green color is obtained on mixing, becoming red on dilution, and blue-green with excess sodium hydroxide solution.

EKKERT TEST REACTION FOR TARTARIC ACID. On mixing 0.01 g. tartaric acid with 0.02 g. pyrogallol, adding 5 ml. sulfuric acid, and heating on the water bath, a violet color is obtained. With β-naphthol instead of pyrogallol, a blue-green color is produced. Citric acid produces no color or a light yellow color; lactic acid, a red or brown color.

EKKERT TEST REACTIONS FOR VARIOUS AROMATIC COMPOUNDS. Dissolve 0.01 g. of the substance in 1 ml. ethyl alcohol, and add 5 drops 10% *p*-dimethylaminobenzaldehyde solution in sulfuric acid, or 1 mg. nitroso-β-naphthol. Shake this solution with 1 ml. sulfuric acid. Characteristic colors are given by benzene, quinone, quinoline, and other aromatic compounds.

ELAEOPTENE. (Elaoptene. Eleoptene. Oleoptene.) The liquid portion of an essential oil as distinguished from the stearoptene or solid which is often dissolved in it.

ELAIDIC. Related to elaidic acid,

For gases the formula $E = pV/v$ is used, in which E = elasticity; p, the increase in pressure; V, the original volume; and v, the diminution in volume. Cf. **modulus, Young.**

ELASTOMER. Any substance, especially a synthetic polymer, having properties of natural, reclaimed, vulcanized, or synthetic rubber.

ELBS OXIDATION REACTION. The oxidation of phenols to dihydric phenols by the action of alkaline potassium persulfate solution, followed by hydrolysis of the persulfate compound formed.

$CH_3(CH_2)_7CH{=}CH(CH_2)_7COOH$, which is trans-oleic acid.

ELAIDIN TEST. A test for acids of the **oleic** series and their compounds in oils which depends upon the fact that nitrous anhydride or nitrous acid converts them into solid substances known as elaidins.

ELBS REACTION. The formation of anthracene derivatives by cyclodehydration of diaryl ketonic compounds, which have a methyl group, or a methylene group, adjacent to the carbonyl group. The reaction is commonly accomplished by heating, usually to fairly elevated temperatures.

ELAIOMETER. An apparatus for determining the percentage of oil in a mixture and also the purity of an oil.

ELASTIC FLUID. See **fluid, elastic.**

ELASTICITY. (1) A property of bodies by virtue of which they resist deformation and resume their original form or volume when the stress ceases to act. (2) The ratio of the stress to the strain which it produces.

ELBS TEST FOR NAPHTHANTHRAQUINONE. Naphthanthraquinone in alcoholic solution develops a violet-colored zone about sodium amalgam, the solution becoming red on heating.

ELECTRICAL AXIS. The axis of a crystal which offers minimum resistance to the passage of current.

ELECTRICAL BATTERY. See **cell.**

ELECTRICAL CELL. See **cell.**

ELECTRICAL CURRENT. The quantity of electricity passing a given point per unit time.

ELECTRICAL DOUBLE LAYER. A region of characteristic properties which exists at the surface of separation between two **phases.** Present-day opinion tends to the view that at a solid-liquid boundary, for example, the double-layer consists of a monomolecular or monoionic layer of liquid that is closely held to the solid surface, and then a diffuse layer which extends into the liquid for some distance.

ELECTRICAL POTENTIAL. See **potential.**

ELECTRICAL RESISTANCE. See **resistance.**

ELECTRICITY. A form of energy which produces a great variety of effects, and whose ultimate nature may be interpreted in light of these phenomena, as a variation in distribution of uniform, small negative charges called electrons with or without other ultimate particles, such as protons; as a field of force associated with magnetic properties; as a continuous train of waves traveling at the speed of light, which is itself, from this point of view, a train of electromagnetic waves; or as other possible physical entities.

ELECTROANALYSIS. Analytical operations involving the use of the electric current. Many metals may be rapidly and accurately determined by depositing them on a weighed **cathode** and subsequently determining the difference in weight. Concentrations may be determined by measuring **potentials** and **conductivities,** the end point of a **titration** may be determined by the use of a **galvanometer** in place of an indicator, and the concentration of hydrogen ions in acids and bases may be determined electrolytically.

ELECTROCAPILLARY CURVE. The curve expressing the variation of the **surface tension** of a solution of an electrolyte with a variable applied potential. It is usually measured experimentally as the interfacial tension at a mercury-solution interface.

ELECTROCHEMICAL CONSTANT. The **faraday** (q.v.).

ELECTROCHEMICAL EQUIVALENT. (1) Of elements. The mass of any chemical substance liberated by one **coulomb** of electricity in electrolysis. For hydrogen it is 0.00001036 g., and this figure multiplied by the gram-equivalent weight of any substance will furnish its electrochemical equivalent. (2) Of electricity, the **faraday** (q.v.).

ELECTROCHEMICAL PASSIVITY. See **passivity, electrochemical.**

ELECTROCHEMISTRY. A branch of chemistry which studies the chemical changes associated with electrical phenomena.

ELECTRODE. (1) The means whereby the electric current gains entrance to or leaves a cell. (2) The ends of a metallic circuit between which the current travels in a medium different from the rest of the circuit are termed electrodes. The negative electrode, or cathode, is that through which the current leaves the cell; the positive electrode, or anode, is that through which the current enters the cell. This discussion follows the convention of positive current; actually, electrons leave the cell at the anode and enter at the cathode. (3) In emission spectroscopy, either of two terminals between which an electrical discharge occurs.

ELECTRODE, AUXILIARY. A standard electrode used to measure the potential at which electrodeposition takes place.

ELECTRODE, CALOMEL. A standard electrode of mercury, mercurous chloride (calomel), and potassium chloride. Its potential, if a molar potassium chloride solution is used, is 0.2800 volt at 25° C. See also **Hildebrand electrode.**

ELECTRODE, COUNTER. In emission spectroscopy, the electrode, in an analytical pair, which is not composed of the sample to be analyzed.

ELECTRODE, DROPPING. An electrode consisting of a steady flow of droplets of mercury into the **electrolyte** of a **cell.**

ELECTRODE, GAS. An electrode that contains a gas by **adsorption, absorption, or** other means which presents a gaseous surface to a solution in contact with the **electrode.**

ELECTRODE, GLASS. A thin-walled glass membrane, separating a solution of known **pH** from another solution whose pH is to be determined. A standard electrode dips into each of these two solutions. From the total **electromotive force** of the cell and the pH of the standard solution, the pH of the unknown may be calculated.

ELECTRODE, HILDEBRAND. See **Hildebrand electrode.**

ELECTRODE, HYDROGEN. A gas electrode (see **electrode, gas**) in which hydrogen is the gas contained.

ELECTRODE, NORMAL CALOMEL. An **electrode** of mercury in contact with a **normal** solution of potassium chloride saturated with calomel.

ELECTRODE OF THE SECOND ORDER. An **electrode** of metal in contact with one of its difficultly soluble salts in the presence of a solution of a salt which has the same anion as the less soluble salt. E.g.,

$$Hg/Hg_2Cl_2/KCl.$$

Electrodes of this type are not essentially different from an ordinary electrode in contact with a solution of one of its salts.

ELECTRODE POTENTIAL. The **potential** of a metal in **equilibrium** with a solution of its ions. The establishment of electrode potential is regarded as the resultant of the rates of two processes, passage of ions from the electrode into solution, and discharge of ions from solution upon the electrode.

ELECTRODE, QUINHYDRONE. A standard **electrode** used in **pH** determinations. Its potential is derived from the reversible oxidation-reduction reaction of quinone-quinhydrone, in a saturated aqueous solution of quinhydrone. Its electromotive force is read against a calomel electrode.

ELECTRODE, REVERSIBLE. An electrode used in a reversible electrochemical reaction. There are three types of reversible electrodes used in reversible cells. The first type consists of a metal which is in contact with a solution containing its ions. The second type consists of a metal and one of its insoluble salts in contact with a solution containing a soluble salt with the same anion. This type of electrode is reversible with respect to the anions. The third type of electrode is a metal which is resistant to acids and bases, in contact with a solution which contains ions in two valence states. Oxidation or reduction is the reversible reaction which occurs at this type of electrode.

ELECTRODE, SELF. In emission spectroscopy, an **electrode** composed of the material being analyzed.

ELECTRODE, SUPPORTING. In emission spectroscopy, an **electrode,** other than a self-electrode, on or in which the sample is supported.

ELECTRODEPOSITION. Any electrochemical process in which an element or mixture of elements, usually a metal or alloy, is deposited upon an **electrode.**

ELECTRODIALYSIS. See **dialysis, electro.**

ELECTROENDOSMOSIS. **Cataphoresis** in which the solid is stationary and the water phase is displaced and migrates toward the electrode.

ELECTROFORMING. The production by electrodeposition of metal in finished or semifinished form, as the production of sheets or tubes, or of electrotypes for use in printing.

ELECTROKINETIC EFFECTS. Movements of particles under the influence of an applied **electromotive force.**

ELECTROLYSIS. The process of decomposing a chemical compound by passing a current of electricity through it either in its natural form, or in solution, or in molten form.

ELECTROLYTE. (1) Any substance whose solutions have the property of conducting the electric current. All soluble acids, bases, and salts are electrolytes. (2) A solution which conducts the electric current.

ELECTROLYTIC. Pertaining to electrolysis and electrolytes.

ELECTROLYTIC DISSOCIATION, ARRHENIUS THEORY OF. To explain the properties of solutions of various acids, bases, and salts, Arrhenius suggested that in solution in water, a considerable proportion of the molecules dissociate spontaneously into positive and negative ions. He also suggested that the extent of this dissociation increases with dilution, becoming practically complete at "infinite dilution." (See **Arrhenius Theory.**)

ELECTROLYTIC RECTIFIER. An electrolytic system which converts alternating current to direct current. It consists essentially of a combination of two **electrodes** and an **electrolyte** which produces a polarizing film on one of the electrodes that practically bars the flow of current into it from the solution, while freely permitting flow in the opposite direction. Groups of these cells may be arranged to utilize both halves of the alternating-current cycle.

ELECTROLYTIC SOLUTION PRESSURE. The tendency of a metal or other substance to **dissolve** in solution with the formation of **ions.** It has been found impossible to devise a satisfactory method for measuring the absolute value of this solution pressure. The establishment of **electrode potential** is now regarded as the resultant of the rates of the two processes, passage of ions from the electrode into solution, and discharge of ions from solution upon the electrode.

ELECTROLYTIC TAUTOMERISM. See tautomerism, electrolytic.

ELECTROLYZE. To submit to the process of electrolysis; to decompose by means of an electric current.

ELECTROMAGNETIC LAW. See **law of Coulomb, electromagnetic.**

ELECTROMAGNETIC UNITS. A system of electrical units derived from dynamic data usually written e.m.u. or emu. The starting point in this system is the unit magnetic pole, which is defined by the expression $m = r\sqrt{F\mu}$, where m is the magnitude of the pole, r is its distance from a like pole, F is the force of repulsion between them, and μ is the magnetic permeability (unity for air). Then the unit of magnetic field intensity H is defined by the expression

$$H = \frac{F}{m}, \text{ etc.}$$

ELECTROMETER. An instrument for measuring electric current or potential.

ELECTROMOTIVE FORCE. A difference of potential, or electrical intensity, which may cause an electrical flow through a circuit against a resistance.

ELECTROMOTIVE FORCE SERIES. An arrangement of **elements** in order of decreasing potentials of their **electrodes** in equilibrium with solutions of their ions. Since the electrode potential of a metal in equilibrium with a solution of its ions cannot be measured directly, the values in the electromotive force series are, in each case, the difference between the electrode potential of the given metal in equilibrium with a solution of its ions, and that of hydrogen in equilibrium with a solution of its ions. In experimental procedure, the hydrogen electrode is used as the standard with which the electrode potentials of other substances are compared.

ELECTRON. A fundamental particle, carrying a discrete negative electric charge of 4.8022×10^{-10} e.s.u., which seems to be the fundamental carrier of electric current. It has a rest mass of 9.1072×10^{-28} g.

ELECTRON ACCEPTOR. See electron donor.

ELECTRON AFFINITY. The degree of **electronegativity,** or the extent to which an atom holds valence electrons in its immediate neighborhood, compared to other atoms of the molecule.

ELECTRON BEAM. A stream of electrons moving with about the same velocity and in the same direction, so as to form a beam.

ELECTRON, BINDING. One of the electrons which *were once believed* to be in atomic nuclei, and to assist in holding the protons together. It is no longer believed that electrons exist as such in the nucleus, although they are emitted by it in many natural and artificial radioactive disintegrations.

ELECTRON, BONDING. An electron in a molecule which serves to hold two adjacent **nuclei** together.

ELECTRON CONCENTRATION. The ratio of the number of **valence electrons** to the number of atoms in a molecule. This quantity is useful in studying the intermetallic **compounds,** where it is correlated with the crystal structure.

ELECTRON, CONDUCTION. An electron which plays an important part in electrical or thermal conduction by metals. These electrons were once called "free" electrons, although present views of the structure of metals have somewhat modified this view. (See **bond, metallic.**)

ELECTRON COUNTER. See **counter.**

ELECTRON COUPLING. The combination of the **orbital** and **spin angular momentum** vectors for a group of electrons. Various types of electron coupling have been postulated for different groups of electrons, especially those of the elements; and have been applied in calculating resultant **quantum** numbers, which are useful in interpreting the **multiplet terms** in spectra.

ELECTRON DIFFRACTION. Beams of high-speed electrons exhibit **diffraction** phenomena analogous to those obtained with light, thus showing the wave-like character of electron beams. Such patterns are useful in the interpretation of the structure of gases or solids.

ELECTRON DISTRIBUTION. An arrangement of electrons, especially the arrangement of electrons in **orbits** or **shells** around the **nucleus** of an atom or an ion.

ELECTRON DONOR. When the valence **bond** between two atoms is that type of covalent linkage in which both the electrons of the duplet are supplied by one atom, then that atom, or portion of the molecule of which it forms a part, is called the electron donor, and the other atom in the linkage is called the electron acceptor.

ELECTRON DUPLET. A pair of electrons which is shared by two atoms, and is equivalent to a single, nonpolar chemical **bond.**

ELECTRON, EXTRANUCLEAR. In an atom, any one of the electrons that surround the positive **nucleus.**

ELECTRON, FREE. (1) An electron which is not restrained to remain in the immediate neighborhood of a **nucleus** or an **atom.** (2) The term free electron is also applied to any electron in the outer electronic shell of an atom, when that electron is not shared by another atom, and especially when that electron is free to be so shared (to form a covalent bond).

ELECTRON GAS. A system of mobile electrons, generally as it exists within a metal.

ELECTRON GROUP or SHELL. A number of electrons occupying similar relative positions, as those extranuclear electrons which possess the same **principal quantum number.**

ELECTRON LENS. An electric field used to focus a stream of electrons on a target. This may be achieved, for example, by use of a circular hole in a charged conductor.

ELECTRON MICROSCOPE. An apparatus which utilizes **electron diffraction** (q.v.) patterns to investigate the submicroscopic structure, especially the atomic arrangement, of substances.

ELECTRON MULTIPLIER. An arrangement of **electron emission** surfaces such that, for each impinging electron, a large number of additional electrons are expelled toward the next surface. In such a manner a cascading electron stream may be obtained.

ELECTRON, NUCLEAR. An electron which is emitted from the **nucleus** of an atom. Its formation within the nucleus is believed to be due to the transformation of a **proton** into a **neutron.** It is not now believed that electrons exist as such inside the nucleus.

ELECTRON OCTET. An **electron group** or **electron shell** (q.v.) containing eight electrons.

ELECTRON, OPTICAL. See **electron, valence.**

ELECTRON OPTICS. The control of the movement of free electrons by means of electric fields, and their utilization in research investigation of electronic diffraction phenomena, in direct analogy to the effect of lenses on light. Electron beams are used to determine the microstructure of crystals and many other materials. (See **electron microscope** and **electron diffraction.**)

ELECTRON, ORBITAL. An electron remaining with a high degree of probability in the immediate neighborhood of a **nucleus,** where it occupies a quantized **orbital.**

ELECTRON PAIR. A general feature of the architecture of many molecular structures, in which neighboring atoms or nuclei are bonded by sharing a pair of valence electrons, forming a nonpolar bond. (See **bond, nonpolar.**)

ELECTRON, PAIRED. One of two electrons which are shared by two atoms to form a valence **bond.**

ELECTRON, PHOTO. An electron ejected from a substance by the action of light or other **radiation.**

ELECTRON POLARIZATION. The part of the total induced **polarization** of a molecule that is due to the distortion or deformation of the electron shells or orbits under the influence of external electric fields.

ELECTRON, POSITIVE. See **positron** and also **electron.**

ELECTRON SHELL. The arrangement of extranuclear electrons in different groups of **orbitals** which are characterized by different **principal quantum numbers.** In the old Bohr model of the atom, all electrons in a given shell moved in orbits of approximately the same distance from the nucleus. Different shells are then characterized by different dimensions of the electronic orbits.

ELECTRON SPIN. Rotation of the electron about its own axis. This rotation contributes to the total angular momentum of the electron and is quantized. It gives rise to **multiplicity** in line spectra, which may be characterized by introduction of the **spin quantum number.**

ELECTRON THEORY OF MATTER. Any one of several hypotheses which postulate that the atoms are constituted of nuclei, surrounded in varying numbers and arrangements by electrons.

ELECTRON TRANSFER. The process of the shifting of an electron from one electrical field to another, as in the formation of an electrovalent bond, in which an electron moving in an orbit about one atom shifts to move in an orbit about the two bonded atoms.

ELECTRON-TRANSFER REACTION. See **reaction, electron-transfer.**

ELECTRON, VALENCE. The electrons in the outermost shell of the structure of an atom. Since these electrons constitute the means by which the atom enters into chemical combinations — either by giving them up, or by adding others to their shell, or by sharing electrons in this shell — these outermost electrons are called valence electrons.

ELECTRON VOLT. A unit of energy defined as the energy gained by an electron in moving through a fall of potential of one volt.

ELECTRON WAVE LENGTH. The wave length, λ, of the **wave train** which characterizes electrons moving with momentum p. These two quantities are related by the equation $\lambda = h/p$, where h is **Planck's constant.**

ELECTRONEGATIVE. Elements and radicals which bear a negative electric charge. In **electrolysis** they are deposited on the **anode.**

ELECTRONEGATIVE ELEMENT. An element which has a relatively great tendency to attract electrons, whereby the **bond energy** of its **linkage** with another and different atom is found to exceed the mean of that found in linkages between the two pairs of identical atoms (i.e., the $X-Y$ bond energy exceeds the mean of the values for $X-X$ and $Y-Y$). Electronegative elements are, generally, acid forming; their outer shell contains four or more electrons, and they tend to add electrons to complete it. They are commonly nonmetals.

ELECTRONEGATIVITY. The extent, relative to other atoms, to which a given atom or group of atoms tends to attract and hold valence electrons in its immediate neighborhood.

ELECTRONIC. Pertaining to or carrying electrons.

ELECTRONIC EQUATION. See **equation, electronic.**

ELECTRONIC THEORY OF VALENCE. The explanation of the nature of chemical **bonds,** i.e., the forces linking atoms to form molecules, as well as certain higher aggregates, in terms of the electrostatic forces between negatively-charged electrons and positively-charged atomic nuclei. Certain differences in characteristics of substances are explained by differences in the method by which these forces are established. Thus the electrovalent bond arises in compound formation where there is transfer of an electron from one atom to another, resulting in the formation of oppositely

charged ions which attract each other. Covalent bonds arise by the sharing of electrons between atoms. Compounds having electrovalent bonds usually ionize and exhibit electrolytic properties; while the covalent bonds are characteristic of organic substances. There are, of course, other types of linkages within these two groups, as well as special or intermediate cases. These statements are general and the ultimate statements of structure must be made in terms of quantitative measurements of bond distances and energies.

ELECTROOSMOSIS. A process of **osmosis** taking place within an electric field.

ELECTROPHORESIS. The movement of particles, usually suspended particles, through a fluid under the action of an **electric field.**

ELECTROPLATING. (Electrodeposition) The process of depositing a smooth, homogeneous coating of a metal or mixture of metals upon a metallic or a conducting surface by means of **electrolysis.** Nickel, copper, zinc, silver, and gold are the metals commonly deposited.

ELECTROPOSITIVE. Elements and radicals which readily give up valence electrons and accumulate a positive charge. In **electrolysis** they are deposited on the cathode. Electropositive elements are generally metallic and base-forming; they tend to lose electrons, and thus to acquire a positive character, and enter into combination with nonmetals.

ELECTROREFINING. Any method for the purification of elements, chiefly metals, by electrodeposition.

ELECTROSCOPE. An apparatus for detecting electrical charges; in its best-known form, it consists of two strips of gold-leaf suspended from the top of a glass container. Charged bodies or particles striking the top of the apparatus cause the leaves to become charged and thus to separate, due to the repulsion of charges of like sign.

ELECTROSOL. A **colloidal solution** produced by electrical means, as by passing a spark between metal electrodes in a liquid.

ELECTROSTATIC BOND. See **bond, electrostatic.**

ELECTROSTATIC UNITS. A system of electrical units derived from static data, usually written e.s.u. or esu. The electrostatic unit of quantity is the quantity of electricity which at one centimeter distance in air exerts a force of one **dyne** on a similar quantity. It is equal to $\dfrac{1}{3 \times 10^9}$ coulomb. The electrostatic unit of potential is the potential difference existing between two points when one erg of work is done in the movement of one electrostatic unit of quantity of electricity from the one point to the other point.

ELECTROSTATIC VALENCE. The type of **valence** which involves electron transfer. It is also known as ionic valence.

ELECTROSTRICTION. The phenomenon of the contraction of a solvent attributable to the **electrostatic field** in a dissolved **electrolyte.**

ELECTROSYNTHESIS. The production of synthetic reactions by means of the electric current. The **electrolysis** of a mixture of potassium acetate and potassium ethyl succinate yields ethyl butyrate, viz.,

$$C_2H_5OOC—CH_2—CH_2—COOK + CH_3COOK + 2H_2O \rightarrow$$
$$C_2H_5OOC—CH_2—C_2H_5 + 2CO_2 + 2KOH + H_2.$$

This type of reaction might well be termed electrocondensation.

ELECTROVALENCE. See **bond, electrovalent.**

ELECTROWINNING. The recovery of metals from their ores by electrodeposition.

ELEMENT. A collection of atoms of one type which cannot be decomposed into any simpler units by any chemical transformation. To date 98 different elements are known; these may be grouped into an ascending series according to the nuclear charge; some elements (those in the so-called radioactive series) spontaneously decompose into simpler elements; radio-active decomposition can be induced artificially where it does not occur in nature; and for each element there is known a number of isotopes, i.e., atoms with the same nuclear charge but different nuclear masses which may vary within certain limits. There are also instances in which atoms have the same nuclear charge and nuclear mass, but differ only in nuclear energetics, and hence stability and behavior.

ELEMENT, ACID-FORMING. An element which has an oxide or oxides that form acids by reaction with water.

ELEMENT, ALKALINE. Any one of the metals of the alkalies, **potassium, sodium, lithium, cesium,** or **rubidium.**

ELEMENT, ARTIFICIAL RADIOACTIVE. A **radioactive** element produced from another element, or from a nonradioactive **isotope** of the same element, by the bombardment of **protons, neutrons, deuterons, gamma rays,** or other particles or radiations.

ELEMENT, BRIDGE. The elements in the first short series in the periodic table, **helium to fluorine,** so called because they show a "notable graduation of properties from one to another."

ELEMENT, ELECTRONEGATIVE. See **electronegative element.**

ELEMENT, ELECTROPOSITIVE. See **electropositive.**

ELEMENT, GASEOUS. An element which is in the gaseous state under normal conditions. The gaseous elements are **argon, chlorine, fluorine, helium, hydrogen, krypton, neon, nitrogen, oxygen, radon** (emanation), and **xenon.**

ELEMENT, INERT. The noble or inactive gaseous elements, which form no chemical compounds — **helium, argon, neon, krypton, xenon,** and **radon.**

ELEMENT, METALLIC. An element which exhibits the properties of a metal, which usually yields base-forming oxides, and which usually yields electrons when it enters into chemical combinations.

ELEMENT, NEGATIVE. This term was originally applied to certain elements which readily form acids, such as nitrogen, phosphorus, chlorine, fluorine, bromine, oxygen, etc., and which, therefore, yield negative radicals. Such an element frequently enters into reactions by which it gains electrons, and thus forms negative ions.

ELEMENT, NONMETALLIC. An element which does not exhibit the properties of a metal, which usually yields acid-forming oxides, and which usually adds electrons (or shares them) when it enters into chemical combinations.

ELEMENT, RADIO-. An artificially radioactive element, obtained by bombardment of another element with certain particles or radiations.

ELEMENT, RADIOACTIVE. A term applied to certain elements that disintegrate spontaneously with the emission of various rays and particles. Most commonly it denotes elements such as radium, radon (emanation), thorium, uranium, which occupy a definite place in the periodic table because of their atomic number and relative stability (long life-period). The term radioactive element is also applied to the various other nuclear species (which are produced by the disintegration of radium, uranium, etc.), including the uranium, actinium, thorium, and neptunium families of radioactive elements, which differ markedly in their stability, and are isotopes of elements from thallium (atomic number 81) to uranium (atomic number 92), as well as the partly artificial actinide group, which extends from actinium (atomic number 89) to californium (atomic number 98), and includes the transuranic elements neptunium (atomic number 93), plutonium (atomic number 94), americium (atomic number 95), curium (atomic number 96), berkelium (atomic number 97), as well as

californium. The radioactive elements produced from nonradioactive ones are discussed under **element, artificial radioactive** (q.v.).

ELEMENT, RADIOACTIVE SERIES. By making physical or chemical separations when possible, by studying radioactive decay and growth curves, by determining the specific properties of the emitted radiations, and in other ways, the naturally occurring radioelements of high atomic weight, at the end of the periodic system, have been grouped into three distinct series. These are known as the thorium series, the uranium series, and the actinium series, respectively. In the first two cases, the series are named after the longest-lived precursors, thorium and uranium, with half-lives of 1.39×10^{10} and 4.5×10^9 years, respectively. The parents of these elements undoubtedly had shorter lives, and consequently no longer exist in any detectable amounts. The parent of the actinium series is not, as was originally supposed, the element actinium, the first member of the series to be discovered, but rather a much longer lived element, sometimes referred to as actinouranium (uranium-235), with a half-life of 7.07×10^8 years.

In the accompanying tables there are recorded details of the thorium, uranium, and actinium series, as well as the new, artificially produced, neptunium series, including the nature of the radiations, and the half-lives of the respective members. In addition to the somewhat unsystematic names given to the various elements as they were discovered, but now becoming obsolete, each is associated in the table with the name of a familiar element; e.g., thorium B, uranium B, and actinium B with lead; thorium C, radium C, and actinium C with bismuth; and so on.

The atomic weight of thorium is 232, to the nearest whole number, which is equivalent to the quantity 4×58. Since an α-particle disintegration results in a decrease of 4 in the atomic weight, whereas there is no appreciable change accompanying β-particle emission, it is evident that the atomic weights of all members of the thorium series may be represented by $4n$, where n is an integer varying from 58 (thorium) to 52 (thorium D). In exactly the same way, it can readily be seen that all atomic weights in the neptunium series are given by the expression $4n + 1$, those in the uranium series by $4n + 2$, and those in the actinium series by $4n + 3$. As stated above, most of the elements in the neptunium series are produced artificially. They are named after neptunium because Np^{237} is the longest-lived member of the series. The four series are given in the following tables:

THE ACTINIUM SERIES

Radioelement	Corresponding Element	Symbol	Radiation	Half Life
Actinouranium	Uranium	U^{235}	α	7.07×10^8 yr.
Uranium Y	Thorium	Th^{231}	β	25.6 hr.
Protactinium	Protactinium	Pa^{231}	α	3.4×10^4 yr.
Actinium 98.8% | 1.2%	Actinium	Ac^{227}	β and α	21.7 yr.
Radioactinium	Thorium	Th^{227}	α	18.6 days
Actinium K	Francium	Fr^{223}	β	21 min.
Actinium X	Radium	Ra^{223}	α	11.2 days
Ac Emanation	Radon	Rn^{219}	α	3.92 sec.
Actinium A ~100% | ~5 × 10⁻⁴%	Polonium	Po^{215}	α and β	1.83×10^{-3} sec.
Actinium B	Lead	Pb^{211}	β	36.1 min.
Astatine-215	Astatine	At^{215}	α	~10^{-4} sec.
Actinium C 99.68% | 0.32%	Bismuth	Bi^{211}	β and α	2.16 min.
Actinium C′	Polonium	Po^{211}	α	5×10^{-3} sec.
Actinium C″	Thallium	Tl^{207}	β	4.76 min.
Actinium D (End Product)	Lead	Pb^{207}	Stable	—

THE THORIUM SERIES

Radioelement	Corresponding Element	Symbol	Radiation	Half Life
Thorium	Thorium	Th^{232}	α	1.39×10^{10} yr.
Mesothorium I	Radium	Ra^{228}	β	6.7 yr.
Mesothorium II	Actinium	Ac^{228}	β	6.13 hr.
Radiothorium	Thorium	Th^{228}	α	1.90 yr.
Thorium X	Radium	Ra^{224}	α	3.64 days
Th Emanation	Radon	Rn^{220}	α	54.5 sec.
Thorium A ~100% | 0.014%	Polonium	Po^{216}	β and α	0.158 sec.
Thorium B	Lead	Pb^{212}	β	10.6 hr.
Astatine–216	Astatine	At^{216}	α	3×10^{-4} sec.
Thorium C 66.3% | 33.7%	Bismuth	Bi^{212}	β and α	60.5 min.
Thorium C'	Polonium	Po^{212}	α	3×10^{-7} sec.
Thorium C''	Thallium	Tl^{208}	β	3.1 min.
Thorium D (End Product)	Lead	Pb^{208}	Stable	—

THE URANIUM SERIES

Radioelement	Corresponding Element	Symbol	Radiation	Half Life
Uranium I	Uranium	U^{238}	α	4.5×10^9 yr.
Uranium X_1	Thorium	Th^{234}	β	24.1 days
Uranium X_2	Protactinium	Pa^{234}	β	1.2 min.
Uranium II	Uranium	U^{234}	α	2.50×10^5 yr.
Ionium	Thorium	Th^{230}	α	8.0×10^4 yr.
Radium	Radium	Ra^{226}	α	1.62×10^3 yr.
Ra Emanation	Radon	Rn^{222}	α	3.82 days
Radium A 99.96% | 0.04%	Polonium	Po^{218}	α and β	3.05 min.
Radium B	Lead	Pb^{214}	β	26.8 min.
Astatine-218	Astatine	At^{218}	α	1.3 sec.
Radium C 99.96% | 0.04%	Bismuth	Bi^{214}	β and α	19.7 min.
Radium C'	Polonium	Po^{214}	α	1.64×10^{-4} sec.
Radium C''	Thallium	Tl^{210}	β	1.3 min.
Radium D	Lead	Pb^{210}	β	22 yr.
Radium E ~100% | ~10^{-5}%	Bismuth	Bi^{210}	β and α	5.0 days
Radium F	Polonium	Po^{210}	α	138.3 days
Thallium-206	Thallium	Tl^{206}	β	4.23 min.
Radium G (End Product)	Lead	Pb^{206}	Stable	—

THE NEPTUNIUM SERIES

Element	Symbol	Radiation	Half Life
Plutonium	Pu^{241}	β	~14 yr.
Americium	Am^{241}	α	470 yr.
Neptunium	Np^{237}	α	2.20×10^6 yr.
Protactinium	Pa^{233}	β	27.4 days
Uranium	U^{233}	α	1.63×10^5 yr.
Thorium	Th^{229}	α	7.4×10^3 yr.
Radium	Ra^{225}	β	14.8 days
Actinium	Ac^{225}	α	10.0 days
Francium	Fr^{221}	α	4.9 min.
Astatine	At^{217}	α	2.0×10^{-2} sec.
Bismuth 96% | 4%	Bi^{213}	β and α	47 min.
Polonium	Po^{213}	α	3.2×10^{-6} sec.
Thallium	Tl^{209}	β	2.2 min.
Lead	Pb^{209}	β	3.3 hr.
Bismuth (End Product)	Bi^{209}	Stable	—

ELEMENT RADIOACTIVE, COLLATERAL SERIES. In addition to the three main natural and one artificial disintegration series of radioelements, each has been found to have at least one parallel or collateral series. The main series and the collateral series have different parents, but become identical in the course of disintegration, when they have a member in common.

ELEMENT, TRANSITION. One of the elements which occupy the middle position in the long periods or form group VIII in the periodic classification, i.e., **iron, cobalt, nickel, ruthenium, rhodium, palladium,** etc.

ELEMENTARY ANALYSIS. The quantitative determination of the elements in a compound, the term being applied to the analysis of an organic compound by combustion, followed by determination of the products obtained.

ELEMENTARY CHARGE. See **charge, elementary.**

ELEMENTS, DEVOLUTION OF. The disintegration of the elements, i.e., such as occurs in radioactive substances.

ELEMENTS, EVOLUTION OF. The formation of complex elements, those of high atomic weight, from simpler elements of low atomic weight.

ELIXIR. A pharmaceutical preparation of drugs, in solution with sugar, alcohol, or other material to render them palatable.

ELLMS-HAUSER TEST. To detect free chlorine in water, add to 100 ml. of water, 1 ml. of a 0.1% solution of *o*-tolidine in 10% hydrochloric acid. In the presence of free chlorine a yellow to green color develops, useful in colorimetric determination.

ELLRAM REAGENT FOR ALKALOIDS, RESINS, AND VOLATILE OILS. A 1% solution (by weight) of vanillin in concentrated sulfuric acid.

ELLRAM TEST REACTION FOR VANADATES AND MOLYBDATES. Vanadates and molybdates give, respectively, a blue color and a yellow to blood-red color when added in powdered form to a thiocyanate solution, to which sulfuric acid is then added.

ELSNER TEST REACTION. Pyrocatechol in solution precipitates, with barium hydroxide solution, silvery-gray leaflets which darken on drying.

ELTESTE REAGENT. A paper impregnated with a 0.1 N aqueous barium hydroxide solution containing phenolphthalein, used as a reagent for carbon dioxide.

ELUTION. In general, a process for **extracting** a solid substance from a mixture of solids by means of a liquid; as in the recovery of a vitamin adsorbed on an adsorbent by means of a solution. Specifically, a process for the recovery of sucrose from molasses. Quicklime in the proportion of 25% of the weight of the molasses is added, the resulting mass is freed from much impurity by percolating (in "elutors") with 35% alcohol and is then decomposed by carbon dioxide which liberates the sucrose.

ELUTRIATION. The separation of solids by the action of water or other liquids: hence, also the washing of a solid by decantation or a related process.

EMANATION. In general, a gaseous substance given off from **radioactive** material. Specifically, the radium emanation, which has a half-period of 3.82 days, emits α-rays, and is transformed into radium A. It is the element radon, of atomic number 86, which has among its isotopes actinon, an actinium emanation with a half-period of 3.92 seconds, and thoron, a thorium emanation with a half-period of 54.5 seconds. Radon decomposes (99.96%) by α-ray emission to give a series of radioelements, terminated by Pb^{206}, a stable isotope of lead. All emanations possess the power to ionize gases, i.e., to make them conductors of an electric current. Also see **element, radioactive series.**

EMBRITTLEMENT, CAUSTIC. See **caustic embrittlement.**

EMDE DEGRADATION REACTION. A method of breaking carbon-nitrogen bonds, often opening ring-structures in the process, by treating a quaternary ammonium halide, in alcoholic or aqueous solution, with sodium amalgam.

$$\text{N(CH}_3)_2\text{Cl} \xrightarrow{\text{NaHg}} \begin{array}{c} \text{CH=CH}_2 \\ \\ \text{CH}_2 \cdot \text{N(CH}_3)_2 \end{array} + \text{HCl.}$$

This reaction is a modification of the **Hofmann degradation** (q.v.).

EMDE TEST REACTION. Methylaniline is differentiated from dimethylaniline by recrystallization of the platinic chloride double salts from hot water. The latter decomposes, the former does not.

EMETIC. A drug that induces vomiting.

EMISSION SPECTRUM. See **spectrum, emission.**

EMISSIVE POWER. The intensity of radiation of given wave length emitted at a given temperature.

EMISSIVE POWER, MONOCHROMATIC. The energy emitted per unit time per unit area per unit wave length for an infinitesimal frequency range near a given frequency in the spectrum of a **black body.**

EMISSIVE POWER, TOTAL. The **total radiant energy** emitted by a **black body** per unit time per unit surface area.

EMISSIVITY. The **total emissive power** of a surface divided by that of a **black body** at the same temperature.

EMISSIVITY, MONOCHROMATIC. The ratio of the monochromatic emissive power (see **emissive power, monochromatic**) of an actual surface to that of a **black body** at the same temperature.

EMMENAGOGUE. A drug that initiates or increases the menstrual flow.

EMMERIE TEST REACTIONS. Ascorbic acid (vitamin C) is detected as follows:

(1) Its 0.1% solutions give an orange-red color with a 5% aqueous solution of selenous acid.

(2) Its dilute solutions reduce gold trichloride.

(3) Its solutions give a brown-red color with uranyl acetate.

EMOLLIENT. A pharmaceutical preparation, or drug, which soothes irritated skin when applied externally.

EMPIRICAL FORMULA. A formula which states only the constituent elements of a substance and their relative proportions and gives no information as to molecular weight or structural constitution. CH_2O is the empirical formula of dextrose. Also see **formula.**

EMULSIFICATION. The process of preparing an emulsion.

EMULSIFYING AGENT. A substance which aids the formation of an **emulsion,** or which extends the range of temperature, concentration, etc., over which the emulsion remains dispersed, and, in general, increases the stability of the emulsion.

EMULSION. A suspension of small droplets (often of colloidal dimensions) of one liquid in another in which it is insoluble.

EMULSION POLYMERIZATION. See **polymerization, emulsion.**

EMULSOID. See **emulsion.**

ENAMEL. In general, a material which, upon application to a surface, yields a glossy, hard finish. Two important classes of enamels are (1) liquid mixtures of pigments and varnishes or lacquers which are applied to the surface and yield the desired finish upon drying, or (2) vitreous glazes which are obtained by fusion of solids upon surfaces of heat resistant substances, such as metals or ceramics.

ENANTHIC (OENANTHIC). Related to enanthic (oenanthic) acid, $C_6H_{13} \cdot COOH$.

ENANTHYL (OENANTHYL). The radical $CH_3(CH_2)_5CO-$.

ENANTIOMORPHOUS. Substances that exist in optically active modifications and crystallize as enantiomorphs.

ENANTIOMORPHS. Crystals that possess neither a plane nor a center of **symmetry** and cannot be brought into coincidence with their reflected image. They are distinguished as right and left forms and commonly exhibit optical activity, the right and left forms rotating the ray of polarized light in opposite directions. Cf. **isomerism, optical.**

ENANTIOTROPY. The property possessed by a substance of existing in two crystal forms, one stable below, and the other stable above, a certain temperature called the **transition point.**

END POINT. (1) A position, established in the course of a dynamic process, at which an **equilibrium** is reached. (2) The point in a **titration** at which the reaction is just complete.

ENDO-. Combining term used in chemical nomenclature to indicate an inner position, specifically (1) in the ring and not in a side chain; or (2) attached to a bridge within the ring.

ENDOCRINE. Pertaining to ductless glands, or to their products or secretions.

ENDOCYCLIC COMPOUNDS. Unsaturated cyclic derivatives in which the double bond or bonds occur in the nucleus.

ENDOSMOSIS. A type of **osmosis** in which the solvent dialyzes into the system. Exosmosis is the reverse process. The two processes may be illustrated by the condi-

tions in the living cell; when the plasma is **hypertonic,** solvent passes from the cell into the plasma (exosmosis); when the plasma is **hypotonic** the solvent passes from the plasma into the cell (endosmosis).

ENDOTHERMIC. Characterized by the absorption of heat. Endothermal reactions absorb heat as they progress. An endothermal cell is an electrical cell in which the production of a current is attended by an absorption of heat.

ENDOTHERMIC REACTION. See **reaction, endothermic.**

-ENE. A suffix indicating unsaturation, or specifically, a double bond.

ENERGY. Energy is an intangible quality by which a body is enabled to deliver work (against an external resistance or force) to the surroundings.

ENERGY, AVAILABLE. Free energy (see **energy, free**).

ENERGY BINDING. The energy which would be released if a given **nuclide** were formed by coalescence of its constituent neutrons and protons.

ENERGY CHANGE, STANDARD FREE. See **standard free energy change.**

ENERGY, CHEMICAL. A form of energy that manifests itself in chemical transformations.

ENERGY, COHESION. The energy a body possesses by virtue of the tendency of its particles to attract each other.

ENERGY, CONSERVATION. See **law of conservation of energy.**

ENERGY, DEGRADATION. Changes in form of **energy** take place in the direction of increasing **entropy,** hence lesser availability.

ENERGY, DISGREGATION. The energy a body possesses by virtue of the tendency of its particles to repel each other.

ENERGY, FIRST LAW OF. See law of conservation of energy.

ENERGY, FORM. Elasticity.

ENERGY, FREE. A thermodynamic concept defined by the relation

$$F = H - TS$$

where H is the **enthalpy** (q.v.), T the absolute temperature, and S the **entropy** (q.v.).

ENERGY, INTERNAL. The energy or energy content of a system. This quantity includes all forms of energy other than that resulting from the position of the system in space.

ENERGY ISOMERISM. Dynamic isomerism. See **isomerism, dynamic.**

ENERGY, KINETIC. Energy possessed by a moving body by virtue of its motion. It is proportional to half the mass of the body multiplied by the square of its velocity.

ENERGY, LATTICE. The potential energy of a **crystal lattice,** which is a measure of the stability of the atomic or ionic lattice system.

ENERGY LEVEL. One of a series of discrete energy values which characterize a quantized system. As an example one may consider the case of an electron in the neighborhood of the nucleus. The energy of the electron is restricted to a series of discrete values, termed energy levels. Transitions between these levels may be accomplished by the absorption or emission of radiation corresponding to the difference in energy between levels.

ENERGY, MECHANICAL. The energy of relatively large (well above molecular size) objects, which is primarily of interest in relation to mechanical work.

ENERGY OF ACTIVATION. See **activation energy.**

ENERGY OF OSCILLATOR. See **oscillator, energy of.**

ENERGY, POTENTIAL. Energy possessed by a body by virtue of its position or condition. The potential energy possessed by a body may be released by altering the position or condition of the body.

ENERGY, RADIANT. A form of energy propagated in definite **wave lengths** at a velocity of 299,790 kilometers per second. Radiant energy is electromagnetic in nature. It is readily transformed into other forms of energy, especially chemical energy (photochemical processes). The main source of radiant energy is the sun.

ENERGY, RESIDUAL. See **residual energy.**

ENERGY, RESONANCE. See **resonance energy.**

ENERGY, SPECIFIC DENSITY OF. The energy in unit volume of space.

ENERGY, THERMAL. Heat energy.

ENERGY, VOLUME. Energy attributable to volume change.

ENFLEURAGE. A process for the extraction of volatile oils and odoriferous substances from plants. The plants or flowers are spread on glass plates which have been coated with grease, fat, vaseline, or glycerol, that absorbs the oils. The essential oils are subsequently extracted from the absorbent by alcohol, or other solvents.

ENGEL TEST REACTIONS. (1) Glycocoll is detected by its deep red color (destroyed by acid) with ferric chloride.
(2) With one drop phenol, and then some sodium hypochlorite solution, glycocoll gives a blue color in a short time.

ENGEL-VILLE TESTS. Free alkali hydroxide is detected in the presence of carbonate as follows: (1) a solution of indigosulfuric acid neutralized with calcium carbonate is colored yellow by alkali hydroxides, but not by carbonates. (2) A 0.2% solution of Poirrier's soluble blue C4B is colored red only by alkali hydroxides.

ENGLER-WILD TEST. Ozone is detected by filter paper treated with concentrated manganese chloride solution, which is turned brown.

ENHANCED LINES IN SPECTRA. Spectral lines yielded by atoms which have been ionized by loss of one or more electrons. Such spectra possess terms in which the **Rydberg constant** R (q.v.) obtained for ordinary spectra (those of neutral atoms) is replaced by $4R$, $9R$, or p^2R, depending on whether one, two, or $(p\text{-}1)$ electrons have been removed from the neutral atom.

ENIMIZATION. A reversible intramolecular rearrangement of **amines** to yield **imines.**

$$RC\!=\!CH\!-\!NHR' \rightleftarrows RCH\!-\!CH\!=\!NR'.$$
enamic form   enimic form

ENLARGEMENT HEAD. See **head, enlargement.**

ENOL FORM. One of two tautomeric forms of a substance of the general type

$$\begin{array}{c} R \\ \diagdown \\ R' \diagup \end{array}\!\!CH\!-\!\underset{\underset{R}{|}}{C}\!=\!O \quad \text{(the keto form)}.$$

The enol form is formed from the keto form by migration of hydrogen atom from the adjacent carbon atom to the carbonyl group, producing the type

$$\begin{array}{c} R \\ \diagdown \\ R' \diagup \end{array}\!\!C\!=\!\underset{\underset{R}{|}}{C}\!-\!OH.$$

See also **isomerism, dynamic.**

ENTHALPY. A thermodynamic concept defined by the equation $H = E + PV$ where H is the enthalpy, E is the energy, P the pressure, and V the volume of a system. At constant pressure the change in enthalpy measures the quantity of heat exchanged by the system with surroundings.

ENTRAINMENT. The process by which a liquid boils so violently that the escaping vapor carries liquid with it as suspended droplets.

ENTROPY. The internal and unavailable energy of a system, a quantity which rarely enters directly into calculations, but rather in the form of its increments or changes. It is arrived at in thermodynamics in the form of the conception of a change in the entropy of a system, which change in entropy is equal to the heat taken up during each infinitesimal stage of a reversible and **isothermal** process, divided by the temperature at which it is absorbed. For the entire change in the system, the change in entropy is equal to the summation of the infinitesimal terms as denoted by the expression,

$$\Delta S = \Sigma \frac{q}{T},$$

where ΔS is the change in entropy and $\Sigma \dfrac{q}{T}$ is the sum of the terms obtained by dividing the infinitesimal amounts of heat by the temperatures at which they are gained or lost. At absolute zero the entropy of a system becomes zero; it is a maximum usually when the available energy is a minimum.

ENTROPY, COMMUNAL. See **communal entropy.**

ENTROPY OF ACTIVATION. See **activation, entropy of.**

ENTROPY OF FUSION. The unavailable energy during a **fusion,** which is the quantity obtained when the heat absorbed in the conversion of a given substance from the solid to the liquid state is divided by the temperature at which the process takes place.

ENTROPY OF MIXING. The unavailable energy of a mixture, defined as the difference between the **entropy** of the mixture and the sum of the entropies of the **components** of the mixture.

ENTROPY, RESIDUAL. See **residual entropy.**

ENTROPY, STANDARD. The total **entropy** of a substance in a state defined as standard. Thus, the standard states of a solid or a liquid are regarded as those of the pure solid or the pure liquid, respectively, and at a stated temperature. The standard state of a gas is at 1 atmosphere pressure and specified temperature, and its standard entropy is the change of entropy accompanying its expansion to zero pressure, or its compression from zero pressure to 1 atmosphere. The standard entropy of an ion is defined in a solution of unit activity, by assuming that the standard entropy of the hydrogen ion is zero.

ENZYME. One of a class of **colloidal,** soluble, organic substances produced by living cells which have the power to catalyze chemical reactions, one specific enzyme rarely catalyzing more than one type of reaction. The exact composition of most enzymes is unknown, but they are organic compounds related to the proteins. Enzymes are named usually according to the type of action they influence, the suffix "ase" being added as characteristic of this class of substances. Representative classes of enzymes are lipase, amylase, catalase, and oxidase. Pepsin, trypsin, rennin, emulsin, and erepsin are enzymes which were named before the general use of the suffix "ase." Enzymes are also termed ferments, and unorganized ferments.

ENZYME, AMYLOLYTIC. An enzyme which acts upon starch, catalyzing its hydrolysis to substances of simpler molecular structure.

ENZYME, APO. That portion of an enzyme which contains the characteristic protein portion.

ENZYME, AUTOLYTIC. (1) One of a group of **proteolytic** and carbohydrate splitting enzymes present in living cells and capable of digesting the cells themselves under favorable circumstances. (2) An enzyme that acts without external stimulation.

ENZYME, DEAMIDIZING. An **enzyme** that catalyzes the removal of the **amino** group from **amino acids.**

ENZYME, DECARBOXYLIZING. An **enzyme** that catalyzes the loss of carbon dioxide by an organic acid.

ENZYME, EXOCELLULAR. (Extracellular enzyme) An **enzyme** that may readily be isolated from association with living cells, e.g., pepsin, maltase, zymase. See also **enzymes, intracellular.**

ENZYME, GLYCOLYTIC. See **enzyme, sucroclastic.**

ENZYME, HYDROLYTIC. An enzyme that catalyzes hydrolysis, such as pepsin, maltase, emulsin, invertase.

ENZYME, INORGANIC. See **ferment, inorganic.**

ENZYME, INTRACELLULAR. An enzyme that has not yet been separated from association with living matter.

ENZYME, INVERTING. An **enzyme** that catalyzes the inversion of a sugar, i.e., its **hydrolysis** to yield simpler sugar molecules, as invertase hydrolyzes sucrose to yield glucose and fructose.

ENZYME, LIPOLYTIC. (Lipase. Steatolytic enzyme) An enzyme that catalyzes the **hydrolysis** of fats and other esters to yield alcohols and acids.

ENZYME, OXIDIZING. An **enzyme** that catalyzes an organic oxidation, e.g., oxidase, phenolase.

ENZYME, PROTEOLYTIC. (Protease. Proteoclastic enzyme) An **enzyme** such as pepsin and papain, that catalyzes the **hydrolysis** of proteins.

ENZYME, REDUCING. An **enzyme** that reduces certain organic or inorganic substances, e.g., catalase.

ENZYME, SUCROCLASTIC. (Glycolytic enzyme) An **enzyme** that catalyzes the splitting of a sugar into simpler sugar molecules.

ENZYME, URICOLYTIC. An **enzyme** that catalyzes the metabolizing of uric acid to urea.

ENZYMOLYSIS. A term applied to any reaction catalyzed by an **enzyme.**

EÖTVÖS EQUATION. A relation for the rate of change of **molar surface energy** with temperature of liquids. Theoretically this quantity

$$k = -\frac{d[\gamma(Mv)^{\frac{2}{3}}]}{dT}$$

should be a constant for all liquids. Actually, deviations are frequently encountered. In the above relationship, γ is the **surface tension** of the liquid, v is its **specific volume**, M is its molecular weight, T is temperature, and k is, ideally, a constant for all liquids.

-EPANE. A suffix indicating a seven-membered ring.

EPHRAIM REACTION FOR THALLIUM (THALLOUS) SALTS. The reagent is prepared by making a solution of antimony trichloride in a slight excess of hydrochloric acid, adding water until no further precipitation occurs, then treating with solid potassium iodide. This solution gives a bright red to orange precipitate with an acid or neutral solution of a thallium salt.

EPHRAIM REAGENT FOR COPPER. A solution of 1 g. salicylaldoxime in 5 ml. of alcohol, which is then diluted to 100 ml. with hot water; used as a test reagent for copper. A green precipitate indicates the presence of copper.

EPHRAIM TEST FOR VANADIUM. Evaporate a mixture of 1 ml. of the solution and 1 ml. concentrated hydrochloric acid down to 0.4 ml. volume. Cool, add 1 drop freshly prepared 0.1% ferric chloride solution and 2 drops 1% dimethylglyoxime solution, and alkalinize with ammonia. A red color indicates vanadium.

EPI-. (Greek, upon, on, to) Denoting certain relations, as follows: (a) the 1,5-positions in naphthalene; as epidichloronaphthalene; (b) in aldoses and related compounds, identity of structure except arrangement about the α-carbon atom; as, epirhodeose (epimer of rhodeose); (c) a bridge connection; as, 9,10-epidioxyanthracene (anthracene 9,10-peroxide).

EPIMER. One of a pair of **isomeric substances** which differ in structure only in the positions of one hydrogen atom and one hydroxyl radical, both of which are on the same asymmetric carbon atom, usually the carbon atom is at the end of a chain. Epimers are fairly common among the sugars.

EPIMERIDE. The same as **epimer** (q.v.).

-EPIN, -EPINE. A suffix indicating a seven-membered ring.

EPOXY. The radical $-O-$ (joined to different atoms already united in some other way).

EPPINGER TEST REACTION. Glyoxylic acid is detected in solution by adding a 0.1% indole solution, and floating the mixture on concentrated sulfuric acid. A red ring indicates the presence of glyoxylic acid.

EPSILON (E, ϵ or $\mathcal{E}$). The fifth letter of the Greek alphabet, used to denote the fifth carbon atom in a straight-chain compound, or a derivative in which a substituted group is attached to that carbon atom (ϵ-). Symbol for ergon (ϵ). Symbol for **electrode potential** ($\mathcal{E}$). Symbol for **dielectric constant** in cgs units (ϵ). Symbol for dielectric constant (ϵ). Symbol for **emittance** of radiation (ϵ). Symbol for **electromotive force** (ϵ). Symbol for **emissivity** (ϵ'); total emissivity (ϵ' or ϵ_t'). Symbol for monochromatic emissivity (ϵ_{λ}'). Symbol for average molecular energy (ϵ). **Extinction coefficient** (ϵ).

EQUATION. An expression in mathematics of the equality (denoted by the symbol $=$) between two quantities or terms, or two groups of quantities or terms. Usually the groups of expressions on one or both sides of the equality symbol contain directions for various mathematical operations to be performed, as multiplication, division, differentiation, integration, etc. In this way the equation acquires, in addition to its meaning of simple equality, also a meaning of the result of a process, and this is the significance of a chemical equation. (See **equation, chemical.**) In addition to the equations listed below, see also equations listed under proper names, as **Berthelot equation.**

EQUATION (ADSORPTION), LANGMUIR. See **Langmuir equation (adsorption).**

EQUATION, BEATTIE AND BRIDGEMAN. See **Beattie and Bridgeman equation.**

EQUATION, BERTHELOT. See **Berthelot equation.**

EQUATION, CLAPEYRON-CLAUSIUS. See **Clapeyron-Clausius equation.**

EQUATION, CLAUSIUS. See **Clausius equation.**

EQUATION, DIETERICI. See **Dieterici equation.**

EQUATION, ELECTRONIC. An equation, or partial equation, showing the transfer or liberation or absorption of electrons. An example of such an equation is the following:

$$2I^- \rightleftarrows I_2 + 2e.$$

This equation shows the loss of two electrons by the oxidation of two iodide ions to form an iodine molecule, a process which frequently occurs when the iodide ion functions as a reducing agent.

EQUATION, EÖTVÖS. See **Eötvös equation.**

EQUATION, FANNING. See **Fanning equation.**

EQUATION, GEIGER-NUTTALL. See **Geiger-Nuttall rule.**

EQUATION, GIBBS-HELMHOLTZ. See **Gibbs-Helmholtz equation.**

EQUATION, IONIC. An equation expressing an **ionic reaction** (q.v.) in terms of the symbols or formulas of the ions or molecules which react, and the ions or molecules which are formed by the reaction, with in-

tegral coefficients showing the proportional number of ions or molecules involved (which is the proportional number of equivalent weights of each ion or of **gram-molecular weights** of each molecule). For example:

$$Ba^{++} + SO_4^{=} \rightleftarrows BaSO_4 \text{ (precipitate)}$$
$$Pb^{++} + 2CH_3COO^- \rightleftarrows Pb(CH_3COO)_2$$
$$Zn + Pb^{++} \rightleftarrows Zn^{++} + Pb.$$

The symbol $\rightleftarrows$ is used to express the reversible nature of the ionic reaction which results in the establishment of an equilibrium between all the reactants. Even though the position of the equilibrium may be far to one side or the other as, for example, the mixture of solutions of barium ions and sulfate ions results in almost complete precipitation, there is always some concentration, however slight, present in an equilibrium reaction.

EQUATION, KEYES. See **Keyes equation.**

EQUATION, KIRCHHOFF. See **Kirchhoff equation.**

EQUATION, MOLECULAR. An equation expressing a **molecular reaction** (q.v.) in terms of the formulas of the molecules which react and those which are formed by the reaction, with integral coefficients showing the proportional number of gram-molecular weights of each substance. For example:

$$2SO_2 + O_2 \rightarrow 2SO_3$$

is the molecular equation for the combination of sulfur dioxide and oxygen to form sulfur trioxide, in the proportions of two **gram-molecular weights** of sulfur dioxide and one of oxygen to yield two gram-molecular weights of sulfur trioxide.

EQUATION, MORSE. See **Morse equation.**

EQUATION OF CONTINUITY. An expression of the **conservation of mass** for a fluid, wherein the excess of flow of fluid mass into a region, over the flow from the region, is equated to the time rate of increase of density. The equation is commonly written in the form:

$$\frac{\partial \rho}{\partial t} = - \nabla \cdot \mathbf{V}$$

where $\frac{\partial \rho}{\partial t}$ is the rate of increase of density, ∇ is the vector differential operator, $\mathbf{V}$ is the mass of fluid flowing through unit cross-section in unit time, and $-\nabla \cdot \mathbf{V}$ is the excess of inward over outward flow, or the convergence of the fluid.

EQUATION OF STATE. A relationship which defines, or partly defines, the physical conditions of a homogeneous system by relating its pressure, temperature, volume or concentration, and the gas constant. Furthermore, all equations of state, except the simple $PV = RT$, contain additional constants or variables. (Also see **equation of state, general; equation of state, thermodynamic; Keyes equation; Berthelot equation; Beattie and Bridgeman equation; van der Waals equation; Dieterici equation; and Clausius equation.**)

EQUATION OF STATE, GENERAL. The most general form of the equation of state, relating the pressure, volume, and temperature of a gas, and the gas constant. It is of the form

$$PV = RT \left(1 + \frac{B}{V} + \frac{C}{V^2} + \frac{D}{V^3} \cdots \right)$$

in which P is the pressure, V the volume, T the absolute temperature, R the gas constant, and B, C, D, etc., are constants, dependent upon the temperature and called virial coefficients. The equation is sometimes referred to as the virial equation of state.

EQUATION OF STATE, REDUCED. See **reduced equation of state.**

EQUATION OF STATE, THERMODYNAMIC. Any equation derived by consideration of reversible energy changes, which gives a relationship between pressure, volume, and temperature for a state of matter.

EQUATION OF STATE, VIRIAL. See **equation of state, general.**

EQUATION, OXIDATION-REDUCTION. A chemical equation expressing a reaction in which there is a **transfer of electrons** between ions, atoms, or molecules.

EQUATION, STARK-EINSTEIN. See **Stark-Einstein equation.**

EQUATION, STEFAN-BOLTZMANN. See **Stefan-Boltzmann equation.**

EQUATION, SUTHERLAND. See **Sutherland equation.**

EQUATION, SVEDBERG. See **Svedberg equation.**

EQUATION, TRANSMUTATION. An equation for the change of one atom into another, which differs from it in nuclear charge, mass, or stability. Such changes occur in natural **radioactive processes,** but the general need for a systematic notation for expressing them came only with the investigation of **artificial radioactivity,** and the great number of changes discovered.

Two representative **transmutation** equations are

$$_{13}\text{Al}^{27} + _{0}n^{1} \rightarrow _{12}\text{Mg}^{27} + _{1}\text{H}^{1}$$

which shows the transmutation of aluminum atoms of mass number 27, and of atomic number 13, by bombardment with neutrons, to magnesium atoms of mass number 27, and of atomic number 12, with the emission of a proton, and

$$_{4}\text{Be}^{9} + \gamma \rightarrow _{4}\text{Be}^{8} + _{0}n^{1}$$

which shows the transmutation of beryllium atoms of mass number 9, under gamma ray bombardment, to beryllium atoms of mass number 8, with the emission of a neutron.

The two reactions above may also be expressed in condensed form as:

$$\text{Al}^{27} (n; p) \text{Mg}^{27}$$

and $\text{Be}^{9} (\gamma; n) \text{Be}^{8}.$

EQUATION, VAN DER WAALS. See **van der Waals equation.**

EQUILIBRIUM. A condition in which all the forces or tendencies present are exactly counterbalanced or neutralized by equal and opposite forces and tendencies. In chemical theory, the term is applied especially to reversible reactions, in which case equilibrium is reached when the velocity of the "opposing" reaction, i.e., the interaction of the products to regenerate the initial reactants, equals the velocity of the forward reaction.

EQUILIBRIUM, APPARENT. (False equilibrium) A condition of apparent equilibrium in a system which is brought about by the interference of some factor (usually accidental) that prevents the system from proceeding to a true equilibrium. Often the interfering factor is a great diminution in the velocity of one of the reactions.

EQUILIBRIUM, CHEMICAL. The condition of a system undergoing a **reversible chemical reaction** at which the rate of the forward reaction is equal to the rate of the reverse reaction, and the concentrations of all of the reacting substances remain constant.

EQUILIBRIUM, CHEMICAL LAW OF. See **law of chemical equilibrium.**

EQUILIBRIUM CONSTANT. See **law of chemical equilibrium.**

EQUILIBRIUM DIAGRAM. A graphical representation, commonly plotted from temperature and pressure data, which shows the condition of equilibrium between various **phases** of a substance, or system of substances.

EQUILIBRIUM, DISPLACEMENT OF. See **law of chemical equilibrium.**

EQUILIBRIUM, HETEROGENEOUS. (Polyphase equilibrium) Equilibrium between two or more phases, as between a solid and a gas, or a liquid and its saturated vapor. The system calcium oxide-calcium carbonate-carbon dioxide is an example of an heterogeneous equilibrium state.

EQUILIBRIUM, HOMOGENEOUS. Equilibrium conditions in a system that constitutes a single phase, i.e., reactions

in solution or among gases the products of which remain in the same phase as the reactants.

EQUILIBRIUM, ISOTHERMAL. An **equilibrium** (q.v.) reached by a system that remains at constant temperature during the entire process.

EQUILIBRIUM, METASTABLE. A definite **equilibrium** state which is not the most stable equilibrium under the given conditions. A metastable system will undergo a spontaneous change upon addition of the stable phase, or frequently under the action of vibratory forces.

EQUILIBRIUM, ORDER OF. A method of classifying equilibria. Equilibria of the first order embrace cases where only one component is present; equilibria of the second order embrace two-component systems and so on for higher orders.

EQUILIBRIUM, PHOTOCHEMICAL. A position of **equilibrium** (q.v.) reached in a reversible chemical change in which one or both of the reactions are sensitive to light, and with the presence of the effective radiation postulated as one of the conditions under which the equilibrium is reached.

EQUILIBRIUM POINT. The external conditions (such as temperature or pressure) at which a system is in **equilibrium.**

EQUILIBRIUM, POLYPHASE. See **equilibrium, heterogeneous.**

EQUILIBRIUM, RADIOACTIVE. In a system containing two or more radioactive elements, in which each element (except the first) is formed by radioactive disintegration of the element preceding it in the series present, radioactive **equilibrium** is reached when the rate of formation of any element from its parent is equal to its own rate of disintegration. This statement does not apply to the terminal element of the series present which is nonradioactive.

EQUIPARTITION OF ENERGY, MOLECULAR. A principle according to which the total energy of a molecule is divided equally among the various **degrees of freedom;** in classical mechanics each degree of freedom contributes the quantity $\frac{1}{2}kT$ to the total energy, where k is the **Boltzman constant,** and T is the absolute temperature.

EQUIVALENCE. Valence.

EQUIVALENCE POINT. The stage in a **titration** at which the reacting substances, as the alkali and acid, are present in exactly equivalent proportions. It is the theoretical end point of the titration, which differs from that found on analysis, because of the limitations of the indicator or indicating system, and of the observational error.

EQUIVALENT. A term used generally in chemistry to connote equal combining power. Thus the equivalent weight of an element is its **atomic weight** divided by its **valence** in the particular reaction in question. This is by definition the weight of an element which combines with one-half atomic weight (8 grams) of oxygen, or one atomic weight of hydrogen (1.008 grams). Therefore, the equivalent weight of a compound is its molecular weight divided by the valence change, or hydrogen-combining equivalent, in the particular reaction.

EQUIVALENT CONDUCTANCE. See conductance, equivalent.

EQUIVALENT CONDUCTIVITY. See conductivity, equivalent.

EQUIVALENT, ELECTROCHEMICAL. See electrochemical equivalent.

EQUIVALENT, GRAM. See gram-equivalent.

EQUIVALENT, TOXIC. The minimum lethal dose. The smallest amount of a poisonous substance needed to kill an animal, divided by the weight of the animal in kilograms.

EQUIVALENT WEIGHT. See equivalent.

Er Symbol for the element **erbium.**

ERBIUM. Rare earth metallic element. Symbol Er. Atomic number 68. Atomic weight 167.2. Density 4.77. Valence 3. Oxide Er_2O_3. Erbium occurs in samarskite, gadolinite, and other rare minerals.

ERDMANN REAGENT FOR POTASSIUM AND RUBIDIUM. Dissolve 30 g. cobalt nitrate in 60 ml. water and add 100 ml. 50% sodium nitrite solution and 10 ml. glacial acetic acid. This reagent gives a yellow precipitate with potassium and rubidium salts. Many modifications of this reagent have been developed.

ERDMANN SOLUTION. A mixture of 60 ml. concentrated sulfuric acid and 1 ml. dilute nitric acid, used in the identification of alkaloids. Characteristic color reactions are obtained.

ERDMANN TEST FOR NITRITE. Fifty ml. of the solution to be tested are mixed with 5 ml. of an acidified solution of 2 g. per liter sodium sulfanilate, and there is added 0.5 g. 1-amino-8-hydroxynaphthalene-4,6-disulfonic acid. A bright Bordeaux-red color indicates nitrite.

EREMACAUSIS. Slow combustion or **oxidation** such as the rusting of iron, decay of wood, or oxidation of phosphorus in air.

ERÉNYI TEST. To detect zinc in the presence of iron, acidify the sample with 0.5–1.0 ml. 2 N hydrochloric acid, add sufficient alkali fluoride to decolorize the solution, filter, wash, and add 1–2 ml. potassium ferrocyanide solution to the filtrate. A white precipitate, formed in 2–3 minutes, indicates zinc. Potassium ferricyanide gives a brown-yellow precipitate.

ERG. The unit of **work** in the **c.g.s. system,** defined as the work done when a body acted upon by a force of one dyne moves through one centimeter in the direction of the force.

$$1 \text{ joule} = 10^7 \text{ ergs.}$$

ERGO-, ERGOT-. Relating to ergot, as ergosterol, ergotamine.

ERGON. (1) A **quantum** of **energy** ϵ, which is calculated for any given oscillator by multiplying the frequency of the oscillator by **Planck's constant.** (2) This term is used also by some writers to denote an **enzyme** which has a **vitamin** as part of the prosthetic group.

ERGOT-. A prefix meaning related to ergot.

ERLENMEYER FLASK. A flask of conical shape, extending from a relatively narrow neck to a large flat base.

ERLENMEYER-PLÖCHL AZLACTONE AND AMINO ACID SYNTHESIS. A reaction of carbonyl compounds and acylglycines which yields unsaturated azlactones, which undergo reduction and hydrolysis to yield amino acids.

ERLICKI SOLUTION. A solution of 1 g. cupric sulfate and 2.5 g. potassium dichromate in 100 ml. water, used as a hardener for organic tissues.

ERLICKI STAIN. A solution of 2.5 g. methyl green, in 100 ml. 1% acetic acid, used as a tissue stain.

ERROR. (1) Departure from the truth. (2) The limit of precision of a determination in terms of the precision of the experimental results.

ERROR OF OBSERVATION. The difference between the observed value and the true value.

ERROR OF SAMPLING. The difference between the statistic of the sample

R′CHO + CH₂ C=O
NH OH
O
C
R″
Sod. acet.
Acet. anhyd.
−H₂O
R′CH=C C=O
N O
C
R″
+H₂ +H₂O
R′CH₂CHCOOH + R″COOH
NH₂.

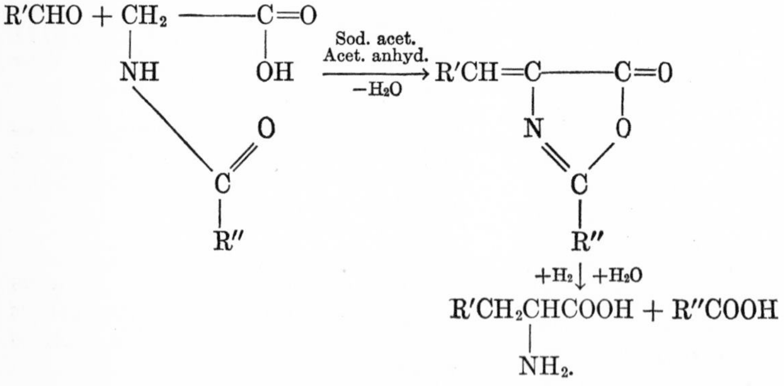

ERLENMEYER RULE. A free **hydroxyl** group usually adds to a carbon atom in double union with its neighboring carbon atom. When intramolecular atomic **rearrangements** occur the hydrogen of the hydroxyl migrates to the adjacent carbon atom and the hydroxyl oxygen unites doubly with the first carbon atom. For example:

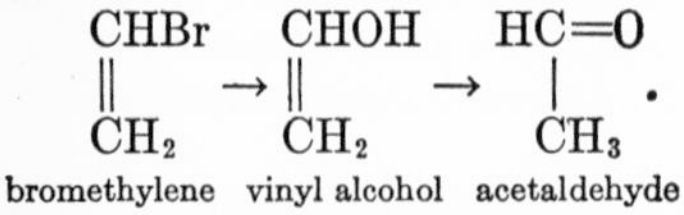

CHBr CHOH HC=O
CH₂ CH₂ CH₃
bromethylene vinyl alcohol acetaldehyde

Erlenmeyer recognized that the attachment of two hydroxyl groups to the same carbon atom is unstable; loss of water usually occurs and a >C=O group remains.

(such as its mean value or variance or coefficient of correlation or other quantity) and the population value, which consists of all the items from which the sample is drawn.

ERYTHRIC. Related to erythric acid, $CH_2OH(CHOH)_2COOH$.

ERYTHRO-, ERYTHR-. (Greek) Red; as erythrolitmin, erythritol.

ESBAUCH REAGENTS. Aminopyrine and ammonium thiocyanate, used as reagents for copper. In Martini's microtest, a drop of dilute copper solution is treated with a drop of saturated ammonium thiocyanate solution, and then with a drop of aminopyrine. A grey-brown precipitate is obtained.

ESCAPING TENDENCY. The tendency of a substance to change from one state to another.

ESCHAICH TEST FOR CYANIDE. One ml. of a 10% aminopyrine solution is mixed with 1 ml. 25% cupric sulfate solution and 10–12 drops glacial acetic acid; then the solution to be tested is added in drops. A blue color, followed by a turbidity, indicates the presence of cyanide.

ESCHAICH TEST FOR NITRATE AND NITRITE. A modified Curtman test, in which 5 ml. of the solution tested and 4 drops **Denigès** (q.v.) acid mercuric sulfate reagent are added successively to 2 ml. of a 1:10 aqueous solution of antipyrine. Stir, add 1 drop 5% solution of potassium ferricyanide and stir again. Nitrite produces a red color. For the detection of nitrate, an amalgamated aluminum wire is first left in the solution to reduce the nitrate to nitrite.

ESCHAICH TEST FOR PHENOL. Add to the solution to be tested, 10 drops ammonia, 0.05 g. sodium or ammonium persulfate and 4–5 drops 0.1 N sodium nitrite. A green color, changing to blue, indicates phenol.

ESCHBAUM TEST. To detect ozone in water, dissolve 1 g. tetramethyl-p-phenylenediamine in 100 ml. hot water, add 20 drops glacial acetic acid, and decolorize with zinc dust. This reagent gives a deep blue color with water containing ozone.

ESCHKA REAGENT. A mixture of 1 part anhydrous sodium carbonate and 2 parts magnesium oxide, used in determining sulfur in coal and other solids.

ESCHWEILER-CLARK MODIFICATION OF LEUCKART REACTION. See **Leuckart reaction.**

ESO-. (Greek) *Within;* a prefix denoting immediate attachment to a ring atom.

ESSENCE. (1) A proximate principle of a plant. (2) An alcoholic solution of the volatile constituents of a plant. A spirit.

ESSENTIAL OIL. A volatile oil obtained by distillation, extraction, expression, or other process of a naturally-occurring material, generally of vegetable origin. Essential oils are obtained from individual plants, and also from specific parts, such as leaves, fruit, flowers, buds, seeds, roots, bark, etc., of individual plants.

ESTER. (Compound ether. Ethereal salt) A compound formed from an **alcohol** and an organic or inorganic **acid** by the elimination of water. The alcohol residue takes the position assumed by **cations in** the inorganic salts. For example:

$$CH_3OH + CH_3COOH \rightarrow CH_3COOCH_3 + H_2O.$$

methyl alcohol   acetic acid   methyl acetate   water

The nomenclature of the esters is similar to that of the inorganic salts; they are named as if they were salts of the alcohol radicals.

ESTER, ACID. (Ether acid) An ester of a **polybasic acid** in which only part of the hydrogen atoms have been replaced by alcohol radicals.

ESTER, BASIC. An ester of a **polyhydric alcohol** in which only part of the hydroxyl hydrogens have been replaced by acid radicals, for example, α-propylene chlorohydrin.

$$CH_3\!-\!CHOH\!-\!CH_2Cl.$$

ESTER GUM. A synthetic gum **resin** prepared by the reaction of a natural gum resin with a **polyhydric alcohol**, such as glycerol, at moderate temperatures.

ESTER, MIXED. An **ester** consisting of two different groups joined to the char-

acteristic 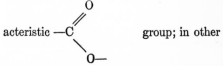 group; in other

words, a compound of the general form,

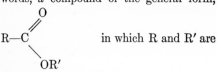

different organic radicals.

ESTER, NEUTRAL. An **ester** of a **polybasic acid** in which all the acidic hydrogens have been replaced by alcohol radicals.

ESTER NUMBER. A "constant" of a **fat** or **wax.** It is calculated from the amount of alkali needed to saponify the neutral esters in a given fat and is equal to the **saponification number** minus the **acid number.** Specifically the number of milligrams of potassium hydroxide required to saponify 1 gram of oil, fat, or wax.

ESTERASE. Any **enzyme** or **ferment** which brings about the **hydrolysis** of **esters.**

ESTERIC HINDRANCE. Same as **steric hindrance.**

ESTERIFICATION. The process of converting an **acid** into an **alkyl** or **aryl** salt or **ester.** Dehydrating and catalytic agents are often used to bring about the reaction, e.g., sulfuric or hydrochloric acid. In another esterification method, acyl chloride may be added to the alcohol, when hydrochloric acid is split out and the ester is formed.

ESTERIFICATION CONSTANT. A constant that depends upon the velocity of the **esterification** of an acid dissolved in an alcohol in the presence of $N/20$ alcoholic hydrochloric acid. As the **reaction velocity** varies with the temperature and the alcohol employed the constant is qualified thus:

$$E_{EtOH}^{20°} \quad or \quad E_{MeOH}^{15°}.$$

ESTERIFICATION LAW. See **law of esterification.**

ESTES TEST REACTION. Vanillin is detected by a violet color formed on boiling the solution to be tested with a solution of mercury in nitric acid and water.

ESTÈVE TEST. To detect barium in the presence of strontium and calcium, add to 5 ml. of the solution 1 ml. 1:100 sulfuric acid and 1 ml. 1:1000 potassium chromate solution (without mixing the liquids). A white ring, changing to yellow, at the interface indicates barium.

ESTILL-NUGENT TEST. Aluminum is detected by dissolving the sample to be tested in hot $6 N$ sulfuric acid, adding 5–10 ml. water and enough alkanet tincture to color the solution ruby-red. Add $6 N$ ammonium hydroxide until the color changes to blue, plus 3–5 ml. in excess. A purple precipitate which appears in about 5 minutes (rising to the surface as a compact mass) indicates aluminum.

Et. Abbreviation for **ethyl.**

ETA (H or η). The seventh letter of the Greek alphabet, used to denote the seventh carbon atom in a straight-chain compound, or a derivative in which a substituent group is attached to that carbon atom (η-). Symbol for **efficiency** (η). Coefficient of **viscosity** (η).

-ETANE. A suffix indicating a four-membered ring.

ÉTARD REACTION. The direct **oxidation** of an **aromatic** or **heterocyclic** bound methyl group to an **aldehyde group** by chromyl chloride or certain metallic oxides.

$$RCH_3 \xrightarrow{CrO_2Cl_2} RCHO$$

(R denotes an aryl or heterocyclic radical).

-ETE. A suffix indicating a four-membered ring.

-ETENE. A suffix indicating a four-membered ring.

ETHANOLYSIS. Alcoholysis in which the alcohol split out is ethyl alcohol.

ETHENE. See **ethylene.**

ETHENOID. Containing an ethene or **ethylene** linkage.

ETHENYL. See **ethylidyne** or **vinyl.**

ETHER. A compound derived from two **alcohol** molecules by the elimination of water.

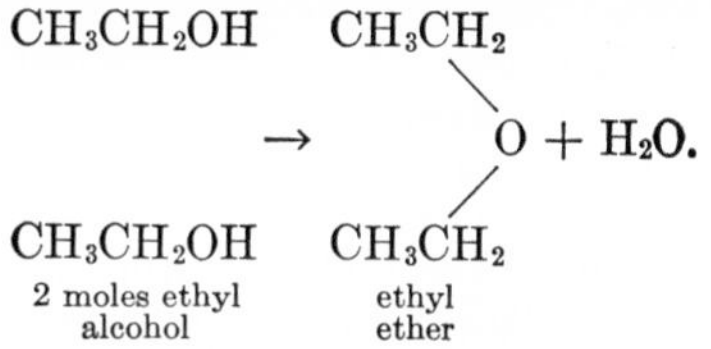

$$CH_3CH_2OH \quad CH_3CH_2$$
$$\rightarrow \quad O + H_2O.$$
$$CH_3CH_2OH \quad CH_3CH_2$$

2 moles ethyl   ethyl
alcohol   ether

Ethers in which the alcohol radicals are identical are termed simple ethers; those in which they are different are mixed or complete ethers.

ETHER ACIDS. See **ester, acid.**

ETHER, COMPOUND. (Obs.) (Complex ether) An **ester.**

ETHER, LACTAM. A derivative of one of the **tautomeric** forms of m-oxybenzoxazole having the structure,

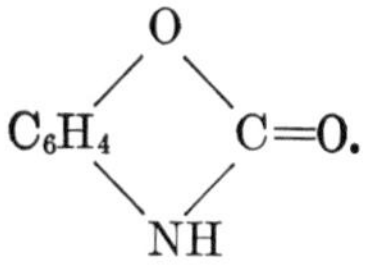

$$C_6H_4 \quad C=O.$$
$$NH$$

ETHER, MIXED. An **ether** consisting of two different groups joined to the characteristic oxygen atom, in other words, a compound of the general form R—O—R', in which R and R' are different organic radicals.

ETHER, THE. An hypothetical medium postulated to pervade all space and to permeate all matter, of enormous elasticity, offering no resistance to the passage of bodies through it but capable of resisting a shearing stress. It was considered the medium for the transmission of radiation through space.

ETHEREAL OIL. A volatile or **essential oil** (q.v.).

ETHEREAL SALT. An **ester.**

ETHEREOUS OIL. A volatile or **essential oil** (q.v.).

ETHERIFICATION. A chemical reaction which results in the formation of an **ether** (q.v.).

ETHIDE. A compound of a metal and the ethyl radical, as zinc ethide, $Zn(C_2H_5)_2$. The ethides may be regarded as ethane in which one hydrogen atom has been substituted by a univalent metal.

ETHINYL. See **ethynyl.**

ETHOXALYL. The radical

$$C_2H_5OOCCO-.$$

ETHOXY. The radical C_2H_5O-.

ETHYL. The radical CH_3CH_2-.

ETHYLATION. The formation of a compound by introduction of the **ethyl** radical.

ETHYL-DOW PROCESS. A method for the recovery of bromine from sea water. Treatment with chlorine displaces the bromine from the bromides present, then air is passed through the acidulated sea water to remove the bromine, and this air is passed through bromine-absorption columns where the bromine is absorbed in a solution of sodium carbonate, which is then acidified, and steam-distilled to obtain the bromine.

ETHYLENE. The radical $-CH_2CH_2-$.

ETHYLENEDIOXY. The radical

$$-O(CH_2)_2O-.$$

ETHYLIDENE. The radical $CH_3CH=$.

ETHYLIDYNE. The radical $CH_3C\equiv$.

ETHYNYL. The radical $CH\vdots C-$.

ETHYNYLENE. The radical $-C\vdots C-$.

-ETIDINE. A suffix indicating a four-membered ring.

-ETINE. A suffix indicating a four-membered ring.

ETIO-. (Greek *aitia*) *cause:* a prefix used to denote certain **degradation** products.

ETTI TEST REACTION. Resorcinol is detected by a violet color formed on triturating a solution containing it with vanillin and hydrochloric acid. (This test is also used to detect vanillin.)

ETTINGSHAUSEN (VON ETTINGSHAUSEN) EFFECT. When an electric current flows across the lines of force of a magnetic field, an **electromotive force** is observed which is at right angles to both the primary current and the magnetic field; a temperature gradient is observed which has the opposite direction to the **Hall electromotive force.**

Eu (1) Symbol for the element **europium.** (2) A prefix derived from the Greek word meaning good.

EUCOLLOID. A **colloid** composed of relatively large particles, i.e., exceeding 0.25 micron in length.

EUDIOMETER. A graduated tube closed at one end in which two platinum wires are sealed so that a spark may be passed through the contents of the tube. Used to measure the volume changes in the combustion of gases.

EUDIOMETRY. Gas analysis.

EUROPIUM. Rare earth metallic element. Symbol Eu. Atomic number 63. Atomic weight 152.0. Valence 3. Oxide Eu_2O_3.

EURY TEST. Formaldehyde in milk is detected by heating to boiling 5 ml. of the milk, 5 ml. sulfuric acid, and 5 drops 0.01 N ferric chloride solution. A violet color indicates formaldehyde. (See **Linder Test** and **Leach Test.**)

EUSTON PROCESS. A procedure for the manufacture of white lead. Refined metallic lead is treated to obtain a solution of basic lead acetate, which then reacts with carbon dioxide to form white lead, which precipitates.

EUTECTIC. A minimum temperature and corresponding composition (in other words, a minimum point upon a temperature-composition diagram) at which a liquid consisting of two or more **components** is in equilibrium with its components in the solid state, or with a particular group of solid substances derived from its components, and which may include one or more elements, compounds or solid solutions. Material of this composition is often called an "eutectic"; and the temperature of this point is sometimes called the eutectic temperature. It represents the lowest melting point of the system. This temperature is constant, and is analogous in many respects to constant boiling mixtures of liquids. Cryohydrates are eutectic mixtures. Cf. **dystectic.**

EUTECTIC COMPOSITION. See **eutectic.**

EUTECTIC TEMPERATURE. See **eutectic.**

EUTECTOID. A minimum temperature and corresponding composition (in other words, a minimum point upon a temperature-composition diagram) at which a solid solution is in equilibrium with its **components** in the solid state, or with a particular group of solid substances derived from its components, and which may include one or more elements, compounds or solid solutions. The temperature of this point is sometimes called the eutectoid temperature; and material of this composition is sometimes called the eutectoid.

EUTECTOID TEMPERATURE. See **eutectoid.**

EUTROPY. The effect of the **atomic number** of an element upon the **isomorphous series** of salts which it forms.

EVAPORATING DISH. An article of laboratory equipment used to evaporate or concentrate solutions. It usually has a large diameter in relation to its depth, which provides a large liquid surface and so increases the rate of evaporation.

EVAPORATION. The conversion of a substance from the liquid state into the vapor state. As a **unit operation** in chemical engineering, the process of evaporation, and the apparatus designed to carry it out, have been developed to obtain the maximum thermal efficiency and over-all efficiency of operation, including removal of solids, if any, and use of reduced pressures. The latter is combined with the use of multiple units, in such an arrangement as to utilize the heat of condensation of the vapor from one unit to evaporate liquid in the next.

EVAPORATION, FLASH. See **flash evaporation.**

EVAPORATION, MOLAR HEAT OF. See **vaporization, molecular heat of.**

EVAPORATION, SPONTANEOUS. Evaporation at ordinary temperature.

EVASION COEFFICIENT. A factor which expresses the number of milliliters of a gas under standard conditions evolved per minute from one square centimeter of the surface of its solution in a liquid.

EVERS-BELLIER TEST. A test for peanut oil in other oils, in which 1 ml. of the oil is saponified with 5 ml. 1.5 N alcoholic potassium hydroxide solution by heating on a water bath for 5 minutes, avoiding loss of alcohol. Add 50 ml. of 70 per cent alcohol and then 0.8 ml. of hydrochloric acid, specific gravity 1.16. After heating to dissolve any precipitate that may be formed, cool the solution in water, stirring continuously with a thermometer, so that the temperature falls at the rate of about 1° C. per minute. If a turbidity appears before the temperature reaches 9° C., it is best to check the presence of arachis oil by isolating the acid and determining the melting point. If the liquid remains clear at this temperature arachis oil may be regarded as absent.

EVOLUTION APPARATUS. Any form of apparatus used in gas analysis in which a gas may be set free from a measured amount of substance, collected, and directly measured. **Nitrometers, azotometers.**

EVRARD REAGENT. Allyl-iodo-hexamethylenetetramine, used to precipitate cadmium.

EWALD REAGENT. A solution of ferric chloride and potassium thiocyanate used in determining hydrochloric acid in gastric juice.

EWINS TEST REACTIONS. One ml. of an 0.001% epinephrine (adrenalin) solution, with 1 ml. 1% sodium acetate solution and 4–5 drops 0.1% mercuric chloride solution gives a rose-red color when heated to 40–50° C. Epinephrine solutions give a red color on heating with potassium persulfate solution.

EXALTATION. The positive difference between the observed and the calculated values of the **molar refractivity of a substance.** See **optical exaltation.**

EXCHANGE REACTION. See **reaction, exchange.**

EXCIPIENT. A substance used in a pharmaceutical preparation to add bulk or form, in order to produce a medication that can be conveniently administered. Thus, excipients are used to absorb oily or sticky drugs, or to dilute powerful drugs to obtain the desired dosage in a portion that is easily handled or measured.

EXCITATION. **Activation** by absorption of radiation, usually effected by the transfer of an **oscillator** (commonly an electron) to a higher energy level.

EXCITATION FUNCTION, NUCLEAR. The variation, with the energy of the incident particle, of the efficiency, or yield, of a nuclear reaction. (See **reaction, nuclear.**)

EXCLUSION PRINCIPLE. See **Pauli's exclusion principle.**

EXHAUSTER. An apparatus used in the purification of gas during the manufacture of coal gas. The exhauster moves the gas along the purification system by maintaining a constant pressure.

EXHAUSTING AGENT. A substance which is added to a dye bath to effect a greater absorption of dye by the cloth, and to cause a high exhaustion of dye from the dye bath.

EXHAUSTIVE METHYLATION. The introduction of methyl groups into a compound until all the replaceable hydrogen atoms have been replaced. See **Hofmann degradation.**

EXO-. (Greek) Outside, out of; as, exotoxin (an excreted toxin); specifically, denoting attachment in a side chain. See **endo-, eso-.**

EXOCYCLIC COMPOUND. An unsaturated cyclic compound in which the **double bond** occurs in the side chain.

EXOSMOSIS. An **osmotic** process by which a diffusible substance passes from the inner or closed, to the outer parts of a system, as in the loss of substances, from a portion of a plant root to water in the surrounding soil.

EXOTHERMIC. A term denoting evolution of heat.

EXOTHERMIC REACTION. See **reaction, exothermic.**

EXPANSION. Increase in size, in length, width, or volume.

EXPANSION, ADIABATIC. An expansion of a substance or system of substances without gain or loss of heat by the substance or system.

EXPANSION, COEFFICIENT OF LINEAR. The change in the length of an expanding body per length per degree, **or**

$$\alpha = \frac{L_2 - L_1}{L_1(t_2 - t_1)}$$

where α is the coefficient of linear expansion, L_1 is the length at $0°$ C. or the length at any other reference temperature, L_2 is the observed length, t_1 is $0°$ C., or any other reference temperature, and t_2 is the observed temperature.

EXPANSION, POLYTROPIC. One of the infinite number of ways in which it is theoretically possible to expand a gas from an initial pressure and volume to a final pressure and volume. The funda-

mental mathematical relationship for all such expansions of an *ideal* gas is

$$PV^n = C$$

with n having a value of 0 for an isobaric expansion (constant pressure); of 1 for an isothermal expansion (constant temperature); of γ (the ratio of the specific heat at constant pressure to the specific heat at constant volume, C_p/C_v) for an isentropic expansion (constant entropy — no heat gained or lost by the system); and other values for combinations of these processes.

EXPECTORANT. A drug which promotes the secretion of mucus from tissues of the **respiratory system.**

EXPERIMENT. An operation conducted for the purpose of determining some unknown fact or of obtaining knowledge concerning a general principle of truth.

EXPLOSION. A chemical change that produces large quantities of energy or an increase in the volume of the system, or both at a rate sufficiently rapid to have considerable effects, often destructive, upon the surroundings.

EXPLOSIVE. A compound or mixture used to release, by a chemical reaction, considerable amounts of energy in a confined space and so rapidly that mechanical movement or shattering of surrounding objects is obtained.

EXPLOSIVE MIXTURE. A mixture of substances which may explode, or undergo sudden, noisy, and violent reactions.

EXPOSURE. The **irradiance** (q.v.) of a given area of a photographic emulsion integrated over the **exposure time** (q.v.).

EXPOSURE TIME. The interval during which the receiver is irradiated. It is important to distinguish this term from exposure.

EXSICCATION. Desiccation.

EXTENSIVE PROPERTY. See **property, extensive.**

EXTERNAL COMPENSATION. See compensation, external.

EXTERNAL STANDARD. A standard sample used for direct comparison with the unknown sample.

EXTINCTION COEFFICIENT, MOLAR. A constant quantity that appears in one of the forms of statement of **the law of Beer** (q.v.) expressing the amount of light absorption of a solution at various wave lengths, as in the relationship:

$$I = I_o 10^{-\epsilon cd}$$

in which I is the **intensity** of light transmitted and I_o is the intensity of incident light (both for a given wave length), ϵ **is** the **molar extinction coefficient** for that wave length, c is the concentration of the solution in moles per liter, and d is the thickness of the transmitting layer of solution.

EXTRACT. The material extracted from a plant by a solvent. Specifically the total solids in a liquid of organic nature, as the extract in a tincture or wine.

EXTRACT, FLUID. An extract of a drug in aqueous or alcoholic solution prepared in a standard strength, usually such that 1 cubic centimeter of the solution represents 1 gram of the drug, or its active principle.

EXTRACTION. A process of separating certain substances from mixtures usually by means of **solvents,** as the extraction of the soluble matters from a drug by percolation.

EXTRACTION APPARATUS. Various types of apparatus used in plant and laboratory for the separation of one or more substances from a mixture, by the action of solvents.

EXTRACTION THIMBLE. A small container, porous and open at one end, used to hold substances to be extracted by solvent action.

EXTRACTOR. An apparatus used in the wood distillation industry for refining the products of wood distillation, or more gen-

erally a vessel used for extraction on an industrial scale.

EXTRANUCLEAR ELECTRON. See electron, extranuclear.

EYKMAN FORMULA. An empirical relationship for the molal refraction of a liquid, of the form:

$$R = \frac{M(n^2 - 1)}{d(n + 0.4)} = \frac{V(n^2 - 1)}{n + 0.4}$$

in which R is the **molal refraction** for a given optical frequency, n is the **index of refraction** for that frequency, M is the molecular weight, V is the **molecular volume,** and d is the density.

F. Symbol for the element **fluorine** (F). Symbol for Fahrenheit temperature (F.). Abbreviation for function (f). Abbreviation for force $(F$ or $f)$. Abbreviation for the **faraday,** unit of electrical quantity (F). Abbreviation for the **farad,** unit of electrical capacity (f). Abbreviation for **magnetomotive force** (F). Abbreviation for acceleration (f). Abbreviation for **degree of freedom** $(F$ or $f)$. Abbreviation for **free energy** (F). Symbol for **Fanning friction factor** (f). Symbol for **activity coefficient,** molal basis [f]. Symbol for **friction coefficient** (f). Symbol for rate of feed (F). Abbreviation for **fugacity** (f). Symbol for **distribution function** $(f$ or $F)$. Symbol for focal length of object space (f). Symbol for focal length of image space (f'). Abbreviation for **formality** (F). Abbreviation for frequency (electrical, mechanical, acoustical), (f). Abbreviation for resonant frequency (f_r). Symbol for **hyperfine quantum number** $(= I + J)$ (F).

FABINYI TEST. To 0.25 ml. acetone, add 1 g. salicylaldehyde and 4 ml. N sodium hydroxide. A red color on shaking, after standing for 15 minutes, is obtained. To test for benzaldehyde, add a particle of potassium hydroxide and a little acetone to the alcoholic solution of the material under examination. A red color indicates the presence of benzaldehyde.

FACT. In science, a circumstance that has been confirmed by at least two independent investigators by experiment,

FACTITIOUS. Not produced by natural process.

FACTOR. (Reactant) **A component.** Any one of the substances that take part in a chemical reaction, or a numerical quantity or a unit which, in mathematical combination with other units or numerical quantities, expresses the components of another quantity or unit, or a **vitamin** (q.v.), which is sometimes called a food factor.

FACTOR, CONVERSION. A number used to multiply a quantity in order to obtain its equivalent value in other units, which may be either in the same system of weights and measures, or in another system.

FACTOR, CORRECTION. A quantity used to multiply an experimental result in order to correct for a source of error of known magnitude.

FACTOR, GRAVIMETRIC. A number used to multiply the weight result of a given quantitative analysis in order to obtain the amount of a substance to be determined.

FACTOR, TITRIMETRIC. A number used to multiply the volume result of a given titrimetric analysis in order to obtain the amount of the substance to be determined; often termed the volumetric factor.

FACTOR, VAN'T HOFF. See **reaction isotherm** and **isochore.**

FACTOR, VOLUMETRIC. See **factor, titrimetric.**

FADEOMETER. An instrument for determining the resistance to fading of substances and materials upon exposure to the action of radiant energy (commonly artificial sunlight or ultraviolet light) under controlled conditions.

FADING. Lightening of the color of an article or material as the result of exposure to the action of radiant energy, such as sunlight or ultraviolet light, or to other weathering action.

FADING TEST. A test used to determine the fastness of a color to light. A portion of the material is covered while the rest is exposed to the radiant energy, usually sunlight, artificial sunlight, or ultraviolet light.

FAGÈS TEST REACTION. To detect stannous salts in alkaline solution, add a few drops sodium nitroprusside solution. Stannous salts give a grey-red color, changing to blue with hydrochloric acid, but decolorized by an excess.

FAHRENHEIT. (F.) A thermometric scale devised by Fahrenheit (1686–1736), on which the freezing point of water is 32 degrees, and the boiling point 212 degrees, both at standard pressure.

FAIRHALL TEST. Lead is detected by the formation of a black hexanitrite of potassium, copper, and lead, showing rectangular plates or cubes under the microscope.

FAJANS METHOD. The use of a dye which is adsorbed near the end of a titration, thus producing a clearly visible color change. An example is the use of dichlorofluorescein in titration of chloride with silver nitrate solution.

FAJANS-SODDY LAW. See **law of radioactive displacement.**

FALCIOLA TEST REACTION FOR COBALT. A strongly ammoniacal cobalt solution gives a yellow, orange, or red color with sodium bisulfite.

FALCIOLA TEST REACTION FOR MOLYBDENUM. A solution of molybdenum in hydrochloric acid, on addition of a 25% solution of sodium thiosulfate, colors ethyl acetate lilac, red, or red-brown.

FALCIOLA TEST REACTION FOR SELENIUM. A selenium solution gives an orange-red precipitate on application to a little thiourea on a filter paper; and a hydrochloric acid solution of selenium is colored red by thiourea.

FALCIOLA TEST REACTION FOR TELLURIUM. A tellurium solution gives a yellow spot on application to a little thiourea on a filter paper; tellurium solutions of moderate strength give a yellow crystalline precipitate with thiourea.

FAMILY. A group of **elements** characterized by similar chemical properties such as **valence,** solubility of salts, behavior toward reagents, etc. The alkali family includes sodium, potassium, lithium, rubidium, cesium, and trancium. The halogen family consists of fluorine, chlorine, bromine, iodine, and astatine.

FANNING EQUATION. An equation expressing the drop in pressure, because of friction, in a fluid flowing in a pipe. It is of the form:

$$\Delta p_f = 2f\left(\frac{v^2}{g}\right)\left(\frac{l}{d}\right)$$

where Δp_f is the frictional drop in pressure, f is a function of the **Reynolds number,** v is the rate of flow, g is the acceleration of gravity, l is the length of the pipe element, and d is its diameter.

FANSTEEL ABSORBER. An apparatus for the absorption of gaseous hydrochloric acid by water. It consists essentially of a tower, packed with suitable rings, and containing a tantalum condenser near the top. The heat of solution of the hydrochloric acid evaporates water from the lower part of the tower, which is condensed at the top, and thus provides reflux of weak acid down the tower.

FARAD. The name of the practical **electromagnetic unit** of capacity. It is defined as that capacity which is charged to a difference of potential of one volt by one coulomb. The microfarad (10^{-6} farad) is the unit in common use. Cf. **Faraday.**

FARADAY. The quantity of electricity that can deposit one electrochemical equivalent in grams, equal to approximately 96,500 coulombs. Cf. **farad.**

FARADAY EFFECT. See **magnetic rotation.**

FARADAY LAWS. See **laws of Faraday.**

FARADIC CURRENT. An electric current produced by certain forms of high frequency apparatus.

FARADIZATION. Therapeutic use of induced currents.

FARINACEOUS. Containing starch.

FARINOGRAPH. A device for testing flour, in which the resistance of the dough to a given mechanical mixing operation is recorded graphically throughout a continuous mixing period; or in which the dough is stretched until it breaks, generally a matter of seconds, and the stretching force and the corresponding amount of stretch are recorded in graphical form.

FARRANT SOLUTION. A solution of 2 g. arsenious oxide and 50 g. gum acacia in 50 ml. glycerol and 50 ml. water, used as a preservative.

FARRAR PROCESS. A method of producing high-quality case-hardened iron from pig iron by treatment with manganese dioxide, ammonium chloride, and potassium ferrocyanide.

FAT. The mixed glyceryl **ester** of higher "fatty" acids such as stearic, palmitic, and oleic acids, etc., or any mixture of such glyceryl esters. The term is not narrowly limited, because it is indefinite which aliphatic acid forms the fat of lowest molecular weight. See also **fatty oil.**

FATTY ACID. (1) A general term for a group of monobasic **organic acids** derived from hydrocarbons by the equivalent of oxidation of a methyl group. They include both saturated and unsaturated acids; for example, formic acid, $HCOOH$; propionic acid, CH_3CH_2COOH; sorbic acid,

$$CH_3 \cdot CH : CH \cdot CH : CH \cdot COOH.$$

(2) Three members of the fatty acid series (those whose glyceryl esters compose the largest part of the most fats), namely, palmitic acid, $C_{15}H_{31}COOH$; stearic acid, $C_{17}H_{35}COOH$; and oleic acid, $C_{17}H_{33}COOH$.

FATTY OIL. A nonvolatile oil of vegetable or animal origin, and consisting of glyceryl (and other) esters of fatty acids (sometimes other organic acids), often with some of the free acid present.

FATTY SERIES. The aliphatic series of organic compounds.

FAUSER PROCESS. A process for the production of ammonia by direct combination of nitrogen and hydrogen that is similar to the **Casale process** (q.v.). The chief differences are somewhat lower pressures in the Fauser process, with less ammonia recirculation, and use of some of the liquid ammonia product to absorb heat by evaporation in the condenser.

FAVORSKII REARRANGEMENT. One of a number of rearrangements of α-halo-ketones to acids or esters, catalyzed by bases.

reagent for glyoxylic acid. A blue color, changing to red on dilution with water, indicates the presence of glyoxylic acid.

FEARON-MITCHELL TEST FOR ALCOHOLS. Primary and secondary alcohols are given a blue-violet or blue color if 0.1–1.0 ml. of a solution containing them is treated with a mixture of 5 drops 5% potassium dichromate solution and 5 ml. 7.5 N nitric acid.

FEARON TEST REACTION FOR CYANATE. To a slightly acid or neutral cyanate solution, add 2–5 drops 6% alcoholic benzidine solution and a few drops cupric acetate solution. A red color is formed, becoming brown.

FEARON TEST REACTION FOR VITAMIN A. Vitamin A is given a pink color

$$
\begin{array}{c}
\mathrm{CH_2-CH_2-CHX} \\
| \qquad\qquad | \\
\mathrm{CH_2-CH_2-CO}
\end{array}
\xrightarrow{\text{KOH}}
\begin{array}{c}
\mathrm{CH_2-CH_2-CH-CO_2K} \\
| \qquad\qquad \diagup \\
\mathrm{CH_2\!-\!-\!-CH_2}
\end{array}
$$

$$
\begin{array}{c}
\mathrm{CH_2-CH_2-CHX} \\
| \qquad\qquad | \\
\mathrm{CH_2-CHX-CO}
\end{array}
\xrightarrow{\text{KOH}}
\begin{array}{c}
\overset{\displaystyle \mathrm{OH}}{\underset{\displaystyle |}{}} \\
\mathrm{CH_2-CH_2-C-COOH} \\
| \qquad\qquad \diagup \\
\mathrm{CH_2\!-\!-\!-CH_2}
\end{array}
$$

$$
\downarrow \mathrm{o}
$$

$$
\begin{array}{c}
\mathrm{CH_2\!-\!-\!-CH_2-CO} \\
| \qquad\qquad \diagup \\
\mathrm{CH_2\!-\!-\!-\!-CH_2}
\end{array}
$$

The second of these reactions, i.e., formation of the 1-hydroxyacid, which can be oxidized to the cyclopentanone, is called the **Wallach degradation reaction** (q.v.). It commonly starts from the α,α'-dibromo-cyclohexanone.

FAVREL TEST REACTION. Citric acid is detected by heating for 5–10 minutes with sulfuric acid, cooling, diluting with water, and extracting with ether. On evaporation of the ether, the extract gives a red color with ferric chloride solution.

Fe Symbol for element **iron.**

FEARON SOLUTION FOR GLYOXYLIC ACID. A solution of 1 g. pyrogallol in 100 g. concentrated sulfuric acid, used as a

by the presence of pyrogallol, trichloracetic acid, and an oxidizing agent.

FEDER SOLUTION FOR ALDEHYDES. A solution of 1 g. sodium thiosulfate and 0.8 g. sodium hydroxide in 10 ml. water, to which is added 10 ml. of a 2% aqueous solution of mercuric chloride. It is a test reagent for aldehydes, becoming turbid in their presence.

FEDER TEST FOR HYDROGEN PEROXIDE. To detect hydrogen peroxide in milk, warm 5 ml. milk with 5 ml. concentrated hydrochloric acid, add a few drops formaldehyde and hold at 60° C. for a few minutes. A blue-violet color indicates the presence of hydrogen peroxide.

FEHLING SOLUTION. A freshly mixed solution of cupric sulfate, sodium potassium tartrate, and sodium hydroxide, used for determining reducing compounds, especially reducing sugars, by reduction of the cupric ions to insoluble cuprous oxide. Fehling solution is commonly prepared by mixing two solutions — (1) a solution of 34.65 g. cupric sulfate in 500 ml. water; and (2) a solution of 173 g. of Rochelle salt and 125 g. potassium hydroxide in 500 ml. distilled water.

FEIGL-ANGER TEST. To detect sulfonic acids, evaporate 1 drop of the test solution in a micro-crucible, heat with a few drops sulfuryl chloride to fumes, and add 2 drops saturated alcoholic solution of hydroxylamine hydrochloride. Then add 1 drop acetaldehyde, render alkaline with 5% sodium carbonate solution, let stand a few minutes, acidify with alcoholic hydrochloric acid, and add 1 drop ferric chloride solution. Red or violet colors indicate sulfonic acids.

FEIGL-CHARGAV TEST REACTION. Carbon disulfide produces an evolution of nitrogen if 5 ml. of its aqueous solution is treated with 1–2 ml. of 0.5 N sodium azide solution and 0.1 N iodine solution. Hydrogen sulfide interferes.

FEIGL-DEMANT TEST. Selenium is detected in solution by mixing 4 drops of a 1% solution of as-diphenylhydrazine in glacial acetic acid on a spot plate with 1 drop 2 N hydrochloric acid and 1 drop of the solution tested. A red color indicates the presence of selenium.

FEIGL-FREHDEN TEST. If oxalate is present, a fragment of the material gives an aniline blue color on melting with diphenylamine over a small flame.

FEIGL-KRUMHOLZ TEST FOR PALLADIUM. When a rapid stream of carbon monoxide is passed through a boiling acid solution containing palladium and phosphomolybdic acid, a blue to green color appears in a few minutes.

FEIGL-LEITMEIER TEST. An alcoholic solution of diphenylcarbazide colors magnesite red-violet, but does not affect dolomite.

FEIGL MICRO-REACTION FOR COPPER. Warm a drop of copper solution with a drop of alcoholic cupron solution on a slide. A green copper precipitate mixed with oxime crystals is seen under the microscope.

FEIGL MICRO-REACTION FOR PHOSPHATE. A drop of acid molybdate solution is added to a drop of the solution to be tested, and allowed to partially evaporate. On addition of a drop of benzidine hydrochloride solution and a little dilute ammonia, a blue to black color is seen under the microscope, if phosphate is present.

FEIGL-NEUBER TESTS FOR COPPER. (1) On spot test, a drop of copper solution gives a blue color with potassium cyanide solution followed by phosphomolybdic acid solution.

(2) On spot test, a drop of copper solution gives a blue color with hot saturated potassium bromide solution followed by a drop of benzidine hydrochloride solution.

FEIGL-NEUBER TEST FOR MERCURY. On spot test on filter paper, an alcoholic solution of diphenylcarbazide gives a violet spot with a mercury solution, which darkens on exposure to ammonia.

FEIGL-NEUBER TEST FOR TIN. A filter paper which has been moistened with phosphomolybdic acid solution, then held over ammonia, gives a blue color with stannous chloride solution.

FEIGL-PAVELKA TEST. Calcium or magnesium salts in solution give white precipitates with potassium or ammonium ferrocyanide dissolved in water and alcohol.

FEIGL-POLLAK REAGENT FOR SILVER. Rhodanine or isonitrosorhodanine.

FEIGL TEST REACTION FOR ANTIMONY. Antimony (trivalent ionic) is precipitated as white, lustrous crystals, insoluble in acids, from solution in dilute hydrochloric acid, by adding a slight excess of Rochelle Salt, followed by a concentrated aqueous solution of resublimed pyrogallol.

FEIGL TEST REACTION FOR CE-RIUM. When cerium oxide is moistened with a solution of benzidine in acetic acid, a bright blue color is obtained. Other cerium salts act similarly, but not the fluoride, bisulfate, or carbonate.

FEIGL TEST REACTION FOR MER-CURIC SALTS. The compound phenyl-urazol, $C_6H_5 \cdot N \begin{smallmatrix} NH-CO \\ \ \ \ \ | \\ CO-NH \end{smallmatrix}$, gives peach-blossom colored precipitates with mercuric ion in the presence of sodium acetate.

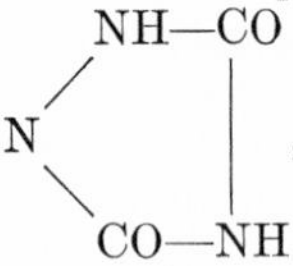

FEIGL REAGENT FOR COPPER. An ammoniacal or alcoholic solution of cupron, $C_6H_5 \cdot CHOH \cdot C(:NOH) \cdot C_6H_5$, gives a green precipitate with copper in neutral or alkaline solutions.

FEIGL REAGENT FOR GOLD, SIL-VER, AND PALLADIUM. A solution of 0.3 g. p-dimethylaminobenzylidenerhoda-nine in 100 ml. acetone. It precipitates these three metals.

FEIGL REAGENT FOR SULFIDES (METALLIC). A mixture in equal volume of a 0.2 N solution of sodium azide and a

FEIGL TEST FOR NICKEL. A modi-fied **Tschugaev test** (q.v.). The solution tested is treated with an excess of ammonia, a little lead dioxide, several drops dilute sodium hydroxide and 8–10 ml. 1% al-coholic dimethylglyoxime solution. On boiling and filtering, nickel produces a yellow-red to deep red color.

FEIGL-ZAPPERT-VASQUEZ TEST FOR ACETIC ACID. Acetic acid is detected by evaporating 1 or 2 drops of solution with a little calcium carbonate, heating the residue in a micro-distilling flask, and exposing to the vapors a paper moistened with an alka-line solution of o-nitrophenol. An indigo color indicates the presence of acetic acid.

FEIGL-ZAPPERT-VASQUEZ TEST FOR METHYL KETONES. The material is dissolved in a solvent other than alcohol, heated and treated with 1 drop alkaline solution of o-nitrobenzaldehyde, and evap-orated. On treatment with chloroform, a blue color indicates the presence of methyl ketones.

FEIST-BENARY SYNTHESIS. A method of formation of **furans** from α-chloro-carbonyl compounds (or α,β-chloroethers) and β-dicarbonyl compounds in the pres-ence of ammonia or pyridine.

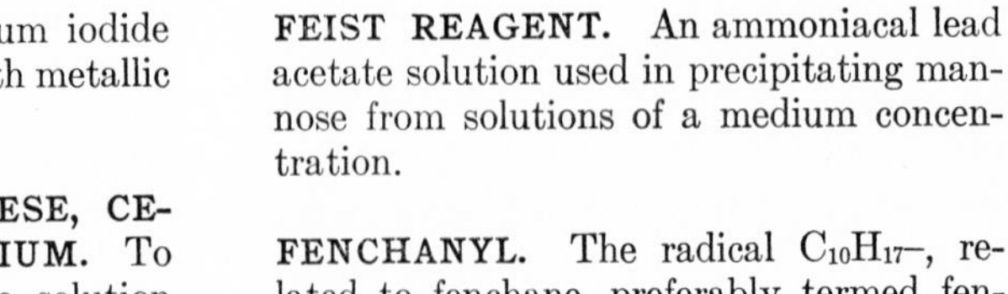

$$CH_3COCH_2Cl + \begin{smallmatrix} CH_2-COOR \\ \ \ \ | \\ CO-CH_3 \end{smallmatrix} \xrightarrow[-HCl]{-H_2O}$$

0.2 N iodine solution in potassium iodide solution. It evolves nitrogen with metallic sulfides.

FEIGL TEST FOR MANGANESE, CE-RIUM, COBALT, AND TITANIUM. To a volume of 50–150 ml. of the solution tested, dilute sodium hydroxide solution containing a little sodium carbonate is added until an alkaline reaction is obtained, then the mixture is heated to boiling, filtered, and spot-tested with benzidine acetate solution. One or more of the above metals is indicated by a blue color.

FEIST REAGENT. An ammoniacal lead acetate solution used in precipitating man-nose from solutions of a medium concen-tration.

FENCHANYL. The radical $C_{10}H_{17}-$, re-lated to fenchane, preferably termed fen-chyl.

FENCHYL. The radical $C_{10}H_{17}-$, related to fenchane.

FENTON-BARR TEST REACTIONS. Characteristic colors are obtained when various organic acids are treated with various phenols in the presence of concentrated sulfuric acid.

FENTON REAGENT FOR KETOHEXOSES. *p*-Phenylhydrazinesulfonic acid.

FENTON REAGENT FOR SODIUM. Dihydroxytartaric acid gives a yellow precipitate with sodium. This test is unaffected by the presence of ammonium and potassium.

FENTON TEST FOR MALONIC ACID. The substance tested is allowed to stand with anhydrous alcohol containing hydrochloric acid. After a few minutes, it is neutralized, bromomethylfurfurol is added, and the mixture barely alkalinized with potassium hydroxide solution. A blue fluorescence indicates the presence of malonic acid.

FENTON TEST REACTION FOR TARTARIC ACID. On addition to a tartrate solution of a little ferrous sulfate, 2 drops hydrogen peroxide, and an excess of alkali, a violet color is obtained.

FERMENT. A material which catalyzes certain organic reactions and which consists of an **enzyme** (q.v., a catalyst which is the product of a living organism or organisms, and which has an organic chemical composition) in association with other substances produced by the living organism, or with the organism or cell itself.

FERMENT, INORGANIC. A term sometimes used, improperly, for a **colloidal solution** of a metal which acts catalytically in a similar manner to organic ferments, showing analogous changes of activity by time and temperature, and whose activity is destroyed by substances which render the enzymes inert.

FERMENT OIL. A **volatile oil** produced by the fermentation of plant material in which the oils are not pre-existent.

FERMENTATION. The process in which an organic substance or substances undergo a change or a variety of changes attributable to the activity of certain living organisms, or of substances derived from animal or vegetable sources, called ferments or **enzymes.**

FERMENTATION, ACETIC. A fermentation which produces acetic acid, commonly in the dilute form (vinegar) from alcohol-containing solutions or substances.

FERMENTATION, ALCOHOLIC. A fermentation which produces ethyl alcohol, commonly by the action of a yeast, such as *Saccharomyces cerevisiae*, on a sugar, or a sugar-containing solution.

FERMENTATION, AMYLOLYTIC. In general, this term means a fermentation of starch; specifically, it is an incomplete fermentation of starch that does not yield simple sugars.

FERMENTATION, BUTYRIC. A fermentation which produces butyric acid.

FERMENTATION, LACTIC. A fermentation that produces lactic acid; generally this term is applied specifically to the fermentation of milk.

FERMENTATION PROCESS FOR STARCH. A method of producing wheat starch by decomposing the glutenous matter by fermentation, releasing the starch granules, which are washed and dried.

FERMENTATION, SELECTIVE. Biochemical resolution of **inactive compounds** (q.v.).

FERMI-DIRAC STATISTICS. A system of **quantum** statistics in which the **eigenfunction** of the system is postulated as being antisymmetric. This system is especially applicable to electrons, and to atoms or molecules containing an odd number of fundamental particles.

FERMI PLOT. See **Kurie plot.**

FERNBACK FLASK. A flask having a flat bottom of large diameter and sides tapering to a much smaller neck. It is used for mold work, especially glucose oxidation by molds, where large surface area is necessary.

FERRARIO REACTION. A reaction of diphenyl ethers and sulfur to yield phenoxathiin and its derivatives.

FERRATE (II). The anion FeO_2^-, $Fe(OH)_4^-$, or $Fe(OH)_6^{4-}$ or a compound containing one of these anions. The last two of these ions, and their compounds, are called hydroxoferrates (II).

FERRATE (II), HYDROXO-. See ferrate (II).

FERRATE (III). The anion FeO_2^-, $Fe_2O_4^-$, or $Fe(OH)_6^{5-}$, or a compound containing one of these anions. The last of these ions, and its compounds, are called hydroxoferrates (III).

FERRATE (III), HYDROXO-. See ferrate (III).

FERRATE (IV). The anion FeO_3^-, or a compound containing it.

FERRATE (VI). The anion FeO_4^-, or a compound containing it.

FERREIRA DA SILVA SOLUTION. A solution of 0.5 g. ammonium selenite in 10 g. concentrated sulfuric acid, used as a test reagent for alkaloids. Characteristic color reactions are obtained.

FERRI-. A prefix indicating content of ferric iron, as in ferricyanide.

FERRIC. Containing or pertaining to trivalent iron.

FERRICYANIC. Related to the ferricyanides, compounds containing the anion $Fe(CN)_6^{3-}$.

FERRICYANIDE. The anion $Fe(CN)_6^{3-}$, or a compound containing it.

FERRIFERROUS. Containing both trivalent and divalent iron.

FERRIOXALATE. See oxalatoferrate.

FERRITE. See ferrate (III).

FERRO-. A prefix indicating content of ferrous iron, as in ferrocyanide.

FERROCYANIC. Related to the ferrocyanides, compounds containing the anion $Fe(CN)_6^{4-}$.

FERROCYANIDE. The anion $Fe(CN)_6^{4-}$, or a compound containing it.

FERRON SOLUTION. A solution of 2 g. 7-iodo-8-hydroxyquinoline-5-sulfonic acid in 100 ml. water, used in the colorimetric determination of iron. A green color in a solution acid to methyl orange is positive for ferric iron.

FERROSILICON PROCESS FOR HYDROGEN. A method of preparing hydrogen of high purity by reaction of powdered ferrosilicon with a 20% aqueous solution of caustic soda at about 90° C.

FERROUS. Containing or pertaining to divalent iron.

FERRUGINOUS. Containing iron.

FERTILIZER. A substance added to soils to replace plant foods abstracted from the soil by vegetation, or as in sandy soil, to furnish nutritive material for plant life. They may be classified as: natural fertilizers, e.g., manure, urine, vegetable compost; and artificial fertilizers, e.g., ammonium salts, nitrates, potassium salts, phosphates, nitrolime, etc.

FICK LAW OF DIFFUSION. See law of diffusion, Fick.

FIEHE REAGENT FOR ARTIFICIAL HONEY. A solution in 100 g. hydrochloric acid of 1 g. resorcinol, used in testing honey for invert sugar, a substance used in making artificial honey. A violet red color indicates the presence of invert sugar.

FIEHE TEST FOR GLUCOSE. To detect commercial glucose in food products, dilute or dissolve 10 g. of the sample with 10 ml. of water, warming if necessary to effect solution. Add 10 ml. of a saturated solution of ammonium oxalate and boil. Add animal charcoal and boil again. Filter and place 2 ml. of the clear filtrate in a test tube, add 2 drops of hydrochloric acid and 20 ml. of 95% alcohol and mix. In the presence of commercial glucose or dextrins a marked white turbidity will be formed.

FIELD. (1) The region in which an event takes place, or a process is carried out. (2) The area visible through an optical instrument.

FIELD, ATOMIC. The region surrounding an atom in which the **repulsion forces** for other particles are considerable.

FIELD, ELECTRIC. The region surrounding an electrically charged body or region of electrical potential; while this region is indefinite in extent, its bounds are considered in practice to be those of the observable effect of the particular electrical process under investigation.

FIELD-INTENSITY, ELECTRIC. The force exerted by an **electric field,** at a given point, upon unit electric charge.

FIELD-INTENSITY, MAGNETIC. The force exerted by a magnetic or electromagnetic field, at a given point, upon unit magnetic pole.

FIELD, MAGNETIC. The region surrounding a magnet or a body exhibiting magnetic properties, or a region of **magnetomotive force;** although this region is indefinite in extent, its bounds are considered in practice to be those of the observable effect of the particular magnetic process under investigation.

FIELD TEST REACTION. Certain organic substances often present in water give a rose-red color with a very dilute aqueous solution of platinic chloride and potassium iodide.

FILHOL TEST. Alkali hydroxides are detected by a blue color given with an aqueous solution of sodium nitroprusside saturated with hydrogen sulfide.

FILLER. A material used to add to the bulk of a mixture or substance; or to occupy the pores and other imperfections in a surface.

FILM. In general, any thin sheet of material used for covering, coating or wrapping, or any thin layer that enters into the structure, usually on or near the surface, of a substance or an object, as the membrane of an organism. Photographic film is a flexible, transparent sheet of material containing substances which undergo a permanent change by action of light.

FILM CONCEPT. The hypothesis that there exists, at surfaces of contact between solids and fluids (liquids or gases), a relatively slowly moving film of the fluid, which decreases in thickness with increasing velocity, parallel to the surface of the main body of fluid.

FILOMUSI-GUELFI TEST. Human blood is differentiated from animal blood because only the latter gives characteristic crystals with a 2% solution of sodium fluoride. In several instances, the crystal form is characteristic of the particular animal.

FILTER. In the most general sense of the term, a filter is a device for removing one or more components of a mixture on passage through it. The nature of the mixture is widely variable. It may be any kind of matter, or material particles, or not matter at all, as in the case of an optical filter, which absorbs certain frequencies of radiant energy and transmits others. Chemists use various methods for separating particles by passage of a liquid containing solid particles through porous media, the size of the pores determining, in the main, the size of the largest particle that will pass through the medium.

FILTER AID. A substance added to a solution to be filtered to assist **filtration,** usually by forming on the filter a bed of material which functions as an auxiliary filter, arresting particles that would otherwise pass through or clog the filter.

FILTER, BACTERIOLOGICAL. A filter designed for filtering small quantities of liquid, such as broth cultures. A common form is a cylindrical chamber designed to contain suitable **filter blocks,** to yield a sterile filtrate from cultures of various bacilli.

FILTER, BAG. An apparatus used for separating solids from gases. It consists essentially of a bag of cloth or wire-mesh having apertures smaller than the solid particles, through which the air or other gas passes, leaving the solids inside.

FILTER, BECKHOLD. An apparatus for the filtration of colloids. It commonly consists of porous discs coated with nitrocellulose.

FILTER, BERKEFELD. An apparatus for filtration made of porous earthenware used to strain out minute particles such as bacteria.

FILTER BLOCK. A porous block of porcelain or similar material used in filtration of small particles, such as microorganisms.

FILTER, BUTTERS. A vacuum leaf filter consisting of a series of rectangular leaves, consisting of a filtering medium such as cocoa matting or wood riffles over which is sewed filter cloth.

FILTER CLOTH. A heavy textile material used in large pressure or vacuum filtering apparatus.

FILTER, COLOR. An apparatus or material capable of absorbing certain wave lengths of light and transmitting others.

FILTER CONE. A small hollow cone, usually metallic, containing small holes or pores, which is placed in the apex of a funnel to hold the end of the folded filter paper away from the outlet, and thus to assist filtration.

FILTER CYLINDER. A porous tube used for filtration.

FILTER, DISC. (1) A type of rotary filter consisting of a series of discs, each of which is covered with filter cloth, and having suction applied to its interior to draw the filtrate through the cloth and build up a cake of solid upon its external surface.

(2) A circular, perforated plate of porcelain or alundum which can be placed in an ordinary funnel, open-bottom crucible or glass holder, in order to support the mass to be filtered.

FILTER, DRUM. See **filter, rotary.**

FILTER, GLASS. A small porous glass cup used to separate precipitated solids from liquids by filtration, usually in quantitative determinations.

FILTER, KELLY. A leaf filter used to filter **slurries** under pressure.

FILTER, LEAF. A type of filter, in which a partial vacuum is applied to the interior of a group of filter leaves, which consist of frames covered with filter cloth and which are immersed in the solution to be filtered. The filtrate is drawn into the apparatus, and the solids are deposited on the leaves.

FILTER, LIGHT. An apparatus capable of absorbing rays of certain wave length so that light which has passed through it is qualitatively modified. (See **filter, color.**)

FILTER, MANTLE. A tube, commonly of metal or glass, around a **filter cylinder** (q.v.).

FILTER, OLIVER. A rotary filter (see **filter, rotary**).

FILTER PAPER. A porous paper used in **filtration.**

FILTER PAPER ANALYSIS. (1) **Filter paper test** (q.v.). (2) **Chromatography** (q.v.). (3) A germination test of seeds on moist filter paper.

FILTER PAPER TEST. A method of testing in which a reagent or reagents and a solution or liquid to be tested are successively applied to filter paper.

FILTER, PASTEUR. A cylindrical tube of unglazed porcelain, or similar material, used in the **filtration** of solid particles, by passage of liquids containing them under pressure or vacuum.

FILTER PLATE. A porous, circular disc used in funnels or other supports for purposes of **filtration**; it may be packed around the edges with asbestos or secured permanently with cement.

FILTER PRESS. A type of apparatus consisting of alternate plates and frames with filter paper or cloth between each frame and the adjacent plate. The materials to be filtered are forced through by a pumping device, the residue is left in the hollow spaces inside the frames, and the effluent is discharged through a manifold.

FILTER PUMP. Any vacuum pump used to assist filtration by evacuating the receiver. The term is used specifically to designate a short tube containing a tapered constriction, which is attached to the water faucet and develops a vacuum in accordance with the **Bernoulli principle.** Filter pumps are also available in positive pressure types.

FILTER, ROTARY (or ROTATORY). A filter consisting of a cylindrical drum covered with a filter cloth, and dipping into a trough or tank containing the solution to be filtered. As the drum rotates, the filtrate is drawn into it usually by suction, and discharged at ports in the end, while the filter cake is removed by a scraper mounted against its periphery.

FILTER STICK. A short tube of glass or porcelain having a porous filter disc (usually integral) on one end, and used most commonly to draw off supernatant liquid from precipitates, especially in micro work.

FILTER STONE. A porous circular disc of ceramic material, used most commonly in soil permeability apparatus.

FILTER TUBE. Any tube used to support or contain the apparatus or medium used in filtration, and to connect it to a filter flask.

FILTER, VACUUM. A filter in which a partial vacuum is used to assist the passage of the liquid through the filtering medium. Since the pressure above the liquid being filtered usually remains atmospheric, and thus relatively constant, the application of the partial vacuum to the other side of the medium induces a pressure differential which forces the liquid through the medium.

FILTRATE. The liquid that has been strained through a filter.

FILTRATION. A **unit operation** in which a solid phase, consisting of discrete particles, is separated from a liquid phase in which it is suspended by passage through a porous medium, whereby some or all of the solid particles are arrested and the liquid passes through.

FILTRATION, PERCOLATION. A process for the purification of liquids by adsorption, in which the liquid flows through or over the bed of adsorbent.

FILTRATOR. An apparatus used in vacuum filtration, consisting of a glass bell with an integral glass neck, and a metal base with suction connector. The bell jar fits tightly into a circumferential slot in the circular base so that the space within the bell jar can be exhausted. The neck can be closed by a one-hole rubber stopper carrying a funnel; filtration can be carried out so that the filtrate runs directly into a beaker within the bell jar.

FINE STRUCTURE CONSTANT. See **atom, Bohr-Sommerfeld.**

FINENESS. (1) The extent of subdivision of a substance. (2) The number of particles in a unit volume of a material. (3) The gold content of an alloy, expressed in parts per thousand.

FINES. Finely-divided material; especially material which is finer than desired, or which passes through a screen on which larger particles are retained.

FINING AGENT. A substance added to a liquid to clarify it. Examples are the addition of certain colloids or other materials to fermented beverages to remove suspended matter, and the use of certain oxides, such as arsenious oxide, in molten glass to aid in the removal of air bubbles.

FINISHING AGENT, MATERIAL, or SUBSTANCE. A substance used to confer certain desired properties upon another substance, such as resistance to shrinking,

oxidation, combustion, etc., and which is commonly applied or incorporated in the latter stages of the manufacturing process.

makes it relatively resistant to fire. (2) Material which will not support combustion.

FIRST LAW OF THERMODYNAMICS. See **law of conservation of energy,** and **thermodynamics.**

FISCHER-HEPP REARRANGEMENT. The rearrangement of a **nitroso** derivative of a secondary aromatic amine to a p-nitrosoarylamine, which is brought about by an alcoholic solution of hydrogen chloride, and similar reagents.

$$(C_6H_5)_2N \cdot NO \rightarrow C_6H_5 \cdot NH \cdot C_6H_4 \cdot NO(p).$$

FISCHER INDOLE SYNTHESIS. A method of formation of **indole** derivatives by ring closure of aromatic **hydrazones.**

FIRE. Burning gas or other material, at a temperature at which it is luminous.

FIRE FOAM. A multi-phase system containing carbon dioxide gas-bubbles, commonly consisting of a viscous or heavy colloidal solution in water of some suspended solid, from which the gas bubbles escape slowly.

FIRE POINT. The minimum temperature at which a substance burns continuously, usually under specified test conditions.

FISCHER-JENNINGS TEST. To differentiate aldoses and ketoses, add 0.2 g. resorcinol to 2 ml. of the sugar solution, then treat with hydrogen chloride gas. Allow to stand for 12 hours, dilute with water, alkalinize with sodium hydroxide, and warm with **Fehling solution** (q.v.). Aldoses give a red-violet color; ketoses do not.

FISCHER OXAZOLE SYNTHESIS. A method of formation of oxazoles from aldehyde cyanhydrins and aldehydes.

$$R'CHOHCN + R''CHO \xrightarrow[\text{ether}]{\text{HCl}} \begin{array}{c} R' \quad O \quad R'' \\ \text{(oxazole ring)} \\ N \end{array} + H_2O.$$

FIRE-POLISHING. A method of smoothing the sharp edges of glass by slightly fusing them in a flame.

FIREPROOF. (1) To impregnate combustible material with a substance that

FISCHER PEPTIDE SYNTHESIS. A method of synthesis of peptides in which α-amino acids (or peptides containing a free amino group) react with acid halides of α-haloacids, followed by amination with ammonia.

$$Cl \cdot CHR' \cdot COCl + H_2N \cdot CHR'' \cdot COOH \xrightarrow{-HCl} Cl \cdot CHR' \cdot CONH \cdot CHR'' \cdot COOH \xrightarrow{NH_3}$$
$$\text{(1)} \qquad \qquad \text{(2)} \qquad \qquad \text{(3)}$$

$$NH_2 \cdot CHR' \cdot CONH \cdot CHR'' \cdot COOH.$$
$$\text{(4)}$$

The above reaction can be used repeatedly by forming the acid chloride of the intermediate product (3), and condensing it with another molecule of an α-amino acid, (2), to form another intermediate molecule of type (3), before the final amination of the terminal carbon atom.

FISCHER PHENYLHYDRAZINE SYNTHESIS. The method of production of aromatic hydrazines by reducing diazo compounds to hydrazine-sulfonic acids, followed by hydrolysis.

$$RN_2Cl + 2Na_2SO_3 + H_2O \rightarrow RNHNHSO_3Na + NaCl + Na_2SO_4$$
$$ H_2O \downarrow HCl$$
$$RNH \cdot NH_2 \cdot HCl + NaHSO_4$$

FISCHER PHENYLHYDRAZONE AND OSAZONE REACTION. The reaction of phenylhydrazine with sugars with the formation of phenylhydrazones and diphenylhydrazones (osazones).

FISCHER REAGENT FOR ALDEHYDES AND KETONES. A solution of 1 part phenylhydrazine hydrochloride and 1 part sodium acetate in 10 parts water. It forms hydrazones with aldehydes and ketones.

FISCHER REAGENT FOR BERYLLIUM. An alkaline, violet solution of quinalizarin, which changes to blue with alkaline solutions of beryllium ion.

FISCHER REAGENTS FOR COBALT. (1) Glyoxaline, which gives violet-blue precipitates; and (2) an ammoniacal solution of diphenylthiocarbazone, which gives a violet color.

FISCHER REAGENT FOR METALS. Diphenylthiocarbazone, which gives red, brown, or purple precipitates with many metals when they are in solution made alkaline by ammonium hydroxide.

FISCHER REAGENT FOR WATER. A reagent prepared by mixing 8 moles pyridine and 2 moles sulfur dioxide, adding about 15 moles methanol, and then 1 mole iodine. The reagent is used in the accurate determination of water.

FISCHER-SPEIER ESTERIFICATION METHOD. The method of forming esters directly from acids and alcohols by heating in the presence of a mineral acid. If they are volatile, as is often the case, a reflux condenser is used.

FISCHER TEST FOR FLUORIDE. Add to 1 ml. of an acetic acid solution of the substance tested, 0.5 ml. saturated sodium acetate solution, 1 drop 0.2% eosin solution, and 0.5 ml. 1% solution of lanthanum acetate in very dilute acetic acid. A red precipitate shows fluoride.

FISCHER TEST FOR HYDROGEN SULFIDE. A modified **Lauth and Caro test** (q.v.). On addition to a hydrogen sulfide solution of p-dimethylphenylenediamine sulfate, then ferric chloride in strong hydrochloric acid solution, a deep (methylene) blue color appears.

FISCHER TEST REACTION FOR BENZALDEHYDE. When benzaldehyde is heated with twice its volume of dimethylaniline and sulfuric acid, leucomalachite green is formed. On dilution with water, and addition of potassium dichromate and sodium acetate, the green color of malachite green appears.

FISCHER TEST REACTION FOR COBALT. An aqueous solution of potassium nitrite and acetic acid produces a yellow precipitate with a cobalt salt solution.

FISCHER TEST REACTION FOR TERTIARY AMINES. An aqueous solution of potassium ferrocyanide, when added in amount equivalent to that of the hydrochloride of the tertiary amine in aqueous solution, gives a precipitate which recrystallizes from alcohol to yield colorless leaflets, becoming blue in air.

FISCHER-TROPSCH PROCESS. A process for the synthesis of **hydrocarbons** and their oxygen derivatives by the combination of hydrogen and carbon monoxide, under carefully controlled conditions of temperature and pressure, and in the presence of certain **catalysts.**

FISHEL-KETOSE TEST REACTION. A method for determining levulose by treatment with a freshly-prepared aqueous solution of Rochelle salt, disodium phosphate, sodium carbonate, and cupric sulfate.

FISSION. A process undergone by certain atomic nuclei in which they break up into atoms of much lower atomic weight, and of an aggregate mass less than that of the parent nucleus; the lost mass appears as energy in amount $\Delta E = c^2 \Delta m$, where Δm is the change in mass, and c^2 the square of the velocity of light (approx. 9×10^{20} (cm/sec)^2).

The process of fission is initiated by the bombardment with certain particles and radiations, especially **neutrons** of **resonance energy,** of certain fissionable atomic species, such as the uranium isotopes $_{92}U^{235}$ and $_{92}U^{238}$, the transuranic element plutonium $_{94}Pu^{239}$ (which may also have other fissionable isotopes), a certain isotope or isotopes of the transuranic element neptunium $_{93}Np$, etc. An equation for the fission reaction has been given for $_{92}U^{235}$ as follows:

$$100\ _{92}U^{235} + 100\ _{0}n^1 \rightarrow$$
$$29.1\ Zr + 25.2\ Mo + 22.2\ Nd + 19.7\ Ba$$
$$+ 13.0\ Xe + 12.5\ Ce + 12.4\ Ru$$
$$+ 11.0\ Cs + 6.5\ La + 6.2\ Pr +$$
$$+ 6.2\ Tc + 4.6\ Y + 4.0\ Rb$$
$$+ 3.7\ Sr + 3.05\ Kr + 2.7\ Pm$$
$$+ 2.15\ Te + 1.88\ Sm + 1.52\ Pd$$
$$+ 0.75\ Eu + 0.23\ Ag + 0.18\ I$$
$$+ 0.081\ Sn + 0.062\ Cd$$
$$+ 0.052\ Gd + 0.031\ Sb + 0.010\ In$$
$$+ 200\text{–}300\ _{0}n^1 + \Delta E.$$

Fission reactions have also been observed in processes carried out in powerful modified cyclotrons, such as the one at Berkeley, which has produced fission of atoms of elements extending down the atomic number range as far as lead, platinum, and tantalum, by bombardment with 200 m.e.v. protons and 400 m.e.v. α-particles. These fissions, unlike some of those produced by resonance neutrons in elements of higher atomic number such as uranium, neptunium, plutonium, etc., are not chain reactions. They also differ from the other type of fission in that the various atoms produced by the cyclotron fission all lie in the same mass number range, while those from the resonant neutron-induced fissions are commonly of two mass number ranges, as seen in the reaction written above for the uranium 235 fission.

FITTIG REACTION. The synthesis of aryl **hydrocarbons** by treatment of halogen-substituted aryl compounds with metallic sodium. Thus, bromobenzene yields diphenyl:

$$2C_6H_5Br + 2Na \rightarrow C_6H_5 - C_6H_5 + 2NaBr.$$

The formation of hydrocarbons from equimolar proportions of an aryl halide and an alkyl halide is sometimes called the Fittig reaction, although it is more commonly known as the **Wurtz-Fittig** reaction. Cf. **Wurtz reaction** and **Wurtz-Fittig reaction.**

FIXATION. In general, the act or process of making secure or permanent. Examples are found in microscopy, where the term is applied to the preparation of slides from specimens or sections cut from them; in photography, where the term is applied to the removal from photographic film or other media, after exposure, of the unchanged light-sensitive substances, to prevent further change and hence marring the picture; in immunology, to the method of preventing **hemolysis** by the **complement;** in perfume and flavor formulation, to the use of high boiling components to make the evaporation of the mixture uniform; and chemistry, to reactions and processes by which free nitrogen enters into chemical combination. (See **nitrogen fixation.**)

FIXATIVE. A substance which is employed to increase the durability, or resistance to decay or wear, of another substance or product. Thus, fixatives are used in perfumes to reduce evaporation losses of important components; in dyeing to form less soluble compounds with the dyes; and in histology, to preserve tissues.

FIXED OIL. A fatty or nonvolatile oil, e.g., olive, linseed, castor oils, etc. (See **fatty oil.**)

FIXING AGENT. See **fixative.**

FIXING BATH. A solution of sodium thiosulfate ("hypo") used in photography to dissolve the silver salts which remain unreduced in a photographic emulsion that has been exposed and developed.

FLAME. A reaction or reaction-product, partly or entirely gaseous, which yields heat and more or less light, as the result of a chemical reaction, commonly oxidation.

FLAME COLOR. A characteristic color imparted to a nonluminous flame by certain atoms or substances containing them, due to the excitation of their flame spectra. (See **spectrum, flame.**)

FLAME, LUMINOUS. A pale or bright colored flame, as a candle flame or a sodium light. This term is also applied to the inner cone or reducing portion of the Bunsen flame, and to the inner parts of other gas flames that show two portions.

FLAME, NONLUMINOUS. A flame that is dark in color, and of little brightness; or the oxidizing or outer part of the Bunsen flame, and outer parts of other gas flames that show two portions.

FLASH EVAPORATION. Very rapid evaporation, especially as applied in industrial processes, in which liquids are heated under pressure, and the pressure is subsequently suddenly reduced causing the liquid, which is then superheated, to evaporate rapidly.

FLASH POINT. In general, the minimum temperature that will enable combustion or explosion to take place. It is an important property of lubricating oils, other oils, and some solvents, being the minimum temperature at which the vapor from a liquid will ignite under specified conditions of testing.

FLASH ROASTER. A furnace used for the combustion of very fine ores, in which the pulverized ore is blown from a nozzle into a combustion chamber.

FLASH SPECTRUM. See **spectrum, flash.**

FLASK. A container, most commonly of glass, used to hold substances in the laboratory and provided with a neck for handling and pouring; occasionally the term is used in industry, as a mercury flask.

FLASK, ACETYLIZATION. A small (usually 50–100 ml.) round-bottom flask with a condensing tube fitted to its stopper, usually of ground glass. This apparatus is often used for determining menthol in oil of peppermint.

FLASK, ASSAY. A flask of conical shape.

FLASK, BOILING. A flask having a long, cylindrical neck and a spherical body.

FLASK, CLAISEN. A distilling flask with two necks; usually the vapor tube is connected to the branch-neck, allowing the main neck to be used for introducing materials or holding a stirrer.

FLASK, CULTURE. A flask designed for growing one or more kinds of microorganisms. Many variations of such flasks have been developed for specific microorganisms. See **Pasteur flask** and **Koble flask.**

FLASK, DELIVERY. A flask calibrated to deliver a specified volume of liquid.

FLASK, DEWAR. A double-walled flask, the space between the walls of which is evacuated to reduce heat transmission so that the flask may be used to hold liquefied gases.

FLASK, DISTILLING. Basically, a flask with spherical body and cylindrical neck, carrying a tube that is directed downward. Many additions and modifications are known, some under special names. See **flask, Claisen** and **Ladenburg flask.**

FLASK, ERLENMEYER. See **Erlenmeyer flask.**

FLASK, FERNBACK. See **Fernback flask.**

FLASK, FILTERING. A flask used for vacuum filtration. It is made of heavy glass and has a side tube for attachment of the suction tube.

FLASK, FLORENCE. A flask having a spherical body, flattened on the bottom, and a cylindrical neck.

FLASK, IODINE. A flask designed to be used for the determination of **iodine absorption number** (q.v.). Such flasks are often provided with a glass stopper having a mercury-seal rim.

FLASK, JACOBS-SINGER. See **Jacobs-Singer separatory flask.**

FLASK, KJELDAHL. See **Kjeldahl flask.**

FLASK, KNORR. See **Knorr flask.**

FLASK, KOBLE. See **Koble flask.**

FLASK, KOHLRAUSCH VOLUMETRIC. See **Kohlrausch volumetric flask.**

FLASK, LADENBURG. See **Ladenburg flask.**

FLASK, MOJONNIER. See **Mojonnier flask.**

FLASK, PASTEUR. See **Pasteur flask.**

FLASK, VACUUM. A flask of the Dewar type (see **Dewar flask**).

FLASK, VOLUMETRIC. A flask calibrated to contain or deliver a definite volume of liquid.

FLAVO-, FLAV-. (Latin) *Flavus*, yellow; as flavoprotein, flavone; specifically, designating certain series of coordination compounds.

FLAVORING SUBSTANCE. Any material used principally to add flavor to an industrial product, a food or a pharmaceutical preparation.

FLECK TEST REACTION. A solution of picric acid in 10% hydrochloric acid gives a blue color on addition of zinc. Dinitrocresol gives a blood-red color.

FLEIG BLOOD REAGENT. A test reagent for blood in urine, made by adding 10 g. powdered zinc to a solution of 0.25 g. fluorescein and 20 g. potassium hydroxide in 100 ml. water. A fluorescence, in the presence of hydrogen peroxide, indicates the presence of blood.

FLEIG TEST REACTIONS FOR CARBO-HYDRATES. (1) On heating 0.5 ml. of a dilute solution of many of the carbohydrates with 4 ml. hydrochloric acid, a yellow to orange-red color forms on addition of 4 drops 0.1% alcoholic indole solution. (2) On addition of 2 drops of a saturated solution of carbazole in alcohol, and 1 ml. sulfuric acid to 0.5 ml. of the carbohydrate solution, a violet-red color is produced.

FLEISCHMANN TEST. Alcohol is detected in volatile oils by shaking the oil with water, and adding potassium dichromate and sulfuric acid to the water-extract. A green color indicates alcohol.

FLEMING TUBE. A laboratory apparatus used for the determination of carbon. The gases obtained by combustion of the sample pass through the tube, where the carbon dioxide is taken up by suitable absorbents.

FLEMMING SOLUTION. An aqueous solution of osmic acid, chromic acid, and acetic acid, used as a fixative for specimens.

FLETCHER-HOPKINS TEST. Lactic acid is detected by heating a few drops of the liquid containing it for 1–2 minutes on the water bath with 5 ml. sulfuric acid and

1 drop saturated cupric sulfate solution. Cool, add 2–3 drops of a solution of 10–20 drops thiophene in 100 ml. alcohol and heat on the steam bath. A cherry-red color indicates lactic acid.

FLEURY TEST REACTION FOR BENZOIC ACID. To 10 ml. benzoic acid solution, add 3 drops dilute ferric chloride solution, 3 drops hydrogen peroxide, and 3 drops 3% ferrous sulfate solution. A violet color results.

FLICK SOLUTION. A solution of 15 ml. hydrochloric acid and 10 ml. hydrofluoric acid in 90 ml. water, used in etching aluminum.

FLOAT. A small air-filled tube of glass used in a burette to facilitate reading, or a bobbin or other device made of some material like talc, glass, or metal, etc., used in a **rotameter** (q.v.) to indicate velocity of fluid flow.

FLOCCULENT. Woolly; occurring in indefinite masses like locks of wool. This term is used to describe the characteristic appearance of certain precipitates or organisms.

FLOOD REACTION. A method for the preparation of trialkylhalosilanes from (1) trialkylsilylsulfates and hydrogen chloride, or from (2) hexaalkalyldisiloxanes on treatment with sulfuric acid and ammonium halide. On treatment with sulfuric acid, the hexaalkyldisiloxanes yield the trialkylsilylsulfates that are the initial reactants in (1).

separated from the **gangue** by establishing a differential **surface tension** that causes segregation of particles. The usual method is to treat the finely-ground material with oils or other agents which modify the surface tension of a water-air-particle system, then mix the material with water and blow with air. The concentrated ore is skimmed off in the foam, and the gangue settles to the bottom.

FLOW CURVE. A graphical relationship between the pressure applied to a liquid or plastic solid, or system containing such substances, and the resulting rate of flow.

FLOW METER (FLOWMETER). (1) An instrument used to measure the rate of flow of a fluid in pipes or other restricted areas. Most flow meters operate on the **Venturi principle.** Recording flow meters are provided with a clockwork mechanism and means for recording the rate of flow, so that the total quantity over any period may be computed, or reported directly by the apparatus.
(2) An instrument used to measure the flowing quality of a paint or other finishing material.

FLOW METER (ORIFICE). An instrument which measures the rate of flow of a fluid from the pressure differential across a calibrated orifice introduced into the pipe carrying the fluid.

FLOW, MOLECULAR. See **molecular flow.**

$$(R_3Si)_2SO_4 + 2HCl \xrightarrow{(NH_4)_2SO_4} 2R_3SiCl + H_2SO_4$$

$$R_3SiOSiR_3 + H_2SO_4 + 2NH_4Cl \rightarrow 2R_3SiCl + (NH_4)_2SO_4 + H_2O.$$

FLORENCE REAGENT. A mixture of 50 g. alcohol, 50 g. chloroform, and 50 g. pyridine, containing 7.5 g. zinc acetate, used in testing for blood and bile pigments in urine. The bile pigments cause a fluorescence, whereas blood gives a pink to cherry-red color.

FLOTATION OF ORES. A process for concentrating ores in which the mineral is

FLOW SHEET. A chart or diagram listing the various stages or operations in the manufacture of one or more products, arranged in the sequence in which they take place and showing their interrelationships.

FLOWING JUNCTION. A method of setting up a junction between two **electrolytes** which has important advantages for use in electrochemical measurements, especially of **electrode potential.** In its simplest form, this arrangement consists of an upward current of the heavier electrolyte meeting a downward current of the other at a point where a horizontal outlet tube joins the vertical tube through which the liquids enter.

FLÜCKINGER TEST REACTIONS FOR ALKALOIDS. Atropine, on heating with equal volumes glacial acetic acid and concentrated sulfuric acid, gives a green-yellow fluorescence, and on cooling, a pleasant odor.

Brucine when dissolved in dilute sulfuric acid, on addition of 1 drop dilute potassium dichromate solution, becomes raspberry red, then orange-red, then brown.

Cocaine hydrochloride mixed with caramel gives a black color with dilute alcohol.

Colchicine is colored yellow in dilute solution by sulfuric acid, and blue-violet by nitric acid.

Digitalin is colored green by hot concentrated phosphoric acid, the acid turning yellow.

FLÜCKINGER TESTS FOR PHENOL AND NAPHTHOLS. When ammonia is added to a phenol solution, and the mixture exposed to bromine vapor, a blue color results.

α-Naphthol, with a few drops 10% ferric chloride solution, gives a white precipitate and then a violet color; β-naphthol gives a green solution and then a white turbidity.

FLUCTUATION. Any erratic, momentary deviation of a physical quantity from its mean (average) value.

FLUID. A state of matter which is unable to support a steady longitudinal stress without lateral support; therefore, a gas or liquid.

FLUID DRAM. A unit of volume in the apothecary's system, equal to 60 minims or $\frac{1}{8}$ fluid ounce.

FLUID DYNAMIC PRESSURE. The pressure necessary to accelerate a fluid from rest to a given velocity. This pressure may be calculated by the expression:

$$P_D = \frac{\rho V^2}{2}$$

where P_D is the dynamic pressure, ρ is the **density** of the fluid, and V is its velocity.

FLUID, ELASTIC. A condition of matter in which the molecules flow without apparent resistance, i.e., a gas.

FLUID EXTRACT. See **extract, fluid.**

FLUID HEAD. The height of a column of a fluid which exerts a pressure equal to that of the fluid itself at a given point.

FLUID OUNCE. A unit of volume in the apothecary's system equal in the United States to $\frac{1}{128}$ American gallon. The fluid ounce in the British Apothecary's System is equal to $\frac{1}{160}$ Imperial gallon.

FLUIDITY. The property of a substance that expresses its ability to flow, as contrasted with **viscosity,** which is the resistance to flow. Fluidity is a measure of the rate at which a fluid is deformed by a shearing stress, and is mathematically the reciprocal of the viscosity.

FLUO- (or FLUOR- or FLUORO-). A prefix indicating content of fluorine, as fluobenzene, fluorochloroform. The prefix fluo- also indicates the presence of **fluorescence** (q.v.).

FLUOALUMINATE. The anion AlF_4^-, $AlF_5^=$, AlF_6^{3-}, or $Al_3F_{14}^{5-}$, or a compound containing one of these anions.

FLUOANTIMONATE (III). The anion SbF_4^-, $SbF_5^=$, or SbF_6^{3-}, or a compound containing one of these anions.

FLUOANTIMONATE (V). The anion SbF_6^- or $SbF_4(OH)_2^-$, or a compound containing one of these anions.

FLUOARSENATE (V). The anion AsF_6^-, or a compound containing it.

FLUOBERYLLATE. The anion BeF_3^- or $BeF_4^=$, or a compound containing one of these anions.

FLUOBORATE. The anion $BO_2F_2{}^{3-}$ or $BF_4{}^-$, or a compound containing one of these anions.

FLUOCHROMATE (III). The anion $CrF_6{}^{3-}$, or a compound containing it.

FLUOCHROMATE (VI). The anion CrO_3F^-, or a compound containing it.

FLUOFERRATE (III). The anion $FeF_4{}^-$ or $FeF_6{}^{3-}$, or a compound containing one of these anions.

FLUOGERMANATE. The anion $GeF_6{}^=$, or a compound containing it.

FLUOHAFNATE. The anion $HfF_6{}^-$, or a compound containing it.

FLUOIODATE (V). The anion $IO_2F_2{}^-$, or a compound containing it.

FLUOMOLYBDATE (VI). The anion $MoO_3F_2{}^=$, $MoO_2F_3{}^-$, $MoO_3F_3{}^{3-}$, $MoO_2F_4{}^=$, or $MoOF_5{}^-$, or a compound containing one of these anions.

FLUONIOBATE (V). The anions $NbOF_4{}^-$, $NbOF_5{}^=$, $NbF_6{}^-$, $NbOF_6{}^{3-}$, or $NbF_7{}^-$, or a compound containing one of these anions.

FLUOPHOSPHATE. The anion $PO_3F^=$, $PO_2F_2{}^-$, or $PF_6{}^-$, or a compound containing one of these anions.

FLUORATE. The anion $FO_3{}^-$, or a compound containing it.

FLUORENYL. The radical $C_{13}H_9$— derived from fluorene. This radical has 5 isomers.

FLUORENYLIDENE. The radical $C_{13}H_8=$,

Derived from fluorene.

FLUORESCENCE. (Epipolism, epipolic dispersion) A property possessed by certain substances of absorbing **radiant energy** of definite wave length and of emitting it as waves of different length, characteristic of the substance. The phenomenon ceases when the illumination is cut off (difference from phosphorescence). Chlorophyll solutions show a red fluorescence, quinine sulfate solutions a pale blue, fluorspar a violet fluorescence.

FLUORESCENCE ANALYSIS. Methods of analysis based upon irradiation with **ultraviolet light,** and observation of the color and intensity of the fluorescent radiation emitted by the sample.

FLUORESCENCE MICROSCOPE. See **microscope, fluorescence.**

FLUORESCENCE, RESONANCE. See **resonance fluorescence.**

FLUORESCENT SCREEN. A plate coated with a material readily fluorescent. It is used to observe certain patterns or other properties of invisible radiations, such as x-rays, from the fluorescent radiations emitted by the screen.

FLUORHENATE (IV). The anion $ReF_6{}^-$, or a compound containing it.

FLUORHODATE (III). The anion $RhF_6{}^{3-}$, or a compound containing it.

FLUORIC. Containing or derived from fluorine.

FLUORIDATION. Treatment with **fluorine;** as for example, the treatment of water supplies, to which fluorine is often added to benefit the teeth of the members of the community.

FLUORIDE. (1) The ion F^-, or a compound containing it. (2) Hence, a salt of hydrofluoric acid (H_2F_2). (3) A binary compound of **fluorine.**

FLUORIDE ("ACID"). The ion $HF_2{}^-$, or a compound containing it.

FLUORINATION. The introduction of fluorine into an organic molecule.

FLUORINE. Gaseous element. Symbol F. Atomic number 9. Atomic weight 19.00. Molecular weight 38.00. Density of the liquid fluorine 1.108. Melting point $-218°$ C. Boiling point $-187°$ C. Valence 1. Fluorine occurs in cryolite and fluorspar. It is very reactive. Acid H_2F_2.

FLUORO- See fluo.

FLUOROCARBON. A compound of fluorine and carbon. Large numbers of such compounds are known; in many of their properties they resemble the hydrocarbons. The series C_nF_{2n+2} shows a sequence of increasing boiling points in successive members that is closely analogous to that of the paraffin hydrocarbons. The chemical inertness of the fluorocarbons makes them useful as solvents, lubricants, and insulators.

FLUOROCHROME. A substance that causes another material, upon contact, to become fluorescent.

FLUOROGEN. A radical which, by its presence in a compound, causes fluorescence.

FLUOROMETRY. Measurement of the intensity and color of fluorescent radiations.

FLUOROPHORE. See fluorogen.

FLUOROSCOPE. (1) An apparatus for the determination of fluorescence by visual comparison, by means of an optical system, with a standard. (2) A screen of fluorescent material used to transform invisible radiation (x-rays, γ-rays, etc.) to visible light.

FLUOSILICATE. The anion $SiO_4F_2^{6-}$ or $SiF_6^=$, or a compound containing one of these anions.

FLUOSILICIC. Related to fluosilicic acid, H_2SiF_6.

FLUOSTANNATE (IV). The anion $SnF_6^=$ or $HSnF_8^{3-}$, or a compound containing one of these anions.

FLUOSULFONATE. The anion SO_3F^-, or a compound containing it.

FLUOTANTALATE. The anion $TaOF_5^=$, TaF_6^-, $TaOF_6^{3-}$, $TaF_7^=$, or TaF_8^{3-}, or a compound containing one of these anions.

FLUOTELLURATE. The anion $TeO_3F_2^=$, or a compound containing it.

FLUOTELLURITE. The anion TeF_5^-, or a compound containing it.

FLUOTHORATE. The anion ThF_5^-, or a compound containing it.

FLUOTITANATE (III). The anion TiF_6^{3-}, or a compound containing it.

FLUOTITANATE (IV). The anion $TiF_6^=$ or TiF_7^{3-}, or a compound containing one of these anions.

FLUOTUNGSTATE (VI). The anion $WO_3F_3^{3-}$ or $WO_2F_4^=$, or a compound containing one of these anions.

FLUOURANATE (VI). The anion $UO_2F_3^-$ or $UO_2F_5^{3-}$, or a compound containing one of these anions.

FLUOVANADATE (III). The anion VF_6^{3-}, or a compound containing it.

FLUOVANADATE (V). The anion $VO_2F_3^=$, $VO_2F_4^{3-}$, $VOF_5^=$, or VF_6^-, or a compound containing one of these anions.

FLUOZIRCONATE. The anion $ZrF_6^=$ or ZrF_7^{3-}, or a compound containing one of these anions.

FLUSHED COLORS. Pigments which have been mixed while wet with vehicles and other components of paints. Flushed colors have higher tinting strength and give more gloss than dry colors.

FLUX. (1) Any substance used to facilitate the fusion of a metal or mineral, as borax, lime, or fluorite. (2) The quantity of a force which passes through unit area in a given time. (3) Flow, often with the connotation of periodic reversal in direction.

FOAM. A system containing gaseous and liquid phases, in which the former is more or less intimately dispersed throughout the latter.

FOG. (1) A two-phase system consisting of liquid particles or droplets dispersed in a continuous gaseous phase. (2) Extra-spectral blackening of a photographic emulsion.

FOG CHAMBER. A confined space in which **supersaturation** of air or other gas is produced by reduction of pressure, cooling, or other means, in order to study the movement and interaction of electrified particles by the condensation (fog tracks) they produce.

FOG TRACKS. Linear regions of **condensation,** produced in air or other gases that are supersaturated with water vapor, by the passage of electrified particles. Fog tracks are useful in following the courses and collisions of such particles.

FOGES TEST. Chlorates and bromates are detected by treating a solution containing a few drops of either of them with 1 ml. of a solution of 0.8 g. strychnine in 24 ml. nitric acid (sp. gr. 1.334). A red color is obtained.

FOLIN APPARATUS. Laboratory apparatus used in the determination of ammonia, urea, and other nitrogenous substances in solution.

FOLIN-DENIS REAGENT FOR PHENOLS. A solution of 100 g. sodium tungstate, 20 g. phosphomolybdic acid, and 50 ml. 85% phosphoric acid in water, adjusted to a volume of 1 liter, used as a test reagent for phenols. A blue color indicates the presence of phenols.

FOLIN-DENIS REAGENT FOR TYROSINE. An aqueous solution containing 10% sodium tungstate, 2% phosphomolybdic acid, and 10% phosphoric acid, used as a test reagent for tyrosine. A blue color indicates the presence of tyrosine.

FOLIN-DENIS REAGENT FOR URIC ACID. A solution of 10 g. sodium tungstate in 80 ml. 85% phosphoric acid and 750 ml. water, which is refluxed for two hours and made up to 1 liter. It gives a blue color with uric acid and sodium carbonate solution.

FOLIN-McELLROY REAGENT. A solution of 50 g. sodium carbonate, 100 g. sodium pyrophosphate, and 30 g. disodium phosphate dissolved in 1 liter of water, the resulting solution being then mixed with a solution of 13 g. cupric sulfate in 1 liter water. This reagent is used for testing for glucose in urine. A greenish-yellow or red precipitate indicates the presence of glucose.

FOLIN MIXTURE. An aqueous solution of 500 g. ammonium sulfate, 5 g. uranium acetate, and 6 g. acetic acid in a volume of 1 liter, used in testing for uric acid.

FOOD. A substance used to maintain certain essential biological processes in living organisms, notably to furnish cell and tissue-building materials, and to provide heat and energy, as well as to supply auxiliary substances needed for the functioning of these processes.

FOOD, PROTECTIVE. Any food commonly used to supplement nutrition by supplying certain **vitamins** or other factors that may be deficient.

FOOT. A unit of length in the **English system.** One foot = $\frac{1}{3}$ yard = 12 inches. One foot = 0.305 meter.

FOOT, CUBIC. A unit of volume in the **English system.** 1 cubic foot = 0.0283 cubic meter.

FOOT POUND. A unit of **work** defined as the work necessary to lift a pound mass through a distance of one foot against the force of gravity.

FOOT POUNDAL. A unit of force, defined as the force that produces an acceleration of one foot per second in a mass of one pound.

FOOT, SQUARE. A unit of area in the **English system.** 1 square foot = $\frac{1}{9}$ square yard. 1 square foot = 0.0929 square meter.

FOOTS. Sediment that accumulates at the bottom of a tank or other vessel containing crude liquids, such as vegetable oils.

FORCE. A fundamental physical entity derived from the universal experience of the effects produced upon objects by the application of muscular effort, and which connotes that which tends to produce a change in the direction or magnitude of the motion of a body upon which it acts, or to produce a change in shape or form. Force is defined in terms of the acceleration imparted to a body per unit mass, and such units of force are the **dyne** in the metric system and the **poundal** in the English system; however, they are replaced in the practical engineering use of these systems by gravitational units, which are simply the weights of unit mass in each system.

FORCE, CATABIOTIC. Energy derived from the **metabolism** of food.

FORCE, CATALYTIC. See **catalysis.**

FORCE, CENTRIFUGAL. In uniform circular motion, the reaction of a moving body against being pulled out of a straight line. It is measured by the product of the mass times the acceleration,

$$F = mv^2/r,$$

where m is mass, v, velocity, and r, the radius of the circle described by the moving body. The force required to counteract centrifugal force and to continue the body in circular motion is known as "centripetal" force.

FORCE CONSTANTS OF LINKAGES. Expressions of the forces acting between **nuclei** to restrain relative displacement. They provide the means of measurement of the resistance to stretching of the **valence bond** and the resistance to deformation of the **valence angle,** and they express these factors mathematically.

FORCE, ELECTROMOTIVE. See **electromotive force.**

FORCE, VITAL. Force inherent in and characteristic of living organisms. It was formerly considered that vital force modified the chemical reactions of the organism and produced compounds which could not be synthesized without its aid. This view

has been thoroughly disproved especially by organic chemistry which has synthesized, *in vitro,* a large number of the products of living cells.

FORD CONTINUOUS SHEET PROCESS. A continuous process for the manufacture of sheet glass, in which the molten glass flows onto a metal table, where it is leveled by metal rollers, and then passed through an annealing furnace.

FORMAMIDO. The radical $HCONH-$.

FORMANEK REACTION FOR METALS. Five ml. of an alcoholic extract of alkanna root is added to a solution of metallic chlorides or nitrates, and the absorption spectrum is observed. Then the effects of adding traces of ammonia are noted.

FORMATE. A compound containing the

radical H—C ⟨with O double-bonded above and $O-$ below⟩ .

FORMATION, HEAT OF. See **heat of formation.**

FORMAZYL. The radical

$$C_6H_5N:N$$
$$\searrow$$
$$C-.$$
$$\nearrow$$
$$C_6H_5NHN$$

FORMIC. Related to formic acid, $HCOOH$.

FORMOL TITRATION. The addition of formaldehyde in quantity sufficient to combine with any **amino groups** in a compound, prior to the titration of carboxy groups, or other acid groups, with standard alkali. This method is used in the analysis of **amino acids.**

FORMOLITE. The solid product obtained by treating with sulfuric acid and formaldehyde those mineral oils which contain unsaturated cyclic hydrocarbons.

The process is known as the formolite reaction, and the weight of air-dry formolite obtained from 100 g. of oil is known as the formolite number of the oil. The reaction is also called the "formalin" reaction.

FORMOLITE NUMBER. See **formolite.**

FORMULA. (1) A statement in chemical symbols of the composition of a substance. (2) A recipe for the preparation of some mixture or compound. (3) A mathematical statement of a law.

FORMULA, ATOMIC. A term sometimes used for a **structural formula.** (See **formula, structural.**)

FORMULA, CONSTITUTIONAL. A formula that shows the molecular structure (or constitution) of a substance in two dimensions, e.g.,

$$\begin{array}{c} H \\ C \\ HC \quad CH \\ HC \quad CH \\ C \\ H \end{array}$$

is a constitutional formula for benzene, and CH_3—COOH is the constitutional formula for acetic acid. It is to be noted that the constitutional formula shows the atomic **linkages** when they are most significant to the chemist, and does not show, as in the case of the structural formula, the valence linkages of every atom.

FORMULA, COORDINATION or CO-ORDINATE. A formula of a **coordination compound** (q.v.) that shows the groupings of the individual coordinated groups around the central atom, as

$$K_2 \left(\begin{array}{cc} CN \cdot & \cdot CN \\ CN \cdot & Ni & \cdot CN \end{array} \right).$$

FORMULA, ELECTRONIC. A formula that shows the electronic state of each atom in a compound, i.e., the number of positive or negative elementary charges which the atom has acquired by loss or gain, respectively, of its valency electrons.

FORMULA, EMPIRICAL. A formula that indicates only the elements in a given compound and their proportions, which are expressed by subscripts indicating the number of **gram-atomic weights** of the various elements in a molecular weight of the compound (or the number of atoms of each kind in its molecule), e.g., H_2O, $C_2H_4O_2$.

FORMULA, GENERALIZED. A formula that represents the composition of more than one substance by the use of symbols which represent more than one kind of atom or more than one number, as HX represents hydrochloric, hydrobromic, or hydriodic acids, and as $FeCl_n$ might represent ferrous chloride and ferric chloride.

FORMULA, GRAPHIC. A formula that represents the actual spatial **orientation** of the atoms or radicals in a molecule or, more commonly, some aspect of that orientation which has a bearing upon a particular problem, or comparative relationship.

FORMULA, IONIC. The formula of an ion. In the case of a mono-atomic ion, this formula would consist only of the symbol of the element and the number of elementary charges, positive or negative, carried by the ion. In the case of an ionized radical, it would consist of the symbols of all elements contained, their atomic proportions (number of gram-atomic weights), and the number of net elementary charges carried by the ionized radical, positive or negative.

FORMULA, LEWIS-LANGMUIR. A formula for a substance which shows each atom and the electrons that participate in the valence bonds uniting it to other atoms. For example, this type of formula for methane,

$$\begin{array}{c} H \\ H \colon \overset{\cdot\cdot}{C} \colon H, \\ H \end{array}$$

shows the central carbon atom joined to four hydrogen atoms, in each case by a valence bond composed of a pair of shared electrons. To consider another type of compound, the formula for sodium chloride,

$$\overset{+}{Na} \colon \overset{\cdot\cdot}{\underset{\cdot\cdot}{Cl}} \colon,$$

shows an ionized sodium atom joined to an ionized chlorine atom by electrostatic forces. See **atom, Lewis-Langmuir.**

FORMULA, MOLECULAR. A formula that indicates composition of a substance, which contains two or more molecules. Hydrates, for example, are commonly represented by molecular formulas, as $CuSO_4 \cdot 5H_2O$ or $CaSO_4 \cdot 2H_2O$. In such formulas the period ($\cdot$) indicates the intramolecular valence **bond** or bonds.

FORMULA, NONPOLAR. See **formula, Lewis-Langmuir.**

FORMULA, OCTET. See **formula, Lewis-Langmuir.**

FORMULA, POLAR. See **formula, Lewis-Langmuir.**

FORMULA, POLARITY. A formula which indicates in some manner whether a pair of bonding electrons is located equidistantly between the two atoms bonded, as in the case of methane, illustrated under **formula, Lewis-Langmuir** (q.v.), or whether it is displaced toward one of the atoms, as in the case of a **dative bond** (q.v.) or the extreme case of sodium chloride, where the bond has become truly electrovalent.

FORMULA, RATIONAL. An **empirical formula** (q.v.).

FORMULA REARRANGEMENTS. Changes in structural relationships within the molecule which result in formation of new compounds. See **intramolecular change,** and **isomerism, dynamic.**

FORMULA, STEREOISOMERIC (or STEROMETRIC). A formula which shows enough of the interatomic valences in a compound to make clear the difference

in spatial configuration between two **stereoisomers** (q.v.). The formulas of the two forms of lactic acid are shown as:

$$CH_3-\overset{\displaystyle OH}{\underset{\displaystyle H}{\overset{|}{\underset{|}{C}}}}-COOH \quad \text{and} \quad CH_3-\overset{\displaystyle H}{\underset{\displaystyle OH}{\overset{|}{\underset{|}{C}}}}-COOH.$$

FORMULA, STRUCTURAL. A formula which shows all the valence **bonds** and the atoms that they join within the molecule, as the formula for ethyl acetate,

$$H-\overset{\displaystyle H}{\underset{\displaystyle H}{\overset{|}{\underset{|}{C}}}}-\overset{\displaystyle O}{\overset{\|}{C}}-O-\overset{\displaystyle H}{\underset{\displaystyle H}{\overset{|}{\underset{|}{C}}}}-\overset{\displaystyle H}{\underset{\displaystyle H}{\overset{|}{\underset{|}{C}}}}-H.$$

FORMULA, SYSTEMATIC. A constitutional formula. (See **formula, constitutional.**)

FORMULA, TRANSMUTATION. See **equation, transmutation.**

FORMULA WEIGHT. The **gram-molecular weight** or **mole.** Sometimes the term formula weight is applied to the molecular weight calculated from the composition on the assumption that the element present in the smallest proportion is represented by only one atom, as in the case of substances of uncertain molecular weight such as certain proteins.

FORMYL. The radical OCH–.

FORMYLATION. The introduction of the **formyl** radical into a compound.

FORSTER-DECKER AMINE METHOD. A method of formation of secondary **amines** by reaction of an alkyl halide with one of the **Schiff bases** (q.v.), with subsequent hydrolysis.

$$RX + R'N:CH \cdot C_6H_5 \rightarrow C_6H_5 \cdot CH{=}NRR'X$$
$$\downarrow H_2O$$
$$C_6H_5CHO + HNRR' + HX.$$

FOSSÉ REAGENT FOR UREA. Xanthydrol, which precipitates dixanthylurea.

FOUCHET SOLUTION. Ten ml. of a 10% solution of ferric chloride and 25 g. trichloroacetic acid dissolved in 100 ml. water, used in testing for bile pigments in urine.

FOUCRY TEST REACTION. To test for amines, add to 5 ml. of the aqueous solution tested, which has been neutralized with acetic acid, 5 ml. of a solution of 1 part quinone and 5 parts glacial acetic acid in 100 parts alcohol. A currant-red to violet color is given, on boiling, by many amines.

FOULGER REAGENTS. Two solutions — (1) a solution of 40 g. urea in 80 ml. (40% by volume) sulfuric acid, to which 2 g. stannous chloride is added, and the solution diluted to 100 ml. with 40% sulfuric acid; and (2) a solution of 25 g. quinidine in 100 ml. 40% sulfuric acid, which is then saturated with stannous chloride. These solutions give characteristic colors with sugars. Solution (1) is useful in differentiating between aldose and ketose sugars.

FOUNDATION COKE OVEN. A by-product coke oven for the production of coke by the regenerative heating and distillation of coal.

FOURDRINIER SCREEN. A rugged, fine screen used in the major primary stage of paper manufacture, in which the matted sheet is formed from the suspended fibers by separation of the suspending medium (water).

FOURIER, LAW OF. See law of Fourier.

FOWLER SOLUTION. A solution of potassium arsenite, used as an antiseptic.

FOX TEST. Hydrocyanic acid in air decolorizes the bluish cloudiness present in a solution of 1 drop 5% potassium iodide solution and 1 drop 0.001 N silver nitrate solution in 1 ml. 5% potassium hydroxide solution.

Fr Symbol for the element **francium.**

FRACTIONAL COMBUSTION. See combustion, fractional.

FRACTIONAL CONDENSATION. See condensation, fractional.

FRACTIONAL CRYSTALLIZATION. See crystallization, fractional.

FRACTIONAL DISTILLATION. See distillation, fractional.

FRACTIONATE. To separate a substance into parts.

FRACTIONATING COLUMN. An apparatus used to separate, or partly separate, the **components** of a vapor by selective **condensation.** This apparatus is generally supplied with vapor from a still, and it consists commonly of a vertical series of small chambers or baffles, designed mechanically to accomplish three objectives: (1) to retain a small amount of liquid in each chamber, this liquid being continually displaced by liquid flowing down from chambers above; (2) to permit the passage upward of vapor rising from a still below, and also to bring that vapor into close contact with the descending liquid so that the vapor is enriched in the more volatile components of the liquid; and (3) to provide sufficient external surface to condense, in its upper portion, enough of the ascending vapor to insure the required "reflux" (flow of liquid down the column).

FRACTURE. The character of the new surfaces produced on breaking a solid substance. The fracture is one of the specific properties of a mineral, and of certain other solid materials.

FRANCHIMONT REACTION. A method whereby α,β-dicarboxylic acids may be obtained. The reaction is that of KCN on α-bromo acids or esters. The resulting α-cyano-α,β-dicarboxylic acid derivatives yield the α,β-dicarboxylic acids on hydrolysis and decarboxylation.

water, used in testing for ammonia in methylamine. A red-brown precipitate,

$$2C_6H_5CHBr \cdot COOR + KCN \rightarrow \begin{array}{c} CN \\ | \\ C_6H_5-C-COOR \\ | \\ C_6H_5-C-COOR \\ | \\ H \end{array} + HBr + KBr$$

$$\downarrow H_2O$$

$$\begin{array}{c} C_6H_5-CH-COOH \\ | \\ C_6H_5-CH-COOH \end{array} + 2ROH + NH_3 + CO_2$$

FRANCIUM. Radioactive element. Symbol Fr. Atomic number 87. This element was named upon the discovery, by Marguerite Perey, of the Paris Radium Institute, of an atomic species of it of mass number 223, with a half-period of 21 minutes. It emits an electron and gamma radiation. Other isotopes include an atomic species of isotopic mass number 221, which is an alpha-emitter of a half-period of 4.9 minutes, and isotopes of mass numbers 211, 212, 218, 219, 220 and 222. It is a member of the Neptunium Series of **radioactive elements.**

FRANCK-CONDON PRINCIPLE. Electronic **transitions** in a diatomic molecule occur with greatest probability when the internuclear distance corresponding to a given vibrational energy level is at the maximum or minimum value. The time required for the transitions is small compared to the time required for oscillations of **nuclei;** hence electronic transitions occur without change in internuclear distance.

FRANCOIS REAGENT FOR AMMONIA IN METHYLAMINE. A solution of 22.7 g. mercuric iodide, 33.0 g. potassium iodide and 35.0 g. sodium hydroxide in 1 l.

formed on heating, is given by ammonia.

FRANK TEST. To test for magnesium in water, add to 10 ml. of the water, 2–3 drops of a solution of 0.02 g. p-nitrobenzeneazoresorcinol in 100 ml. sodium hydroxide solution, and then add concentrated sodium hydroxide solution until the solution becomes red or violet in color. Magnesium is present if a blue precipitate forms after agitation.

FRANKLAND-DUPPA REACTION. A reaction of dialkyl oxalates and alkyl halides, with zinc and HCl, yielding α-hydroxyesters.

$$2RI + R'OOC \cdot COOR' + 2Zn + 2HCl \rightarrow R_2C(OH)COOR' + R'OH + ZnCl_2 + ZnI_2.$$

FRANKLAND REACTION. A condensation similar in principle to the **Wurtz reaction** (q.v.) but using zinc alkyls or zinc alkyl halides to react with the halogenated hydrocarbons, instead of metallic sodium as a condensing agent. The zinc alkyls or zinc alkyl halides are prepared by action of metallic zinc on alkyl halides. Many of these metal alkyl compounds are spontaneously flammable and, therefore, this reaction is limited to specific syntheses which cannot well be accomplished by other methods, such as the production of certain hydrocarbons:

$$2(CH_3)_3CCl + (C_3H_7)_2Zn \rightarrow 2(CH_3)_3CC_3H_7 + ZnCl_2.$$

FRANZEN REAGENT. A mixture of a solution of 50 g. sodium hydrosulfite in 250 ml. water; and a solution of 5 g. sodium hydroxide in 40 ml. water, used as an oxygen absorbent.

FRASCH PROCESS. A process used in mining sulfur, in which the sulfur is melted by superheated water, emulsified, and forced to the surface by compressed air. This process is especially important because it makes possible the mining of sulfur from such deep or inaccessible beds as can be reached by the water and air piping.

FRASES TEST REACTION. A solution of 0.1 g. vanadium pentoxide in 10 ml. sulfuric acid gives an emerald-green color with quinine hydrochloride; a blood-red color, becoming violet, with quinine sulfate; and with rotenone, a dark red color with violet streaks.

FRAUDE SOLUTION. A solution of 25 g. perchloric acid in 100 ml. water, used in testing for alkaloids. Various color reactions are obtained.

FRAUNHOFER LINES. A series of dark lines which cross the solar spectrum and whose location is fixed. They are designated by letters and occur in great numbers. They are produced by atoms in the cooler outer atmosphere of the sun, which absorb principally radiations of those wave lengths they would emit if heated to a high temperature. Therefore the missing wave lengths correspond to the **spectra** of various elements, which are thus identified as present in the solar atmosphere. (In applying this method, attention must be paid to selective absorption of solar radiation by atoms and molecules as it passes through the earth's atmosphere.)

FREDHOLM TEST REACTION. Potassium is detected by a crystalline precipitate given with 5-nitrobarbituric acid.

FREDIANI MICRO-TEST FOR POTASSIUM. Potassium solutions give with an aqueous solution of naphthol yellow S, saturated at 20° C., well-defined needle-like crystals. Several other metals may interfere.

FREE. (1) Uncombined, as a free element. (2) Active, as a free charge. (3) Isolated, as free carbon dioxide.

FREE ELECTRON. See **electron, free.**

FREE ENERGY. Also called the **thermodynamic potential,** or the Gibbs function. It is a property of a system defined as the difference between the **heat content** and the product of the **entropy** and temperature. In the older literature, the term "free energy" was used for the quantity now called the **work function** (q.v.).

FREE RADICAL. An unsaturated molecular fragment in which some of the valence electrons remain free, i.e., do not partake in bonding. Examples are methyl $(CH_3 \cdot)$ or phenyl $(C_6H_5 \cdot)$ radicals. Clear experimental evidence is available of their existence in various systems, especially in gaseous ones, although their **half-life period** is of the order of thousandths of a second.

FREEDOM, DEGREES OF. The number of **variables** which must be fixed before the state of a system may be defined according to the **phase rule.** The relationship between the number of degrees of freedom (F), the **components** (C), and the phases (P) of a system is expressed by the formula,

$$F = C + 2 - P.$$

Thus a pure gas has two degrees of freedom. At any temperature its volume and pressure are variable, but if one of these is fixed then the other is automatically determined for, at any given temperature and pressure, each pure gas assumes one, and only one, volume at equilibrium.

FREEZE. To solidify, especially at low temperatures.

FREEZING MIXTURE. Two or more substances which initiate, upon being brought together, an endothermic process. They are used in chemical work to absorb heat, as in conducting freezing point determinations, reactions at lower temperatures, etc.

FREEZING POINT. The temperature at which a liquid becomes a solid. This is not always identical with the melting point of the solid for many mixtures, particularly of fats and waxes, do not solidify until they have been cooled several degrees below their melting points. If a liquid be cooled under pressure the freezing point rises if the solid is of higher specific gravity than the liquid; if it is of lower specific gravity, as in the case of water, the freezing point is lowered. Since the freezing point varies slightly with pressure, the pressure should be stated in reporting a freezing point. However, atmospheric pressure is commonly understood unless otherwise specified.

FREEZING POINT, DEPRESSION OF. The freezing point of a solution is, in general, lower than that of the pure solvent and the depression is proportional to the active mass of the solute. Abnormal depressions are due to **ionization, association,** and sometimes, chemical action. Cf. law of **Blagden.**

FREEZING POINT, MAXIMUM. See **maximum freezing point.**

FREHDEN-FÜRST SPOT-TEST. Chloroform reacts with ammonia and sodium hydroxide to form sodium cyanide, which gives a blue spot-test with cupric acetate and benzidine acetate.

FREHDEN-GOLDSCHMIDT TEST FOR AMINES. Amines are detected by treating them in a crucible with 2 drops of a solution of 10 drops furfural in 10 ml. glacial acetic acid. On gentle evaporation, and moistening with a few drops of acetic acid, characteristic colors are obtained. *p*-Dimethylaminobenzaldehyde solution may be used instead of furfural.

FREHDEN-GOLDSCHMIDT TEST FOR PROTEIN. The material is treated with 2 drops of a saturated solution of *p*-dimethylaminobenzaldehyde in glacial acetic acid, and 1 drop hydrochloric acid is added. A violet color appears if protein is present.

FREMY REAGENT. Potassium pyroantimonate solution used to precipitate sodium.

FRENCH PROCESS (ZINC OXIDE). A process for the manufacture of zinc oxide, in which the metal or spelter is volatilized, and its vapors are oxidized by air to form the oxide. Because the metal or spelter must first be produced from the ore, this process is also called the Indirect Process. (See **American process, zinc oxide,** for the direct method.)

FRENCH-WITTEL REAGENT. α-Naphthylisocyanate used to identify phenols and aliphatic amines by forming urethanes with characteristic melting points.

FREQUENCY. From its general meaning of rapidity of repetition, this term has acquired the specific meaning of the number of complete repetitions per unit time. When applied to **electromagnetic radiation,** the frequency is defined by the expression:

$$\nu = \frac{c}{\lambda}$$

in which ν is the frequency of the radiation, λ is its **wave length,** and c is the velocity of light.

FREQUENCY CURVE. A probability function for finding, from a series of values, the particular value most nearly representative. The curve is obtained by plotting the number of values in each range class against the values.

FRESENIUS TEST REACTION FOR ANTIMONY. The solution tested is acidified with hydrochloric acid, and 1 drop of it is placed on platinum foil and a particle of metallic zinc added. A black film appears on the platinum if antimony is present.

FRESNEL. A unit of **frequency** equal to 10^{12} cycles per second.

FREUND REACTION. A method of preparation of alicyclic hydrocarbons by the action of sodium on open-chain dihalo compounds

$$BrCH_2-CH_2-CH_2-CH_2Br + 2Na \rightarrow \begin{matrix} H_2C-CH_2 \\ | \quad\ | \\ H_2C-CH_2 \end{matrix} + 2NaBr.$$

FREUNDLER-MENAGER REAGENT.
Silicotungstic acid, used to precipitate rubidium in the presence of sodium and potassium.

FREUNDLICH ADSORPTION ISOTHERM. An empirical equation for variation of **adsorption** with pressure at constant temperature. It applies over a somewhat limited range of pressure. It takes the form:

$$\frac{x}{m} = kp^{1/n}$$

where x is the mass of gas adsorbed; m is the mass of adsorbent; p is the pressure; and k and n are constants.

FREUNDLICH EQUATION. In an **adsorption** process between a gas or vapor and a solid, the amount of gas or vapor adsorbed per unit quantity of adsorbent is an exponential function of the **partial pressure,** of the form:

$$p = Cx^n$$

where p is the partial pressure, x is the amount of gas adsorbed per unit amount of adsorbent, and C and n are constants. In certain systems, it is necessary to express this relationship in the form:

$$x = C(h\gamma)^{1/n}$$

where x, C, and n have the same meaning as above, h is the ratio of the partial pressure of the vapor to its saturation value, and γ is the surface tension.

FREYTAG TEST FOR SULFONATED OILS. The substance tested is boiled with sodium hydroxide and pyridine, then treated with β-naphthylamine or p-nitroaniline and dilute acid. A pink to red color indicates sulfonated oils.

FREYTAG TEST FOR SULFUR DIOXIDE. Paper treated with green 2-benzylpyridine turns red on treatment with sulfur dioxide in air (stannous chloride gives the same reaction).

FRICTION. The resistance offered to the motion of one body upon or through another.

FRICTION HEAD. See **head, friction.**

FRICTION, INTERNAL. Viscosity.

FRIEDEL-CRAFTS REACTION. The synthesis of aromatic hydrocarbon derivatives by the action of anhydrous aluminum chloride upon a mixture of a hydrocarbon and an alkyl or acyl halide.

$$C_6H_6 + CH_3Cl \xrightarrow{AlCl_3} C_6H_5CH_3 + HCl.$$

This reaction applies also to many benzene derivatives and related compounds. Thus acetyl chloride with benzene yields acetophenone, phthalic anhydride with benzene yields o-benzoylbenzoic acid (readily converted to anthraquinone), and carbon dioxide with benzene yields benzoic acid.

FRIEDENWALD-EHRLICH DIAZO REAGENT. Two solutions — (1) a solution of 0.5 g. sodium nitrite in 100 ml. water; and (2) a solution of 0.5 g. p-aminoacetophenone and 50 ml. concentrated hydrochloric acid in 1 liter water. These solutions are mixed (1:50) and used in testing for pathological urine which gives a red color.

FRIEDLÄNDER PICROCARMINE SOLUTION. A solution of 1 g. carmine and 1 ml. ammonium hydroxide in 50 ml. water, to which enough of a saturated aqueous solution of picric acid is added to cause a permanent turbidity. This solution is a differential stain for tissue substances.

FRIEDLANDER SYNTHESIS. A method of formation of quinoline derivatives by condensation of o-aminobenzaldehydes with aldehydes or ketones.

FRIES REARRANGEMENT. The rearrangement of phenol ethers into substituted phenols; and of phenol esters into phenol ketones,

$$C_6H_5OR \xrightarrow{AlCl_3} C_6H_4 \begin{array}{c} OH \\ \diagup \\ \diagdown \\ R \text{ (ortho or para)} \end{array}$$

$$C_6H_5OCOR \xrightarrow{AlCl_3} C_6H_4 \begin{array}{c} OH \\ \diagup \\ \diagdown \\ COR \text{ (ortho or para)} \end{array}$$

FRIES RULE. During the course of a reaction, or whenever change is possible, any aromatic ring in a polynuclear compound tends to assume the bond structure most nearly approaching that of the benzene ring.

FRIES-VOGT TEST REACTION. Sulfoxides give a yellow color with a solution of hydrobromic acid in glacial acetic acid; sulfones do not.

FRIGORIFIC. An agent which produces cold.

FRITSCH TEST. Acetone is detected by a fuchsin-red color appearing when a solution containing it is heated with an equal volume of a 5% solution of rhamnose in concentrated hydrochloric acid.

FRITZMANN TEST. Nitrate in milk is detected by a blue to violet ring which appears when milk containing formaldehyde and nitrate is floated over concentrated sulfuric acid. Various modifications of this test have been developed. (See **Barth test.**)

FRÖHDE TEST REACTION FOR ALBUMIN. Albumin gives a blue color with a solution of molybdic acid in concentrated sulfuric acid.

FRÖHDE REAGENT. A solution of 0.1 g. sodium molybdate in 100 ml. concentrated sulfuric acid. It is used in the detection of alkaloids, which give characteristic colors.

FROMMHERZ REAGENT. Two solutions — (1) a solution of 41.76 g. cupric sulfate in 200 ml. water, and (2) a solution of 20.88 g. potassium bitartrate and 10.44 g. potassium hydroxide in 600 ml. water — which are mixed, diluted with water to 1 l., and used in testing for glucose.

FROTH. A gas-in-liquid dispersion.

FROTHER. A substance used to produce froth, as in the flotation industry.

FROTHING. (1) The process by which a liquid boils so violently or is agitated so vigorously by a stream of gas that the escaping vapor or gas carries liquid with it as bubbles. (2) Foaming.

FRY REAGENT. A solution of 90 g. cupric chloride in 120 ml. hydrochloric acid and 100 ml. water, used in etching steel.

FRYER-WESTON REAGENT FOR FATS. A mixture of methyl and amyl alcohols, with which fats and fatty oils produce clear solutions at various temperatures.

FUCO-, FUC-. Derived from, or related to, the alga called fucus, as fucoxanthin, fucose.

FUGACITY. A quantity which measures the true **escaping tendency** of a gas, a sort of idealized pressure. If primes and double primes refer, respectively, to an ideal gas and a real gas, then $dF' = V'dp = RT\,d\ln p$, and $dF'' = V''dp = RT\,d\ln f$, where dF is a change in **free energy** or **chemical potential,** produced by a change in pressure, dp; V is the volume of the gas at the absolute temperature T, f is its fugacity and R is the gas constant.

FUJITA-IWATAKE-MIYATA TEST FOR ASCORBIC ACID. To 4 ml. of a solution of the substance tested in 2% metaphosphoric acid, add 1 ml. of a freshly-made solution of 2 g. sodium tungstate in 10 ml. N sulfuric acid, and follow with 0.4 ml. 2 N sodium hydroxide solution. A sky-blue color is given by ascorbic acid.

FUJIWARA TEST FOR STRYCHNINE. Concentrated sodium molybdate gives a red color, with strychnine and concentrated sulfuric acid, and also with strychnine nitrate and concentrated hydrochloric acid.

FUJIWARA TEST REACTION. When a solution containing chloroform or other trihalogenated compound is treated with pyridine and sodium hydroxide solution, a pink color is produced.

FUKAI TEST. Methylpentose, on distillation with hydrochloric acid, gives a distillate that produces a violet-red color with a 0.5% solution of vanillin in sulfuric acid.

FULD REAGENT. A solution of 0.2 g. rhodamine B-Extra in 60 ml. alcohol, reduced with 5 g. zinc dust, and with 5 ml. 10% sodium hydroxide solution added, used to detect blood in feces. A red color is imparted to an alcohol-acetic acid extract of the feces, in the presence of hydrogen peroxide, if blood is present.

FULGURATOR. An apparatus used in **spectroscopy,** consisting of an atomizer to spray salt solutions into a flame.

FULMINATING. Causing an explosion by detonation, as by using a salt of fulminic acid to initiate the explosion.

FULTON REACTIONS FOR PHENOLS. (1) To 0.5 ml. alcoholic solution of the substance tested, add on the spot plate 3 drops hydrogen peroxide and 2 drops 1:2 ammonium hydroxide solution. On stirring with copper wire, phenols give a pink color changing to yellow or brown.
(2) To 5 ml. alcoholic or aqueous solution of the substance tested, add 0.5–1.0 ml. hydrogen peroxide, 0.5 ml. ammonium hydroxide, and a 0.1% cupric sulfate solution drop by drop. Phenols give a red or pink color.

FULTON SOLUTIONS. A modification of **Marquis reagent** (q.v.), by the addition of a 10% aqueous solution of ferric sulfate. The reagent is used to identify opium alkaloids.

FULTON TEST FOR COPPER. In 2 ml. alcohol, dissolve 0.4 g. β-naphthol, add 0.5 ml. 1:4 ammonium hydroxide solution, and 5 ml. of the solution tested. A cloudy yellowish-green color with an oily appearance indicates copper.

FUMARIC. (1) Related to fumaric acid,

$$HOOC—CH$$
$$\|$$
$$HC—COOH$$

(2) Related to a group of acids of type formula $C_nH_{2n-2}(COOH)_2$; thus in fumaric acid itself (and maleic acid) n has a value of 2; in glutaconic acid, n has a value of 3, etc.

FUMAROID FORM. The axial symmetric or *trans*-form of ethylene geometrical isomers, named from fumaric acid

$$HOOC—C—H$$
$$\|$$
$$H—C—COOH.$$

(See **isomerism, geometrical.**)

FUME. Fine particles (0.2 to 1 micron in diameter) of a solid or liquid suspended in a gas; technically fumes are colloidal systems formed from chemical reactions like combustion, distillation, sublimation, calcination, and condensation.

FUME CLOSET. An enclosed space that is ventilated for the safe removal of gases, vapors, smokes, etc. It is essential for performing experiments that produce unpleasant or toxic gases or vapors. (Commonly called "hood.")

FUME HOOD. An enclosed ventilating shaft or flue in the laboratory designed to carry off fumes. Sometimes this ventilating system is connected to "canopy-like" covers of metal or glass, arranged so that apparatus evolving fumes may be manipulated under them. These "canopies" are sometimes called "hoods."

FUMIGATION. Treatment with gases or vapors for the destruction of pests such as rodents, insects, fungi, bacteria, etc.

FUNAKOSHI REAGENT. A 0.03% alcoholic solution of *p*-dimethylaminobenzylidenerhodanine, which gives a red-violet precipitate with even very dilute neutral or slightly acid cuprous solutions. Cupric ions give colors when in concentrated solutions. Various modifications of this test have been developed.

FUNCTION. (1) A mathematical quantity or quality so related to another quantity that an alteration in one is accompanied by an alteration in the other. The circumference of a circle is a function of the diameter. (2) A chemical type radical or type structure which has characteristic properties, as hydroxyl-function, acid-function, or to carry the concept to a higher order of generalization, oxygen-function, nitrogen-function, etc. Functional conceptions in chemistry often furnish a useful basis for the classification of reactions and properties of substances. (3) Physiological performance of an organ.

FUNDAMENTAL SERIES. A series of lines in the spectra (see **spectrum**) of many atoms which have one, two, or three electrons in their outer shells, either in their neutral state or as a result of ionization. (Excluded are the atoms which have only one electron in all, such as hydrogen, singly-ionized helium, doubly-ionized lithium, etc.). The fundamental series differs from the other series for such elements in having a somewhat distinctive physical appearance, and in having a characteristic formula,

$$\bar{\nu}_F = L - \frac{R}{(m + c)^2},$$

where $\bar{\nu}$ is the wave number of a line in the fundamental series, L and c are constants for the fundamental series, m is a variable integer, whose values give the various lines in the fundamental series, and R is the **Rydberg constant.**

FUNNEL. A glass cone, terminating in a glass tube, used for conducting filtrations or for transferring a liquid from one vessel to another.

FUNNEL, BÜCHNER. A porcelain funnel having in its wide top portion a perforated, integral plate, on which a filter paper or other filtering medium is placed for suction filtration.

FUNNEL, DROPPING. A closed glass vessel, with a long stem containing a stopcock, and usually with a short neck containing a ground-glass stopper.

FUNNEL, HOT WATER. A double-walled funnel with a short nipple and cap or other provision for filling the space between the walls with hot water. It is used for conducting filtrations at higher temperatures.

FUNNEL, SEPARATORY. A closed (occasionally open-top) glass vessel, usually pear-shaped or cylindrical, with a stopcock on the stem, and a glass stopper in the short neck, used to separate immiscible liquids.

FURFURAL. See **furfurylidene.**

FURFURAL PROCESS OR FURFURAL REFINING. A process for the refining of lubricating oils, involving extraction with furfural, $C_4H_3O \cdot CHO$.

FURFURYL. The radical

$$\overline{O \cdot CH : CH \cdot CH : CCH_2} -.$$

FURFURYLIDENE. The radical

$$\overline{O \cdot CH : CH \cdot CH : CCH} =.$$

FURNACE. An apparatus enclosing a space which is heated by combustion of fuel, passage of electric current, or other source of thermal energy; doors, parts, etc., are provided for the introduction, and subsequent removal, of material to be heated, or the furnace is placed in contact with a surface to be heated, or some other arrangement is made to utilize the heat produced.

FURNACE, ARGALL. A metallurgical furnace in which the charge is moved across the hearth continuously by mechanical rabbles.

FURNACE, BALLING. (Black ash furnace) A long reverberatory furnace, equipped with two hearths, used in the Leblanc process for soda. The pasty product is removed in balls, hence the name.

FURNACE, CARIUS. A furnace for heating Carius tubes in the determination of sulfur and halogens by the **Carius method.** This type of furnace is usually rectangular in shape, and is designed to operate in such ranges as 150–300° C. and to protect the operator from explosion hazards.

FURNACE, COAL ASH. A furnace designed to reach temperatures required for the rapid and complete combustion of coal as required in ash determinations. This furnace has a heating chamber large enough to accommodate several crucibles, and is usually electrically heated and rectangular in shape.

FURNACE, COMBUSTION. A laboratory apparatus used to produce controlled high temperatures, as for heating materials to combustion temperatures in organic analysis.

FURNACE, CRUCIBLE. A furnace of cylindrical shape with a cylindrical chamber, concentric with its axis, in which crucibles or other containers of small, i.e., laboratory-size, charges are placed.

FURNACE, INDUCTION. An electric furnace heated by induced currents; as those produced within the charge by alternating currents in coils which surround the furnace.

FURNACE, MUFFLE. A furnace containing a **muffle** (q.v.) lining which is used in laboratory work or in small-scale, high quality production. A high temperature furnace, usually rectangular in shape.

FURNACE, REDUCING. A furnace in which metals are obtained by the reduction of their ores. Such furnaces are commonly of the shaft type designed so that ores and reducing substances are charged at the top.

FURNACE, RESISTANCE. A furnace in which heat is generated by resistance to the passage of electric current and in one of two ways — either by passing the current through resistance coils in or on the walls of the furnace, or by conducting the current directly into the charge by electrodes.

FURNACE, REVERBERATORY. An oven for smelting and for roasting metal ores, in which the flames come in contact with the material being heated (the charge) by reflection from the curved roof. One of the characteristic features of this construction is that the fuel does not come in contact with the charge.

FURNACE, SIEMENS. A furnace, originally designed for steel making by Siemens, which was essentially a gas-heated reverberatory type. The term is now commonly applied to all furnaces so made.

2-FUROYL. The radical

$$O \cdot CH:CH \cdot CH:CCO-.$$

3-FUROYL. The radical

$$CH:CH \cdot O \cdot CH:CCO-.$$

FÜRTH-HERMANN TEST REACTION. On warming with pyridine and acetic anhydride, aconitic acid gives a violet-red color, citric acid a carmine-red, and tartaric acid an emerald-green. Other dicarboxylic acids give browns or no color.

FURYL. The radical

$$O \cdot CH:CH \cdot CH:C-$$

(2 isomers).

FURYLIDENE. The radical

$$CH:CH \cdot O \cdot CH_2 \cdot C=$$

(2 isomers).

FUSE. (1) To melt. (2) A device for igniting a charge of an explosive. (3) A device for breaking an electric circuit by the melting of a short conductor when the current exceeds a specified value.

FUSED RING. A structural element in the formula of a chemical compound consisting of two rings that are joined by having two atoms in common.

FUSION. The process of converting a solid into a liquid by raising its temperature.

FUSION, ALKALINE. Fusion with an alkali metal **hydroxide.**

FUSION, HEAT OF. See **heat of fusion.**

FUSION, WATERY. The melting of an hydrated substance below 100° C. with consequent solution in its own water of crystallization.

G. Abbreviation for gram (g.). Symbol for the acceleration due to gravity (g). Symbol for standard acceleration due to gravity (g_o). Symbol for local value of acceleration due to gravity (g_L). Symbol for acceleration of free fall (g). Symbol for

GABRIEL ISOQUINOLINE SYNTHESIS. A method of formation of isoquinoline derivatives by the reaction of sodium ethylate on phenylglycine esters, which may be prepared from potassium phthalimide.

$$
\underset{\text{CO}}{\overset{\text{CO}}{\diagup}}NK + CH_2ClCOOR \xrightarrow{-KCl} \underset{\text{CO}}{\overset{\text{CO}}{\diagup}}NCH_2COOR
$$

$$\downarrow \text{NaOC}_2\text{H}_5$$

electric conductance (g or G). Symbol for degeneracy (statistical weight) (g). Symbol for modulus of shear elasticity (G). Abbreviation for Gibbs function, total (G), per unit mass (g), per mole (g, G, or G_M), per atom or molecule (g or g_m). Landé

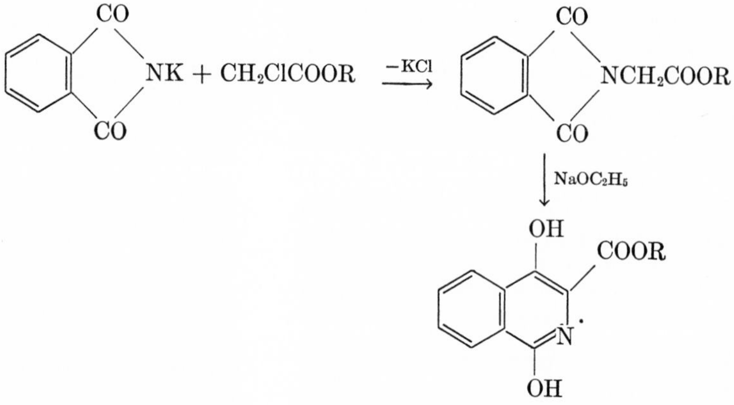

GABRIEL SYNTHESIS. A method of preparing primary amines, usually by reaction of an alkyl iodide and potassium phthalimide, followed by hydrolysis with hydrochloric acid under pressure, or dilute alkali.

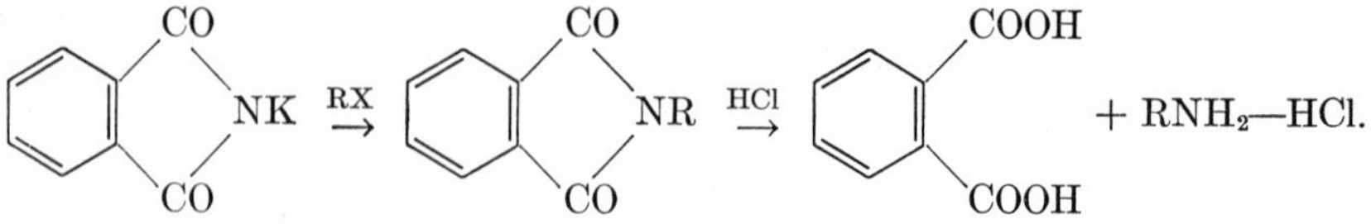

$$
\underset{\text{CO}}{\overset{\text{CO}}{\diagup}}NK \xrightarrow{RX} \underset{\text{CO}}{\overset{\text{CO}}{\diagup}}NR \xrightarrow{HCl} \underset{\text{COOH}}{\overset{\text{COOH}}{\diagup}} + RNH_2—HCl.
$$

factor (g). Symbol for mass velocity (G). Symbol for the gravitational constant (G). See also **gamma**.

Ga Symbol for the element **gallium**.

GABRIEL ETHYLENIMINE METHOD. A method for the formation of ethylenimines from aliphatic compounds having terminal halogen and amino groups, by elimination of HX by the action of an alkali.

GABUTTI REAGENT FOR MORPHINE AND CODEINE. A solution of chloral in sulfuric acid, which gives a violet color with a sulfuric acid solution of morphine, and green-blue with codeine.

GABUTTI TEST FOR FORMALDEHYDE. A solution of carbazole in sulfuric acid becomes violet red at *room temperature* if formaldehyde is present, and turns blue or gives a blue-green precipitate on heating.

$$
XCH_2 \cdot CH_2 \cdot CH_2 \cdot NH_2 \xrightarrow{KOH} \underset{H_2C—NH}{\overset{H_2C—CH_2}{\mid \quad \mid}} + H_2O + KX.
$$

GADOLINIUM. Rare earth metallic element. Symbol Gd. Atomic number 64. Atomic weight 156.9. Density 1.31. Valence 3. Oxide, Gd_2O_3. Gadolinium occurs in samarskite and other minerals.

GAGE. An instrument used to measure a quantity, to determine the state of a phenomenon, or the numerical quality of a system at any given time, as a pressure gage or a rain gage.

GAGE, IONIZATION. See **ionization gage.**

GAGE, McLEOD. See **McLeod gage.**

GAGE, MULTIPLYING. A gage incorporating a device to multiply its reading, as by the use of an inclined column of liquid, or a properly placed reduction in area in conjunction with the use in the gage of two immiscible fluids.

GAGE PRESSURE. See **pressure, gage.**

GAGLIO TEST. Mercury vapors in air produce a turbidity or precipitate in a

galalith, galactose; (b) galactose, as gala-heptose, galactolipide.

GALACTOGOGUE. A substance or drug that stimulates the secretion of milk.

GALACTOMETER. An **hydrometer** graduated to read in per cent of cream, used in testing the quality of milk. A lactometer.

GALENICAL. A liquid mixture of medicinal substances compounded according to the art of pharmacy and used in the treatment of disease.

GALL-, GALLO-. Relating to gallnuts or gallic acid, as gallotannic acid, galactolipide.

GALLAGHER-HOLLANDER DEGRADATION. A series of reactions for the **degradation** of **amino acids** by which *two* carbon atoms are eliminated. This method has been applied effectively to side chains of bile acids and other polynuclear compounds. The method, as usually applied, involves a series of some seven reactions.

$$R(CH_2)_2COOH \xrightarrow{SOCl_2} R(CH_2)_2CO \cdot Cl \xrightarrow{CH_2N_2} R(CH_2)_2CO \cdot CHN_2$$
$$\downarrow HCl$$
$$R \cdot CH_2 \cdot CHBr \cdot CO \cdot CH_3 \xleftarrow{Br_2} R(CH_2)_2CO \cdot CH_3 \xleftarrow[CH_3COOH]{Zn} R(CH_2)_2CO \cdot CH_2Cl$$
$$\downarrow (Collidine)$$
$$RCH{=}CH \cdot CO \cdot CH_3 \xrightarrow{CrO_3} RCOOH + [CH_3 \cdot CO \cdot COOH].$$

1:500 aqueous solution of palladous chloride.

GAILLARD-PARRISH CHAMBER. A chamber used in the **chamber process** for sulfuric acid. It has one or more centrifugal dispersers near its top wall, which are run by motors whose shafts pass through the roof. These dispersers throw the acid around the chamber, thus obtaining better contact with the gases, better cooling of the walls, and improved production.

GAILLARD TOWER. A tower in which a spray of sulfuric acid falls through rising heated gases and is concentrated.

GALA-, GALACTO-, GALACT-. (Greek, milk, milky) Relating to: (a) milk, as

GALLATE (ORTHO). The anion GaO_3^{3-}, or a compound containing it.

GALLIC. (1) Containing trivalent **gallium.** (2) Related to gallic acid, which is 3,4,5-trihydroxybenzoic acid.

GALLIUM. Metallic element. Symbol Ga. Atomic number 31. Atomic weight 69.72. Density 5.903. Specific heat 0.080. Melting point 30.15° C. Boiling point 2000° C. Valence 1, 2 and 3. Oxide Ga_2O_3. Gallium sulfate forms a true alum with ammonium sulfate. Gallium occurs in zinc blende.

GALLON. A unit of liquid measure. The United States gallon is 231 cubic inches in volume. The imperial gallon used in

England contains 277.46 cubic inches and is equivalent to 1.20032 U.S. gallons. The U.S. gallon of water weighs 8.345 pounds at 4° C. and is divided into four quarts, 8 pints, or 128 fluid ounces.

1 U.S. gallon = 3.78543 liters.
1 imperial gallon = 4.54345 liters.

GALLOUS. Containing divalent **gallium.**

GALVANIC. Pertaining to electricity produced by chemical action in cells.

GALVANIZING. The treatment of iron sheets with hot zinc so as to coat them with an adherent layer of pure zinc. The iron is first cleaned by pickling with dilute acid, and is then treated with the molten zinc.

GALVANOMETER. An electrical instrument used for detecting or measuring the strength of an electric current by observing the deflection of a magnetic needle produced by the passage of the current. In the astatic galvanometer two needles, of almost equal magnetic moment, are suspended on the same axis, and the direction of the poles of one is opposite that of the other. The tangent and sine galvanometers in which the strength of the current is proportional to the tangent or sine respectively of the angle of deflection are used in measuring and comparing currents.

GALVANOMETER, ASTATIC. A galvanometer which gives readings independent of the earth's magnetic field by means of a construction feature in which readings of current are obtained by passing the current through a coil around a system of two movable needles with opposing magnetic fields.

GALVANOMETER, BALLISTIC. A galvanometer which is used most commonly to measure the total quantity of electricity in a transient current, and is accordingly designed to have a long period of swing (high moment of inertia) of its moving element and little friction or other damping action to retard its motion.

GALVANOMETER, D'ARSONVAL. A galvanometer in which a light wire carrying

a mirror is suspended inside a current-carrying coil. A beam of light directed upon the mirror is used for reading the deflections of the wire.

GALVANOMETER, EINTHOVEN. A very sensitive galvanometer consisting of a strong magnet and a fine quartz or metallic thread, whose movement is observed optically. Also called the string galvanometer.

GALVANOMETER, KELVIN. See **galvanometer, mirror.**

GALVANOMETER, MIRROR. Any galvanometer in which the deflection produced by induction of the current to be measured is amplified by a mirror attached to the galvanic element.

GALVANOMETRY. The art and process of detecting and measuring the strength of electric currents.

GALVANOSCOPE. A sensitive **galvanometer.**

GAMMA (γ or Γ). (1) The third letter of the Greek alphabet, used as a prefix to denote the third carbon atom in a straight chain compound, or a derivative in which a substituted group is attached to that carbon atom (γ-). (2) The position in a polycyclic compound following the β-position (see beta), and away from the α-position (see alpha), or a derivative in which a substituted group occupies that position (γ-). (3) Symbol for microgram (γ). (4) Symbol for **activity coefficient,** molal basis (γ). (5) Symbol for weight rate of flow per unit width (γ). (6) Symbol for 0.00001 gauss (γ). (7) Ratio of specific heats of a gas C_p/C_v(γ). (8) The slope of the straight line portion of the **H and D curve** (q.v.). See also **contrast factor** and **gradient.** Symbol for angular magnification (γ). Symbol for **surface tension** (γ). Symbol for **specific weight** (γ).

GAMMA RAYS. Electromagnetic radiations, ranging in wave length from 10^{-10} meters to 10^{-13} meters (1.0 to 0.001 Ångström units). They are emitted in the course of many radioactive changes.

GAMMA SPACE (γ-SPACE). A hyperspace of $2nr$ dimensions, where n is the number of (identical) molecules, and $2r$ is the number of coordinates required to specify the exact mechanical condition of a molecule, both its instantaneous position and its momentum.

GANASSINI REAGENT FOR HYDROGEN SULFIDE. A reagent prepared by mixing (1) a solution of 1.25 g. ammonium molybdate in 50 ml. water, and (2), a solution of 2.5 g. potassium thiocyanate in 45 ml. water, to which is then added 5 ml. hydrochloric acid and enough oxalic acid to produce a yellow-green color. This solution is used as a test reagent for hydrogen sulfide. A violet color indicates the presence of hydrogen sulfide.

GANASSINI TEST FOR ACROLEIN. Add to 10 drops of the aqueous solution to be tested 2 drops of a solution of 2 ml. phenylhydrazine in 3 ml. glacial acetic acid and 5 ml. water; after shaking, add 5 ml. concentrated hydrochloric acid and 1 drop 0.5% aqueous potassium chloride solution. A violet-red color indicates acrolein.

GANASSINI TEST FOR MERCURY. Shake the solution that is to be tested with metallic copper. Wash with water, and alcohol, and dry the amalgam. Place in a test tube, introduce a piece of paper that is wet with cuprous iodide solution, and heat. If mercury is present, the paper is colored rose.

GANASSINI TEST FOR QUINOTOXINE IN QUININE. (1) Moisten the quinine with nitric acid, and dry. A dark yellow color, changed to brown-yellow by ammonia, indicates quinotoxine.
   (2) A filtered, dilute acetic acid solution of the quinine gives a precipitate with sodium nitrate, and an orange-yellow precipitate with phenylhydrazine on heating, if quinotoxine is present.

GANASSINI TEST FOR URIC ACID AND ZINC. A zinc sulfate solution precipitates from an alkali urate solution, a precipitate changing to green or blue in color.

GANGUE. The material in an ore other than the metals to be separated. In the course of various processes of extracting metals, such as reduction, flotation, etc., the gangue is removed, commonly as a waste product.

GAPCHENKO-SHEINTZIS MICROTEST FOR BISMUTH. One drop of the solution tested, acidified with nitric acid, is treated with a saturated quinoline solution in the presence of ammonium thiocyanate. Bismuth produces a golden-yellow amorphous precipitate, quickly changing to x-shaped crystal groups.

GAPCHENKO-SHEINTZIS MICROTEST FOR MAGNESIUM. Addition of 8-hydroxyquinoline to a drop of solution containing magnesium gives a green-yellow amorphous precipitate, changing to crystalline rosettes.

GAPCHENKO-SHEINTZIS TEST FOR BISMUTH. A solution of 1 g. quinoline in 100 ml. alcohol mixed with 20 ml. 25% potassium iodide solution gives a red-orange color with bismuth.

GAPCHENKO-SHEINTZIS TEST FOR TITANIUM. Saturate a filter paper with a 10% tannin solution. Apply to it a drop of 20% antipyrine solution, and to the latter a drop of the solution to be tested. Titanium gives a red color, which is *not* removed by 1:4 sulfuric acid solution.

GARBY SOLUTION. One hundred ml. of an aqueous solution containing 10 g. mannite, to which is added, successively, 40 ml. concentrated ammonium hydroxide, 15 ml. 25% potassium hydroxide solution, and 40 g. nickel nitrate, used as a test reagent for biguanide.

GARDINER TEST. Tannic acid is detected by a deep yellow-brown to dark brown color which it gives with ammonium molybdate. If the ammonium molybdate contains nitric acid, the yellow-brown color appears with very dilute tannic and gallic acid solutions.

GARELLI-TETTAMANZI TEST REACTION. When 2 drops cobalt chloride 5%

solution are added to an aqueous solution of triethanolamine made alkaline with 1 drop of ammonia, a deep purple-violet color appears, which changes to blue on warming. The reaction can be used to detect either cobalt or triethanolamine.

GARMASK TEST FOR STRONTIUM. To the solution tested, add one-fifth its volume of a saturated solution of sodium acetate, acidify with acetic acid, and add an excess saturated potassium dichromate solution. Filter, add an equal volume saturated ammonium sulfate solution, and heat to boiling. If strontium is present, a precipitate is formed.

GAS. A state of matter, in which the molecules move freely, and consequently the entire mass tends to expand indefinitely, occupying the total volume of any vessel into which it is introduced. Gases follow, within considerable degree of fidelity, certain laws relating their conditions of pressure, volume, and temperature (see **equations of state**); they mix freely with each other; and they can all be liquefied.

GAS ABSORBENT. See **absorbent, gas.**

GAS, AIR. An illuminating and fuel gas made by blowing air through layers of volatile petroleum distillates.

GAS AMPLIFICATION. See **counter, gas amplification.**

GAS ANALYSIS. See **analysis.**

GAS BALANCE. An instrument for measuring the density of a gas. Regnault used a globe or "balloon" which was filled with gas and weighed, its weight when evacuated being known. The Whytlaw-Gray microbalance is a delicate "buoyancy" apparatus. An industrial type of gas balance measures the **specific gravity** of a mixture of gases in order to determine approximately the completeness of combustion in a heating plant. It consists of a sensitive balance one arm of which holds a closed glass vessel with a pan and weights, the other holds another glass vessel open at the bottom into which cleaned and dried gases from the chimney

are continuously aspirated. The pointer moves over a graduated scale which reads directly in per cent of carbon dioxide.

GAS BATTERY. (Gas cell) A concentration cell (see **cell, concentration**) in which the electrodes are virtually gaseous.

GAS, BLAU. A gaseous mixture of aliphatic **hydrocarbons** with hydrogen and ethylene obtained by cracking gas oil. It is used as a fuel.

GAS BURETTE. See **burette, gas.**

GAS CALORIMETER. See **calorimeter, gas.**

GAS CELL. An electrolytic **cell** (q.v.) which has two gas electrodes.

GAS, COAL. A combustible gas produced by the distillation of coal, and used as a domestic and industrial fuel and illuminant. It consists of methane, hydrogen, carbon monoxide, and other components and is most commonly used in mixtures with other industrial gases.

GAS CONSTANT. See **constant, gas,** and also **equation of state.**

GAS CONVERSION PROCESS. A method of petroleum **cracking** in which thermal cracking and naphtha reforming take place in the same reaction zone, specifically by subjecting the C_3 and C_4 hydrocarbons to partial conversion before the naphtha is added to the stream.

GAS CYLINDER. A long, thick, steel tank used for shipping liquefied gases, as oxygen, hydrogen, carbon dioxide, etc.

GAS, DISSOCIATION. See **dissociation.**

GAS, ELECTROLYTIC. A mixture of hydrogen and oxygen in 2:1 proportion by volume. This mixture is produced by the complete **electrolysis** of water.

GAS, ELEMENTARY. A gaseous element (see **element, gaseous**).

GAS, EXCITED. A gas in which some of the atomic or molecular electrons are in levels above the **ground state** (minimum) levels, as a result of absorption of energy.

GAS, EXPANSION. See **law of Boyle** and **law of Charles**.

GAS FILTER. A filter for removing particles from gases.

GAS GENERATOR. An apparatus in which a reaction may be carried out to produce a gaseous substance, usually equipped with some device for controlling the rate of evolution of gas, e.g., Kipp generator; Ostwald generator.

GAS HOLDER. A tank used for storing manufactured gas. The holder is an iron cylinder, supported in a steel frame and free to rise and fall in a deep circular trough filled with water, which acts as a seal.

GAS, IDEAL. A gas which would behave exactly in accordance with the **law of Boyle**, the **law of Gay-Lussac**, and the **law of Avogadro**, under all conditions, without any of the deviations from them that are exhibited by real gases.

GAS, ILLUMINATING. A gas which burns under specific conditions with a flame sufficiently luminous so that it is useful for lighting, often used synonymously for manufactured gas (see **gas, manufactured**).

GAS, INERT. A gas that does not react chemically, such as **helium, argon, neon, krypton,** and **xenon**.

GAS IONIZATION. See **ionization, gaseous**.

GAS LAWS. See **law of Charles, law of Boyle, law of Gay-Lussac,** and **equation of state**.

GAS LIQUOR. See **gas, water**.

GAS MANOMETER. A pressure gage used for gases.

GAS, MANUFACTURED. A term often applied to ordinary city illuminating and fuel gas, when it is produced essentially from coal. It consists of water gas (see **gas, water**), to which may be added some coal gas (see **gas, coal**), and some illuminants, the last by spraying oil into hot portions of the apparatus.

GAS, NOBLE. The same as **gas, inert** (q.v.).

GAS, OIL. A gas produced from petroleum by simple stripping, or distillation.

GAS, OLEFIANT. Ethylene, $CH_2{=}CH_2$. So called from its formation of an oil on combining with chlorine. From this the "olefin" series of hydrocarbons derives its name.

GAS, PERMANENT. Oxygen, nitrogen, hydrogen, and other gases which require low temperatures and (in practice) high pressures for their liquefaction. In the early days of scientific investigation, before methods had been developed for obtaining these conditions, it was believed that these gases could not be liquefied at all, and hence they were called "permanent" gases.

GAS, PINTSCH. A compressed oil gas (see **gas, oil**) of high illuminating value which was once used extensively in railway cars and other movable lighting installations.

GAS PIPETTE. See **pipette, gas**.

GAS POLYMERIZATION. See **polymerization, gaseous**.

GAS REGULATOR. Devices for controlling the pressure or temperature of a gas.

GAS, SOLUBILITY COEFFICIENT. See **solubility coefficient of gases**.

GAS TAR. Coal tar, the tarry matter produced in the distillation of bituminous coal, and obtained from coal gas by separation.

GAS THERMOMETER. A temperature-measuring device which uses as its variable substance a gas, and determines temperature from the variation in volume of the gas at constant pressure, or the variation in pressure at constant volume, by the use of data on the departure of the behavior of that gas from the ideal gas laws.

GAS, TWO-DIMENSIONAL. A layer of adsorbed gas, of monomolecular thickness.

GAS, WATER. A combustible gas manufactured by the reaction between steam and glowing coal, by which the steam loses oxygen to the carbon, forming hydrogen and carbon monoxide. In using water gas for household consumption, it is further processed by adding unsaturated hydrocarbons, in order to increase the candle power of its luminous flame.

GASES, ABSORPTION COEFFICIENT OF. See absorption coefficient of gases.

GASES, BUNSEN COEFFICIENT OF. See Bunsen coefficient.

GASOMETER. An apparatus for holding and measuring large quantities of gas.

GASOMETRIC. Pertaining to the measurement of gases, e.g., the methods of gas analysis.

arsenite in 100 g. alcohol used in testing for lithium. A white or rose precipitate on heating indicates the presence of lithium.

GASPAR Y ARNAL TEST REACTION FOR AMMONIUM, POTASSIUM, CESIUM, AND RUBIDIUM. A solution of sodium ferrocyanide and calcium chloride in 50% alcohol, when added to a few drops of a solution containing any of the four alkali ions above, produces a white precipitate.

GASPAR Y ARNAL TEST REACTION FOR PHOSPHATE. A solution of sodium molybdate gives with antimony trichloride a yellow precipitate soluble in excess of the latter. If an orthophosphate is added before the precipitate dissolves, a blue solution or precipitate results.

GASPAR Y ARNAL TEST REACTION FOR THALLOUS SALTS. With calcium acetate and sodium ferrocyanide, the thallous ion gives a precipitate, insoluble in water and soluble in mineral acids.

GASTALDI SYNTHESIS. A method of forming dicyanopyrazines from isonitrosoketones by reaction with sodium bisulfite and potassium cyanide, followed by the condensation of two molecules by action of HCl.

$$RCOCH{=}NOH + 2NaHSO_3 + KCN \rightarrow RCOCH(CN)NHSO_3K + Na_2SO_3 + H_2O$$

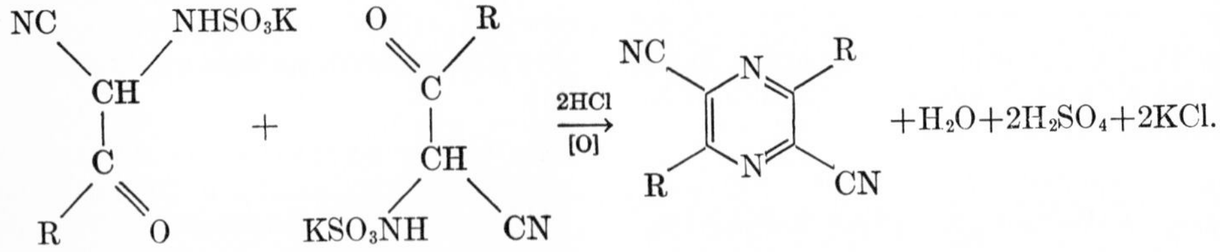

GASPAR Y ARNAL REAGENT FOR ALUMINUM. A solution of 20 g. calcium ferrocyanide in 675 ml. water and 400 ml. alcohol, used as a precipitant for aluminum.

GASPAR Y ARNAL REAGENT FOR LITHIUM. A solution of 5 g. sodium

GATTERMANN ALDEHYDE OR KETONE SYNTHESIS. A reaction between phenols, hydrogen chloride, and hydrogen cyanide in the presence of aluminum or zinc chloride to yield, on hydrolysis, hydroxy aldehydes. Ketones are produced by using organic cyanides instead of hydrogen cyanide.

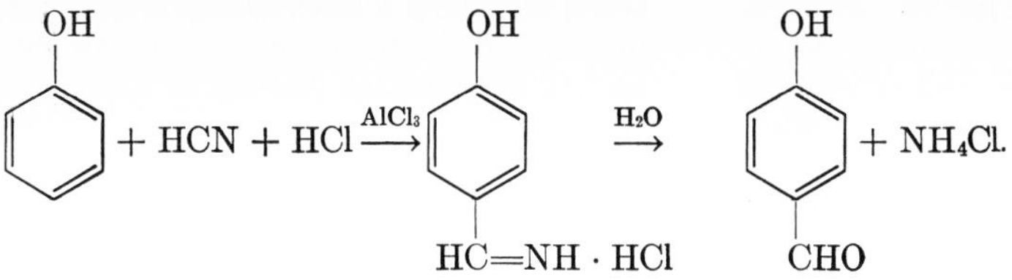

For ketones:

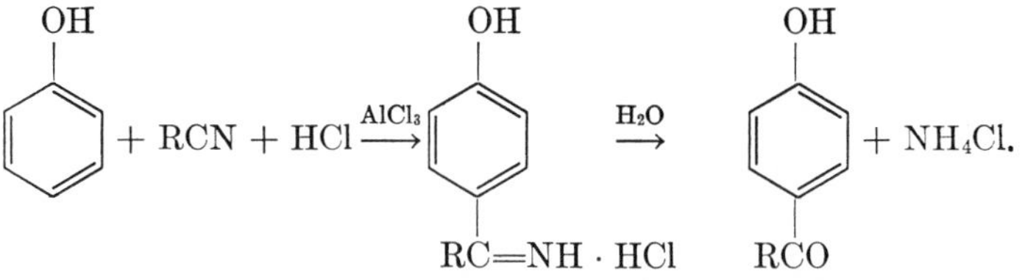

A special case of this reaction is the production of benzaldehyde by the reaction of benzene, hydrogen chloride, and carbon monoxide in the presence of aluminum chloride and cuprous chloride. See **Gattermann-Koch reaction.**

GATTERMANN DIAZO REACTION. The preparation of halogen-substituted aromatic compounds from the corresponding diazonium compounds by treatment with finely-divided copper and the appropriate halogen acid. From phenyl diazonium chloride, chlorobenzene is formed as follows:

$$C_6H_5N_2Cl \xrightarrow[HCl]{Cu} C_6H_5Cl + N_2.$$

Similarly, treatment with KCN yields the nitrile. See also **Sandmeyer reaction** and **Körner-Contardi reaction.**

GATTERMANN-KOCH REACTION. The direct synthesis of aromatic aldehydes from aromatic hydrocarbons and carbon monoxide, in the presence of hydrogen chloride and certain metallic chlorides which act as catalysts.

$$C_6H_6 + CO \xrightarrow[Cu_2Cl_2]{HCl} C_6H_5CHO.$$

GATTERMANN-SKITA SYNTHESIS. A method of formation of pyridine derivatives by condensation of esters of the type of diethyl sodiomalonate with amines such as dichloromethylamine.

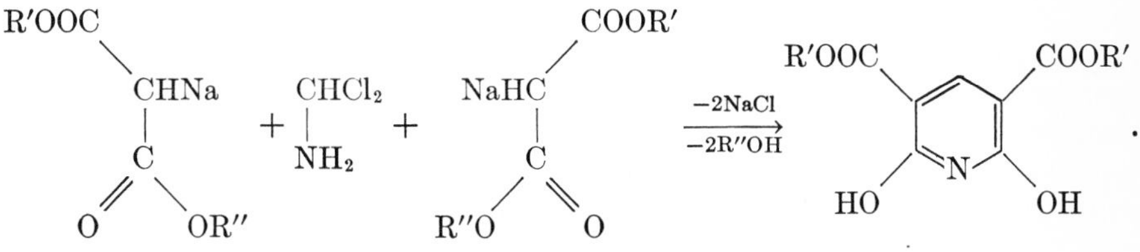

See also **Hantzsch pyridine synthesis.**

GAUCHER HEMATIN SOLUTION. A solution of 1 g. hematin in 100 ml. water used in detecting unboiled milk. A rose red color, that is permanent, indicates the presence of unboiled milk.

GAUGE. See **gage.**

GAUSS. The unit of intensity of a **magnetic field,** namely a field which exerts a force of one dyne upon unit pole.

GAUSS PRINCIPLE OF "LEAST CONSTRAINT." (1) The motion of connected points is such that, for the motion actually taken, the sum of the products of the mass of each particle into the square of the distance of its deviation from the position it would have reached if free, is a minimum.

(2) The motion of a system of material points interconnected in any way and submitted to any influences, agrees at each instant as closely as possible with the motion the points would have if they were free. The actual motion takes place so that the constraints on the system are the least possible. For the measurement of the constraint, during any element of time, take the sum of the products of the mass of each point by the square of its deviation from the position the point would have occupied at the end of the element of time, if it had been free.

GAY-LUSSAC TOWER. A tower used in the **chamber process** for sulfuric acid. It is built very much like the Glover tower but is commonly twice as high. Two towers are sometimes used. The function of the tower is to remove oxides of nitrogen from the waste gases of the process. To accomplish this, concentrated sulfuric acid is allowed to flow down through the packing of the tower, while the gases enter at the bottom, pass upward and escape at the top. The oxides of nitrogen are absorbed by the acid which is collected at the bottom of the tower and pumped to the Glover tower.

Gd   Symbol for the element **gadolinium.**

Ge   Symbol for the element **germanium.**

GEE-CHAIKOFF REAGENT. The compound dimethylhydroresorcinol, used as a reagent for acetaldehyde in blood.

GEIGER FORMULA. A relationship between the initial velocity of **α-particles** and their range. This relationship, which was derived from measurements on radium C and was later found to apply to α-particles from various sources, which have ranges from 3 to 7 cm., is of the form

$$V_0^3 = aR$$

where V_0 is the initial velocity of the α-particles at the source; a is a constant having the same value for α-particles from various sources, namely 1.03×10^{27}, provided V_0 is given in centimeters per second; and R, the usual range of the α-particles, is given in the number of centimeters of air at 15° C. and a pressure of one atmosphere, which the α-particles traverse from their source to a point at which they no longer produce appreciable ionization.

GEIGER-MUELLER COUNTER. See **counter.**

GEIGER-NUTTALL RULE. The equation relating the **radioactive constant** (decay constant) of a radio element, and the range of the α-particles which it emits. This relationship takes the form

$$\log \lambda = b + c \log R$$

where λ is the radioactive constant, b is a constant for each series, c is a constant, and R is the range of the α-particles.

GEIGER REGION. The part of the characteristic curve of **pulse size** versus voltage in which the pulse size is independent of the number of ions produced in the initial ionizing event.

GEIGER THRESHOLD. See **threshold voltage for Geiger counting action.**

GEILMANN-WRIGGE-WEIBKE TEST FOR RHENIUM. Add to the neutral solution to be tested 10 ml. 20% hydrochloric acid and 2 ml. 10% potassium thiocyanate. Then dilute to 50 ml., shake with 10 ml. 2% stannous chloride solution in a separatory funnel, and after 30 seconds shaking add 20 ml. ether and drain off the aqueous layer. A yellow color in the ether indicates rhenium. Many other metals interfere.

GEISSLER-OLIVER TESTING PAPERS. Papers impregnated with various solutions, such as citric acid-picric acid, potassium ferrocyanide-picric acid, sodium tungstate-citric acid, which are used in testing for albumin and related compounds.

GEISSLER TEST PAPERS. Strips of filter paper impregnated with mercuric chloride and potassium iodide, others with citric acid, used in testing for albumin.

GEISSLER TUBE. A partially evacuated glass tube provided with electrodes and used to investigate electric discharges through gases.

GEL. (1) A jelly. (2) A solid gelatinous form in which a colloidal system is sometimes obtained as distinguished from the liquid form, or "sol." Sols and gels are mutually transformable. The terms hydrogel and alcogel have been applied to gels in which one of the components is water or alcohol.

GELATE. To form a gel, especially when a **sol** solidifies.

GELATION. The process of forming a **gel.** Pectization.

GELLING POINT. The temperature at which various **colloidal solutions,** or other semi-liquids, become solid. It is a function of the concentration as well as of the temperature of the substance or substances.

GEM-. Abbreviation of geminate (said of two groups attached to the same atom), as the *gem*-dimethyl grouping in camphor.

GEN-. (Greek *genes*) Born, hence producing; used as a prefix in naming the *N*-oxide of an alkaloid, or as a suffix to mean producing or produced by.

GENERAL CHEMICAL PROCESS. A process, similar to the **Haber process** (q.v.), for the production of ammonia by direct combination of nitrogen and hydrogen. Points of difference are the more sensitive catalyst, which requires a more careful purification of the gases, and the use of pressures around 125 atmospheres.

GENERAL EQUATION OF STATE. See **equation of state, general.**

GENERATOR. An apparatus for the preparation of a gas or vapor by chemical action. See **gas generator.**

GENEVA NOMENCLATURE. An accepted international system of nomenclature for carbon compounds. See **chemical nomenclature.**

GENLIS REAGENT. Stir 5 g. starch flour with 100 ml. water, add 20 g. zinc chloride and boil 1 hour. After cooling add 2 g. zinc iodide and make up to 1 liter. Used as a reagent for free chlorine.

GEOMETRICAL ISOMERISM. See **isomerism, geometrical.**

GERANYL. The radical $C_{10}H_{17}-$ (from geraniol).

GERHARDT REACTION FOR PICRIC ACID. Picric acid, when heated with chlorinated lime solution, gives chloropicrin (characteristic odor).

GERMANATE (META). The anion $GeO_3^=$, $Ge_2O_5^=$, or $Ge_4O_9^=$ or a compound containing one of these anions.

GERMANIC. Containing or pertaining to tetravalent **germanium.**

GERMANITE. The anion $GeO_2^=$, or a compound containing it.

GERMANIUM. Metallic element. Symbol Ge. Atomic number 32. Atomic weight 72.60. Density 5.35. Specific heat 0.074. Melting point 958.5° C. Boiling point 2700° C. Valence 2 and 4. Oxides GeO and GeO_2.

-GERMANONIC. A suffix indicating the radical $-Ge\overset{\displaystyle O}{\underset{\displaystyle OH}{\diagup}}$.

GERMANOUS. Containing or pertaining to divalent **germanium.**

GERMICIDE. A substance or chemical which kills disease germs and other microorganisms.

GERMUTH-MITCHELL REAGENT FOR INORGANIC SALTS. A 0.5% aqueous solution of sodium alizarin sulfonate which gives colored flocculent precipitates with 1% solutions of metallic salts.

GERMUTH REAGENT FOR NITRITE. Two solutions: (1) a solution of 1 g. sulfanilic acid in 100 ml. water; and (2) 5.25 g. dimethyl-α-naphthylamine in 1 liter of a 4 N methanol solution of acetic acid. These solutions are used in the determination of nitrite which gives a purple-red color.

GERMUTH TEST REACTION FOR LACTATE. To a solution of 0.5–5.0% lactic acid, or a weakly-acid (hydrochloric acid) lactate solution, add 0.5 ml. 15% potassium thiocyanate solution for each 1% lactic acid present. An orange to red color develops, which is unchanged by heating.

GERRARD SOLUTION. Fehling solution (q.v.) modified by the addition of an aqueous solution of potassium cyanide and used in testing for glucose.

GEUTHER REAGENT AND TEST. A modified Welman test for detecting vegetable oils in animal oils or fats, in which the reagent is a solution of 5 g. sodium phosphomolybdate in 25 ml. water and 25 ml. nitric acid (sp. gr. 1.4). On treatment with this reagent and chloroform, vegetable oils give a dark green color in *2 minutes or less.*

GIBBS-DUHEM EQUATION. In a system of two or more **components** at constant temperature and pressure, the sum of the changes for the various components, of any **partial molar quantity,** each multiplied by the number of moles of the component present, is zero. The special case of two components is the basis of the Gibbs-Duhem equation of the form:

$$n_1 d\overline{X}_1 = - n_2 d\overline{X}_2$$

in which n_1 and n_2 are the number of moles of the respective components and $\overline{X}_1$ and $\overline{X}_2$ are the partial molar values of any extensive property of the components.

GIBBS FUNCTION. See **free energy.**

GIBBS-HELMHOLTZ EQUATION. A thermodynamic relationship useful in calculating changes in the energy or enthalpy (**heat content**)(q.v.) of a system, from certain other data. Two useful general forms of this equation are:

$$\Delta A - \Delta E = T\left(\frac{\partial(\Delta A)}{\partial T}\right)_V$$

$$\Delta F - \Delta H = T\left(\frac{\partial(\Delta F)}{\partial T}\right)_P$$

in which A is the work function (which in earlier literature was called the "free energy," E is the energy of the system, T is the absolute temperature, V is the volume, P is the pressure, F is the free energy, or thermodynamic potential, and H is the heat content of the system.

GIBBS PHTHALIC ANHYDRIDE PROCESS. An industrial method of producing phthalic anhydride by atmospheric oxidation of naphthalene at 400–450° C. Vanadium pentoxide is an effective catalyst.

GIBBS TEST. Dilute solutions of phenols, with a pH adjusted to 9.4, give a blue color when 20 ml. of the solution are treated with 2–3 drops of an aqueous suspension of 2,6-dibromoquinonechloroimide.

GIBLIN-CHAPMAN TEST. A modified Griess test (q.v.) in which nitrite is detected by a red color formed on addition to 10 ml. of the solution tested of 2 drops of a solution of 1 g. dimethylaniline and 1.5 g. sulfanilic acid in 100 ml. 0.5 N hydrochloric acid.

GIEMSA REAGENT. Two solutions: (1) a solution of 27 g. mercuric chloride in 1500 ml. water; and (2) a solution of 10 g. potassium iodide in 50 ml. water. They are mixed, acidified with acetic acid, and used in testing for quinine. An opalescence is produced in the presence of quinine.

GIES BIURET SOLUTION. An aqueous solution of potassium hydroxide to which has been added a solution of cupric sulfate. It is used as a test reagent for proteins.

GIL TEST REACTIONS. Polysulfides are detected by boiling 96% alcohol in a flask until the air has been displaced by alcohol vapor, then adding at once the solution tested. Polysulfides give a blue color.

GILL. A unit of liquid measure equal to the fourth part of a **pint.**

1 gill = 4 fluid ounces
1 gill = 7.219 cubic inches
1 gill = 118.29 cubic centimeters

GILLET-HAINS TEST REACTION. Ketones in dilute aqueous solution give a yellow crystalline precipitate with **Nessler solution** (q.v.).

GILMAN-NELSON REAGENTS. Triethylbismuth and tetraethyllead used for the detection of the sulfhydryl group by the **Zerevitwinov procedure** (q.v.).

GILMAN-SWEENEY-HECK REACTION. Michler's ketone is detected by the greenish color produced on dissolving 0.05 g. of the substance in 10 ml. anhydrous benzene, adding 2 ml. 0.001 M dimethylaniline to 2 ml. of this solution, shaking, adding 1 ml. 2.25 M phenylmagnesium bromide and shaking, then adding 3 ml. water.

GILMOUR REAGENT. A solution of 317.5 g. sucrose in 100 ml. water, to which is added, after boiling, 2.5 ml. 3 N sulfuric acid, followed by 150 ml. of aqueous solution containing 2.5 ml. 3 N sodium hydroxide solution. The reagent is used for the titration of boric acid.

GILSON FLUID. A fixative, consisting of 3 g. mercuric chloride, 1 ml. glacial acetic acid, and 3.75 ml. 80% nitric acid dissolved in 230 ml. water and 15 ml. alcohol.

GIRARD-FOURNEAU REAGENT. Tetraacetylammonium hydroxide which, when added, with potassium iodide, to a bismuth solution, gives a red color to petroleum benzine used to extract the solution.

GIRARD REAGENT. Various quaternary ammonium compounds which form soluble compounds with substances containing carbonyl groups; the latter being readily regenerated by treatment of the compound formed. The Girard reagents are used in certain separations of carbonyl-containing substances, especially in separation of the sex hormones from urine. A representative reagent of the group is Girard's reagent T, which is trimethylacethydrazine ammonium chloride.

GIRARD TEST REACTION. Picric acid gives a red color on heating with ammonium sulfide.

GIRBOTOL PROCESS. A method for purification of manufactured gases, in which the gas is scrubbed with a solution of an organic base, such as triethenolamine, which absorbs acidic gases such as hydrogen sulfide.

GIRI REAGENTS. Aqueous solutions of trichloroacetic acid, and of potassium ferricyanide, and a sulfuric acid solution of ammonium molybdate, used in testing for vitamin C.

GLACIAL. Resembling a clear solid, a term used to distinguish certain chemical compounds from their liquid analogues, as glacial acetic acid, or glacial phosphoric acid (metaphosphoric acid).

GLADSTONE-DALE FORMULA. An empirical relationship for the molal **refraction** of a liquid, of the form:

$$R = \frac{M(n-1)}{d} = V(n-1)$$

in which R is the molal refraction for a given optical frequency, n is the **index of refraction** for that frequency, M is the **molecular weight,** V is the **molecular volume,** and d is the density.

GLASS. A hard, amorphous mixture of silicates, an alkali silicate always being present. Transparent glass usually contains potassium or sodium, and lead or calcium silicates. Other metals are added to furnish special qualities as color, hardness, low coefficient of expansion, insolubility, etc.

GLASS BEADS. Small hollow or solid glass spheres. They have various uses in the chemical laboratory, such as in fractionating columns to increase the surface of contact between ascending vapor and descending liquid.

GLASS, CLOCK. A circular piece of glass used for covering beakers and other apparatus. (See **glass, watch.**)

GLASS, COVER. A square of thin, flat glass used for protecting microscopic specimens on the slide.

GLASS, CROWN. An optical glass, containing sodium silicate.

GLASS FILTER. See **filter, glass.**

GLASS, FLINT. An optical glass, containing the silicates of lead and potassium.

GLASS, ORGANIC. An absolute term for certain glass-like resins.

GLASS, POLARIZING. A thin film of plastic material, in which oriented sub-microscopic crystals of iodoquinine sulfate are suspended, which is pressed between two pieces of glass, and is used to produce or analyze polarized light.

GLASS, "PYREX." A sodium aluminum borosilicate glass used in construction of laboratory apparatus. It has a low coefficient of expansion, and is, therefore, resistant to thermal stress.

GLASS, SAFETY. A glass consisting of a thin sheet of flexible transparent plastic, or similar material, sandwiched between two pieces of thin plate glass.

GLASS, TOUGHENED. Glass that has been heat-treated for resistance to shock.

GLASS TUBING. A hollow glass rod of varied diameter and wall thickness used for connecting laboratory apparatus.

GLASS WOOL. Thin glass threads used as packing for laboratory apparatus, especially for filtering gases or liquids.

GLAZE. A smooth glass-like coating applied to ceramic ware. Salt glaze is a double silicate of sodium and aluminum produced during the firing of earthenware by throwing common salt into the kiln. Transparent glazes are made of various glasses. Enamels are suspensions of metallic oxides and other substances in a transparent glaze. Porcelain glaze is a mixture of feldspar, quartz, and lime, and is fused into the body of the ware.

GLOSS. The shine or luster of a material or surface.

GLOVER AND WEST COKING RETORT. A vertical retort for the distillation of coal to form coke. It is continuous in operation; coal enters at the top and coke is periodically withdrawn at the bottom; gas, tar, and ammonia are obtained from the distillate.

GLOVER TOWER. A tower, commonly made of sheet lead, lined with acid resisting material and filled with packing used in the **chamber process** for the manufacture of sulfuric acid. The gases from the pyrites or sulfur burners enter at the bottom, pass up through and are conducted from the top to the first lead chamber. Meanwhile a mixture of acid from the Gay-Lussac tower and of dilute acid from the chambers is allowed to drip through, whereby it is freed from oxides of nitrogen, much water, and the gases are cooled to 50–60° C. Some sulfuric acid is formed from the gases in the tower.

GLUC-, GLUCO-. (a) Relating to glucose; as glucopyranose, glucuronic; (b) less properly see **glyc-, glyco-**

GLUCINIUM. A name for the element **beryllium** (q.v.).

GLÜCKSMANN REACTION FOR PYROGALLOL. A trace of pyrogallol is dissolved in 1 ml. glacial acetic acid, 3–5 drops formaldehyde added, the solution is heated to boiling and a few drops concentrated hydrochloric acid added. A deep cherry-red color, which changes to rose-red with acetic acid in excess, indicates the presence of pyrogallol.

GLUCOPHORE (GLUCIPHORE). A radical or atomic grouping which is supposed to impart a sweet taste to many compounds in which it appears. Common glucophore groups are

$$—CHOH—CH_2OH; \quad —CO—CH_2OH;$$
$$—CHNH_2—COOH; \quad and \quad —CH_2ONO_2.$$

GLUCOSIDE. See **glycoside.**

GLUCOSIDE (CYANOGENETIC). See glycoside (cyanogenetic).

GLUTAMIC. Related to glutamic acid,

$$NH_2 \cdot CH \cdot COOH$$
$$|$$
$$CH_2 \cdot CH_2 \cdot COOH.$$

GLUTAMINYL. The radical

$$H_2NCOCH_2CH_2CH(NH_2)CO-.$$

GLUTAMOYL. The radical

$$-COCH_2CH_2CH(NH_2)CO-.$$

GLUTAMYL. The radical

$$-OCCH(NH_2)(CH_2)_2CO-.$$

GLUTARIC. Related to glutaric acid,

$$HOOC(CH_2)_3COOH.$$

GLUTARYL. The radical

$$-OC(CH_2)_3CO-.$$

GLYC-, GLYCO-. (Greek) Sweet, or relating to sugars or glycine, as glycogen, glycoside, glycocholic.

GLYCERIC. Related to glyceric acid,

$$CH_2OH \cdot CHOH \cdot COOH.$$

GLYCERIDE. An organic ester in which the alcohol radical is glyceryl derived from glycerol. Thus

$$CH_2O-OC-CH_3 \qquad CH_2O-OC-C_{17}H_{35}$$
$$|\qquad\qquad\qquad\qquad |$$
$$CHO-OC-CH_3 \qquad CHO-OC-C_{17}H_{35}$$
$$|\qquad\qquad\qquad\qquad |$$
$$CH_2O-OC-CH_3 \qquad CH_2O-OC-C_{17}H_{35}$$
$$\text{Triacetin} \qquad\qquad \text{Tristearin}$$

The natural fats are mixed triglycerides. Mixed glycerides contain two or three different acid residues in the same molecule.

GLYCERYL. The radical $-CH_2\overset{|}{C}HCH_{2}-.$

GLYCOL. A dihydric alcohol, so called from glycol,

$$CH_2OH$$
$$|$$
$$CH_2OH$$

the simplest member of the class. Glycols are named according to the Geneva convention by adding the suffix "diol" to the stem of the parent hydrocarbon, e.g., glycol is ethanediol. Glycols are distinguished as α, β, γ, δ, etc., according to the relative positions of the hydroxyl groups (1:2, 1:3, 1:4, etc.) in the carbon chain and as diprimary, primary-secondary, primary-tertiary, disecondary, secondary-tertiary, ditertiary, according to the nature of the alcohol groups. Compounds in which two hydroxyls are attached to the same carbon atom are not regarded as glycols.

GLYCOLIC. Related to glycolic acid,

$$HO \cdot CH_2 \cdot COOH.$$

GLYCOLYL. The radical $HOCH_2CO-.$

GLYCOSIDE. (Glucoside) An ethereal compound of a **carbohydrate** formed by the union of a sugar with a nonsugar, water being eliminated. The term is used to include the whole class and is also applied to the subclass which yields glucose on hydrolysis. Glycosides are classified in several ways; as α and β according to the constitution of the molecule:

$$
\begin{array}{cc}
CH_2OH & CH_2OH \\
| & | \\
CHOH & CHOH \\
| & | \\
CH & CH \\
| & | \\
CHOH & CHOH \\
| & | \\
CHOH & CHOH \\
| & | \\
H \cdot C \cdot OR & RO \cdot CH \\
\text{α-glycoside} & \text{β-glycoside}
\end{array}
$$

Emulsin hydrolyzes the β-glycosides only and the α-glycosides only are hydrolyzed by maltase. Glycosides are further classified according to the sugar formed during their hydrolysis as glucosides, fructosides, rhamnosides, galactosides, mannosides, arabinosides, xylosides, sorbosides, glucoheptosides, etc., or as aldosides, or ketosides if formed from aldoses or ketoses. Other classifications are based upon the nature of the nonsugar or "aglycone" group formed when glycosides are hydrolyzed. Glycosides may also be classed as disaccharoses.

GLYCOSIDE, CYANOGENETIC. A glycoside which yields hydrocyanic acid among its hydrolytic products, e.g., amygdalin, on hydrolysis yields dextrose, benzaldehyde, and HCN. A large number of cyanogenetic glycosides are known.

GLYCYL. The radical H_2NCH_2CO-.

GLYOXYLIC. Related to glyoxylic acid,

$$HOOC \cdot CH:O \cdot H_2O$$

GLYOXYLYL. The radical $OCHCO-$.

GOADBY SOLUTION. A solution of 0.33 g. mercuric chloride, 200 g. sodium chloride, and 100 g. alum in 5 liters water, used as a preservative.

GÖBEL REAGENT FOR METALS. An aqueous solution of sodium formate which reduces salts of some of the metals.

GODEFFROY TEST REACTION FOR ALKALOIDS. (1) A solution of ferric chloride in hydrochloric acid gives yellow-red precipitates with many alkaloids in solutions of moderate concentration. Preliminary moistening with sulfuric acid increases the range of color changes.

(2) Stannous chloride gives crystalline precipitates with hydrochloric acid solutions of many alkaloids.

GOGTE SYNTHESIS. A method of formation of α-pyrone derivatives by treatment of β-substituted glutaconic anhydrides with acyl chlorides, followed by decarboxylation.

GOLD. Metallic element. Symbol Au. Atomic number 79. Atomic weight 197.2. Density 19.3. Specific heat 0.0297. Melting point 1063° C. Boiling point 1880° C. Valence 1 and 3. Oxides, Au_2O, Au_2O_3. Gold forms two series of salts, although a number of auroauric compounds containing both univalent and trivalent gold are known. It occurs native and in combination.

GOLD NUMBER. An index of the protective action of a **colloid.** It is found by determining the value of the colloid in preventing **coagulation** of a metal sol by an ionic solution. It is defined as the weight, in milligrams, of the colloid necessary to prevent 10 cubic centimeters of a 0.005% red gold sol changing to a blue color when 1 cubic centimeter of a 10% sodium chloride solution is added.

GOLDSCHMIDT DETINNING PROCESS. A process for the recovery of tin, based on the action of dry chlorine on scrap tin-plate. The tin reacts readily to form stannic chloride, and the iron reacts only slightly. By fractional distillation the stannic chloride is separated from the small amount of ferric chloride that is formed.

GOLDSCHMIDT PROCESS. A method of direct synthesis of formates by heating sodium hydroxide with carbon monoxide under pressure. Further heating yields oxalates.

$$NaOH + CO \xrightarrow{200° C.} HCOONa$$

$$2HCOONa \xrightarrow{375° C.} \underset{\underset{COONa}{|}}{COONa} + H_2.$$

GOL'BRAIKH TEST FOR NITROGEN. The sample is heated with manganese dioxide in a tube having an air-inlet tube and an outlet tube leading to distilled water, which is then tested for nitrite.

GOLDSCHMIDT REDUCTION PROCESS. A process based on the reaction of various metallic oxides with metallic aluminum, resulting in the oxidation of the aluminum to its oxide, and the reduction of the metallic oxide to the free metal. This process is used in the production from their oxides of many metals, such as chromium, zirconium, cobalt, etc. Furthermore, the reaction is strongly exothermic and is applied in welding by igniting a mixture of aluminum and ferric oxide, which is known as thermite.

GOLDSCHMIDT TEST FOR SILVER HALIDES. On fusion with bismuth sulfide on charcoal by means of a blowpipe, silver iodide gives a red deposit, silver bromide, yellow, and silver chloride, white.

GOLDSMITH FLUID. A tissue fixative consisting of 1 part glacial acetic acid, 15 parts of 1% aqueous chromic acid solution, and 4 parts 2% aqueous potassium dichromate solution.

GOLDSMITH TEST FOR TUNG OIL. Two or three ml. of the oil are mixed with petroleum benzine (and filtered if neces-

GOLSE TEST FOR MERCURY OXYCYANIDE. Add to 2 ml. of a 1% solution of the substance tested, 1 ml. 5% potassium iodide solution, 1 ml. ammonium hydroxide, and 1 ml. sodium carbonate solution. A brown precipitate indicates mercury oxycyanide.

GOLSE TEST REACTION FOR ARSONIC ACIDS. On mixing 5 ml. of 1:3 sulfuric acid solution with 1 drop of a 1:20 aqueous solution of sodium methyl arsenate, or other derivatives or salts of arsonic acid, and adding with agitation several drops of 1:10 potassium iodide solution, a brown solution, turbid when warm, is obtained.

GOMBERG-BACHMANN-HEY REACTION. The formation of biaryl compounds from aromatic compounds and aryl diazonium compounds in the presence of alkaline substances such as sodium hydroxide.

$$\langle\!\!\rangle\!\!-\!N_2Cl + \langle\!\!\rangle \xrightarrow{\text{NaOH}} \langle\!\!\rangle\!\!-\!\langle\!\!\rangle + N_2 + NaCl + H_2O.$$

sary). On the addition of sodium nitrite and dilute sulfuric acid, a yellow precipitate indicates tung oil. If the oil was boiled, add 4% absolute alcohol to the petroleum benzine.

GOLDSTEIN SOLUTION. A solution of 2 g. iodine and 6 g. potassium iodide in 120 ml. water, used to test for glycogen. A brown color is positive.

GOLDSTÜCK REAGENT. An aqueous solution of 2,4-dinitroresorcinol, strong enough to be brown in color. It gives a greenish-blue precipitate with ferrous salts.

GOLENKIN REAGENT. Quinoline blue (cyanine) used for the micro-chemical detection of free iodine in plant tissues. Iodine colors it brown.

GOLODETZ TEST REACTION. A solution of a few granules benzoyl peroxide in concentrated sulfuric acid gives a blood-red color with formaldehyde.

GOMBERG FREE RADICAL REACTION. The formation of free radicals by the action of certain metals upon triarylmethyl halides,

$$R_3CCl + Ag \rightarrow R_3\dot{C} + AgCl$$

(in which R is an aryl radical).

GONIOMETER. An instrument for measuring angles, especially the angles of **crystals.**

GONIOMETRIC. Pertaining to the measurement of angles with a goniometer.

GOOCH CRUCIBLE. See **crucible, Gooch.**

GOODMAN-SUZANNE REAGENT. A solution of 1.5 g. phosphoric acid and 5 g. hydrochloric acid in 93.5 g. ethyl alcohol, used in testing for albumin in urine.

GOPPELSRÖDER REAGENT. A 0.1% alcoholic solution of morin which gives a strong green fluorescence with aluminum salts.

GOULD-JACOBS REACTION. A method of formation of 4-hydroxyquinolines by ring closure of α-carbalkoxy-β-aniloacrylic esters.

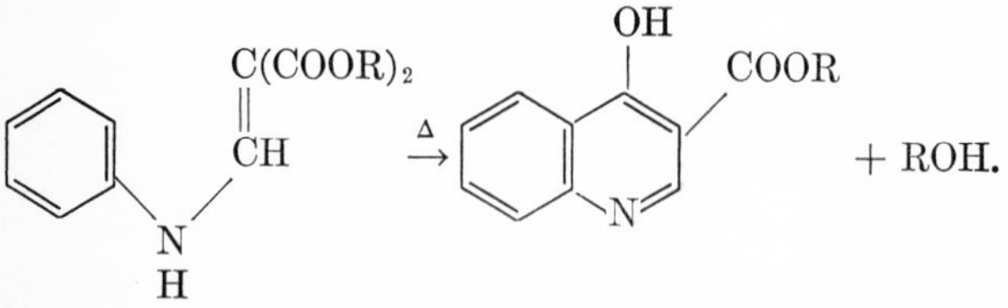

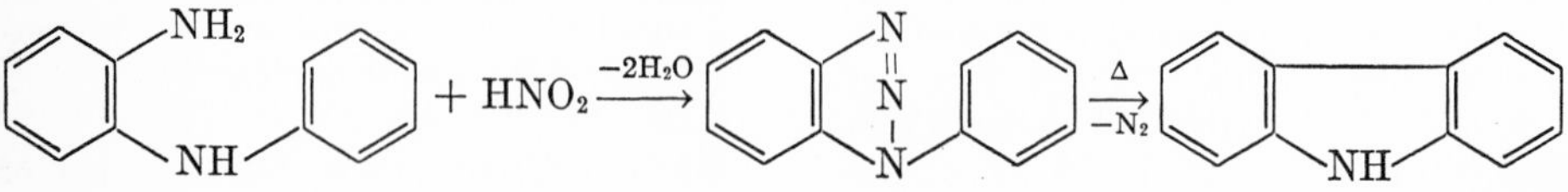

GRÄFE REAGENT FOR FORMALDE-HYDE IN MILK. A solution of 1 g. diphenylamine in 100 g. concentrated sulfuric acid used as a reagent for formalde-

$$+ \text{ROH}.$$

GOVER PROCESS. A process for the **dewaxing** (q.v.) of petroleum oils by the use of a solvent consisting of a mixture of benzene and acetone, which may be partly replaced by various other ketones or mixtures of them. Since ethyl methyl ketone (2-butanone) is one of these solvents the process is also known as the ethyl methyl ketone process, as it was once known as the benzol-acetone process. The final separation of the wax is done by filtration.

GOWER SOLUTION. An aqueous solution of mercuric cyanide and potassium iodide, used as a reagent for albumin. A white precipitate is obtained.

GRADIENT. A mathematical operator with **vector** properties that describes the change of the operand over a small distance along three mutually perpendicular directions.

GRADUATE. A vessel calibrated either in fluid ounces or milliliters or both, of a conical shape, and used to measure liquids.

GRADUATED CYLINDER. See **cylinder, graduated.**

GRAEBE-ULLMANN SYNTHESIS. A method of formation of carbazoles from 2-aminodiphenylamines, by treatment with nitrous acid, and heating of the intermediate compound.

hyde in milk. A green color indicates the presence of formaldehyde.

GRAHAM LAW OF DIFFUSION. See **law of diffusion, Graham.**

GRAHAM-MENTEN REAGENT. A solution of 0.5 g. benzidine in 100 g. 75% alcohol with 0.2% hydrogen peroxide added, used in testing for oxidases.

GRAIN. A unit of weight in the **English system** equal to the 480th part of an apothecaries' ounce, or equal to the 5760th part of an apothecaries' pound. The conversion factors of grains to avoirdupois units, and to metric units, are as follows:

$$437.5 \text{ grains} = 1 \text{ avoirdupois ounce}$$
$$15.4324 \text{ grains} = 1 \text{ gram}$$
$$1 \text{ grain} = 0.0648 \text{ gram}.$$

GRAINER PAN. An open evaporator in which solutions are placed to evaporate water so that crystallization may occur. The heat is usually supplied by steam pipes.

GRAM. A unit of weight in the **metric system.** It is the thousandth part of the international **kilogram** and is very nearly the weight of one cubic centimeter of distilled water at 4° C.

1 gram = 15.4324 grains
28.3495 grams = 1 avoirdupois ounce
31.10348 grams = 1 troy ounce
453.59 grams = 1 avoirdupois pound
1 gram = 1,000 milligrams
1,000 grams = 1 kilogram.

-GRAM. A suffix meaning the record produced by an instrument, as in telegram and spectrogram.

GRAM-ATOM. The **atomic weight** of an element stated in grams.

GRAM-ATOMIC WEIGHT. See **gram-atom.**

GRAM-EQUIVALENT. The **atomic weight** of an element (or formula weight of a radical) divided by its **valence.** In the case of multivalent substances there will be more than one value for the gram-equivalent, viz., $Fe^{++} = 27.92$, $Fe^{+++} = 18.61$, and the proper value for the particular reaction must be chosen.

GRAM MOLE. A **mole** or **gram molecular weight.**

GRAM-MOLECULAR VOLUME. The volume occupied by 1 mole of an element at 0° C. and 760 mm. pressure. For an ideal gaseous element it is 22.242 liters.

GRAM-MOLECULAR WEIGHT. The expression in grams of the **molecular weight** of a substance. It is also designated as the mole or mol.

GRAM-NEGATIVE. Not stained by Gram stain; a valuable distinguishing characteristic of bacteria.

GRAM-POSITIVE. Stained by Gram stain; a valuable distinguishing characteristic of bacteria.

GRAM STAIN. A solution used for differential staining, especially for bacteria. A widely-used formula for this stain consists of 7 ml. of a saturated alcoholic solution of methyl violet 6B, 15 ml. aniline, 10 ml. ethyl alcohol, and 100 ml. water.

GRANDMOUGIN-HAVAS REAGENT. A solution of 3 g. sodium hydrosulfite and 5 ml. sodium hydroxide solution in 1 liter of boiled water used in the determination of azo dyes by titration.

GRAPH. A line drawing expressing a function of two variables; or more generally, any record produced by physical methods.

-GRAPH. A suffix meaning a device to produce a record of observations as in telegraph and spectrograph.

GRAPHIC FORMULA. See **formula, graphic.**

GRATING. Any frame-work or lattice-work, consisting of a regular arrangement of bars, rods, or other long, narrow objects with interstices between them. A **diffraction** grating consists of rulings upon the surface of a light-transmitting or light-reflecting substance; it is used for the production of spectra.

GRAVELER. A cylindrical vessel containing stones through which a solution is passed in order to remove relatively insoluble impurities by crystallization of them upon the cool stones.

GRAVES TEST. Ammonia is detected in water by a white precipitate or turbidity formed by addition of a few ml. of a mixture of 50 ml. saturated mercuric chloride solution, 35 ml. saturated lithium carbonate solution, and 15 g. sodium chloride.

GRAVIMETRIC ANALYSIS. See **analysis, quantitative.**

GRAVIMETRIC FACTOR. See **factor, gravimetric.**

GRAVITATION. The force of attraction between material bodies, which varies directly as the product of their masses, and inversely as the square of the distance between their centers of mass.

GRAVITATION, LAW OF. See **law of Newton (gravitation).**

GRAVITATIONAL EFFECT. A variation in the weight obtained on a beam balance of a body when it is weighed underneath another body.

GRAVITY. The attraction which exists between all material bodies anywhere in the universe. Specifically, the attraction of the earth for bodies near its surface. The attraction between the earth and a mass of one gram is 980 dynes. The force of the attraction is measured from the center of the two bodies, is proportional to the product of their mass (m_1, m_2) divided by the square of the distance between them (d), or,

$$F = G(m_1 m_2/d^2),$$

where G is the Newtonian constant, 980 dynes.

GRAY BODY. A substance having a **spectral distribution curve** such that the amount of energy it emits at each wave length is the same fraction of the energy emitted by a **black body** at that wave length.

GREASE. In general, any material consisting entirely or largely of fats and related materials. Lubricants for high-pressure service often contain greases. Waste products often consist largely of greases. Specifically, a grease is a fat that is soft at atmospheric temperatures.

GREGOR MICROCHEMICAL RE-AGENT. A solution of cobalt thiocyanate, used in testing flour and in the histological detection of cacao shells.

GRIESS DIAZO REACTION. See **Diazo reaction** (Griess).

GRIESS PHENYLENEDIAMINE TEST FOR NITRITE. A solution of 5 g. *m*-phenylenediamine dissolved in 1 liter water acidified with sulfuric acid gives a brownish-yellow color with even traces of nitrite in solution.

GRIESS REAGENT AND TEST FOR NITRITE. The solution tested is acidified with sulfuric acid, and a solution of sulfanilic acid added, followed after a few minutes by a colorless solution of α-naphthylamine sulfate. A red color is given even with traces of nitrite. Many modifications of this test have been developed.

GRIESSMEYER REACTION FOR TANNIC ACID. Add to an aqueous tannic acid solution a 0.01 N iodine solution as long as decolorization occurs. Then the addition of a very little alkali colors the liquid a brilliant red.

GRIGGI REACTION FOR GALLIC ACID. A 1:30 potassium cyanide solution gives a light ruby-red color when shaken with a 1% solution of gallic acid. The color disappears on standing and reappears on shaking.

GRIGNARD DEGRADATION. A method of removing the halogen atoms from a polyhalo compound, step-by-step, by formation of the magnesium-addition compound (Grignard reagent) and decomposition with water.

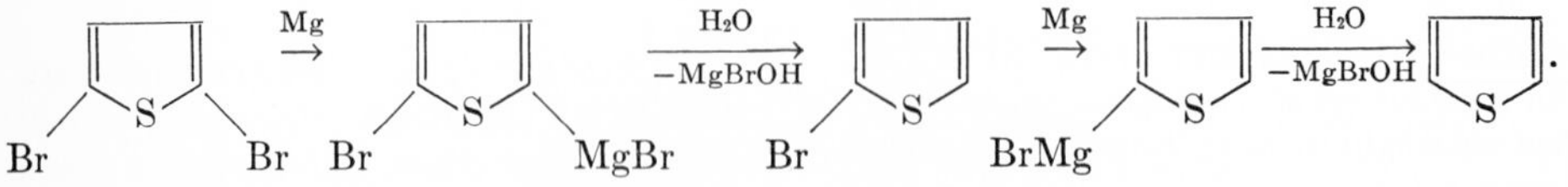

GRIEBEL TEST FOR HYDROGEN PEROXIDE. A drop of a solution containing hydrogen peroxide gives a dark brown color, later forming violet or blue crystals, with 1 drop of 1% vanillin solution in 25% hydrochloric acid. The test can also be used for vanillin.

GRIGNARD REACTION. Any one of a vast number of reactions, commonly condensations, involving the various Grignard reagents, which are usually, but by no means always, magnesium alkyl monohalides or magnesium aryl monohalides, which may be prepared, for example, by reaction between the alkyl or aryl halide, commonly dissolved in ethyl ether, and magnesium. The great variety of products obtainable from these Grignard reagents is due, not only to the ease with which they are reduced, oxidized, hydrolyzed, etc., but also to their ready condensation with many types of compounds. Since the magnesium and halogen atoms are readily removed from the final product, commonly by hydrolysis, the use of these reagents offers a convenient way to prepare many compounds, ranging in diversity from acetals to carbithionic acids, and including tertiary alcohols (as well as primary and secondary alcohols), cyanides, keto-alcohols, nitrites, and many others. One of the most useful properties of these reagents is their reactivity with inorganic compounds of other elements, whereby it is possible to prepare organic compounds of the other element by way of the Grignard reagent. By such means organic compounds have been conveniently prepared of arsenic, bismuth, boron, germanium, lead, mercury, and many other elements.

GRIGORIEW REAGENTS. Three solutions used as solvents for blood stains for spectroscopic examination. They consist of (1) a solution of 12 g. potassium hydroxide and 40 g. Rochelle salt in 100 ml. water; (2) a solution of 1.5 g. potassium hydroxide and 1 g. Rochelle salt in 2 ml. water; and (3) a solution of 1 g. sodium carbonate in 5 ml. water and 95 ml. alcohol.

GRILLO-SCHROEDER PROCESS. A contact process (q.v.) for the manufacture of sulfuric acid in which the catalyst is platinized magnesium sulfate.

GRIMAUX REAGENT FOR NITRATE. An aqueous solution of nitroquinetol acidified with sulfuric acid, and used to precipitate nitrates.

GRIMBERT-DUFAU REAGENT. A solution of 100 g. citric acid in 75 ml. water used to test urine for mucus and albumin. This is a ring test, showing a characteristic difference between mucus and albumin, confirmed by repeating the test with nitric acid.

GRIMBERT TEST REACTION FOR MAGNESIUM. A modified **Schlagdenhauffen reaction** (q.v.). Add to 5 ml. 10% potassium iodide solution, 2–3 drops concentrated sodium hypochlorite solution, add this to 10 ml. of the solution tested. A reddish-brown flocculent precipitate indicates magnesium.

GRIZZLEY. A heavy classifying device consisting of a number of heavy, wedge-shaped metal bars fastened together.

GRODZKI TEST REACTION. Acetal is detected, in its acidified (with hydrochloric acid) aqueous solution, by a precipitate of iodoform on addition of sodium hydroxide solution and iodine solution.

GROSHEINTZ-FISCHER-REISSERT SYNTHESIS. See **Reissert reaction.**

GROSSFELD REAGENT FOR OXALATES. A solution of 5 g. citric acid, 5 g. calcium chloride, and 30 g. sodium acetate in 100 ml. hot water, used to detect oxalates in beverages. A white precipitate, obtained upon addition of reagent until the solution is acid to methyl orange, shows the presence of oxalates.

GROSSFELD TEST FOR BENZOIC ACID. Evaporate an ethereal extract of the sample, acidified with sulfuric acid if necessary, to dryness in a test tube. Add 0.1 g. potassium nitrate and 1 ml. sulfuric acid, and heat 20 minutes on the water bath. Cool, add 2 ml. water, alkalinize with 15% ammonia and add 2 ml. 2% aqueous solution of hydroxylamine hydrochloride. A red color indicates benzoic acid.

GROSSMAN TEST REACTION FOR COBALT. Solutions containing cobalt give with potassium ferrocyanide a green precipitate, changed to red by ammonium hydroxide.

GROSSMAN TEST REACTIONS FOR TITANIUM. Solutions of trivalent titanium give: (1) colored precipitates with potassium thiocyanate, sodium nitroprusside and ferro- and ferricyanides; (2) colored solutions, precipitated on heating, with sodium acetate and sodium formate; (3) precipitates with strong oxalate and tartrate solutions.

GROSSMANN-MAUNHEIM REAGENT. Dicyanodiamine, used to precipitate copper.

GROSSMANN-SCHÜCK REAGENT FOR METALLIC SALTS. Guanidine carbonate, used to precipitate certain metals from solution.

GROSSMANN-SCHÜCK REAGENT FOR NICKEL. A 10% solution of dicyanodiamine sulfate, acidified with hydrochloric acid and boiled for one minute. If a nickel solution is added to this reagent, followed by potassium hydroxide solution, a yellow precipitate is obtained.

GROTE REAGENT. A solution in 10 ml. water of 0.5 g. sodium nitroferricyanide, 0.5 g. hydroxylamine hydrochloride, and 1 g. sodium bicarbonate, to which 2 drops bromine are added, and the volume made up to 25 ml. It is used to test for sulfur in organic compounds and for thiourea in orange juice. A purple color indicates the presence of organic sulfur, and a blue or blue-green color is given by thiourea in orange juice.

GROTTHUS-DRAPER LAW. See **law of Grotthus-Draper.**

GROUND COLOR. A foundation coat of a color which will intensify the chromatic value of more transparent colors that are to be applied later.

GROUND STATE. The lowest permissible **energy level** which can be assumed by a system quantized with respect to energy.

GROUP, ATOMIC. (1) A number of atoms which remain together and act as a unit during various reactions, or, in other words, a radical. (2) Certain arrangement of atoms which confer specific properties upon the compounds in which they occur, as the **amine** ($-NH_2$), **carboxyl** ($-COOH$), **carbonyl** ($> C=O$) groups, etc. See **atomic.**

GROUP DISPLACEMENT LAW. See **Law of radioactive displacement.**

GROUP, FUNCTIONING. An organic radical which has one or more replaceable hydrogen atoms, as $-NH_2$, $-OH$, etc.

GROUP OF ELEMENTS. A number of elements placed together because they have similar properties from the standpoint of a particular system of classification, as the **periodic system,** a system of qualitative **analysis,** etc.

GROUP PRECIPITANT. A substance or reagent which precipitates the elements of an entire analytical group, as hydrochloric acid for the first group, hydrogen sulfide for the second, etc.

GROUP PROPERTY. A property common to a group of substances, i.e., **colligative properties,** the property of ionizing, etc.

GROUP REACTION. The reaction of a **group precipitant** (q.v.).

GROVE CELL. An electrical **cell** consisting of an amalgamated zinc electrode in an electrolyte of sulfuric acid solution, and a platinum electrode in concentrated nitric acid.

GRÜSS SOLUTION FOR WOOD AND VANILLIN. A solution of 5 g. vanadic acid in 100 ml. water, to which phosphoric acid is added until solution is complete. This reagent is used in testing for wood and vanillin. Wood is colored red-brown, leaving a blue solution, while vanillin yields red-brown crystals.

GRUTTERINK REAGENTS FOR ALKALOIDS. The nitrobenzoic acids, the di- and trinitrobenzoic acids, naphthalenesulfonic acids and certain related compounds, used in microchemical detection of the alkaloids.

GRUZEWSKA-ROUSSEL TEST. To detect copper in organic matter, dissolve the ash in dilute nitric acid and precipitate iron with excess ammonia. Concentrate to small volume and add an alcoholic solution of benzoinoxime. A green precipitate indicates copper.

GRYSZKIEWICZ-TROCHIMOWSKI AND McCOMBIE METHOD. A method of formation of fluorine compounds from chlorine compounds and potassium fluoride at high temperatures and pressure (autoclave). The reaction applies particularly to chloroesters and chloroalcohols.

$$ClCH_2 \cdot COOR + KF \xrightarrow{190° C.} FCH_2 \cdot COOR + KCl.$$

GUAIACYL. See *o*-methoxyphenyl.

GUANIDO. The radical

$$H_2NC(:NH)NH-.$$

GUANYL. The radical $H_2NC(:NH)-$.

GUARESCHI TEST FOR BROMINE. Moisten starch-free paper with a 1% fuchsin-sulfurous acid solution and hang over the solution tested, to which chlorine water has been added. A violet or purple color indicates bromine. Instead of chlorine water, a 25% solution of chromic acid may be used.

GUARESCHI TEST REACTION FOR PHENOLS. Phenols on heating with potassium hydroxide and chloroform form a red mass which dissolves in dilute alcohol to give a red solution. Many modifications of this test have been developed.

GUARESCHI-THORPE SYNTHESIS. See **Hantzsch pyridine synthesis.**

GUERBET REACTION. The direct condensation of **alcohols,** in the presence of alkali and metallic **catalysts,** and at elevated pressure and temperature. Straight chain alcohols add to form a single molecule containing one hydroxyl group and twice the number of carbon atoms, some of which are in a side chain. Close control of conditions is necessary to minimize the extent of the side reactions.

GUERIN SOLUTION FOR SELENIUM. A solution of 10 g. mercuric nitrate and 10 ml. nitric acid in 100 ml. water, used as a reagent for selenium. Characteristic precipitates are obtained with selenic acid and selenites.

GUERIN TEST FOR ZINC. To test ethyl or methyl alcohol for zinc, add 25–50 ml. of the alcohol to 2–3 ml. of a chloroform solution of urobilin, dilute with half the volume of water, and add 3–4 drops ammonium hydroxide. A characteristic fluorescence indicates zinc.

GUERIN TEST REACTIONS FOR GUAIACOL. (1) An aqueous guaiacol solution gives a brown color and precipitate with 2% chromic acid solution. (2) Guaiacol gives an orange-brown color and precipitate with 2% iodic acid solution.

GUGGENHEIM PROCESS. A method used for mining and refining sodium nitrate from the nitrate deposits of Chile. Mechanical means are used to strip-mine the nitrate fields, and they are followed by crystallization from solution of the sodium nitrate.

GUGLIALMELLI-DELMON TEST FOR CARBOHYDRATES. A mixture of 0.5 ml. of an alcoholic solution or suspension of the carbohydrate and 2–3 drops of a 2% alcoholic solution of fluorene is treated with twice the volume of sulfuric acid. Many carbohydrates give a red to indigo-violet color, and a dark yellow precipitate on dilution. The test can also be used for fluorene.

GUGLIALMELLI REAGENTS FOR PHENOLS. Two solutions giving color reactions with phenols: (1) a solution of 20 g. sodium tungstate in 150 ml. water, to which 50 g. arsenious acid is added followed by refluxing for $1\frac{1}{2}$ hours; and (2) a solution of 20 g. sodium tungstate and 4 g. sodium molybdate in 150 ml. water followed by addition of 50 g. arsenious acid, refluxing for $1\frac{1}{2}$ hours, and dilution to 200 ml.

GUIGNARD TEST FOR HYDROCYANIC ACID. Filter paper is saturated with 1% picric acid solution, and, after drying, impregnated with 10% sodium carbonate solution. This paper is colored red by hydrogen cyanide (gas).

GUILLAUME PROCESS. A continuous process, operated in a group of stills and condensers, for the concentration and rectification of alcohol, from fermented sugar and starch solutions. The alcohol is concentrated up to 95%, with separation of higher alcohols and esters.

GULDBERG AND WAAGE, LAW OF. See **law of mass action.**

GUM. A class of amorphous transparent substances allied to the **carbohydrates,** characterized by insolubility in alcohol and organic solvents. The "real gums" dissolve in water, the vegetable mucilages (which belong to the class of gums) swell up in that solvent to form sticky masses.

On oxidation with nitric acid all gums yield mucic and oxalic acids. Gum arabic, gum tragacanth, cherry gum, and plum gum are examples of this class.

in water, used as a test for acetone. When it is added in excess to an ammoniacal solution containing acetone, a turbidity or yellow precipitate of iodoform is obtained.

GÜNZBERG REAGENT. A solution of 4 g. phloroglucinol and 2 g. vanillin in 80 ml. 95% alcohol, used as a test reagent for free hydrochloric acid in gastric juice. On evaporation of the reagent with gastric juice, the residue has a red tinge if free hydrochloric acid is present.

GUSTAVSON REACTION. A method of formation of alicyclic hydrocarbons by the action of zinc on open-chain dihalocompounds.

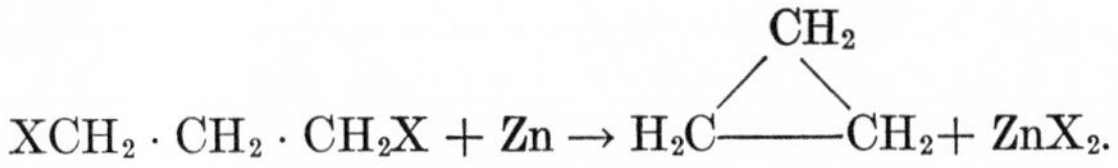

$$XCH_2 \cdot CH_2 \cdot CH_2X + Zn \rightarrow H_2C \underset{}{\overset{CH_2}{\diagup \diagdown}} CH_2 + ZnX_2.$$

GUTKNECHT PYRAZINE SYNTHESIS. A method of formation of dihydropyrazines by reduction of α-oximinoketones and condensation.

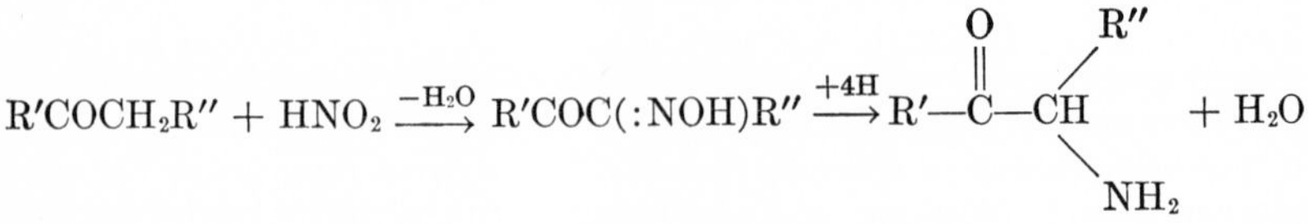

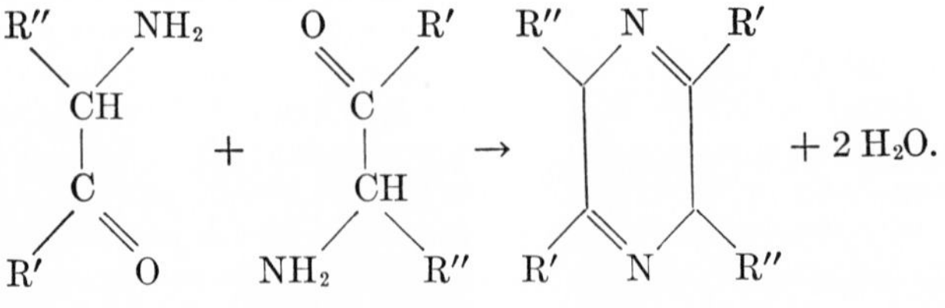

$$R'COCH_2R'' + HNO_2 \xrightarrow{-H_2O} R'COC(:NOH)R'' \xrightarrow{+4H} R'-\overset{O}{\overset{\|}{C}}-\overset{R''}{\underset{NH_2}{\overset{\diagup}{CH}}} + H_2O$$

Further oxidation yields **pyrazines.**

GUM RESIN. A resinous substance which generally contains essential oil as well as resin. Several of them, asafoetida, gamboge, and galbanum, are important pharmaceutically.

GUNNING REAGENT. A zinc acetate solution, used for precipitating blood pigments.

GUNNING REAGENT FOR ACETONE. A solution of iodine and ammonium iodide

GUTMANN REAGENT FOR HALOGENS. A solution of 35 g. arsenic trioxide in 200 g. 40% sodium hydroxide solution, used to test for certain organic halogen compounds. A crystalline precipitate is given by the organic halogen compounds.

GUTMANN REAGENT FOR MERCURY. A solution of 5 g. potassium iodide in 12 ml. 10% sulfuric acid, used to test for mercury in urine.

GUTMANN TEST FOR THIOSULFATE. Heat the solution tested with potassium cyanide on the steam bath. Acidify, and treat with ferric chloride. A red color indicates thiosulfate.

GUTZEIT-MONNIER-BACHOULKOVA-BRUN REAGENT FOR MAGNESIUM. An alkaline solution of 5-*p*-acetamidophenylazo-8-hydroxyquinoline, which gives a violet color with magnesium solutions stronger than 1:10000.

GUTZEIT-MONNIER REAGENT FOR VANADIUM AND IRON. The compound 5,7-dibromo-8-hydroxyquinoline in nitric acid solution, which gives green and brown precipitates, respectively, with iron and vanadium in nitric acid solution. To detect vanadium in presence of iron, first precipitate the latter with sodium hydroxide.

GUTZEIT TEST. A test for arsenic based on the addition of metallic zinc and hydrochloric acid. If arsenic is present, the evolved gases form a yellow to black discoloration on paper that has been dipped in mercuric chloride or mercuric bromide solution. Many variations and modifications of this test have been described.

GUTZEIT-WIEBEL SPOT TEST FOR ANTIMONY. To detect antimony in a mixture of sulfides, dissolve in aqua regia, evaporate to dryness, take up in hydrochloric acid. Add to 1 drop of the solution on filter paper, 5 drops 35% formaldehyde; then after 2–3 minutes, add 1 drop potassium iodide-antipyrine reagent. Antimony gives a yellow-brown stain.

GUY TEST REACTION. A solution of potassium permanganate in sulfuric acid gives characteristic color reactions with many alkaloids.

GUYOT TEST REACTION FOR FORMIC ACID. On warming an alkaline formate solution with potassium permanganate solution, a precipitate of manganese dioxide is obtained.

GUYOT REAGENT FOR AMMONIA. Potassium bromide solution is added to an acid solution of mercuric nitrate until the precipitate formed redissolves. Then potassium hydroxide solution is added until a permanent precipitate is formed. The clarified liquid gives a white precipitate or turbidity with ammonia.

GUYOT REAGENT FOR EPINEPHRINE. A solution of 1.5 g. sodium vanadate and 2 ml. sodium hydroxide solution in 30 ml. water, used in testing for epinephrine. A red color is given by epinephrine in dilute sodium hydroxide solution.

GYRO PROCESS. A petroleum-cracking process that operates on crude oil which is preheated and flashed. The reduced crude oil is introduced into the fractionator and the "bottoms" from the tower are sent to a viscosity-breaking coil.

H. Symbol for **hydrogen** (H). Symbol for **Planck's constant** (h). The symbol for the **gauss**, unit of magnetic field strength (H). The symbol for the **henry**, unit of inductance (H). Abbreviation for hour (h). Abbreviation for hetero- (h). Symbol for individual **heat transfer** coefficient (h). Abbreviation for **humidity** (H). Symbol for relative humidity (H_R). Abbreviation for height or altitude (h). Symbol for **Boltzmann function** (H). Symbol for enthalpy (**heat content**) per atom or molecule (h or h_m), per mole (h, H, or H_M), per unit mass (h), total value H. Henry Law constant (H). Symbol for degree of **hydrolysis** (electrolysis) (h). Miller indices (h, k, l). In naming almost completely fluorinated organic compounds, the prefix (H) may be used under certain conditions to designate the position of hydrogen atoms. The letter (H) is preceded by the numbers of the carbon atoms to which the hydrogen atoms are attached, as for example, the compound $CHF_2CF_2CF_2CHFCF_3$ is named $1H$, $4H$-decofluoropentane. As yet, this usage has not been extended to almost completely substituted organic compounds other than the fluorinated ones.

***H*-THEOREM.** The **entropy** of a system always increases, as concluded by Boltzmann from his calculations of the kinetics of ideal gases. Boltzmann defined a function H by the equation:

$$H = N_0 \int \ln f \cdot f \, d\xi \, d\eta \, d\zeta \, dV$$

where N_0 is the number of molecules, f is the **distribution function** for all the molecules, ξ, η, and ζ are components of the molecular velocity, and V is the volume. He demonstrated that H is a quantity which decreases in all possible processes involving deviations from the equilibrium value of f, and is therefore analogous to negative entropy.

HAAKH TEST REACTION. Naphthalene, anthracene, and other higher aromatic hydrocarbons, when mixed with chloranil and warmed, give colored quinhydrones, which become colorless on cooling.

HABER-BOSCH PROCESS. A process for the synthesis of ammonia from nitrogen and hydrogen under a pressure of about 200 atmospheres, and at a temperature of about 500° C., in the presence of a special iron catalyst, plus oxides of potassium, aluminum, and other metals to promote the catalytic activity.

HAEMOLYSINS. See **hemolysins.**

HAEMOLYSIS. See **hemolysis.**

HAFNATE. The anion HfO_3^-, or a compound containing it.

HAFNIUM. Metallic element. Symbol Hf. Atomic number 72. Atomic weight 178.6. Density 13.3. Melting point 2207° C. Boiling point > 3200° C. Valence 4, 3, 2. Hafnium is found chiefly in zirconium minerals. The chemical properties of hafnium are similar to those of zirconium.

HAGAN-SIEVERT TEST REACTION. Rhenium heptoxide is detected by its reaction with a few drops 30% hydrogen peroxide, to give a dark red solution, stable only in little water, and destroyed on heating with sulfuric acid.

HAGER-GAWALOWSKI REAGENT. A neutral aqueous solution of ammonium molybdate used as a test reagent for glucose and some other carbohydrates. A blue color on heating is given by these carbohydrates.

HAGER REAGENT. A mixture of 1 g. ferric chloride solution, 1 g. saturated potassium ferricyanide solution and 60 ml. water containing 5 drops dilute hydrochloric acid.

HAGER REAGENT FOR ALKALOIDS. A cold saturated aqueous solution of picric acid, which gives precipitates with many alkaloids.

HAGER REAGENT FOR AŁKALI SALTS. A solution of potassium chlorostannite, which gives a white turbidity with solutions of sodium, ammonium or lithium salts.

HAGER REAGENT FOR FREE CHLORINE. Diphenylamine sulfate.

HAGER REAGENT FOR GLUCOSE. A solution of 12 ml. glacial acetic acid, 15 g. sodium acetate, 25 g. sodium chloride, and 15 g. mercuric oxide in 200 ml. water, used as a reagent for glucose. A precipitate of mercurous chloride is given by glucose on heating.

HAGER TEST FOR FREE CHLORINE or BROMINE. Superimpose 0.5 ml. of a 1% solution of naphthol in alcohol on 4–5 ml. of the solution tested. A milky ring at the interface indicates free chlorine or bromine.

HAGER TEST FOR NITRATE AND NITRITE. Solutions of nitrates or nitrites in concentrated sulfuric acid give with a 1% solution of naphthol in alcohol a yellow to dark cherry-red color.

HAGER TEST REACTION FOR GLYCEROL. An aqueous solution of borax colored blue by litmus becomes red when added to glycerol or to neutral solutions containing it.

HAGER TESTS FOR ALCOHOL IN VOLATILE OILS. (1) On shaking 10 drops of the oil with a little tannin, a gelatinous mass forms if alcohol is present.

(2) On shaking the oil with twice its volume of glycerol, alcohol increases the volume of the glycerol.

HAHN REAGENT. The compound 8-hydroxyquinoline, which is called "oxine." It is used in 5% alcoholic solution in the determination of zinc, aluminum, and magnesium, in certain analytical separations, etc.

HAHN REAGENT FOR NITRITE. The compound 2,4-diamino-6-hydroxypyrimidine, which gives a strawberry-colored precipitate with sodium nitrite.

HAHN-SCHUTZE-PAVLIDES REAGENT. A 0.1% alcoholic solution of α-naphthoflavone, used to determine free chlorine in water. The method includes the addition of potassium iodide to the water tested before the reagent is added, and depends upon the subsequent color change from blue to pink in a titration with sodium thiosulfate.

HAHN TEST FOR BORIC ACID (BORON). A solution of glycerin in an equal volume of water is heated to boiling, phenolphthalein added, and then enough 0.01 N sodium hydroxide solution to give a permanent light red color. Then add phenolphthalein to the solution tested, and bring to the same shade with 0.01 N sodium hydroxide or hydrochloric acid. On mixing the two solutions, the presence of boron, even in micrograms per ml., causes decolorization.

HAHN TEST FOR BROMATE. Dissolve 0.1 g. fluorescein in 5 ml. 0.1 N sodium hydroxide solution and make up to 1 liter. Add 0.1 ml. of this reagent to 1 ml. of the solution tested, then a little oxalic acid, heat to boiling and cool. On adding 1–3 drops 0.1 M chloramine, a characteristic color change is obtained.

HAHN-WOLF-JÄGER REAGENT. A solution of 0.1 g. quinalizarin in 1 liter alcohol, which is used in testing for magnesium. A neutral solution containing magnesium (and free from ammonium) gives a cornflower blue color or flocculent precipitate with a few drops of the reagent.

If the solution tested is acid, the color is yellow-red, and in that case confirm by neutralizing and adding some excess of 2 N sodium hydroxide solution, which destroys the brown-red color if magnesium is not present.

HAINE REAGENT. A solution of 8.314 g. cupric sulfate and 40 ml. glycerol in 400 ml. water, to which is added 500 ml. 5% aqueous potassium hydroxide solution. It is a test reagent for glucose, yielding a precipitate of cuprous oxide.

HALDEN SOLUTIONS. Two solutions — (1) a solution of 0.1 g. pyrogallol in 100 g. absolute alcohol; and (2) 10 g. anhydrous aluminum chloride in 110 ml. absolute alcohol. They are used in testing for vitamin D. A deep violet color is given by vitamin D dissolved in benzene, chloroform or ether.

HALF-CELL. An electrochemical system consisting of a single electrode and an electrolytic solution, with usually a (reversible) ionization process in progress between electrode and electrolyte.

HALF-LIFE or HALF-PERIOD. (1) The time required for the radioactivity of a given radioactive element to decrease to one-half its value. Since the half-life is constant for each radioactive element, the measurements may be made over any range of absolute activities.
(2) The half-life of a first order chemical reaction (see reaction, first order) is the time required to reduce the concentration of the reacting substance to one-half its initial value.

HALF-ROTATION. See mutarotation.

HALF-THICKNESS. The thickness of an absorbing medium necessary to reduce the intensity of the transmitted radiation to one-half its incident value.

HALIDE. A binary compound of a halogen (fluorine, chlorine, bromine, or iodine) and another element, most commonly a metal. (See halogen family, which also includes the element astatine).

HALIDE, ACID. An organic compound of the type R–COX, in which R is an **alkyl** or **aryl** group, and X is a **halogen** atom.

HALIDE, ALKYL. An organic compound of the type RX, in which R is an **alkyl** group, and X a **halogen** atom.

HALIDE, ARYL. An organic compound of the type RX, in which R is an **aryl** group, and X is a **halogen** atom.

HALL EFFECT. A difference of **electrical potential** within an electrically conducting body produced by the action of a magnetic field, such as that of an electromagnet when the conducting body is placed traversely between its poles.

HALL-HÉROULT CELL. A **cell** for the production of aluminum by electrolysis of alumina dissolved in a bath of molten salts. This cell uses six or more preformed carbon electrodes which are suspended in the cell by means of copper bars.

HALL PROCESS. A process for the production of aluminum by electrolysis of alumina (Al_2O_3) in a bath of molten cryolite and fluorspar, or in a bath of the fluorides of sodium, aluminum, and calcium in suitable proportions. Carbon anodes and carbon cell linings are used.

HALL REHEATING PROCESS. A process for the removal of organic sulfur compounds from petroleum oils before they are used in gas manufacture.

HALLER-BAUER REACTION. A reaction for the preparation of trisubstituted acetic acids. The usual starting substance is a phenyl alkyl ketone in which (1) the α-methylene group is fully alkylated by the action of an alkyl halide and sodamide, then (2) the resulting compound is split between the phenyl and carbonyl groups by action of sodamide and hydrolysis and (3) the trisubstituted amide is oxidized to the acid.

HALLORAN PROCESS. A low temperature, multi-operation process for the purification of gasoline produced by cracking.

HALOCHROMISM. The phenomenon of color-development from colorless **carbonyl** compounds when they are dissolved in mineral acids. It is thought to be due to the formation of an **oxonium** salt, e.g.,

$$\begin{array}{c} R_1 \\ \diagdown \\ \diagup C{=}O + H_2SO_4 \rightarrow \\ R_2 \end{array} \qquad \begin{array}{c} R_1 \qquad\quad H \\ \diagdown \quad\; \diagup \\ C{=}O \\ \diagup \qquad\quad \diagdown \\ R_2 \qquad\quad HSO_4 \end{array}$$

HALOCHROMY. The property of forming colored salts by **halochromism**.

HALOFORM REACTION. See **reaction, haloform**.

HALOGEN. As commonly used in chemistry, one or more of the elements **fluorine, chlorine, bromine** or **iodine**, which constitute, with **astatine**, the **halogen family.**

HALOGEN FAMILY. A family of elements including **fluorine, chlorine, bromine, iodine,** and **astatine**. They are characterized by the presence of seven electrons in the outermost, or valency shell, and hence they readily gain an electron to form negative **ions** with a completed octet of valence **electrons.**

HALOGENATION. The introduction of **halogen** into an organic compound either by addition or by substitution.

HALOGENIDE. (1) A **halide**. (2) A **halogen** substitution product of an organic compound.

HALOGENOUS. Pertaining to or containing halogen. (See **halogen family**).

HALOHYDRIN. A primary **halogen** ester of a **glycol**, e.g., glycol chlorohydrin, CH_2Cl-CH_2OH.

$$C_6H_5 \cdot CO \cdot CH_2R' + 2R''X + 2NaNH_2 \rightarrow C_6H_5 \cdot CO \cdot CR'R''_2 + 2NH_3 + 2NaX$$
$$C_6H_5 \cdot CO \cdot CR'R''_2 + NaNH_2 + H_2O \rightarrow H_2N \cdot CO \cdot CR'R''_2 + C_6H_6 + NaOH$$
$$CR'R''_2 \cdot CO \cdot NH_2 + HNO_2 \rightarrow CR'R''_2 \cdot COOH + H_2O + N_2$$

HALOID. Halogenous (q.v.)

HALPHEN REAGENT FOR COTTON-SEED OIL. A solution of 1 g. sulfur in 100 ml. carbon disulfide, used in detecting cottonseed oil. Three ml. of this reagent is heated with 3 ml. of the oil tested and 3 ml. amyl alcohol for 15 minutes, in a concentrated aqueous solution of sodium chloride. A red color is given by cottonseed oil.

HALPHEN REAGENT FOR LINSEED OIL. A solution of sufficient bromine in 10 ml. carbon tetrachloride to bring the volume to 15 ml., used in detecting linseed oil. One ml. of the reagent is added to 0.5 ml. of the oil tested and 30 ml. ether at 25° C. A turbidity that appears in 2 minutes is given by linseed oil.

HALPHEN REAGENT FOR ROSIN OIL. Two solutions, consisting of (1) a

solution of 10 ml. phenol in 20 ml. carbon tetrachloride; and (2) a solution of 10 ml. bromine in 10 ml. carbon tetrachloride.

HALPHEN TEST FOR BENZENE IN ALCOHOL. Mix the alcohol with brine, extract with carbon disulfide, and treat the extract with a mixture of fuming nitric acid and concentrated sulfuric acid. Separate the acid layer, dilute with water, and extract with ether. Evaporate the ether, and reduce the residue with zinc and hydrochloric acid. Filter, add a few drops sodium nitrite solution, and neutralize with sodium carbonate. On adding an alkaline solution of α-naphthol, an orange-red color indicates benzene.

HAMBURGER TEST REACTION. To detect lecithin, add 3 volumes of alcohol to the solution, filter, and add 1:5 sulfuric acid solution. A cloudy precipitate, dissolving on warming, and reappearing on cooling, indicates lecithin.

HAMMER MILL. See **mill, hammer.**

HAMMERSTEN SOLUTION. A mixture of 5 ml. 25% nitric and 95 ml. 25% hydrochloric acids, used in testing for bile pigments in urine. A green color is given by bilirubin.

HAMMETT-SOTTERY TEST FOR ALUMINUM. A precipitated hydroxide to be tested for aluminum is dissolved in 5 ml. N hydrochloric acid, and 5 ml. 3 N ammonium acetate solution and 5 ml. 0.1% aluminon reagent is added. On making alkaline with ammonium hydroxide containing ammonium carbonate, a light red precipitate insoluble in the ammonium solution indicates aluminum.

HAMMICK REACTION. A method of formation of heterocyclic carbinols by decarboxylation of picolinic or related acids by reaction with carbonyl compounds.

HANNAY TEST REACTION. When a manganous ion solution is warmed with potassium chlorate and concentrated nitric acid, the manganese is completely precipitated as manganous manganate.

HANSEN REAGENT. Two solutions consisting of (1) a solution of 2 g. thymol in 90 ml. water and 10 ml. 2 N sodium hydroxide solution; and (2) a mixture of 100 ml. bromine water with 35 ml. 2 N sodium hydroxide solution. This reagent is used in testing for ammonia, by adding 1 ml. (1) and 1 ml. (2) to 5 ml. of the dilute alkaline or neutral solution tested. A blue-green color, soluble in ether, is given by ammonia.

HANSGRIG PROCESS. A process for the production of metallic magnesium from magnesium oxide by reduction with carbon at high temperatures, followed by quenching in a blast of hydrogen or natural gas.

HANTZSCH PYRIDINE SYNTHESIS.

A method of formation of pyridine derivatives by condensation of ammonia (or amines) with acetoacetic ester and acetaldehyde.

In other variants of this reaction, cyanoacetic acid derivatives may be used instead of acetoacetic ester (**Guareschi-Thorpe**); or a mole of malonic ester may be used instead of a mole of acetoacetic ester (**Knoevenagel-Fries**).

HANTZSCH PYRROLE SYNTHESIS.

A method of formation of pyrrole derivatives, using as starting materials an α-chlorocarbonyl compound, a β-ketoester, and ammonia (or an amine).

HANUS REAGENT FOR CINNAMALDEHYDE. An aqueous solution of semioxamazide, used to precipitate cinnamaldehyde quantitatively.

HANUS REAGENT FOR VANILLIN. *m*-Nitrobenzoylhydrazide, used to precipitate vanillin quantitatively.

HANUS SOLUTION FOR DETERMINING IODINE NUMBER. A solution of 13.2 g. iodine in 1 liter glacial acetic acid is cooled to 25° C., and the iodine in 25 ml.

determined by titration with 0.1 N sodium thiosulfate solution. To the remainder of the solution a quantity of bromine is added equivalent to the iodine present. Keep in the dark.

HAPTOPHORE. The chemical group which joins with the amboceptor which is a heat resistant substance found in blood that unites the **cell** body with the **complement**.

HARCOURT LAMP. See **lamp, Harcourt**.

HARDEN-NORRIS DIACETYL REACTION. Diacetyl solution gives a violet color with proteins and amino acids in alkaline solution.

HARDENING OF FATS. The **hydrogenation** (q.v.) of fats.

HARDNESS. The property of firmness or resistance possessed by solids and very viscous liquids. The degree of hardness of a substance is shown by its resistance to cutting, scratching, or abrasion. Hardness also means the presence in water of certain salts which form insoluble deposits in boilers, which form precipitates with soap, and which have other objectionable effects. Temporary hardness is caused by the presence of **bicarbonates**, chiefly of calcium or magnesium, which can be removed by boiling; permanent hardness is due to the presence of **carbonates** and **sulfates** of calcium and magnesium.

HARDNESS, BIERBAUM. The relative hardness of a micro-constituent of an alloy, determined by an instrument called the Bierbaum microcharacter. The method involves the measurement of the width of a scratch produced by a standard diamond point, under a standard pressure.

HARDNESS, BRINNELL. A measure of the relative hardness of the surface of a substance, obtained by measuring the depth of indentation of a standard steel ball at a standard pressure; and then computing the hardness by an expression whereby the value obtained is directly proportional to the applied pressure, and inversely proportional to the depth of penetration.

HARDNESS, ROCKWELL. A measure of relative hardness of the surface of a substance, based on the indentation made by a $\frac{1}{16}''$, $\frac{1}{8}''$ or $\frac{1}{4}''$ standard steel ball, or a conical diamond with an apex angle of 120°. The results are reported by using numbers to denote the pressure in kilograms, and letters to denote the ball or diamond producing a given indentation.

HARDNESS, DEGREE OF. An index of the amount of alkaline earth metal, calculated as calcium carbonate, present in a sample of water. Clark's scale used a degree based on one grain of calcium carbonate per imperial gallon. The French scale used a degree corresponding to one part of the same in 100,000 of water. The German degree corresponded to one part of calcium oxide per 100,000 of water. These scales have been discarded in favor of the more uniform method of reporting the hardness as the number of parts of calcium carbonate per million of water.

HARDNESS, PERMANENT. The presence in water of certain salts, chiefly sulfates or carbonates of calcium or magnesium, which can not be removed by boil-

ing, and require chemical treatment of the water (or its passage through ion-exchange media) to prevent scale formation in boilers, the precipitation of soap, and other undesired effects.

HARDNESS SCALE, MOH. A system in which all solid substances are classified in order of increasing hardness, so that the hardness of any particular substance may be expressed by a number. The numbers were established by assigning the integers from one to ten to arbitrarily chosen substances of increasing hardness, ranging from talc which was given the number one, to diamond which was given the number ten. This was the original Moh scale and is still generally used. In the new Moh scale, fifteen substances are used, and diamond has the number fifteen. The hardness of any substances not on the scale is determined by the scratch test, i.e., by comparing its hardness with that of the various substances in the standard scale, utilizing the principle that the harder of the two substances will scratch the softer one, and will not be scratched by it. When a substance is found to have hardness between two of the standard substances in the scale, this fact is expressed by use of decimal notation. Thus, the mineral having hardness of 6.65 would be harder than feldspar 6, and softer than quartz 7.

The original Moh's scale assigned the integral numbers as follows: 1 — Talc; 2 — Gypsum; 3 — Calcite; 4 — Fluorite; 5 — Apatite; 6 — Orthoclase; 7 — Quartz; 8 — Topaz; 9 — Corundum; 10 — Diamond. In the new Moh's scale the numbers above five have been re-assigned as follows: 6 — Orthoclase, Periclase; 7 — Vitreous Pure Silica; 8 — Quartz, Stellite; 9 — Topaz; 10 — Garnet; 11 — Tantalum Carbide, Fused Zirconia; 12 — Tungsten Carbide, Fused Alumina; 13 — Silicon Carbide; 14 — Boron Carbide; 15 — Diamond.

HARDNESS, TEMPORARY. The presence in water of certain salts, such as bicarbonates of calcium or magnesium, which can be removed by boiling, and which, if not removed, cause scale formation in boilers, the precipitation of soap, and other undesired effects.

HARGREAVES-BIRD CELL. A type of electrolytic **cell** for the manufacture of chlorine and sodium hydroxide from sodium chloride solution. It uses an anode having a surface of carbon and a cathode of copper gauze.

HARGREAVES TEST REACTION. Quinine in aqueous solution is treated with bromine water dropwise until a pale yellow color appears, then 3–5 ml. 2% phenylhydrazine hydrochloride solution and a slight

presence of tungsten in ores, boil 0.2 g. ore with hydrochloric acid (if necessary fuse the ore with 8 times its weight sodium carbonate and add hydrochloric acid). Heat the acid solution with tin; a blue color indicates tungsten.

HASS CYCLOPROPANE REACTION. A method of preparation of cyclopropane by chlorination of propane, and treatment of the resulting 1,3-dichloropropane with zinc dust in aqueous alcohol.

$$ClCH_2-CH_2-CH_2Cl + Zn \rightarrow H_2C\overset{\displaystyle CH_2}{\underset{\displaystyle \diagup \diagdown}{\rule{1.5cm}{0pt}}}CH_2 + ZnCl_2.$$

excess of ammonia is added. A pink to red color results.

HARRIS HEMATOXYLIN. A mixture of a solution of 20 g. alum in 200 ml. water, with a solution of 1 g. hematoxylin in 10 ml. ethyl alcohol, to which are then added 0.5 g. mercuric oxide and 8 ml. glacial acetic acid, used as a stain.

HARRIS PROCESS. A process for the "softening" (partial purification) of lead, in which the oxidized impurities are treated by certain sodium salts (sodium nitrate, sodium hydroxide, etc.) in a specially-designed cylindrical chamber provided with means for agitating, mixing, removal of molten impurities (salts of arsenic, antimony, tin, etc.) and removal of the "softened" lead.

HARTLEY TEST REACTION. Ceric salts in acid or neutral solution give a brown precipitate, which later darkens, on addition of sodium acetate and hydrogen peroxide.

HARTMANN TEST. To determine the

HAUSER-HERZFELD TEST. Methane is detected in gas mixtures by its oxidation to formaldehyde by ozonized air.

HAUSER-LEWITE REAGENT. A concentrated solution of titanium dioxide in concentrated sulfuric acid, or fuming hydrochloric acid, which gives a red to violet color with phenols on heating.

HAUSHOFER TEST REACTION. Cupric salt solutions, on addition of excess ammonium hydroxide, give a yellow to yellow-brown crystalline precipitate with potassium ferrocyanide solution upon evaporation of the ammonia.

HAUSSLER TEST REACTION. Citric acid solutions, when evaporated to dryness with vanillin, followed by warming with sulfuric acid, give a violet color, which dissolves in water with a green color, changed to red by ammonia.

HAWORTH METHYLATION REACTION. The use of dimethyl sulfate and sodium hydroxide to prepare methyl ethers of carbohydrates.

$$\begin{array}{l} | \\ CHOH \\ | \\ CHOH \\ | \end{array} + (CH_3)_2SO_4 + 2NaOH \rightarrow \begin{array}{l} | \\ CH_2OCH_3 \\ | \\ CH_2OCH_3 \\ | \end{array} + 2H_2O + Na_2SO_4.$$

HAWORTH SYNTHESIS. A method for the preparation of multi-ring hydrocarbons by preparing the substituted butyric acids with aromatic radicals in the γ-position, followed by reduction of the carbonyl group, cyclization, reduction, and aromatization.

and prevent the reduction of the iron oxides. The briquettes are crushed, and the tin removed partly by gravity concentration, partly by flotation, and the last by leaching with sodium hydroxide solution.

He Symbol for the element **helium.**

HAYEM SOLUTION. A solution used in counting corpuscles in blood containing 2.5 g. mercuric chloride, 5 g. sodium chloride and 25 g. sodium sulfate in 1 liter water.

HAYWARD-SCHLEICHER PROCESS. A process for the production of alumina (chiefly for use in obtaining aluminum) by treatment with sulfuric acid and water, heating, leaching with water, adjusting the aluminum sulfate-potassium sulfate ratio by adding potassium sulfate, crystallizing the alum, recrystallizing, heating to expel water, calcining at 1000° C. to decompose the aluminium sulfate to alumina, leaching out and recovering the potassium sulfate.

HAYWARD-WRIGHT PROCESS. A method of recovering tin, in which the cassiterite concentrates are briquetted to walnut size, introduced into the top of a heated vertical tube, up which a hydrogen-steam mixture is passed, controlling the temperatures to favor the reduction of tin dioxide

HEAD. The height of a fluid above a reference point. It is often used as a means of expressing pressure since the equivalent height of a fluid that corresponds to any pressure may be found by dividing the pressure by the density of the fluid, if that can be assumed to be uniform.

HEAD CONTRACTION. The loss in pressure of a moving fluid attributable to contraction in cross-sectional area of the conduit through which the fluid is moving. This pressure loss is expressed in the equivalent height of the fluid above a reference point.

HEAD, ENLARGEMENT. The change in pressure of a moving fluid attributable to enlargement of the cross-sectional area of the conduit through which the fluid is flowing. This change in pressure is expressed in the terms of the equivalent height of fluid above a reference point.

HEAD, FRICTION. The loss in pressure of a moving fluid as a result of friction with the walls of the conduit, expressed in terms of the equivalent height of the fluid above a reference point.

HEAD, IMPACT. The pressure of a moving fluid, measured in the direction of flow, as expressed in terms of the equivalent height of that fluid above a reference point.

HEAD, POTENTIAL. The pressure in a fluid attributable to its height above a reference point.

HEAD, STATIC. The pressure of a fluid that is exerted normal to the surface of which it acts, expressed in terms of the equivalent height of the fluid above a reference point. If the fluid is moving, the static head is measured at right angles to the direction of flow.

HEAD, VELOCITY. The pressure of a fluid that is due to its motion, and is equal to the difference between inpact head and static head. The velocity head is expressed in terms of the equivalent height of the fluid above a reference point.

HEAD, WORK. The pressure corresponding to external work done on a fluid, expressed in terms of the equivalent height of the fluid above a reference point.

HEARON-GUSTAVSON REAGENT. Two solutions: (1) a solution of 25 g. ferrous ammonium sulfate and 2 ml. concentrated sulfuric acid in 500 ml. water; and (2) a solution of 30 g. potassium hydroxide in 30 ml. water, made up to 200 ml. with ethyl alcohol; used in detecting the nitro group in organic compounds. Add .01 g of the substance tested to 0.7 ml. of (1), then add 0.5 ml. of (2), expel the air by a stream of inert gas, and shake. A red-brown precipitate indicates the presence of the nitro group.

HEAT. A form of energy that can be transmitted from one body to another by conduction, convection, and radiation. Its intensity is measured by the **temperature** (q.v.) of the body or system or other material entity or aggregate. It is con-sidered to be associated with the chaotic motion of molecules, because, when a substance gains heat, its molecules exhibit an acceleration of their motion of translation, rotation, and internal vibration; calculations made upon the basis of the **kinetic theory** (q.v.) from specific heat data of diatomic molecules show that at ordinary temperatures about 60% of an increment in heat energy is converted into translational molecular motion, and about 40% into rotational molecular motion. No appreciable amount of the heat energy is converted into internal vibrations until higher temperatures are reached.

HEAT, ATOMIC. The product of the **atomic weight** of an element and its **specific heat.** The result is the atomic heat capacity per gram-atom. For many solid elements, the atomic heat capacity is very nearly the same, especially at higher temperatures.

HEAT CAPACITY. The amount of heat necessary to raise the temperature of a system, entity, or substance by one degree of temperature. It is most frequently expressed in calories per degree centigrade. If the mass of a substance is specified, then certain derived values of the heat capacity can be obtained, such as the atomic heat, molar heat, or specific heat. (See **heat, atomic; heat, molecular;** and **heat, specific**).

HEAT CONDUCTIVITY. See **thermal conductivity.**

HEAT CONTENT. A thermodynamic property which may be regarded as the total heat of a substance or system, and is defined as the sum of its internal energy plus the product of its pressure and volume, as in the relationship:

$$H = E + PV$$

where H is the heat content, E is the internal energy (see **energy, internal**), P is the pressure, and V is the volume. Heat content is also called the heat function, and the enthalpy. The form in which this concept enters most commonly into chemical calculations is that of changes in heat content when a system changes from one state to another.

HEAT ENGINE. A machine operating on a thermodynamic **cycle** for the transformation of heat energy into mechanical energy.

HEAT EQUIVALENT. See **heat, mechanical equivalent of.**

HEAT EXCHANGER. An apparatus used widely in industry to transfer heat from one medium to another. For example, heat exchangers are used in reactions conducted at higher temperatures, in order to transfer heat from products leaving the reaction chamber, to reactants entering it. Heat exchangers are used widely to heat cold incoming material with hot finished material thereby cooling the latter, as in using hot pasteurized milk to preheat cold raw milk.

HEAT FUNCTION. See **heat content.**

HEAT INDEX. (HEAT NUMBER). This quantity is essentially the same as the **Maumené number.** It is determined by mixing a given amount, such as 20 ml. of an oil with a given amount, such as 4 or 5 ml. of sulfuric acid and noting the temperature rise. Its magnitude indicates the degree of unsaturation of the oil, and hence its effectiveness as a **drying oil.**

HEAT, LATENT. Heat which is gained by a substance or system without an accompanying rise in temperature during a change of state. (See **heat of fusion, latent; heat of sublimation, latent;** and **heat of vaporization, latent.**)

HEAT, MECHANICAL EQUIVALENT OF. The proportionality factor between mechanical energy and thermal energy, i.e., between work and heat, expressed commonly in terms of the number of energy units per unit of heat, and representing the complete conversion of work into heat.

HEAT, MOLECULAR. (Heat, Molar) The product of the **molecular weight** of a compound and its specific heat. (See **heat, specific.**) The result is the heat capacity per gram-molecular weight.

HEAT NUMBER. See **heat index.**

HEAT OF ACTIVATION. The increase in heat content accompanying the transformation of a substance from a less active to a more reactive form. This process applies commonly to **enzymes,** and to many instances of the **excitation** of atoms or molecules, as well as to the **irradiation** of molecules.

HEAT OF ADSORPTION. The increase of **heat content** when one **mole** of a given substance is adsorbed upon another specified substance. It is also necessary to state whether the **adsorption** is of the van der Waals type or of the activated type, since higher values are obtained from the latter process. Since gaseous adsorption is frequently a function of the pressure, one defines a differential heat of adsorption, as the difference between values of the heat of adsorption at two different neighboring pressures. (See **Langmuir adsorption isotherm.**)

HEAT OF AGGREGATION. The increase of **heat content** accompanying the formation of various aggregates of matter, such as crystals, etc.

HEAT OF ASSOCIATION. The increase of **heat content** when one **mole** of a **coordination compound** is formed from its constituent molecules or other particles.

HEAT OF COMBINATION. See **heat of formation.**

HEAT OF COMBUSTION. The increase in the **heat content** when one **mole** of a substance undergoes oxidation, whereby the products obtained in complete **combustion** are produced. The heat of combustion is very nearly an additive property; it depends, however, slightly upon molecular constitution, so that isomers do not give identical heats of combustion.

HEAT OF CONDENSATION. The increase of **heat content** when unit mass, or one **mole** of a vapor is converted into liquid at its boiling point under isobaric conditions without change of temperature. This quantity is the reverse of the latent **heat of vaporization.**

HEAT OF COOLING. An increase in the **heat content** of a substance or system at certain temperatures on its cooling curve, because of an internal change, commonly to an **allotropic** modification, which produces an increase in heat content. See **heat of transition.**

HEAT OF CRYSTALLIZATION. The increase in the **heat content** of one **mole** of a substance attributable to its transformation to the crystalline state.

HEAT OF DECOMPOSITION. The change of **heat content** when one **mole** of a compound is decomposed into its elements. This is equal in quantity, but opposite in sign, to the **heat of formation.**

HEAT OF DILUTION, DIFFERENTIAL. The increase in **heat content** of a system resulting from addition of an infinitesimal quantity of solvent to the solution.

HEAT OF DILUTION, INTEGRAL. The increase in **heat content** occurring when a specified amount of the solvent is added to a solution. This quantity is called the integral heat of dilution (or the total heat of dilution) in contrast with the differential heat of dilution.

HEAT OF DISSOCIATION. The increase of **heat content** occurring as a result of the breaking apart of molecules or, in general, in the rupture of valence **linkages.**

HEAT OF EVAPORATION. See **heat of vaporization, latent.**

HEAT OF FORMATION. The increase of **heat content** of the system when one **mole** of a substance is formed from its elements. If the physical state of the various elements are not specified they are assumed to be in the state at which they would normally exist at atmospheric pressure and ordinary temperature.

HEAT OF FUSION, LATENT. The increase of **heat content** when unit mass, or one **mole** of a solid is converted into a liquid at its melting point (without change of temperature). The value of this quantity is commonly determined at constant pressure.

HEAT OF HYDRATION. The increase of **heat content** when one **mole** of a **hydrate** is formed from the anhydrous form of the compound, and from liquid water.

HEAT OF HYDROGENATION. The increase of **heat content** when one **mole** of an unsaturated compound is converted into the corresponding saturated compound with gaseous hydrogen.

HEAT OF IONIZATION. The increase of **heat content** accompanying the complete **ionization** of one **mole** of a substance.

HEAT OF LINKAGE. The **bond energy** of a particular valence **linkage** between atoms, as determined by the average amount of energy required to **dissociate** bonds of that type in one **mole** of a given compound. This is illustrated by the case of methane, in which the bond energy of the C–H bond is taken to be one-quarter of the heat required to dissociate one mole of methane into carbon and hydrogen atoms.

HEAT OF NEUTRALIZATION. The increase in **heat content** of a system undergoing a **neutralization** reaction involving molar quantities of reactants.

HEAT OF RACEMIZATION. The increase in **heat content** when one **mole** of an optically active substance changes to its **racemic** form.

HEAT OF REACTION. The increase in **heat content** resulting from a chemical **reaction,** dependent, of course, upon the amounts of the substances involved, which are assumed to be, unless otherwise specified, the number of **moles** in the equation of the reaction.

HEAT OF SOLIDIFICATION. The increase in **heat content** upon the formation of one **mole** of a solid from a substance commonly in the liquid state.

HEAT OF SOLUTION, DIFFERENTIAL. A partial differential quantity obtained by differentiating the total heat of solution (see **heat of solution, integral**) with respect to the **molal concentration** of one **component** of the solution, while the concentration of the other component or components, the temperature, and pressure remain constant.

HEAT OF SOLUTION, INTEGRAL. The difference between the **heat content** of a solution, and the heat contents of its **components.** This quantity is also called the total heat of solution.

HEAT OF SUBLIMATION, LATENT. The increase of **heat content** when unit mass, or one **mole,** of a solid is converted into a vapor under **isobaric** conditions.

HEAT OF TRANSITION. The increase in heat content when one **mole** of a substance changes to an **allotropic** form, at the **transition temperature.**

HEAT OF VAPORIZATION, LATENT. The increase of **heat content** when unit mass, or one **mole,** of a liquid is converted into a vapor at the boiling point, without change of temperature.

HEAT PUMP. An apparatus designed to convert mechanical energy into thermal energy, as, for example, by the compression of a gas.

HEAT, RADIANT. Heat energy that is transmitted from one place or object to another without direct contact transfer, as by transmission through space, or through matter without the transfer process being dependent upon absorption of the heat by the transmitting medium.

HEAT, SPECIFIC. Also called the specific heat capacity. The quantity of heat required to raise the temperature of unit mass of a substance by one degree of temperature. The units commonly used for its expression are the unit mass of one gram, the unit quantity of heat in terms of the **calorie.**

HEAT SUMMATION, LAW OF. See **law of heat summation.**

HEAT TRANSFER, COEFFICIENT OF. The rate of flow of heat through a medium or a system, expressed as the amount of heat passing through unit area, per unit

time, and per degree temperature difference. In the **English system** of units, the coefficient of heat transfer is usually expressed in B.T.U. per square foot per hour per degree Fahrenheit.

HEAT TRANSFER SALT. A mixture of salts, commonly 50% sodium nitrite and 50% potassium nitrate, used in molten form (melting point of this mixture 282°F.) as a heat transfer medium in high temperature processes.

HEATH REAGENT. A mixture of three solutions: a solution of 5 g. cupric sulfate in 15 ml. water, a solution of 5 g. stannous chloride in 10 ml. water, and a solution of 2 g. potassium iodide in 10 ml. water, plus 100 ml. ammonium hydroxide, used in testing for tungsten. A red ring test, given by the substance tested (in acetic acid solution) indicates the presence of tungsten.

HEATING VALUE OF FOODS. The amount of heat liberated by complete combustion of unit mass, commonly one gram, of a food. See **heat of combustion.**

HEATING VALUE OF FUELS, FORMULAS. The caloric value of fuels may be approximated from the analysis. If C, H, N, and O represent the percentage of carbon, hydrogen, nitrogen, and oxygen,

$$Q = \frac{8,149C + 34,500H - 3,000(O - N)}{100}$$

(Mahler's formula)

Q, the heating value, is expressed in calories (15°) per gram.

HEAVY CHEMICALS. Chemicals that are produced, or were once produced, in very large quantities, such as sulfuric acid, caustic soda, chlorine, etc.

HEAVY HYDROGEN. See **hydrogen, isotopes.**

HEAVY METAL. A metal having a specific gravity greater than four.

HECHENBELIKNER CONCENTRATOR. A nitric acid concentrator, consisting of a short packed tower, into which dilute nitric acid with or without weak sulfuric acid enters at the top. Steam from a boiler enters at the bottom and boils off strong nitric acid (90–96%), which is condensed externally.

HECHT REAGENT FOR MUCUS. A mixture of 50 ml. of a 2% aqueous solution of Brilliant Green and 50 ml. of a 1% aqueous solution of Neutral Red, used in testing for mucus in urine or feces. A red color is given if mucus is present.

HECTARE. A measure of area in the metric system equal to 10,000 square meters.

$$1 \text{ acre} = 0.4047 \text{ hectare}$$
$$2.471 \text{ acres} = 1 \text{ hectare}$$

HECTOGRAM. One hundred **grams.**

HECTOLITER. One hundred **liters.**

HECTOMETER. One hundred **meters.**

HECZKO SOLUTION. A solution prepared by dissolving 55 g. phosphorus pentoxide and 12 ml. 30% hydrogen peroxide in 500 ml. water, and adding a little 85% phosphoric acid. It is used in the determination of manganese.

HEERMANN REAGENT. A solution of stannous chloride in absolute alcohol saturated with hydrogen chloride gas. It gives a turbidity or precipitate with sodium.

HEGLER TEST REACTION. Lignin is colored orange-yellow by a concentrated solution of thallium sulfate in dilute alcohol.

HEHNER NUMBER. The percentage of water insoluble **fatty acids** obtainable from a fat. This constant is lower for butter than for most fats and is of value in testing its purity. (A Hehner solution is used in determining the **iodine number** of oils.)

HEHNER TEST FOR FORMALDE-HYDE AND PHENOL. To test for formaldehyde add 1 drop phenol to the solution. A carmine-red ring test with sulfuric acid indicates the presence of formaldehyde.

HEHNER TEST FOR FORMALDE-HYDE IN MILK. If formaldehyde is present, milk gives a violet ring test with concentrated sulfuric acid.

HEIDENHAIN REAGENT FOR CAR-BON DIOXIDE. An alcoholic solution of Nile Blue A, to which is added enough 0.1 N sodium hydroxide solution to change the color to red. It becomes blue again with carbon dioxide.

HEIMROD-LEVINE TEST. Aldehydes are detected by mixing 1 drop of the solution tested with 2 ml. phosphoric acid, 1 drop of a weak solution of tryptophane in phosphoric acid and 1 drop 5% ferric chloride solution. The mixture gives a violet ring test with sulfuric acid if aldehydes are present.

HEINTZ TEST FOR POTASSIUM. Aqueous potassium solutions, acidified with hydrochloric acid, on mixing with double their volume of a mixture of equal parts ether and alcohol, give an octohedral crystalline precipitate on addition of platinic chloride solution and standing.

HEINTZ TEST FOR SULFITE. Heating with stannous chloride and hydrochloric acid gives a precipitate if sulfites are present. If only a color develops, add cupric sulfate, which gives a black precipitate of copper sulfide.

HEISENBERG PRINCIPLE. See **uncertainty principle.**

HEITLER-LONDON METHOD. A **quantum** mechanical theory describing the nature of homopolar bonds. According to this theory the **orbital wave functions** for the complete molecule are determined by summing over products of the **atomic wave functions.**

HELFERICH METHOD. The replacement of an acetoxy group on the first carbon atom of an acetylated aldose, by a phenoxy group, by heating with phenol. Acid catalysts are used, and influence the configuration of the resulting compound.

$$\left.\begin{array}{l} H-C-O-CO-CH_3 \\ | \\ H-C-O-CO-CH_3 \\ | \end{array}\right] O + C_6H_5OH \xrightarrow{POCl_3} \left.\begin{array}{l} C_6H_5O-C-H \\ | \\ H-C-O-CO-CH_3 \\ | \end{array}\right] O + CH_3COOH.$$

$$\left.\begin{array}{l} H-C-O-CO-CH_3 \\ | \\ H-C-O-CO-CH_3 \\ | \end{array}\right] O + C_6H_5OH \xrightarrow{ZnCl_2} \left.\begin{array}{l} H-C-OC_6H_5 \\ | \\ H-C-O-CO-CH_3 \\ | \end{array}\right] O + CH_3COOH.$$

HELIUM. Gaseous element. Symbol He. Atomic number 2. Atomic weight 4.003. Density (grams per liter at S.T.P.) 0.1785. Melting point $-271.9°$ C. (26 atmospheres). Boiling point $-268.9°$ C. Helium forms no known compounds; 1,000 volumes of air contain 0.0014 volume of helium. Emitted during many radioactive processes as its ion with two positive charges, which is its atomic nucleus (α-particle).

HELIUM NUCLEUS. See **alpha particle.**

HELL-VOLHARD-ZELINGSKY REACTION. The direct halogenation of an anhydrous aliphatic acid, using phosphorus as a reactant, with the production of the α-halogenated acid halide. This reaction is used extensively in the production of pure α-halogenated acids, which are obtained by hydrolysis of the acid halides.

$$6RCH_2COOH + 3X_2 + 2P \rightarrow 6RCH_2COX + 2H_3PO_3$$
$$6RCH_2COX + 6X_2 \rightarrow 6RCHX \cdot COX + 6HX$$
$$6RCHX \cdot COX + 6H_2O \rightarrow 6RCHX \cdot COOH + 6HX.$$

HELLY FLUID. A solution of 1.0 g. sodium sulfate, 5.0 g. mercuric chloride and 2.5 g. potassium dichromate in 100 ml. water, to which 5 ml. formalin is added, used as a fixative.

HELVETIUM. A name assigned to element 85 on the report of its discovery by Minder in 1940. See **astatine.**

HEM-, HEMO-. (Greek) Relating to blood or its color; as, hemoglobin, hemin.

HEMAGOGUE. A drug that promotes the discharge of blood, especially from the uterus.

HEMAT-, HEMATO-. (Greek) Relating to blood or its color; as, hematoporphyrin, hematein.

HEMATOLOGY. The science of blood, its chemical, biological and serological properties, and their relation to the functioning of the organism in health and in disease.

HEMICELLULOSE. One of a number of substances resembling, but having simpler structures than that of **cellulose,** and sometimes resulting from the partial hydrolysis of cellulose. The term hemicellulose is also applied to certain constituents of starch, and of the cells of animals.

HEMICOLLOID. A **colloid** composed of particles of small size, i.e., ranging from 0.005 to 0.0025 micron in length.

HEMIHEDRITY. A term describing **crystal** phenomena, to indicate that only half of a symmetrical structure undergoes modification. For example, if in truncating a cube the process is carried out symmetrically on four out of the eight solid angles the resulting structure exhibits hemihedral symmetry.

HEMITERPENE. One of a class of substances related to the **terpenes** of the formula C_5H_8, e.g., isoprene.

HEMITROPE. A twin **crystal.**

HEMOLYSIN. One of a group of metabolic products of **bacteria,** some plants, snakes, toads, bees, spiders, etc., which have the power of producing hemolysis. Certain of these exist normally in blood serum or are produced during immunization.

HEMOLYSIS. (1) The separation of **hemoglobin** from the stroma of the blood and its appearance in the serum. This is effected by **hypotonic** solutions, a number of chemical compounds (ether, chloroform, alkalies, biliary acids, and especially saponins) and by hemolysins. (2) The actual destruction of red blood corpuscles.

HEMOSTATIC. A drug or other agent which, upon external application, arrests or retards the flow of blood from the body, as from wounds or lesions.

HEMPEL BURETTE. A graduated glass **burette,** used with a leveling tube and absorption apparatus, for measuring gas volumes in analysis.

HENDECYL. The radical $CH_3(CH_2)_{10}-$.

HENDERSON EQUATION. An equation for the calculation of the **neutralization** curves of a weak acid by a strong base of the form:

$$pH = pK_A + \log [\text{salt}]/[\text{acid}]$$

where the square brackets represent concentrations, and pK_A is the logarithm of the reciprocal of the **dissociation constant** of the weak acid, and pH is the logarithm of the reciprocal of the **hydrogen ion concentration.** The results are satisfactory for solutions between pH 4 and pH 10 if they are not too dilute.

HENDERSON PROCESS. A metallurgical process for the recovery of copper, by converting it to the water-soluble chloride by roasting the ore with salt.

HENLE REAGENT. A preparation made by heating 27 g. metallic aluminum and 0.2 g. mercuric chloride in 276 g. absolute alcohol under reflux until crystallization occurs. Then the alcohol is distilled off, and the residue heated at 340° C. until its temperature drops to 330° C. It is cooled and dissolved in 1 liter xylene. It is used in detecting water in organic solvents. A white precipitate indicates the presence of water.

HENNING FLUID. A mixture of 12 ml. of a saturated solution of mercuric chloride in 60% alcohol, 6 ml. of saturated aqueous solution of picric acid, and 8 ml. of a $\frac{1}{2}\%$ aqueous solution of chromic acid, to which is then added 21 ml. absolute alcohol and 8 ml. concentrated nitric acid. It is used as a fixative.

HENRY. The unit of **inductance** and self-inductance, defined as the inductance in a circuit in which the induced E.M.F. is one volt when the inducing current changes at the rate of one ampere per second.

1 henry (absolute) = 10^9 electromagnetic units (c.g.s.) = 0.99948 international henry.

HENRY ALCOHOL REACTIONS. (1) Acetyl chloride forms acetates with primary and secondary alcohols, but gives chlorides with tertiary alcohols.
(2) On solution in fuming hydrochloric acid, tertiary alcohols yield an oil (the chloride) which rises to the surface. Primary and secondary alcohols may give an upper layer, but it contains unchanged alcohol.
(3) Bromine is used to distinguish between secondary and tertiary alcohols.

HENRY LAW. See **law of Henry.**

HENRY REACTION. A method of formation of nitroalcohols by the condensation of nitroparaffins (primary or secondary) with aldehydes in the presence of a base.

$$CH_3 \cdot CH_2 \cdot NO_2 + RCHO \rightarrow RCHOH \cdot CH_2 \cdot CH_2 \cdot NO_2.$$

See also **reaction, Kamlet.**

HEPAR TEST. A qualitative test for sulfur, made by alkaline fusion with carbon to reduce the sulfur to sodium sulfide and placing the fused mass on a silver coin, which darkens on moistening with water if sulfur is present.

HEPTYL. The radical $CH_3(CH_2)_6-$.

HERB. A plant, or portion of a plant, used in medicine, in cookery, for the extraction of certain essential oils, etc.

HERBERT-HEIM TEST. Arsine in air is detected by passing the air through a solution of cuprous chloride in hydrochloric acid, and then over mercuric chloride paper. A yellow color indicates the presence of arsenic.

HERMANN FLUID. A mixture of 3 ml. of a 10% aqueous solution of platinic chloride, 2 ml. glacial acetic acid and 16 ml. of a 1% aqueous solution of osmic acid and 19 ml. water, used as a fixative.

which the ore is mixed with 4% to 6% coke, and charged at intervals to a roasting bed where an ore column 3 feet or more in depth is maintained. The ash and residue are withdrawn through the grates. The oxide is passed through cooling tubes, and a coke-tower down which water trickles.

HERSCHKIND FURNACE. An apparatus in which hydrochloric acid is manufactured from chlorine by its passage with steam through hot coal. The reaction is of the form:

$$C + 2H_2O + 2Cl_2 \rightarrow 4HCl + CO_2.$$

As in a gas producer, sufficient air is admitted to maintain the coal at the reaction temperature.

HERZ REACTION. A method of formation of the so-called "Herz-Compounds," which are arylthiazathionium chlorides, from aromatic amines (primary) and sulfur chloride.

HERMANS TEST FOR NITRITE. Two ml. of the liquid tested are mixed with a few drops acetic acid, 2 ml. 5% potassium oxalate solution, 1 ml. 5% manganous sulfate solution, and a few drops hydrogen peroxide. A red color indicates nitrite. The test may be rearranged to detect manganese.

HERMITE PROCESS. An electrolytic process for producing sodium hypochlorite solution from sodium chloride.

HERNANDEZ TEST PAPER. Paper impregnated first with a 6% zinc sulfate solution, then with 10% sodium nitroprusside solution. It gives a red color with sodium sulfite.

HERRENSCHMIDT FURNACE. A furnace for the production of antimony in

HERZIG-MEYER DETERMINATION OF ALKIMIDES. Compounds containing N-alkyl group(s) are heated under reflux with hydriodic acid to form the quaternary ammonium iodides, which break up on heating to give alkyl iodides which can be determined quantitatively.

HERZOG REAGENT FOR LYSINE AND ORNITHINE. Phenylthiocarbamide ($H_2N \cdot CS \cdot NH \cdot C_6H_5$), which forms addition products with lysine and ornithine.

HERZOG TEST REACTION FOR HISTIDINE. A modified **biuret reaction,** in which histidine gives a red-violet color with alkali and cupric sulfate.

HESS-IVES PHOTOMETER. A colorimeter using numbered series of colored glass slides to match and designate the color of a substance or solution.

HESS LAW. See **law of Hess.**

HESSE TEST FOR PYROCATECHNIC ACID. Ferric chloride colors an alkaline solution of the acid deep green.

HETER-, HETERO-. (Greek *heteros*, other) Other, different; as, heteropolyacids, heterocyclic.

HETEROATOM. A term applied to the members of a ring structure other than carbon atoms; as in pyridine, the nitrogen atom, and in thiophene, the sulfur atom, are heteroatoms.

HETEROCYCLIC. Containing atoms of more than one element in a ring.

HETEROCYCLIC ATOM. See **heteroatom.**

HETEROCYCLIC COMPOUND. See **compound, heterocyclic.**

HETEROGENEOUS. Consisting of more than one phase. See **equilibrium, reaction, catalysis.**

HETEROION. A complex **ion** consisting of a simpler ion adsorbed upon a molecule. The term is commonly applied in cases where the adsorbing molecule is large, e.g., a protein molecule.

HETEROLOGY. Relationship between substances of partial identity of structure but of different properties, as benzene, phenol, benzoic acid, aniline. Cf. **homology, isology.**

HETERONUCLEAR. A condition in which two (or more) **substituents** occur in different rings or nuclei of compounds which contain two or more rings, as, e.g., 1,8-dichloronaphthalene. When substituents are both located in the same ring the condition is termed isonuclear.

HETEROPOLAR BOND. See **bond, heteropolar.**

HETEROPOLYACIDS. Acids derived from two or more other acids, under such conditions that the negative radicals of the individual acids retain their structural identity within the complex radical or molecule formed. The term heteropolyacids is usually restricted to complex acids in which both radicals are derived from oxides, such as phosphomolybdic acid.

HETEROPOLYMERIZATION. See **polymerization, hetero.**

HETEROPOLYSALTS. The salts of **heteropolyacids** (q.v.).

HETEROTOPIC. Having a different **atomic number** or nuclear charge, the opposite of **isotopic.**

H.E.T.P. The height of packing equivalent to one theoretical **plate.** This is a quantity used in the design of packed towers. It is obtained by determining the number of theoretical plates which would be necessary if the process were conducted in a plate tower; and then applying that figure to the case of the packed tower.

HEUMANN INDIGO SYNTHESIS. A method of synthesis of indigo by fusion of phenylglycine with sodamide to form indoxyl, which is then oxidized to indigo.

The *o*-carboxy derivative of phenylglycine may be used, yielding on fusion with caustic soda, indoxylic acid, which gives indigo on decarboxylation and oxidation.

HEWERA-BERMEJO TEST REACTION. Mercaptans give a red-violet color with sodium nitroprusside.

HEXAD. (1) An element which has a **valence** of six, as chromium in the chromates, and sulfur in many of its compounds. (2) A crystal having six similar faces.

HEXADECYL. The radical

$$CH_3(CH_2)_{14}CH_2-,$$

also termed cetyl.

HEXAGONAL SYSTEM. One of the seven **crystallographic systems** (q.v.).

HEXATHIONATE. The anion $S_6O_6^=$, or a compound containing it.

HEXATHIONIC. Related to hexathionic acid, $H_2S_6O_6$.

HEXON BASES. The **amino acids** lysine, arginine, and histidine which contain six carbon atoms.

HEXOSE. A **carbohydrate** consisting of a six-carbon chain, as dextrose and fructose. These carbohydrates are classified as aldohexoses and ketohexoses according to whether they exhibit the properties of aldehydes or ketones.

HEXYL. The radical $CH_3(CH_2)_5-$.

HEYN-BAUER REAGENT. A solution of 25 g. cadmium acetate in 200 ml. acetic acid which is then diluted with water to 1 liter, used in a test procedure for sulfur, selenium, and tellurium in crude metallic copper, which is dissolved in potassium cyanide solution and treated with alcohol and the reagent. A yellow precipitate indicates sulfur; orange-red, selenium; and gray-black, tellurium.

Hf Symbol for the element **hafnium.**

Hg Symbol for the element **mercury.**

HICK REAGENT. Two solutions: (1) a solution of 10 ml. phenol in 20 ml. carbon tetrachloride; and (2) a solution of 5 ml. bromine in 20 ml. carbon tetrachloride, used in testing for resins. Characteristic color reactions are obtained.

HIDING POWER. The **opacity,** or ability of a pigment or finishing material to cover completely another color.

HIGH ORDER REACTION. See **reaction, high order.**

HILDEBRAND ELECTRODE. Two electrodes bear the name of Hildebrand. (1) A modified calomel electrode (see **electrode, calomel**). (2) A platinum electrode in an apparatus containing hydrogen and used as a hydrogen electrode. (See **electrode, hydrogen.**)

HILDEBRAND RULE. The **entropy of** vaporization, i.e., the ratio of the heat of vaporization to the temperature at which it occurs, is a constant for many substances if it is determined at the same **molal concentration** of vapor for each substance.

HILGER-ROTHENFUSSER REAGENT. β-Naphthylhydrazine in alcoholic solution, which forms hydrazones with certain sugars in concentrated aqueous solution.

HILGER TEST REACTION FOR MALIC ACID. On heating to boiling with palladous chloride in neutral or weakly alkaline solution, malic acid gives a dark-colored precipitate of palladium.

HILGER TEST REACTION FOR SELENITE AND TELLURITE. With an excess of magnesium chloride and ammonium chloride solution, selenite gives a crystalline precipitate and tellurite an amorphous one. Phosphates interfere.

HILLEBRAND TEST FOR VANADIUM IN ROCKS. Several drops of hydrogen peroxide added to an appropriately prepared extract of the rock give a brownish yellow color if vanadium is present. If chromium is present, hydrogen peroxide and ether are added to an acidified portion of the extract. The ether is colored blue by the chromium; and the aqueous solution, yellow by vanadium.

HILPERT-WOLF REAGENT. A mixture of 1 volume antimony pentachloride and 2 volumes carbon tetrachloride, which gives characteristic colors with many aromatic hydrocarbons in carbon tetrachloride solution.

HINDERED SETTLING. See **settling, hindered.**

HINSBERG INDOLE SYNTHESIS. A method of synthesis of oxindoles by formation of the third (indole) ring by the action of the sodium bisulfite addition product of glyoxal on such aromatic amines as β-naphthylamine.

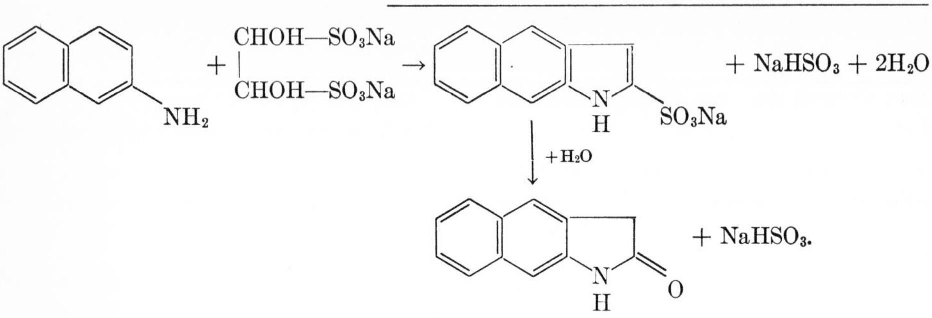

HINSBERG TEST REACTION FOR o-DIAMINES. Prepare a solution of phenanthrenequinone in glacial acetic acid, by heating, and add 1 drop of it to an alcoholic solution to be tested, then heat to boiling. A yellow precipitate, colored deep red by hydrochloric acid, is given by *o*-diamines.

HINSBERG TEST REACTION FOR PRIMARY AND SECONDARY AMINES. On reaction with benzene sulfonylchloride ($C_6H_5SO_2Cl$) and dilute aqueous alkali, primary amines give sulfonamides soluble in potassium hydroxide solution, while secondary amines give sulfonamides insoluble in alkali, and tertiary amines do not react.

HIPPURIC. Related to hippuric acid, $C_6H_5 \cdot CO \cdot NH \cdot CH_2COOH$.

HIPPURYL. The radical

$$C_6H_5CONHCH_2CO-.$$

HIRSCH TEST REACTION FOR OSMIUM. A solution of osmium tetroxide in mineral acids, on addition of concentrated potassium thiocyanate solution, followed by shaking with ether or amyl alcohol, gives a deep blue color.

HIRSCHBERG TEST REACTION FOR SUGAR. Sucrose is differentiated from other sugars by its failure to decompose when incubated for 24 hours with 0.1 *N* sodium hydroxide solution.

HIRSCHFELD REAGENT FOR PUS. Two ml. 1% solution of α-naphthol in 70% alcohol mixed with 2 ml. of an aqueous solution of dimethyl-*p*-phenylenediamine hydrochloride. The reagent develops a blue color when floated on a body fluid containing pus or its products.

HIRSCHSOHN COTTONSEED OIL REAGENT. A solution of 1 g. gold chloride in 150 ml. chloroform, used in testing for cottonseed oil. A red color on heating is given by cottonseed oil.

HIRSCHSOHN MYRRH REAGENT. A solution of 4 g. chloral hydrate in 1 g. trichloroacetic, used in testing for myrrhs. Herabol myrrh gives a violet color with this reagent, but bissabol myrrh does not.

HIRSCHSOHN REAGENT FOR VOLATILE OILS. (1) A solution of 2–4 drops ferric chloride solution in 40 ml. alcohol. It is added by drops to an alcoholic solution of the volatile oil, yielding characteristic colors. (2) A solution of 0.1 g. fuchsin in 1 l. water, which is decolorized with sulfur dioxide. On addition of 2–3 ml. of this reagent to 1 ml. of an alcoholic solution of a volatile oil, characteristic colors are obtained.

HIRSCHSOHN TEST REACTION FOR CHLORESTEROL. Nine g. trichloracetic acid mixed with 1 ml. water gives on heating with chloresterol a red, slightly fluorescent solution, changing to raspberry-red, blue-violet, and blue in 24 hours.

HISTIDYL. The radical

$$N_2C_3H_3CH_2CH(NH_2)CO-.$$

HISTONES. A class of proteins related to the protamines and characterized by the property of being precipitated from solution by ammonia. See **proteins.**

HITTORF NUMBER. The fraction of the current carried by a given **ion** in electrolytic conduction. See **transport number**.

Ho Symbol for the element **holmium** (q.v.).

HOCH-CAMPBELL ETHYLENIMINE SYNTHESIS. A Grignard method for the preparation of ethylenimines from ketoximes.

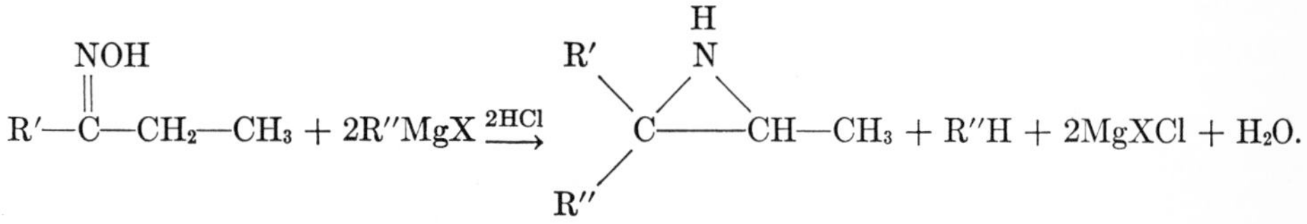

HOFFER TEST REACTION. An antimony solution gives a black spot when applied, with zinc and hydrochloric acid, to a mercury mirror on copper, prepared by treating the clean metal with mercuric chloride solution.

$$R'-\underset{\underset{\displaystyle NOH}{\|}}{C}-CH_2-CH_3 + 2R''MgX \xrightarrow{2HCl} \underset{\underset{\displaystyle R''}{\diagup}}{\overset{\overset{\displaystyle H}{\underset{\displaystyle N}{R'}}}{C}}-CH-CH_3 + R''H + 2MgXCl + H_2O.$$

HOESCH SYNTHESIS. A method of formation of ketophenols or ketophenolic ethers from phenols or phenolic ethers and organic nitriles.

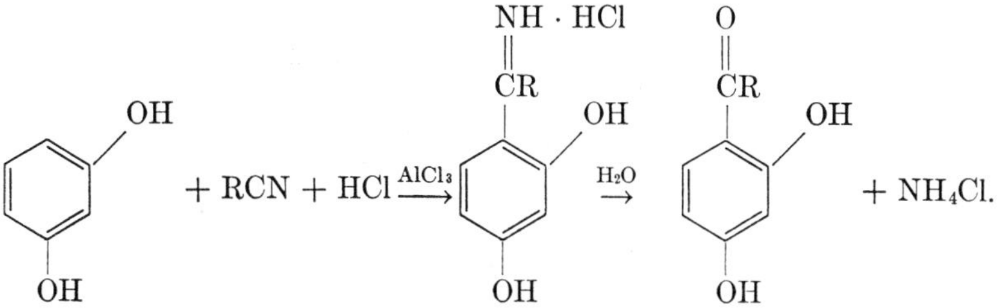

HOFER-MOEST REACTION. A method of obtaining methyl alcohol by the electrolysis of an acetate in the presence of strong electrolytes.

$$CH_3COONa + NaOH + \tfrac{1}{2}O_2 \rightarrow CH_3OH + Na_2CO_3.$$

See also **Kolbe reaction**.

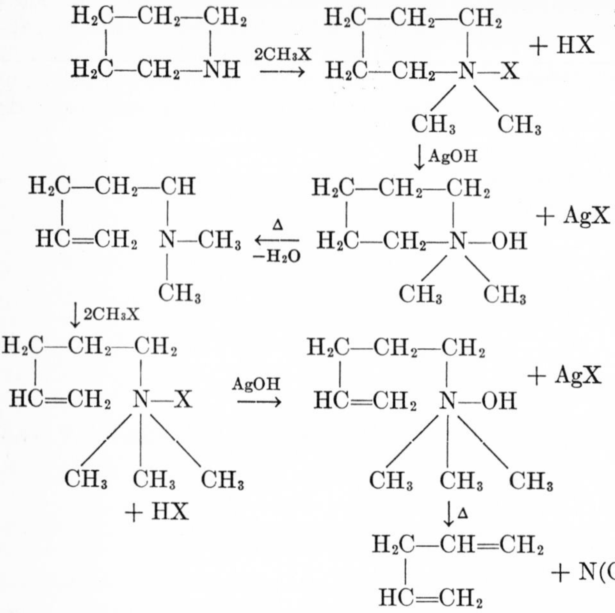

$$\begin{array}{c} H_2C-CH_2-CH_2 \\ | \quad\quad\quad | \\ H_2C-CH_2-NH \end{array} \xrightarrow{2CH_3X} \begin{array}{c} H_2C-CH_2-CH_2 \\ | \quad\quad\quad | \\ H_2C-CH_2-N-X \\ \diagup\;\;\diagdown \\ CH_3 \quad CH_3 \end{array} + HX$$

$$\downarrow AgOH$$

$$\begin{array}{c} H_2C-CH_2-CH \\ | \quad\quad\quad | \\ HC=CH_2 \;\; N-CH_3 \\ | \\ CH_3 \end{array} \xleftarrow[-H_2O]{\Delta} \begin{array}{c} H_2C-CH_2-CH_2 \\ | \quad\quad\quad | \\ H_2C-CH_2-N-OH \\ \diagup\;\;\diagdown \\ CH_3 \quad CH_3 \end{array} + AgX$$

$$\downarrow 2CH_3X$$

$$\begin{array}{c} H_2C-CH_2-CH_2 \\ | \quad\quad\quad | \\ HC=CH_2 \;\; N-X \\ \diagup\;|\;\diagdown \\ CH_3\; CH_3\; CH_3 \\ + HX \end{array} \xrightarrow{AgOH} \begin{array}{c} H_2C-CH_2-CH_2 \\ | \quad\quad\quad | \\ HC=CH_2 \;\; N-OH \\ \diagup\;|\;\diagdown \\ CH_3\; CH_3\; CH_3 \end{array} + AgX$$

$$\downarrow \Delta$$

$$\begin{array}{c} H_2C-CH=CH_2 \\ | \\ HC=CH_2 \end{array} + N(CH_3)_3 + H_2O.$$

HOFMANN DEGRADATION.

A method of breaking carbon-nitrogen bonds, especially useful in opening nitrogen-membered ring compounds, by pyrolysis of the quaternary ammonium hydroxide derivative; the reaction forms an olefin and a tertiary amine. The quaternary ammonium hydroxide derivative can be prepared by methylating the nitrogen-containing ring compound.

HOFMANN-HÖCHTLEN REAGENT.

Dissolve (1) 5 g. nickel sulfate in 20 ml. water; and (2) 2.5 g. potassium cyanide in 10 ml. water. Mix (1) and (2), and add 20 ml. ammonium hydroxide; then after standing 15 minutes at 0° C., filter and add enough 60% acetic acid to produce turbidity. This reagent is used to test for phenol, aniline and benzene which give characteristic precipitates.

HOFMANN-MARTIUS REARRANGEMENT.

The formation of C-alkylaniline hydrohalides by rearrangement upon heating of N-alkylaniline hydrohalides.

HOFMANN REACTION (HOFMANN REARRANGEMENT).

The reaction of an acid amide with halogen and an alkali, or with a hypohalite. Most commonly the product is an amine with one less carbon atom, by elimination of CO from the molecule. With certain acid amides higher in the aliphatic series, the reaction does not stop at the amine, but the latter is oxidized by the hypohalite to the corresponding cyanide. With α-halogen acid amides, the Hofmann reaction yields an aldehyde or ketone with one less carbon atom, instead of the amine. The general equation for the reaction is:

$$RCONH_2 + NaOX + 2NaOH \rightarrow RNH_2 + NaX + Na_2CO_3 + H_2O.$$

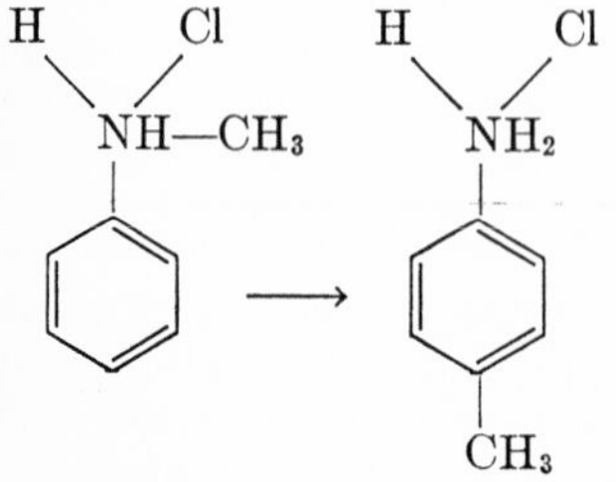

Isocyanates are intermediate in the reaction, and may yield other products.

HOFMANN RULE.

In the decomposition of a quaternary ammonium hydroxide containing different primary alkyl radicals, the products are such that the ethylene formed will contain the least number of alkyl substituents.

$$\begin{array}{c}
CH_3 \\
\diagdown \\
CH-CH_2 \\
\diagup \qquad\qquad \diagdown \\
CH_3 \qquad\qquad NH \xrightarrow[\text{AgOH}]{2CH_3X} \\
\diagup \\
CH_3-CH_2
\end{array}
\qquad
\begin{array}{c}
CH_3 \\
\diagdown \\
CH-CH_2 \quad CH_3 \\
\diagup \quad\qquad \diagdown \ \diagup \\
CH_3 \qquad\qquad N-OH \\
\diagup \quad \diagdown \\
CH_3-CH_2 \quad CH_3
\end{array}$$

$$\downarrow \Delta$$

$$\begin{array}{c}
CH_3 \qquad\qquad\qquad CH_3 \\
\diagdown \qquad\qquad\qquad \diagup \\
CH-CH_2-N \qquad + CH_2{=}CH_2 + H_2O. \\
\diagup \qquad\qquad \diagdown \\
CH_3 \qquad\qquad CH_3
\end{array}$$

HOFMANN-SAND REACTION. A general reaction of olefins with mercuric salts in alkaline solution, to form compounds containing mercury.

$$RCH{:}CH_2 + Hg(NO_3)_2 + NaOH \rightarrow HOCHRCH_2HgNO_3 + NaNO_3.$$

HOFMANN-STORM REAGENT. Tetraformyl-trisazine (made from formaldehyde and hydrazine hydrate) used as an analytical reducing reagent.

HOFMANN TEST REACTION FOR BENZENE. Benzene is detected by nitration and reduction, followed by treatment of the aniline formed, in ethereal solution, with chlorinated lime to give a purple-violet color.

HOFMANN TEST REACTIONS FOR ANILINE. (1) Aniline in hydrochloric acid solution is precipitated by platinic chloride. (2) Aniline in alcoholic solution is precipitated by mercuric chloride in alcoholic solution. (3) By fuming nitric acid, aniline is colored blue, changing to yellow and scarlet on warming. (4) A solution of aniline in dilute hydrochloric or sulfuric acid gives reddish crystals with bromine water.

HOFMANN TEST REACTIONS FOR PRIMARY AMINES. (1) On warming with chloroform and potassium hydroxide, primary amines give isonitriles (characteristic odor).

(2) Concentrated solutions of primary amines in alcohol and carbon disulfide give, on heating with mercuric chloride, the odor of mustard oil.

(3) Primary aromatic amines give crystalline salts with sulfuric and hydrochloric acids.

HOFMANN TEST REAGENT FOR CARBON DISULFIDE. Triethylphosphine, which gives a red crystalline compound with carbon disulfide.

HOFMANN TEST REAGENT FOR TITANIC ACID. Chromotropic acid (1.8-dihydroxynaphthalene-3, 6-disulfonic acid), which gives a deep red color with solutions of titanic acid in hydrochloric acid or sulfuric acid.

HOFMEISTER REACTIONS FOR ALIPHATIC AMINO ACIDS. Amino acids give a red color with ferric chloride, and blue with cupric sulfate. They reduce mercuric nitrate to mercury, which they precipitate in the presence of sodium carbonate, and they bring about the solution of cupric hydroxide in alkalies.

HOFMEISTER SERIES. A definite order of arrangement of **anions** and **cations** according to their powers of coagulation when their salts are added in quantity to lyophilic sols. Thus, the order of cations is $Mg^{++} > Ca^{++} > Sr^{++} > Ba^{++} > Li^+ > Na^+ > K^+ > Rb^+ > Cs^+$. The Hofmeister series is also called the **lyotropic series** (q.v.), and the effect is called salting-out, a term applied strictly to the effect of electrolytes upon true solutions.

HOGSHEAD. A unit of volume in the English system, containing 52.5 imperial gallons, or 238.5 liters. In common usage, the term is applied to a number of casks of various sizes.

HÖHNEL REAGENT FOR SILK. A saturated solution of chromic acid which has been diluted with an equal volume of water, used in testing for silk, which dissolves rapidly in this reagent.

HÖHNEL REAGENTS FOR WOOD. (1) A concentrated solution of phenol in hydrochloric acid (sp. gr. 1.19), which colors lignin green. (2) A solution of potassium iodide and sulfuric acid, which colors wood blue and mechanical pulp dark yellow.

HOLE THEORY OF LIQUIDS. A theory for analyzing the properties of liquids, by use of a model in which the liquid is considered to be an imperfect crystal — imperfect in the sense that not all the crystal lattice sites are occupied by molecules, the vacant sites being equivalent to "holes."

HOLL REAGENT. A solution of 0.2 g. ferric chloride and 0.5 g. potassium ferricyanide in 250 ml. water, used in detecting pine oil in oil of turpentine. A blue turbidity is given by pine oil.

HOLMES-MANLEY PROCESS. A process for the simultaneous **cracking** and **distillation** of crude oil (or a fraction distilled therefrom) by the application of heat and pressure. The oil is heated with stirring in large stills, 40 feet high and 3 feet in diameter, to a pressure of about 175 pounds per square inch.

HOLMIC. Containing or pertaining to trivalent **holmium.**

HOLMIUM. Rare earth metallic element. Symbol Ho. Atomic number 67. Atomic weight 164.94. Valence 3, Oxide, Ho_2O_3. Holmium occurs in gadolinite.

HOLO-. (Greek) Whole, complete; as holoquinoid, holocellulose; specifically, denoting the completely hydrated form of an acid; as, holophosphoric acid, H_5PO_5.

HOLOHEDRAL CRYSTAL. A **crystal** in which the full number of faces are developed, corresponding to the maximum and complete **symmetry** of the system.

HOLOPHOSPHATE. The anion PO_5^{5-}, or a compound containing it.

HOLT-DERN PROCESS AND FURNACE. A concrete furnace for chloridizing ground silver ores, equipped with bottom grates through which air is blown and chloridized ore discharged. The ore is crushed to 20-mesh, mixed with 6% sodium chloride, 10% water and 2% charcoal, and roasted under an air pressure of 1–4 inches of water.

HOLTON TEST. Iodine is detected in the presence of bromine by boiling 0.5 ml. of the solution tested with 15 ml. saturated sodium carbonate solution, filtering, adding excess nitric acid to 1 ml. of the filtrate, then 3 drops 8% potassium chromate solution and 1 ml. carbon disulfide, which becomes violet if iodine is present.

HOLZER-REIF TEST REACTION. α-Naphthylamine gives a blue or red-violet precipitate with gold chloride, palladium chloride, or ferric chloride.

HOMO-. (Greek) Same, similar; as, homocyclic, homologous; specifically, designating a homolog (ordinarily the next higher homolog) of a compound, differing in formula from the latter by an increase of CH_2; as, homophthalic acid.

HOMOCENTRIC RAYS. Rays having the same **focal point.** (It may be at infinity; in other words, the rays may be parallel.)

HOMOCHROMOISOMERISM. The phenomenon in which different structural modifications of organic compounds exhibit the same color and identical **absorption bands** in solution.

HOMOCYCLIC. A ring or nucleus composed of atoms of the same element, e.g., the benzene ring. Cf. **heterocyclic.**

HOMOISOHYDRIC SOLUTIONS. Solutions having the same **hydrogen ion concentration,** and consisting of the same ions.

HOMOLOGOUS SERIES. A series of carbon compounds of the same type which conform to a general formula and in which each member differs from the preceding member by a constant increment of the atomic group CH_2. For example, in the paraffin series we have the general formula C_nH_{2n+2}, and the compounds

HOOGOLIET TEST PAPER FOR CHLORIDE. Strips of filter paper saturated with an ammoniacal solution of silver chromate, which are drawn through dilute nitric acid, so that the red silver chromate precipitates evenly. The dried paper is decolorized by chloride ion.

HOOKER REACTION. A shifting of substituent groups in certain naphthoquinones which accompanies side-chain oxidation with alkaline permanganate.

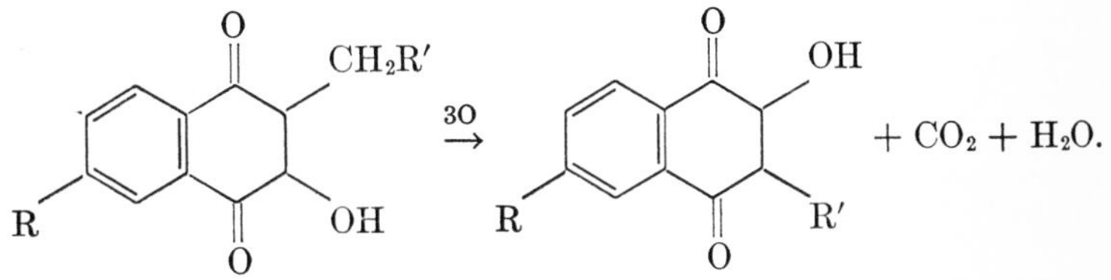

$$\xrightarrow{30} \quad + CO_2 + H_2O.$$

CH_4	methane
C_2H_6	ethane
C_3H_8	propane
C_4H_{10}	butane
C_5H_{12}	pentane
etc.	

The phenomenon is known as homology, the compounds are homologous and any one of them is the homologue of any other in the series. Cf. **homo-, isology.**

HOMOLOGUE. A member of an **homologous series.**

HOMOLOGY. The phenomenon exhibited by an **homologous series** (q.v.).

HOMOPIPERONYL. The radical

$$3,4\text{-}(CH_2O_2)C_6H_3CH_2CH_2\text{--}.$$

HOMOPOLAR BOND. See **bond, homopolar.**

HOMOTOPE. One of the elements in a vertical group of the **periodic system,** as sodium is a homotope of lithium, potassium, rubidium, cesium, and francium.

HOOD. A curved flue, provided with connection to a chimney or ventilating system, used to remove fumes resulting from chemical plants, laboratories or processes.

HOOPES PROCESS. A method of refining impure metallic aluminum by its electrolysis in a cell in which the anode of the crude aluminum rests on the bottom, the electrolyte is molten cryolite containing some barium fluoride, and the cathode is a layer of pure aluminum floating on the surface.

HOOVER TEST REACTION. Carbon monoxide imparts a green color to a mixture of pumice, iodine pentoxide, and pyrosulfuric acid.

HOPKINS-COLE REAGENT FOR TRYPTOPHANE. A solution of 10 g. mercuric sulfate in 90 g. 5% sulfuric acid, used in the precipitation of tryptophane from dilute sulfuric acid solution.

HOPPE-SAYLOR TEST REACTION FOR PHENOL. Pine wood gives a blue color when treated with phenol and hydrochloric acid.

HORMONE. One of a class of substances elaborated within a living organism, in animals by the ductless glands, to control many or all of the **metabolic** processes of the organism. They act as **catalysts,** or to modify the action of catalysts, or directly upon certain organs.

HORMONE, PLANT. See **plant hormone.**

HOROSZKIEWICZ-MARX TEST. To detect carbon monoxide in blood, add 2 ml. blood to 4 ml. hot aqueous 8% quinine hydrochloride solution. Heat to boiling. Cool, add 2 drops fresh ammonium sulfide solution. A bright red color indicates the

HOUBEN-FISCHER SYNTHESIS. Preparation of aromatic nitriles by hydrolysis of trichloromethyl-aryl ketimines; the hydrolysis must be carried out in an alkaline medium, since acid hydrolysis yields ketones instead of nitriles. The trichloromethylaryl ketimines are prepared from aromatic hydrocarbons and trichloroacetonitrile as in the **Hoesch synthesis.**

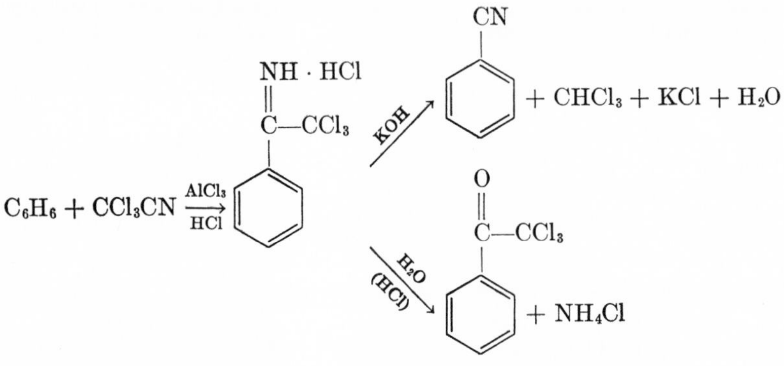

$$C_6H_6 + CCl_3CN \xrightarrow[HCl]{AlCl_3} \underset{\text{C—CCl}_3}{\overset{NH \cdot HCl}{\|}}$$

$$\xrightarrow{KOH} CN + CHCl_3 + KCl + H_2O$$

$$\xrightarrow[\text{(HCl)}]{H_2O} \underset{\text{C—CCl}_3}{\overset{O}{\|}} + NH_4Cl$$

presence of carbon monoxide in the blood. Normal blood gives a dirty blue-green color.

HORSEPOWER. A unit of power in the **English system** defined as the power to do 33,000 foot-pounds of work per minute or 550 foot-pounds per second.

1 kilowatt = 1.34 horsepower.
1 horsepower = 746 watts.

HORSEPOWER, FRENCH or METRIC. A unit of power defined as the power required to raise 75 kilograms through one meter in one second.

HOSHIDA REAGENT. A freshly prepared solution of 0.5 ml. formaldehyde and 0.3 g. sodium molybdate in 60 ml. sulfuric acid, used as a reagent for morphine and pseudomorphine. A violet color, changing to a dirty green, is given by morphine; pseudomorphine gives a violet color changing to a stable blue-green.

HOT PLATE. An apparatus used in laboratories for heating flasks, beakers, etc. It consists of a metal plate, heated usually electrically, but sometimes by gas or steam.

HOUBEN-HOESCH REACTION. See **Hoesch synthesis.**

HOUDRY PROCESS. A process for the catalytic **cracking** of crude oil by the action of **activated** aluminum hydrosilicate. The charge is heated in a still to about 475° C., whence it passes to a vaporizer, from which the vaporized fractions pass to catalyst chambers, after which they are fractionated. The process varies considerably with the nature of the oil charged and the products desired.

HOUZEAU REAGENTS FOR OZONE. Red litmus paper and potassium iodide-starch paper, both of which are colored blue by ozone.

HOVORKA-SÝKORA REAGENT. A 1% alcoholic solution of isatin-β-oxime, which precipitates many metals, often with characteristic colors, from acetate solutions.

HTS. See **heat transfer salt.**

H.T.U. The height of a **transfer unit.** The number of transfer units theoretically required in a packed tower process is calculated mathematically; and the height of the tower for the process, divided by the number of transfer units calculated, yields the height of one transfer unit.

HUBER SOLUTION. An aqueous solution of ammonium molybdate and potassium ferrocyanide, used in testing for free mineral acids. An orange to brown precipitate indicates the presence of free mineral acids.

HÜBL NUMBER. The **iodine number** of a fat or oil.

HÜBL SOLUTION. A solution of 5.2 g. iodine and 6 g. mercuric chloride, in 200 ml. 95% alcohol, used in the detection of unsaturated compounds in fats, or in the quantitative determination of their iodine numbers.

HÜBL-WALLER REAGENT. A reagent for determining iodine number. This reagent is **Hübl solution** (q.v.), each liter of which contains 50 g. of hydrochloric acid (sp. gr. 1.19).

HUDSON ISOROTATION RULES. The rotational contribution of the terminal carbon atom of an aldose sugar is affected only slightly by changes in any other part of the molecule than a contiguous atom; and changes in the atoms or radicals attached to the terminal carbon atom affect only slightly the rotation of the remainder of the molecule.

HUDSON LACTONE RULE. When γ-lactones of aldonic acids are represented by the usual planar projection formula, the lactones having the γ-hydroxyl on the right will be dextrorotatory, and those having it on the left, levorotatory.

HUFF SEPARATOR. A separating apparatus for concentrating crushed ores by means of the attraction of an electric field for the metallic particles, which are charged by an electrified belt.

HUIZINGA REAGENT FOR OZONE. Filter paper impregnated with thallous hydroxide, which is colored brown by ozone.

HUME-ROTHERY RULE. An empirical rule governing the composition of structurally analogous **phases** in **alloy** systems, to the effect that the deciding factor is the ratio of the total number of valence electrons in the system to the number of atoms. Many alloy systems, including those formed between the transition metals and the more common of the B sub-group metals, usually have three ordered phases, known as the β, γ, and ϵ phases. For these three phases, this ratio is $3:2$ (or $21:14$), $21:13$, and $7:4$ ($21:12$), respectively. Thus the composition of the β, γ, and ϵ phases of the copper-zinc system is represented by $CuZn$, Cu_5Zn_8, and $CuZn_3$.

HUMFREY REAGENT. A solution of 100 g. cupric ammonium chloride and 50 ml. concentrated hydrochloric acid in 1 liter water, used in etching steels.

HUMIDIFICATION. A process for increasing the water content of air or other gases.

HUMIDITY. The quantity of water vapor in the atmosphere.

HUMIDITY, ABSOLUTE. The concentration of water vapor in the atmosphere, commonly expressed in grams per cubic centimeter.

HUMIDITY, RELATIVE. The ratio of the amount of water vapor present in the atmosphere at any given temperature to the amount needed for saturation at that temperature, expressed as a percentage.

HUMPHREY PROCESS. A process for the **hydrogenation** of rosin acids. It is usually conducted under pressure, in the presence of a base-metal catalyst, and results in the addition of hydrogen in about half the amount necessary for saturation of the double bonds present.

HUND RULE. In atomic spectra, the **ground term** is associated with the largest **multiplicity** possible for the available electrons. In general, the lowest energy state of any atom or ion is considered to be the one in which the maximum number of electrons, compatible with the **Pauli principle,** have unpaired spins.

HUNEFELD SOLUTION. An alcoholic solution of glacial acetic acid, turpentine, and chloroform, used to detect blood.

HUXLEY-BROOK REAGENT. Potassium lead iodide ($PbI_2 \cdot 2 KI$), which becomes yellow in the presence of water in ether or chloroform.

HUYSSE REAGENT FOR POTASSIUM, RUBIDIUM, AND CESIUM. Bismuth subnitrate is dissolved in the minimum amount of hydrochloric acid, and water

HYDRAMINE. One of a series of **amines** derived from the **glycols** in which one hydroxyl is replaced by an amino group, e.g., oxyethylamine, $CH_2OH \cdot CH_2NH_2$.

HYDRAMINE FISSION. A reaction characteristic of **alkaloids** having a hydroxyl group in the α-position to the aromatic nucleus and an amino-group in the β-position. The nitrogen from the β-position is removed as an ammonia derivative, and the alcoholic group is converted into a carbonyl group:

$$\text{CHOH—CH—R}' \quad \xrightarrow{\Delta} \quad \text{CO—CH}_2\text{—R}' \quad + \text{H}_2\text{NR}$$

added to precipitation. Enough sodium thiosulfate is added to dissolve the precipitate, then enough alcohol is added to form a permanent turbidity, which is dissolved by addition of water. On treatment with this reagent, a solution containing potassium, rubidium, or cesium forms yellow-green needles (visible microscopically).

HUYSSE TEST FOR INDIUM. The solution tested is evaporated with sulfuric acid, the residue taken up with water, and cesium chloride or ammonium fluoride added. Indium forms colorless octohedra.

HYBINETTE PROCESS. A method of producing electrolytic nickel from ore (especially of Sudbury type) by direct electrolysis of a copper-nickel alloy.

HYDNOCARPOYL. The radical $C_5H_7(CH_2)_{10}CO-$. It is derived from hydnocarpic acid.

HYDNOCARPYL. The radical $C_5H_7(CH_2)_{10}CH_2-$. It is derived from hydnocarpyl alcohol.

HYDR-, HYDRO-. (Greek) (1) denoting presence or addition of hydrogen, as hydrochloric, hydracrylic; (2) sometimes relating to water, as hydrate.

HYDRACRYLIC. Related to hydracrylic acid, $HO \cdot CH_2 \cdot CH_2 \cdot COOH$.

HYDRARGYRIC. Containing or pertaining to divalent mercury.

HYDRARGYROUS. Containing or pertaining to monovalent mercury.

HYDRARGYRUM. The Latin name for the metal **mercury,** whence the symbol Hg is derived.

HYDRATE. (1) A compound which contains combined water as water of crystallization, as $CuSO_4 \cdot 5 H_2O$. (2) A hydroxide which may be converted into the corresponding oxide by heat $Ca(OH)_2$, $Al(OH)_3$. (3) A substance which contains water. (4) As a combined term, a substance which contains hydrogen and oxygen in the proportions in which they occur in water, e.g., carbohydrate.

HYDRATED. See **hydrate.**

HYDRATED ION. An ion which is in combination with one or more water molecules, as $H^+(H_2O)$, or H_3O^+.

HYDRATION, HEAT OF. See **heat of hydration.**

HYDRATION, WATER OF. Water of crystallization.

HYDRATOR. An apparatus used to produce **hydrates,** or any compounds by reaction with water. The term is applied especially to the apparatus used to produce calcium hydroxide from calcium oxide (quicklime) and water.

HYDRAULIC CLASSIFICATION. See classification, hydraulic.

HYDRAULIC PRESS. A press which secures great mechanical advantage by the use of a fluid, commonly water, as a pressure — transmitting medium.

HYDRAULIC RADIUS. The cross-sectional area of a stream of fluid moving in a conduit, divided by the wetted perimeter.

HYDRAULIC SEPARATION. See separation, hydraulic.

HYDRAZI. The radical

$$\begin{array}{c} NH \\ | \\ NH \end{array} \Big\rangle \text{ (to same atom).}$$

HYDRAZI COMPOUND. A compound containing the group $\Big\langle \begin{array}{c} NH \\ | \\ NH \end{array}$, that has its two nitrogen atoms attached to a single other atom.

HYDRAZIDE. A compound of the general type, $R-\overset{\overset{\textstyle O}{\|}}{C}-NH-NH_2$, in which R is commonly an alkyl group.

HYDRAZINE. (1) The compound $H_2N \cdot NH_2$. (2) A derivative of that compound in which one or more of the hydrogen atoms are substituted by alkyl or aryl groups.

HYDRAZINO. The radical H_2NNH-.

HYDRAZO. The radical $-HNNH-$ (the two bonds are not attached to the same atom).

HYDRAZO COMPOUND. Compounds of the general type $R-NH-NH-R'$, in which R and R' may be identical or different organic radicals. Produced by the reduction of the azo compounds.

HYDRAZOATE. See azide.

HYDRAZONE. A compound of the general type $RNH \cdot N{=}CR'R''$ formed by reaction between a hydrazine and a compound containing a carbonyl group.

HYDRAZONO. The radical $H_2NN{=}$.

HYDRIC. Pertaining to or containing hydrogen.

HYDRIDE. A compound of hydrogen with any other element arsine (AsH_3, arsenic hydride), stibine (SbH_3, antimony hydride), phosphine (PH_3, phosphorus hydride), etc.

HYDRIN. A substituted alcohol, such as ethylene chlorhydrin, $ClCH_2CH_2OH$, ethylene cyanohydrin, $CNCH_2CH_2OH$, etc.

HYDRIODIC. See hydroiodic.

HYDRION. A name applied to the hydrogen ion.

HYDRO-. See hydr-.

HYDROBROMIC. Related to hydrobromic acid, HBr.

HYDROCARBON. Any compound which contains carbon and hydrogen only. These are regarded as the parent substances in organic chemistry from which all other organic compounds may be considered derived. They are classed as saturated, unsaturated, aliphatic, aromatic, etc.

HYDROCARBON, ALICYCLIC. (1) A compound of hydrogen and carbon having a saturated ring. (2) More specifically, one of a group of hydrocarbons derived from the corresponding aliphatic compounds by ring formation.

HYDROCARBON, ALIPHATIC. A compound of carbon and hydrogen only, in which the atoms are linked only or substantially in open chains.

HYDROCARBON, AROMATIC. A compound of carbon and hydrogen only, which contains in its structure one or more groups of carbon atoms linked in a **benzenoid** (q.v.) ring or rings.

HYDROCARBONATE. The anion HCO_3^-, or a compound containing it. (See **carbonate.**)

HYDROCARBONATO. The radical $HOO_2C\big\langle$.

HYDROCARBON, LIMIT. A saturated hydrocarbon of the paraffin series, so called because they contain the limit of hydrogen.

HYDROCARBON, SATURATED. A compound of carbon and hydrogen only in which each **valence** linkage between carbon atoms consists of only one pair of electrons, there being no double or triple linkages or bonds between carbon atoms.

HYDROCARBON, UNSATURATED. A compound of carbon and hydrogen only, in which there are one or more pairs of carbon atoms possessing a multiple valence linkage. Two carbon atoms may share two pairs of electrons, in which case they are said to be joined by a double bond; or the two carbon atoms may share three pairs of electrons, when they are joined by a triple bond.

HYDROCHLORIC. Related to hydrochloric acid, HCl.

HYDROCHLORIDE. A compound formed commonly by the addition of one or more molecules of hydrochloric acid to a molecule of a different kind. For example, the alkaloid strychnine adds hydrochloric acid to form strychnine hydrochloride.

HYDROCINNAMOYL. The radical $C_6H_5CH_2CH_2CO-$.

HYDROCYANIC. Related to hydrocyanic acid, HCN.

HYDRO-DIFFUSION. **Diffusion** in aqueous media.

HYDROFINING. A high-pressure catalytic process for the hydrogenation of low-grade petroleum fractions, to produce gasolines and lubricating oils that are exceptionally high in quality. Pressures are used as high as 3500 pounds per square inch, temperatures of 410–430° C., and a widely-used catalyst is molybdenum oxide.

HYDROFLUORIC. Related to hydrofluoric acid, H_2F_2 (which also contains HF, H_3F_3, etc.).

HYDROFORMING. The operation of converting **hydrocarbons** of low **octane number** and other undesirable properties into a stable fuel of higher octane rating. The operation may be conducted by subjecting the material to temperatures ranging from 480° C.–540° C., at a pressure of 150–300 pounds per square inch, including a high partial pressure of hydrogen to minimize carbon formation, and a suitable catalyst. During the process various reactions occur, including considerable cracking and **aromatization** (q.v.).

HYDROGEN. Gaseous element. Symbol H. Atomic number 1. Atomic weight 1.008. Molecular weight 2.016. Melting point −256.5° C. Boiling point −252.7° C. Valence 1. Hydrogen combines with all elements except the five noble gases. 1 liter of hydrogen under standard conditions weighs 0.08987 gram. One gram of hydrogen at S.T.P. occupies 11.117 liters.

The three **isotopes** of hydrogen have been assigned names. Ordinary hydrogen consists largely of protium, which consists, in its normal atomic form, of one proton and one electron. The second isotope of hydrogen is deuterium, which has an atomic weight of 2.0136 (on the chemical atomic weight scale) and a molecular weight of 4.0272. It is widely used in chemical research, as a means of identifying hydrogen atoms in particular positions; and its nuclear particle (by ionization of the atom with the loss of one electron) is used in nuclear investigations. Deuterium is present in ordinary water. The third isotope of hydrogen is tritium, which has a mass number of 3, and an atomic weight of 3.0221 (on the chemical atomic weight scale). Tritium is radioactive, having a half-period of 12.4 years, emitting electrons. It has been detected in ordinary hydrogen from various sources, and has been prepared by a number of nuclear reactions, e.g., the neutron bombardment of lithium and nitrogen, and the collision of two deuterons.

Hydrogen has also been found to exist in two molecular forms, para hydrogen and ortho hydrogen (See **hydrogen, ortho** and **para.**) which differ in the relation between the directions of the spins of the two nuclei in the molecule.

HYDROGEN, ATOMIC. Hydrogen partially in the atomic state produced by **dissociation** of molecular hydrogen at very high temperatures, as those of the **electric arc.** Since a large amount of heat is produced when hydrogen atoms combine to form hydrogen molecules, atomic hydrogen is used in welding to produce temperatures far beyond those obtainable by mere combustion of molecular hydrogen.

HYDROGEN BOND. See **bond, hydrogen.**

HYDROGEN ELECTRODE. (1) An **electrode** in which hydrogen gas at atmospheric pressure bubbles past a platinum-black electrode maintained in contact with an acid solution. (2) More generally, any electrode which can be used in the measurement of hydrogen ion concentration, such as the quinhydrone electrode, the glass electrode, and many others.

HYDROGEN EQUIVALENT. The effective acidity of an acid, or basicity of a base, as measured by the number of hydrogen equivalents per mole of acid (or, in other words, the number of replaceable or reactable hydrogen atoms per molecule), or the number of hydroxyl equivalents per mole of the base.

HYDROGEN, HEAVY. See **hydrogen** and **hydrogen, isotopes.**

HYDROGEN ION. An atom of hydrogen which has lost its one electron, and thus carries an elementary unit positive charge, equal in magnitude to that of the electron. Since the hydrogen atom consists of a proton and an electron, the hydrogen ion is a proton, which it is commonly called. Hy-

drogen ions are present in solution largely in solvated form, i.e., combined with molecules of solvent.

HYDROGEN ION CONCENTRATION. The concentration of ionic hydrogen in any system. This concentration $[H^+]$ is often expressed in terms of the pH of the system, where $pH = \log 1/[H^+]$.

HYDROGEN ION, NORMAL SOLUTION. A solution which contains one gram equivalent of hydrogen ion. Used as a basis in computing **pH.**

HYDROGEN, ISOTOPES. Three isotopes of hydrogen are known: protium which has a mass of 1.00756 (on the chemical atomic weight scale) is by far the most abundant isotope and is denoted by the symbol p or H^1; deuterium which has a mass of 2.0136 (on the chemical atomic weight scale) and is denoted by the symbol d or H^2; and tritium which has a mass of 3.0221 (on the chemical atomic weight scale) and is denoted by the symbol t or H^3. Deuterium is called heavy hydrogen.

HYDROGEN MOLECULE. The ordinary form of hydrogen, in which it is diatomic, H_2.

HYDROGEN, ORTHO AND PARA. Two forms of hydrogen, which constitute about 75%, and 25%, respectively, of ordinary hydrogen at room temperature, and which differ somewhat in their physical properties, especially in their specific heats. At very low temperature, as for liquid hydrogen, the para form is present to the extent of 99.7%. The difference between the two forms is explained on the assumption that the two nuclei in the H_2 molecule are spinning in anti-parallel directions in the case of para hydrogen and in parallel directions in ortho hydrogen.

HYDROGEN, PARA. See **hydrogen, ortho.**

HYDROGENATE. To cause to combine with hydrogen, as to hydrogenate oils which contain fats derived from unsaturated acids for example, oleic acid, in which case the unsaturated acids are converted into saturated fatty acids.

HYDROGENATION. See **hydrogenate** (q.v.).

HYDROGENATION PROCESS. A method of introducing hydrogen into a molecule. Representative cases include the synthesis of methanol and ammonia from carbon monoxide and nitrogen, respectively, and the saturation of unsaturated organic compounds.

HYDROGENIDE. A hydride.

HYDROGENIZE. To **hydrogenate.**

HYDROIODIC. Related to hydroiodic acid, HI.

HYDROLYSIS. Literally water-splitting. A process of **decomposition** in which the products of the reaction take up the elements of water in the sense that one product combines with a hydrogen atom and the other with an hydroxyl group derived from water in the system. E.g., methyl acetate on hydrolysis yields methyl alcohol and acetic acid, viz.,

acid, and a_{A^-} is the activity of the anions of the weak acid.

HYDROLYSIS, REVERSIBLE. Hydrosynthesis.

HYDROLYSIS, ZYMO. See **zymohydrolysis.**

HYDROLYTIC. See **hydrolysis.**

HYDROLYTIC DISSOCIATION. (1) The **hydrolysis** of a salt upon solution in water, e.g., sodium phenolate hydrolyzes as follows: $C_6H_5ONa + H_2O \rightarrow NaOH + C_6H_5OH$. (2) **Ionization** upon solution in water.

HYDROLYTIC FERMENT. See **enzyme.**

HYDROMETER. An instrument used for determining the **specific gravity** of a liquid, depending upon the principle that the exposed volume of a floating body immersed in a liquid is inversely proportional to the density of the liquid. Hydrometers are commonly graduated to read directly in

$$CH_3COOCH_3 + H_2O \rightarrow CH_3COOH + CH_3OH.$$

The adjective hydrolytic is used to denote the process of hydrolysis and the agents which catalyze it.

HYDROLYSIS CONSTANT. The **equilibrium constant** of a hydrolysis reaction, being equal to the ratio of the product of the activities of the substances yielded by the hydrolysis, to the product of the activity of the substance hydrolyzed.

HYDROLYSIS CONSTANT (OF A SALT). The **equilibrium constant** of a hydrolytic reaction of a salt. In the case of a salt of a weak acid and a strong base, the most general expression for this constant is expressed by the following relationship:

$$k_h = \frac{a_{OH^-} \times a_{HA}}{a_{A^-}}$$

in which k_h is the hydrolysis constant, a_{OH^-} is the hydroxyl ion activity, a_{HA} is the **activity** of the molecules of the weak

specific gravity, but forms are made for special purposes which are graduated differently. "Alcoholometers" are graduated to read directly in per cent of absolute alcohol or of proof spirit.

HYDROMETER SCALES. 1. Baumé scale, for liquids lighter than water,

Degrees Baumé =

$$\frac{140}{\text{Specific gravity (60° F./60° F.)}} - 130.$$

2. Baumé-Beck scale, for liquids heavier than water,

Degrees Baumé (American) =

$$145 - \frac{145}{\text{Specific gravity (60° F./60° F.)}}.$$

3. Twaddle scale,

Degrees Twaddle =
$1000(\text{Specific gravity (60° F./60° F.)} - 1)$.

4. Gay-Lussac scale,

Degrees Gay-Lussac =
$$\frac{100}{\text{Specific gravity (60° F./60° F.)}}.$$

5. A.P.I. scale,

Degrees A.P.I. =
$$\frac{141.5}{\text{Specific gravity}} - 131.5.$$

6. Balling scale. A saccharometer indicating directly per cent sucrose at 60° F. or otherwise at 17.5° C.

7. Brix scale. A saccharometer indicating directly per cent sucrose at various temperatures, frequently at 20° C.

HYDROMETRY. The process of determining the density or specific gravity of liquids (by means of an hydrometer).

HYDRONE PROCESS. A method of preparing hydrogen of high purity by reaction of a lead-sodium alloy with water.

HYDRONIUM ION. An ion found in water and all its solutions, which has the formula H_3O^+ and which consists of a **hydrogen ion** combined with a water molecule. It has been established that hydrogen ions do not exist free in aqueous solution, but are present as hydronium ions.

HYDROPEROXIDE. The anion HO_2^-, or a compound containing it. (See **peroxide.**)

HYDROPEROXO. The inorganic group HOO-.

HYDROPHILE. A substance or system which absorbs or adsorbs water.

HYDROPHOBE. A substance or system, colloidal or otherwise, which repels water.

HYDROSOL. A colloidal system in which the dispersion medium is water.

HYDROSULFATE. An addition compound of sulfuric acid. Cf. **hydrochloride.**

HYDROSULFIDE. The anion SH-, or a compound containing it. (See **sulfide.**)

HYDROSULFIDO. The inorganic group HS-.

HYDROSULFITE. See **dithionite.**

HYDROSULFURIC. Related to hydrogen sulfide, H_2S.

HYDROSYNTHESIS. The correlative of **hydrolysis** or **condensation** reaction in which water is eliminated.

HYDROUS. Containing either admixed or combined water.

-HYDROXAMAMIDE. A suffix indicating the group $-C(:NOH)NH_2$, commonly introduced by replacement of the carboxy radical.

-HYDROXAMIC. A suffix indicating the radical $-C(:NOH)(OH)$ or its tautomer $-C(:O)(NHOH)$, commonly introduced by replacement of the carboxy radical.

HYDROXAMINO. The radical HONH-.

HYDROXIDE. The anion OH-, or a compound containing it.

HYDROXIDION. The hydroxyl ion, OH-. It is characteristic of bases.

HYDROXIMINO. See **isonitroso.**

HYDROXOCHLOROPLATINATE. The anions chloroplatinate, hydroxo- (IV), $Pt(OH)_4Cl_2^-$, or $Pt(OH)_2Cl_4^-$, etc., or a compound containing one of them.

HYDROXY. The radical or group HO- (hydroxo in coordination compounds).

HYDROXY SALT. See **salt, hydroxy.**

HYDROXYACETIC. See **glycollic.**

HYDROXYFORMIC. See **carbonic.**

HYDROXYL. See **hydroxy.**

HYDROXYL BOND. See **bond, hydroxyl.**

HYDROXYL GROUP. The univalent group -OH, characteristic of bases, many acids, phenols, alcohols, carboxylic, and sulfonic acids, as well as amphoteric compounds. In combination with metallic radicals it confers strong basic properties upon the resulting compounds; with non-metals like sulfur and phosphorus, it forms strongly acid compounds. In solution, if ionized, the hydroxyl group forms the basic hydroxide ion.

HYDROXYMALONIC. See **tartronic.**

HYDROXYSUCCINIC. See **malic.**

HYENIC. Related to hyenic acid,

$$C_{24}H_{49}COOH.$$

HYGIRTAL PROCESS. A process for the production of hydrogen from gaseous **hydrocarbons,** involving their catalytic reaction with steam to yield hydrogen and carbon dioxide, or hydrogen, carbon dioxide, and carbon monoxide.

HYGROMETER. An instrument used to measure the amount (usually relative to saturation) of moisture in the atmosphere. There are various types of hygrometers, such as the psychrometer and the hair hygrometer.

HYGROSCOPIC. Becoming wet, or capable of becoming wet, by absorption of water from the atmosphere. Substances exhibiting this behavior at atmospheric temperature and humidity are called hygroscopic substances.

HYLON. A term in limited use to designate the positive nucleus of the atom.

HYNES-YANOWSKI MICRO RE-AGENT. Flavocobaltic nitrate (1,2-dinitratotetraamminocobaltic nitrate) which gives characteristic microscopic precipitates with chromate, dichromate, dithionate, and silicotungstate ions.

HYO-. (Greek) Derived from, or related to, swine; as hyodesoxycholic acid (from hog bile).

HYPER-. A prefix which indicates "over," "excess," "greater"; equivalent to per- and super-, e.g., hyperoxide.

HYPERACIDITY. Extreme or excessive **acidity.**

HYPERCHROMIC RADICAL. A radical which causes an increase in the color intensity of a coloring material.

HYPERCONJUGATION. The description of the properties of a molecule in terms of **resonance** structures in which an atom or group is not joined by any sort of bond to the atom to which it is ordinarily considered linked. Also called no-bond resonance.

HYPERFINE STRUCTURE. The existence in certain spectra of extremely fine lines, which become evident only at very high resolution, or very high sensitivity, and were overlooked in early investigations of the fine structure. The hyperfine structures are explained in some cases as due to the presence of **isotopes** and, in others, as due to the **spin momentum** of the atomic nucleus, which produces, by interaction with the resultant **quantum number** of the electronic system, a series of values for the total angular momentum of the whole atom.

HYPERISOTONIC. See **hypertonic solution.**

HYPERTONIC SOLUTION. A solution having a higher **osmotic pressure** than blood or another solution with which it is compared.

HYPNOTIC. A drug used to produce sleep.

HYPO-. (Greek: Under, beneath) Indicating (1) down, under, or less than ordinary; (2) a low, lower, or the lowest state of oxidation; as hypochlorous, hypoxanthine.

HYPOACIDITY. Subnormal acidity.

HYPOBROMITE. The anion BrO^-, or a compound containing it.

HYPOCHLORITE. The anion ClO^-, or a compound containing it.

HYPOCHLOROUS. Related to hypochlorous acid, HClO.

HYPOFERRITE. See ferrate (II).

HYPOFLUORITE. The anion FO⁻, or a compound containing it.

HYPOIODITE. The anion IO⁻, or a compound containing it.

HYPOMANGANITE. See **manganate (III).**

HYPONITRITE. The anion $N_2O_2^=$, or a compound containing it.

HYPOPHOSPHATE (meta). The anion $P_2O_6^{4-}$, or a compound containing it.

HYPOPHOSPHITE. The anion $H_2PO_2^-$, or a compound containing it.

HYPOSULFATE. A thiosulfate or a **dithionate** (q.v.).

HYPOSULFITE. A **dithionite** and **thiosulfate** (q.v.).

HYPOSULFURIC. See **dithionic.**

HYPOTHESIS. A purely ideal supposition which may be true or untrue. As used in chemistry it appears to be confirmed by facts but is not as certain as a theory. Cf. **laws.**

HYPOTHESIS, ATOMIC. The **atomic theory** (q.v.).

HYPOTHESIS, AVOGADRO. See **Avogadro hypothesis.**

HYPOTHESIS, MOLECULAR. The **molecular theory** (q.v.).

HYPOTONIC SOLUTION. A solution having a lower **osmotic pressure** than blood or another solution with which it is compared.

HYPSO-. A prefix meaning height.

HYPSOCHROME. An atom or radical which, by its substitution in a molecule, tends to shift its optical **absorption bands** in the direction of shorter wave length.

HYPSOFLORE. An atom or radical which, by its substitution in a molecule, tends to shift its **fluorescent radiation bands** in the direction of shorter wave length.

HYSTERESIS. (1) Thermodynamically, a retardation of the movement of a system to a condition of stable **equilibrium.** Probably responsible for metastable equilibrium. (2) The lag of a substance in a changing magnetic field, in acquiring an induced magnetization equal to that of the same material under steady-state conditions. (3) The lag of a chemical system in reaching equilibrium; this usage is applied particularly to colloidal systems.

I. The symbol for iodine (I). Symbol for **moment of inertia** (I). The iodide ion (I^-). Symbol for light intensity (I). Symbol for electric **current** (I). Symbol for instantaneous electric current (i or I). Symbol for maximum of electric current (I_m or I_{max}). Symbol for peak electric current (I_p or I). Symbol for saturation current (I_s). Abbreviation for iso or inactive (i). The **van't Hoff factor** (i). Symbol for **ionic strength** (I). Symbol for **vapor pressure** constant (i). Symbol for **radioactivity,** initial (I_o). Symbol for radioactivity at time t (I). Symbol for candle power, or **luminous intensity** (I). Symbol for integration constant of **Gibbs function** equation (I). **Mole factor** or van't Hoff coefficient (i). Symbol for **nuclear spin** (I). Symbol for strength of magnetic shell (I). See also **iota.**

IATROCHEMISTRY. A doctrine of therapeutics based on chemistry, applied especially to the 16th century physicians who followed the principles of Paracelsus.

IDEAL GAS. See **gas, ideal.**

IDEAL SOLUTION. A solution which behaves exactly in accordance with the **law of Raoult,** and various relationships derived from it, at all temperatures and concentrations. Many real solutions approach ideal behavior more or less closely when highly dilute, deviations from ideality becoming more marked the higher the concentration.

-IDENE. This suffix or word-part, added to any radical, usually means a double bond at the point of attachment.

IDENTITY PERIOD. The distance between identical atomic groupings in the chain molecule of an associated or polymerized substance or in a crystal lattice. The magnitude of this dimension, which is commonly expressed in **Ångström units,** plays an important part in descriptions of structure.

IDIOMORPHOUS. Appearing in distinct crystals.

IGNITION. (1) The process of complete oxidation. (2) The initiation of such a process. (3) The process of heating a substance until it ceases to lose weight, indicating that all thermal decomposition, including losses of moisture and volatile matter, which may occur up to the temperature of heating, has been completed.

IGNITION POINT. (Kindling point) The minimum temperature which will enable combustion or explosion to take place. The **flash point** of gases.

IHL TEST REACTION FOR VOLATILE OILS. Various oils in alcoholic solution give characteristic colors with sucrose or lepidine and hydrochloric acid.

IHL TEST REACTIONS FOR CARBO-HYDRATES. Many sugars, starches, and gums give color reactions, when added to alcoholic solutions of various phenols, followed by the addition of hydrochloric or sulfuric acid and gentle heating.

ILINSKI-KNORRE REAGENT FOR COBALT AND NICKEL. A solution of α-nitroso-β-naphthol in 50% acetic acid which gives a red precipitate with cobalt solutions, and a brown precipitate with nickel solutions.

ILLINIUM. The name once applied to element of atomic number 61 (see **promethium**), in consequence of the report of its discovery in 1926.

ILLUMINATION, DARK-GROUND. See **illumination, indirect.**

ILLUMINATION, DIRECT. (1) Lighting by visible radiation that passes from light source to object without reflection. (2) In microscopy, light falling directly on the stage of a microscope from above without being reflected by the mirror.

ILLUMINATION, INDIRECT. (1) Lighting by visible radiation that undergoes one or more reflections in its journey from light source to object. (2) In microscopy, light which strikes the object at right angles to the direction of the axis of a microscope.

ILLUMINATION INTENSITY. The **flux density** of light incident upon a surface, divided by the surface area.

ILOSVAY REAGENT FOR ACETYLENE. A solution of definite proportions of cupric sulfate, ammonia, and hydroxylamine hydrochloride (such as 1 g. cupric sulfate in 8 ml. 10% ammonia to which 3 g. hydroxylamine hydrochloride is added, and water to make 50 ml.). A red precipitate is given by acetylene with this reagent.

ILOSVAY REAGENT FOR HYDROGEN PEROXIDE. A solution of 5 drops dimethylaniline and 0.03 g. potassium dichromate in 1 liter water, used in testing for hydrogen peroxide. A yellow color in the presence of oxalic acid is given by solutions containing hydrogen peroxide, on treatment with this reagent.

IMAZINE. The radical

$$=C=N-CH=N-.$$

IMBIBITION. The penetration of a liquid into a solid system, colloidal or otherwise.

IMIDAZOLIDYL. The radical $C_3H_7N_2-$. Derived from imidazolidine.

IMIDAZOLE. The compound

$$\begin{array}{c} HC-N \\ \| \quad \diagdown \\ \quad \quad \quad CH. \\ \| \quad \diagup \\ HC-NH \end{array}$$

IMIDAZOLYL. The radical $C_3H_3N_2-$. Derived from imidazole (4 isomers).

-IMIDE. A suffix indicating the radical

$\diagdown$NH or –CONHCO–, introduced, in the

case of the former, by replacement of two
acid hydroxy groups, or in the case of the
latter, by replacement of two methyl
groups.

-IMIDIC. A suffix indicating the radical
–C(:NH)OH introduced by replacement
of a carboxy group.

IMIDO. The radical NH= (properly in
acid groups only; sometimes used synonymously with imino).

IMIDODIPHOSPHATE. The anion
$NHP_2O_6^{4-}$, or a compound containing it.

IMIDODISULFATE. The anion

$$NH(SO_3)_2^- \text{ or } N(SO_3)_2^{3-},$$

or a compound containing one of these
anions.

-IMINE. A suffix indicating the $\diagdown$NH

radical, introduced by replacement of two
hydrogen atoms attached to the same atom.

IMINO. The radical NH=.

IMINOQUINOLE. One of a series of
compounds of the general type formula:

in which R is an **alkyl radical.**

IMMISCIBLE SOLVENT. See **solvent,
immiscible.**

IMMUNITY. The ability of an organism
to resist the action of a disease-producing
agent, and thus to withstand **infection.**

IMMUNOLOGY. The science dealing
with immunity, i.e., the power of resistance
of an organism to **infection.**

IMPACT HEAD. See **head, impact.**

IMPACT PRESSURE. See **pressure, impact.**

IMPREGNATION. The incorporation of
one substance into another, usually in a
finely-divided or finely-separated form.

IMPROVER. A bleaching or whitening
agent, as nitrosyl chloride, or chlorine,
which is added to flour to remove or mask
the color; or a mixture of starch and salts
added to flour to stimulate the yeast and
improve the rising properties of the bread.

In Symbol for element **indium.**

INACTIVE COMPOUND. (1) One of
two **optical isomers** that does not rotate
the plane of **polarized light.** (2) A nonradioactive compound.

INACTIVE, DIVISIBLE COMPOUND.
A substance which does not rotate the
plane of **polarized light** but which may be
separated into equal amounts of dextrorotatory and levorotatory compounds,
e.g., racemic compounds. Such substances
are inactive by external compensation.

INACTIVE, INDIVISIBLE COMPOUND.
A compound which, although containing
asymmetric atoms, does not rotate the
plane of **polarized light.** The effect is
supposed to be due to equal and opposite
rotations of two asymmetric atoms, e.g.,
mesotartaric acid. These compounds cannot be separated into optically active
isomers and are said to be inactive by
internal compensation. See **isomerism,
optical.**

INCH. A unit of linear measure in the
English system, equal to $\frac{1}{36}$ yard.

1 inch = 25.4001 millimeters.

INCINERATION. Complete **oxidation.**

INCIDENCE. Impact of one material or
body or radiation upon another body.

INCIDENCE, ANGLE OF. The angle at
which one body or material or radiation
strikes a surface, measured from the line

of direction of the moving entity to a line perpendicular to the surface at the point of impact. The term is used commonly in regard to the impact of radiant energy upon a material surface.

INCLINATION TO REACTION. Tendency to reaction. A condition where a difference in the intensity of the chemical energy of different substances in a system will equalize itself if an opposing influence is withdrawn.

INCLINATOR. A support for large bottles that facilitates pouring.

INCOMBUSTIBLE. Not consumed or decomposed by heat or flame.

INCOMPATIBILITY. In pharmacy a condition which arises when two substances possess properties which cannot be harmonized. Incompatibility is termed chemical, pharmaceutical, or physiological according to whether the compounds react upon each other in an undesirable manner, are immiscible like oil and water, or liquefy like mixtures of camphor and menthol, or are physiological antagonists like atropine and pilocarpine or strychnine and chloral hydrate.

INCOMPRESSIBLE VOLUME. That portion of the total volume of a gas which consists of the actual bulk of the gas molecules, rather than the spaces between molecules. It is because of the large amount of empty space between molecules that gases are easily compressible; the ideal gas law describes the behavior of a (hypothetical) gas which has no incompressible volume. Denoted by the quantity b in the van der Waals equation. See co-volume.

INCONGRUENT MELTING POINT. See melting point, incongruent.

INCONGRUENTLY SATURATED SOLUTION. See saturated solution, incongruent.

INCONSTANT ELEMENTS. Volatile elements.

INDAMINES. Dyestuffs derived from one of the indoanilines by substitution of $>$NH for the quinone oxygen. Phenylene blue, $C_6H_4-N-C_6H_4NH_2$ is a representative indamine.

$$\underset{NH}{\diagdown\diagup}$$

INDANYL. The radical C_9H_9- (from indan, 4 isomers).

INDATE. The anion InO_2^-, or a compound containing it.

INDENYL. The radical C_9H_7- (from indene, 7 isomers).

INDEX OF REFRACTION. See refraction, index of.

INDICATOR. A substance which shows by a color change, or other visible manifestation, some change in, or particular condition of, the chemical nature of a system. Thus acid-base indicators may be used to indicate the end point of a particular neutralization reaction, or they may also be used to indicate the pH value of a system. Indicators also are useful in following oxidation-reduction reactions, precipitation reactions, and, in general, throughout all volumetric analysis, and in many other chemical control operations.

INDICATOR, ACHROMATIC. A mixture of indicators so chosen that they possess complementary colors at the end point of the particular reaction, and therefore, the solution becomes colorless when the end point is reached.

INDICATOR, ADSORPTION. An indicator which shows the end point of a titration by a change in its colloidal condition, commonly by being released from adsorption, or by being adsorbed upon the precipitate, so that the precipitate, which had been colored by the adsorbed dye, becomes colorless, or much less strongly colored; or vice versa.

INDICATOR, EXTERNAL. See indicator, outside.

HYDROGEN ION CONCENTRATION RANGES (pH) AND COLOR CHANGES OF INDICATORS

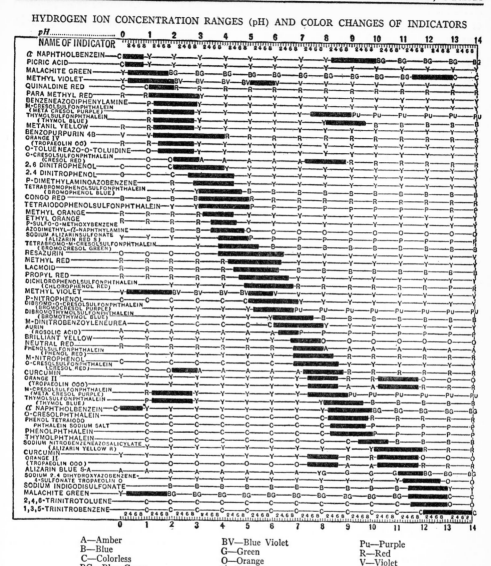

The pH ranges shown are approximations and are intended to aid in selecting the proper indicator. (*Eastman Kodak Co.*)

A—Amber	BV—Blue Violet	Pu—Purple
B—Blue	G—Green	R—Red
C—Colorless	O—Orange	V—Violet
BG—Blue Green	P—Pink	Y—Yellow

INDICATOR, FLUORESCENT. An indicator which shows a change in a chemical system, such as the **end point** of a reaction, by an increase or decrease in fluorescence.

INDICATOR, INTERNAL. An indicator used in the usual way, by adding it to the system under analysis or control. Contrast **indicator, outside.**

INDICATOR, NEUTRALIZATION. A substance which undergoes a characteristic color change at the point where an acid has been neutralized by a base used in titrating it, or a base by an acid used in its **titration.**

INDICATOR, OUTSIDE. An indicator used outside the solution that is being titrated, as by the spot-plate method; in which a drop or two of the solution being titrated is removed and treated on a spot-plate with the indicator. The **titration** is continued until this test shows that the **end point** of the reaction has been reached.

INDICATOR, OXIDATION-REDUC-TION. A substance that undergoes a characteristic color change at a definite state of oxidation of a solution or, rather, at a definite value of the **oxidizing potential.**

INDICATOR, TURBIDITY. An **indicator** that shows the **end point** of a reaction by an increase in turbidity or actual precipitation. Such indicators are usually **colloidal** solutions.

INDICATOR, UNIVERSAL. An **indicator** that gives characteristic color reactions over a wide range of pH values. Universal indicators are generally prepared by mixing selected indicators.

INDICATORS, CHROMOPHORIC THEORY OF. The hypothesis that the change in color exhibited by **indicators** is due to intramolecular transitions from quinoid (**chromophore**) to benzenoid forms and vice versa.

INDICATORS, IONIZATION THEORY OF. The hypothesis that the color of an **indicator** in solution is due to its degree of **ionization.** In alkaline solutions there will be more negative ions than in neutral solutions and in acid solutions still less of the negative ions. If the color of the negative ion of an indicator differs from that of the molecule (as in the case of methyl orange) there will be a difference in color of its acid and alkaline solutions.

INDIFFERENT GAS. A gas that does not react chemically with the system under observation.

INDIRECT ILLUMINATION. See **illumination, indirect.**

INDIRECT PROCESS (ZINC OXIDE). See **French process (zinc oxide).**

INDISSOLUBLE. Insoluble.

INDIUM. Metallic element. Symbol In. Atomic number 49. Atomic weight 114.76. Density 7.3. Specific heat 0.0303. Melt-ing point 155° C. Boiling point 1450° C. Valence 3, 2, 1. Oxide In_2O_3. Indium occurs in zinc blende and other minerals.

INDOLYL. The radical C_8H_6N- (from indole, 7 isomers).

INDOLYLIDENE. The radical

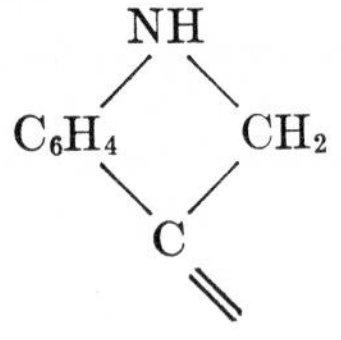

$$
\begin{array}{c}
NH \\
C_6H_4 \qquad CH_2 \\
C \\
\end{array}
$$

[3(2) form shown].

INDUCED POLARIZATION. See **polarization, molar.**

INDUCED RADIOACTIVITY. See **radioactivity, induced.**

INDUCED REACTION. A **reaction** that is accelerated when one or more, but not all, of its reactants enter into another reaction with one or more other substances.

INDUCTION. (1) The initiation or occurrence of an **induced reaction** (q.v.). (2) The production of an electric charge or magnetic field in a substance by the approach or proximity of an electrified body, a magnet or any other source of an electric or magnetic field, the term induction implying that there is a relatively poor conduction of electricity, or a relatively non-magnetized medium, between the body in which the electric or magnetic effect is induced and the electrified body, or other source of the electric or magnetic field.

INDUCTION EFFECT. An attractive force between molecules, or a component of such force, due to the moment induced by an adjacent **dipolar** molecule.

INDUCTION FACTOR. If the substances entering into a simple induced reaction (see **reaction, induced**) are designated as follows:
For the induced reaction,

$$A + B \rightarrow X \cdots$$

and for the reaction which accelerates the induced reaction,

$$A + C \rightarrow Y \cdots$$

then the induction factor is:

$$\frac{\text{Rate at which } B \text{ is transformed}}{\text{Rate at which } C \text{ is transformed}}.$$

INDUCTION, PERIOD OF. A period of acceleration of a chemical reaction from zero to a maximum rate, found in many cases, often occupying measurable time, as in the combination of impure hydrogen and chlorine when exposed to light. It may be due to the main reaction being compounded of a number of consecutive reactions, to time consumed in overcoming passive resistance, to slow catalysis, to negative catalysis, etc. With photochemical reactions the phenomenon is known as the period of photochemical induction.

INDUCTOMERIC EFFECT. A time-variable effect operating by the inductive mechanism; i.e., a general displacement of electrons in a molecule under the influence of electrical fields.

INDUCTOR. In induced reactions, the substance which takes part in the accelerating reaction as distinguished from the actor which takes part in both, and from the receptor which takes part only in the induced reaction. Thus if the induced reaction is

$$A + B \rightarrow X \cdots$$

and the reaction which accelerates it is

$$A + C \rightarrow Y \cdots$$

then C is the inductor, A, the actor, and B, the receptor.

INDULINE. One of a group of black or blue dyes containing the ring structure

$$HN{=}C_6H_3 \overset{\displaystyle N}{\underset{\displaystyle NR}{\diagup\hspace{-0.5em}\diagdown}} C_6H_4.$$

INDUSTRIAL CHEMISTRY. See **chemistry, industrial.**

INDYL. See **indolyl.**

-INE. A suffix meaning a base or a potential base.

INEQUALITY OF CLAUSIUS. The **entropy** of a system undergoing an irreversible cyclic process tends to increase. This is one of the statements of the Second Law of Thermodynamics. See **thermodynamics, second law of.** It is equivalent to the statement that the entropy of the universe tends toward a maximum.

INERT GAS. See **gas, inert.**

INERT SUBSTANCES. Elements and compounds that react very slowly or not at all. Nitrogen is very inert. The noble gases are all completely inert.

INERTIA. Inertia is one of the few properties manifested by all kinds of matter. Although its name implies inaction (no doubt from the fact that bodies do not set themselves into motion), inertia is an actual opposition to any alteration of motion. That is, the acceleration of a body in any sense, either as to speed or direction of motion, requires the application of force proportional to the mass of the body and to the amount of acceleration. The reaction to this force, acting always through the center of mass, is a measure of the inertia of the body.

INFECTION. (1) The invasion and successful growth in an organism of one or more species of bacteria or parasites. (2) Transmission of disease by contact.

INFILTRATION. In general, the passage of a liquid or gas through interstices, or into restricted spaces. Specifically, the passage of injected liquids from the point of introduction into the tissues; or the penetration of a liquid or solution into the interstices of a rock, usually with subsequent solidification and modification of the composition of the original rock.

INFRARED ABSORPTION SPECTRA (MOLECULAR). See **spectrum, infrared absorption.**

INFRARED SPECTRUM. A portion of the invisible part of the **electromagnetic spectrum** consisting of radiations varying in wave length from about 3×10^{-4} meters to the longest visible red, at 7.7×10^{-7} meters. The term infrared spectrum is also applied to the characteristic radiations emitted (or absorbed) in this region by some particular substance.

INFUSIBLE. Solid substances which cannot be transformed into the liquid state under specified or implied conditions.

INFUSION. An aqueous solution of the soluble components of a plant made by immersing a quantity of the plant in water, allowing the mixture to steep until cold, and straining off the liquid portion. Cf. **decoction.**

INHIBITOR. A negative **catalyst,** i.e., a substance that diminishes the rate of a chemical reaction.

-INIUM. A suffix meaning the cation of an -ine base.

INKOMETER. A device for measuring **adhesion** of liquids. The rotation of one drum transmits a torque to another by virtue of the adhesive placed in contact with both, and the magnitude of the torque is measured.

INNER COMPLEX. A compound formed by many types of substances with metals, in which a cyclic structure is usually effected within the compound by the establishment of a coordination linkage. (See **bond, coordinate.**) Molecules containing both an acid radical and an electron-rich group form many stable compounds of this type with various metals. There are nonionic as well as salt-forming substances among the substances defined as inner complex salts.

INNER COMPOUND. See **compound, inner.**

INNER QUANTUM NUMBER. The number used in quantizing the angular momentum of an electron as a basis for explaining the multiplet lines in atomic spectra. The inner **quantum number** is the sum of the azimuthal quantum number and the **spin** quantum number, or in physical terms, the resultant of the spin of the electron and the azimuthal contribution to the angular momentum.

INORGANIC. (1) Not derived from a living organism. (2) Any chemical compound that does not contain carbon, with the exception of carbonates, cyanides, and a few other simple carbon compounds which are usually considered inorganic in nature.

INORGANIC COMPOUND. See **compound, inorganic.**

INSECTICIDE. A substance used to kill insects.

INSOLUBLE. Not dissolving in a solvent (except in minute amounts).

INSTABILITY CONSTANT. The **dissociation constant** for a complex ion, which may be expressed in terms of **activities,** by dividing the product of the activities at **equilibrium** of each of its simpler ions (raised to the proper power) by the activity of the complex ion; or in terms of concentrations, where permissible, by dividing the product of the concentrations at equilibrium of each of its simpler ions (raised to the proper power) by the concentration of the complex ion.

INTEGRAL. (1) A whole, or composed of constituent parts making a whole. (2) An essential part, either a constituent or a component. (3) A mathematical symbol denoting summation, or a mathematical expression carrying such a symbol.

INTEGRAL HEAT OF DILUTION. See **heat of dilution, integral.**

INTEGRAL HEAT OF SOLUTION. See **heat of solution, integral.**

INTENSIVE PROPERTY. See **property, intensive.**

INTERACTION. (1) Identical with **reaction** (q.v.). (2) Mutual effect due to proximity of charges, ions, dipoles, or molecules on each other's properties.

INTERACTION TERMS. Terms in the **van der Waals equation** for gases representing the forces of interaction between gas molecules of different substances when this equation is applied to mixtures of gases.

INTERFACE. A surface which forms the boundary between two phases or systems.

INTERFACIAL SURFACE ENERGY. The work necessary to enlarge the surface of separation between two immiscible or partially-miscible liquids.

INTERFACIAL TENSION. The contractile force of an interface between two liquids, resulting from their surface tensions, and the attraction between the molecules of the two liquids. It is commonly determined by measuring the interfacial surface energy.

INTERFERENCE. An opposing action, commonly between two forces or force systems, which results in partial or complete nullification of their individual effects. The term arises most commonly in chemistry in regard to wave systems, especially of radiant energy, where the process results in partial or even complete loss of energy in certain areas (destructive interference) and exaltation of energy in other areas (constructive interference).

INTERHALOGEN COMPOUND. A binary compound composed of two elements of the **halogen family.**

INTERIONIC ATTRACTION THEORY. Even in concentrated solutions, there is a high degree of **ionization.** The reason, therefore, that the properties of strong electrolytes depart from those calculated under the **Arrhenius ionic theory** is not solely attributable to incomplete ionization, but involves the electrostatic attractions between ions of opposite charge, and the repulsions between ions of like charge. In solution, each positive ion is surrounded, on the average, with an **"ionic atmosphere"** (q.v.) of negative ions, and vice versa.

INTERMEDIATE. A substance used in the manufacture of dyes, drugs, and other organic products, which has been obtained usually by chemical treatment of crudes or other chemical raw materials.

INTERMEDIATE PHASES. Intermetallic compounds, which are sometimes called intermediate phases because they are commonly found in the matrix of another phase at intermediate compositions in an alloy.

INTERMITTENCY EFFECT. The departure from the **reciprocity law** when the **exposure** of a photographic emulsion is made in a series of discrete installments rather than in a continuous exposure to the same total energy.

INTERMOLECULAR REACTION. A reaction between individual molecules, which is the usual kind of reaction. The term is used to distinguish these reactions from intramolecular reactions, where the action takes place between portions of the same molecule.

INTERNAL. A term used frequently in chemistry to express the idea that a phenomenon is confined within a molecule, as internal compensation, internal oxidation.

INTERNAL COMPENSATION. A condition of optical inactivity in a molecule containing two, or a multiple of two, **asymmetric carbon atoms,** due to the fact that two carbon atoms, one of which is dextrorotatory, the other of which is levorotatory, neutralize the optical effect of each other.

INTERNAL CONVERSION. The process by which a γ-ray emitted by an atomic nucleus will, on its way out from the nucleus, give up its entire energy to one of the extra-nuclear electrons of the atom in which it originated.

INTERNAL CONVERSION COEFFICIENT. The fraction of the γ-ray photons emerging from the atomic nucleus which undergo **internal conversion.**

INTERNAL ENERGY. See **energy, internal.**

INTERNAL REACTION. An **intramolecular reaction** (q.v.).

INTERNAL SALT. See **salt, internal.**

INTERNAL STANDARD. A material present in or added to samples in known amount to serve as a reference for spectral measurements.

INTERNAL STANDARD LINE. A spectral **line** of an internal standard, with reference to which the **radiant power** of an analytical line is measured.

INTERPHASE. The boundary surface between two **phases.**

INTERSTICE. A small space within a **phase** or, more commonly, between particles.

INTERSTITIAL COMPOUND. See **compound, interstitial.**

INTERTRACTION. Increase in density of a **colloidal solution** caused by loss of solute by diffusion into a salt solution which is in contact with the colloidal solution.

INTRA-ATOMIC. Within an atom, as intra-atomic structure is the internal structure of an atom.

INTRAMOLECULAR. Within a molecule.

INTRAMOLECULAR CONDENSATION. A **condensation reaction** (q.v.) between two portions of the same molecule.

INTRAMOLECULAR OPPOSITION. Assumed tension or opposition between the elements in a compound because of their **potential differences.**

INTRAMOLECULAR OXIDATION. The **oxidation** of a compound in which the oxygen required by the reaction is furnished by the compound itself, e.g., nitrolactic acid oxidizes itself to oxalic acid, hydrocyanic acid and water, viz.,

$$\begin{array}{ccc} CH_3 & COOH & \\ | & | & \\ CHNO_3 \rightarrow & | & + HCN + H_2O. \\ | & | & \\ COOH & COOH & \end{array}$$

INTRAMOLECULAR REACTION. A reaction taking place within a molecule. Contrast **intermolecular reaction.**

INTRAVENOUS. Inside or within the blood vessels.

INTRINSIC VISCOSITY. See **viscosity, intrinsic.**

INTROFACTION. The effect of an **introfier** upon a liquid, whereby its rate and extent of penetration or impregnation is increased. The effect is due primarily to **dissociation** of complex molecules.

INTROFIER. A substance added to liquids to increase their **penetrating power,** or to accelerate their rate of penetration into substances to be impregnated.

INVASION. The solution of a gas in a liquid. See **absorption of gases.**

INVASION COEFFICIENT. A factor used to denote the number of milliliters of a gas under standard conditions absorbed by one square centimeter of surface in one minute.

INVERSION. (1) The conversion of a stereo-chemical **isomer** into its opposite form, as a levorotatory to a dextrorotatory substance or a cis to a trans form. (2) The decomposition, as by hydrolysis, of an optically active substance, thereby producing an oppositely optically active substance, e.g., the inversion of dextrorotatory sucrose to a levorotatory mixture of dextrose and levulose.

INVERSION, GEOMETRICAL. The conversion of a geometrical **isomer** into its opposite form by physical or chemical means. Fumaric acid, on heating, is converted into the anhydride of maleic acid; nitrous acid converts oleic into elaidic acid.

INVERSION, OPTICAL. The conversion of optically active substances into derivatives of identical structure but of opposite rotation. *l*-Malic acid with phosphorus pentachloride yields *d*-chlorosuccinic acid; *d*-malic acid under the same conditions yields *l*-chlorosuccinic acid. Walden's inversion is the classical instance of optical inversion.

INVERSION TEMPERATURE. See Joule-Thomson inversion temperature.

INVERSION, WALDEN. Optical inversion. The following scheme illustrates the phenomenon:

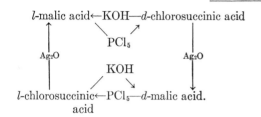

l-malic acid←KOH—d-chlorosuccinic acid

PCl$_5$

Ag$_2$O   Ag$_2$O

KOH

l-chlorosuccinic←PCl$_5$—d-malic acid.
acid

Thus, l-malic acid may be converted into d-malic acid, and vice versa.

IODATE. The anion IO$_3^-$, or a compound containing it.

IODATO. The inorganic radical O$_3$I–.

IODIC. (1) Related to iodic acid, HIO$_3$. (2) Containing or pertaining to pentavalent **iodine.**

IODIDE (TRI-). The anion I$_3^-$, or a compound containing it.

IODINE. Non-metallic element. Symbol I. Atomic number 53. Atomic weight 126.91. Density 4.93 (solid). Specific heat 0.054. Melting point 113.5° C. Boiling point 184.4° C. Valences 1, 3, 5, and 7. Oxides I$_2$O, I$_2$O$_3$, I$_2$O$_5$. Acids, HI, HIO, HIO$_3$, HIO$_4$.

IODINE CARRIERS. Substances added to organic reaction mixtures to cause combination of **iodine** with various compounds or to direct the course of the reaction in some specific way. Phosphorus, iron wire, ferrous iodide, ferric chloride, mercuric oxide, etc., are examples.

IODINE NUMBER. (Iodine value. Hübl number.) A "constant" of unsaturated fats and waxes; numerically the percentage of iodine absorbed by the sample. Iodine chloride or bromide may be used in the determination of the constant, in which cases the results are calculated to iodine.

IODITE. A compound containing the radical —IO$_2$.

IODO. The radical I–, in organic compounds.

IODO COMPOUND. An organic compound which may be regarded as derived from hydriodic acid, as iodobenzene, C$_6$H$_5$I, iodomethane, CH$_3$I.

IODOAURATE (III). The anion AuI$_4^-$, or a compound containing it.

IODOBISMUTHATE (III). The anion BiI$_4^-$, BiI$_5^=$, or BiI$_6^{3-}$, or a compound containing one of these anions.

IODOMERCURATE (II). The anion HgI$_4^=$, or a compound containing it.

IODOMETRY (IODIMETRY). Analysis by means of **iodine,** commonly consisting of the titrimetric determination of substances which can, under certain conditions, oxidize an iodide, such as potassium iodide, to free iodine; or else of substances which combine with iodine or reduce it. In any case, the iodine formed or remaining after the reaction is determined by titration with standard sodium thiosulfate solution.

IODONIUM COMPOUNDS. Compounds derived from the hypothetical iodonium hydroxide, IH$_2$OH, as diphenyliodonium hydroxide (C$_6$H$_5$)$_2$IOH, and diphenyliodonium iodide (C$_6$H$_5$)$_2$I · I. The iodonium compounds contain trivalent iodine.

IODOÖSMATE (IV). The anion OsI$_6^=$, or a compound containing it.

IODOPALLADATE (II). The anion PdI$_4^=$, or a compound containing it.

IODOPLATINATE (II). The anion PtI_4^- or a compound containing it.

IODOPLATINATE (IV). The anion PtI_6^-, or a compound containing it.

IODORHENATE (IV). The anion ReI_6^-, or a compound containing it.

IODOSO. The radical OI–, usually in organic compounds.

IODOSO COMPOUNDS. Organic compounds which contain the group –IO, as iodosobenzene, C_6H_5IO.

IODOSTANNATE (IV). The anion SnI_6^-, or a compound containing it.

IODOTELLURATE. The anion TeI_6^-, or a compound containing it.

IODOTHALLATE (III). The anion TlI_4^-, or a compound containing it.

IODOTITANATE (IV). The anion TiI_6^-, or a compound containing it.

IODOUS. (1) Related to iodous acid, HIO_2. (2) Containing trivalent iodine.

IODOXY. The radical O_2I–, in organic compounds.

IODOXY COMPOUNDS. Organic compounds which contain the group $–IO_2$, as iodoxybenzene, $C_6H_5IO_2$. Formerly termed iodo compounds.

IODOZINCATE. The anion ZnI_4^-, or a compound containing it.

IODOZIRCONATE. The anion ZrI_6^-, or a compound containing it.

ION. An electrically-charged particle, atom, molecule, or radical, in which the charge is due to the gain or loss of one or more electrons and is, accordingly, negative or positive in electrical sign, and equal in magnitude to the number of electrons gained or lost. Ions exist in various media and under various conditions, for example, in water, liquid ammonia, and other ionizing solvents, whose molecules are considered to form complexes with the ions, in crystals, in gases conducting electricity, and under other conditions.

ION, AMPHOTERIC. An **ion** which carries both a positive and a negative charge, commonly at opposite ends of a long, or fairly long, chain, as in the case of ions of **amino acids.**

ION, AQUO. A complex particle consisting of an ion combined with one or more molecules of water, as $H^+(H_2O)$ or H_3O^+. The strongly-ionizing solvents are considered to form such aquo ions with all, or virtually all, the ions in solution.

ION BEAM. A beam of charged particles which compare in velocity to those yielded by **radioactive** substances, or which exceed that velocity. Ion beams are produced by the application of electrical forces to ordinary ions and other particles, as in the production of a beam of α-particles by applying potentials in the millions of volts to the particles from a helium discharge tube; or as in the acceleration of ionic particles to great velocities by use of the cyclotron.

ION, COMPLEX. See **complex ion.**

ION-DIPOLE INTERACTION. A reaction between an **ion** and a dipole (i.e., a molecule having a **dipole moment**) which results in the formation of an aggregate of particles, in which the ion is at the center, surrounded by a number of molecules which are oriented so that their regions of polarity of sign unlike the charge on the ion, are closest to it. Thus, if the ion has a negative charge, the neighboring molecules will orient so that their regions of positive polarity are closest to the ion.

ION EXCHANGE. An exchange of **ions** that occurs at a **phase** boundary. Although most applications of the phenomenon occur in systems involving electrolyte solutions and ionic solids, the distribution of **electrolytes** between immiscible solutions of electrolytes, for example, may be considered an ion-exchange phenomenon.

ION EXCHANGE RESIN. A **resin** capable of exchanging **ions** readily enough for useful applications. Originally confined to water-softening, these applications now extend widely throughout chemical technology, chemical research, agriculture, and medicine. Various theories of the mechanism proposed include the **double layer** theory, the **crystal lattice** theory, and the **Donnan membrane** theory. Resins are available that will exchange OH^- for all anions in solution; others will exchange H^+ for all cations in the solution, etc.

ION, MOLECULAR. A charged molecule, commonly produced by electrical discharges through gases in which a gaseous molecule has lost (or gained) one or more electrons.

ION, NEGATIVE. An ion carrying a negative charge; an **anion.**

ION PAIR. As postulated in the **Debye-Hückel theory,** in concentrated solutions of strong electrolytes (two or more) ions may occasionally approach each other so closely that they may form pairs (or groups) without entering into permanent chemical combination.

ION, POSITIVE. An ion carrying a positive charge; a **cation.**

ION, SOLVATED. See **ion, aquo.**

ION, ZWITTER. See **ion, amphoteric.**

IONIC ATMOSPHERE. As outlined under the definition of **Debye-Hückel Theory of Conductivity,** every ion attracts ions of opposite sign. Therefore, there are more ions of unlike than of like sign in the neighborhood of any individual ion in a solution and it is, in effect, surrounded by an ionic atmosphere of opposite charge.

IONIC CHARGE. Either the total charge carried by an ion, or the charge carried by an ion which has unit charge. Since ions owe their charges to gain or loss of electrons, unit charge is the charge on an **electron** (q.v.), and all ionic charges are either equal to this value, or integral multiples of it.

IONIC COMBINATIONS. Reactions between salts, salts and bases, salts and

acids, or acids and bases which do not involve transfer of electrons, and which proceed by the removal of a product from the system as in the evolution of a gas or the precipitation of a solid; or by the formation of a product which, while remaining in the system, is of such nature that the properties of the system are changed, as in the formation of a weak electrolyte.

IONIC COMPOUND. See **compound, ionic.**

IONIC CONDUCTANCE. See **conductance, ionic.**

IONIC EQUILIBRIUM. In any **ionization,** at any particular temperature and pressure, the conditions at which the rate of **dissociation** of unionized molecules, or other particles to form ions, is equal to the rate of combination of the ions to form the unionized molecules, or other particles so that activities and concentrations remain constant as long as the conditions are unchanged.

IONIC MICELLES. Aggregates of **ions** exhibiting characteristic properties. The conception was applied by McBain to explain the behavior of soaps in very dilute solutions, in which aggregates of ten or more of the anions form ionic micelles containing a number of water molecules.

IONIC MIGRATION. The movement of charged particles of an **electrolyte** toward the electrodes under the influence of the electric current.

IONIC MOBILITY. The absolute velocity of an ion when moving under a **potential gradient** of one volt per centimeter.

IONIC POTENTIAL. The ratio of the charge on an **ion** to its radius.

IONIC RADIUS. The distance usually measured in **Angstrom units,** from the center of a charged atom or group of atoms to the periphery of the effective sphere, generally calculated from crystal structure data.

IONIC REACTION. See **reaction, ionic.**

IONIC STRENGTH. A mathematical quantity used to evaluate the effectiveness of the forces restricting the freedom of **ions** in an **electrolyte,** and defined as one-half the sum of the terms obtained by multiplying the total concentration of each ion by the square of its valence.

IONIC VELOCITY. The actual speed with which, and direction in which, an **ion** moves. The ionic velocity may be calculated by multiplying the **ionic mobility** by the **potential gradient.**

IONIUM. Naturally occurring radioactive element. Symbol Io. It is an isotope of **thorium** (atomic number 90), and has a mass number of 230. Ionium has a half-period of 8.3×10^4 years, emitting α-particles and γ-rays.

IONIZATION. A process which results in the formation of ions (q.v.). Such processes occur in water, liquid ammonia, and certain other solvents when polar compounds (such as acids, bases, or salts) are dissolved in them. **Dissociation** of the compounds occurs, with the formation of positively- and negatively-charged ions, the charges on the individual ions being due to the gain or loss of one or more electrons from the outermost orbits of one or more of their atoms. The ionization of gases is a process by which atoms in gases similarly gain or lose electrons, usually through the agency of an electrical discharge, or passage of radiation, through the gas.

IONIZATION CHAMBER. One of a variety of enclosures used in the study of ionized gases and of ionizing agencies. The essential features are a closed vessel containing a gas at normal or altered pressure, and furnished with two electrodes held at different potentials. When the gas between the electrodes is ionized by the passage of radiations or other means, the ions move to the electrode of opposite sign, thus producing an ionization current measurable by a sensitive galvanometer or other such instrument.

IONIZATION CONSTANT. The **equilibrium constant** (q.v) for the **dissociation** of an **electrolyte,** which is equal to the

product of the activities of each of the ions produced by the dissociation (if more than one ion of a given kind is produced, its **activity** is raised to the corresponding power) divided by the activity of the unionized molecules. Concentrations may be substituted for activities, if the result is multiplied by a similar term consisting of the corresponding activity coefficients of ions and unionized molecules, or if activity coefficients are assumed to have values of unity as in dilute solutions.

IONIZATION, DEGREE OF. The ratio, usually stated as a percentage, of the number or the concentration of the particles in a system which become ionized, to those which remain unionized. If the system is a solution, the reference particles are the molecules of a specified component.

IONIZATION, GASEOUS. The process by which charged particles are formed from neutral atoms or molecules of gases.

IONIZATION, HEAT OF. See **heat of ionization.**

IONIZATION ISOMERISM. Two compounds having the same atomic composition which yield different **ions.** This phenomenon is exhibited, for example, by certain complex salts which have two forms differing only in that two atoms may occupy positions within the complex or outside it. Thus, the following compounds are ionization isomers:

$$[XA]\, B \rightleftarrows [XA]^+ + B^-$$
$$[XB]\, A \rightleftarrows [XB]^+ + A^- \cdot$$

IONIZATION POTENTIAL. The work necessary to remove an **electron** from a normal **atom,** leaving it positively charged.

IONIZATION, THEORY OF. See **electrolytic dissociation.**

IONIZING EVENT. Any event in which **ionization** is produced, such as the passage of a charged particle through a **counter.**

IONIZING EVENT, PRIMARY. A term used in **counter** technology to denote the ionizing event which initiates the count.

IONOGENIC. Forming or furnishing ions, e.g., all **electrolytes.**

IONOTROPY. The **ionization** of a **tautomeric** form of a substance in which a charged atom or radical separates from an unsaturated molecule, having an oppositely charged fragment. If the atom or radical is negative, the process is called anionotropy; if positive, cationotropy.

IOTA (I or ι). The ninth letter of the Greek alphabet, used to denote the ninth carbon atom in a straight-chain compound or a derivative in which a substituent group is attached to that carbon atom (ι-).

IPATIEV REACTION. An organic reduction, most commonly of **ketones** to **alcohols,** brought about by heating under pressure with hydrogen in the presence of a metallic oxide catalyst, usually nickel oxide.

Ir Symbol for **iridium.**

-IRANE. A suffix indicating a 3-membered ring.

-IRENE. A suffix indicating a 3-membered ring.

IRIDESCENCE. The exhibition of the colors of the rainbow, commonly by diffraction of light of the various wave lengths reflected from superficial layers in the surface of a substance.

IRIDIC. Containing or pertaining to tetravalent **iridium.**

-IRIDINE. A suffix indicating a 3-membered ring.

IRIDIUM. Metallic element. Symbol Ir. Atomic number 77. Atomic weight 193.1. Density 22.42. Specific heat 0.0323. Melting point 2450° C. Boiling point $>4800°$ C. Valence 1, 2, 3, and 4. Oxides Ir_2O_3, IrO_2. Iridium is found in platinum ores.

IRIDOUS. Containing or pertaining to trivalent **iridium.**

-IRINE. A suffix indicating a 3-membered ring.

IRON. Metallic element. Symbol Fe. Atomic number 26. Atomic weight 55.85. Density 7.86. Specific heat 0.113. Melting point 1535° C. Boiling point 3000° C. Valence 2, 3, and 6. Oxides FeO, Fe_2O_3, Fe_3O_4. Ores, magnetite, hematite, limonite, franklinite, siderite, etc. Acid, ferric acid, H_2FeO_4 known only in its salts. Iron forms two series of compounds, ferrous and ferric.

IRON-STEAM PROCESS. A method used for the manufacture of hydrogen. Steam is passed over heated iron at high temperatures, producing iron oxide and hydrogen.

IRRADIANCE (OF A RECEIVER). The radiant power per unit area incident on a receiver. See **exposure.**

IRRADIATION. Subjection to radiation, as for example, subjection to ultraviolet radiation for the formation of vitamin D from various sterols and related compounds.

IRREVERSIBLE REACTION. See **reaction, irreversible.**

IRVINE-PURDIE METHYLATION. See **Purdie methylation.**

ISENTROPIC CHANGE. A change that is accomplished without any increase or decrease of **entropy.**

ISHIBASHI-MORI TEST. Tellurium in minerals is detected by adding copper to a dilute solution of the mineral in hot sulfuric acid. A red precipitate indicates the presence of tellurium.

ISIDIOMS. A term suggested by Ladenberg to describe different compounds or different elements that behave in a similar chemical manner, as pseudotropine and scopoline, benzene and thiophene, cobalt and nickel, niobium and tantalum.

ISO-. (Greek) Equal, alike, as **isomer;** usually, denoting an isomer of a compound, as isocyanic acid; specifically, denoting an isomer having a single, simple branching at the end of a straight chain, as isopentane $(CH_3)_2$—$CHCH_2CH_3$.

ISOALLYL. See **propenyl.**

ISOAMOXY. The radical

$$(CH_3)_2CHCH_2CH_2O-.$$

ISOAMYL. The radical

$$(CH_3)_2CHCH_2CH_2-.$$

ISOAMYLIDENE. The radical

$$(CH_3)_2CHCH_2CH=.$$

ISOBAR. (1) A line connecting points at equal pressure, such as that which appears on a meteorological chart. (2) One of two or more atomic species, or elements, which have the same mass number, but which differ in other respects, such as atomic number.

ISOBUTENYL. See 2-methylpropenyl.

ISOBUTOXY. The radical

$$(CH_3)_2CHCH_2O-.$$

ISOBUTYL. The radical $(CH_3)_2CHCH_2-.$

ISOBUTYRYL. The radical

$$(CH_3)_2CHCO-.$$

ISOCHORE. The variation of the pressure of a gas or liquid with variation in temperature, at constant volume; or the graph of that function.

ISOCHORE, REACTION. See **reaction isochone.**

ISOCHROMATIC. Of the same color, as of lines of the same tint in the interference figures of biaxial crystals.

ISOCHRONE. A line connecting points having the same time values, as points of the same gelation time for colloidal solutions.

ISOCYANATE. The anion NCO^-, or a compound containing it.

ISOCYANATO. The inorganic group $OC:N-.$

ISOCYANIDE. An **isonitrile.**

ISOCYANO. The radical $C:N-.$

ISODIMORPHISM. (Double isomorphism) The condition in which both crystalline forms of a dimorphous substance which is isomorphous with a second dimorphous compound are **isomorphous** with both forms of the second compound. Example: arsenious oxide and antimonious oxide, which crystallize in rhombs and also in regular octahedra.

ISODYNAMIC. Furnishing the same amount of energy in the organism. 100 grams of fat are isodynamic with about 230 grams of protein or carbohydrate.

ISOELECTRIC POINT. The point at which a substance or system is electrically neutral, usually expressed in **pH** value. At points above or below this value, the substance accepts or yields protons. The isoelectric point is an important property of proteins and other complex organic substances. The isoelectric point of an **ampholyte** is that pH at which the extent of **ionization** of the ampholyte as an acid is equal to that as a base.

ISOELECTRONIC. Pertaining to similar electronic arrangements. This term is applied, for example, to two or more atoms or atomic groups having an analogous arrangement of the same number of valency electrons, and similar physical properties.

ISOHEXYL. The radical

$$(CH_3)_2CH(CH_2)_3-.$$

ISOHYDRIC SOLUTIONS. Solutions that possess the same concentration of **hydrogen ions.** They may be mixed without alteration of the degree of ionization of either solute. By extension the term is applied to all solutions which have a common ion in the same concentration.

ISOINDOLYL. The radical C_8H_6N- (from isoindole, 4 isomers).

ISOLABLE. Capable of being isolated or obtained in a pure condition.

ISOLATE. To separate in a pure condition from all foreign admixture, as to isolate an alkaloid; specifically, a pure organic compound separated by crystallization, distillation, or other physical process from a natural material, as eugenol from clove oil, safrole from sassafras oil, etc.

ISOLEUCYL. The radical

$$CH_3CH_2CH(CH_3)CH(NH_2)CO-.$$

ISOLOGOUS SERIES. Carbon compounds, similar chemically, but differing from one another in composition by a difference other than nCH_2 (characteristic of homology) are isologous and form an isologous series as

ethane	C_2H_6	benzene	C_6H_6
ethylene	C_2H_4	naphthalene	$C_{10}H_8$
acetylene	C_2H_2	anthracene	$C_{14}H_{10}$.

ISOLOGUE. A member of an **isologous series.**

ISOLOGY. The relationship between isologous substances.

ISOM PROCESS. An early petroleum-cracking process that is still in use. In this process, the oil is forced to circulate within the still by a driven impeller.

ISOMER. (1) One of two or more substances which have the same elementary composition, but differ in structure, and hence in properties. (2) One of two or more nuclides which have the same mass number and atomic number, but differ in energetics and behavior. (See **isomeric isotopes.**)

ISOMERIC. (1) Pertaining to isomers. (2) Exhibiting isomerism.

ISOMERIC IONS. See **isomerism, ionic.**

ISOMERIC ISOTOPES. Two (or more) atomic species with the same mass number and the same atomic number, but with different radioactive properties. They are believed to have isomeric nuclei, i.e., nuclei which are composed ultimately of the same number of protons and the same number of neutrons, but which differ in their energy levels. Such isomeric nuclei are found among naturally radioactive elements as well as artificially radioactive ones. Two well-known examples of the latter are radio-zinc of isotopic atomic weight 69, which emits a gamma radiation to yield another radioactive zinc of isotopic atomic weight 69; and a radioactive krypton which has an atomic weight of 83 and is, therefore, an isomeric isotope of ordinary nonradioactive krypton.

ISOMERIDE. One of two or more substances having the same structure, but not necessarily the same composition.

ISOMERISM. (1) A phenomenon attributable to the structure of chemical compounds in which two or more compounds of different properties may possess identical ultimate compositions, e.g., two substances of the formula C_4H_{10} are known, viz., butane, $CH_3-CH_2-CH_2-CH_3$, and isobutane, CH$_3$

$$\begin{array}{c} \diagdown \\ CH-CH_3. \\ \diagup \\ CH_3 \end{array}$$

There are many types of isomerism, as will be apparent from the listings that follow. (2) See **isomeric isotopes.**

ISOMERISM, CHAIN. A form of structural isomerism in which two or more substances, of the same composition, differ in the manner of linkage of atoms which are considered to form the essential structure of the substance. Moreover, this type of isomerism is concerned, in primary conception at any rate, with open-chain compounds. It is illustrated by the difference between normal pentane

$$CH_3-CH_2-CH_2-CH_2-CH_3,$$

and, for example, tetramethylmethane

$$\begin{array}{ccc} CH_3 & & CH_3 \\ \diagdown & & \diagup \\ & C & \\ \diagup & & \diagdown \\ CH_3 & & CH_3 \end{array}$$

which is isomeric with it.

ISOMERISM, CIS-TRANS. (Ethylene isomerism. Alloisomerism.) Geometrical isomerism of carbon compounds arising from the hindrance to free rotation about a double bond or as a consequence of a ring structure. Thus, for example,

$$
\begin{array}{cc}
\text{H—C—COOH} & \text{H—C—COOH} \\
\parallel & \parallel \\
\text{H—C—COOH} \;\;\text{and}\;\; & \text{HOOC—C—H} \\
\text{Maleic acid} & \text{Fumaric acid} \\
\text{(Cis form)} & \text{(Trans form)}
\end{array}
$$

ISOMERISM, DESMOTROPIC. A form of dynamic isomerism in which two or more substances, of the same composition, differ in the manner of linkage of certain of their atoms and commonly in the nature of one or more of their characteristic radicals, but not in their valency, or in the grouping of their other atoms.

$$
\begin{array}{cc}
\text{O} & \text{OH} \\
\diagup\!\!\diagup & \diagup \\
\text{R—C} & \text{R—C} \\
\diagdown & \diagdown\!\!\diagdown \\
\text{NH}_2 & \text{NH} \\
\text{Acid amide} & \text{Acid imide}
\end{array}
$$

$$
\begin{array}{cc}
\text{O} & \text{OH} \\
\diagup\!\!\diagup & \diagup \\
\text{R—C} & \text{R—C} \\
\diagdown & \diagdown\!\!\diagdown \\
\text{CH}_2\text{R}' & \text{CHR}' \\
\text{Ketone} & \text{Enol}
\end{array}
$$

ISOMERISM, DYNAMIC. (1) (Energy isomerism. Dynamical isomerism.) Isomerism due to difference in internal energy between isomers. (2) (Tautomerism, tautomery, pseudomerism, desmotropy, desmotropism, merotropy.) Isomerism due to intramolecular rearrangements by virtue of which one substance may react in accordance with two structural formulas, viz., cyanamide may react as $N{\equiv}C{-}NH_2$ or $HN{=}C{=}NH$. The terms dynamic isomerism and desmotropism have also been applied to the cases where the two forms have been found to exist, usually they are interconvertible; in fact, the compound exists as a mixture of the two forms in equilibrium.

ISOMERISM, GEOMETRICAL. Isomerism between unsaturated and optically inactive compounds due to the relative spatial positions of various groups attached to the same nucleus. Cis-trans and syn-anti isomerism are examples.

ISOMERISM, IONIC. (1) The isomerism of the acid and non-acid forms of pseudo-acids and the basic and non-basic forms of pseudo-ammonium bases. (2) Isomerism between ions attributable to valence differences, as Fe^{2+} and Fe^{3+}, Cr^{2+} and Cr^{3+}. These ions are considered isomeric and are termed ionic isomers.

ISOMERISM, KETO-ENOL TAUTOMERISM. A type of desmotropic isomerism observed in certain carbonyl containing compounds in which, by intramolecular change, a hydrogen atom from an adjacent carbon atom combines with the carbonyl oxygen with consequent production of a double bond between the carbon atoms concerned, viz.

$$
\begin{array}{ccc}
\text{R—CH}_2 & & \text{R—CH} \\
\mid & \rightleftarrows & \parallel \\
\text{R—C}{=}\text{O} & & \text{R—C—OH} \\
\text{Keto form} & & \text{Enol form}
\end{array}
$$

ISOMERISM, LACTONE TAUTOMERIC. Dynamic isomerism between groups in the γ-, δ-, etc., positions in alicyclic compounds, and in the o-position in carbocyclic compounds, as shown in the following example of o-position lactone dynamic isomerism:

$$
\begin{array}{ccc}
\begin{array}{c}\text{COCl}\\ \text{COCl}\end{array} & \rightleftarrows & \begin{array}{c}\text{C}{\diagdown}^{\text{Cl}}_{\text{Cl}}\cdot \\ \text{C}{=}\text{O}\end{array}
\end{array}
$$

ISOMERISM, META- (Metamerism). A form of structural isomerism in which two or more substances, of the same composition, differ in the position of one or more atoms or radicals or double bonds or triple bonds or other special valences. Frequently the compounds are of different types, but the valency and linkages are the same:

$$
\begin{array}{cc}
\text{H} & \text{R}'\text{O} \\
\diagdown & \diagdown \\
\;\;\;\;\text{C}{=}\text{NOR}' \;\;\text{and}\; & \;\;\;\;\text{C}{=}\text{NH} \\
\diagup & \diagup \\
\text{R} & \text{R} \\
\text{Ketoxime} & \text{Imido compound}
\end{array}
$$

$$H_2N \diagdown C=NH \diagup RO \qquad \text{and} \qquad RHN \diagdown C=NH \diagup HO$$

Pseudo ureide   Hydroxylimide

$$CH_3{-}CH{=}CH{-}CH_2{-}CH_3$$
Pentene-2.

and

$$CH_2{=}CH{-}CH_2{-}CH_2{-}CH_3$$
Pentene-1.

ISOMERISM, NUCLEAR. (1) A form of isomerism in which two compounds of the same composition differ in the valence linkages by which certain of their atoms are joined in ring structures, or in the relative positions of substituents in a ring. (2) See **nuclear isomers.**

ISOMERISM, OPTICAL. A type of isomerism in which the isomers are identical in composition, constitution, molecular weight, chemical properties, and most physical properties and differ only in the way their solutions (or liquid states) affect the rays of polarized light. The plane of the ray may be rotated to the right, in which case the substance is termed the dextrorotatory (d) form; to the left, in which case the substance is termed the levorotatory (l) form; or the ray may not be affected, when the substance is termed inactive. Such inactivity may be due to several causes: the substance may be a molecular mixture of the opposite forms (dl); it may be a racemic mixture (r); or it may be a meso form inactive by internal compensation. Optical isomerism is due to differences in the relative positions in space assumed by certain of the constituent atoms and/or groups in the compound. The active isomers are variously termed enantiomorphs, antipodes, and active components.

ISOMERISM, PLACE. A form of isomerism in which two or more substances possess the same composition, but differ in the position assumed by a substituent, or in the relative positions of two or more substituents, e.g., the isomerism between propyl and isopropyl chlorides and the isomerism between ortho, meta, para, etc., derivatives of cyclic nuclei.

ISOMERISM, PSEUDOMERIC. A form of isomerism in which two or more substances of the same composition differ in the valence of certain atoms and in their chemical nature. The classic examples are the cyanates KOCN and the isocyanates KCNO; as well as the cyanides and the isocyanides KCN and KNC.

ISOMERISM, RING. A form of isomerism in which two or more substances have the same composition, but differ in the relative positions of distinctive atoms in a ring, or the positions of the ring atoms to which substituent atoms or groups are attached.

ISOMERISM, STEREOCHEMICAL. A form of isomerism in which two substances of the same composition and constitution differ in the relative positions in space assumed by certain of their constituent atoms and/or groups. This isomerism may be due to the relative spatial position of groups attached to atoms joined by a double bond (geometrical isomerism), or it may be due to the presence of one or more asymmetric atoms — i.e., quadrivalent atoms of carbon, silicon, etc., to which four different atoms or radicals are attached and which, therefore, possess two spatial geometrical forms that cannot be coincident, but are in fact mirror images. Many such compounds, containing such atoms, exhibit optical isomerism. (See **isomerism, optical.**)

ISOMERISM, STRUCTURAL. A form of isomerism in which two or more substances possess the same elementary composition, but differ in their structures, commonly their plane-structures, by having the same substituent attached to different atoms in a chain, the same atoms or groups in different positions on a ring, double or triple bonds in different positions, or a difference in the chain arrangement of the atoms.

ISOMERISM, SYN-ANTI. Geometrical isomerism of certain compounds about double bonds. Thus there are syn- and anti-forms of the diazoates about the —N=N— bond and there are other examples among nitrogen-carbon compounds, e.g., with monoximes,

$$C_6H_5—C—H \qquad C_6H_5—C—H$$
$$\| \qquad\qquad \|$$
$$N—OH \qquad\quad HO—N$$

syn-Benzaldoxime   *anti*-Benzaldoxime
(m. p. 35° C.)   (m. p. 130° C.)

and with dioximes, e.g., benzildioximes,

$$R—C—C—R \qquad R—C———C—R$$
$$\| \ \ \| \qquad\qquad \| \qquad\quad \|$$
$$HON \ NOH \qquad NOH \ HON$$

anti-form   *syn*-form

$$R—C———C—R$$
$$\| \qquad\quad \|$$
$$NOH \ NOH$$

amphi-form

ISOMERISM, TAUTOMERIC. A form of dynamic isomerism in which two or more substances, of the same composition, differ in the manner of linkage of certain of their atoms, and in the nature of one or more of their characteristic radicals, and the grouping of important atoms, but not in valency.

RNO_2	and	$RONO$
Nitro-compound		Nitrite
$RCNO$	and	$RONC$
Isocyanate		Fulminate

ISOMERIZATION PROCESS. A process by which isomeric compounds are produced from the corresponding normal form of the substance, e.g., isobutane from normal butane, isopentane from normal pentane, etc. The process is used in the petroleum industry to increase the octane rating of gasoline. Thus, the catalytic isomerization of *n*-butane to isobutane by aluminum chloride takes place at 175° C., and 525 pounds per square inch pressure.

ISOMEROMORPHISM. Isomorphism between isomeric substances.

ISOMORPH. (1) One of two or more substances that crystallize in the same form. (2) One of a group of elements whose compounds with the same other atoms or radicals crystallize in the same form. The elements may be classified on this basis into eleven groups.

ISOMORPHIC. Exhibiting **isomorphism.**

ISOMORPHISM. Literally, having the same form, a term applied to substances of different composition, which crystallize in the same form, or different elements which, when combined with the same atoms or radicals, crystallize in the same form. For example, the chlorides of the alkali metals crystallize in the same form.

ISOMORPHOUS. Exhibiting **isomorphism.**

ISONITRILE. (Carbylamine, isocyanide) A compound of the general formula RNC, as ethyl isocyanide, C_2H_5NC.

ISONITRO. The radical $HOON=$.

ISONITROSO. The radical $HON=$.

ISONITROSO COMPOUND. A compound which contains the group $HON=$, other than the oxime. A representative isonitroso compound is

$$CH_3$$
$$|$$
$$C=O$$
$$|$$
$$CH=N—OH$$

Isonitrosoacetone

ISONUCLEAR. Occurring in the same nucleus.

1-ISOPENTENYL. See 3-methyl-1-butenyl.

ISOPHTHALAL. See **isophthalylidene.**

ISOPHTHALOYL. The radical

$$-OCC_6H_4CO-(m).$$

ISOPHTHALYLIDENE. The radical

$$=HCC_6H_4CH=(m).$$

ISOPIESTIC SOLUTION. See **solution, isopiestic.**

ISOPLERE. A curve or graph corresponding to the condition of constant volume, as e.g., a plot of pressure versus temperature for a gas held at constant volume. Also termed isochore, isometric, and isopycnic.

ISOPROPENYL. The radical

$$CH_2:C(CH_3)-.$$

ISOPROPOXY. The radical $(CH_3)_2CHO-$.

ISOPROPYL. The radical $(CH_3)_2CH-$.

ISOPROPYLIDENE. The radical

$$(CH_3)_2C=.$$

ISOPYCNIC. See **isoplere.**

ISOQUINOLYL. The radical C_9H_8N- (from isoquinoline, 7 isomers).

ISOROTATION RULES (HUDSON). In many **carbohydrates,** changes in the structure of the molecule have very little effect upon the magnitude and sign of the contribution made by the first asymmetric carbon to the rotation of the plane of polarized light of the molecule; and changes in the atoms and groups linked to the first carbon atom have little effect upon the rotation of polarized light by the molecule. (See **Hudson isorotation rules.**)

ISOSMOTIC. Having an identical **osmotic** pressure.

ISOSTERE, ADSORPTION. See **adsorption isostere.**

ISOSTERES. Pairs of compounds which show notable agreement in physical properties (as carbon dioxide and nitrous oxide; carbon monoxide and nitrogen) and which (according to the octet theory) have the same number and arrangement of electrons in the molecule. The term applies also to radicals and groups of atoms which hold pairs of electrons in common. These are termed isosteric compounds, and the phenomenon is called isosterism (Langmuir).

ISOSTERIC. See **isosteres.**

ISOSTERISM. See **isosteres.**

ISOTENISCOPE. An instrument used to measure **vapor pressure.** It consists essentially of a U-tube containing the liquid of which the vapor pressure is to be measured. One arm of the tube connects with a closed vessel containing the same liquid; the other arm is connected to a manometer. The pressure in the latter is adjusted to the value at which the liquid levels in both arms of the U-tube are the same. This is the vapor pressure of the liquid at the temperature of the test.

ISOTHERM. A relationship, or its mathematical or graphical expression, for which the temperature is constant.

ISOTHERM, ADSORPTION. See **adsorption isotherm.**

ISOTHERM, REACTION. See **reaction isotherm.**

ISOTHERMAL. (1) Of constant temperature. Isothermal processes are those conducted without temperature change. (2) A line or curve expressing a relationship between variables such as pressure and volume, for all values of which the temperature remains constant. (3) A line or curve joining points at the same temperature.

ISOTHERMIC. Isothermal.

ISOTHIOCYANATE. The anion NCS^-, or a compound containing it.

ISOTHIOCYANATO. The radical $S:C:N-$, in organic compounds.

ISOTHIOCYANO. The radical $S:C:N-$.

ISOTONES. Elements having equal numbers of **neutrons.**

ISOTONIC. Having the same **osmotic pressure;** or, specifically, having the same osmotic pressure as normal blood serum.

ISOTOPE. One of two or more atoms or elements which have the same atomic number but which differ in other respects, such as atomic weight. In cases where both atomic number and atomic weight are the same, two atoms or elements may differ in the energy levels of their nuclei, and hence in their radioactive behavior.

ISOTOPIC ATOMIC WEIGHT.

The comparative **atomic weight** of an **isotope,** or a distinct atomic species, calculated on the basis of an atomic weight of 16.0000 for the lighter isotope of oxygen. This differs from the standard chemical practice, which uses as standard an atomic weight of 16.0000 for ordinary oxygen, which contains small percentages of isotopes having approximate isotopic atomic weights (mass numbers) of 17 and 18.

ISOTOPIC COMPOSITION OF THE NATURALLY-OCCURRING ELEMENTS

Symbol	Atomic Number	Mass Number	Per Cent Abundance
H	1	1	99.98
		2	0.02
He	2	3	1.3×10^{-4}
		4	100
Li	3	6	7.5
		7	92.5
Be	4	9	100
B	5	10	18.83
		11	81.17
C	6	12	98.9
		13	1.1
N	7	14	99.62
		15	0.38
O	8	16	99.76
		17	0.04
		18	0.20
F	9	19	100
Ne	10	20	90.00
		21	0.27
		22	9.73
Na	11	23	100
Mg	12	24	77.4
		25	11.5
		26	11.1
Al	13	27	100

Symbol	Atomic Number	Mass Number	Per Cent Abundance
Si	14	28	92.21
		29	4.70
		30	3.09
P	15	31	100
S	16	32	95.0
		33	0.74
		34	4.2
		36	0.016
Cl	17	35	75.4
		37	24.6
A	18	36	0.307
		38	0.061
		40	99.632
K	19	39	93.381
		40(r)	0.012
		41	6.61
Ca	20	40	96.96
		42	0.64
		43	0.15
		44	2.06
		46	0.0033
		48	0.19
Sc	21	45	100
Ti	22	46	7.95
		47	7.75
		48	73.45
		49	5.51
		50	5.34
V	23	50	0.25
		51	99.75
Cr	24	50	4.49
		52	83.78
		53	9.43
		54	2.30
Mn	25	55	100
Fe	26	54	6.04
		56	91.57
		57	2.11
		58	0.28
Co	27	57	100
		59	

Symbol	Atomic Number	Mass Number	Per Cent Abundance	Symbol	Atomic Number	Mass Number	Per Cent Abundance
Ni	28	58	67.4	Zr	40	90	48
		60	26.7			91	11.5
		61	1.2			92	22
		62	3.8			94	17
		64	0.88			96	1.5
Cu	29	63	70.13	Nb	41	93	100
		65	29.87				
				Mo	42	92	14.9
Zn	30	64	50.9			94	9.40
		66	27.3			95	16.1
		67	3.9			96	16.6
		68	17.4			97	9.65
		70	0.5			98	24.1
						100	9.25
Ga	31	69	61.2				
		71	38.8	Ru	44	96	5.7
						98	2.22
Ge	32	70	21.2			99	12.8
		72	27.3			100	12.7
		73	7.9			101	17.0
		74	37.1			102	31.3
		76	6.5			104	18.3
As	33	75	100	Rh	45	103	100
Se	34	74	0.9	Pd	46	102	0.8
		76	9.5			104	9.3
		77	8.3			105	22.6
		78	24.0			106	27.2
		80	48.0			108	26.8
		82	9.3			110	13.5
Br	35	79	50.6	Ag	47	107	51.9
		81	49.4			109	48.1
Kr	36	78	0.342	Cd	48	106	1.4
		80	2.23			108	1.0
		82	11.50			110	12.8
		83	11.48			111	13.0
		84	57.02			112	24.2
		86	17.43			113	12.3
						114	28.0
Rb	37	85	72.8			116	7.3
		87(r)	27.2				
				In	49	113	4.5
Sr	38	84	0.56			115(r)	95.5
		86	9.86				
		87	7.02	Sn	50	112	1.1
		88	82.56			114	0.8
						115	0.4
Y	39	89	100			116	15.5

Symbol	Atomic Number	Mass Number	Per Cent Abundance	Symbol	Atomic Number	Mass Number	Per Cent Abundance
		117	9.1	Nd	60	142	25.95
		118	22.5			143	13.0
		119	9.8			144	22.6
		120	28.5			145	9.2
		122	5.5			146	16.5
		124	6.8			148	6.8
						150	5.95
Sb	51	121	56				
		123	44	Sm	62	144	3.1
						147(r)	15.0
Te	52	120	0.088			148	11.2
		122	2.83			149	13.8
		123	0.85			150	7.4
		124	4.59			152	26.8
		125	6.93			154	22.7
		126	18.71				
		128	31.86	Eu	63	151	49.1
		130	34.52			153	50.9
I	53	127	100	Gd	64	152	0.2
						154	2.86
Xe	54	124	0.094			155	15.1
		126	0.088			156	20.59
		128	1.92			157	16.42
		129	26.23			158	23.45
		130	4.05			160	20.87
		131	21.14				
		132	26.93	Tb	65	159	100
		134	10.52	Dy	66	156	0.052
		136	8.93			158	0.090
						160	2.29
Cs	55	133	100			161	18.9
						162	25.5
Ba	56	130	0.101			163	25.0
		132	0.097			164	28.2
		134	2.42				
		135	6.59	Ho	67	165	100
		136	7.81				
		137	11.32	Er	68	162	0.136
		138	71.66			164	1.56
						166	33.4
La	57	138(r)	0.089			167	22.9
		139	99.911			168	27.1
						170	14.9
Ce	58	136	0.19	Tm	69	169	100
		138	0.26				
		140	88.47	Yb	70	168	0.14
		142	11.08			170	3.03
						171	14.3
Pr	59	141	100			172	21.8

Symbol	Atomic Number	Mass Number	Per Cent Abundance	Symbol	Atomic Number	Mass Number	Per Cent Abundance
		173	16.2	Tl	81	203	29.1
		174	31.8			205	70.9
		176	12.7				
				Pb	82	204	1.48
Lu	71	175	97.5			206	23.59
		176(r)	2.5			207	22.64
						208	52.29
Hf	72	174	0.18				
		176	5.2	Bi	83	209	100
		177	18.4				
		178	27.1	Th	90	232(r)	100
		179	13.8				
		180	35.3	Pa	91	231(r)	
Ta	73	181	100	U	92	234(r)	0.00518
						235(r)	0.719
W	74	180	0.122			238(r)	99.274
		182	25.80				
		183	14.26				
		184	30.74				
		186	29.22				

(r) indicates a radioactive isotope.

Note: Certain naturally-occurring radioactive elements, such as radium and radon (emanation), are omitted from this table.

Symbol	Atomic Number	Mass Number	Per Cent Abundance
Re	75	185	38.1
		187(r)	61.9
Os	76	184	0.018
		186	1.59
		187	1.64
		188	13.3
		189	16.1
		190	26.4
		192	41.0
Ir	77	191	38.5
		193	61.5
Pt	78	190	0.012
		192	0.78
		194	32.8
		195	33.7
		196	25.4
		198	7.2
Au	79	197	100
Hg	80	196	0.15
		198	10.1
		199	17.0
		200	23.3
		201	13.2
		202	29.6
		204	6.7

ISOTOPIC DILUTION ANALYSIS. A special method for determining the concentration of an **element** in a system. A compound containing a **radioactive isotope** of the element at known concentration is added to the system. A pure sample of the compound is then isolated from the system. From the decrease in activity of the tracer element the original concentration of the element in the system can be computed.

ISOTRIMORPHISM. (Triple **isomorphism**) The condition in which two isomorphous substances are each trimorphous and each of the three pairs of forms is isomorphous. Cf. **isodimorphism.**

ISOTROPISM. Possessing isotropic properties, i.e., properties whose physical magnitude is independent of **orientation.**

ISOVALERYL. The radical

$$(CH_3)_2CHCH_2CO-.$$

ISOXAZOLYL. The radical C_3H_2NO- (from isoxazole, 5 isomers).

-ITOL. A suffix indicating a **polyalcohol.** (The suffix -ite was formerly used for this purpose.)

ITTNER PROCESS. A process for refining glycerol by repeated steam distillation. The vapor from the first still passes through a condenser which condenses out the glycerol, so that the steam can be used in a second still, and so on.

ITTNER TEST FOR CYANIDES. Alkalinize the solution to be tested, add a little ferrous sulfate and ferrous chloride, warm gently, and add an excess of hydrochloric acid. A blue color indicates cyanides.

-ITY. A suffix meaning a property of a substance. For example, absorptivity, density, solubility, resistivity (which is simpler than the older term, specific resistance), conductivity, and so on.

IWANOW IRIDIUM CHLORIDE SOLUTION. A solution of 25 mg. iridium chloride or iridium potassium chloride in 5 ml. water, to which is added 100 ml. concentrated sulfuric acid, and the solution is heated until colorless. It is used in the detection of nitrate. A blue color indicates the presence of nitrate.

IWANOW REAGENT. A solution of 2 g. sodium bisulfite in 100 ml. water, used in

nous chloride solution turn brown and then raspberry-red.

J. Abbreviation for **joule** (*J*). Symbol for **mechanical equivalent of heat** (*J*). Symbol for **heat transfer factor** (*j*). Abbreviation for **gram-equivalent weight** (*J*). Symbol for **action variable** (*J*). Symbol for electric current density (**J**). Symbol for polar moment of inertia (*J*). **Inner quantum number** (*j*). Total inner quantum number (*J*). Symbol for **spectral radiant intensity** (J_λ).

JABLOKOFF TEST. To detect mineral oils in fatty oils, mix 1 part of the oil with 4 parts aniline. The presence of mineral oils causes turbidity.

JACKSON REACTION FOR TITANIUM. Hydrogen peroxide colors an aqueous solution of titanium yellow to orange-yellow.

JACOBS-SINGER SEPARATORY FLASK. A flask or tube for extracting fats, dyes, drugs, etc., by means of immiscible solvents.

JACOBSEN REACTION. The migration of an alkyl group or a halogen atom in a benzenesulfonic acid which has several substituted alkyl or halogen groups. The migration may be intramolecular, or may take place from one molecule to another.

testing for lead in water. A white turbidity is given by lead (and some other metals).

IWANOW TEST FOR RHODIUM. Rhodium solutions on heating with stan-

JACOBSEN REAGENT. Rosaniline, used to detect rancidity in fatty oils, by giving a red color with the free fatty acids.

JACOBY REAGENT FOR PEPSIN AND TRYPSIN. A solution of 1 g. ricin and

1.5 g. sodium chloride in 100 ml. water, used as a test reagent to precipitate pepsin and trypsin.

JACQUEMART REAGENT. An aqueous solution of mercuric nitrate acidified with nitric acid, used as a test reagent for ethyl alcohol. A black precipitate, produced upon addition of concentrated ammonium hydroxide, indicates the presence of ethyl alcohol.

JACQUEMIN TEST FOR FIBERS. With a lukewarm 1 N solution of chromic acid, wool and silk are colored yellow; cotton is unchanged.

JACQUEMIN TEST FOR PHENOL. The liquid tested is treated with a little aniline and sodium hypobromite solution. Phenol gives an intense blue color, changed to red by acids and restored to blue by alkalies.

JAEGER CONVERTOR. A convertor used in the manufacture of sulfuric acid by the **contact process.** The Jaeger convertor is constructed in two parts, each containing catalytic material, and both provided with cooling elements in the form of open-end tubes. The purpose of this arrangement is to permit control of the temperatures in order to maintain, as nearly as possible, the temperatures for optimum yield of SO_3, from the standpoints of theoretical equilibrium and reaction rates.

JAFFE TEST FOR SULFUR OILS. Dissolve the oil in chloroform, shake with silver nitrate and triethanolamine in alcoholic solution. A yellow-brown color of the chloroform layer indicates sulfur.

JAFFE TEST REACTION FOR BISMUTH AND ANTIMONY. A solution of 8 g. iodine in 100 ml. triethanolamine gives a scarlet precipitate with a bismuth solution acidified with hydrochloric acid. Antimony solutions give a golden-yellow precipitate.

JAFFE TEST REACTION FOR BORIC ACID. On slow addition of a cupric sulfate solution, a mixture of boric acid and triethanolamine gives a green color.

JAFFE TEST REACTION FOR FERRIC SALTS. A solution of a ferric salt in triethanolamine, on treatment with potassium ferrocyanide, followed by the dropwise addition of hydrochloric acid to the neutral point, gives a color change from red to violet to deep blue: more acid gives a blue precipitate.

JAFFE REAGENT FOR GOLD AND SILVER. Tris(hydroxyethyl)amine, which forms metallic mirrors with small amounts of gold and silver salts, or gives, with gold salts, red or blue colloidal solutions.

JAFFE TEST REACTION FOR MERCURY. An acid solution of iodine in triethanolamine, on addition of mercuric chloride, forms a yellow precipitate, turning green and soluble in excess triethanolamine, then reduced to mercury on heating.

JAFFE TEST REACTION FOR MOLYBDENUM. Two to three ml. of the molybdate solution are acidified with hydrochloric acid. With triethanolamine, this solution gives a green ring test, becoming turbid and forming a blue precipitate, soluble in excess triethanolamine.

JAFFE TEST REACTION FOR VANADIUM. A boiling acid solution of a vanadate gives a green color with triethanolamine; after standing, the green color changes to bright blue.

JÄGER TEST REACTION FOR CHOLESTEROL. On heating with isobutyric anhydride, cholesterol forms its isobutyrate (m.p. 128.5° C.).

JAMIN EFFECT. A column of air- and water-bubbles can exist in a capillary tube against a definite pressure.

JANDRIER TEST FOR COTTON. On treatment with sulfuric acid (20° Bè.), cotton forms compounds that give red and violet colors, respectively, with resorcinol and α-naphthol in sulfuric acid solution.

JANDRIER TEST FOR OXYCELLULOSES. Oxycelluloses in a solution containing a little phenol give a gold-yellow ring test with sulfuric acid. Other phenols give other colors.

JANNASCH-BIEDERMANN REAGENT.
A 3% aqueous solution of hydrazine sulfate, which precipitates copper quantitatively in the cuprous or metallic state from hot alkaline solutions.

JANNASCH REAGENT. A mixture of 15-20% hydrogen peroxide and 65% nitric acid, used in oxidizing organic matter, as a preliminary step in determination of inorganic substances present.

JANVILLIER REAGENT FOR ANTIPYRINE AND AMINOPYRINE. Silicotungstic acid, which gives a white precipitate with antipyrine solutions in hydrochloric acid, and a yellow one with aminopyrine solutions in hydrochloric acid.

JAPAN. A hard varnish.

JAPANNING. The application of a japantype varnish or lacquer; the coated articles are usually baked to obtain a more permanent surface.

JAPP-KLINGEMANN REACTION. A method of formation of **hydrazones** by the action of aryl diazo compounds on various activated methylene groups.

JAWOROWSKI REAGENT FOR AMMONIA. A solution of 8 g. sodium chloride, 2 g. mercuric chloride, and 2 g. sodium carbonate in 60 ml. water. A yellow precipitate or coloration is given by solutions containing the ammonium ion.

JAWOROWSKI TEST FOR COBALT IN PRESENCE OF NICKEL. Neutralize the liquid tested with sodium carbonate, shake with sodium pyrophosphate until the precipitate has dissolved, dilute until almost colorless, shake 8 ml. of this solution with 1.5 g. sodium carbonate and 8 drops bromine water. A green color indicates cobalt.

JAWOROWSKI TEST FOR COPPER. Five ml. of the liquid tested are treated with an excess of ammonium hydroxide and 2 drops phenol. A blue color develops in 1 hour if copper is present.

JEAN TEST FOR SOAP IN LUBRICATING OILS. An ethereal solution of the oil gives a precipitate of the soap on addition of an alcoholic solution of metaphosphoric acid.

JEANS VISCOSITY EQUATION. An equation relating the **viscosity** of a gas to

$$CH_3 \cdot CO \cdot \overset{\overset{\displaystyle R}{|}}{C}Na \cdot COONa + ArN_2Cl + HCl \rightarrow CH_3CO\overset{\overset{\displaystyle R}{|}}{C}=NNHAr + 2NaCl + CO_2.$$

JAW CRUSHER. See **crusher, jaw.**

JAWOROWSKI REAGENT FOR ALBUMIN. A solution of 8 g. citric acid and 2 g. ammonium molybdate in 80 ml. water, used in testing for albumin in urine. A lasting turbidity indicates the presence of albumin.

JAWOROWSKI REAGENT FOR ALKALOIDS. A mixture of a solution of 0.3 g. sodium vanadate in 10 ml. water, with a solution of 0.2 g. cupric sulfate in 100 ml. water, to which acetic acid is then added until the solution is clear. This reagent yields a precipitate or turbidity with alkaloids dissolved in 5% acetic acid (or their salts dissolved in water).

the temperature, having the form $\eta = kT^n$, where k is a constant, T is the absolute temperature, and n is an empirical constant differing for different gases.

JEHN TEST REACTION FOR POLYVALENT ALCOHOLS. A test solution of borax gives, with certain indicators, an alkaline reaction that is changed to acid by polyvalent alcohols.

JELINEK TEST FOR MUSTARD GAS. To a concentrated ammoniacal solution of isatin, add ammoniacal silver nitrate solution. Paper impregnated with this reagent gives a Bordeaux red color with mustard gas in 1-60 minutes, depending upon the temperature of the gas.

JELLYING POWER. The ability to solidify in solution, as exemplified by such **colloidal** substances as gelatin, Irish moss, etc.

JENDRASSIK SOLUTION. A mixture of 5 ml. 0.1 N ferric chloride solution and 5 ml. 0.1 N potassium ferricyanide solution, used in testing for vitamin B_1. A dark blue color or precipitate indicates the presence of vitamin B_1.

JENNER STAIN. (1) A precipitate obtained by mixing a 1.25% aqueous solution of water-soluble eosin with an equal volume of a 1% aqueous solution of methylene blue. It is used in methanol solution as a stain. (2) A mixture in proportions of 5:4 of a $\frac{1}{2}$% methanol solution of eosin with a $\frac{1}{2}$% methanol solution of methylene blue.

JENSEN TEST FOR MANGANESE. To 1 ml. of the solution tested, add 2 ml. concentrated hydrochloric acid, and 4 ml. of ether saturated with hydrogen chloride, then a particle of potassium chlorate. A green color in the ether indicates manganese.

JENSEN-URBAIN REAGENT. A reagent consisting of two solutions: (1) a solution of 1 g. sodium hyposulfite in 1 liter water, and (2) a solution of 1 g. sodium nitrite in 1 liter water. Material to be tested for blood is soaked for several minutes in (1), washed, soaked in (2), washed again, and treated with hydrogen peroxide. A green color is given by hemoglobin.

JET CONDENSER. See **condenser, jet.**

JIG. An apparatus for classifying particles by size or weight, consisting of a vibrating screen, which may be partly or entirely submerged in water.

JINDAL TEST REACTION. A dilute cobalt solution forms with sodium silicate solution a blue precipitate, which dissolves in excess reagent. The blue solution formed is decolorized by acids, restored by ammonia.

JODLBAUER REAGENT. A solution of 50 g. phenol in sufficient concentrated sulfuric acid to make 100 ml. of solution, used for the determination of nitrogen.

JOHANNSON REAGENT. A solution of 13.5 g. mercuric chloride and 50 g. potassium iodide in 1 liter water, used in testing for colchicine. A turbidity in sulfuric acid solution indicates the presence of colchicine.

JOHNSTONE TEST. To detect silver in lead, dissolve the lead in nitric acid, nearly neutralize with sodium carbonate and introduce strips of zinc and of copper. Lead is precipitated on the zinc and silver on the copper.

JOLLES FORMAL REAGENT. A solution of 15 g. sodium chloride in 50 ml. 37% formaldehyde and 50 ml. 1% acetic acid, used as a precipitant for albumin.

JOLLES REAGENT FOR ALBUMIN IN URINE. A solution of 20 g. citric acid (or succinic acid), 20 g. sodium chloride, and 10 g. mercuric chloride in 500 ml. water, used in testing for albumin in urine. A turbidity in the presence of acetic acid is given by urine containing albumin.

JOLLY BALANCE. See **balance, jolly.**

JOLY STEAM COLORIMETER. A differential method of measuring **specific heats** of gases at constant volume based upon the difference in amount of condensation of steam on an evacuated metal sphere and that on an identical sphere filled with the gas under investigation.

JONES PROCESS. A process for the manufacture of a fuel gas from oil, which consists essentially of thermal decomposition of the oil to yield gaseous hydrocarbons, and production of water gas by the intermittent admission of steam. A relatively small amount of lampblack is formed.

JONES REDUCTOR. An apparatus used for reducing certain substances, commonly solutions of metallic ions, to a lower state of oxidation so they can be determined by titration with solutions of oxidizing agents. The apparatus consists essentially of a glass tube, filled with amalgamated particles of zinc, through which the solution to be reduced is poured.

JONES-SMITH TEST. Rotenone is detected by adding 1 ml. 1:1 nitric acid to 1 ml. of an acetone solution of the substance tested, allowing it to stand 1 minute, then adding 9 ml. water and 1 ml. ammonium hydroxide. A blue color indicates rotenone.

JONES-TASKER TEST REACTION. Cobalt in solution forms a deep red-brown color with potassium dithioxalate. Nickel gives a deep magenta color.

JONESCU TEST. To detect benzoic acid in foods, acidify with sulfuric acid and distill with steam. Extract the distillate with ether and evaporate it. The residue is dissolved in water, and treated with ferric chloride solution and hydrogen peroxide. A violet color indicates benzoic acid.

JORDAN REFINER. A machine used in paper-making to separate and shorten the fibers further after beating. It consists of a conical plug which turns in a conical shell, both provided with bars running lengthwise.

JÖRGENSEN SOLUTION. A solution of 1.96 g. iodine, 10 g. 10% hydriodic acid, and 10 g. 10% sulfuric acid in sufficient alcohol to make 250 ml. of solution. It is used as a test reagent for quinine.

JORISSEN REAGENT FOR GLYCOSIDES AND ALKALOIDS. A solution of 2 g. fused zinc chloride in 60 ml. concentrated hydrochloric acid, and 60 ml. water, used in testing for glycosides and alkaloids. Various color reactions are obtained.

JORISSEN REAGENT FOR NITRITE. A solution of 0.01 g. fuchsin in 100 ml. glacial acetic acid, which is colored violet, changing to blue, to green and then to yellow by nitrite.

JORISSEN REAGENT FOR PEROXIDE IN ETHER. A solution of 0.4 g. vanadic acid in 4 ml. concentrated sulfuric acid and 100 ml. water. Shake 10 ml. of the ether with 2 ml. of reagent. A rose-red to blood-red color is given if peroxide is present.

JORISSEN TEST FOR FORMALDEHYDE. Ten ml. of the liquid tested are treated with 1–2 ml. 0.1% aqueous phloroglucinol solution, then a few drops sodium hydroxide solution are added. Formaldehyde gives a red color. The test can be used for detecting formaldehyde in milk.

JORISSEN TEST FOR TITANIUM. Fuse the material tested in potassium bisulfate bead and dissolve in a solution of 0.1–0.2 g. salicylic acid in 20–30 drops concentrated sulfuric acid. A red color of solution and residue indicates titanium.

JOULE. A unit of work equal to ten million **ergs**.

$$1 \text{ joule} = 1 \text{ volt-coulomb}$$
$$3600 \text{ joules} = 1 \text{ watt-hour (1 kelvin)}$$
$$1 \text{ joule} = 0.2390 \text{ calorie}$$
$$1 \text{ calorie} = 4.185 \text{ joules}$$

JOULE-CLAUSIUS VELOCITY. A quantity used in describing the kinetic behavior of gases, and defined by the equation $p = \frac{1}{3} dG^2$, where p is the pressure of the gas, d is the density, and G is the Joule-Clausius velocity.

JOULE LAWS. See **laws of Joule.**

JOULE-THOMSON COEFFICIENT. The ratio of the change in temperature to the change in pressure when a gas expands at constant **enthalpy** to a lower pressure through a small aperture or porous plug.

JOULE-THOMSON EFFECT. In passing a gas at high pressure through a porous plug or small aperture, a difference of temperature between the compressed and released gas may be noticed. Hydrogen and helium become warmer and all other gases cooler at ordinary temperatures and pressures. This phenomenon is called the Joule-Thomson effect. It is due to the departure of real gases from the **ideal gas laws.** With a perfect gas no difference should be observed.

JOULE-THOMSON INVERSION TEMPERATURE. The temperature, or one of the two possible temperatures, at which the Joule-Thomson coefficient changes its sign for a given gas.

JOURDAN-ULLMANN-GOLDBERG SYNTHESIS. A method of synthesis of acridones by ring closure of diphenylamine o-carboxylic acids. The diphenylamine

o-carboxylic acid may be obtained from arylamines and o-halobenzoic acids as well as the aryl halide and anthranilic acid method shown.

JUERST EBULLIOSCOPE. An apparatus for measuring accurately the boiling point of alcohol-water solutions, usually to determine their composition.

JULIUS TEST REACTION. Benzidine in aqueous solution gives a voluminous deep blue precipitate with potassium dichromate solution.

JUNGMANN SOLUTION. A solution of 1 g. sodium phosphomolybdate in 10 ml. hydrochloric acid and 20 ml. water, used as a test reagent for arbutin. A blue color indicates the presence of arbutin.

JUSTIN-MUELLER CUPROSODIC REAGENT. A solution of 1 g. cupric sulfate pentahydrate in 10 ml. water to which is added dropwise, with stirring, 100 ml. sodium hydroxide solution (sp. gr. 1.332). Ten ml. of this reagent is equivalent to 0.013 g. dextrose.

K. Symbol for the element potassium (K). Symbol for **Kelvin temperature** (° K). Symbol for specific **reaction rate** or reaction velocity constant (k). Symbol for individual **mass transfer coefficient** (k). Symbol for gas-film mass transfer coeffi-

cient (k_G). Symbol for liquid-film mass transfer coefficient (k_L). Symbol for overall mass transfer coefficient (K). Symbol for over-all mass transfer coefficient, gas film basis (K_G). Symbol for over-all mass transfer coefficient, liquid film basis (K_L). Symbol for **thermal conductivity** (k). Expression for **equilibrium constant** (K). Symbol sometimes used for **specific heat ratio** $K = \dfrac{C_p}{C_v}$; γ is much more commonly used for this meaning. Symbol for **Boltzmann constant** (k). Symbol for compressibility factor, or **coefficient of compressibility** (k). Symbol for curvature (K). Symbol for force constant (k). **Miller indices** (h, k, l). Symbol for **radius of gyration** (k). Symbol for specific **magnetic susceptibility** (k). See also **kappa.**

K-ELECTRON. An electron in the first shell surrounding the atomic nucleus; such electrons (two in number) are statistically nearest to the nucleus.

K-ELECTRON CAPTURE. Capture by a nucleus of an electron of the "K" shell, or the innermost shell of electrons surrounding the nucleus. This process accompanies the decay processes of artificially-radioactive atomic nuclei, notably those emitting **positrons.**

K-LINE. (1) One of the characteristic lines in the **x-ray spectrum** of an atom produced by K-electron excitation. (2) The designation used for a strong line in the **emission spectrum** of calcium, useful in fixing spectrographic positions.

K-ORBIT. The orbits of the **K-electrons**.

K-RADIATION. The radiation, or rather radiations, emitted when **K-electrons** are excited. These radiations are **x-rays** of relatively high frequency, and of similar spectral distribution for the various elements, except that they are displaced in the direction of decreasing wave length as the **atomic number** of the element increases. They are commonly obtained by bombardment with high-speed electrons of the particular element, usually in the form of the metal.

K-SHELL. The innermost shell of electrons surrounding the atomic nucleus; this shell consisting of the **K-electrons**.

KAISER TEST FOR WOOD PULP. Equal parts of amyl alcohol and concentrated sulfuric acid are heated at 90° C. until gas evolution begins. Pure filter paper becomes red in this reagent. Poorer grades become violet, and wood pulp papers, blue.

KALIUM. Latin and German name of **potassium**.

KAMLET REACTION. A method of formation of nitroalcohols by the condensation of the sodium salts of *aci*-nitroparaffins with the sodium bisulfite addition products of aldehydes in the presence of weak acid or alkali.

KAO-FANG-SAH REAGENT. The substance *p*-chlorobenzazide, used as a reagent for primary and secondary amines.

KAO-TAO-SAH REAGENT. The substance *m*-bromobenzhydrazide, which gives compounds of definite melting point with aldehydes and ketones.

KAPNOMETER. An apparatus used to determine the concentration of solid or liquid particles dispersed in a gas, such as the density of smoke or fog.

KAPPA (K or κ). The tenth letter of the Greek alphabet, used to denote: (1) the tenth carbon atom in a straight-chain compound, or a derivative in which a substituent group is attached to that carbon atom (κ-); (2) **ratio of specific heats** of a gas $C_p/C_v = \kappa$; γ is more commonly used for this meaning; (3) prefix designating the kata-position, e.g., the 1,7 substitution in naphthalene, (κ).

KARN TEST. To detect cadmium in the presence of copper add 3–4 ml. 10% ammonium chloride solution to the neutral copper solution and then an equal volume of saturated ammonium bicarbonate solution. If cadmium is present, a white precipitate appears.

KAROGLANOV TEST. Nitrite is detected in the presence of nitrate and chlorate by dissolving the material tested in 2 N acetic acid, passing hydrogen through the solution and suspending in the exit gas

$$CH_2 : NO_2Na + RCHOH \cdot SO_3Na \rightarrow RCHOH \cdot CH_2 \cdot NO_2 + Na_2SO_3$$

KAMLET REAGENT. A solution of 15 g. sulfosalicylic acid, 85 g. citric acid, and 25 g. commercial ammonium molybdate, in 1 liter of water to which 2 ml. chloroform are then added. This solution is used as a reagent for albumin in urine.

KAMPOMETER. An instrument used to measure **radiant energy**, especially in the thermal region.

KAO-CHEN REAGENT. A 1% solution of *p*-homosalicylic acid, used in copper determinations.

current a drop of a sulfuric acid solution of diphenylamine. A blue color indicates nitrite.

KARAGLANOV SULFITE TEST. To detect sulfite in the presence of thiosulfite, dilute the solution until addition of acetic acid causes no precipitation. Then add 2 N acetic acid, and pass in hydrogen. The vapors will decolorize starch iodine solution if sulfite is present.

KASERER REAGENT. Dissolve 38 g. pyrogallol and 36.3 g. formanilid in absolute ether and add 15.2 g. phosphorus oxy-chloride. After 12–18 hours, filter by suction and recrystallize the precipitate from alcohol with the addition of sodium chloride. While warming, decompose with sodium hydroxide solution in a current of hydrogen, acidify, extract with ether, and purify the aldehyde by means of the bisulfite compound. This reagent gives a bright yellow liquid with thorium sulfate and nitrate, and later a dirty yellow precipitate. Zirconium acts similarly, while cerous ion produces a brown-yellow color resistant to boiling.

KASSNER MIXTURE. A mixture of 1 part barium peroxide and 3 parts potassium ferricyanide, used to produce oxygen.

KASTLE REAGENT FOR BROMINE AND IODINE. Dichlorobenzenesulfonamide, which liberates bromine from bromides and iodine from iodides.

KASTLE-SHEDD REAGENT. A solution of phenolphthalein, used as a reagent for oxidases.

KATA-. (Cata-) A prefix, from the Greek, which indicates "down," "below," "under," "opposed to," etc.

KATABOLISM. See **catabolism.**

KATAKOUZINOS TEST REACTION. *m*-Phenylenediamine gives characteristic colors with various metallic ions in dilute solution; chromium can be detected in the presence of iron by preliminary oxidation with sodium peroxide.

KATHAROMETER. An instrument for determining the composition of a gas mixture by measuring variations in its **thermal conductivity.**

KATIONOID REAGENT. A positive, or electron-seeking reagent. Also called cationoid, electrophilic, and Lewis acid.

KATION. Cation (q.v.).

KAUFLER CONFIGURATION OF BI-PHENYL. A folded structure in which one benzene ring lies directly above the other.

KAWAI REACTION FOR EUGENOL. A chloroform solution of antimony trichloride gives a blue color with a solution of eugenol in chloroform after standing 1 hour.

KAWAI TEST FOR BLOOD. Blood in alkaline medium gives a red color with orcin.

KEESOM EQUATION. An expression giving the mean energy of interaction between a pair of **dipoles** having free rotation and with random orientation of axes.

KEKULÉ STRUCTURE OF BENZENE. See **benzene, formulas.**

KELLER SOLUTION. A solution of 1 ml. concentrated hydrofluoric acid, 1.5 ml. concentrated hydrochloric acid, and 2.5 ml. concentrated nitric acid, used for etching aluminum alloys.

KELLOGG EQUATION. An **equation of state,** relating the pressure, absolute temperature, and density of a gas. It is of the form:

$$p = RT\rho + \left(B_o RT - A_o - \frac{C_o}{T^2}\right)\rho^2 + \left(bRT - a - \frac{c}{T^2}\right)\rho^3$$

in which p is the pressure, T the absolute temperature, ρ the density, R the **gas constant,** and A_o, B_o, C_o, a, b, and c are constants.

KELLY FILTER. See **filter, Kelly.**

KELM-WILKINSON TEST. Potassium is detected by treatment of the analytical residue (after removal of alkaline earths and ammonia), with 1 drop 0.1 N hydrochloric acid, adding 0.01 g. cobalt nitrate and lead nitrate, and adding 4 drops saturated sodium nitrite solution. A black precipitate indicates potassium.

KELVIN GALVANOMETER. See **galvanometer, Kelvin.**

KELVIN TEMPERATURE SCALE. A thermodynamic temperature scale based upon the efficiency of a reversible heat engine, operating in cycles between two heat reservoirs. The temperatures of the two reservoirs are in the same ratio as the quantities of heat transferred between the reservoirs and the machine. In this manner the temperature ratio becomes independent of the working substances. To fix the temperature values themselves, zero on this scale is defined as that temperature of the heat sink at which the efficiency of the heat engine is 100%. The scale may be identified with the ideal gas scale by defining the size of the degree to be the same in both cases, and by defining the ice point on the Kelvin scale as occurring at 273.16 degrees.

KENDALL–SHERMAN TEST. To determine reducing sugars, treat 0.03 g. sugar with 0.06 g. *p*-bromobenzylhydride in alcohol solution and evaporate to dryness. Several reducing sugars give hydrazones which can be separated by their solubility in alcohol and chloroform.

KENTMANN REAGENT. A solution of 10 g. morphine hydrochloride, in 100 ml. concentrated sulfuric acid, used as a test reagent for formaldehyde. If a liquid containing formaldehyde is floated on the reagent, a reddish-violet color in the aqueous layer indicates the presence of formaldehyde.

KERBOSCH REAGENT. A solution of 5 g. cesium iodide and 1.8 g. cadmium iodide in 100 ml. water, used in testing for alkaloids. Precipitates are obtained.

KERN TEST REACTION. Gold in solution gives an orange precipitate on warming with a potassium thiocyanate solution.

KERNEL, ATOMIC. An atomic **nucleus** surrounded by all the electrons present in the normal atom with the exception of the **valence** electrons of the outermost **shell.**

KERR CONSTANT. A constant in the relationship between the different refractive indices of the same medium when exhibiting the properties of double **refraction** by electrical polarization (Kerr effect). The reduced form (independent of wave length of light) for the expression for K is:

$$K = \frac{n_p - n_s}{nE^2},$$

in which n is the **refractive index** of the medium for the incident light, and n_p and n_s are the refractive indices of the emergent **polarized light** vibrating in planes parallel and perpendicular to the direction of the field, and E is the field strength.

KERR EFFECT. The property of double refraction, induced in a transparent, isotropic substance by the action of a stationary electrical field.

KERSHNER–DUFF SOLUTION. A solution of 0.4 g. purpurin and 0.01 g. gum sandarac, in 1 liter ethyl ether, used as a test reagent for aluminum. A pink foam, on shaking the strongly ammoniacal solution to be tested with 1 ml. of the reagent and with 10 ml. *N* ammonium chloride solution, indicates the presence of aluminum.

KERSTING TEST FOR NITRITE. Mix 1 ml. of the liquid tested with 1 ml. of a 1 : 1000 aqueous brucine solution. A red ring test with concentrated sulfuric acid indicates nitrite.

KET-, KETO. From ketone; as ketohexose, ketoxime. (See **keto-**.)

KETAZINE. One of a class of nitrogenous derivatives of the **ketones,** of the type

$$RR'C{=}N{-}N{=}CR''R'''$$

in which R terms represent univalent aryl or alkyl groups. For example, tetramethyl ketazine,

$$(CH_3)_2C{=}N{-}N{=}C(CH_3)_2.$$

KETENE. One of a class of organic compounds having the general formula

$$\begin{array}{c} R \\ \diagdown \\ C=C=O. \\ \diagup \\ R \end{array}$$

If both the R symbols are organic radicals, the compound is a keto-ketene; whereas if one of the R symbols should be a hydrogen atom, the compound is an aldo-ketene.

KETIMINE. A compound in which the oxygen atom in the keto-group $\begin{array}{c} \diagdown \\ C=O, \\ \diagup \end{array}$ has been replaced by the imino, $=NH$ group. The type formula is

$$\begin{array}{c} R \\ \diagdown \\ C=NH. \\ \diagup \\ R' \end{array}$$

KETO-. A prefix which indicates content of the **carbonyl group,** $=CO$, which confers ketonic properties.

KETOAMINE. A compound containing a **carbonyl group** $(=CO)$, and an amino group $(-NH_2)$.

KETO-HEXOSE. A six-carbon monosaccharose which contains a **carbonyl group,** e.g., fructose.

KETOKETENE. A compound containing

the group $\begin{array}{c} \diagdown \\ C=C=O. \\ \diagup \end{array}$

KETOL. A compound containing a **carbonyl group** $(=CO)$, and an **alcohol group** $(-OH)$.

KETOL, SATURATED. A saturated ketol, in which the carbonyl group is usually in the α- or β-position to the alcohol group.

KETOL, UNSATURATED. An oxymethylene **ketone** of the general type, $R \cdot CO \cdot CR' : CHOH$, in which R represents

an alkyl or aryl group and R' may be hydrogen; e.g., oxymethylene acetone,

$$CH_3 \cdot CO \cdot CH : CHOH.$$

KETONE. An organic compound characterized by content of the **carbonyl group,** as

acetone, $\begin{array}{c} CH_3 \\ \diagdown \\ C=O. \\ \diagup \\ CH_3 \end{array}$ The ketones are

named in various ways: (1) By combining the names of the radicals (alkyl or aryl) with "ketone," as dimethyl ketone, ethyl methyl ketone, etc. (2) The Geneva names are formed by adding the suffix "one" to the root of the parent hydrocarbon. Thus, acetone is propanone; ethyl methyl ketone is butanone. Simple ketones contain two alkyl or aryl groups of one kind; in mixed ketones the alkyl or aryl groups are different, e.g., ethyl methyl ketone.

KETONE, MIXED. A ketone consisting of two different groups joined to the characteristic carbonyl group, in other words, a compound of the general form

$$\begin{array}{c} O \\ \parallel \\ R-C-R' \end{array}$$

in which R and R' are different organic radicals.

KETOSE. (See **Carbohydrate**) Any sugar that contains a **carbonyl group.**

KETOSIDE. Any **glycoside** which, on hydrolysis, yields a **ketose,** e.g., methylfructoside.

KETOXIME. An **oxime** of a **ketone** of the

general type $\begin{array}{c} R \\ \diagdown \\ C=N-OH, \\ \diagup \\ R' \end{array}$ e.g., acet-

oxime, $\begin{array}{c} CH_3 \\ \diagdown \\ C=NOH. \\ \diagup \\ CH_3 \end{array}$

KEYES EQUATION. An **equation of state** for a gas, deduced from the concept of the nuclear atom. This equation is designed to correct the **van der Waals equation** for the effect upon the term b of the surrounding molecules. The equation is written as

$$P = \frac{RT}{V - Be^{-\alpha/V}} - \frac{A}{(V + l)^2}$$

in which P is pressure, T is absolute temperature, V is volume, R is the **gas constant**, e is the base of natural logarithms, 2.718 ..., and A, α, B, and l are constants for each gas.

KHARICHKOV REAGENT FOR ORGANIC BASES. This reagent consists of two solutions: (1) a solution of inactive oleic or naphthenic acid in ether; and (2) a 3% aqueous solution of cupric sulfate. On shaking with 2 volumes of (1) and 1 volume of (2), organic bases yield a green color.

KHARICHKOV TEST FOR COPPER, COBALT, AND NAPHTHENIC ACID. Concentrated solutions of naphthenic acid in petroleum benzine or in benzene give deep green colors with cupric salts in neutral or weak acid solution; with cobalt salts, an eosin-red color changed to green-brown on shaking the benzine layer with hydrogen peroxide.

KHARICHKOV TEST FOR FERROUS SALTS. To a concentrated solution of naphthenic acid in petroleum benzine, ferrous salts in neutral or weak acid solutions impart a deep chocolate-brown color.

KHARICHKOV TEST FOR HYDROGEN PEROXIDE. Filter paper impregnated with a concentrated solution of naphthenic acid in benzine to which has been added a neutral or weakly-acid cobalt solution, changes from a rose color to olive-green when moistened with a hydrogen peroxide solution.

KICK, LAW OF. See **law of Kick.**

KIKUCHI LINES. A series of spectral lines obtained by directing an **electron** stream against the surface of a **crystal**, due to the **scattering** of electrons by layers of atoms in the crystal structure.

KILIANI REAGENT FOR DIGITALIS GLUCOSIDES. A mixture of 1 ml. 5% ferric sulfate solution with 100 ml. concentrated sulfuric acid, used to test for the digitalis glucosides and their decomposition products. Characteristic color reactions are obtained.

KILIANI SYNTHESIS (KILIANI-FISCHER SYNTHESIS). An application of the cyanhydrin synthesis (see **synthesis, cyanhydrin**) to increase the number of carbon atoms in the carbon chain of sugars. The acid **lactones** are reduced by sodium amalgam to **aldoses,** and the **carbonyl** group in the latter, upon treatment with hydrogen cyanide, yields a cyanhydrin, which upon hydrolysis gives an α-hydroxy acid group. Thus, l-arabinose by the cyanhydrin treatment and hydrolysis gives a mixture of l-mannonic and l-gluconic acids.

KILN. One of a number of types of furnaces or ovens. The most common type is that used for drying or roasting ores or rocks, such as the lime kiln used for producing crude calcium oxide from limestone.

KILO-. A Greek prefix which signifies one thousand as used in the metric system and for scientific units. The word kilo is sometimes used colloquially for kilogram.

KILOCALORIE. One thousand calories. This is the so-called "large" **calorie,** in which calorific values, especially of foods, are so often reported under the designation "calorie."

KILOGRAM. One thousand **grams.**

1 kilogram = 2.20462 (avoirdupois) pounds.
1 kilogram = 2.67923 troy pounds.

KILOGRAM METER. A unit of **work** in the gravitational system defined as the work done in raising a mass of one **kilogram** through a distance of one **meter** against gravity. It equals 98,065,504 ergs.

KILOJOULE. One thousand **joules.**

KILOLITER. One thousand **liters.**

1 kiloliter = 264.18 U.S. liquid gallons
1 kiloliter = 283.774 U.S. bushels.

KILOMETER. One thousand **meters.**

1 kilometer = 3,280.83 feet
1 kilometer = 0.62137 mile
1 kilometer = 1,093.611 yards
1 mile   = 1.60935 kilometers.

KILOWATT. One thousand **watts.**

1 kilowatt = 1,000 joules per second
746 kilowatt = 1,000 horsepower
1 kilowatt = 1.341 horsepower
1 kilowatt = 238.9 calories per second.

KILOWATT HOUR. A commercial unit of energy equal to 1,000 **watt-hours** or 3,600,000 joules.

KIMPFLIN TEST. To detect formaldehyde in green leaves, impregnate them with a solution of methyl-*p*-amino-*m*-cresol and sodium bisulfite, and examine microscopically for red colored areas.

KINDLER REACTION. See **reaction, Kindler.**

KINDLING TEMPERATURE. The lowest temperature at which a substance will burn in air with sufficient rapidity to maintain its **combustion.**

KINETIC ENERGY. Energy possessed by a body because of its motion; it is equal to the product of one half the mass of the body by the square of its velocity.

KINETIC THEORY. An explanation of many of the properties of matter, and many of the relationships between matter and energy, on the basis that all matter is composed of molecules in motion, which possess kinetic energy. Thus, evaporation is caused by the escape from the surface of a liquid of its (relatively) faster-moving molecules; the pressure of a gas is the sum effect of the impacts of gas molecules upon a surface; and increase in temperature of a substance is accompanied by increasing speed, and hence energy, of molecular motion.

KINKEAD TEST. Mercerized fabrics give a reddish-purple color (other fabrics blue) when heated with 0.001% methylene blue solution and 0.5% sodium carbonate solution.

KINNERSLEY-PETERS TEST FOR VITAMIN B₁ (THIAMINE). A solution of 5.76 g. sodium bicarbonate in 100 ml. water is mixed with 100 ml. *N* sodium hydroxide solution. To 1.25 ml. of this solution, 0.5 ml. diazotized sulfanilic acid is added, and after 1 minute 1 drop 40% formaldehyde, and immediately 0.3 ml. of the dilute vitamin solution (pH above 3.5). A pink color deepening for 30–60 minutes indicates thiamine.

KIPP GENERATOR. A glass apparatus used in the laboratory to generate gases, such as carbon dioxide, hydrogen sulfide, by the interaction of a solid and a liquid, such as an acid solution. It is of characteristic form, and is designed to provide space for (1) the reacting liquid, (2) the reacting solid, and (3) the product gas. Its arrangement tends to restrain the flow of acid into the section containing the solid as the gas pressure increases and forces the acid or reacting liquid away from the solid.

KIRCHHOFF EQUATION. The basic relationship between the variation of **heat of reaction** with temperature to the change in **heat capacity** accompanying the process. The generalized form of this equation is

$$\left(\frac{\partial(\Delta H)}{\partial T}\right)_p = \Delta C_p$$

in which ΔH is the heat of reaction at constant pressure, T is the absolute temperature, ΔC_p is the difference in heat capacities of the final and initial states. A similar equation can be deduced for reactions at constant volume.

KIRCHHOFF LAW, OPTICAL. See **Law of Kirchhoff, optical.**

KIRCHHOFF LAWS OF NETWORKS. See **laws of Kirchhoff for networks.**

KIRSCHNER VALUE. A number dependent on the amount of soluble silver salts of fatty acids in a **Reichert-Meissl** distillate. The Kirschner value may be calculated by the following formula:

$$K = \frac{A \times 121(100 + B)}{10,000}$$

where K is the Kirschner value, A is the number of ml. of 0.1 N Ba(OH)$_2$ used to neutralize the distillate from the soluble silver salts of the fatty acids; and B is the number of ml. of 0.1 N Ba(OH)$_2$ used to neutralize the 100 ml. of Reichert-Meissl distillate.

KISHNER CYCLOPROPANE SYNTHE-SIS. A method of formation of cyclopropane derivatives from α,β-unsaturated **ketones** or **aldehydes** by reaction with **hydrazine.**

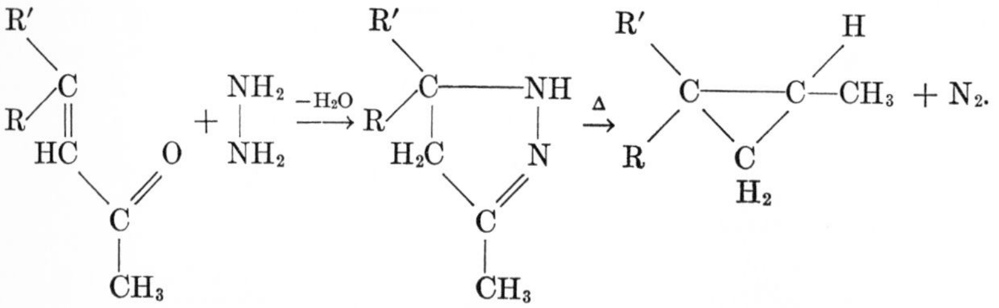

used by mineralogists. Its specific gravity is 3.28.

KLEIN SOLUTION FOR NITRATE. A solution of elementary tellurium in fuming sulfuric acid, used as a test reagent for nitrates (it gives a red color).

KLEINMANN-PANGRITZ REAGENT. One volume 1% sodium molybdate solution mixed with 2 volumes N hydrochloric acid, and then 1 volume 2% cocaine hydrochloride solution. This reagent gives a turbidity with solutions of arsenic, and is used in the nephelometric determination of arsenate.

KLEMON TEST. Coniferous pulps are colored yellow by a solution of aniline sul-

KISSER REAGENT. A solution of 2.64 g. picrolonic acid in 1 liter water, used as a test reagent for calcium and thorium. It forms yellow precipitates with these cations, and generally with those of the alkali and alkaline earth metals.

KJELDAHL FLASK. A pear-shaped flask with round bottom and cylindrical neck.

KJELDAHL NITROGEN METHOD. An analytical method for the determination of nitrogen in an organic compound by its reduction to ammonium salts, from which the ammonia is liberated by a nonvolatile alkali, and then distilled into a standard acid. The initial decomposition of the organic material is effected by sulfuric acid digestion, which converts aminoid nitrogen to ammonium sulfate.

KLEIN MINERAL SOLUTION. A saturated solution of cadmium borotungstate

fate and of methylene blue; deciduous wood pulps are colored blue-green.

KLING REAGENT. Racemic tartaric acid, used in the quantitative determination of barium, strontium, and calcium, and the quantitative separation of calcium salts.

KNAPP SOLUTION. A solution of 10 g. mercuric cyanide and 100 ml. 3 N sodium hydroxide solution in sufficient water to make a liter. It is used in the quantitative determination of glucose.

KNAPPER-CRAIG-CHANDLEE TEST. To detect tin, the solution tested is acidified with concentrated hydrochloric acid and heated to boiling. Then a boiling, saturated solution of phenylarsonic acid is added. A turbidity or white precipitate forms at once if tin is present.

KNECHT REAGENT. A standard solution of titanium trichloride, used in many determinations, including those of ferric ion, azo-group, nitro-group, persulfate, and hydrogen peroxide.

KNECHT TEST REACTION FOR COPPER. A solution of titanous sulfate precipitates metallic copper from a copper

acid), and an aldehyde, in the presence of ammonia or a primary or secondary amine, frequently piperidine. The methylene hydrogen atoms of the acid are replaced in an aldol condensation type of reaction, followed by loss of water, yielding α,β-unsaturated acids, or their esters.

$$RCHO + H_2C(COOH)_2 \rightarrow [RCH = C(COOH)_2] \rightarrow RCH{=}CHCOOH + H_2O + CO_2$$

solution.

KNECHT TEST REAGENT FOR TITANIUM. A solution of Rochelle salt colored just blue by an indigo solution. After heating, add the solution to be tested, prepared with hydrochloric acid. The indigo solution is decolorized by titanium, but its color is restored on shaking with air.

KNIGA TEST. To test for ferricyanide, treat one drop of the unknown solution on filter paper, with one drop alkaline phenolphthalein. A brilliant red color shows ferricyanide.

KNOCK. A term used in engineering to denote an undesirably rapid **combustion** of the fuel-air mixture in the cylinder of an internal combustion engine. The effect is to produce a momentary pressure far in excess of that for which the engine was designed, and thus to reduce its thermodynamic **efficiency.** The method of control is by the addition of **catalysts** (anti-knock substances) to the fuel, by the use of fuels which burn more slowly, and by cleaning the cylinder walls of possible contamination with substances, such as carbon deposits, which may tend to preignite the mixture.

KNOEVENAGEL CONDENSATION. A reaction of a dicarboxylic acid, such as malonic acid, (or an ester of a dicarboxylic

Knoevenagel's name is sometimes applied to any condensation of carbonyl groups with reactive methylene groups, in the presence of amino-function compounds.

KNOEVENAGEL DIAZO REACTION. See **Diazo (Knoevenagel) reaction.**

KNOEVENAGEL-FRIES SYNTHESIS. See **Hantzsch Pyridine synthesis.**

KNOP TEST REACTION FOR SILICIC ACID. A soluble silicate gives a yellow color on addition to a solution of ammonium molybdate in nitric acid.

KNORR FLASK. An extraction flask, commonly provided with a countersunk neck, which forms a trough for a mercury seal and has holes for the return flow of the extraction solvent.

KNORR PYRAZOLE SYNTHESIS. A method of formation of pyrazoles from β-dicarbonyl compounds and hydrazines.

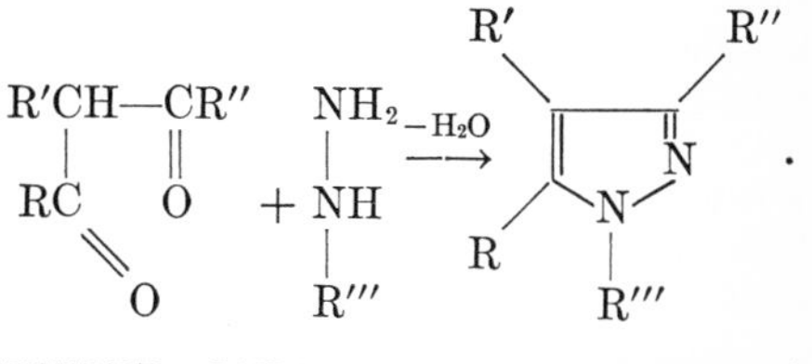

KNORR PYRROLE SYNTHESIS. A method of formation of pyrrole from carbonyl compounds with α-active methylene groups, and α-amino ketones.

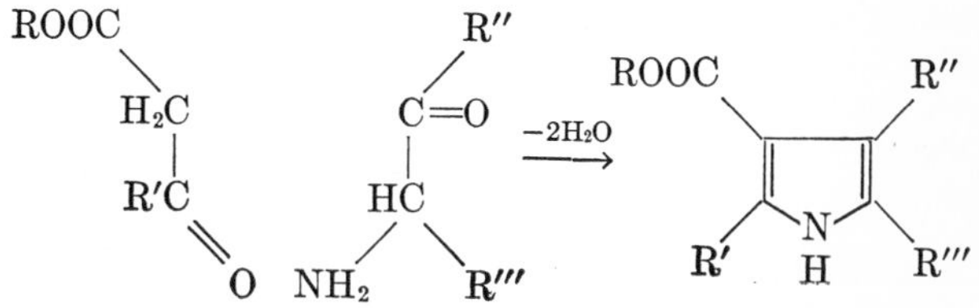

The α-amino ketone above may be replaced by an isonitroso ketone yielding it on reduction.

KNORR QUINOLINE SYNTHESIS. A method of formation of α-hydroxy quinolines by ring closure of aromatic amides of β-keto esters.

KNORR REAGENT FOR ALKALOIDS. Picrolonic acid, which precipitates salts with most alkaloids.

KNORR TEST REACTION FOR PYRAZOLINE BASES. Red and blue colors are obtained by oxidizing pyrazoline bases with chromic acid, hydrogen peroxide, and other oxidants.

KNOWLES REAGENT. An alcoholic solution of α-benzoinoxime used to precipitate molybdenum from slightly acid solution.

KNUDSEN ABSOLUTE MANOMETER. A device for measuring gas pressures below about 0.006 mm. Hg pressure. Two metal plates are kept at slightly different temperatures. One plate is fixed in position, the other is suspended close to it. The force on the suspended plate is measured.

KO REAGENT. A solution of 1 g. hexamethylenetetramine in 100 ml. concentrated sulfuric acid, used in testing for β-naphthol in foods. A green color, in the absence of water, is given by β-naphthol.

KOBER TEST. Determination of proteins in milk by their precipitation with sulfosalicylic acid.

KOBERT TEST REACTION FOR ALLYL COMPOUNDS. On treatment with 1 ml. of a 10% alcoholic phloroglucinol solution and 9 ml. concentrated hydrochloric acid, allyl compounds give a red color. The test applies to allyl compounds in volatile oils.

KOBLE FLASK. A watch-shaped culture flask with a wide indented neck and two parallel flat walls.

KOBULADZE REAGENT. A solution of 10 g. mercuric chloride, 2 g. tartaric acid, and 2 g. sodium chloride in 500 ml. water, used in determining albumin in urine. A turbidity is given by albumin.

KOCH-EHRLICH STAIN. Two aqueous solutions: (1) a solution of 1 g. methylene blue in 200 ml. water, alkalinized with 10% potassium hydroxide solution; and (2) a saturated aqueous solution of vesuvin. They are used in staining tuberculosis bacilli.

KOCH SOLUTION. A solution prepared by adding 0.5 ml. of a saturated alcoholic solution of methylene blue, and 0.1 ml. 10% potassium hydroxide solution, to 100 ml. water. It is used as a stain for bacteria.

KOENIGS-KNORR SYNTHESIS. A method of formation of glycosides from acetylglycosyl halides and alcohols (or phenols).

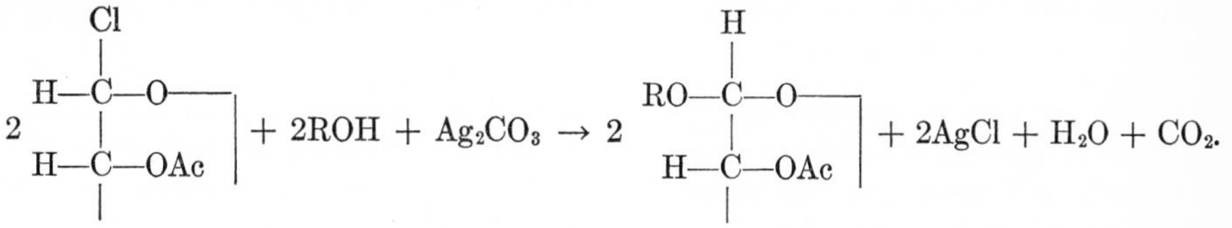

See also **Crum Brown-Walker reaction** and **Hofer-Moest reaction.**

KOLBE-SCHMITT REACTION. The

$$2\ \underset{\displaystyle\begin{array}{c}H-\overset{\displaystyle Cl}{\underset{\displaystyle |}{C}}-O-\!\!\!\\[2pt] H-\underset{\displaystyle |}{\overset{\displaystyle |}{C}}-OAc\\[2pt]|\end{array}}{}\ +\ 2ROH\ +\ Ag_2CO_3\ \rightarrow\ 2\ \underset{\displaystyle\begin{array}{c}RO-\overset{\displaystyle H}{\underset{\displaystyle |}{C}}-O-\!\!\!\\[2pt] H-\underset{\displaystyle |}{\overset{\displaystyle |}{C}}-OAc\end{array}}{}\ +\ 2AgCl\ +\ H_2O\ +\ CO_2.$$

When the halogen atom and the acetyl group have the trans-configuration, orthoesters are the chief product.

KOESSLER-HANKE ESTIMATION OF IMIDAZOLES. Phenyldiazonium sulfonate in alkaline solution reacts with com-

synthesis of aromatic hydroxy acids by heating phenates with carbon dioxide under pressure. For example, sodium phenate yields salicylic acid (o-hydroxybenzoic acid) at temperatures below 130° C., but the potassium phenate, and higher temperatures, yield the p-hydroxybenzoic acid.

$$C_6H_5ONa + CO_2 \rightarrow C_6H_5OCO_2Na \rightarrow o\text{-}C_6H_4(OH)COONa$$
$$C_6H_5OK + CO_2 \rightarrow C_6H_5OCO_2K \rightarrow p\text{-}C_6H_4(OH)COOK.$$

pounds containing the imidazole nucleus to give a characteristic color.

KOETTSTORFER NUMBER. See **saponification number.**

KOHLRAUSCH LAW. See **law of Kohlrausch.**

KOHLRAUSCH VOLUMETRIC FLASK. A volumetric flask with an enlargement in diameter of the upper part of the neck, used considerably in the analysis of sugar presscake.

KOHN TEST FOR GLYCERIN. The glycerin is oxidized with potassium bisulfate to acrolein, which is detected by **Schiff reagent** (q.v.).

KOLBE ELECTROLYSIS REACTION. Electrolysis of the alkali salts of aliphatic acids results in the loss of carbon dioxide, and the combination of the remaining fragments of the molecule to form hydrocarbons. Thus the electrolysis of sodium propionate yields butane:

KOLISCH SOLUTION. A solution of 30 g. mercuric chloride, 3 drops glacial acetic acid, and 1 g. sodium acetate, in 125 ml. absolute alcohol, used as a reagent for creatinine.

KOLTHOFF-HAMER REAGENT FOR ZINC IN THE PRESENCE OF CADMIUM. A solution of potassium thiocyanate and antipyrine which precipitates zinc in the presence of cadmium.

KOLTHOFF-HAMER REAGENTS FOR HEAVY METALS. Solutions of pyridine and thiocyanate, of pyridine and bromide, or of antipyrine and thiocyanate. They precipitate metals.

KOLTHOFF-NAPONEN TEST FOR NITRATE. To the aqueous solution tested, add enough potassium chlorate to give a concentration of 8–12 g. per liter, add 10 ml. sulfuric acid from a pipette, place in cold water and mix. When cooled, add 0.1 ml. 0.006 N sodium diphenylamine sulfonate solution and mix. A blue color indicates nitrate.

$$C_2H_5COONa + NaOOCC_2H_5 + 2H_2O \rightarrow C_2H_5 \cdot C_2H_5 + 2CO_2 + 2NaOH + H_2.$$

KOLTHOFF REACTIONS FOR BERYL-LIUM. (1) To 10 ml. of the solution tested, add 0.1 ml. of 0.1% alcoholic solution of 1,2,5,8-hydroxyanthraquinone and 6–8 drops 4 N ammonia, and boil. Beryllium gives a dark blue color or flocculent precipitate after 5 minutes standing.

(2) To 10 ml. of the solution tested, add 1 drop 0.1% alcoholic curcumin solution, 0.5 ml. 4 N ammonium chloride solution, and 6–8 drops 4 N ammonia. Beryllium gives a red to orange-red precipitate.

KOLTHOFF REAGENT AND REACTION FOR MAGNESIUM. A 0.05% aqueous solution of Titian yellow (Azidin Yellow 5 G, Clayton Yellow) is added to the solution tested, which is then strongly alkalinized with sodium hydroxide solution. A red color indicates magnesium. Calcium must be removed, and aluminum, zinc, and tin must be absent.

KOLTHOFF REAGENT FOR BARIUM, STRONTIUM, AND LEAD. Sodium rhodizonate, which gives a red precipitate or solution with neutral solutions of salts of barium, strontium, and lead.

KOLTHOFF REAGENT FOR FREE CHLORINE IN WATER. Dimethyl-p-phenylenediamine, which gives a red color with free chlorine.

KOLTHOFF REAGENT FOR METALS. A solution of 0.1 g. diphenylcarbazide in 100 ml. 50% alcohol used as a test reagent for metals. Characteristic colors are obtained.

KOLTHOFF REAGENTS FOR SODIUM. Modified Streng reagents, consisting of: (1) An aqueous solution of 10 g. uranyl acetate and 6 g. 30% acetic acid in a volume of 50 ml. Also an aqueous solution of 33 g. magnesium acetate and 6 g. acetic acid in a volume of 50 ml. The two solutions are mixed, allowed to stand for several days and filtered. This solution precipitates sodium from an aqueous alcoholic solution.

(2) A hot solution of 10% uranyl acetate and 6 g. 30% acetic acid in 34 ml. water that is mixed with a hot solution of 30 g. zinc acetate and 3 g. acetic acid in 17 ml. water. Allow to stand 1 day, and filter.

This solution precipitates sodium from aqueous solution, but more readily if alcohol is added.

KOLTHOFF-STANSBY REAGENT FOR FLUORINE. Dissolve 0.16 g. zirconium oxychloride in 100 ml. concentrated hydrochloric acid and add 100 ml. water. Dissolve 9 g. purpurin (1,2,4-trihydroxyanthraquinone) in 30 ml. alcohol, and add it slowly to the zirconium solution. To the mixture add 620 ml. concentrated hydrochloric acid, and make up to 1 liter with water. With fluorine compounds in hydrochloric acid solution, this reagent changes in color from pink to yellow.

KOLTHOFF TEST FOR ALUMINUM. Prepare a buffer solution consisting of 10 parts 5 N acetic acid and 9 parts 5 N ammonia. Add 0.25–1.0 ml. of this solution to 10 ml. of the almost neutral aluminum solution, then add 3 ml. 0.1% alcoholic quinalizarin solution. Aluminum gives a violet-colored solution.

KOLTHOFF TEST FOR COPPER IN WATER. To 10 ml. of the water, add 0.2–0.3 ml. alcoholic dimethylglyoxime solution and 1 ml. saturated potassium periodate solution. A violet-red color is given by copper.

KOLTHOFF TEST FOR CYANIDE. To 5–10 ml. of the solution tested, add 1 ml. 1% sodium tetrathionate solution, and 5 drops 6 N ammonium hydroxide. Heat 5 minutes at 50–55° C., cool, add 2 ml. 4 N sulfuric acid and 3 drops N ferric chloride. A red color indicates cyanide.

KOMAROVSKII-KORENMANN SPOT TEST FOR CERIUM. One drop of the solution tested, with one drop saturated phosphomolybdic acid solution, and then 1 drop 40% potassium hydroxide solution, gives a blue color if cerium is present.

KOMAROVSKII-POLUEKTOV TEST FOR COPPER. Apply 1 drop saturated 8-hydroxyquinoline solution in 80% acetic acid to filter paper, add 1 drop of the solution tested, after absorption, add another drop of the reagent and 1 drop 25% potassium cyanide solution. A raspberry-red color indicates copper.

KOMAROVSKII-POLUEKTOV TEST FOR GERMANIUM. Apply 1 drop alkaline or slightly acid solution tested to filter paper, add one drop of a solution of 1.5 g. ammonium molybdate in 10 ml. water and 10 ml. concentrated nitric acid, then 1 drop 0.1% acetic acid solution of benzidine, and

KONDAKOFF RULE. Those **alkenes** which add mineral acids easily react with bromine or chlorine by *replacement* to yield unsaturated monohalides, while those alkenes which react sluggishly with mineral acids, add the bromine or chlorine to give dihalides.

$$(CH_3)_2C{=}CH_2 \xrightarrow{Br_2} (CH_3)_2C{=}CHBr \text{ or } CH_2{=}C(CH_3)CH_2Br + HBr.$$

$$CH_2{=}CH_2 \xrightarrow{Br_2} CH_2Br{-}CH_2Br.$$

blow ammonia across the paper. A blue color indicates germanium. Silica and phosphate give similar reactions.

KOMAROVSKII-POLUEKTOV TEST FOR INDIUM. To 1 drop of the solution tested, add concentrated sodium thiosulfate solution until no more violet color is produced. Then add a grain of sodium sulfite and 6–8 drops 5% potassium cyanide solution. Place this solution on filter paper moistened with a saturated solution of alizarin in alcohol, then dip the paper in a saturated aqueous solution of boric acid. A red color in the center of the spot indicates indium.

KOMAROVSKII-POLUEKTOV TEST FOR MOLYBDENUM. Add to the solution tested 2 drops 3% alcoholic solution of $\alpha\alpha'$-dipyridyl, then a drop of a solution of 5 g. stannous chloride in 10 ml. hydrochloric acid. An intense violet color indicates molybdenum.

KOMAROVSKII-POLUEKTOV TEST REACTION FOR BERYLLIUM. A yellow alkaline solution of p-nitrophenylazoresorcinol becomes orange-red with a beryllium salt.

KOMAROVSKII-SHAPIRO REAGENT FOR NIOBIUM AND TANTALUM. A freshly-prepared mixture of equal volumes of 1% sodium thiosulfate solution, 25% barium chloride solution, 0.1 N acetic acid and 0.7% hydrogen peroxide solution. The reagent gives a barium sulfate precipitate when treated with neutral niobium or tantalum solutions.

KÖNIG REAGENT. An aqueous solution of the acid disodium salt of 1,8-dihydroxynaphthalene-2, 6- disulfonic acid. It gives with chromate and dichromate ions a dark red-violet to cherry-red color.

KONOWALOFF RULE. An empirical conclusion reached by Konowaloff independently of the fundamental theoretical deductions of physical chemistry. It states that the vapor over a liquid system is relatively richer in the **component** whose addition to the liquid mixture results in an increase of the total **vapor pressure.**

KONOWALOFF TEST REACTION FOR PRIMARY AND SECONDARY NITRO COMPOUNDS. On shaking with a slight excess of aqueous potassium hydroxide solution, extracting with water, then adding ether, then ferric chloride, nitroethane becomes red; nitroisopropane first red, then green, and finally blue.

KOPP LAW. See **law of Kopp.**

KOPP SOLUTION. A solution of 0.1 g. diphenylamine in 5 ml. concentrated sulfuric acid and 5 ml. water, which is then made up to a volume of 1 liter with concentrated sulfuric acid. It is used in testing for nitrates and nitrites, which give a blue color with it. Many modifications of this test have been reported.

KOPPERS COKE OVEN. A by-product coke oven for the production of coke by the regenerative heating and distillation of coal.

KOPPERS PROCESS. A method used for the removal of ammonia from manufactured gases. The gas is separated from ammonia liquors, and is then cooled, causing most of the ammonia to condense together with water vapor present, in the form of ammonium hydroxide. The gas is then treated with sulfuric acid and ammonium sulfate precipitates.

KOPPESHAAR REAGENT. A solution of 25 g. potassium bromide and 3 g. potassium bromate, in water, diluted to a volume of 1 liter of solution, used in the determination of unsaturated organic substances.

KORENMAN-FURSINA MICRO-REACTION FOR LITHIUM. To 1 drop of the solution tested, add 1 drop 15% methenamine solution and 1 drop 15% potassium ferricyanide solution. Shiny-yellow octohedrons are visible under the microscope if lithium is present.

KORENMAN-LUBASHEVICK TEST FOR COPPER. To a few drops of the solution tested, add an excess of 10% ammonia, filter if necessary, and acidify with acetic acid. Treat with 1 drop 20% cadmium nitrate or zinc sulfate solution and 1 drop ammonium-mercuri-thiocyanate solution. Copper gives a blue precipitate.

KORENMAN MICRO-CHEMICAL TEST FOR IODIDE. Mix 1 part phenylhydrazine with 5 parts sulfuric acid and add 2–3 crystals potassium dichromate. One drop of this solution, and the same amount of the solution tested, give characteristic microscopic crystals if iodide is present.

KORENMAN MICRO-CHEMICAL TESTS FOR PERMANGANATE. (1) One crystal of alkali perchlorate is dissolved in 1 drop of the solution tested, then 1 drop rubidium nitrate solution added. A pink or pink-violet color indicates permanganate.
(2) To 1 drop of the solution tested, add 1 crystal each of sodium sulfate and silver nitrate. If permanganate is present, the silver sulfate formed is colored black, brown-violet, gray-violet, or pink.

KORENMAN REAGENT FOR FREE AMMONIA IN PYRIDINE. A mixture of 10 ml. of a 0.1% aqueous solution of

cupric sulfate and 10 ml. of a saturated aqueous solution of picric acid, used in determining free ammonia in pyridine. A precipitate is produced if free ammonia is present.

KORENMAN REAGENT FOR HEAVY METALS. Quinoline, which gives characteristic crystalline precipitates with salts of several heavy metals.

KORENMAN TEST FOR BROMATE. Two ml. of the solution tested are treated with 1 ml. 3 N hydrochloric acid and 1–2 drops 0.015% methyl orange solution. Bromate gives immediate decolorization.

KORENMAN TEST REACTION FOR FERRICYANIDES. Three ml. of the solution tested are treated with 10 drops saturated sodium carbonate solution and 2–3 drops 0.02% indigo-carmine solution. Ferricyanides cause decolorization.

KÖRNER-CONTARDI REACTION. The preparation of halogen-substituted aromatic compounds from the corresponding diazonium compounds by treatment with cupric salts and the corresponding halogen acid.

$$C_6H_5N_2Cl \xrightarrow[HCl]{CuCl_2} C_6H_5Cl + N_2.$$

Similarly, treatment with KCN and the cupric salt yields the nitrile. See also **Gattermann reaction** and **Sandmeyer reaction**.

KORNER METHOD. An absolute method for the establishment of the **orientation** of the **substituents** in derivatives of benzene based upon the number of **isomers** that can be produced by further substitution in the ring. For example, nitration of *o*-dibromobenzene leads to two isomeric (mono-nitro) derivatives; *m*-dibromobenzene leads to three isomers; *p*-dibromobenzene can lead to only one isomer.

KOSTANECKI-ROBINSON REACTION. The Kostanecki reaction is a method of acylation of *o*-hydroxyarylketones by anhydrides and sodium salts of aliphatic acids to form chromones or coumarins. If the sodium salt of an aromatic acid is used instead, yielding flavones, the reaction is called the Allan-Robinson condensation. In the Bargellini reaction, sodium phenyl acetate is used as the acid component to give coumarins.

KOURBATOFF REAGENT. One of several etching solutions used to develop the crystal structure of steel for microscopic examination. They are all solutions of hydrochloric or nitric acids in various simple alcohols, and are sometimes used in conjunction with solutions of nitroaniline in alcohol.

KOWALEWSKY SOLUTION. A solution of 0.5 g. uranium acetate in 100 ml. water, used as a test reagent for albuminous substances. A yellow precipitate is given by albumin.

Kr Symbol for the element **krypton.**

KRAFT METHOD. See **degradation of acids.**

KRASE PROCESS. A process for the production of urea by the reaction of liquid carbon dioxide and liquid ammonia in an autoclave.

KRATZMANN CESIUM CHLORIDE SOLUTION. A mixture of a 33.6% solution of cesium chloride with an equal volume of a 39.2% solution of sulfuric acid, used in testing for aluminum in plants. Formation of crystals of cesium alum is positive.

KRAUSKOPF-PURDY REAGENT. A solution of 100 g. cuprous chloride in 1 liter hydrochloric acid, heated at 60° C. with copper turnings until decolorized. It is used, after dilution and addition of stannous chloride, in carbon monoxide absorption apparatus.

KRAUSKOPF-SWARTZ TEST FOR MOLYBDENUM. The nitrate residue is extracted with ammonia, filtered and neutralized with hydrochloric acid. Add potassium thiocyanate, extracting any red color with ether, then add zinc and hydrochloric acid until gas evolves. Molybdenum gives a deep red color.

KRAUT REAGENT. A mixture of a concentrated aqueous solution containing 27.2 g. potassium iodide, and a solution of 8 g. bismuth subnitrate in 20 g. of nitric acid (sp. gr. 1.18), which is filtered and diluted with water to 100 ml. after separation of the potassium nitrate crystals. It is used in testing for choline, which gives a brick-red precipitate with it.

KREIS REAGENT FOR DETECTING RANCIDITY. A solution of 0.1 g. phloroglucinol in 100 ml. ether, used in detecting rancidity in fats and oils. The material to be tested yields with this reagent, after treatment with hydrochloric acid, a red color if rancid fats are present.

KREIS-STUDINGER REAGENT. A reagent prepared by dissolving 4.4 g. potassium nitrite in 100 ml. of a saturated solution of mercuric chloride, and then adding 1 ml. of a 10% sodium carbonate solution. It is used in testing for vanillin in brandy. A wine-red color indicates the presence of vanillin.

KREIS TEST REACTION FOR OXALIC ACID. On heating with resorcinol and sulfuric acid, oxalic acid gives an indigo blue color which changes to violet with further heating and addition of acid.

KRÖHNKE SOLUTION. A solution of 1.49 g. isonitrosoacetophenone, in 100 ml. chloroform used as a test reagent for ferrous iron. A blue coloration, imparted by an ammoniacal solution of the sample, is given by ferrous iron.

KROMAYER LAMP. See **lamp, Kromayer.**

KRONBERGER SOLUTION. Two solutions: (1) a solution of 1 g. iodine and 2 g. potassium iodide in 200 ml. water; and (2) a solution consisting of 1 ml. of a saturated solution of gentian violet in 200 ml. water. These two solutions, and absolute alcohol, give a red color with pathological urine.

KRONMAN-BIBIKOVA MICRO-CHEMICAL REACTION FOR RHENIUM. A drop of the nitric acid solution tested is placed on a slide together with 1 drop nitron acetate solution and 1 drop sodium sulfide solution. One drop hot 10% gelatin solution is added, and when the gelatin has solidified, place on it 1 drop titanium trichloride solution. After an hour the nitron perrhenate crystals become colored brown-yellow with rhenium sulfide.

KRUISHEER TEST FOR IODIDE. A
yellow color, which can be extracted with amyl alcohol, is produced when an alkaline solution of an iodide is treated with excess hydrochloric acid and sodium sulfite solution.

KRUMHOLZ-FEIGL-RAJMANN REAGENT FOR PALLADIUM AND PLATINUM. p-Dimethylaminobenzylidenerhodanine, which gives violet precipitates with palladium and platinum; used in spot tests.

KRUMHOLZ-FEIGL-RAJMANN REAGENT FOR ZIRCONIUM. p-Dimethylaminoazobenzenearsonic acid, which is used to saturate filter paper. A drop of the solution to be tested is then applied, and the paper is immersed in warm $0.2 N$ hydrochloric acid. Brown spots indicate zirconium.

KRUMHOLZ-HÖNEL REAGENTS FOR MERCURY, COPPER, IRON, AND CADMIUM. Various dinaphthyl- and diphenylcarbazones, prepared by action of phosgene on ethereal solutions of the aryl hydrazines.

KRUMHOLZ-KRUH TEST FOR CADMIUM. Decolorize the ammoniacal solution tested with potassium cyanide, add 5 drops of a solution of 1 g. sodium selenite and 0.5 g. potassium cyanide in 100 ml. water. On cooling, shake with 1 ml. ether. A red-brown color in the interface indicates cadmium.

KRUMHOLZ-SANCHEZ REAGENT. A
solution of 8 g. mercuric chloride and 9 g. ammonium thiocyanate, in 100 ml. water, used as a test reagent for zinc. One ml. of this reagent and 1 ml. 0.02% cobalt chloride solution are added to 1 ml. of the neutral solution to be tested. A blue precipitate, formed in the interface on shaking with ether, indicates zinc.

KRYPTOMERISM. See tautomerism.

KRYPTON. Gaseous element. Symbol Kr. Atomic number 36. Atomic weight 83.8. Density (g. per liter at S.T.P.) 3.733. Melting point $-157°$ C. Boiling point $-152.3°$ C. 1,000,000 volumes of air contain (about) 0.05 volumes of krypton.

KUBIERSCHKY TOWER. A compartmented, stoneware tower used in the chlorination of brines containing magnesium bromide. The chlorine is admitted at the bottom, and the bromine (together with some chlorine and steam) is discharged at the top.

KUBINA-PLICHTA TEST REACTION FOR BISMUTH. Hot solutions of bismuth chloride or nitrate, on addition of 1% dimethylglyoxime solution and ammonia, give a quantitative, voluminous yellow precipitate.

KUCHEROV REACTION. The direct hydration of triple bonds in hydrocarbons to give carbonyl compounds. Mercuric salts catalyze the reaction.

$$HC\vdots CH + H_2O \rightarrow CH_3 \cdot CHO.$$

KUEVER SOLUTION. A solution of 2 g. precipitated sulfur in 100 ml. pyridine and 100 ml. carbon disulfide, used in testing for cottonseed oil. A wine-red color on heating with a sample of olive oil indicates the presence of cottonseed oil.

KUHN REAGENT. Two solutions: (1) a solution made by mixing 20 ml. 5% cupric sulfate solution with 10 ml. 20% ammonium hydroxide; and (2) a mixture of 20 ml. 85% phosphoric acid and 20 ml. water. They are used in testing for bile pigments in urine. A green color, formed in an alcoholic layer, is given by bile pigments.

KUHN-ROTH METHOD. A method of determination of terminal methyl groups by oxidation of the compound with chromic acid-sulfuric acid. The terminal methyl groups are converted to acetic acid, which is easily determined.

KUL'BERG-MATVEEO TEST FOR HYDROGEN PEROXIDE. Hydrogen

peroxide gives a blue color with *o*-toluidine in the presence of ferrous iron.

KUL'BERG TEST REACTION FOR CERIUM. On precipitation of its hydroxide with sodium hydroxide and treatment with leucomalachite green, cerium gives a blue color.

KUL'BERG TEST REACTION FOR COBALT. Acidify the solution tested with acetic acid and place a drop on filter paper, plus 1 drop ammonium mercuric thiocyanate solution, and 1 drop sodium pyrophosphate solution. A blue spot on drying indicates cobalt.

KUL'BERG TEST REACTION FOR ZINC. To the solution tested, which should be slightly acid, add 4 drops of a dilute cobalt acetate solution, and 0.5 ml. ammonium mercuric thiocyanate solution. Zinc is indicated by a blue precipitate.

KUNDT EFFECT. The rotation of the plane of **polarized light** by certain liquids and gases when they are placed in a **magnetic field.**

KUNDT METHOD. A method of measuring the velocity of sound by means of longitudinal vibrations set up in a metal rod placed so as to develop stationary waves in air or other gas within a glass tube. A light powder, spread over the interior of the tube, is lumped together at the nodal points.

KUNDT RULE. When the **refractive index** of a solution increases, because of changes in composition or other causes, its **optical absorption bands** are displaced toward the red.

KUNZ-KRAUS REAGENT FOR CYANOGEN. A mixture of 10 ml. freshly-prepared 1:1000 aqueous cupric sulfate solution, with 15 ml. alcohol in which a granule of guaiaconic acid has been dissolved. Traces of cyanogen give a blue color at once.

KUNZ-KRAUSE REAGENT FOR DICYANOGEN. A mixture of 5 ml. of a 15% solution of potassium hydroxide and 2 ml.

of a saturated solution of picric acid, dissolved in 18 ml. alcohol. This solution is used in testing for dicyanogen. A purple color, changing to brown, is obtained if dicyanogen or hydrogen cyanide is present.

KURIE PLOT. A graphical relationship resulting from the Fermi equation for β-decay. The quantity $(N/f)^{\frac{1}{2}}$ is plotted against $E + 1$, where N is the number of β-particles that have a momentum, or energy, lying within a certain narrow range, and f is a function of the corresponding calculated values of the β-particle energy E. In accordance with the Fermi neutrino theory, this plot should be a straight line. This plot is also called the Fermi plot.

KUROWSKI REAGENT. A solution prepared by boiling thallium carbonate with an alcoholic solution of acetylacetone. It gives a yellow color or orange precipitate with carbon disulfide.

KURT MEYER METHOD. A method of analysis of keto-enol tautomeric mixtures, based upon the fact that the enol form absorbs bromine rapidly, whereas the keto form does not. (See **tautomerism.**)

KUTZLNIGG TEST FOR ISOBUTYL ALCOHOL. On heating with 1% potassium ferrocyanide solution, isobutyl alcohol gives a light brown to orange color.

KYANIZE. To protect against decay by saturating with aqueous mercuric chloride.

L. Abbreviation for molar latent heat (L). (The particular inter-state change is indicated by subscript letters.) Symbol for **solubility product** (L). Abbreviation for liter (l). Abbreviation for **latent heat per gram** (l). Abbreviation of levo- or levorotatory (l). Denoting configurational relationship *l*-glyceraldehyde (l). Abbreviation for length (l or L). Symbol for liquid rate (L); (liquid rate above feed L_n; below feed L_m). Symbol for **mass velocity** of liquid (L). Symbol for direction cosine (l, m, n). Symbol for **free path** (l or λ). Symbol for mean free path (l or λ). Symbol for Tait free path (l_T or λ_T). Symbol for relative **heat content** (L). Symbol for length of heat flow path (L, l). Symbol for **inductance** (*L*). Symbol for mutual inductance (L_{12}). **Miller indices** (*h, k, l*). Symbol for kinetic potential (*L*). Azimuthal or orbital **quantum number** (*l*). Total azimuthal or orbital quantum number (*L*). See also **lambda.**

L-ELECTRON. An electron having an orbit of such dimensions that the electron constitutes part of the second shell of electrons surrounding the atomic nucleus, counting out from the nucleus; orbitals in the L-shell are characterized by the **principal quantum number** value of 2 (i.e., the L-shell follows the K-, or innermost, shell).

L-LINE. One of the lines in the L-series of **x-rays,** which are characteristic of the various elements, and are produced by **excitation** of the electrons of the L-shell.

L-RADIATION. One of a series of **x-rays** characteristic of each element, that is emitted when that element, commonly as the metal, is used as an anti-cathode in an x-ray tube, and the electrons of its L-shell are excited.

L-SHELL. The second layer of electrons about the **nucleus** of an atom, the first or innermost being the K-shell, which consists of two electrons in the case of all elements, except hydrogen. The L-shell contains eight electrons in the case of neon (atomic number = 10) and of all elements of atomic number greater than ten. The L-shell is started with lithium (atomic number = 3), which has an L-shell containing one electron, and the L-shell of each atom of successively increasing atomic number has one more additional electron in its L-shell until neon, containing 8 electrons in its L-shell, is reached, at which point the L-shell is complete.

La Symbol for the element **lanthanum.**

LABICHE REAGENT. A solution of 50 g. lead acetate, in 100 ml. warm water, used in testing for cottonseed oil. Mix 25 ml. of this reagent with 25 ml. of the oil, heat to 35° C., and add 5 ml. ammonia. A yellow-red emulsion on mixing indicates the presence of cottonseed oil.

LABILE. A system or compound that is **unstable,** suffering conversion into a more stable form on slight disturbance. Thermolabile means modified by moderate heating, as certain **isomers, enzymes,** and **bacteria.**

LACHMAN PROCESS. A purification process for petroleum products obtained by **cracking,** in which the hot hydrocarbon vapor is treated with concentrated zinc chloride solution.

LACHRYMATOR. A substance which causes tears to form in the eyes.

LACQUER. A term originally applied to a varnish, which has since been extended to denote any coating solution which dries rapidly by evaporation of its solvent or solvents. In recent years the term lacquer has been used widely to denote specifically a coating solution which contains a cellulose ester as its chief ingredient.

LACROIX TEST. Titanium solutions give a wine-red color with solutions of morphine in sulfuric acid.

LACTAM. One of a group of cyclic **amides** containing the —NH—CO— grouping. For examples, two of the more common types of lactams are derived from the γ and δ amino-carboxylic acids by elimination of water — an intramolecular condensation. They correspond to the γ and δ lactones and are of the general type

$$\overline{NH—CH_2—CH_2—CH_2—C}=O$$

(γ lactam), and

$$\overline{NH—CH_2—CH_2—CH_2—CH_2—C}=O$$

(δ lactam). They are named from the **fatty acids** of like carbon content.

LACTATE. A compound containing the radical

$$\underset{O}{\overset{O}{\|}}C—CHOH—CH_3.$$

LACTAZAM. A type of compound which may be regarded as a **lactam** (group —NH—CO—), in which the lactam-nitrogen is joined to a second nitrogen atom, e.g., 3-methylpyrazolone.

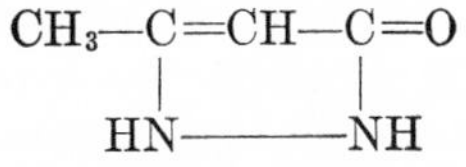

$$CH_3—C=CH—C=O$$
$$HN————NH$$

LACTAZON. See **lactoxime**.

LACTIC. Related to lactic acid,

$$CH_3 \cdot CHOH \cdot COOH.$$

LACTIDE. One of a group of cyclic double esters of the α-hydroxy acids. The lactides have the general type-formula:

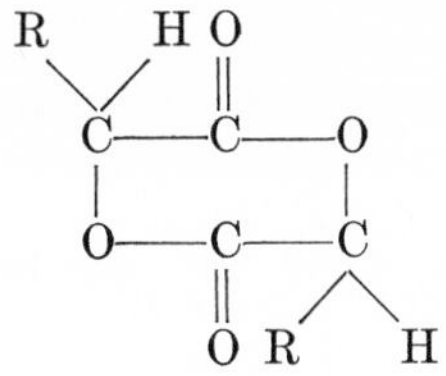

The two hydrogen atoms may be replaced by organic radicals, or the two radicals (R)

in the above formula may be replaced by hydrogen atoms to give glycollide, the simplest lactide.

LACTIM. One of a group of cyclic compounds, isomeric with the **lactams**, of which they are the enol forms.

Lactam form   Lactim form

LACTONE. One of a group of cyclic inner esters of the hydroxy acids formed by the elimination of the elements of water from one molecule of the hydroxy acid. They

are classified as α, β, γ, and δ according to the position relative to the carboxy carbon atom of the carbon atom connected to the hydroxy group.

Thus, the γ-hydroxy acid of type-formula,

$$RCHOH—CH_2—CH_2—COOH$$

yields a γ-lactone,

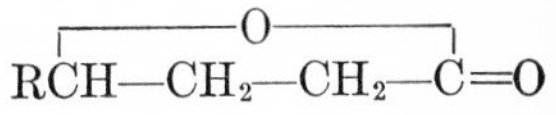

and the δ-hydroxy acid of type formula

$$RCHOH—CH_2—CH_2—CH_2—COOH$$

yields a δ-lactone

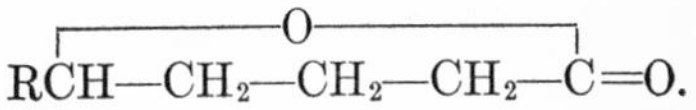

LACTONE RULES. See **Hudson lactone rules.**

LACTOXIME. (Lactozone. Isoxazolon.) One of a group of cyclic keto derivatives of the hypothetical dihydroisoxazole. They can be variously formulated,

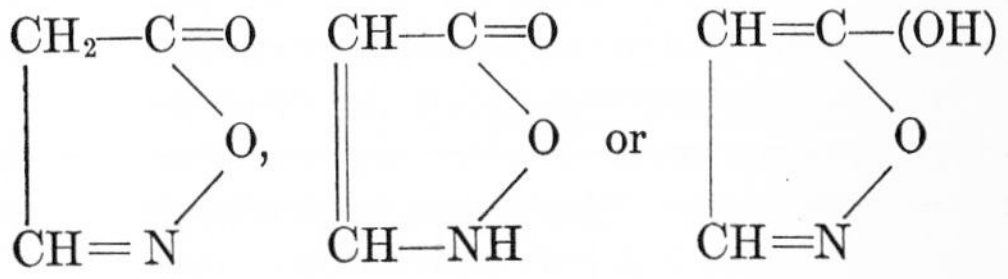

LACTYL. The radical $CH_3.CHOH.CO=$, derived from lactic acid.

LADENBURG FLASK. A distilling flask having bulbs (commonly 3) in its neck to give increased reflux area and permit closer fractionation.

LADENBURG, LAW OF. See **law of Ladenburg.**

LADENBURG STRUCTURE OF BENZENE. See **benzene, formulas.**

LADENBURG TEST FOR *o*-DIAMINES. On heating for a few minutes at 110–120° C. with benzaldehyde, an *o*-diamine hydrochloride evolves hydrogen chloride.

LAEVO-, LEVO-. (Latin *laevus*, left) To the left, as in levorotation; rotating the plane of polarization to the left; as, levovaline. Abbreviation, *l*; as, *l*-valine.

LAEVOROTATORY.   See **isomerism, optical.**

LAILLER REAGENT. A solution of 3 g. chromic acid in 22 ml. water, to which is added half its volume of concentrated nitric acid. This reagent is used in testing the purity of olive oil. On shaking 2 g. of the reagent with 8 g. of the oil, the mixture will solidify and turn blue on standing for a few days if the oil is pure.

LAKE. A precipitate of **dyestuff** or other coloring material, of natural or synthetic origin, with a metallic salt or other metallic compound. Lakes are widely used in dyeing, where they are commonly produced within the fiber by successive treatment with solutions of the metallic compound (called, in this connection, a mordant) and the color or dyestuff. Permanent dyeing results if the lake formed is insoluble, or is adsorbed upon the fiber, or is otherwise stabilized. Lakes are also used in ink manufacture, and for many other purposes. In dyeing, the color produced can often be varied, for the same dyestuff, by changing the metallic salt. Thus, alizarin produces blue lakes with calcium and barium, reddish with aluminum and tin, black-violet with ferric iron, and violet-brown with chromium.

LAKING. The process of forming an insoluble substance, in general, from soluble organic substances. See **lake.**

LAMBDA (Λ or λ). The eleventh letter of the Greek alphabet, used to denote: (1) the eleventh carbon atom in a straight-chain compound, or a derivative in which a substituent group is attached to that carbon atom (λ-). (2) Symbol for latent **heat of evaporation** (λ). (3) Symbol for equivalent **conductivity** (Λ). (4) Symbol for **microliter** (λ). Symbol for **wave length** (λ). Symbol for linear charge density (λ).

Decay or **radioactive disintegration constant** (λ). Symbol for linear mass density (λ). Symbol for **nuclear dissociation energy** (Λ). Symbol for mass per unit length (λ).

LAMBDA POINT (λ-POINT). The temperature at which the transition of helium I to helium II takes place. Under **orthobaric** conditions, liquid helium undergoes this change at 2.19° K.; but the temperature at which this change occurs decreases with increasing external pressure.

LAMBDA-S COUPLING. A type of **coupling** of the electrons of the atoms in a diatomic molecule, in which **S,** the resultant **spin vector** for all optical electrons, precesses about Λ, the resultant **orbital angular momentum** of the electrons about the internuclear axis.

LAMBERT. A unit of brightness equal to one **lumen** per square centimeter.

LAMBERT, LAW OF. See **law of Lambert.**

LAMP. In its derivation, this term denoted a device for producing light by combustion; its application has been extended to cover a wide range of devices for giving light and/or other radiant energy.

LAMP, ARC. A source of light consisting essentially of **electrodes** between which an electric **arc** is maintained.

LAMP, BLAST. A burner to which air or oxygen is supplied under pressure, to obtain a hotter flame with the (usually) gaseous fuel.

LAMP, FILAMENT. A device for producing light by an electrically-heated wire in a glass bulb that has been evacuated, or partially filled with an inert gas.

LAMP, HARCOURT. A standard of **intensity of illumination,** which produces light by the combustion of pentane.

LAMP, KROMAYER. A mercury vapor lamp, used as a source of **ultraviolet radiation.**

LAMP, MERCURY VAPOR. A lamp containing mercury in a previously-evacuated bulb or tube. The mercury-vapor conducts electricity between the electrodes, and yields a blue-green light, rich in ultraviolet. For uses where that radiation is wanted, the tube is made of quartz instead of glass.

LAMP, NERNST. An electric lamp in which the filament is composed of a metal oxide, which has the required conductivity only when heated. The lamp contains a starting device for furnishing the initial heat.

LAMP, QUARTZ. A lamp having a quartz bulb to transmit ultraviolet radiation; such lamps are commonly of the mercury-vapor type, or of other light-source rich in ultraviolet radiation.

LAMP, SPECTRUM. A lamp giving a nonluminous flame, used in the **spectroscopic** examination of radiation from solids, liquids, or solutions introduced into the flame.

LANDÈ SPLITTING FACTOR. A numerical factor introduced into calculations of the **magnetic moments** of atoms. The factor is related to the **spin, orbital angular,** and **total angular momentum** numbers of the atom.

LANDMARK PROCESS. A process for the production of ammonia from nitrogen, steam and carbon, using titanium nitride as an intermediate substance. Carbon monoxide is also a product of the process, and must be utilized for economic operation. The basic reaction is

$$2TiN_2 + 3H_2O + 3C \rightarrow 2TiN + 2NH_3 + 3CO.$$

followed by the renitrification of the titanium nitride,

$$2TiN + N_2 \rightarrow 2TiN_2.$$

LANDOLT REACTION. The reaction of iodic and sulfurous acids in the presence of starch. The blue color, due to the starch-iodide complex, is not observed at first, but appears after some time, depending on the concentration of the solution. It has been proved that the reaction takes place in three steps, and only at the third stage is there sufficient free iodine in the solution to produce the blue color with starch.

LANDSBERGER METHOD. A procedure for determining the boiling point of a solution by heating it with vapor from the boiling solvent. Superheating by this method is theoretically impossible.

LANE SYSTEM. A process for the manufacture of hydrogen. Iron ore is treated with Blau gas in heated retorts, and the result of the reaction is to reduce the iron oxide to metallic iron. Steam is then turned into the retorts and yields its oxygen to the iron, forming iron oxide and hydrogen. The cycle is continuous.

LANGE SOLUTION. A solution of 30 g. zinc chloride, 5 g. potassium iodide and 1 g. iodine, in 25 ml. water used as a test reagent for mercerized cotton.

LANGEVIN FORMULA. An expression relating **paramagnetic susceptibility** with temperature.

LANGHELD TEST REACTION. Benzaldehyde, on heating with dimethylaniline and ethyl metaphosphate, forms malachite green.

LANGMUIR ADSORPTION ISOTHERM. The relation between the amount of gas adsorbed by a definite mass of adsorbent, and the pressure. One form of this relationship is the following:

$$\theta = \frac{bp}{1 + bp}$$

where θ is the fraction of the surface covered by adsorbed gas, b is a constant, p the gas pressure. This equation is commonly known as the Langmuir isotherm. It can be obtained in the form:

$$\frac{p}{X/m} = \frac{1}{K_1 K_2} + \frac{p}{K_2}$$

in which X is the amount of gas adsorbed, m is the mass of adsorbent, p is the gas pressure, and K_1 and K_2 are constants. As is evident from the relationship, by the plotting of $\frac{p}{X/m}$ against p, a straight line should be obtained.

LANO-. (Latin, *lana*, wool) Relating to wool, as lanosterol.

LANTHANUM. Rare earth metallic element. Symbol La. Atomic number 57. Atomic weight 138.92. Two solid forms known, the α-form, stable at ordinary temperatures, density 6.194; the β-form obtained by heating at 350° C., density 6.17. Melting point 810° C. Valence 3 and possibly 2. Oxide La_2O_3. Lanthanum occurs in cerite, samarskite, and other minerals.

LA ROSA TEST REACTION. A solution containing magnesium, on addition of a few drops of a 0.5% aqueous solution of p-diaminobenzene, followed by potassium hydroxide solution drop-by-drop, gives a red-violet precipitate, forming a colorless solution with acids, but restored by alkalies.

LARSON TEST REACTION. Cholesterol and its esters are detected by a dark brown color given by a 25% solution of antimony pentachloride in chloroform.

LASSAIGNE REACTION FOR NITROGEN. Organic substances containing nitrogen form sodium cyanide on heating with metallic sodium. The cyanide may be detected by the blue color formed when its aqueous extract is treated with ferrous sulfate, ferric chloride, and hydrochloric acid.

LASSAIGNE SOLUTION FOR DIFFERENTIATING WOOL AND SILK. A solution of 10 g. lead acetate in 100 ml. water, to which potassium hydroxide is added until the initial precipitate redissolves. It is used in differentiating wool and silk; the former is colored brown, while the latter is unchanged.

LASSAR-COHN REAGENT FOR ALDEHYDES. A solution of 10 g. mercuric iodide and 5 g. potassium iodide in 50 ml. water, to which is added a solution of 20 g. barium hydroxide (or equivalent sodium hydroxide) in 50 ml. water. (Cf. **Nessler Reagent.**) The Lassar-Cohn reagent gives with aldehydes a brown precipitate insoluble in potassium cyanide.

LATENT HEAT OF FUSION. See **heat of fusion, latent.**

LATENT HEAT OF SUBLIMATION. See **heat of sublimation, latent.**

LATENT HEAT OF VAPORIZATION. See **heat of vaporization.**

LATHERING POWER. The power of a solution to produce foam, measured by the relative amount produced.

LATTICE PLANE. See **net plane.**

LAUE METHOD. A basic method of **diffraction of x-rays** by **crystals,** or prepared sections of crystals, to produce diffraction patterns, usually recorded photographically.

LAUE PHOTOGRAPH. A photograph of the diffraction pattern obtained from an **x-ray** beam after its passage through a **crystal.**

LAURIC. Related to lauric acid, $C_{11}H_{23}COOH$.

LAUROYL. The radical $CH_3(CH_2)_{10}CO-$ (from lauric acid).

LAURY FURNACE. A direct-fired rotary furnace for the production of salt cake and hydrochloric acid by the heating of an intimate mixture of niter cake and salt. The basic reaction is of the form:

$$NaHSO_4 + NaCl \rightarrow Na_2SO_4 + HCl.$$

LAUTH TEST FOR HYDROGEN SULFIDE. Hydrogen sulfide in weakly acid solution is colored violet by p-phenylenediamine hydrochloride and ferric chloride.

LAUTH TESTS FOR AROMATIC AMINES. One drop, or a tiny particle, of the amine is treated on a watch glass with ten drops 30% acetic acid. A little lead peroxide is placed on the edge of the watch glass, and moistened by the solution. Characteristic colors are obtained with many aromatic amines.

LAVOYE TEST FOR METALS. On adding to 1 ml. of the solution tested, a mixture of 1 ml. 10% resorcinol solution with 2 ml. 10% ammonium hydroxide, heating, and allowing to stand, characteristic colors are obtained with many metals.

LAW. A statement describing a general truth or general relationship, which formulates the conditions applying to various phenomena or their relationships.

LAW OF ALTERNATION. The spectra of the elements in successive groups of the periodic table of elements are characterized by alternations of odd and even term multiplicities. Thus the arc spectrum of potassium has a multiplicity of 2, calcium has values of 1 and 3, scandium, 2 and 4, titanium 1, 3, and 5, etc. In general, the elements of even valence have odd multiplets, whereas those of odd valence have even multiplets. A spectral multiplicity or multiplet is the number of spectral lines in an associated group of fine lines relatively close together.

LAW OF APPEARANCE OF UNSTABLE FORMS. The unstable forms of monotropic substances are obtained from a liquid or vapor state before the stable form appears.

LAW OF BABO. The addition of a nonvolatile solid to a liquid in which it is soluble lowers the vapor pressure of the solvent in proportion to the amount of substance dissolved.

LAW OF BEER (Absorption Law). A relationship applying to the absorption of a beam of parallel, monochromatic radiation in a homogeneous, isotropic medium. The law is expressed quantitatively in the equation:

$$P = P_o 10^{-\alpha bc}$$

in which:

P = transmitted radiant power.

P_o = incident radiant power, or a quantity proportional to it as measured with pure solvent in the beam.

α = absorptivity, a constant characteristic of the material and the frequency.

b = internal cell length, usually in centimeters.

c = concentration.

A = αbc absorbance.

LAW OF BEHRING. The blood serum of an animal which has been artificially rendered immune to a certain infectious disease, when injected into the body of another animal, has power to protect the latter individual against the same disease and to cure the disease after infection has occurred.

LAW OF BERTHOLLET. Different substances have different affinities for each other; which are evident only when they are in immediate contact with each other. The condition of equilibrium depends not only upon the chemical affinity but also upon the relative masses of the reacting substances.

LAW OF BERTHELOT-NERNST. The ratio of the activities of a substance in two phases is constant at a given temperature.

LAW OF BLAGDEN. The depression of the freezing point of a solution is, for small concentrations, proportional to the amount of dissolved substance.

LAW OF BOLTZMANN. A name sometimes given to the application of the principle of the equipartition of energy to a molecular system.

LAW OF BOUGUER. In a homogeneous medium, the absorption of radiant energy is directly proportional to the thickness of a small region of the medium through which the radiation passes; i.e., each layer of equal thickness absorbs an equal fraction of the light which traverses it. (See law of Beer.)

LAW OF BOYLE. (Mariotte's law. Law of Boyle-Mariotte.) At constant temperature the volume of a gas varies inversely as the pressure, and the pressure varies inversely as the volume. In other words, the product of the pressure and volume of a gas is constant at a given temperature. This law holds only for the ideal or perfect gas; all real gases depart from it to a greater or less extent.

LAW OF BREWSTER. The polarizing angle of a substance; i.e., the angle of incidence of light at which **polarization** of the reflected light is a maximum, is such that the reflected and refracted rays are at right angles to each other. Therefore, the index of refraction is equal to the tangent of the angle of polarization.

LAW OF BUNSEN-ROSCOE. In photochemical reactions, the extent of the change is proportional to the amount of radiant energy absorbed, which is a product of the intensity of the radiation and the time.

LAW OF CAILLETET AND MATHIAS. Also called the law of the rectilinear diameter. The mean value of the densities of a substance in the saturated vapor state and in the liquid state, at the same temperature, is a linear function of the temperature.

LAW OF CHARLES. The volume of a gas held at constant pressure varies directly as the absolute temperature. This law holds only for the ideal or perfect gas; all real gases depart from it to a greater or less extent.

LAW OF CHEMICAL EQUILIBRIUM. When a reversible chemical **reaction** of the type

$$aA + bB = pP + qQ \ldots$$

has reached **equilibrium,** one can define a quantity

$$K = \frac{C_P^p C_Q^q \cdots}{C_A^a C_B^b \cdots}$$

where C_A represents the activity of species A, etc., and where K is a constant at a given temperature.

LAW OF CLAUSIUS. The **specific heat** of a perfect gas at constant volume is independent of the temperature.

LAW OF COMBINING VOLUMES. See **law of Gay-Lussac** (2).

LAW OF COMBINING WEIGHTS. In every chemical compound the proportion by weight of each element may be denoted by a fixed number (a different one for each element) or by some integral multiple of that number.

LAW OF CONSERVATION OF ENERGY. The total quantity of energy in a closed system is constant. This law has been restated, in light of the relativistic relationship between matter and energy, in a form that applies to the total quantity of matter and energy in a system, taken together as a single entity.

LAW OF CONSERVATION OF MASS. (Law of the conservation of matter) This law has been put in the form that matter can neither be created nor destroyed. More accurately, the total mass of any system remains constant under all transformations. In light of the relativistic relationship between mass and energy, this law has been restated in a form that applies to the total quantity of mass and energy in a system, taken together as a single entity.

LAW OF CONSTANT COMPOSITION. See **law of definite proportions.**

LAW OF CONSTANT HEAT SUMMATION. (Law of Hess) The energy change involved in a chemical reaction or series of reactions in going from the initial condition of the system to the final condition is always the same and is independent of the intermediate course the reaction takes.

LAW OF CONSTANT PROPORTIONS. See **law of definite proportions.**

LAW OF CORRESPONDING STATES. If any two or more substances have the same **reduced pressure** (the same fraction or multiple of their respective critical pressure) and are at equal **reduced temperature**

(the same fraction or multiple of their respective critical temperature), their **reduced volumes** should be equal. These substances are said to be in corresponding states.

LAW OF COULOMB, ELECTROMAGNETIC. The force between two **electromagnetic poles** is directly proportional to the product of their pole-strengths, and inversely proportional to the square of the distance between them. The energy of attraction or repulsion between the two poles is proportional to the product of their pole strengths, and inversely proportional to the distance between them.

LAW OF COULOMB, ELECTROSTATIC. The force between two **electric charges** in a vacuum is directly proportional to the product of their magnitudes, and inversely proportional to the square of the distance between them.

LAW OF CURIE. For **paramagnetic** substances, the **susceptibility** is nearly inversely proportional to the absolute temperature.

LAW OF DALTON. The pressure exerted by a mixture of gases which do not react with each other is equal to the sum of the pressures which each gas would exert separately if it were alone in the containing vessel at the given temperature, that is, in a mixture each gas behaves as if it were alone. Cf. **law of Gay-Lussac** (1).

LAW OF DEFINITE PROPORTIONS. (Law of constant proportions, law of constant composition, Proust's law) Any specific compound always contains the same elements united in the same proportions by weight.

LAW OF DEGRADATION OF ENERGY. A name applied to the second law of thermodynamics (see **thermodynamics, second law of**), because of the statement that the **entropy** of an isolated system is increased by irreversible processes involving energy changes, and that therefore, the sum of the available energy tends to decrease.

LAWS OF DESLANDRES. 1st Law. In **band spectra**, the oscillation **frequencies** of the lines starting from one head form arithemetical series. More than one such series can proceed from the same head.

2nd Law. The differences in frequency of the heads of the bands in each group form an arithmetical series, but the arrangement of the heads is reversed from that of the lines forming each band.

LAW OF DIFFUSION, FICK. The rate of **diffusion** of particles across a given area is proportional in amount, and opposite in sign, to the **concentration** gradient. This relationship is defined by the equation:

$$dw = -D \frac{dc}{dx} dt,$$

where the diffusion coefficient D is the weight or material diffusing across a plane 1 square centimeter in area, and dw is the quantity diffusing across the plane in time dt when the concentration gradient is $-\frac{dc}{dx}$.

LAW OF DIFFUSION, GRAHAM. The rate of **diffusion** of a gas is inversely proportional to the square root of its density.

LAW OF DILUTION. See **law of Ostwald, dilution.**

LAW OF THE DISPLACEMENT OF EQUILIBRIUM. See **law of Le Chatelier.**

LAW OF DISTRIBUTION. (The partition law, distribution law of Nernst) If two partly or nearly immiscible liquids are in contact and a substance which is soluble in both liquids be added to the system, the addend will be distributed between them in such a way that the ratio of the concentrations of the two solutions formed is a constant regardless of the quantity of solute. (Measurable deviations from this law take place, especially in concentrated solutions, because of association, ionization, chemical action, etc.) The constant is termed the distribution ratio, constant, or coefficient, and the partition coefficient.

LAW OF DISTRIBUTION OF MOLECULAR VELOCITIES. At any given temperature different molecules of a gas have different velocities which range from very small to very large values. A large majority of molecules have velocities falling in a narrow range, but a small fraction of molecules have very low or high velocity. As the temperature is raised the maximum in the velocity distribution curve shifts to higher velocities and flattens out.

LAW OF DRAPER. The only radiation which is effective in causing a chemical change is that which is absorbed.

LAW OF DUANE-HUNT. The increment in energy of an electron passing through an **x-ray tube** determines directly the maximum frequency of x-rays obtainable.

LAW OF DULONG AND PETIT. The product of the **atomic weights** and the **specific heats** of the solid elements (i.e., their atomic heats or thermal capacities) have nearly always the same numerical value, about 6.4. Many substances obey the law. Exceptions include silicon, boron, beryllium, and carbon; at high temperatures even these substances give values approaching 6.

LAW OF ELECTROLYSIS. See **laws of Faraday.**

LAW OF EQUIVALENT RATIOS. See **law of Richter.**

LAW OF EQUIVALENT WEIGHTS. See **law of Richter.**

LAW OF ESTERIFICATION. (Victor Meyer's esterification law) When the hydrogen atoms in the two positions **ortho** to the **carboxyl group** in a substituted benzoic acid are replaced by radicals such as chlorine, bromine, nitro, methyl, and carboxyl, an acid results which can be esterified by means of hydrochloric acid and alcohol only with difficulty or not at all.

LAWS OF FARADAY. (1) The quantity of an electrolyte decomposed by the passage of an electric current is proportional to the quantity of electricity which passes. (2) The masses of any substances deposited or dissolved by a given quantity of electricity are proportional to their chemical equivalent weights.

LAW OF FERMAT. In the case of **refraction** and **reflection,** the path of a ray from one point to another by way of a refracting or a reflecting surface is either a maximum, or a minimum. This is true only of plane surfaces.

When the light ray travels from one point to another in a medium, the ray pursues that path which requires the least time.

LAW OF FOURIER. The rate of heat flow at a given point in a body is proportional to the area of the cross-section and the temperature gradient, both at the given point. The form of this relationship is:

$$\frac{dQ}{dt} = -kA\,\frac{dT}{dl}$$

where Q is quantity of heat, t is time, k is the proportionality constant (**thermal conductivity**) A is the cross-sectional area, T is temperature, and l is distance in the direction of heat flow.

LAW(S) OF FRESNEL-ARAGON. (1) Two rays of light polarized in the same plane interfere in the same manner as ordinary light.

(2) Two rays polarized at right angles do not interfere.

(3) Two rays polarized at right angles from ordinary light and brought into the same plane of polarization, do not interfere in the ordinary sense.

(4) Two rays polarized at right angles (obtained from plane **polarized light**) interfere when brought into the same plane of polarization.

LAW OF GAS VOLUMES. See **law of Gay-Lussac** (1).

LAW OF GASES, IDEAL. An **equation of state** relating the pressure, volume, and temperature of a gas as follows:

$$pV = RT$$

where p is the pressure, V the **molar volume,** T the absolute temperature, and R the **gas constant** (0.082 if p is in atmospheres, and V in liters/mole). This relation is not obeyed by real gases, although at low pressures the values obtained are close enough for most purposes.

LAW(S) OF GAY-LUSSAC. (1) (Law of volumes, law of Charles) The volume of a gas held at constant pressure varies directly as the absolute temperature. This law holds only for the ideal or perfect gas; all real gases depart from it to a greater or less extent. This law is also known as the law of Charles. (2) In all reactions involving gases, either as initial reactants or as products, or both, the proportions by volume of the gaseous substances can be expressed accurately by ratios of small whole numbers.

LAW OF GLADSTONE AND DALE. When a substance is compressed, or its temperature varied, the density alters and there is a corresponding variation in the **refractive index.** The form of this relationship is:

$$\frac{n+1}{\rho} = k$$

where n is the index of refraction, ρ is the density, and k is a constant.

LAW OF GRAHAM. See **law of diffusion, Graham.**

LAW OF GROTTHUSS-DRAPER. Only those radiations which are absorbed by the reacting system are effective in inducing chemical change.

LAW OF GROUP DISPLACEMENT. See **law of radioactive displacement.**

LAW OF GULDBERG AND WAAGE. A theory which embodied the principle that the rate of a chemical reaction is proportional to the active masses of the reacting substances. Guldberg and Waage were interested in the "affinity" coefficients, later "velocity" coefficients for reactions, which they found were especially useful for reversible reactions because they furnished a means for "determining the result of the reaction from any original condition of the four substances."

LAW OF HAÜY. Every crystalline substance of definite chemical composition has a specific crystalline form characteristic of that substance.

LAW OF HELMHOLTZ. See **law of Thompson.**

LAW OF HENRY. The amount of a gas dissolved by a given volume of a solvent at constant temperature is directly proportional to the pressure of the gas with which it is in equilibrium.

LAW(S) OF HESS. See **law of constant heat summation,** and **law of thermoneutrality.**

LAW OF IMPENETRABILITY OF MATTER. Two bodies cannot occupy the same region of space at the same time.

LAW OF INDEPENDENT MIGRATION OF IONS. See **law of Kohlrausch.**

LAW OF INTERMEDIATE REACTIONS. See law of successive reactions.

LAW OF ISOMORPHISM. See **law of Mitscherlich.**

LAW(S) OF JOULE. (1) The heat produced by a current is proportional to the square of the current and the time during which it flows, or $H = I^2Rt$ (R is the resistance). (2) (Kopp's law or rule, Woestyn's law or rule) The **molar heat** of a solid compound is approximately the sum of the **atomic heats** of its constituent elements.

LAW OF KICK. An expression for the energy consumed in grinding in terms of the fractional reduction in average size of the particles. It is of the form:

$$E = k \log \frac{l_1}{l_2}$$

where E is the energy consumed, k is a proportionality constant, and l_1 and l_2 are the linear dimensions of the initial and final particles, respectively.

LAW(S) OF KIRCHHOFF FOR NETWORKS. Two laws relating to electric networks carrying steady currents. The general case is that of n points or junctions, each one of which is connected with each of the $n - 1$ remaining points by a conductor containing a source of electromotive force. Kirchhoff's two statements are as follows:

(1) If conductors forming part of a network carrying a steady current meet at one point, the sum of the currents flowing toward the point is equal to the sum of those flowing away from it; or the algebraic sum of all the currents in these conductors is zero.

(2) Starting at any one of the junctions of such a network and following any succession of the conductors which form a closed path, around either way to the starting point, the algebraic sum of the products formed by multiplying the resistance of each conductor by the current through it is equal to the algebraic sum of the electromotive forces encountered on the journey. (In this reckoning, we call all currents moving with us positive, and all electromotive forces tending to cause such currents positive.)

LAW OF KIRCHHOFF, OPTICAL. The relation between the powers of **emission** and the powers of **absorption** for rays of the same wave length is constant for all bodies at the same temperature. First, a substance when excited by some means or other possesses a certain power of emission; it tends to emit definite rays, whose wave lengths depend upon the nature of the substance and upon the temperature. Second, the substance exerts a definite absorptive power, which is a maximum for the rays it tends to emit. Third, at a given temperature the ratio between the emissive and the absorptive power for a given wave length is the same for all bodies and is equal to the emissive power of a perfect **black body.**

LAW OF KOHLRAUSCH. The **conductivity** of a neutral salt in dilute solution is the sum of two values, one of which depends upon the **cation,** the other upon the **anion.** In other words, each ion contributes a definite amount to the total conductance of the electrolyte, independent of the nature of the other ion.

LAW OF KOPP. The **molar heat** of a solid compound is equal approximately to the sum of the **atomic heats** of its constituents.

LAW OF LADENBURG. The speed of a **photoelectron** is proportional to the square root of the **excitation voltage.**

LAW OF LAMBERT. The absorption of radiation by a homogeneous absorption medium is a function of its thickness. The mathematical expression is:

$$I = I_0 e^{-\alpha l}$$

in which I_0 is the intensity of **incident radiation,** I is the intensity of **emergent radiation,** e is base of natural logarithms, α is its absorption coefficient, and l is the thickness of the absorbing layer traversed by the light. Cf. **law of Beer.**

LAW OF LANDOLT-OUDEMAN. See **law of Oudeman.**

LAW OF LE CHATELIER. If a system in physical or chemical equilibrium be subjected to a change of temperature, pressure, concentration, or similar condition under which the system is in equilibrium, the state of the system will automatically tend to alter so as to minimize (or undo) the effect of the change. This law is also known as the **law of mobile equilibrium.**

LAW OF MARIOTTE. The product of the pressure and the volume of a gas is constant.

LAW OF MASS ACTION. For a homogeneous system the rate of a chemical reaction is proportional to the active masses of the reacting substances. This was the basic postulate of Guldberg and Waage. See **law of Guldberg and Waage.**

LAW OF MAXWELL, DISTRIBUTION. A mathematical relationship, derived by statistical mechanics, which expresses the distribution of molecular velocities at a given temperature of a gas which is at a steady state, i.e., one in which the number of molecules possessing a given velocity is constant. The term distribution of molecular velocities denotes the fraction of total number of molecules possessing a given velocity, or rather having velocities within a given range. See **law of distribution of molecular velocities.**

LAW OF MEYER. See **law of esterification.**

LAW OF MITSCHERLICH. Substances that are similar in crystalline form and chemical nature usually have similar chemical formulas. Mitscherlich extended this conception by concluding that the crystalline form of compounds was determined only by the number and arrangement of their constituent atoms, but this is by no means a general law.

LAW OF MOBILE EQUILIBRIUM. See **law of Le Chatelier.**

LAW OF MODULI, VALSON. For moderate concentrations, the densities of salt solutions show constant differences for substitutions of **anion** or **cation,** i.e., the difference in density in normal solutions of potassium and ammonium salts of the same acid is 0.280 to 0.288; and that between chlorides and nitrates of the same base in normal solution is 0.0141 to 0.0150.

LAW OF MOLECULAR CONCENTRATION. A slightly-modified form of the **law of mass action** (q.v.) also proposed by Guldberg and Waage. Instead of relating the rate of reaction of a system to the active masses of the reactants, as is done by the law of mass action, the law of molecular concentration relates the rate of reaction to the **molecular concentrations** of the reactants. Cf. **law of chemical equilibrium.**

LAW OF MOSELEY. The square root of the frequency of a line in the **x-ray series** of a given element varies directly with the **atomic number** of the element. The relationship is of the form:

$$\sqrt{\nu} = a(Z - \sigma)$$

where ν is the frequency of the given line in the x-ray series of an element, Z is the atomic number of the element, and a and σ are constants, σ having the same value for all the lines of a given series.

LAW OF MULTIPLE PROPORTIONS. When two elements combine in more than one proportion the quantities of the first which are combined with a given amount of the second stand in the ratio of small whole numbers.

LAW OF THE MUTUALITY OF PHASES. If two phases, with respect to a certain definite reaction, at a certain temperature, are in equilibrium with a third phase, then at the given temperature and for the same reaction, they are in equilibrium with each other.

LAW OF NERNST. See **law of distribution.**

LAW OF NEUMANN. With chemical compounds of the same formula, and of a similar chemical constitution, the product of the **molecular weight** by the **specific heat** is a constant quantity.

LAW OF NEWTON FOR HEAT LOSS (COOLING). The heat lost by radiation and convection from one body to another is proportional to the temperature difference between the two bodies. This law holds only for small temperature differences and then only approximately.

LAW OF NEWTON (GRAVITATION). Every body attracts every other body with a force that is directly proportional to the product of their masses, and inversely proportional to the square of the distance between their centers of mass.

LAW(S) OF NEWTON (MOTION). (1) Every body persists in its state of rest or of uniform motion in a straight line, unless it is compelled by some force to change that state. (2) The rate of change of the momentum of a body is proportional to the force acting and is in the direction of the force. (3) For every action there exists an equal and oppositely directed reaction.

LAW OF OCTAVES. Newland's name for his hypothesis of the periodic system. His arrangement was a simple grouping of the elements in order of increasing atomic weight, beginning with lithium, in horizontal rows of eight elements each, beginning each new row directly beneath the previous one.

LAW OF OHM. The strength of a direct, continuous electric current is directly proportional to the **electromotive force** and inversely proportional to the resistance in the circuit.

LAW OF OSTWALD (DILUTION). The relationship:

$$K = \frac{\alpha^2 C}{1 - \alpha}$$

where α is the degree of **dissociation,** and C is the total concentration of solute. This expression is only approximate, because the effect of the **activities** of the ions and molecules has been disregarded.

LAW OF OUDEMAN. (Law of Landolt-Oudeman) The **molecular rotations** of the salts of **optically active** acids or bases always tend to a definite limiting value as the concentration of the solution diminishes; e.g., the soluble salts of α-bromosulfocamphoric acid show identical molecular rotations in hundredth normal solutions.

LAW OF PARTIAL PRESSURES. See law of Dalton.

LAW OF PARTITION. See **law of distribution.**

LAW OF PASCAL. In an incompressible fluid, pressure is equally transmitted in all directions and, therefore, if the pressure at any point is increased, there will be an equal increase of pressure at every point. Moreover, in a fluid at rest, the difference of pressure between two points depends only on the difference of level and the density.

LAW OF PASCHEN. The **sparking potential** between electrodes in a gas depends on the length of the spark gap and the pressure of the gas in such a way that it is directly proportional to the mass of gas between the two electrodes, i.e., the sparking potential is a function of the pressure times the density of the gas.

LAW OF PEPTIC ACTIVITY. The amount of coagulated protein digested by a peptase is proportional to the time.

LAW OF PHOTOCHEMICAL ACTION. See **law of Draper.**

LAW OF PHOTOCHEMICAL EQUIVALENT. See **law of Stark-Einstein.**

LAW OF PROPORTIONALITY. See **law of Richter.**

LAW OF PROUT. See **law of definite proportions.**

LAW OF RADIOACTIVE DECAY. The rate of decay (i.e., rate of decrease in activity) of a radioactive substance is proportional to the **radioactivity** of the substance at that time; expressed mathematically,

$$-\frac{dI}{dt} = \lambda I$$

where $-\dfrac{dI}{dt}$ is the rate of decay of the substance, I is the instantaneous value of its radioactivity, and λ is the **radioactive constant.**

LAW OF RADIOACTIVE DISPLACEMENT OR THE GROUP DISPLACEMENT LAW. The **atomic number** of an element produced by a radioactive disintegration is determined by the atomic number of the parent element and by the particle emitted. Specifically, emission of an α- or a β-particle by an element results in a new element with atomic number 2 units lower or 1 unit higher, respectively, than that of the parent element.

LAW OF RAOULT. The **vapor pressure** of a **solution** is given by

$$p = p_0 x$$

where p_0 is the vapor pressure of the pure solvent, and x is the **mole fraction** of solvent.

LAW OF RECIPROCAL PROPORTIONS. (Law of equivalent proportions) The weights, or their multiples and submultiples, of elements reacting with a definite fixed weight of another element, also react with each other. Cf. **law of Richter.**

LAW OF RECTILINEAR DIAMETER. See **law of Cailletet and Mathias.**

LAW OF RETGERS. The physical properties of isomorphous mixtures (mixed crystals) are continuous functions of the percentage composition.

LAW OF RICHTER. (Law of Wenzel, law of proportionality, law of equivalent ratios) The weights of various acids which will neutralize a certain fixed weight of one of the bases will neutralize certain fixed weights of all the bases, and the bases will neutralize the acids according to the same weights, i.e., each acid and base may be assigned an equivalent weight. Cf. **law of reciprocal proportions.**

LAW OF ROBIN. When a system is in a condition of either chemical or physical **equilibrium,** an increase of pressure favors the system formed with a decrease in volume; a reduction in pressure favors the system formed with an increase in volume; and a change of pressure has no effect upon a system formed without a change in volume. Cf. **law of Le Chatelier.**

LAW OF SCHÜTZ AND BORRISSOW. The amount of material digested by an **enzyme** is proportional to the square root of the amount of enzyme. Where t = the time, C_f = concentration of the enzyme, and x = the amount digested,

$$x = tK\sqrt{C_f}.$$

Cf. **law of peptic activity.**

LAW(S) OF SNELL. (1) When light passes from one medium to another, the incident ray, the normal to the surface at the point of incidence, and the refracted ray are all in the same plane.

(2) The sine of the angle of incidence bears to the sine of the **angle of refraction** a ratio which is constant for the same two media, and depends only on the nature of those media.

$$\frac{\sin i}{\sin r} = \mu, \text{ index of refraction}$$

i = angle of incidence.

r = angle of refraction.

LAW OF SPECIFIC HEATS. See **law of of Dulong and Petit.**

LAW OF SPECTROSCOPIC DISPLACEMENT. The arc spectrum (see **spectrum, arc**) of an element is similar, especially in regard to **fine structure,** to the first spark spectrum (see **spectrum spark**) of the element one place higher in the periodic table, to the second spark spectrum of the element two places higher, and so on. Since the lines in the arc spectrum are commonly those of the normal atom, while the first spark spectrum contains lines of the singly-ionized atom, the second spark spectrum, those of the double-ionized atom, and so on, this law asserts a similarity between the spectrum of an unionized atom, and that of a singly-ionized atom of an element one place higher in the periodic table, and that of a doubly-ionized atom two places higher in the table, etc.

LAW OF STARK-EINSTEIN. Also known as the law of photochemical equivalence. Each molecule entering into a photochemical reaction (i.e., a reaction induced by exposure to light) absorbs one **quantum** of the characteristic radiation by which the reaction is induced.

LAW OF STEFAN AND BOLTZMANN. A relationship between quantity of **thermal radiation** and the temperature of its source. It states that the total radiation energy radiated from a perfect radiator, such as the ideal **black body,** is directly proportional to the fourth power of the absolute temperature.

LAW OF STEWART AND KIRCHHOFF. See **law of Kirchhoff, optical.**

LAW OF STOKES. A basic relationship applying to the motion of a small sphere through a fluid. In a simple form, representing the force required to sustain the motion of a small sphere through a fluid, the relationship is:

$$f = 6\pi r \eta V$$

where f is the required force to maintain motion at velocity V of a sphere of radius r in a fluid of viscosity η. For a solid sphere falling through a fluid (or a liquid one through a gas), the relationship is:

$$V_m = \frac{2gr^2(\rho_s - \rho_l)}{9\eta}$$

where V_m is the maximum velocity attained by a sphere of radius r falling in a fluid of viscosity η, and ρ_s is the density of the sphere and ρ_f that of the fluid, and g is the acceleration of gravity.

LAW OF STUFFER. All **sulfones** in which sulfone groups are attached to two adjacent carbon atoms can be saponified. Ethylene-diethyl sulfone is an example of such a compound:

$$CH_2—SO_2—C_2H_5$$
$$|$$
$$CH_2—SO_2—C_2H_5.$$

LAW OF SUCCESSIVE REACTIONS. (OSTWALD) In the formation of a consecutive series of intermediate compounds in a chemical process the compound which involves the smallest loss of **free energy** will be formed first, and the one which involves the next smallest loss of free energy second, and so on. This is also known as the law of intermediate reactions, or of intermediate stages.

LAW OF THERMONEUTRALITY (HESS). When solutions of two soluble salts are mixed, no heat effect is observed, provided they do not form a slightly soluble precipitate, a volatile gas, a complex ion, or a weak salt.

LAW OF THOMPSON. (Law of Helmholtz, Thompson's rule) In an electric cell the **heat of reaction** is a direct measure of the **electromotive force**, i.e., the chemical energy is simply converted into electrical energy. This is only approximately true, for part of the energy of an electric cell appears as heat, either absorbed or evolved as the case may be.

LAW OF TROUTON. The ratio of the molar **latent heat of evaporation** of a liquid to its boiling point is a constant, approximately 21. This rule applies only in a limited number of cases.

LAW OF VAN'T HOFF. A dissolved substance has the same **osmotic pressure** as the gas pressure it would exert in the form of an **ideal gas** occupying the same volume as that of the solution.

LAW OF WENZEL. See **law of Richter.**

LAW OF WIEDEMANN - FRANZ - LORENZ. For all good conductors at the same temperature, the ratios of the thermal to the electrical conductivities are closely similar; at different temperatures the ratio is proportional to the absolute temperature.

LAW OF WIEN. There is a definite, direct relationship between the absolute temperature of a perfect radiator, and the wave length at which intensity of radiation is a maximum. As the temperature of the **black body** increases, the position of the maximum is displaced toward shorter wave lengths.

LAW OF WÜLLNER. The modification of the **osmotic** properties of water by a dissolved substance, notably the reduction of the vapor pressure, is a direct function of the concentration of the solute.

LAW, PERIODIC. The properties of the elements are periodic functions of their atomic weights.

LAXATIVE. A drug that causes bowel evacuation.

LAYER, MONOMOLECULAR. See **film, monomolecular.**

LEA REAGENT FOR CYANIDES. A solution of 1 g. ferrous ammonium sulfate, and 1 g. cobalt or uranium nitrate, in 250 ml. water, used as a test reagent for cyanides. A red color (ring test) is given by cyanides.

LEA TEST FOR HYPOSULFUROUS ACID. A solution of hyposulfurous acid, after supersaturating with ammonia, gives a red color on boiling with ruthenium sesquichloride.

LEACH TEST FOR FORMALDEHYDE IN MILK. On heating 10 ml. of milk with 10 ml. of hydrochloric acid (sp. gr. 1.2) containing 2 ml. of 10% ferric chloride per liter, a violet color indicates the presence of formaldehyde.

LEACHING. Treatment of a solid by a liquid, in order to remove soluble components of the solid.

LEAD. Metallic element. Symbol Pb. (Plumbium). Atomic number 82. Atomic weight 207.21. Density 11.36. Specific heat 0.0293. Melting point 327.43° C. Boiling point about 1620° C. Valence 2 and 4. Oxides Pb_2O, PbO (Litharge), Pb_2O_3, Pb_3O_4, (Minium), PbO_2. Metaplumbic acid H_2PbO_3. Lead forms two series of compounds, the plumbic and plumbous. It occurs native as sulfide, carbonate, etc.

LEAD TREE. The precipitate of metallic lead which occurs when a bar of zinc is suspended in an aqueous solution of a lead salt. The lead adheres to the zinc and assumes an arboreal form.

LEAF FILTER. See **filter, leaf.**

LEAKE-GUY FLUID. A solution of 0.05 g. crystal violet, 6 ml. formalin, and 1.6 g. sodium oxalate in 94 ml. water, used for diluting and preserving blood.

LEBEDEV PROCESS. A method of producing butadiene by heating ethanol with a suitable catalyst.

LE CHATELIER RULE. See **law of Le Chatelier.**

LECITHOPROTEIN. One of a group of compounds of lecithins with proteins, as phosphatids. See **proteins.**

LE CLAIRE-SOREL PROCESS (ZINC OXIDE). See **French process (zinc oxide).**

LECLANCHÉ CELL. A primary **cell**, consisting of a single electrolyte of ammonium chloride solution, and electrodes of zinc and carbon. Its modified form is the well-known dry cell.

LECLÈRE TEST FOR NITRITE IN PRESENCE OF NITRATE. To the solution tested, add with mixing an equal volume syrupy citric acid. Float on this mixture a ferrous ammonium sulfate solution. A brown ring at the interface shows nitrite.

LECOCQ REACTION FOR MOLYBDENUM. Solutions of sodium or ammonium molybdate acidified with hydrochloric acid give an indigo-violet color with an alcoholic solution of diphenylcarbazide.

$$2CH_3CH_2OH \xrightarrow{300-400° C} CH_2{=}CH{-}CH{=}CH_2 + 2H_2O + H_2.$$

LE BLANC PROCESS. A method for the production of sodium carbonate from salt, sulfuric acid, limestone, and coal. The salt is treated with the sulfuric acid, forming sodium sulfate, which is reduced to sodium sulfite by fusion with the coal (or coke), and finally the sodium sulfide is heated with the limestone to yield sodium carbonate.

LE CHATELIER-DUPUY REAGENT. A solution of 0.5 g. picric acid, 1–2 ml. concentrated hydrochloric acid, and 1.0 g. cupric chloride in 10 ml. water and 100 ml. alcohol, used for etching steel, to show phosphorus segregation.

LE CHATELIER-LEMOINE REAGENT. A solution of 40 g. magnesium chloride, 20 ml. hydrochloric acid and 10 g. cupric chloride in 180 ml. water and 1000 ml. absolute alcohol, used for etching steel, to show phosphorus segregation.

LEDERER-MANASSE REACTION. A method of preparation of phenolic alcohols by the controlled addition of phenols to formaldehyde.

See also **Baekeland process.**

LEGAL SOLUTION. An alkaline solution of 10 g. sodium nitroprusside in 30 ml. water, used in testing for acetone in urine. A characteristic series of color changes, beginning with red, is obtained.

LÉGER TEST REACTION FOR BISMUTH. A warmed solution of 1 g. cinchonine in 100 ml. water and a little nitric acid, to which 2 g. potassium iodide is added, gives an orange precipitate with bismuth solutions.

LEGLER TEST FOR FORMALDEHYDE. Distill the liquid to be tested, add excess ammonium hydroxide to the distillate, evaporate until little ammonia is left, and add bromine water. A yellow color or precipitate indicates formaldehyde.

LEITMEIER-FEIGL TEST FOR CHROMIUM IN MINERALS. Fuse with sodium carbonate or sodium peroxide, leach with water and add an alcoholic solution of diphenylcarbazide. A color change from red to violet indicates chromium.

LEITMEIER-FEIGL TEST FOR MAGNESIUM IN MINERALS. Heat the powdered mineral with a solution of nitrobenzeneazoresorcinol containing excess sodium hydroxide. (Silicates must first be decomposed, and iron interferes.) A blue color indicates magnesium.

LEITMEIER TEST FOR MANGANESE IN MINERALS. Dissolve the mineral, and, to a drop of the solution on filter paper, add 2–3 drops potassium hydroxide solution and an acetic acid solution of benzidine. A blue color indicates manganese.

LEJUENE SOLUTION. A solution of 2.5 g. p-diaminodiphenylamine sulfate in 250 ml. alcohol, used in testing flour for benzoyl peroxide. A blue-green color, in petroleum benzine solution, is given by benzoyl peroxide.

LELLI REAGENT. A solution of 1 g. gold chloride in 10 ml. concentrated hydrochloric acid, used as test reagent for indican in urine. A violet color is obtained with urine containing indican.

LELLMANN TEST. To differentiate diamines, dissolve the salt of the diamine in water, add ammonium thiocyanate, and evaporate to dryness. Heat residue 1 hour at 120° C., wash with water, and add alkaline lead solution, with heating; m- and p-diamines give a black precipitate; o-diamines do not.

LE MITHONARD SOLUTION. A solution of 20 g. tartaric acid and 4 g. ferrous sulfate, in 200 ml. water, used in testing for picric or picramic acid in urine. The urine

is treated with lead acetate solution, filtered, the excess lead is precipitated with sulfuric acid. After another filtration, the solution is extracted with chloroform, the extract is added to water and ammonia, and the reagent is then added. The appearance of a red ring at the interface indicates the presence of picric or picramic acid.

LEMOULT TEST REACTION. On heating with phosphorous pentachloride at 80–100° C., dimethylaniline produces a blue color, which disappears at higher temperatures.

LENARD RAY. Fluorescence **radiation** of characteristic appearance obtained on passage of cathode rays (electrons) through metallic films or sheets.

LENHER-CRAWFORD TEST. A solution of thymol in alcohol and acetic acid, to which sulfuric acid is added, gives a pale red color with titanium salts.

LENNARD-JONES POTENTIAL. A potential energy function representing the total interaction between two molecules and based on a soft-sphere molecular model. The attractive potential depends inversely on the sixth power of the distance between the molecules, and the repulsive potential on the inverse twelfth power of the distance.

LENS. A device which converges, or diverges, **radiation**; most commonly, a piece of glass or other transparent material, or an assembled group of such pieces, with a curved surface or surfaces.

LENS, ACHROMATIC. A **lens** corrected for **chromatic aberration,** so that light rays of different frequencies are brought to the same focus.

LENS, APLANATIC. A **lens** corrected for **spherical aberration** so that light rays are brought into focus in the same plane.

LENS, APOCHROMATIC. A **lens** corrected for both **chromatic aberration** and **spherical aberration.**

LENS, COMPOUND. A closely-grouped system of two or more lenses, through which the light passes in order.

LENS, CONCAVE. A **lens** having its center thinner than its periphery.

LENS, CONVEX. A **lens** having its center thicker than its periphery.

LENTICULAR. Lens-shaped.

LENZ-RICHTER TEST REACTIONS FOR PER-SALTS. When to a 1% solution of a per-salt, 2 drops 10% potassium iodide solution are added, iodine is liberated by persulfate only. On acidifying with dilute sulfuric acid, iodine is also liberated by perborate and potassium percarbonate, but not by perchlorate.

LENZ-SCHOORL TEST. A microscopic test with ammonium uranyl acetate solution some of which is placed on a slide; and at the margin of the drop is placed some of the powdered material tested. The formation of tetrahedral crystals of sodium uranyl acetate indicates the presence of sodium.

LEONE TEST. Cottonseed oil is detected by the formation of a brown ring on heating the oil tested with a 1% alcoholic solution of silver nitrate to which 0.5% nitric acid has been added.

LEPAGE REAGENT. A solution of potassium cadmium iodide used as a precipitant for alkaloids.

LE ROY REAGENT. A solution of 1 g. hexamethyl-tri-p-aminotriphenylmethane, in 20 ml. of a 1:1 aqueous solution of concentrated hydrochloric acid, which is then diluted to 100 ml. This reagent is used in testing for free chlorine in water. A violet color in dilute solution indicates the presence of chlorine.

LE ROY TEST FOR FREE CHLORINE IN HYDROCHLORIC ACID. The presence of chlorine is indicated by a blue color on the addition of diphenylamine to the acid.

LESSING RING. A type of tower packing, consisting of small-diameter metallic tubing formed into irregular curved shapes.

LETTS SYNTHESIS. A method of formation of nitriles by heating acids with metallic thiocyanates.

$$RCOOH + NaSCN \xrightarrow{\Delta} RCN + NaHS + CO_2.$$

LEUC-, LEUCO-. (Greek) Colorless, white, as leucine; specifically, denoting a colorless or weakly colored compound closely related to a colored compound, as leucomethylene blue.

LEUCEIN. One of a series of unsaturated **glycines** of the general formula:

$$C_nH_{2n-4}O_2N.$$

LEUCHTER REAGENT FOR HYDROGEN PEROXIDE. A mixture of (1) 50 g. of a solution of 0.8 g. borax and 10 g. glycerol in 50 ml. water, with (2) 50 g. of a 1% aqueous solution of cobalt chloride. This reagent is used in making a ring test for hydrogen peroxide. A brown to black ring indicates the presence of hydrogen peroxide.

LEUCHTER REAGENTS FOR PINE OIL AND TURPENTINE OIL. (1) A solution of 1 g. o-nitrobenzaldehyde and 10 g. 15% sodium hydroxide solution in 30 ml. alcohol and 20 ml. water. A yellow-brown to black color is produced by pine oil, and a yellow color by turpentine oil.

(2) A mixture of 0.3 g. phloroglucinol, 3.0 g. ethyl alcohol, 7.5 g. glycerol, 3.75 g. water and 15.0 g. 25% hydrochloric acid. A rose to indigo color is produced by pine oil, and a light yellow to light brown color by turpentine oil.

LEUCKART REACTION. The reductive **alkylation** of ammonia or **amines** (except tertiary amines) by **carbonyl** compounds and formic acid.

$$RNH_2 + \begin{array}{c} R' \\ \diagdown \\ CO \\ \diagup \\ R'' \end{array} + HCOOH \rightarrow \begin{array}{c} R' \\ \diagdown \\ CH.NHR \\ \diagup \\ R'' \end{array} + CO_2 + H_2O.$$

If this reaction is carried out with formaldehyde and formic acid, it is known as the Eschweiler-Clarke modification.

$$RNH_2 + H_2CO + HCOOH \rightarrow CH_3.NHR + CO_2 + H_2O.$$

LEUCKART THIOPHENOL REACTION. A method of formation of **thiophenols** (or their alkyl ethers) from **diazo compounds** and **xanthates.** The reation takes place in two stages.

$$(1) \quad ArN_2Cl + NaS.CS.OR \xrightarrow{\Delta} ArS.CS.OR + N_2 + NaCl.$$

The intermediate compound yields the thiophenol on hydrolysis in alkaline solution, or the thioether by simple heating.

$$(2)\ ArS.CS.OR + H_2O \rightarrow ArSH + HSCOOR$$

$$(2)\ ArS.CS.OR \xrightarrow{\Delta} ArSR + COS.$$

LEUCO BASE. One of a great number of colorless reduction products of certain **dyestuffs,** notably of the triphenylmethane derivatives, which on oxidation are converted back into the dyestuffs.

LEUCOMAINE. One of a number of **protein** degradation products, formed in animal tissues, which are somewhat similar to the ptomaines.

LEUCYL. The radical

$$(CH_3)_2CHCH_2CH(NH_2)CO—$$

(from leucine).

LEVEL WIDTH. The **uncertainty factor** in the determination of the energy of a particular **excited state** of a nucleus. It is proportional to the probability that the nucleus, in the given energy state, will undergo change per unit time.

LEVELER. A substance added to a product to reduce the variation in magnitude of

LEVELING AGENT. A substance which is added to a dye bath to bring about a level precipitation of the **dye** upon the fiber.

LEVELING BULB. A device for adjusting the pressure of gas in laboratory measuring apparatus to the pressure of the atmosphere, usually in order to measure the volume of gas at a pressure that is known.

The leveling bulb is an open glass vessel, connected to the gas burette by a rubber tube that is filled with water or other liquid. By moving the bulb until the liquid level in it is in line with that in the burette, the pressure in the latter is made atmospheric.

LEVELING EFFECT. The effect of a **proptophilic** solvent, such as water, in equalizing the difference between acids in their tendency to ionize.

LEVENE-BEATTY REAGENT FOR AMINO ACIDS. A very concentrated solution of phosphotungstic acid, containing 2–4 parts of the acid to 1 part of water, used as a precipitant for amino acids.

LEVENE-HUDSON ISOROTATION RULE. Certain derivatives of the sugar acids (their phenylhydrazides, amides, salts, and acylated nitriles) are related in their rotations to the configurations of the second carbon atoms; when the hydroxyl group on this carbon is to the right in the ordinary planar sugar formula, these derivatives rotate the plane of polarization of polarized light to the right, and *vice versa.*

LEVENSTEIN PROCESS. An industrial method of producing mustard gas from sulfur chloride and ethylene.

$$2CH_2{=}CH_2 + S_2Cl_2 \rightarrow ClCH_2.CH_2.S.CH_2.CH_2Cl + S.$$

some property during the processing or functioning of the product, e.g., to maintain a more uniform viscosity over a range of temperature or concentration.

LEVIGATION. The process of grinding a wet, insoluble substance to a fine powder. The term levigation is sometimes applied to **sedimentation.**

LEVINE-BIEN REAGENTS FOR DIF-FERENTIATING CAROTENE AND OILS RICH IN VITAMIN A. These reagents are antimony trichloride, trichloroacetic acid, chloral hydrate, and sulfuric acid containing formaldehyde. They give different colors with carotene, halibut and other fish liver oils, ergosterol, cholesterol, etc.

LEVINE-BIEN TESTS FOR CARO-TENE. (1) To 3 ml. of the chloroform solution, add 3 ml. of a 1:50 mixture of 37% formaldehyde and sulfuric acid. A violet ring forms, and, on shaking, the acid is colored violet and the chloroform is colorless.

(2) Add, to 0.1 ml. of a solution of carotene in chloroform, 3 drops of a 9:1 mixture of trichloroacetic acid and water. An intense blue color is formed, stable to heat, but not to dilution.

(3) Heat 0.5 g. chloral hydrate until melted, and add 1 drop hydrochloric acid and 0.1 ml. of the chloroform solution of the substance tested; carotene gives an immediate deep blue color, ergosterol a carmine-red changing to green and blue.

LEVINE-RICHMAN REAGENT FOR TERPENES. A solution of 30 g. antimony trichloride in 100 ml. chloroform, used in testing for terpenes. Characteristic color reactions are obtained in the presence of acetic anhydride.

LEVINE-RICHMAN TEST TO DIFFER-ENTIATE IRRADIATED FROM NON-IRRADIATED STEROLS. Irradiated ergosterol and cholesterol are differentiated from their nonirradiated forms by color tests in 1% and 0.5% chloroform solutions.

LEVINE TEST FOR CARBOHYDRATES. After adding 3–4 drops 5% alcoholic thymol solution to the liquid tested, float the mixture on an equal volume concentrated sulfuric acid. Carbohydrates (and some other substances) are indicated by a pink to deep red ring.

LEVINE TEST FOR PHENOLS. Mecke reagent (q.v.) gives characteristic colors with many phenols, and with α- and β-naphthol.

LEVOROTATORY. Capable of rotating the plane of **polarized light** in a counterclockwise direction.

LEVY REAGENTS FOR ALKALOIDS AND PHENOLS. Solutions of niobic, tantalic and titanic acids in sulfuric acid, which give characteristic color reactions with alkaloids and phenols.

LEWIN REAGENT FOR ALDEHYDES. A mixture of piperidine and sodium nitroprusside solution, which gives colors with aldehydes.

LEWIN REAGENT FOR PROTEINS. A 0.1% solution of triformoxine (trioximinomethylene) in concentrated sulfuric acid, which gives a violet color with proteins.

LEWIS-LANGMUIR THEORY OF ATOMIC STRUCTURE. A fundamental conception of the structure of the **atom,** in which the electrons surrounding the nucleus of an atom are considered to be arranged in shells. The number in the successive shells that appear in atoms of increasing atomic number, are inferred from the total number of electrons in the rare gases of the atmosphere whose chemical inactivity is attributed to their possession of complete shells. Since the atomic numbers of these elements are 2, 10, 18, 36, 54, and 86, the successive differences between these numbers are considered to be the numbers of electrons in the successive shells. Moreover, the theory is extended to explain the properties of other atoms which, by their gain or loss of electrons to achieve a complete shell structure, or by their sharing of electrons with other atoms, form the various types of chemical compounds. (See also **atom, Lewis-Langmuir.**)

LEXASCHOVA SPOT TEST FOR CHRO-MIUM. Place 2–3 drops of a mixture composed of equal parts water, nitric acid, and sulfuric acid on a clean metal surface, transfer to a watch glass, and heat with excess sodium peroxide. Place the suspension on a folded filter paper, and place on the spot formed on the lower segment 1 drop benzidine dissolved in acetic acid and 1 drop hydrogen peroxide. A blue color indicates chromium.

LEY REAGENT FOR HONEY. A solution prepared by dissolving 10 g. silver nitrate in water, and precipitating it completely as silver oxide by adding sodium hydroxide solution. The silver oxide is filtered and dissolved in sufficient 10% ammonium hydroxide solution to make a total volume of 115 ml. It is used in detecting artificial honey.

LEYS REAGENT FOR ALDEHYDES. Warm 1 g. mercuric oxide with 100 ml. freshly prepared 5% sodium sulfite solution, and filter. This solution gives a white precipitate with dilute acetaldehyde and other aldehyde solutions and dilute alkali; but it *does not* do so with formaldehyde.

Li Symbol for the element **lithium.**

LIBERALLI REACTION FOR POLYPHENOLS. Crystals of polyphenol give characteristic colors with a few drops of 10% alkali thiocyanate solution and 1 ml. sulfuric acid.

LIBERALLI REAGENT. A mixture of 32.4 ml. of a 10% aqueous solution of ferric chloride and 58.2 ml. of a 10% aqueous solution of potassium thiocyanate with water to make 100 ml., used as a test reagent for hydroxy acids. A yellow color is produced with this reagent by hydroxy acids.

LICHTHARDT TEST SOLUTION FOR CARAMEL. A solution of 1 g. tannin in 30 ml. water, to which is added 0.75 g. concentrated sulfuric acid, and the volume adjusted with water to 50 ml. This reagent gives a brown precipitate with solutions containing caramel.

LIDOW REAGENT. A solution of 10.08 g. oleic acid in 500 ml. 96% alcohol, which is titrated with a solution of 2.5 g. potassium hydroxide in 100 ml. water and 100 ml. alcohol, until it is alkaline to phenolphthalein. The red solution (color due to phenolphthalein) is then diluted to 1 liter with alcohol. It is used as a reagent for determining hardness of water.

LIDOW TEST FOR PROTEINS. On heating with silver nitrate and a slight excess of potassium hydroxide solution, solutions of proteins give a brown color changing to cinnamon color.

LIEBEN IODOFORM REACTION. A method of formation of haloforms by treatment with hypohalites, of acetaldehyde, methyl ketones, their halogenated derivatives, or compounds yielding them on reaction. The reaction is general for hypohalites, but derives its name from the "iodoform test" whereby the compounds listed above give the characteristic odor of iodoform with iodine in alkaline solution.

$$CH_3CHO + 3NaOX \rightarrow CX_3CHO + 3NaOH.$$

$$CX_3CHO + NaOH \rightarrow CHX_3 + HCOONa.$$

LIEBEN REAGENT. An aqueous solution of 2 g. iodine and 3 g. potassium iodide, in a total volume of 50 ml., used in detecting acetone or ethyl alcohol. Iodoform is produced, in the presence of potassium hydroxide, if acetone is present.

LIEBERMANN REACTION FOR PROTEINS. Many proteins that have been washed with alcohol and with ether give a violet-blue color with hot concentrated hydrochloric acid.

LIEBERMANN REAGENT FOR THIOPHENE. A solution of 8 g. potassium nitrite in a mixture of 100 g. concentrated sulfuric acid and 6 ml. water, used in detecting thiophene in benzene. A green color, changing to blue, indicates the presence of thiophene.

LIEBERMANN TEST FOR CERTAIN STEROLS. Characteristic colors are obtained when cholesterol and certain other sterols, when in saturated solution in acetic anhydride, are treated drop by drop with sulfuric acid.

LIEBERMANN TEST FOR PHENOLS. A characteristic series of color changes obtained by treatment of a phenol with sulfuric acid to which a little sodium nitrite has been added, and then by pouring the mixture into water and alkalinizing. Similar reactions are obtained with nitrosamines; and since nitrosamines are produced by treatment of secondary amines with nitrous acid, the reaction also serves to establish the presence of a secondary amine.

LIEBIG COMBUSTION. The oxidation of organic substances for analytical purposes so that their carbon and hydrogen are quantitatively converted to carbon dioxide and water, respectively, and absorbed in suitable materials.

LIEBIG CONDENSER. See **condenser, Liebig.**

LIEBIG REACTION FOR CYSTINE. On boiling with a solution of lead oxide in aqueous sodium hydroxide solution, cystine gives a black precipitate.

LIESEGANG RINGS. The formation of a banded precipitate by **ions** which react by diffusion through certain **gels.** Thus, for example, if silver nitrate is dissolved in a warm gelatin sol which is then allowed to set, and a drop of sodium dichromate solution is deposited on its surface, the resulting silver chromate precipitate will appear in the gel as a series of rings, with clear areas between them.

LIESEGANG SOLUTION. A mixture of 14 ml. of a 40% aqueous solution of potassium phosphate and 1 ml. of a 10% aqueous solution of cupric chloride, used as a reagent for gelatin. A violet color is obtained.

LIESEGANG TEST FOR IRON AND COPPER. To detect iron and copper in paper and animal tissues, saturate the material with potassium ferrocyanide solution, dry, and expose to fumes of hydrochloric acid. Brown or blue dots appear in a few hours if copper or iron is present.

LIFETIME, MEAN. The period of time, on the average, that an **atom** will remain in a given excited **quantum state** before undergoing a change, i.e., by emission of a particle or emission of radiation.

LIFSCHÜTZ TEST REACTION FOR OLEIC ACID. To a solution of 1 drop oleic acid in 3.4 ml. glacial acetic acid, add 1 drop 10% anhydrous solution of chromic acid in glacial acetic acid, then add 10–12 drops concentrated sulfuric acid. Decolorization on standing, followed by a violet to cherry-red color, indicates oleic acid.

LIGASOID. A **colloidal** system, in which the dispersed particles (or the dispersed phase) are liquid, and the dispersion medium (or the continuous phase) is gaseous.

LIGHT. Radiant energy in a spectral range visible to the normal human eye (approximately 3800 to 7800 angstroms). See also **ultraviolet** and **infrared.**

LIGHT, DEPOLARIZATION FACTOR OF. See **depolarization factor of light.**

LIGHT FILTER. A screen of a substance, solid, liquid or gas, which absorbs certain wave lengths of light and transmits others. Such a screen, or a number of screens, can be used to analyze light by separating the various wave lengths or wave bands.

LIGHT METAL. A metallic element of small density, commonly one with a density below four.

LIGHT, MONOCHROMATIC. Light which consists of only one wave length.

LIGHT, POLARIZED. Light consisting of vibrations in the same plane, or vibrations which follow certain uniformly-changing pathways. When the vibrations occur in a single plane the light is said to be plane polarized. If the vibrations of two plane polarized beams at right angles to each other are so timed that the resultant describes a circular or elliptical path, the light is said to be circularly or elliptically polarized.

LIGHT, TRANSMITTED. Light that has traveled through a medium without being absorbed.

LILENDAHL-PETERSEN REAGENT. An aqueous solution of 6 g. sulfuric acid, 2 g. phosphomolybdic acid, and 6 g. kaolin in a total volume of 400 ml., used as a precipitant for albumin.

LILOLE COMPOUND. One of the compounds derived from the hypothetical hydrocarbon lilole.

LIME-SODA PROCESS. A method of manufacture of sodium hydroxide by treatment of calcium hydroxide (slaked lime) with a solution of sodium carbonate. Calcium carbonate is precipitated, and the sodium hydroxide remains in solution.

LIMINAL VALUE. The minimum concentration, usually expressed in **normality,** of a solution of a drug which produces an observable physiological reaction.

LIMITED PROPORTIONALITY, REGION OF. The part of the characteristic curve of pulse size versus voltage in which the **gas amplification** depends on the number of ions produced in the initial ionizing event, and also on the voltage.

LIMITING CURVES. Any line on a **phase diagram,** or other graphical representation of the conditions of a system, at which two phases are coexistent. Usually these limiting curves are the plotted curves that separate phases.

LIMITING DENSITY. The value which the density of a gas approaches as its pressure-volume relationship approaches the constant value (at constant temperature) of an **ideal gas.**

LIN-. Denoting a straight, linear alignment of rings, as *lin*naphthoanthracene (pentacene).

LINDE TEST FOR GLYCERIN. In the presence of glycerin, borax colors the flame green. A borax solution, to which litmus has been added, changes from blue to red with glycerin.

LINDER TEST FOR MINERAL ACIDS IN GASES. Metanil-yellow paper is colored violet by gaseous mineral acids.

LINDER TEST FOR FORMALDEHYDE. To 10 ml. of the solution tested, add a little casein, a few drops dilute ferric chloride solution, 10 ml. concentrated phosphoric acid, and 10–15 ml. concentrated sulfuric acid. A violet color indicates the presence of formaldehyde.

LINDO TEST FOR NITRATE. To 0.5 ml. of the solution tested, add 1 drop hydrochloric acid, 1 drop 10% aqueous resorcinol solution, and 2 ml. concentrated sulfuric acid. A purple-red color indicates the presence of nitrate.

LINE PAIR. In spectroscopy, an analytical line and the internal standard line with which it is compared.

LINE SPECTRUM. See **spectrum, line.**

LINEAR. Pertaining to a line or to the dimension of length.

LINGERING PERIOD. The length of time which an electron remains in its orbit of highest excitation (highest **energy level**) before jumping to a lower orbit, and radiating the difference in energy.

LINIMENT. A liquid, or solution, applied externally to relieve pain in muscles, superficial tissues, or other outer parts of the body.

LINING, ACID. A ceramic inner wall, or surface, of a furnace or other high temperature apparatus, which is composed of siliceous material.

LINING, BASIC. A ceramic inner wall, or surface, of a furnace or other high temperature apparatus, which is composed of material containing lime, magnesia, and other substances giving basic reactions under the operating conditions.

LINKAGE. The bond used in constitutional formulas to represent one **valency.** Double and triple linkings refer to double and triple bonds. See the various terms under **bond** for definitions of many types of linkages, and their descriptions in terms of conceptions of molecular structure.

LINKAGE, CATENARY. The linking of molecules to one another end to end, as occurs when **amino acids** unite to form polypeptides.

LINKAGE, COORDINATION. See **coordination linkage.**

LINKAGE, HEAT OF. See **heat of linkage.**

LINKAGE, SINGLET. A valence **bond** between two atoms which consists of a single electron. This linkage can exist only under rather exceptional circumstances, as where the electron may resonate between a position close to one atom and one close to the other, and this condition would require little, if any, difference in energy between its two positions.

LINOLEIC. Related to linoleic acid, $C_{17}H_{31}COOH$.

LINOLENIC. Related to linolenic acid, $C_{17}H_{29}COOH$.

LINTNER REACTION FOR DIASTASE. Tincture of guaiac containing a little hydrogen peroxide gives a blue color with an active diastase.

LINTNER REACTION FOR SALICYLIC ACID. On addition of a little 10% acid mercuric nitrate to the solution tested, boiling for 2 minutes and cooling, the addition of a few drops dilute sulfuric acid and a few drops of a solution of sodium nitrite give a red color if salicylic acid is present.

LIOUVILLE'S THEOREM. The time of change of point density near a given point moving through **gamma-space** is zero. This implies that an assembly of points, which fills a certain part of phase space with a given density, will move through phase space in such a manner as to leave its density unaltered.

LIPID, LIPIDE. See **lipin.**

LIPIN. In general, any **fat,** fatty oil, **lipoid,** or related substances preferably termed lipide. Specifically, the substances extracted from protoplasm by treatment with alcohol and ether, which are not soluble in water.

LIPOID. The same as **lipin.**

LIPOLYSIS. The solution or decomposition of fats and fatty substances.

LIPOPROTEIN. See **protein.**

LIPOWITZ TEST FOR NONDRYING OILS. Nondrying oils, on trituration with fresh, moist chlorinated lime, give two layers; drying oils do not.

LIPP SOLUTION. A saturated aqueous solution of monobasic lead acetate, used as a test reagent for dextrin. A white precipitate on boiling indicates the presence of dextrin.

LIPPMANN-POLLACK TEST REACTION. With concentrated sulfuric acid and a few drops of benzal chloride, various aromatic hydrocarbons give characteristic color reactions.

LIQUATION. The method of extraction of certain metals from certain of their ores or their industrial waste products simply by heating the material and "melting out" the desired metal, which collects at the lowest point in the apparatus.

LIQUEFACTION. Transformation to the liquid state; the term is applied more commonly to the change of gases to liquids than to the melting of solids.

LIQUEFON. A unit which expresses the starch liquefying power of **enzymes,** defined by the relationship:

$$\log_{10} L = 0.000565(S - 1078)$$

in which L is the number of liquefons per ten milliliters of infusion, and S is the weight (in milligrams) of starch liquefied per hour.

LIQUID. The second state of matter, the matter occupying a definite volume, but not a definite shape; it flows, more or less freely, in all directions in a plane perpendicular to the direction of gravity. Therefore, it takes the shape of its container.

LIQUID, ASSOCIATED. A liquid containing **associated** molecules, as water is believed to contain associated groups such as $(H_2O)_2$, etc., due possibly to the formation of hydrogen bonds between H_2O molecules. **Polar liquids** associate readily.

LIQUID, COMPLEX. A liquid in which the rate of shear is not a linear function of the shearing stress.

LIQUID, CONSTANT BOILING. See **constant boiling mixture.**

LIQUID JUNCTION POTENTIAL. See **potential, diffusion.**

LIQUID, NORMAL. Also called a nonpolar or nonassociated liquid. It is a liquid in which the molecules do not aggregate or form coordinate **bonds.**

LIQUID, POLAR. A liquid consisting of molecules which are electrically polarized, i.e., which exhibit electrical differences between various points in their structure. Such molecules tend to associate, i.e., to form larger aggregates held together by electrical forces. They are ionizing solvents.

LIQUIDUS CURVE. In a temperature-concentration diagram, the line connecting the temperatures at which fusion is just completed for the various compositions.

LIQUOR. An aqueous solution of gases, liquids, or solids.

LISKA TEST REACTION. Nickel is detected in solution by adding oxamide, heating to boiling, and adding 20% sodium hydroxide solution; nickel gives a deep yellow color.

LISOLOID. A **colloidal** system made up of a liquid phase surrounded by a solid phase.

LISON SOLUTION FOR PEROXIDASES. A solution of 1.5 g. acid fuchsin or acid violet in 100 ml. 2% acetic acid, reduced by addition of 5 g. zinc dust, to which 2 ml. glacial acetic acid is then added, used with hydrogen peroxide in detecting peroxidases.

LITER. The unit of volume in the **metric system,** defined as the volume of one kilogram of water at 4° C., and one atmosphere pressure.

    1 liter = 1000 milliliters
    1 liter = 1000.028 cubic centimeters
    1 liter = 33.82 fluid ounces.

LITER-ATMOSPHERE. A unit of **work** defined as the work done in raising a piston of one square decimeter area one decimeter in a cylinder against an atmospheric pressure of one atmosphere.

    1 liter-atmosphere = 24.25 gram calories.

LITH-, LITHO-. (Greek: *lithos*, stone) Related to stone or calculus, as litharge, lithocholic acid (from gallstones).

LITHIUM. Metallic element. Symbol Li. Atomic number 3. Atomic weight 6.94. Density 0.534. Specific heat .941. Melting point values reported range from 178–186° C. Boiling point 1336° C. ± 5° C. Valence 1. Lithium occurs in triphylite, petallite, spodumene, lithia mica, and other minerals. Oxides Li_2O, Li_2O_2.

LITTROW PRISM. A glass prism that reflects light internally from one surface.

LIXIVIAL SALTS. Salts obtained by lixiviating ashes.

LIXIVIATION. A process for separating soluble from insoluble matter by dissolving out the soluble substances and drawing off the solution from the residue.

LJUNG TEST. Selenium is detected by adding, to 1 ml. of the solution tested, 5 ml. concentrated hydrochloric acid and 2 ml. 0.025 N ammonium thiocyanate solution, and diluting with water to 10 ml. On heating to boiling and boiling for 1 minute, selenium gives a red, yellow, or green precipitate.

LJUNGREN SOLUTION. A solution of 0.1 g. palladium chloride and a little sodium acetate in 100 ml. water, used as an impregnant for test paper for carbon monoxide. A blackening of the moistened paper is given by carbon monoxide.

LLOYD REAGENT FOR ALKALOIDS. Precipitated aluminum silicate, which precipitates alkaloids from neutral or acid solution.

LOBO MICRO-TEST FOR MERCUROUS ION. On the addition to 1 drop of the solution tested of 1 drop 2% solution of sozoiodol (diiodophenol-*p*-sulfonic acid), bright yellow crystals form in the presence of mercurous ion.

LOBRY DE BRUYN-VAN EKENSTEIN CONVERSION. Treatment of a sugar, either a ketose or an aldose sugar, with aqueous alkali, in such a manner that an equilibrium mixture of ketose and aldose sugars is formed.

LODI REAGENTS FOR BLEACHING CHEMICALS IN FLOUR. (1) An acetic acid solution of benzidine.

(2) A mixture of *o*-toluidine, potassium bromide, and hydrochloric acid.

(3) A mixture of *p*-diaminodiphenylamine, potassium bromide, and hydrochloric acid.

LOEBICH REAGENT FOR PERCHLORIC ACID. Nitron, used in the quantitative precipitation of perchloric acid.

LOGARITHM. The power to which an arbitrarily chosen number (called the base) must be raised to yield a given number. Thus, if x is the base of a system of logarithms, then the logarithm l of any number a is calculated by the relationship, $a = x^l$.

LOGARITHM, BRIGGS OR COMMON. A **logarithm** (q.v.) whose base is 10.

LOGARITHM, NAPIERIAN OR NATURAL. A logarithm whose base is the number e, which is calculated by the function:

$$e = 1 + 1 + \frac{1}{2} + \frac{1}{2 \times 3} + \frac{1}{2 \times 3 \times 4} \cdots$$

the value of e, to five places of decimals, being 2.71828 . . . .

LONDON FORCES. Forces due to mutual perturbations of the electron clouds of two atoms or molecules which, when the molecules are in their **ground electronic states,** are always attractive. The principal part of these forces is due to interactions between the instantaneous **dipole moments** and gives a potential energy varying inversely as the sixth power of the molecular separation.

LONG PERIOD. See **period, long.**

LONGI TEST. Nitrate is detected by addition to the solution tested of several drops *p*-toluidine solution in dilute sulfuric acid, and by making a ring test of the mixture with concentrated sulfuric acid. A red ring indicates nitrate.

LOOF REAGENT FOR ARSENIC. A solution of 50 g. sodium hypophosphite in 100 ml. concentrated hydrochloric acid, used as a test reagent for arsenic compounds. They are reduced to metallic arsenic by the action of this reagent.

LOOF TEST FOR NITRATE IN WATER. One-half g. of sodium salicylate is dissolved in 5 ml. of the water, and 10 ml. concentrated sulfuric acid added. A yellow to red color indicates nitrate.

LORD BLOWPIPE REAGENT. Ammonium fluoride, used with sulfuric acid to treat materials tested in the flame for potassium and boron.

LORENTZ-LORENZ EQUATION. A relationship between the **refractive index** of a compound and its density, called the specific refraction, and constant at all temperatures for a given substance. It is of the form

$$[r] = \frac{n^2 - 1}{\rho(n^2 + 2)}$$

in which $[r]$ is the specific refraction, n the index of refraction, and ρ the density.

LORENTZ-LORENZ FORMULA. A relationship for the **molal refraction** of a liquid, derived from the electromagnetic theory of light, of the form:

$$R = \frac{M(n^2 - 1)}{\rho(n^2 + 2)} = V \frac{(n^2 - 1)}{(n^2 + 2)}$$

in which R is the molal refraction for a given optical frequency, n is the **refractive index** for that frequency, ρ is the density, M is the molecular weight, and V is the **molecular volume.**

LORICA. A lute for protecting vessels from fire.

LOSCHMIDT NUMBER. An approximate value of the number of molecules in 1 cubic centimeter of gas at $0°$ C. and 1 atmosphere pressure, calculated from the mean **free path,** and the densities of the substance (commonly a gas) both in the gaseous state and in the liquid state at low temperatures. The values obtained, by disregarding the free space between the molecules of the liquid, range from

$$1.5 \times 10^{18} \text{ to } 2.5 \times 10^{18}.$$

They are probably low.

LOSSEN REARRANGEMENT. The rearrangement of aromatic hydroxamic acids or their derivatives into isocyanates. The change is effected by heat, or by certain reagents, such as thionyl chloride.

are compared with the solution or object under examination.

LOVITON REAGENT. Ammonium nitrate, used in metal analysis because the molten salt dissolves only certain metals, such as copper, zinc, and nickel.

LÖW-BOKORNY REAGENT. Two solutions: (1) a solution of 10 ml. ammonium hydroxide (sp. gr. 0.96) and 13 ml. 33% potassium hydroxide solution in 100 ml. water; and (2) a solution of 1 g. silver nitrate in 100 ml. water. They are used in testing for albumin in living cells. If the cells are alive, their albumin reduces the reagent to metallic silver.

LÖWE REAGENT. A solution of 16 g. cupric sulfate in 64 ml. water, to which is added 80 ml. 35% sodium hydroxide solution and 6–8 ml. glycerol. It is used in testing for glucose, which precipitates cuprous oxide from it.

LOWENTHAL REAGENT. A solution of 5 g. ferric chloride, 60 g. tartaric acid, and 240 g. sodium carbonate in 500 ml. water, used in testing for glucose. A black precipitate is obtained on boiling glucose solutions with this solution.

LÖWY-NEUBERG TEST REACTION: Diamines in ethereal solution give precipitates with phenylisocyanate.

$$C_6H_5.CO.NH.OOC.C_6H_5 \xrightarrow{\Delta} C_6H_5.NCO + C_6H_5COOH.$$

LOTHIAN TEST REACTION FOR ALKALOIDS. On heating with a solution of aloe in dilute alcohol, most alkaloids give cherry-red to purple-red color.

LOUTCHINSKI COLORIMETRIC PHENOL DETERMINATION. On treatment with titanium tetrachloride, phenol forms a red compound.

LOVIBOND TINTOMETER. A colorimeter in which the color of a solution or object is expressed in terms of glass slides of three colors. The instrument is equipped with a series of slides of each color, which

Lu Symbol for the element **lutecium.**

LUBRICANT. See **lubricating agent.**

LUBRICATING AGENT. A substance used to decrease friction between surfaces that move in contact.

LUCAS THEORY. A theory of the effect of substituent groups upon the **electronic configuration** of atoms, which has been applied to explain many structural phenomena, including the differences in properties of position-isomers or place-isomers, especially of benzenoid compounds. One of the salient points of this theory is that a substituting radical, especially in an organic compound, attracts or repels electrons of neighboring and other atoms, and thus modifies the **chemical reactivity** of those atoms.

LUCKOW TEST REACTION FOR ALUMINUM. Carminic acid solution or tincture of cochineal give colored precipitates with neutral or weakly acid solutions containing aluminum.

LUDWIG-HAUPT REAGENT. A mixture of a solution of 0.5 g. aniline hydrochloride in 25 ml. alcohol, 5 ml. of a 1% alcoholic solution of furfural, and 1 ml. phenol, to which is added a 5% ammonium hydroxide solution in water until a yellow-red color is produced. It is used in testing for oleic acid and saturated fatty acids. Oleic acid gives a yellow color, and saturated acids yield a red one.

LUDWIG REAGENT. A reagent used to test for uric acid, consisting of three solutions: (1) an aqueous solution of 10 g. magnesium chloride, 5 g. ammonium chloride, and 15 g. ammonia in a volume of 100 ml.; (2) an ammoniacal aqueous solution of 26 g. silver nitrite in a volume of 1 liter; and (3) an aqueous solution of 15 g. potassium hydroxide and 10 g. sodium hydroxide in a volume of 1 liter, one-half of this solution having been saturated with hydrogen sulfide. This reagent gives a white precipitate under test conditions if uric acid is present.

LUFF REAGENT. An aqueous solution of 63 g. citric acid to which is added 35.9 g. cupric citrate and 67.2 g. potassium hydroxide. It is used in testing for reducing sugars, which precipitate yellow cuprous oxide from it.

LUKAS-JILEK TEST REACTION. A test for certain metals. A 30% hydrogen peroxide solution gives a brown color with vanadium solutions in sulfuric acid, and with similar molybdenum solutions, a yellow-green color, discharged by boric acid; 30% hydrogen peroxide and quinine hydrochloride give a yellow to orange color with neutral cerium solutions.

LUMEN. (1) The diameter of a capillary-tube or other small tube. (2) A photometric unit, the quantity of light emitted by one standard candle.

LUMINESCENCE. The property of emitting light in greater degree than corresponds to the temperature of the emitting body as defined by Stefan's law (see **law of Stefan**).

LUMINESCENCE, CHEMI-. See **chemiluminescence**.

LUMINESCENCE, CRYSTALLO-. Luminescence produced during the separation of crystals from saturated solutions. The phenomenon is shown by arsenious oxide, sodium fluoride, etc.

LUMINESCENCE, ELECTRO-. Luminescence caused by electrical means, as the luminescence of rarefied gases under the influence of a rapidly-alternating, high-potential current.

LUMINESCENCE, PHOTO. The emission of light as a result of the absorption of nonluminous radiations, such as ultraviolet radiations.

LUMINESCENCE, THERMAL. Luminescence at temperatures below red heat, as occurs in diamond, marble, and fluorite.

LUMINESCENCE, TRIBO-. See **triboluminescence**.

LUMINOPHORE. A group which confers or increases the property of **luminescence** in organic compounds. The **amino** and **hydroxyl** groups have this effect.

LUMINOUS FLAME. See **flame, luminous**.

LUND-LIECK TEST REACTION. Ascorbic acid decolorizes methylene blue solutions in 30 seconds on exposure to strong light.

LUND SOLUTIONS. Two solutions for testing honey, consisting of: (1) a solution of 2 g. phosphotungstic acid and 20 g. dilute (1:4) sulfuric acid, dissolved in 80 ml. water, and (2) a solution of 0.5 g. tannic acid in 100 ml. water. The first solution is used to precipitate various nitrogenous compounds and the latter to precipitate albuminoids in honey.

LUNGE SOLUTION. A solution of 0.1 g. α-naphthylamine in 20 ml. distilled water, to which is added 150 ml. 30% acetic acid and 0.5 g. sulfanilic acid dissolved in 150 ml. 30% acetic acid, used in the determination of nitrous acid. The naphthylamine-acetic acid solution and the sulfanilic acid-acetic acid solution may be used separately. A pink color is obtained if nitrous acid is present.

LUSTER. The reflection of the light from the surface of an object or material, and the appearance of the surface by that reflected light. The luster of minerals is a property which is useful in their identification. The luster of a mineral may be metallic, vitreous, adamantine, resinous, pearly, greasy, silky, dull, or earthy.

LUTE. A cement of refractory materials used for sealing the joints or openings of apparatus, or for coating the apparatus to protect it from fire.

LUTECIUM. Rare earth metallic element. Symbol Lu. Atomic number 71. Atomic weight 174.99. Valence 3 or 4. Oxide Lu_2O_3.

LUTEO-. (Latin: *luteus*) Orange-yellow, brownish yellow; specifically, designating certain series of **coordination compounds,** as $[M(NH_3)_6]Cl_3$ (the members of which are not necessarily all yellow).

LUTZ REAGENT FOR TANNIN. A solution prepared by dissolving 1 g. cupric sulfate in 25 ml. water, and adding enough ammonium hydroxide to redissolve the initial precipitate, then diluting with water to a total volume of 50 ml. It is used for detecting tannin in drugs. A brown color is visible on microscopic examination of drugs soaked in the reagent, if tannin is present.

LUTZ TEST REACTION FOR IRON. With a saturated aqueous solution of pyro-

catechuic acid and an excess of sodium carbonate solution, iron salts in solution give a red color.

LYLE-CURTMAN-MARSHALL α-AMINOCAPROIC ACID SOLUTION. A solution of 0.67 g. α-aminocaproic acid in 100 ml. water used as test reagent for copper. A blue-grey precipitate forms in sodium acetate solution if copper is present.

LYLE-CURTMAN-MARSHALL BENZIDINE REAGENT. A solution prepared by dissolving 0.5 g. benzidine in 4.33 ml. glacial acetic acid (heat), and then adding 19 ml. distilled water. A blue color, in the presence of hydrogen peroxide, is obtained if blood is present.

LYMAN SERIES. A series of lines in the **ultraviolet** region of the spectrum of atomic hydrogen. The wave numbers of the lines in this series are given by the relationship:

$$\bar{\nu} = R_H \left(\frac{1}{n_1{}^2} - \frac{1}{n_2{}^2} \right)$$

where $\bar{\nu}$ is the wave number of a line in the Lyman series, R_H is the **Rydberg constant,** n_1 is 1, and n_2 has various integral values.

LYNN-LEE REAGENTS. One per cent solutions of resorcinol and phloroglucinol in concentrated hydrochloric acid. They give characteristic color reactions with many aldehydes (not butyraldehyde).

LYONS TEST FOR IRON. On addition of 1 drop thioglycolic acid and 5 ml. concentrated ammonium hydroxide to 5 ml. of neutral or slightly acid iron solutions, a blue color changing to deep red is obtained.

LYONS-DOX TEST FOR ALKYLBARBITURIC ACIDS. *p*-Nitrobenzoylchloride gives, with alkylbarbituric acids and sodium carbonate, crystalline compounds with characteristic melting points.

LYOPHILE SYSTEM. A **colloidal system** in which there is a marked attraction between the disperse phase and the dispersion medium. When the medium is water, the term hydrophile is applied to the system.

LYOPHOBIC SYSTEM. A colloidal system in which the dispersed phase is a solid that does not attract the dispersion medium.

LYOPHYLIZE. To evaporate water from a frozen product, usually *in vacuo*. This process is used with very unstable substances, such as extracts of penicillin.

LYOTROPIC SERIES. A series of **anions** or **cations** arranged in the order of magnitude of their effect upon reactions in **colloidal solutions**. These ions indirectly influence a reaction by exerting a lyophilic or lyophobic effect upon the solvent. In the hydrolysis of esters by bases the series is as follows:

Anions, I $>$ NO_3 $>$ Br $>$ Cl.

Cations, Cs $>$ Rb $>$ K $>$ Li.

LYSIN. An **antibody** that dissolves cells, usually being specific in its action.

LYSIS. In general, any process of decomposition of a substance or system; specifically the solution of a substance or cell by the action of a lysin.

LYSYL. The radical

$H_2NCH_2CH_2CH_2CH_2CH(NH_2)CO—.$

M. Abbreviation for **molecular weight** (M). Abbreviation for meter (m). Abbreviation for meta, when that prefix is used to denote the relation of the 1 and 3 positions in benzene, or a compound derived from benzene or characterized by its structure (m-). Abbreviation for mesh (M or m). Symbol for slope of equilibrium curve (m). Symbol for metal (M). Abbreviation for one-thousandth (m). Symbol for direction cosine (l, m, n). Symbol for mutual **inductance** (M). Symbol for **magnetization** (M). Symbol for linear magnification (m). Abbreviation for mass (M or m). Symbol for atomic or molecular mass (m or m_m). Symbol for mass of electron (m or m_e). Symbol for **magnetic moment** (m). Symbol for order of spectrum (m). **Magnetic quantum number** (m). Total magnetic quantum number (M).

M-ELECTRON. An electron characterized by having a **principal quantum number** of value 3. (See also **M-shell**.)

M-LINE. One of the lines in the M-series of **x-rays** that are characteristic of the various elements and are produced by **excitation** of the electrons of the **M-shell**.

M-RADIATION. One of a series of **x-rays** characteristic of each element that is excited when that element, commonly as the metal, is used as an **anticathode** in an x-ray tube, thus exciting the electrons of the **M-shell**.

M-SHELL. The collection of all those electrons in an atom that are characterized by the **principal quantum number** three. The M-shell consists of one electron in the case of sodium (atomic number = 11) and increases by one electron for each element of successively higher atomic number until argon (atomic number = 18), which has 8 electrons in its M-shell, is reached. The M-shells of potassium (atomic number = 19), calcium (atomic number = 20), scandium (atomic number = 21), and titanium (atomic number = 22) all contain 8 electrons, the additional electrons of these elements appearing in the beginning N-shell. With vanadium (atomic number = 23), however, there are 10 electrons in the M-shell; in chromium (atomic number = 24), there are 11 electrons in the M-shell; and in manganese (atomic number = 25), there are 13 electrons in the M-shell; and then the elements of successively higher atomic number increase the number of electrons in the M-shell by one each until zinc (atomic number = 30) is reached. All elements of higher atomic number contain 18 electrons in the M-shell.

MAC CALLUM TEST REACTION. Solutions of iron salts give with 5% alcoholic hemotoxylin solution a violet-red to violet-blue color. This reaction is given by iron salts of both inorganic and organic acids.

MACCHIA TEST FOR ALKALINE EARTHS. The mixed carbonate is dissolved in malonic acid, and a slight excess of ammonia precipitates barium. The filtrate on treatment with 4–5 times its volume of methanol, and warming, is filtered and treated with potassium cyanate. A white, flocculant precipitate indicates calcium. The strontium is then precipitated with sodium carbonate.

MACERATION. The steeping of a solid material in a liquid, in order to soften it or break down its structure.

MACHE UNIT. A unit of quantity of radioactive emanation, defined as the quantity of emanation which sets up a saturation current equal to one one-thousandth of the electrostatic unit of current. It is equal to 3.6×10^{-10} **curie** (q.v.).

quantity, as distinguished from microchemistry.

MACROFARAD. A **megafarad.**

MADELUNG CONSTANT. This constant appears in the equation proposed by Born and Mayer in their method of calculating the **lattice energy** of an ionic crystal. The values of this constant have been obtained by adding the mutual potential energy of all the ions in the particular lattice.

MADELUNG SYNTHESIS. A method of formation of indole derivatives from N-acyl-o-toluidine derivatives.

MACLEOD EQUATION. A constant relationship between the **surface tension** of a liquid, its density, and the density of its vapor, of the form:

$$\frac{\gamma^{\frac{1}{4}}}{\rho - \rho'} = \text{Constant}$$

where γ is the surface tension of the liquid, ρ is its density, and ρ' is the density of its vapor.

MACRI TEST REACTION FOR MANGANESE. The slightly-alkalinized manganese solution is treated successively with a few drops sodium oxalate solution and a few drops acetic acid. A persistent rose color is obtained.

MACRI REAGENT. A freshly-prepared mixture of 2 ml. 20% silver nitrate solution and 1 ml. 5% tannin solution. One drop of it is placed on a watch glass and 0.1 ml. of the solution tested is brought near. A silver ring appears in a few seconds if ammonia is present.

MACROCHEMISTRY. The branch of chemistry that deals with substances in

MAGIC NUMBERS. Certain numbers of **neutrons** or **protons** in the nucleus which give rise to increased nuclear stability. The levels that seem certain at this time correspond to values of N (number of neutrons in the nucleus) or of Z (atomic number: number of protons in the nucleus) equal to 2, 8, 20, 28, 50, 82, and 126. For example, tin ($Z = 50$) has as many as ten stable isotopes.

MAGMA. (1) An amorphous mass of finely divided material, which may be wet or dry, but is commonly suspended in water. (2) A molten rock or molten substance that yields igneous rocks on solidification.

MAGNESIA MIXTURE. An aqueous solution of magnesium chloride, ammonium chloride, and ammonium hydroxide, used for the determination of arsenates and phosphates.

MAGNESIUM. Metallic element. Symbol Mg. Atomic number 12. Atomic weight 24.32. Density 1.74. Specific heat 0.222. Melting point 651° C. Boiling point 1110° C. Valence 2. Oxides, MgO (magnesia), MgO_2 (magnesium peroxide). Magnesium occurs abundantly in magnesite, dolomite, kieserite, epsomite, carnallite, asbestos, talc, meerschaum, and other minerals.

MAGNETIC. Having magnetic properties or pertaining to magnetic substances or magnets. (See **magnetism.**)

MAGNETIC FIELD. A region in which a **magnetic force** or the characteristic effects of a magnet are apparent or theoretically apparent. Or the actual force system of a magnet, expressed in terms of lines of force.

MAGNETIC FORCE. The force between a magnetic field and a magnetic pole.

MAGNETIC INTENSITY. The force which a **magnetic field** exerts at a given point, upon a unit magnetic pole; or the **magnetic moment** per unit volume.

MAGNETIC MOMENT. The magnetic moment is the same as the moment of any other force in that it is the product of **magnetic intensity** and the effective distance. Thus, the magnetic moment of a bar-magnet is simply the pole strength multiplied by the length of the magnet. The magnetic moment of an electron rotating in an orbit is expressed by the relationship

$$m_\mu = ep/2mc$$

in which m_μ is the magnetic moment, e is the electronic charge, p is the total mechanical angular momentum of the electron, m is its mass, and c is the velocity of light.

MAGNETIC PERMEABILITY. The value for a given substance of the **magnetic induction** in unit field. It is also defined by the relationship:

$$F = \frac{1}{\mu} \cdot \frac{mm'}{d^2},$$

in which μ is the magnetic **permeability** of a medium, m and m' are the strength of two magnetic poles, d is the distance between them (through the medium, of course), and F is the magnetic force between the poles.

MAGNETIC POLARIZATION. The **optical activity** shown in a magnetic field by an optically inactive substance.

MAGNETIC QUANTUM NUMBER. See **quantum number, magnetic.**

MAGNETIC ROTATION. The rotation of the plane of **polarization** of light by transparent substances when they are placed in a magnetic field. It is a function of the nature of the substance, the frequency of the light, the intensity of the magnetic field, and the temperature. This phenomenon is called the Faraday effect.

MAGNETIC SEPARATOR. An apparatus, usually an electromagnet, used to separate magnetic from nonmagnetic objects or substances.

MAGNETIC SUSCEPTIBILITY. The volume magnetic susceptibility of a medium is expressed in the relationship

$$\mu = 1 + 4\pi\kappa$$

in which μ is the magnetic **permeability** of the medium and κ is its volume magnetic susceptibility. There is also a relationship for specific magnetic susceptibility of the form $\mu = 1 + 4\pi\rho\kappa$ in which μ is the magnetic permeability of the medium, ρ is its density, and κ is its specific magnetic susceptibility.

MAGNETISM. A characteristic property of certain substances by which they exhibit a spatial **polarization** and either attract or repel another fragment or particle of the same substance, or another magnetic substance, depending upon their relative positions. This phenomenon, which was first discovered for certain ferrous substances, acts as if such substances contained two poles, or regions of polarity, such that, when the substances approach each other and like poles are close together, a measurable force of repulsion is exerted, whereas unlike poles attract. The origin of this force is in the molecular or atomic structure, and, therefore, such materials, even though broken into pieces, continue to exhibit this behavior.

MAGNETO-OPTIC METHOD. An experimental method based upon the determination of the time lag in the magnetic rotation of substances, as a basis for their differentiation.

MAGNETOMETER. An instrument for the quantitative measurement of magnetic field intensity or magnetic moment.

MAGNETON. The quantity $eh/4\pi mc$, in which e is the electronic charge, h is **Planck's Constant**, m is the electronic mass, and c is the velocity of light. The numerical value of this quantity, known also as the Bohr magneton, is 9.27×10^{-21} erg gauss^{-1}. This quantity is frequently encountered in quantum mechanics. (See also **Weiss magneton**.)

MAGNIFYING POWER. The ratio of the true size of an object to the size of its image, as produced by a microscope or other optical apparatus.

MAGNUS RULE. A metal is deposited from a solution containing metallic salts, at the voltage which is characteristic for that metal.

MALATE. A compound containing the malic acid radical

$$-OOC-CHOH-CH_2-COO-.$$

MALATESTA-DI NOLA REAGENT FOR COPPER, NICKEL AND COBALT. A solution of 0.5 g. 1, 2-diaminoanthraquinone-3-sulfonic acid in 360 ml. water, 100 ml. concentrated ammonium hydroxide, and 40 ml. sodium hydroxide solution (40° Bé.).

MALATESTA-DI NOLA TEST REACTION FOR GOLD AND PLATINUM. A solution of 1 g. benzidine in 50 ml. water and 10 ml. acetic acid gives a blue color or precipitate with solutions of gold or silver salts.

MALEATE. A compound containing the maleic acid radical

$$-OOC-CH=CH-COO-.$$

MALEIC. Relating to maleic acid,

$$HC=COOH$$
$$|$$
$$HC=COOH$$

MALENOID FORM. The *cis* form of geometrical isomerism. See **isomerism, geometrical**.

MALEYL. Containing the radical

$$-OC-CH=CH-CO-.$$

MALIC. Related to malic acid,

$$HOOC.CH_2.CHOH.COOH.$$

MALITZKII-TUBAKAIEV MICRO-TEST FOR SODIUM. With 1 drop zinc uranyl acetate solution, 1 drop of a neutral solution containing sodium gives characteristic crystals of sodium-zinc-uranium acetate.

MALLEABILITY. The property by which a material may be hammered out or rolled into thin sheets without tearing or fracture, or the extent to which a material possesses that property.

MALLET TEST REACTION FOR TUNGSTEN. When to a tungstate solution, concentrated hydrochloric acid is added until the precipitate which forms redissolves, and metallic zinc is added, a color develops, magenta-red being most characteristic. Adding potassium thiocyanate instead of zinc gives a green color, becoming violet on dilution.

MALONATE. A compound containing the malonic acid radical

$$-OOC-CH_2-COO-.$$

MALONIC. Related to malonic acid,

$$HOOC.CH_2.COOH.$$

MALONIC ESTER SYNTHESIS. See **synthesis, malonic ester**.

MALONYL. The radical $-OCCH_2CO-$.

MALOWAN TEST REACTION. Aldehydes which have a double bond in the α-position to the $-CHO$ group on addition to molybdenum blue solutions form two layers—a colorless aqueous layer and a green aldehyde layer.

MANCHOT-KAMPSCHULTE TEST. Dry or moist ozone is detected by its action in blackening silver.

MANCHOT-SCHERER REAGENT. A mixture of 50 ml. of a 0.1 N aqueous solution of silver nitrate, 50 ml. of a 0.15 N aqueous solution of sodium hydroxide (chloride-free), and 50 ml. pyridine. It is used as a reagent for carbon monoxide, which produces metallic silver by reduction.

MANDEL-NEUBERG REAGENT FOR ALDO- AND KETOACIDS. Naphthoresorcinol, used in testing for many aldo- and ketoacids, with which it gives characteristic colors.

MANDELIC. Related to mandelic acid,

$$C_6H_5.CHOH.COOH.$$

MANDELIN REAGENT FOR ALKALOIDS. A solution of 1 g. ammonium vanadate in 200 g. of mono- or dihydrated sulfuric acid. Characteristic colors are given with many alkaloids.

MANEA TEST REACTION. Vegetable fibers, when dissolved in concentrated sulfuric acid, give with oleic acid a red color, changing to violet on addition of water. Animal fibers do not give this reaction.

MANGANATE (II). The anion $MnO_2^=$, or a compound containing it.

MANGANATE (III). The anion MnO_2^- or MnO_3^{3-}, or a compound containing one of these anions.

MANGANATE (IV). The anion $MnO_3^=$, $Mn_2O_5^=$, or $Mn_3O_7^=$, or a compound containing one of these anions.

MANGANATE (VI). The anion $MnO_4^=$, or a compound containing it.

MANGANESE. Metallic element. Symbol Mn. Atomic number 25. Atomic weight 54.93. Density 7.2. Specific heat

0.093. Melting point 1260° C. Boiling point 1900° C. (?). Valence 2, 3, 4, 6, and 7. Oxides, MnO, Mn_3O_4, Mn_2O_3, MnO_2, MnO_3, Mn_2O_7. Chief ore, pyrolusite (MnO_2). Manganese forms two acids, manganic H_2MnO_4 and permanganic $HMnO_4$.

MANGANIC. Containing or pertaining to trivalent **manganese.**

MANGANICYANIDE. See **cyanomanganate (III).**

MANGANITE. See **manganate (IV).**

MANGANOCYANIDE. See **cyanomanganate (II).**

MANGANOUS. Containing or pertaining to divalent **manganese.**

MANGENT-MARION REAGENT FOR AMMONIA. Diaminophenol, which gives a deep yellow color with ammonia.

MANGENT-MARION TEST FOR FORMALDEHYDE. Milk containing formaldehyde gives a canary-yellow color with aminophenol or 1,2,4-diaminophenol.

MANGIN SOLUTIONS FOR CELLULOSE. A series of eight solutions used in testing for cellulose. They are particularly useful for microscopic examination of materials containing cellulose. They consist of: (1) a solution of 1 g. iodine and 3 g. potassium iodide in 200 ml. water; (2) a solution of 0.2 g. iodine and 1 g. potassium iodide in 20 g. of a concentrated aqueous solution of calcium chloride; (3) a solution of 1.3 g. iodine, 6.5 g. potassium iodide, and 20 g. zinc chloride in 10.5 ml. water; (4) a solution of 0.3 g. iodine and 0.5 g. potassium iodide in 25 g. phosphoric acid; (5) an aqueous solution of stannous chloride and iodine-potassium iodide; (6) an aqueous solution of aluminum chloride and iodine-potassium iodide; (7) hydriodic acid containing iodine; and (8) a solution of copper turnings in concentrated ammonia prepared in air without light.

MANGINI SOLUTION FOR ALKALOIDS. A hydrochloric acid solution of potassium iodide and bismuth triiodide, used as a test reagent for alkaloids. Characteristic color reactions are obtained.

MANNITIC. Related to mannitic acid,

$$CH_2OH(CHOH)_4COOH.$$

MANN TEST PAPER FOR WATER IN ETHER OR ALCOHOL. Soak paper in an aqueous extract of a fusion of 2 parts citric acid and 1 part molybdic acid. The dried paper is blue in color, and is decolorized by water in ether or in alcohol.

MANNHEIM FURNACE. A muffle furnace (see **furnace, muffle**) for the production of salt cake and hydrochloric acid from sulfuric acid and salt by the reaction indicated below (the intermediate product, $NaHSO_4$, or niter cake, may be charged with the salt, so that only the second part of the reaction occurs):

$$NaCl + H_2SO_4 \rightarrow NaHSO_4 + HCl.$$

$$NaCl + NaHSO_4 \rightarrow Na_2SO_4 + HCl.$$

The Mannheim furnace consists of a cast-iron pan with scrapers built in a muffle furnace provided with means for heating, and a collection system for the hydrochloric acid produced.

MANNHEIM PROCESS. A **contact process** (q.v.) for the manufacture of sulfuric acid, in which the conversion of SO_2 to SO_3 takes place in two stages, the first catalyzed by ferric oxide, Fe_2O_3, and the second, by platinized asbestos.

MANNHEIM PROCESS FOR HYDRO-CHLORIC ACID. A method of producing hydrochloric acid gas and sodium acid sulfate from sodium chloride and sulfuric acid which involves:
(1) Cooling the HCl-air mixture by scrubbing with a cold, aqueous solution of HCl (concentrated).
(2) Absorbing the cooled HCl gas in a dilute, cold aqueous solution of HCl.
(3) Stripping HCl gas from the strong HCl solution produced by (2).

MANNICH REACTION. A method of synthesizing **amino** derivatives which consists in replacing active hydrogen atoms by the action of formaldehyde and ammonia, or a primary or secondary amine, usually in the form of the hydrochloride salt. For example,

$$C_6H_5COCH_3 + (CH_3)_2NH.HCl + HCHO \xrightarrow[\text{reflux}]{\text{alcohol}} C_6H_5COCH_2CH_2N(CH_3)_2.HCl + H_2O.$$

MANOCRYOMETER. An instrument invented by de Visser to determine the change in the melting point of a substance due to change in pressure. It consists of a thick-walled thermometer, inverted, with the capillary stem bent upward and then at right angles. The substance under observation is placed in the bulb, and mercury is admitted to the capillary. The whole is then placed in a thermostat, when it assumes the pressure (measured by the mercury) of equilibrium between solid and liquid in the bulb.

MANOMETER. An apparatus used to measure the pressure of liquids and gases. In its simplest form, it consists of a U-tube containing water, mercury, or other liquid, one side of the tube being open to the atmosphere and the other side being connected to the system of which the pressure is to be measured. The resulting difference in height of liquid in the two arms corresponds to the difference between the pressure of the system and that of the atmosphere.

MANOSCOPY. The determination of the densities of gases.

MANSEAU REAGENT FOR OPIUM ALKALOIDS. A 5% solution of methenamine in sulfuric acid, which gives characteristic colors with many opium alkaloids.

MARBLE REAGENT. A solution of 4 g. cupric sulfate and 20 ml. hydrochloric acid in 20 ml. water, used in etching stainless steels.

MARC. Residual vegetable material left after the removal, usually in a press, of the oil or juice of a plant product, such as grapes, oil seeds or kernels, sugar cane, etc.

MARCHAND TUBE. A type of U-shaped tube, having side arms, and used to dry gases, or to absorb them, by the action of calcium chloride, phosphorus pentoxide, or other reactive substances placed in this tube.

MARGARIC. Related to margaric acid,

$$C_{16}H_{33}COOH.$$

MARINO TEST REACTION. To detect thallic salts in presence of thallous, alkalinize the dilute solution tested with potassium hydroxide solution, add saturated α-naphthol solution and a little dimethyl-o-phenylenediamine. An indophenol blue color indicates the presence of thallic salts.

MARIOTTES LAW. The same as the **law of Boyle.**

MARKOWNIKOFF RULE. When an unsaturated molecule adds another molecular system at a low temperature, the most negative element or group combines with the least hydrogenated carbon atom or with that which is already in direct union with some negative element, but at comparatively higher temperatures the more positive element or group adds to the least hydrogenated carbon atom.

A specific application of this principle to the addition of halogen acids to unsaturated ethylenic compounds states that the halogen usually goes to the carbon atom having the smaller number of hydrogen atoms, but this order of addition is often reversed with HBr in the presence of peroxide.

MARME SOLUTION. A solution of 10 g. potassium iodide and 5 g. cadmium iodide in 30 ml. water, to which is then added an equal volume of a saturated aqueous solution of potassium iodide. This reagent is used in testing for alkaloids, which give precipitates in acid solution.

MARQUIS SOLUTION. A solution of 4 ml. 40% formaldehyde in 100 ml. concentrated sulfuric acid, used in the identification of alkaloids. Characteristic color reactions are obtained. Another reagent

is a mixture of 10 drops of concentrated hydroxymethyl sulfuric acid solution and 10 ml. concentrated sulfuric acid. The name is also applied to solutions of certain methylene derivatives in concentrated sulfuric acid.

MARRISON TEST FOR PHOSPHATE AND ARSENATE. One drop of the solution tested is placed on filter paper, and 1 drop 0.02 N sodium sulfide solution is added to it. Then 1 drop 2.5% ammonium molybdate solution is placed on the paper so that its spreading edges meet those of the other spot. A blue color indicates arsenate and the various phosphate ions.

MARSH SOLUTION. An emulsion of 3 ml. phosphoric acid and 3 ml. water in 100 ml. amyl alcohol, used in testing for caramel. A brown color is imparted to the aqueous layer on shaking with material containing caramel.

MARSH TEST. A test for the presence of arsenic, performed by treating the solution to be tested with zinc and hydrochloric acid, whereby the arsenic is reduced to its hydride AsH_3. This hydride and the liberated hydrogen are passed through a long tube that is heated to decompose the arsine, so that a deposit of metallic arsenic forms in the cool portion of the tube, close to its end. An analogous deposit is obtained for antimony, which is differentiated by the fact that the arsenic deposit is soluble in potassium hypochlorite solution, whereas that of antimony is not. Many modifications of this test are known under names of various investigators.

MARSHALL REACTION FOR MANGANESE. A slightly acid manganese solution, on heating with a little silver salt and ammonium persulfate, gives a purple-red color.

MARTIN PROCESS FOR STARCH. A method of producing wheat starch by moistening and mechanically kneading the flour into a dough and working out the starch by jets of water and further mechanical action. This process also includes an alkaline treatment to remove gluten.

MARTINET DIOXINDOLE SYNTHE-SIS. A method of formation of dioxindoles from arylamines and mesoxalic acid esters.

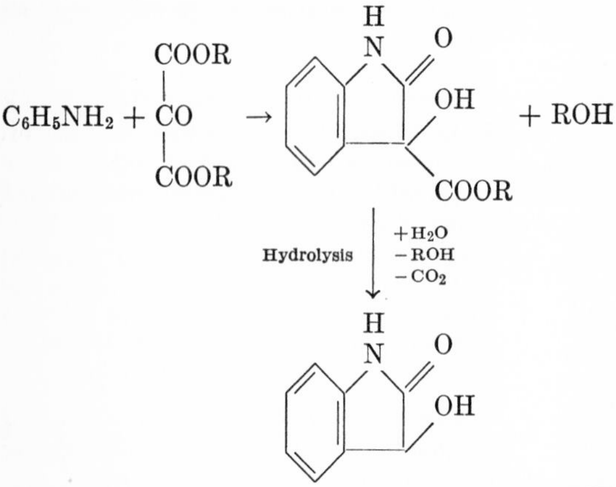

$$C_6H_5NH_2 + \begin{array}{c} COOR \\ | \\ CO \\ | \\ COOR \end{array} \rightarrow$$

$$+ ROH$$

Hydrolysis $\begin{array}{c} +H_2O \\ -ROH \\ -CO_2 \end{array}$

MARTINET REAGENT. A solution of 1 g. vanillin and 20 ml. concentrated hydrochloric acid in 180 ml. alcohol used in differentiating between clove oil and eugenol. The former gives a red color, and the latter, a yellow one.

MARTINI MICRO-TEST FOR ANTIMONY, BISMUTH, AND GOLD. Add sodium iodide to the solution tested to the formation of a yellow color, then add a solution of piperazine in acetone. Golden-yellow oblique prisms form if antimony is present, and red plates with bismuth. To test for gold, use sodium bromide in place of the sodium iodide, whereupon yellow to red plates or prisms are given by the piperazine solution if gold is present.

MARTINI MICRO-TEST FOR CHROMIUM. One drop of a 1% chromium salt solution, on treatment with 1 drop concentrated oxalic acid solution and 1 drop quinoline solution, gives characteristic crystals of the pyridine addition-compound of chromium oxalate.

MARTINI MICRO-TEST FOR PHOSPHATE AND ARSENATE. One drop of 1% disodium phosphate solution or of an arsenate solution, with 1 drop 16.7% cesium chloride solution, 1 drop magnesium chloride solution, and 1 drop quinoline, gives a characteristic precipitate.

MARTINI MICRO-TEST FOR SODIUM. A little powdered ammonium carbonate and 1 drop uranium acetate solution in dilute acetic acid are added to 1 drop 1:100 sodium salt solution; when the effervescence has subsided, add 1 drop pyridine. Characteristic octahedral crystals are formed.

MARTINI MICRO-TESTS FOR COBALT. (1) Cobalt solutions, on addition of hexamethylenetetramine sulfate and ammonium thiocyanate, give blue triclinic crystals.

(2) One drop of a 0.01% solution of a cobalt salt, with 1 drop cold saturated solution of ammonium thiocyanate and 1 drop cold saturated solution of aminopyrine, gives a blue-green precipitate.

(3) Addition of ammonium thiocyanate and pyridine to a neutral cobalt solution gives a rose precipitate, becoming sky-blue and crystallizing on addition of nitric acid.

MARTINI MICRO-TESTS FOR COPPER. (1) An ammoniacal copper solution, containing ammonium thiocyanate, gives green monoclinic crystals with quinoline sulfate.

(2) One drop copper solution, 1 drop saturated hexamethylenetetramine sulfate solution and 1 drop ammonium thiocyanate solution, give yellow crystalline plates.

(3) An ammoniacal copper solution, with single drops of ammonium thiocyanate solution and aniline, gives green triclinic rosettes.

MARTINI MICRO-TESTS FOR IRON, ZINC, AND INDIUM. (1) To a drop of 0.01% solution of the salt, add 1 drop ammonium thiocyanate solution and 1 drop cold saturated aminopyrine solution. Iron forms a red precipitate, zinc a white one.

(2) With dilute acid solutions of aniline hydrochloride, zinc solutions give colorless triclinic crystals.

(3) One drop of a dilute solution of the salt is treated with 1 drop saturated methenamine sulfate solution and 1 drop saturated ammonium thiocyanate solution. Iron gives small reddish crystals; indium, a white precipitate; and zinc, white needle-like crystals.

MARTINI MICRO-TESTS FOR MOLYBDENUM. (1) To 1 drop 0.1–1.0% ammonium molybdate solution add saturated pyrocatechol acetate solution until an orange color appears, then a little aniline. Triclinic crystals are obtained.

(2) To 1 drop 1.0% ammonium molybdate solution add pyrocatechol until a deep orange color forms, then a small drop of benzylamine followed by a little 15% acetic acid. Groups of orange crystals appear on stirring.

MARTINI MICRO-TESTS FOR NICKEL. (1) One drop 1% nickel solution with 1 drop concentrated ammonium thiocyanate solution and 1 drop o-toluidine gives characteristic crystals of the complex compound.

(2) An ammoniacal nickel solution, on treatment with ammonium thiocyanate solution and aniline, gives triclinic prisms.

(3) Nickel ions in dilute solution react with saturated sodium selenite solutions, and cesium chloride, to give characteristic crystals of cesium nickel selenite.

MARTINI MICRO-TESTS FOR TUNGSTEN. (1) One drop 1% tungstate solution is treated with saturated pyrocatechol solution until the orange color appears, then 1 drop aniline or piperazine is added. Yellow crystals are formed.

(2) One drop 1% tungstate solution is treated with pyrocatechol until the orange color appears, then 1 drop benzylamine and a little 15% acetic acid are added. Characteristic groups of crystals appear after mixing.

MARTINI REAGENT. A volume of 25 ml. of a 1% lead nitrate solution to which a saturated aqueous solution of potassium iodide is added in sufficient volume to re-dissolve the initial precipitate. This reagent is used in testing for cocaine hydrochloride, which gives characteristic crystals.

MARVEL-DU VIGNEUD REAGENT. α-Phenyl-β-diethylaminoethyl-p-nitrobenzoate, used to crystallize nitrates and perchlorates.

MASH. A mixture of grain, or bran, and water, used in feeding livestock or in charging fermentation units. In the latter, the grain usually has been malted.

MASKING. The concealing of a substance by another; thus a compound is said to mask the properties of a constituent element or radical if the usual, characteristic reactions of the element or radical are not readily obtained.

MASON-CHAMOT MICRO-TEST FOR BROMIDE. Free the bromine by treatment with chlorine or other reagent, and add a solution of m-phenylenediamine in dilute sulfuric acid. A white crystalline precipitate is produced.

MASS. For many purposes, mass may be defined as the quantity of matter composing a body or entering into a reaction or other process. This definition is adequate for ordinary chemical operations, but says little or nothing about the essential attributes of mass. The only inseparable one of these appears to be inertia, which is an excellent basis for comparing the masses of two bodies at rest. Since in light of the relativity theory, the inertia, and mass, of a body depends upon its motion, the mass of a body moving at very great speeds is appreciably greater than its mass at rest. This relationship is:

$$M = \frac{M_o}{\sqrt{1 - V^2/c^2}}$$

where M is the mass of a body at a given velocity, M_o is its mass at rest, V is the velocity, and c is velocity of light.

MASS ABSORPTION COEFFICIENT. See **absorption coefficient, mass.**

MASS ACTION, LAW OF. See **law of mass action.**

MASS, CONSERVATION OF. See **law of the conservation of matter.**

MASS DEFECT. The difference between the mass of an atom, as calculated from the mass of the **neutrons** and **protons** assumed to be present in its **nucleus** and the electrons surrounding its nucleus; and the mass of the atom as determined by the **mass spectrograph.** Thus, the mass defect is given by the relation:

$$\text{Mass Defect} = Zm_\text{H} + (A - Z)m_n - M$$

wherein Zm_H is the mass of Z hydrogen atoms, Z being the atomic number of the atom; $(A - Z)m_n$ is the mass of $(A - Z)$ neutrons, A being the mass number of the atom; and M is the determined atomic mass.

The energy equivalent of the mass defect is taken as a measure of the **binding energy** of the particular atom.

The mass defect, as defined above, is often called the "true mass defect."

MASS EFFECT. See **packing effect.**

MASS NUMBER. The whole number nearest the precise value for the **atomic weight** of a single atomic species. Mass numbers are of special importance in the study of **isotopes** as by using the **mass spectrograph.** They are commonly written as a superscript before or after symbol of the atom, such as O^{16} or ^{40}K.

MASS POLYMERIZATION. See **polymerization, mass.**

MASS SPECTROGRAM. The photograph of a **mass spectrum** (q.v.).

MASS SPECTROGRAPH. An instrument used to determine the relative masses of atoms and molecules. These are first subjected to electron bombardment and ionized. They are then subjected to **electric fields** and accelerated; finally the ions are placed in a magnetic field and deflected through a certain angle with respect to their original trajectory. From the extent of the deflection their masses may then be determined. The mass spectrograph is widely used in determining the exact masses of **isotopes,** and the relative amounts of each isotope normally present in a given element.

MASS SPECTRUM. The spectrum of atoms of different mass of a sample subjected to mass spectrograph analysis.

MASURIUM. The name assigned to the element of atomic number 43 when its discovery was claimed by Noddack in 1925. The discovery of a radioactive atomic species of atomic number 43 was reported in 1947 and the name assigned to the element of this atomic number was then established as **technetium.**

MATERIALIZATION. The production of matter from energy radiations, as is believed to occur in interstellar space, and in certain recent investigations, from cosmic and high-frequency gamma rays, which are transformed into electron-positron pairs.

MATIGNON TEST REACTION FOR VANADIUM. Solutions of vanadic acid give a blue color with gallic, pyrogallic, and tannic acids.

MATRIX. In general, an aggregate of ground mass in which a discrete object is embedded. Specifically, the material in which a precious or semiprecious stone is embedded; or the earth or rock containing an ore or other mineral; or the impression left in a rock by a precious or semiprecious stone, a crystal, or a fossil. Derivatively, the term matrix is used in mathematics to denote an arrangement of symbols in rows and columns.

MATSUI-NAKAZAWA TEST FOR COBALT. After removal of the nickel with dimethylglyoxime, add 1–2 drops ammonium polysulfide to the filtrate. A red color indicates cobalt.

MATTE. An intermediate, impure product obtained in the process of recovering metals from their ores, which results from smelting operations; or a roughened or fibrous surface which reflects light diffusely, such as the surface of uncoated paper.

MATTER. That which occupies space or which can be perceived by our sense of touch. It presents itself in one of three states of aggregation, the solid, liquid, or gaseous states. It is characterized by association with **mass** (q.v.) possessing the property of inertia.

MATTER, ANNIHILATION. Transformation of matter into energy.

MATTER, CONSERVATION. See **law of conservation of mass.**

MATTER WAVE. See **de Broglie matter waves.**

MAUMENÉ NUMBER. The rise in temperature obtained by mixture of a specified amount of an oil with a specified amount of concentrated sulfuric acid; the magnitude of the rise indicates the degree of unsaturation and hence the effectiveness of the oil as a **drying oil** (q.v.).

MAWAS BRASILIN SOLUTION. A solution of 0.5 g. brasilin in 100 g. water or alcohol. It is used to test for iron in tissues. The nuclei are colored red-violet, and the surrounding tissues are brown, if iron is present.

MAXIMOW FLUID. A solution of 25 g. potassium dichromate, 50 g. mercuric chloride, and 10 g. sodium sulfate, in 1 liter water, to which 100 ml. formaldehyde is then added. It is used as a fixative.

MAXIMUM BOILING POINT. A two-component or multi-component liquid system in which, for a particular composition, the boiling point is higher than that for any other composition or for the pure components is to have a maximum boiling point at that temperature.

MAXIMUM FREEZING POINT. A two-component or multi-component liquid system in which, for a particular composition, the freezing point is higher than that for any other composition or for the pure **components** is said to have a maximum freezing point at that temperature.

MAXWELL DEMON. An imaginary figure pictured by Maxwell to illustrate a concept in gas kinetics. A tiny being was considered to operate a trap door in a partition between two chambers. This "demon" opened the door whenever a molecule of a particular kind approached the door, and so effected separation of a pure gas from a mixture.

MAXWELL, DISTRIBUTION LAW OF. See **law of Maxwell, distribution.**

MAXWELL RELATIONSHIP FOR REFRACTIVE INDEX. See **refractive index, Maxwell's relationship for.**

MAYER. A unit of **heat capacity** proposed by Richards. The mayer is the capacity of a body or system which is warmed 1 degree centigrade by 1 **joule.** The heat capacity of 1 gram of water at 20° is about 4.181 mayers.

MAYER HEMACALCIUM SOLUTION. A solution of 1 g. hematein and 1 g. aluminum chloride in 600 ml. 70% alcohol, to which is then added 10 ml. acetic acid and 50 g. calcium chloride. This reagent is used as a nuclear stain.

MAYER HEMALUM SOLUTION. A solution of 1 g. hematein, or its ammonium salt, in 50 ml. 95% alcohol, to which is then added a solution of 50 g. potassium alum in 1 liter distilled water. Another form of this solution is prepared by dissolving 1 g. hematoxylin in 1 liter distilled water, adding 50 g. potassium alum and 0.2 g. sodium iodate, and diluting with an equal volume of water. These solutions are used as stains.

MAYER PICROCARMINE SOLUTION. A mixture of a solution of 8 g. carmine in 100 ml. ammonium hydroxide and enough of a saturated solution of picric acid to cause formation of a precipitate. It is used as a stain.

MAYER REACTION FOR CHOLESTEROL. Cholesterol gives a violet color on treatment with ferric chloride and hydrochloric acid.

MAYER REAGENT FOR ALKALOIDS. A solution of 13.55 g. mercuric chloride and

50 g. potassium iodide in sufficient water to give 1 liter of solution. It is used as an alkaloidal reagent; white precipitates are obtained.

MAYER-SCHRAMM TEST FOR COPPER. To the acidic solution tested, add sodium bicarbonate until a slight precipitate persists, then add hydrogen peroxide. A bright blue or green color, or a yellow precipitate, indicates copper.

MAYR SOLUTION. A solution of 2 g. α-nitro-β-naphthol in 110 ml. glacial acetic acid and 100 ml. water, used in the quantitative precipitation of cobalt and palladium.

MAYRHOFFER REAGENT. A mixture of 60 ml. of a saturated aqueous solution of picrolonic acid, 30 ml. glycerol, and either 30 ml. absolute alcohol or 10 ml. tincture of iodine, used as a precipitating reagent for hydrastine and berberine.

MAZUIR REACTION FOR TIN. Two ml. of the liquid tested are mixed with 2 ml. 10% potassium iodide solution and then 2 ml. concentrated sulfuric acid are added. A yellow precipitate, soluble in hydrochloric acid, is given by tin salts.

MC AFEE PROCESS. A catalytic cracking process in which the petroleum fraction (which must be free from water) is heated with 5 to 8% by weight of anhydrous aluminum chloride, at a temperature of about 290° C., for about two days.

MC FADYEN-STEVENS ALDEHYDE SYNTHESIS. A method of converting aromatic esters to aldehydes through their benzenesulfonacylhydrazides.

diamine. A black precipitate indicates copper.

MC LEOD GAUGE. A manometer used for determining low gas pressures by compressing a sample until its pressure reaches a measureable value.

ME. Abbreviation for **methyl.**

MEAN. An average. An intermediate numerical value between two or more extremes or variables.

MEAN FREE PATH OF MOLECULES. The average distance traveled by a molecule of a gas or a substance in solution between collision with other molecules.

MEAN LIFETIME. The average period of time that a particle, such as an atom, molecule, nucleus, etc., will remain in a given excited state before undergoing a change.

MEAURIO REAGENT. A solution of 2 g. diphenylamine in 1 liter distilled water used in testing for vanadium. A violet color, developed upon addition of the reagent and hydrochloric acid, is obtained in the presence of vanadium.

MECHANICAL EQUIVALENT OF HEAT. The quantity of heat equivalent to the conversion of a given amount of mechanical energy.

MECHANICAL PASSIVITY. See **passivity, mechanical.**

MECKE SOLUTION. A solution of 0.5 g. selenous acid in 100 ml. concentrated sulfuric acid, used as a test reagent for alkaloids. Characteristic color reactions are obtained.

$$RCOOR' + NH_2NH_2 \rightarrow RCONHNH_2 + R'OH$$

$$RCONHNH_2 + C_6H_5SO_2Cl \rightarrow RCONHNHSO_2C_6H_5 + HCl$$

$$RCONHNHSO_2C_6H_5 + Na_2CO_3 \rightarrow RCHO + C_6H_5SO_2Na + N_2 + NaHCO_3.$$

MC IROY TEST FOR COPPER. Treat a few drops of the ammoniacal solution remaining after removal of the bismuth with 5 ml. saturated solution of potassium thiocyanate and 2–3 drops p-phenylene-

MEDINGER REAGENT. A reagent used in the determination of phosphate in water. It is prepared by adding a 1% aqueous solution of strychnine nitrate to a clear solution of 40 g. ammonium molybdate in

100 ml. water until a permanent precipitate forms, then adding an equal volume of concentrated nitric acid.

MEDIUM. A substance in which a given system of entities exists, or in which a result is accomplished, as the transmission of force or energy, the suspension of particles (colloidal medium) or the growth of micro-organisms (culture medium).

MEERBURG-FILIPPS MICRO-TEST FOR COPPER. Cesium chloride forms red hexagonal prismatic or needle-shaped crystals with copper solutions in hydrochloric acid. Additional cesium chloride gives yellow crystals.

MEERWEIN CONDENSATION. A condensation of diazo compounds with α-γ unsaturated carbonyl compounds. Coupling usually occurs in the α-position.

$$R'CH{=}CHCOR'' + ArN_2Cl \rightarrow R'CH{=}CArCOR'' + N_2 + HCl.$$

MEERWEIN-PONNDORF-VERLEY RE-ACTION. A reductive transformation of hydroxy and carbonyl compounds, using metallic alkoxides as catalysts, in which the hydroxy compound becomes a carbonyl compound, and the carbonyl compound becomes an hydroxy compound. This reaction is reversible.

$$R'CHOHR'' + R'''COR'''' \leftrightarrows R'COR'' + R'''CHOHR''''.$$

This reaction is known as the Meerwein-Ponndorf-Verley reduction or the Oppenauer oxidation, depending on the product sought and the consequent variation in the conduct of the reaction.

MEESEMAECKER TEST REACTION FOR ERGOSTEROL. To 0.0001 g. ergosterol dissolved in 1 ml. chloroform, add 0.5 ml. acetic anhydride and a little zinc chloride. A rose color is given, unless the ergosterol has been irradiated. Ergosterol irradiated with mercury vapor light becomes green when tested.

MEGA-. A prefix meaning (1) large; (2) one million times.

MEGADYNE. One million **dynes.**

MEGAERG. One million **ergs.**

MEGAFARAD. One million **farads.**

MEGAMETER. One million **meters.**

MEHU SOLUTION. A mixture of 5 ml. phenol, 5 ml. glacial acetic acid, and 10 ml. 90% alcohol, used in testing for albumin. A precipitate is obtained upon addition of the reagent and nitric acid.

MEISSNER FLAME TEST. Add hydrochloric acid and zinc to the solution tested. Stir it vigorously with a test tube filled with cold water, and place the test tube at once in the colorless Bunsen flame. A blue flame-color indicates tin.

MEKKER BURNER. See burner, Mekker.

MELDOLA TEST. Nitrite is detected by adding to the solution tested a few drops of a solution of 0.5 g. p-aminobenzeneazodimethylaniline in 1 liter dilute nitric acid, and then adding a few drops hydrochloric acid and, with stirring, a few drops ammonia. If nitrite is present, a blue color appears.

MELISSIC. Related to melissic acid, $C_{30}H_{61}COOH$.

MELLITIC. Related to mellitic acid, $C_6(COOH)_6$.

MELT. To fuse. To pass from the solid to the liquid state (see **fusion**). A "melt" is a fused mass.

MELTING POINT. (1) The temperature at which the solid and liquid states of a substance co-exist in **equilibrium.** The melting point is usually referred to normal pressure, 760 millimeters. Increase or decrease of pressure affects the melting point. If, at the melting point, the specific volume of the liquid is greater than that of the solid, increase of pressure raises the melting point and decrease of pressure lowers it. (2) The "melting point" of **liquid crystals** is the temperature at which the crystals lose their anisotropic properties.

MELTING POINT, CONGRUENT. The melting point of a compound at which the solid phase and the two-component liquid phase present have the same equilibrium composition.

MELTING POINT, INCONGRUENT. In the case of a two-component system which forms a compound that **dissociates** below its melting point, the temperature at which the solid form of that compound is in equilibrium with the two-component liquid and also with one of the solid components, or with the solid form of another compound formed from them.

MELTING POINT TUBE. A device for determining melting points. It is simply a short length of capillary tubing closed at one end in which a sample is placed, and which is then attached to a thermometer and heated slowly in a bath until the sample is seen to fuse.

MELZER REACTIONS FOR ALKALOIDS. Many alkaloids give characteristic colors on treatment with 1 drop 20% solution of benzaldehyde in absolute alcohol, and 1 drop concentrated sulfuric acid.

MEMBRANE. A thin sheet of tissue or other material that lines or divides spaces or organs in plants or animals.

MEMBRANE FILTER. A **filtration** medium consisting of a sheet of nitrocellulose or other plastic material with relatively small apertures, used in bacteriological filtration.

MENDELÉEFF TABLE. See **periodic table.**

MENISCUS. The curved surface of a liquid, particularly noticeable in vessels or tubes of small diameter and due to the surface tension of the liquid. If the liquid wets the containing vessel the meniscus is concave, otherwise it is convex. The meniscus of mercury in glass is convex.

MENKE ISATIN REAGENT. A solution of 0.5 g. isatin in 100 ml. 5% ammonium hydroxide, used in testing for copper and silver. Characteristic crystals are obtained. This is a micro-test.

MENKE MICRO-TEST FOR MANGANESE. A mixture of cyanuric acid and ammonium hydroxide, on addition of a crystal of manganese sulfate, gives a white precipitate, changed on boiling to clusters of crystals.

MENNEL REAGENT. A mixture of 160 ml. 68% sulfuric acid and 130 ml. 37% formaldehyde, used in testing mercerized cotton.

MENSTRUUM. A **solvent,** especially the solvent used in extracting drugs, which is often a complex mixture.

MENTHYL. The radical

$$\overline{CH_3CH.(CH_2)_2.CH(CH(CH_3)_2).CH_2.CH-}$$

(from menthane; 2-*p*-form shown).

MER, MERE, MERI. A combining form used in chemistry with the general meaning of -sided, denoting a member of the (specified) class designated by a corresponding adjective ending in -meric, as in isomer, metamer.

MERCAPTAL. One of a group of sulfur compounds, also known as thioacetals, analogous to the acetals, of the general form $R'S—CHR—SR''$, where R' and R'' are identical or different alkyl or aryl groups.

MERCAPTAN. One of a group of organic compounds, also known as thioalcohols and preferably as thiols, characterized by content of an —SH group, analogous to the alcohols, from which they may be considered derived by the substitution of sulfur for hydroxyl oxygen, e.g., ethyl mercaptan, C_2H_5SH (ethanethiol). They are liquids of extremely disgusting, garlic odor.

MERCAPTIDE. One of a group of metallic derivatives of the mercaptans, e.g., mercury mercaptide, $Hg(C_2H_5S)_2$. They bear the same relation to the mercaptans that the alcoholates do to the alcohols.

MERCAPTO-. The radical HS—.

MERCAPTOL. One of a group of sulfur compounds of the general form

produced by combination of **ketones** and **mercaptans,** in which R′ and R″ may be identical or different aryl or alkyl groups.

MERCERIZATION PROCESS. An operation for improving the working qualities of cotton as a textile, and imparting to it a glossy surface, by treatment with strong sodium hydroxide solution followed by thorough washing and drying.

MERCK REAGENT FOR ALKALOIDS. Sulfuric and nitric acids give characteristic colors with many alkaloids.

MERCK TEST FOR ALCOHOLS. A solution of molybdic acid in sulfuric acid is heated to 60° C., and on it is superimposed the solution to be tested. The presence of alcohols is indicated by a blue ring at the interface.

MERCURATION. The substitution or addition of **mercury** to an organic compound.

MERCURI. The radical —Hg— in organic compounds.

MERCURIC. Containing or pertaining to divalent **mercury.**

MERCURICYANIDE. See **cyanomercurate (II).**

MERCURIDE. A compound of mercury with one or more organic radicals, usually the same radical, as $Hg(C_2H_5)_2$.

MERCURIFY. To combine with mercury, to amalgamate.

MERCURIIODIDE. See **iodomercurate (II).**

MERCURISULFITE. See **sulfitomercurate (II).**

MERCURIZATION. The substitution or addition of mercury to an organic compound.

MERCUROUS. Containing or pertaining to univalent **mercury.**

MERCURY. Liquid metallic element. Symbol Hg (hydrargyrum). Atomic number 80. Atomic weight 200.61. Density 13.456. Specific heat 0.03325. Melting point −39.0° C. Boiling point 356.9° C. Valence 1 and 2. Oxides, Hg_2O and HgO. Mercury occurs native, as sulfide, in cinnabar, etc. Alloys of mercury are termed amalgams. Its salts are poisonous.

MERGET TEST FOR MERCURY VAPOR. Paper marked with ammoniacal silver nitrate solution shows gray lines on exposure to mercury vapor.

MERICA REAGENT. A mixture of 50 ml. 70% nitric acid and 50 ml. 50% acetic acid, used for etching nickel and its alloys.

MERK TEST FOR IODINE. Iodine is detected in inorganic compounds by the appearance of a blue color in trituration with potassium persulfate and soluble starch.

MEROCHROME COMPOUND. A compound having differently-colored isomeric forms occurring together, as in a mixed crystal.

MEROTROPY. Michael's term for desmotropy. See **isomerism, dynamic.**

MERRILL PROCESS. A method of precipitating gold, silver, etc., from cyanide and other solutions by the use of zinc dust.

MERSIBURG PROCESS. A method for the production of ammonium phosphate fertilizer which uses gypsum, ammonia, and carbon dioxide as raw materials.

MES-. See **meso-**.

MESH. The number of open spaces in a screen per unit area.

MESITYL. The radical

$$2,4,6\text{-}(CH_3)_3C_6H_2\text{—}.$$

α-MESITYL. The radical

$$3,5\text{-}(CH_3)_2C_6H_3CH_2\text{—}.$$

MESNARD REAGENT. Mix 50 ml. 5% cupric sulfate solution with 50 ml. 5% potassium cyanide solution, neutralize with sulfuric acid and filter. This reagent gives a blue-violet precipitate with aqueous solutions of methylene blue.

MESO-, MES-. (Greek) Middle, intermediate. Specifically: (1) a prefix designating an intermediate hydrated form of an inorganic acid, as mesoperiodic acid, H_3IO_5; (2) optically inactive owing to internal compensation, as *meso*-tartaric acid; (3) designating a middle position in certain cyclic organic compounds, as *meso*-chloroanthracene (9-chloroanthracene), *meso*-phenylimidazole (2-phenylimidazole); (4) a ring system characterized by the middle position of certain rings, as *meso*-naphthodianthrene.

MESOCOLLOID. A colloid composed of particles of relatively medium size, i.e., ranging from 0.025 to 0.25 micron.

MESOMER. A meso-form (see **meso-**).

MESOMETHYLENE CARBON. A carbon atom which forms a bridge across a ring and is linked to two methyl groups, as the central carbon atom in camphane.

$$
\begin{array}{c}
H_2C\text{———}CH\text{———}CH_2 \\
\quad\ \ CH_3\text{—}C\text{—}CH_3 \\
H_2C\text{———}C\text{———}CH_2 \\
\quad\quad\ \ CH_3
\end{array}
$$

MESOMORPHIC. Having an intermediate form, specifically a form intermediate between the liquid and solid states. The term is applied to the so-called "liquid crystals" which are true liquids having surface tension and free flow, but which are doubly refracting and yield interference patterns in polarized light.

MESON. An elementary particle having a unit positive or unit negative (i.e., the same as that of the electron) electric charge, but with a mass of the order of magnitude of hundreds of times that of the electron. Experimental evidence of the existence of a particle of this order of mass, charged positively or negatively, was obtained in cosmic ray investigations. Later cosmic ray work showed that more than one kind of mesons, with different masses, exist. Prior to this last discovery, several kinds of mesons had been postulated in the construction of a meson theory of nuclear forces. Investigations, both with mesons in cosmic rays and with mesons produced artifically in the laboratory, disclosed the existence of a so-called π(pi)-meson with a mass 285 times that of the electron, and a μ(mu)-meson, into which a π-meson sometimes is transformed. The μ-meson has a mass about 215 times that of the electron.

At least three types of meson theory have been given consideration by physicists. In the neutral meson theory, the proton and neutron are regarded as different energy states of the same fundamental particle; and the meson, which is responsible for energy interactions between them, is supposed to be electrically neutral. This neutral meson is sometimes called a neutretto. The charged meson theory postulates the existence of positive and negative mesons, which are transferred between protons and neutrons in the transformations of those particles. The symmetrical meson theory combines the features of the neutral and the charged meson theories.

MESO-POSITION. See **meso-**.

MESOTHORIUM (I AND II). Radioactive elements of the thorium family. Mesothorium I has an atomic number of 88, and a half-life of 6.7 years. It emits β-rays and is an isotope of **radium.** Mesothorium

II has an atomic number of 89, and a half-life of 6.13 hours. It emits β-rays and is an isotope of **actinium.** Mesothorium I is produced from thorium by α-ray emission. Mesothorium I yields Mesothorium II by β-ray emission, which, in turn, yields radiothorium by β-ray emission.

MESOTOMY. A method of separating the optically active **isomers** from a mixture, or the separation itself.

MESYL. See **methylsulfonyl.**

META-, MET-. (Greek) Indicating changed relations; specifically, a prefix designating (1) a low hydrated form of an acid (usually that derived from the "ortho" form by loss of 1 H_2O from one molecule of acid), as metaphosphoric acid, HPO_3; (2) a closely related compound (sometimes, a polymer), as metaldehyde (trimer of ordinary aldehyde); (3) the relation of the 1 and 3 positions in benzene, or a compound characterized by it, as metaxylene. Abbreviation (in this last sense), m, as m-xylene.

METAANTIMONIC. Related to meta-antimonic acid, $HSbO_4$.

METABISULFITE. See **pyrosulfite.**

METABOLISM. The sum total of the processes occurring in a living cell or organism by which food is transformed into living **protoplasm,** reserve materials are stored, and waste materials are eliminated.

METABORIC. Related to metaboric acid, HBO_2.

METACHROMATISM. Change of the color of an object or substance with a change in the color of the light by which it is viewed.

META-COMPOUND. A compound substituted in the meta-position (see **meta-**).

METAFILTRATION. A method of **filtration** in which the filtering medium is a pile of metallic strips with beveled edges, between which the liquid to be filtered is passed.

METAISOMER. One of two isomeric substances that differ in the position of a double bond.

METAL. (1) Any element that can replace the hydrogen of an acid. (2) A member of a class of elements characterized by the possession of metallic luster, ductility, malleability, high electric and thermal conductivity, and chemically, of forming bases which can react with acids. There is no sharp line of demarcation between metals and non-metals, because many of the latter class possess some metallic properties. The property of forming cations may be considered characteristic of metallic elements. Metals transmit light only through extremely thin layers.

METAL, ALKALI. One of the metals **lithium, sodium, potassium, rubidium, cesium,** and **francium** that constitute the first group in the periodic table.

METAL, ALKALINE EARTH. One of the metals **magnesium, calcium, strontium, barium,** etc., in the second group in the periodic table.

METAL, BASE. One of the more reactive metals (i.e., those which form oxides or bases more or less readily), as contrasted with the noble metals.

METAL BATH. A bath of a fused metal, or mixture of metals, used for heating at controlled temperature.

METAL COMPOUND. See **compound, intermetallic.**

METAL, EARTH. One of the metals **aluminum, scandium, yttrium,** etc., in the third group in the periodic table.

METAL, FUSIBLE. An alloy which melts at low temperatures, viz.,

Alloy	M.P.	Bi	Pb	Sn	Cd
		Composition			
Lipowitz'	60°	15	8	4	3
Rose's	94°	2	1	1	
Wood's	71°	4	2	1	1

METAL, HEAVY. A metal of high specific gravity. The sulfides of such metals are usually insoluble in water and are precipitated by ammonium sulfide.

METAL, LIGHT. A term sometimes used to characterize metals of low specific gravity. Their sulfides are usually soluble in water.

METAL, NOBLE. A term originally applied to gold and silver, and connoting their relative inertness to chemical action, especially to the action of the reagents used by the early chemists and alchemists. Now the term applies generally to the members of the gold and platinum families of elements in the periodic table.

METAL-ORGANIC COMPOUND. A carbon compound, other than a salt, that contains a metal, as zinc ethide $Zn(C_2H_5)_2$, magnesiun alkyl iodides, etc.

METAL, RARE EARTH. One of the elements of the third long period of the **periodic table** from **lanthanum,** atomic number 57, to and including **lutecium,** atomic number 71.

METALAMMINE. See **ammine.**

METALAMMONIUM COMPOUND. See **ammine.**

METALEPSY. Dumas' term for substitution in organic chemistry.

METALLIC. Pertaining to or containing a metal. Possessing the properties of a metal.

METALLIC BOND. See **bond, metallic.**

METALLIC SOAP. See **soap, metallic.**

METALLINE. (1) Resembling or pertaining to a metal. (2) Impregnated with metallic salts, as chalybeate water.

METALLIZATION. The coating of a surface with a metal.

METALLIZING. A process for coating objects with thin layers of metal by spraying them with molten metals.

METALLOGRAPHY. The science that deals with the properties of metals and metallic compounds and mixtures, especially in regard to the study of their surface by microscopical and chemico-microscopical methods, and the interpretation of the results in terms of properties and characteristics.

METALLURGY. The science that deals with the processing of metals, from their recovery from ores to their purification, alloying, and fabrication into industrial articles.

METALLURGY, POWDER. See **powder metallurgy.**

METALORGANIC COMPOUND. See **compound, metalorganic.**

METAMER. See **metamerism.**

METAMERIC. See **metamerism.**

METAMERISM. A form of isomerism that exists between compounds composed of the same atoms, which are linked in different valence groupings. (See **isomerism, meta-.**)

METAPHOSPHATE. The anions of general formula $(PO_3)_n{}^{n-}$, such as (di-) $P_2O_6{}^=$, (hexa-) $P_6O_{18}{}^{6-}$, (tetra-) $P_4O_{12}{}^{4-}$, (tri-) $P_3O_9{}^{3-}$, or a compound containing one of them.

METAPHOSPHITE. The anion $(PO_2)_n{}^{n-}$, or a compound containing it.

METAPHOSPHORIC. Related to metaphosphoric acid, HPO_3.

METAPHOSPHOROUS. Related to metaphosphorous acid, HPO_2.

META-POSITION. The 1,3-positions on the benzene ring. See **meta-.**

METASILICIC. Related to metasilicic acid, H_2SiO_3.

METASTABLE. Moderately unstable. This term is commonly applied to an unstable condition that can change to either a more stable or a less stable condition.

METASTABLE EQUILIBRIUM. See equilibrium, metastable.

METASTASIC ELECTRON. An electron that moves from one atom to another, or from one shell to another in a given atom, or to the nucleus of the atom. K-electron capture, whereby the nucleus, usually in an induced radioactive reaction, captures an electron from the K-shell, is an instance of electron metastasis.

METASTASIS. A fundamental change in the position or orbit of a particle, as in the α-particle emission of certain radioactive nuclei. See metastasic electron.

METASULFURIC. Related to metasulfuric acid, or Caro's acid, $H_2S_2O_5$.

METATHESIS. (Metathetical reaction) A chemical reaction in which an element or radical in one compound changes place with another element or radical in another compound, e.g.,

$$NaNO_3 + KCl \leftrightarrows NaCl + KNO_3.$$

METATITANIC. Related to metatitanic acid, H_2TiO_3.

METAVANADIC. Related to metavanadic acid, HVO_3.

METER. A unit of linear measure (length) in the metric system, intended to be one ten-millionth part of the earth's quadrant from equator to pole. The meter is now an arbitrary unit.

1 meter = 3.28083 feet
1 meter = 1.093611 yards
1 meter = 39.37 inches
1 foot = 0.3048 meter

A meter is also a general term for a measuring device. See electrometer, gas-meter, gasometer, photometer, Venturi-meter.

METHANE SERIES. The paraffin hydrocarbons.

METHANO-COMPOUND. An organic compound containing a —CH₂— bridge within a cyclic structure.

METHANOLYSIS. Alcoholysis in which the alcohol split out is methyl alcohol.

METHENE. See methylene.

METHENYL. See methylidyne.

METHIDE. A metal-organic compound with methyl groups, as zinc methide $Zn(CH_3)_2$.

METHINE. See methylidyne.

METHIONYL. The radical $CH_2(SO_2)_2$=.

METHO-. A prefix used to indicate a methyl group attached to the middle atom of a side chain, or sometimes a methyl group attached to a cyclic nitrogen atom.

METHOXY. The radical CH_3O—.

METHYL. The radical CH_3—.

METHYL-ETHYL-KETONE PROCESS. See Govers process.

METHYLATE. (1) To add a methyl group to or substitute methyl in a compound. (2) A metallic compound of methyl alcohol, as sodium methylate CH_3—ONa.

METHYLENE. The radical CH_2=.

METHYLENEDIOXY. The radical

$$—OCH_2O—.$$

METHYLENEDISULFONYL. See methionyl.

METHYLIDYNE. The radical CH≡.

METHYLOL. Hydroxymethyl.

METHYLPHOSPHENODIIMIDIC. Related to methylphosphenodiimidic acid, HOP=$NCH_3(NH)$ or HOP=$NH(NCH_3)$.

N-METHYLPHOSPHORAMIDIMIDIC. Related to N-methylphosphoramidimidic acid, $(HO)_2(CH_3HN)P(NH)$.

N'-METHYLPHOSPHORAMIDIMIDIC. Related to N'-methylphosphoramidimidic acid, $(HO)_2(H_2N)P(NCH_3)$.

METRIC SYSTEM. A system of weights and measures which was based originally upon a unit of length called the meter (along with a unit of time, the mean solar second). The meter was defined as one ten-millionth of the Earth's meridian quadrant at sea level. The unit of mass then became a secondary standard, viz. the gram, based on the centimeter and the density of water, but this was soon displaced by the standard kilogram, which is defined as the mass of a standard block of metal. Similarly, the meter itself is now defined as the length, under specified conditions, of a standard bar of metal. These standards are preserved at Sèvres, France.

All subdivisions of units in the system are decimal, named by the use of Latin prefixes. Thus, deci- means 1/10; centi-, 1/100; milli-, 1/1000; etc. All multiples of units in the system are decimal, named by the use of Greek prefixes. Thus, deka- means 10 times; hekto-, 100 times; kilo-, 1000 times; etc.

The c.g.s. system is a variant of the metric system in which the measures are founded upon the centimeter and gram (and second), rather than directly upon the kilogram and meter. The c.g.s. system is used in chemical work and many other fields. The following are c.g.s. units of certain familiar magnitudes, together with their dimensional composition in terms of fundamental units of the system:

having advantages in electrical calculations. The following are m.k.s. units of certain familiar magnitudes:

Magnitude	*M.K.S. Unit*	*Dimensions*
Area	Square meter	m.^{2}
Volume	Cubic meter	m.^{3}
Momentum	Kilogram-meter per second	kg. m. sec.$^{-1}$
Energy and Work	Joule	kg. m.^{2} sec.$^{-2}$
Power	Watt	kg. m.^{2} sec.$^{-3}$

MEYER LAW. See **law of Meyer.**

MEYER-JENNEK TEST. Selenite ion is detected by the formation of a yellow-red color on adding 0.1 g. sodium hydrosulfite to 1 ml. of the weakly acid solution to be tested. The orange color of hydrosulfurous acid can be removed by addition of sodium carbonate.

MEYER-LOCHER TEST FOR ALCOHOLS. On distillation with silver nitrate and treatment of the distillate with nitrous acid, then with potassium hydroxide, a red color is given by primary alcohols and blue by secondary alcohols. Tertiary alcohols do not react.

Magnitude	*C.G.S. Unit*	*Dimensions*
Area	Square centimeter	cm.^{2}
Volume	Cubic centimeter	cm.^{3}
	Liter	Volume of 1 kilogram of pure water at its maximum density (1 liter = 1000.028 cm.^{3})
Speed	Centimeter per second	cm. sec.$^{-1}$
Acceleration	Centimeter per second per second	cm. sec.$^{-2}$
Momentum	Gram-centimeter per second	g. cm. sec.$^{-1}$
Force	Dyne	g. cm. sec.$^{-2}$
Torque	Dyne-centimeter	g. cm.^{2} sec.$^{-2}$
Pressure	Barye or Bar	g. cm.$^{-1}$ sec.$^{-2}$
Energy and Work	Erg	g. cm.^{2} sec.$^{-2}$
Power	Erg per second	g. cm.^{2} sec.$^{-3}$

The m.k.s. view of the metric system is based directly upon the meter, kilogram, and second, and was recommended by the International Electrical Commission, as

MEYER METHOD OF MOLECULAR WEIGHT DETERMINATION. See **molecular weight determination, Meyer method.**

MEYER REACTION. A reaction used in the preparation of organic compounds of tin; alkyl halides react with sodium stannite to give alkyl stannates and sodium halides.

$$NaSnOONa + RX \rightarrow RSnOONa + NaX.$$

MEYER REAGENT FOR THORIUM. A solution of 15 g. potassium iodate in 100 ml. water and 50 ml. concentrated nitric acid used as a precipitating reagent for thorium.

MEYER-SCHULZ SOLUTION. A solution of 1 g. lanthanum acetate in 100 ml. water used in the detection and determination of fluorine, by precipitation of lanthanum fluoride upon adding acetic acid to 10 ml. of the solution tested, then solid ammonium acetate, then an excess of the reagent.

MEYER-SCHUSTER REARRANGEMENT. A general rearrangement of acetylenic carbinols into unsaturated ketones by acidic reagents. See (1) below. A special case is the Rupe reaction, whereby an alkylacetylenic carbinol containing a free ethynyl group yields an unsaturated ketone on heating with strong formic acid, instead of the expected unsaturated aldehyde. See (2) below.

MEYER TEST REACTION FOR POTASSIUM. A concentrated solution of sodium phosphotungstate gives a turbidity or precipitate with potassium salt solutions.

MEYER VISCOSITY EQUATION. A relationship of the form:

$$\eta_t = \eta_0(1 + \alpha t)$$

where α = constant, η = gaseous viscosity, and t = temperature.

Mg Symbol for the element **magnesium.**

MHO. The unit of electrical **conductance,** the reciprocal ohm. A conductance of one mho per centimeter cube at a potential of one volt per centimeter permits the passage of a current of one ampere per square centimeter.

MICELLE. In its original meaning, a highly charged and hydrated colloidal aggregate. These micelles are supposed to occur in solutions of certain colloidal electrolytes, such as soaps, and to be responsible for some of the abnormalities exhibited by such solutions. The meaning of the term micelle has been extended to denote any oriented or bound aggregation of molecules.

$$R_2C(OH).C{\equiv}CR' \rightarrow R_2C{=}CH.COR' \qquad (1)$$

$$\overset{\displaystyle R'}{\underset{\displaystyle |}{RCH_2.C(OH).C{\equiv}CH}} \xrightarrow{\text{HCOOH}} RCH{=}CR'.COCH_3. \qquad (2)$$

MEYER SYNTHESIS. See Victor Meyer synthesis.

MEYER TEST FOR BLOOD. Dissolve 1–2 g. phenolphthalein and 25 g. potassium hydroxide in 100 ml. water, add 1 g. zinc dust and heat until decolorized. To 2 ml. of the solution tested, add 1 ml. of this reagent and a few drops hydrogen peroxide. Blood gives a red (phenolphthalein) color.

MICHAEL REACTION. A reaction between esters of α, β-unsaturated acids and other unsaturated systems, and esters having active methylene groups. This reaction takes place in the presence of sodium ethylate. The final result is the addition of the active ester to the double bond. It is used extensively in reactions between such compounds as sodium acetoacetate and sodium malonic ester, and unsaturated compounds of the type

$$R{-}CH{=}CH{-}COOH \quad \text{or} \quad R{-}C{\equiv}C{-}COOH$$

although the carboxyl group may be replaced by a cyanogen or carbonyl group. Cinnamic, fumaric, maleic, and citraconic esters react in this way. A representative reaction is given by the equation:

$$R—CH{=}CH—COOC_2H_5 + NaCH(COOC_2H_5)_2 \rightarrow R—\underset{\underset{CH(COOC_2H_5)_2.}{|}}{CH}—CHNa—COOC_2H_5$$

MICHEL REAGENT FOR BLOOD. A sensitive test reagent for blood, consisting of two solutions: (1) a solution of 0.1 g. leucomalachite green base in 25 ml. 30% acetic acid, to which 100 ml. water is then added; and (2) a mixture of 90 g. 3% acetic acid and 10 g. 30% hydrogen peroxide. Moistening the specimen with these solutions yields a green color if blood is present.

MICHEL REAGENT FOR DIFFERENTIATING OXYHEMOGLOBIN AND CO-HEMOGLOBIN. A solution of 3 g. sodium hydrosulfite ($Na_2S_2O_4$) in a solution of 4 g. sodium hydroxide in 75 ml. water; to which is then added 40 ml. 98% alcohol. This reagent is used in differentiating between oxyhemoglobin and carbon monoxide-hemoglobin, because the latter is changed to hemochromogen at room temperature.

MICHLER KETONE. The compound, $((CH_3)_2NC_6H_4)_2CO$, tetramethyl-p,p'-diaminobenzophenone, used in making dyes, and for various test reactions.

MICRO-. A prefix meaning (1) small; (2) the one-millionth part of a unit.

MICROAMPERE. One millionth of an ampere.

MICROANALYSIS. Analysis, usually qualitative only, by means of the microscope. See microchemical analysis.

MICROBALANCE. An apparatus used to weigh minute quantities of substances; consequently an extremely sensitive balance.

MICROBAR. A unit of pressure equal to one one millionth of a bar.

MICROBE. Any small living organism, usually one of a size visible only under the microscope.

MICROBURETTE. A burette (q.v.) used to deliver extremely small quantities of liquid, as in titrations in microchemical analysis.

MICROBURETTE, SYRINGE. A microburette consisting of a metal holder and glass hypodermic syringe having a special glass tip and provided with the necessary accessory equipment for its use in making microchemical titrations.

MICROCHEMICAL. Pertaining to the processes and data of microchemistry.

MICROCHEMICAL ANALYSIS. (1) Methods of chemical analysis conducted with very small quantities of samples and reagents, by use of small-scale equipment, and often by conducting some of the operations under a microscope. (2) Microchemical analysis is a term also applied to the methods, procedures, and equipment used in the determination or detection of microquantities of a given element or substance in macroquantities of material, as in the determination of arsenic or lead in food, blood, etc.

MICROCHEMISTRY. (1) Colloidal chemistry (This usage is now obsolete). (2) Chemistry which involves the use of the microscope. It deals with microscopical processes in either living or dead material, such as the identification of crystals, the observing of reactions between minute quantities of material, etc. (3) Chemical processes and reactions conducted with very small-scale apparatus, partly with use of the microscope, as in **microchemical analysis** (q.v.).

MICROCOULOMB. One millionth of a coulomb.

MICROFARAD. One millionth of a **farad.**

MICROGRAM. One millionth of a **gram,** sometimes denoted by γ.

MICROLITER. One millionth of a **liter,** sometimes denoted by λ.

MICROMETER. (1) A gage used for the accurate measurement of linear distances, as of the thickness of a sheet of material. (2) An instrument used for the accurate measurement of objects under the microscope. (3) The micron, one millionth of a meter.

MICROMICRON. One millionth of a **micron,** or one trillionth of a meter, sometimes denoted by $\mu\mu$, one micromicron = 10^{-6} micron = 10^{-12} meter.

MICRON. (1) One millionth of a **meter,** sometimes denoted by μ. (2) A colloidal particle having a size between 0.2 and 10 millionths of a meter. (3) A unit of pressure of 0.001 millimeter of mercury.

MICRONIZER MILL. See **mill, micronizer.**

MICROORGANISM. A small living organism, commonly one of microscopic size.

MICROPHOTOGRAM. A greatly-enlarged photograph of a **spectrum,** or of a graphical record of a spectrum.

MICROPHOTOGRAPH. A very small photograph or one that has been greatly reduced in scale. See **photomicrograph.**

MICROREACTION. See **reaction, micro-.**

MICROSCOPE. An optical instrument that magnifies objects of minute size so that the image can be seen clearly with the eye.

MICROSCOPE, COMPOUND. A microscope containing more than one lens or lens-system, commonly the lens-system in the objective and that in the eyepiece. This is the type of microscope in most general use.

MICROSCOPE, ELECTRON. See **electron microscope.**

MICROSCOPE, FLUORESCENCE. A microscope used to examine objects emitting **fluorescent light;** it uses ultraviolet light as a means of illumination.

MICROSCOPE, POLARIZING. A microscope equipped with apparatus to examine objects under illumination by **polarized light.**

MICROSCOPE, ULTRA-. A microscope having transverse illumination, or one in which the direction of illumination is perpendicular to the line of vision. It extends the range of visibility to particles somewhat smaller than those visible with the ordinary microscope.

MICROSCOPE, ULTRAVIOLET. A microscope in which **ultraviolet light** is used to illuminate the object or field under examination.

MICROSPECTROSCOPE. A combination **microscope** and **spectroscope.**

MICROTOME. An apparatus for slicing or cutting thin sections of specimens, tissues, and other objects.

MICROVOLT. One millionth of a **volt.**

MICROWAVE. The region of the electromagnetic spectrum extending from approximately 0.3 mm. (300 μ) to 1 meter in wave length.

MIDDLETON REAGENT. A reagent prepared by saturating a mixture of 30 ml. 10% sulfuric acid and 100 ml. water with carbon dioxide while boiling, then adding 5 g. ferrous sulfate, then adding 30 ml. 10% potassium thiocyanate solution, and then adding enough 0.03 N titanium trichloride solution to decolorize the reagent. This reagent is used to detect peroxides in ether. A brown color indicates the presence of peroxides.

MIESCHER DEGRADATION. This process, which is a modification of the Barbier-Wieland method, accomplishes the removal of three carbons at one time from an aliphatic acid.

$$\text{RR}'.\text{CH}.\text{CH}_2.\text{CH}_2.\text{CO}_2\text{R}'' \xrightarrow{\text{C}_6\text{H}_5\text{MgBr}} \text{RR}'.\text{CH}.\text{CH}_2.\text{CH}_2\overset{\text{OH}}{\underset{\text{C}_6\text{H}_5}{\text{C}}}\!-\!\text{C}_6\text{H}_5$$

$$\Big\downarrow {}_{-\text{H}_2\text{O}}$$

$$\text{RR}'\text{CH}.\text{CHBr}.\text{CH}\!\!=\!\!\overset{\text{C}_6\text{H}_5}{\underset{\text{C}_6\text{H}_5}{\text{C}}} \xleftarrow[\substack{\text{N-bromo}\\\text{succinimide}}]{} \text{RR}'\text{CH}.\text{CH}_2.\text{CH}\!\!=\!\!\overset{\text{C}_6\text{H}_5}{\underset{\text{C}_6\text{H}_5}{\text{C}}}$$

$$\Big\downarrow {\substack{\text{(Dimethylaniline)}\\ \text{C}_6\text{H}_5\text{N}(\text{CH}_3)_2}}$$

$$\text{RR}'\text{C}\!\!=\!\!\text{CH}.\text{CH}\!\!=\!\!\overset{\text{C}_6\text{H}_5}{\underset{\text{C}_6\text{H}_5}{\text{C}}} \xrightarrow[0°\,\text{C.}]{\text{CrO}_3} \text{RCOR}' + \text{CHO}.\text{CH}\!\!=\!\!\overset{\text{C}_6\text{H}_5}{\underset{\text{C}_6\text{H}_5}{\text{C}}} .$$

MIGRATION, ATOMIC. In its simplest form, the transfer of the valence bond of an atom from one atom to another within a molecule. (See **rearrangement**.)

MIGRATION OF IONS. See **ionic migration**.

MIGRATION TUBE. A glass electrolytic apparatus used for investigation of **ionic migrations**. When it is filled with a solution containing ions and an indicator, and an electric current is passed, progress of the color change discloses the progress and rate of the migration of the ions.

MIGRAY TEST. Nitrite is detected by adding, to 100 ml. of the solution tested, 5 drops 10% indigosol 04B solution and 5 ml. 7 N sulfuric acid. A dark blue color indicates nitrite.

MIL. One thousandth of a liter. It is a shortened form of "milliliter."

> 1 mil = 1.000027 cubic centimeter
> 1 mil = 0.03381 U.S. liquid ounce
> 29.573 mils = 1.000 U.S. liquid ounce

The term mil is also used by electricians to mean one thousandth of an inch.

MILL. An apparatus for reducing the size of solid objects or particles by the action of mechanical force, or an installation of such apparatus.

MILL, ATTRITION. A fine-grinding mill which effects reduction chiefly by the rubbing action of the mill elements against the particles to be ground. The old buhr-stone mill, consisting of two flat stones, was an attrition mill.

MILL, BALL. A machine used for grinding solids, or for intimately mixing solids with solids or liquids. It consists of a cylindrical chamber mounted on a shaft and fitted with a tight cover; within are several heavy balls of iron, copper, lead, or stone. When the chamber is rotated the balls roll and tumble together, thus repeatedly pounding the material to be ground into smaller particles. Almost any desired degree of fineness can be secured in the product.

MILL, BRAMLEY. A grinding mill which consists essentially of rotating blades that press against the inside surface of a horizontal cylinder. The blades are driven by radial arms and are adjustable, so that the pressure they exert against the cylinder can be set to suit the product and the fineness of grinding desired.

MILL, BUHR. A stone mill used for grinding. It consists of two stones pressed together, which rotate against each other on a vertical axis. Sometimes only one stone turns.

MILL, CAGE. A mill used for dry grinding. It consists of two concentric cage parts that rotate in opposite directions. The material to be ground is placed in the inner cage.

MILL, EDGE RUNNER. A mill consisting essentially of a large wheel of iron or stone mounted in a framework that is supported at the center of a circular trough, so that the wheel moves around the periphery, or outer portion, of the trough, and rotates at the same time about its axis.

MILL, HAMMER. A type of crushing mill consisting of a shaft to which are attached heavy hammers. As the shaft rotates the hammers swing out and crush the material against the inside surface or lining of the mill.

MILL, MICRONIZER. A mill that owes its disintegrating action entirely to the action of jets of air or steam, which impinge tangentially upon the particles to be ground, and cause them to whirl about and shatter each other.

MILL, PEBBLE. A mill consisting of a rotating chamber containing heavy stones or pebbles, of selected size, which grind by their impacts and resultant forces as the mill turns. Pebble mills are used for fine grinding.

MILL, TUBE. See **tube mill.**

MILLARD TEST REACTION FOR HYPOPHOSPHITE. An aqueous hypophosphite solution gives a blue color on addition of an acid solution of ammonium molybdate and a few drops sulfurous acid.

MILLER INDEX. See **crystal index, Miller.**

MILLER REAGENT FOR CERIUM. A 5% solution of sodium arsanilate, of which 5 ml. is added to a mixture of 45 ml. of the solution to be tested and 5 ml. N sulfuric acid. A pink to red-brown color indicates the presence of cerium.

MILLER REAGENT FOR FLUORINE. A mixture of a solution of 1.84 g. benzidine in glacial acetic acid which has been diluted with water to 500 ml., and 500 ml. of a 0.02 N aqueous solution of mercury succinimide, used as a test reagent for fluorine. A precipitate is obtained under test conditions.

MILLIAMPERE. One thousandth of an **ampere.**

MILLIBAR. A unit of pressure equal to one thousandth of a **bar.**

MILLIGRAM. One thousandth of a **gram.**

$$1 \text{ milligram} = 0.01543 \text{ grain}$$
$$1 \text{ grain} = 64.8 \text{ milligrams}$$

MILLIKAN METER. An **ionization chamber** of integrating type, especially useful for cosmic ray measurements. One of its features is a built-in **electroscope,** consisting of a gold-plated quartz fiber arrangement under torsion, which stands away from (is repelled by) its support when charged. The effect of the arrival of the charge to be measured is to neutralize partly the original charge and permit the fiber to approach its support.

MILLILITER. One thousandth of a **liter.**

MILLIMETER. One thousandth of a **meter.** It is abbreviated mm.

MILLIMICRON. One thousandth of a **micron.** It is sometimes expressed by the symbol $m\mu$.

MILLIMOLE. One thousandth of a **mole.**

MILLINORMAL SOLUTION. A solution which has a concentration of one thousandth of a normal solution (see **solution, normal).**

MILLNER REAGENT FOR ALUMINUM. A 0.1% aqueous solution of Eriochromecyanine-R that gives, with solutions of aluminum salts at pH 4.6–5.6 in the presence of a sodium acetate-acetic acid buffer, a colored lake.

MILLON REAGENT FOR PROTEINS. A 1:1 solution of mercury in fuming nitric acid which is then mixed with 2 volumes of water. On heating a solution with this reagent, a brick-red precipitate appears in the presence of protein.

MILLON TEST FOR SALICYLIC ACID AND PHENOL. A dilute aqueous solution of salicylic acid or phenol is colored red by **Millon reagent for proteins** (q.v.) at the boiling point.

MILLS-PACKARD CHAMBER. A chamber used in the **chamber process** for sulfuric acid. It is cooled by having water running down the outside of its walls, and it gives a much higher acid production rate.

MILROY REAGENT. A solution of 0.4 g. of 1,5-nitroanthraquinonesulfonic acid in 100 ml. water, used in determining blood sugar. A red color is given on heating by glucose in alkaline solution.

MINDES REAGENT. A mixture of 10 ml. of a 1:10 ferric chloride solution, 30 ml. 12% hydrogen peroxide, and 10 ml. alcohol, used in testing for alkaloids and other organic substances. Characteristic color reactions are obtained.

MINERAL. A naturally-occurring inorganic substance which has a characteristic range of chemical composition, usually a definite, crystal form, and which exhibits other specific, physical characteristics such as cleavage, fracture, hardness, luster, color, specific gravity, and index of refraction.

The term mineral is also extended to include various fossilized organized substances found in Nature, such as the bitumens, etc.

MINIM. A unit of liquid measure, the sixtieth part of a fluid **dram.**

1 minim = 0.06161 milliliter.

MINIMUM BOILING POINT. A two-component or multi-component liquid system, in which a particular composition of the components has a lower boiling point than the pure components, or than any other composition of them, is said to have a minimum boiling point. It is the temperature at which boiling begins when the system is heated under conditions of stable equilibrium.

MINOVICI-IONESCU   MICRO-REAGENT. A saturated solution of picric acid in ethyl malonate, used in testing for potassium.

MINOVICI REAGENT. A solution of 20 g. anisaldehyde in 80 ml. absolute alcohol, used as a test reagent for picrotoxin. A deep blue color is obtained under test conditions.

MIPOR. Having small pores.

MISCIBILITY. The ability of two or more substances to mix in all proportions, and to form a single, homogeneous phase.

MISCIBILITY GAP. The range of values in a given condition, usually temperature, under which liquids that are otherwise completely miscible mix only partially, or not at all.

MISCIBLE. See **miscibility.**

MITCHELL SOLUTION FOR GALLIC ACID. A solution of 0.5 g. Rochelle salt and 0.1 g. ferrous sulfate in 100 ml. water, used in testing for gallic acid. A violet color is given by gallic acid and members of the pyrogallol group.

MITCHELL TEST REACTION FOR NITRATE AND SAPONIN. Solutions containing saponin and nitrate ion are colored blood-red upon addition of 1 drop concentrated sulfuric acid.

MITSCHERLICH LAW. See **law of isomorphism.**

MIXED AZO BODIES. Azo compounds of the type R—N=N—R', where R and R' are different radicals, especially where R is aryl and R' is alkyl or heterocyclic.

MIXED CRYSTAL. See **crystal, mixed.**

MIXED ESTER. See **ester, mixed.**

MIXED ETHER. See **ether, mixed.**

MIXED KETONE. See **ketone, mixed.**

MIXED SALT. See **salt, mixed.**

MIXER. An apparatus used to mix, or produce a single homogeneous **phase** or intimate mixture or fine dispersion from two or more substances or materials, commonly by mechanical agitation, as with a paddle or stirrer.

MIXER, ORIFICE. An apparatus for the mixing of liquids consisting of a long pipe or tank into which a number of discs containing many holes have been welded at regular intervals. When the liquid is forced through this apparatus, the extremely turbulent flow assures good mixing at high pressure drops.

MIXTURE. An heterogeneous or homogeneous aggregation of different materials. The components of a mixture may be separated by simple mechanical or physical means, in sharp contrast with a chemical compound which cannot be so separated.

MIXTURE, BECKMANN. See **Beckmann mixture.**

MIXTURE, CONSTANT BOILING. A mixture of two or more liquids of a certain definite composition which distills at a definite boiling point without change in composition, as if it were a single substance.

MIXTURE, FREEZING. See **freezing mixture.**

M.K.S. SYSTEM. See **metric system.**

Mn Symbol for the element **manganese.**

Mo Symbol for the element **molybdenum.**

MOBILE EQUILIBRIUM, PRINCIPLE OF. Any change occurring in one of the conditions, such as temperature or pressure, under which a system is in **equilibrium,** causes the system to tend to adjust itself so as to overcome, as far as possible, the effect of that change.

MOBILITY. Motion. Two important uses of the term in chemistry are to express the random motion of various particles, such as ions, atoms, molecules, and colloidal particles; and also the directed motion that

results when these particles are subjected to the action of forces and fields of force. See **mobility, ionic.**

MOBILITY, IONIC. The absolute velocity of an ion in solution under unit difference of potential. It is expressed by the relationship

$$\mu_+ \text{ or } \mu_- = \frac{\lambda_+ \text{ or } \lambda_-}{F}$$

in which μ_+ or μ_- is the mobility of the ion, λ_+ or λ_- is the conductance, and F is the Faraday constant.

MOBILOMETER. An instrument used to measure the **consistency** or **viscosity** of various liquids by timing the fall of a standard disc through a volume of substance of standard dimensions.

MODIFICATION. A form of a substance or system that differs to some extent, usually slight, from another form, which is sometimes the original form; or the change by which one substance or system is changed to a related one.

MODULUS. A formula, coefficient, or constant that expresses a measure of a property, force, or quality, such as elasticity, efficiency, density, or strength.

MOFFATT-SPIRO TEST. Lead in water is detected by dissolving 0.5 g. hematein in 1 liter of water. A blue color indicates the presence of lead.

MÖHLAU TEST REACTION FOR *p*-DIAMINES. With an alkaline phenol solution and calcium hypochlorite, *p*-diamines give a deep blue color.

MOHLER SOLUTION FOR TARTARIC ACID. A solution of 1 g. resorcinol in 100 g. concentrated sulfuric acid, used in testing for tartaric acid. A red color on heating the substance to be tested to 125–130° C. with 1 ml. of the reagent indicates the presence of tartaric acid.

MOHR LITER. The volume of 1000 grams of water at 17.5° C., adopted as a convenient standard for volumetric work by Mohr.

MOHR PIPETTE. See **pipette, Mohr.**

MOHS HARDNESS SCALE. See **hardness scale, Mohs.**

MOIR REAGENT. A solution of 1 g. *o*-toluidine, 1.5 g. cupric acetate, and 0.5 g. glacial acetic acid in 100 ml. water, used in testing for hydrogen cyanide in air. A blue color, gained by paper moistened with the reagent, is positive.

MOIR TEST FOR NIOBIUM, TANTALUM, AND TITANIUM. On treating a sodium niobate solution with ammonium oxalate, then with zinc and acid, a deep brown color appears, changing to yellow. Titanium solutions give a yellow color, changing to orange.

Niobic acid gives a yellow precipitate with potassium hydrosulfite in acid solution, and an orange-yellow precipitate with pyrogallol and gallic acid; tantalum gives a yellow precipitate. Both niobates and tantalates give color reactions on boiling with sulfuric acid and phenolic compounds.

MOIR TESTS FOR MOLYBDENUM.
(1) In a solution acidified with acetic acid, boiling with hydrazine sulfate gives a blue color if molybdenum is present.

(2) In a solution acidified with acetic acid, boiling with potassium iodide gives a blue color if molybdenum is present.

(3) In a solution acidified with acetic acid, pyrogallol gives an orange color if molybdenum is present.

MOISSAN PROCESS. A method used for the production of metallic chromium by the electric-furnace reduction of chromic oxide with carbon.

MOISTURE. Water or the water content of a solid, liquid, or gas.

MOJONNIER TUBE. A tube or flask for extracting fats.

MOKRANTZA REAGENT. A solution of 0.05 sodium rhenate in 5 ml. water, to which sufficient concentrated sulfuric acid is added to give a volume of 100 ml. This reagent is used in identifying alkaloids. Characteristic color reactions are obtained.

MOL. See **mole.**

MOLAL. Pertaining to moles, as that term is used in chemistry to refer to gram-molecular weights, which are the molecular weights of substances expressed in grams; or as of a solution, containing one gram-molecular weight of solute per kilogram of solvent.

MOLAL CONCENTRATION. The number of moles (gram-molecules) or a substance per unit mass of a phase or a system. For example, a molal solution contains one gram-molecular weight of solute dissolved in one kilogram of solvent.

MOLAL CONDUCTANCE. The **conductance** (q.v.) resulting when one gram-molecular weight of a substance dissolved in one kilogram of solvent is placed between electrodes one centimeter apart.

MOLAL SOLUTION. See **molal concentration.**

MOLAL VOLUME. The volume occupied by one mole of a substance in a specified state under specified conditions. The molal volume of gas, under standard conditions, is approximately 22.4 liters.

MOLAL WEIGHT. One **mole** (q.v.).

MOLALITY. The number of moles (gram-molecules) of a substance per unit mass of a phase or system, as of solute per kilogram of solvent.

MOLAR. Pertaining to molecules, or to moles per unit volume; thus a molar solution is one containing one gram-molecular weight of solute per liter of solution.

MOLAR ABSORPTION COEFFICIENT. See **absorption coefficient, molar.**

MOLAR CONCENTRATION. The number of moles (gram-molecules) of a substance per unit volume of a system. For example, a molar solution contains one mole of solute per liter of solution.

MOLAR CONDUCTANCE. The **conductance** (q.v.) resulting when one gram-molecular weight of a solute dissolved in one liter of solution is placed between electrodes one centimeter apart.

MOLAR DISPERSIVITY. See **dispersivity, molar.**

MOLAR EXTINCTION COEFFICIENT. See **extinction coefficient, molar.**

MOLAR HEAT. The heat required to raise one **mole** of substance by one degree of temperature; the product of the **specific heat** and the **molecular weight.**

MOLAR LATENT HEAT OF VAPORIZATION. The quantity of heat required to convert one **mole** of a substance into vapor at its boiling point under atmospheric pressure.

MOLAR REFRACTION. See **refraction, molar.**

MOLAR ROTATION. See **rotation, molar.**

MOLAR SOLUTION. A solution containing one **mole** of solute per liter of solution.

MOLAR SURFACE. The surface of a sphere the mass of which is one **mole.**

MOLAR SURFACE-ENERGY. The energy necessary to form a sphere (gravitational influences removed) from a mass of any liquid equal to one **mole.** If $V =$ the volume of one mole and $\gamma =$ the **surface tension,** the molar surface energy is $V^{2/3}\gamma$. At the critical point the molar surface energy is zero. It decreases proportionately to increase of temperature, and its temperature coefficient is the same for all homogeneous liquids.

MOLAR VOLUME. The volume occupied by a **mole** of any substance in vapor (reduced to $0°$ C. and 760 mm.). For gases it is approximately equal to 22.4 liters.

MOLAR WEIGHT. See **gram-molecular weight.**

MOLDING, BLOW. A molding process in which air pressure is used to force the material, often a viscous liquid or plastic solid, into the mold.

MOLE (MOL). One gram-molecule of any substance, i.e., the molecular weight of the substance expressed in grams; thus a mole of sulfuric acid weighs 98.08 grams.

MOLE FRACTION. The number of **moles** of one **component** in a **phase** or system containing more than one component, divided by the total number of moles of all the components.

MOLECULAR. Pertaining to, or characteristic of, molecules.

MOLECULAR ASSOCIATION. See **association.**

MOLECULAR ATTRACTION. Intermolecular forces which play an important part in many phenomena. In **van der Waals equation of state** the pressure correction term $\dfrac{a}{V^2}$ is an expression of the magnitude of these forces.

MOLECULAR CRYSTAL. A crystal in which the normal chemical molecule exists as a definite unit in the structure and is situated at each lattice point.

MOLECULAR DIAGRAM. A drawing to scale which shows certain of the structural properties of a molecule, and the constituent atoms, including the **bonds** between the atoms, the **effective radii,** the **ionic radii,** and, in general, the shape of the molecule.

MOLECULAR DIAMETER. Values for the molecular diameter have been obtained by calculation, using the equations for the **mean free path,** for **diffusion,** for **polarization,** for **viscosity,** for **thermal conductivity,** and for **specific heat.** Values for the molecular diameter of the same gas computed by more than one of these methods often agree closely.

MOLECULAR DISPERSION. See **rotation, molar.**

MOLECULAR EQUATION. See **equation, molecular.**

MOLECULAR FIELD. See field, molecular.

MOLECULAR FILM. A monomolecular layer, i.e., a film of a substance, produced on the surface of a liquid, by **adsorption,** or by other means, that has a thickness of the order of molecular dimensions.

MOLECULAR FLOW. The relative rate of flow of gas molecules through a fine orifice, a function of the gas pressure and density, and the size and character of the orifice.

MOLECULAR FORMULA. The formula of a chemical compound, containing the symbols of the atoms or radicals present, followed by subscripts showing the number of each kind of atom or radical in the molecule.

MOLECULAR FREE PATH. The average free path or distance travelled by a molecule between collisions in a gas or in a solution. It is calculated by formulas in which it is directly proportional to the product of the molecular velocity, the viscosity of the medium, and the density of the medium.

MOLECULAR HEAT. See **molar heat.**

MOLECULAR HEAT OF VAPORIZATION. See **molar latent heat.**

MOLECULAR MODEL. A scale model, made of wires, varicolored balls, or other devices, which shows certain of the structural features of a molecule and its constituent atoms—their grouping, relative positions, etc.

MOLECULAR NUMBER. (1) The sum of the **atomic numbers** of the atoms in a molecule. (2) An integral number denoting the position occupied by a given molecule in a series obtained by arranging molecules in order of increasing molecular frequency.

MOLECULAR ORBITAL. The **wave function** of an electron moving in the field of the other electrons and nuclei composing a molecule.

MOLECULAR POLARIZIBILITY. See polarizibility, molecular.

MOLECULAR RAY. A beam of molecules moving in substantially the same direction at roughly similar speed. By deflecting such beams in the mass **spectrograph,** it is possible to determine the relative masses of the molecules of which the beam is composed.

MOLECULAR REARRANGEMENT. Refers to an irreversible reaction which produces a change in the structural arrangement of the molecule with or without the elimination of simple molecules such as water or a hydrogen halide, and which may or may not be unimolecular. Thus Wohler's synthesis of urea to ammonium cyanate is a molecular rearrangement, whereas reactions such as mutarotation, racemization, the Walden inversion, and tautomerism are excluded because they are essentially reversible.

MOLECULAR REFRACTION. See **refraction, molar.**

MOLECULAR ROTATION. The product of the **specific rotation** (q.v.) and the molecular weight, divided by 100.

MOLECULAR SOLUTION. A solution in which the **solute** is present in aggregates not containing more than one molecule of solute; in other words, a solution in which there are no associated molecules.

MOLECULAR SOLUTION VOLUME. The difference in volume between one liter of pure **solvent** and a solution that contains one mole of dissolved substance per liter.

MOLECULAR SPECTRUM. See spectrum, molecular.

MOLECULAR VELOCITY. The mean velocity of a molecule.

MOLECULAR VOLUME OR MOLAR VOLUME. The volume occupied by one **mole** of a solid or liquid which is found by dividing the molecular weight by the density.

MOLECULAR WEIGHT. The relative mass of a compound, calculated on the basis of an atomic weight for ordinary oxygen of 16, and obtained by adding the atomic weights of the elements in the compound, multiplying each atomic weight by the number of atoms of that element present in the formula of the compound.

MOLECULAR WEIGHT DETERMINATION, MEYER METHOD. A method of finding the **molecular weight** of a substance directly, i.e., by converting a known weight of liquid into vapor, and determining the volume of this vapor by collecting in a gas burette (see **burette, gas**) the air which the vapor displaces. The determination is made under **standard conditions,** or calculated to them from observed values.

MOLECULE. The smallest particle of any substance that can exist free and still exhibit all of the properties of the original substance.

MOLECULE, ACTIVATED. A molecule containing one or more excited atoms. (See **atom, excited.**)

MOLECULE, COMPOUND. A large molecule that represents an aggregate of two or more smaller molecules.

MOLECULE, DOUBLED. A molecule formed by the **condensation** of two identical molecules, as by **dehydrogenation.**

MOLECULE, ELEMENTARY. A molecule that is composed of atoms of the same element. (They may be isotopes; thus HD, the molecule which contains one atom of ordinary hydrogen and one of deuterium, the hydrogen isotope of mass number 2, is an elementary molecule.)

MOLECULE, ISOSTERIC. One of two or more molecules possessing essentially the same **valence** configuration, usually the same total number and arrangement of valency electrons.

MOLECULE, NEUTRAL. See **neutral molecule.**

MOLECULE, NONPOLAR. See **compound, nonpolar.**

MOLECULE, POLAR. See **compound, polar.**

MOLECULE, SATURATED. See **compound, saturated.**

MOLECULE, UNSATURATED. See **compound, unsaturated.**

MOLESCHOTT TESTS FOR CHOLESTEROL. Cholesterol gives a red color with concentrated sulfuric acid and a violet color with an aqueous iodine solution. These are microchemical reactions.

MOLINARI-FENAROLI PETROLEUM REACTION. Addition of ozone to petroleum, by reaction with ozonized air at 10° C., whereby white flocculant ozonides are precipitated to a greater or less extent from various petroleums.

MOLISCH REAGENT FOR ALBUMIN. A solution of 20 g. α-naphthol in 100 ml. alcohol. It gives a red or violet color with albumin or peptone on the addition of 5 ml. concentrated sulfuric acid and 2 drops of the reagent to 1 ml. of the liquid to be tested.

MOLISCH TEST FOR SUGARS. To 1 ml. of the solution tested, add 2 drops 15–20% alcoholic α-naphthol solution and 1–2 ml. sulfuric acid. A deep violet precipitate, giving a yellow solution in alcohol or ether, a gold-yellow color in potassium hydroxide solution, and yellow-brown in ammonia, indicates the presence of sugar.

MOLISCH TEST FOR WOOD FIBERS. The reagent is 20 g. thymol dissolved in 80 g. alcohol, diluted with water until thymol begins to separate, at which time potassium chlorate is added. Wood fibers treated with this reagent and concentrated hydrochloric acid become blue.

MOLLIER DIAGRAM. The properties of a vapor, as recorded in vapor tables, may be displayed graphically in a number of ways, among which the most used, and probably the most valuable, is the charting upon a plane whose coordinates are **enthalpy** or total heat and **entropy**. Generally, the total heat is made the ordinate, and entropy the abscissa. This chart of the properties of vapor is named the Mollier Diagram, and is of considerable use in tracing both theoretical and actual expansions of vapor. A throttled expansion on the Mollier Diagram is parallel to the constant heat lines, and adiabatic expansion is parallel to the constant entropy lines. Pressure, quality or superheat, and total temperature are shown on the Mollier Diagram as series of lines curved and inclined to the axes. Thus all characteristics of a vapor except volume may be displayed on the Mollier Diagram.

MOLYBDATE. The anion $MoO_4^=$, or a compound containing it.

MOLYBDATE (PARA). The anion $Mo_7O_{24}^{6-}$, or a compound containing it.

MOLYBDENIC. Containing or pertaining to trivalent **molybdenum.**

MOLYBDENOUS. Containing or pertaining to bivalent **molybdenum.**

MOLYBDENUM. Metallic element. Symbol Mo. Atomic number 42. Atomic weight 95.95. Density 10.2. Specific heat 0.062. Melting point 2620° C. Molybdenum occurs as molybdenite (MoS_2), and as wulfenite. Oxides, Mo_2O_3, MoO_2, MoO_3, Mo_2O_5. Valence 3, 4, and 6 (2 and 5). Molybdic acid, $H_2MoO_4.4H_2O$.

MOLYBDIC. (1) Containing trivalent or hexavalent **molybdenum.** (2) Related to molybdic acid, H_2MoO_4.

MOLYBDICYANIDE. See **cyanomolybdate (V).**

MOLYBDOCYANIDE. See **cyanomolybdate (IV).**

MOLYBDOPHOSPHATE. See **phosphomolybdate.**

MOMENT. The product of a quantity and a distance to some significant point connected with that quantity.

MOMENT, MAGNETIC. See **magnetic moment.**

MOMENT OF FORCE. The product of the magnitude of a force, and the perpendicular distance from the line of action of the force to a point which is the center of the rotation induced by that force.

MON-, MONO-. A prefix meaning one.

MONACID. A base that combines with but one molecule of univalent acid per molecule of base, as sodium hydroxide and strychnine.

MONAD. An element, atom, or radical that has a chief valence of one, as sodium or hydrogen; cuprous copper or mercurous mercury; methyl or hydroxyl.

MONAMIDE. An amide that contains but one **amido** group, as acetamide.

MONAMINE. An amine that contains but one **amino** group, as methylamine.

MONATOMIC. See **monoatomic.**

MOND PROCESS. A method for the purification of nickel, using carbon monoxide to form volatile nickel carbonyl $Ni(CO)_4$, which separates in the vapor phase from other metals and impurities and is later decomposed on heating to yield pure nickel.

MONITRON. An automatic **radiation** monitor, which can be set to sound an alarm when any predetermined intensity of radiation is reached.

MONNIER REAGENT FOR METALS AND CITRIC ACID. A 0.8% solution of titanium trichloride which is used as a reducing agent to precipitate platinum, palladium, etc., as metals, to give colored suspensions by reduction of gold and tungsten, and to give color reactions with selenites, chromates, organic acids, etc.

MONOAMIDE. See **monamide.**

MONOAMINE. See **monamine.**

MONOATOMIC. (1) Containing one atom; a term applied to molecules of certain elements when they are identical with the atoms of that element; or (2) containing one reactive or replaceable atom; a term applied to certain molecules in regard to certain reactions; or (3) having a valence of one (the term **monovalent** is preferred for this usage).

MONOBASIC ACID. An acid which has one ionizable hydrogen atom (yields one **proton**) that is replaceable by one positive atom or radical.

MONOCHROMATIC. Having one color, strictly one frequency or wave length of optical radiation.

MONOCHROMATIC EMISSIVE POWER. See **emission power, monochromatic.**

MONOCHROMATIC EMISSIVITY. See **emissivity, monochromatic.**

MONODISPERSE SYSTEM. A system of **colloidal** particles in which the value of the **sedimentation constant** is constant for successive time intervals, indicating that the system comprises particles of uniform size.

MONOMER. A single molecule, or a substance consisting of single molecules. The term monomer is used in differentiation of dimer, trimer, etc., terms designating polymerized or associated molecules, or substances composed of them, in which each free particle is composed of two, three, etc., molecules.

MONOMOLECULAR. Concerning or involving one molecule.

MONOMOLECULAR FILM. See **film, monomolecular.**

MONOMORPHIC. Having one form, i.e., one **crystal form.**

MONOSE. A sugar containing in its molecule one hexose or pentose chain only.

MONOTROPY. The property of a substance by which it occurs only in one form (commonly only one solid form).

MONOTROPY, PSEUDO. The phenomenon of the existence of a substance in more than one form all but one of which are unstable or metastable under practically all conditions, or under all ordinary conditions.

MONT CENIS PROCESS. A process for the production of ammonia by direct combination of nitrogen and hydrogen. It is a relatively low-pressure process (about one hundred atmospheres) and uses an extremely active catalyst.

MONTEJUS. A small pressure vessel used to elevate liquids upon application of air pressure. It is also known as an acid egg.

MONTEQUI REAGENT FOR ZINC. Two solutions: (1) a solution of 0.5 g. cupric sulfate and 5 drops sulfuric acid in 100 ml. water; and (2) a solution of 8 g. mercuric chloride and 9 g. ammonium thiocyanate in 100 ml. water. This reagent is used in detecting the presence of zinc. Violet crystals are given by neutral or slightly acid solutions of zinc on addition of 1 drop of (1), and 3–4 drops of (2) to 3 ml. of solution.

MONTIGNIE TEST FOR ERGOSTEROL. When dissolved in 5 ml. alcohol, heated to 95° C., and treated with 3–4 ml. 10% selenous oxide solution, ergosterol and its derivatives give a red precipitate in 2 minutes.

MONTIGNIE TEST REACTION FOR HYDRAZINES. Hydrazine and various derivatives reduce 4% selenous acid solution with the formation of red selenium.

MONTIGNIE TEST REACTION FOR MOLYBDENUM. A molybdenum solution gives a rose or red color with a saturated solution of phenylhydrazine acidified with sulfuric acid.

MONTIGNIE TEST REACTION FOR STEROLS. Many sterols give a red-brown color on heating their alcoholic solutions with silicotungstic acid.

MOORE TEST FOR MERCURY. A reagent consisting of 5 ml. 0.5 N potassium iodide solution, 10 ml. 3 N sodium hydroxide solution, and 10 ml. 3 N ammonium hydroxide gives a brown precipitate (at once) with solutions of mercury salts.

MORDANT. A substance used in dyeing to fix or develop a color on the fiber. Salts of ammonium, chromium, iron, tin, antimony, copper, acids, and tannins are used as mordants.

MORDANT DYE. See **dye, mordant.**

MOREL-CHAVASSIEU TEST FOR PURINES. Purine bases give a purple-red color with a solution of m-dinitrobenzene and sodium hydroxide. (Exclude air as much as possible.)

MORGAN TEST REACTION. Mercury salts are detected by placing them on a piece of copper and moistening with concentrated potassium iodide solution. A white spot is given by mercury salts.

MORGAN-WALLS REACTION. See **Pictet-Hubert reaction.**

MÖRNER REAGENT FOR TYROSINE. A solution of 1 ml. formalin in 45 ml. distilled water and 55 ml. concentrated sulfuric acid, used in testing for tyrosine. A green color on heating is given by tyrosine.

MÖRNER TEST REACTION FOR QUINONE. Quinone gives a red color with a colorless solution of ferrous sulfate, ammonium thiocyanate, and sulfuric acid.

MORPHOLINYL. The radical C_4H_8NO— (from morpholine).

MORPHOTROPY. In crystals the change in the ratio in the length of the axes caused by changes in molecular structure such as substitution of certain radicals.

MORPHOUS. A combining term which indicates "form" or "shape," as in isomorphous, dimorphous, etc.

MORRES SOLUTION. A 1% solution of alizarin paste in alcohol, used in making the alizarol test of milk to determine the keeping qualities.

MORSE EQUATION. An expression for the relationship between the **potential energy** of a diatomic molecule, the **dissociation energy** and the **internuclear distance,** from which a curve can be plotted showing the variation in potential energy as the molecule vibrates.

MOSELEY FORMULA FOR THE ENERGY OF K X-RAYS. A relationship of the form:

$$E = 10.25(Z - 1)^2$$

where E is the energy of the K x-rays in electron-volts, and Z is the atomic number of the atom emitting the x-rays.

MOSELEY LAW. See **law of Moseley.**

MOSNIER REAGENT. Lead ammonium iodide ($3PbI_2.4NH_4I$), which is decomposed to give free ammonium iodide on shaking with ether that contains either water or alcohol.

MOTHER LIQUOR. The residual liquid remaining after crystallization has taken place.

MOTILITY. The property of being in a state of motion. The most common usage of this term is in its application to living microscopic organisms, or to particles of colloidal size and smaller, which are observed to move, as in the field of a microscope, and are said to exhibit motility.

MOTION, LAWS OF. See **laws of Newton (motion).**

MOULD (MOLD). (1) To form or shape; or a construction of sand or metal or other material used to form or shape substances which are poured or forced into it while in molten or plastic condition, and which then take the desired shape on solidification. (2) Various fungus growths, including some important in chemical technology.

MOULIN TEST REACTION FOR MERCURY. Dissolve 2 g. diphenylcarbazide in 10 ml. acetic acid and 10 ml. alcohol, and add a few drops of this reagent to the solution tested. Shake, and add some 10% sodium acetate solution. A blue color indicates the presence of mercuric chloride.

MS. Abbreviation for **meso-**.

MU (M OR μ). The twelfth letter in the Greek alphabet, used to denote: (1) The twelfth carbon atom in a straight-chain compound, or a derivative in which a substituent group is attached to that carbon atom (μ-). (2) Abbreviation for **micron** (μ). (3) Symbol for **meso-position** (μ). Symbol for one millionth (μ). (4) Abbreviation for **magnetic permeability** (μ). Symbol for amplification (μ). Symbol for **chemical potential** (μ). Symbol for molecular conductivity (μ). Coefficient of friction (μ). Symbol for partial **molal potential** (μ). Symbol for **electric moment** of atom, molecule or dipole (μ or μ_e). Symbol for **magnetic moment** of atom, molecule, or dipole (μ or μ_m). Symbol for orbital (or Bohr) **magneton** (μ_o). Abbreviation for **meso-** (μ).

MU SPACE (μ-SPACE). A hyperspace of $2r$ dimensions, where $2r$ is the number of coordinates necessary to specify the exact mechanical condition of a molecule, both its instantaneous position and its momentum.

MUCIN. One of the group of **glycoproteins** that occur in the secretions of the organism.

MUCOID. One of a group of **glycoproteins** which are similiar to the mucins but differ from them in solubility and coagulability.

MUFFLE. A refractory container or furnace lining, usually semicylindrical in shape, that protects the charge of the furnace from contamination or sudden temperature changes.

MUFFLE FURNACE. In general, a furnace provided with a lining of ceramic or other refractory material, which prevents direct contact between the charge and the fuel or heat source. Muffle furnaces with electrical heating elements are used extensively in laboratory work.

MUIR SOLUTION. A solution of 9 g. tartaric acid and 3 g. stannous chloride in sufficient potassium hydroxide solution to produce a liquid which remains clear up to 70° C. This reagent yields a dark precipitate at that temperature if bismuth is present. The liquid to be tested is treated with tartaric acid, and alkalinized with potassium hydroxide solution, before adding the reagent and heating.

MULDER SOLUTION FOR GLUCOSE. A solution in water of indigocarmine, alkalinized with sodium carbonate, used as a test reagent for glucose. A color change on heating from green to red to yellow is obtained in the presence of glucose. Several modifications of this method have been reported.

MÜLLER FLUID. A solution of 1.0 g. sodium sulfate and 2.5 g. potassium dichromate in 100 ml. water, used as a fixative.

MÜLLER-KÜHNE PROCESS. A method for the production of sulfuric acid from gypsum.

MÜLLER REAGENT FOR BLOOD. A guaiac resin is dissolved in equal parts acetic acid and alcohol, diluted with twice the volume of water and filtered. The filtrate is added to 100 ml. boiling water. A resin separates, which is then redissolved in alcohol. One ml. hydrogen peroxide is then added to 20 ml. of the solution. This reagent is used to test for blood by adding 3–5 drops of it to a suspected solid or solution.

MÜLLER TEST FOR CARBON IN ORGANIC COMPOUNDS. The substance tested is heated slowly with 20 times its weight of potassium azide in a hard glass tube. At the end of the heating, the temperature is held at red heat for 2 minutes. Carbon in the substance heated produces potassium cyanide in the fusion.

MULLIKAN-BARKER TEST REACTION. The nitro group is detected by dissolving 3–4 drops of the substance tested in 3 ml. 50% alcohol, adding 5–6 drops

10% calcium chloride solution, and heating to violent boiling. Cool and filter. Add ammoniacal silver nitrate. If a nitro compound was present, a silver precipitate is obtained.

MULLIKAN-SCUDDER TEST FOR METHANOL. The methanol is oxidized to formaldehyde by repeated applications of a hot copper wire, resorcinol is added, and a ring test made with concentrated sulfuric acid. A red color at the interface indicates formaldehyde. Various modifications of this test have been developed.

MULTIPLE COIL THERMAL PROCESS. A process for the polymerization of olefinic and paraffinic gaseous hydrocarbons, which operates at a temperature range of 480° to 700° C., and a pressure range of 450 to 800 pounds per square inch. The sequence of reactions is usually the polymerization of the olefinic hydrocarbons, then the cracking of the paraffins to give olefins, and then the polymerization of the latter. The process produces gasoline, fuel oil, and tar. No catalysts are used.

MULTIPLE-EFFECT EVAPORATION. An arrangement of an evaporating system, consisting of more than one unit of evaporating apparatus, in which the vapor evaporated from the charge in the first unit is used as the heating medium for the second unit, and so on. The means by which this plan is accomplished is commonly by maintaining successively lower pressures in the evaporating spaces of the successive units, so that the liquid to be evaporated boils at a lower temperature in each unit than in the preceding one.

MULTIPLE PROPORTIONS, LAW OF. See law of multiple proportions.

MULTIPLICITY. The number $2S + 1$, representing the number of ways of vectorially coupling the orbital angular momentum vector L with the spin angular momentum vector S of an atom. This value represents the number of relatively closely spaced energy levels or terms in an atom which result from the coupling process. The value of the multiplicity is added as a left superscript to the term symbol, as ^3P (triplet P), ^4D (quartet D), etc. The

multiplicity of molecules is analogous to that of atoms, and is expressed also by the number $2S + 1$.

MULTIPLYING GAGE. See gage, multiplying.

MULTIROTATION. See mutarotation.

MULTIVALENT. Having a valence of three or more.

MUREXIDE REACTION. Murexide is the ammonium salt of purpuric acid and is purple-red or violet in color. It is produced by oxidation, with nitric acid (followed by treatment with ammonia), of uric acid and related purine compounds.

MURIATE. An old term for chloride; derived from muriatic acid; an old term for hydrochloric acid.

MURPHREE EFFICIENCY FACTOR. An expression for the efficiency of an individual plate in a fractionating column. This expression corrects for the departure of the vapor from equilibrium composition. It is of the form:

$$E_m = 100\,\frac{(y_n - y_{n-1})}{(y_n{}^* - y_{n-1})}$$

where E_m = Murphree efficiency factor; y_n = actual composition of the more volatile component in the vapor leaving plate "n" (mole fraction); y_{n-1} = actual composition of the more volatile component in the vapor leaving plate "$n - 1$" and entering plate "n" (mole fraction); $y_n{}^*$ = composition of the more volatile component in the vapor in equilibrium (from vapor liquid equilibrium diagram) with the liquid of composition, x_n, on plate "n" (mole fraction).

MUTAMERISM. The process or phenomenon of changing of isomeric form, commonly among optical isomers. See isomerism, optical.

MUTAROTATION. A phenomenon shown by freshly prepared solutions of certain sugars in which a change in specific rotation occurs upon standing. Some sugars show a decrease (i.e., glucose, 50%), whereas others (maltose) show an increase, of specific rotation. The change is not always in any special ratio.

MUTHMANN REAGENT FOR SEPA-RATING MINERALS. Acetylene tetra-bromide.

MYDRIATIC. A drug which causes dila-tion of the pupil of the eye (mydriasis).

MYLIUS SALT TEST. To determine resistance to sea-water erosion of alumi-num and other metals, the metals are immersed in a solution of sodium chloride and hydrogen peroxide and the weight loss determined.

MYRISTIC. Related to myristic acid, $C_{13}H_{27}COOH$.

N. Symbol for the element nitrogen (N). Symbol for **Avogadro number** (N). Symbol for number of molecules (N). Abbreviation for normal (N) or (n) as in a **normal solu-tion;** or as in a straight chain aliphatic com-pound, i.e., n-butane. Symbol for **molec-ular density** (n or N). Symbol for molec-ular density at standard conditions **(Lo-schmidt number)** (n_o or N). Abbreviation for index of refraction (n). Symbol used to designate attachment to a nitrogen atom; thus N-, when attached to a substituent radical in a chemical name, implies the radical is attached to the nitrogen atom. Abbreviation for number in general (N). Symbol for number of plates (N_p). Sym-bol for rate of transfer (N). Symbol for number of transfer units (N_t). Symbol for **intensity of radiation** (N). Symbol for **rotation rate** (n). Symbol for **transport number** (n). Symbol for rotational fre-quency (n). Symbol for **principal quantum number** (n). Symbol for safety factor (N). See also **nu.**

N-ELECTRON. An electron characterized by having a **principal quantum number** of value 4. See also **N-shell.**

N-LINE. One of the lines in the N-series of **x-rays** which are characteristic of the various elements and are produced by exci-tation of the electrons of the N-shell.

N-SHELL. The collection of all those electrons in the atom which have the **prin-cipal quantum number** 4. The N-shell is started with the element potassium, atomic number 19, which has one electron in its N-shell, and the N-shell is finally completed (containing 32 electrons) with the element lutecium, atomic number 71. During the progression from potassium to lutecium the difference between elements of con-secutive atomic numbers is frequently not in the N-shell, but in an electron incre-ment in the M-shell, or in the O-shell, or the P-shell.

Na Symbol for the element **sodium.**

NAEGELI SOLUTION. A strong solu-tion of zinc chloride (made by adding zinc to hydrochloric acid until it no longer dis-solves) saturated with iodine and potassium iodide. This reagent is used in staining cellulose and tannin-containing substances. It gives a blue color with cellulose, and red or violet with tannin.

NAEGELI TEST REACTION FOR AL-DEHYDES AND KETONES. Aldehydes and ketones, on treatment with hydroxyl-amine hydrochloride in the presence of sodium carbonate, form oximes having characteristic physical properties.

NAIMAN REAGENT FOR VITAMIN B_1 (THIAMINE). Potassium bismuth iodide, which gives an orange-red pre-cipitate with vitamin B_1.

NAIMAN TEST REAGENT FOR BIS-MUTH. A mixture of a 1% alcoholic solution of 2-methylbenzothiazole and N potassium iodide solution. It gives a deep red precipitate with bismuth even in the presence of antimony.

NAMETKIN REARRANGEMENT. See **Wagner rearrangement.**

NAPHTH-. See **naphtho-.**

NAPHTHALENE COMPOUNDS, NO-MENCLATURE OF. The positions in the naphthalene ring are designated

or

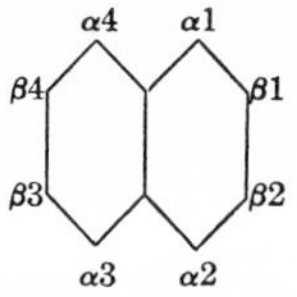

Two monosubstitution products are possible according to whether the substituent is adjacent to the central complex or is separated from it by a CH group, viz.,

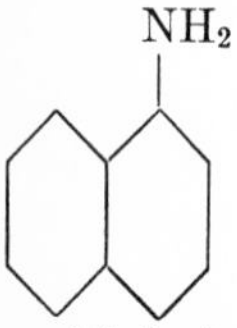

α-naphthylamine 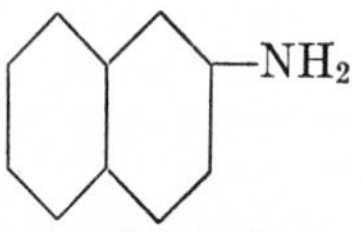   β-naphthylamine

The disubstitution products are named as follows: 1–2 *ortho*, 1–3 *meta*, 1–4 *para*, 1–5 *ana*, 1–6 *epi*, 1–7 *kata*, 1–8 *peri*, 2–3 not named, 2–6 *amphi*, 2–7 *pros*. Polysubstitution products are designated by numbers. Substituents in the same ring are termed isonuclear; those in different rings, heteronuclear.

NAPHTHALIMIDO. The radical (from naphthalimide) $C_{10}H_6(CO)_2N$—.

NAPHTHENE. (Cycloparaffin) One of a series of saturated cyclic **hydrocarbons** of the general formula C_nH_{2n}. They occur in Galician and Russian petroleums.

NAPHTHENYL. See **naphthylmethylidyne.**

NAPHTHO-, NAPHTH-. A prefix meaning related to naphthalene, as naphthoquinone.

NAPHTHODIAZINE COMPOUND. An aromatic compound containing an anthracene-like ring in which two of the ring carbon-atoms are replaced by nitrogen atoms.

NAPHTHOL. A phenolic derivative of naphthalene. Two isomeric monohydroxyl naphthalenes are possible, the α- and β-naphthols, represented by the formulas

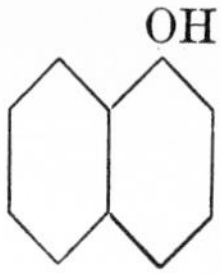

and

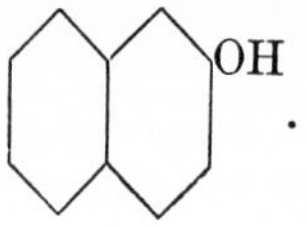

NAPHTHOLATE. A **naphthol** derivative in which the hydrogen atom of the hydroxyl is replaced commonly by a metal atom, analogous to the alcoholate.

NAPHTHOTHIAZOLE. One of a group of naphthalene derivatives in which one of the hydrogen atoms is substituted by a sulfur atom and the other by a nitrogen atom, both of which are connected to a $\equiv$CH group. Type-formula

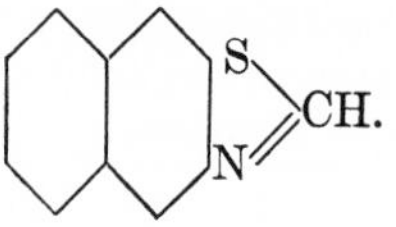

Four isomeric forms are known, the β,β-isomer is shown.

NAPHTHOXAZOLE. One of a group of naphthalene derivatives in which one of the hydrogen atoms is substituted by an oxygen atom and the other by a nitrogen atom, both of which are connected to a $\equiv$CH group. Type-formula

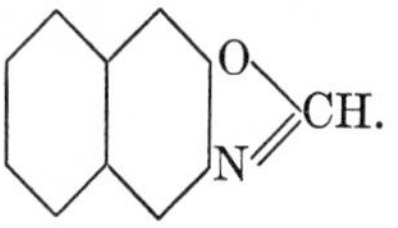

Four isomeric forms are known, the β,β-isomer is shown.

NAPHTHOXY. The radical $C_{10}H_7O$—, derived from **naphthol** by loss of the hydrogen atom from the hydroxyl group.

NAPHTHOYL. The radical $C_{10}H_7CO$—, derived from naphthoic acid.

NAPHTHYL. The radical (1- or 2-) $C_{10}H_7$—, derived from **naphthalene** by loss of a hydrogen atom.

NAPHTHYLENE. The radical —$C_{10}H_6$—, derived from **naphthalene** by loss of two hydrogen atoms.

NAPHTHYLIDENE. The radical

[1(4)-form shown].

NAPIERIAN LOGARITHM. See **logarithm.**

NARCOTIC. A drug that produces sleep or complete insensibility; or a particular group of such drugs, the opium group, which have been the object of legislative control because of the addiction resulting from their improper use.

NASCENT. A term used to designate an element or simple compound just liberated from combination. Some elements show much greater **activity** in this nascent state than they show in their ordinary conditions. Nascent hydrogen will reduce com-

NATURAL CHANGE. A change occurring in nature, chiefly reactions with water (hydrolysis), reactions with air (oxidation), or reactions attributable to bacterial or enzymatic action.

NATURAL LOGARITHM. See **logarithm.**

NAVARRO REAGENTS FOR ALKALOIDS. Alkali xanthogenates that give characteristic crystalline precipitates with many alkaloids.

NAVASHIN SOLUTION. An aqueous solution of chromic acid, acetic acid, and formaldehyde, used as a fixative for vegetable tissues.

Nd Symbol for the element **neodymium.**

Ne Symbol for the element **neon.**

NEBER REACTION. A method of formation of α-amino ketones by reaction of sulfonic esters of ketoximes with potassium ethylate, followed by hydrolysis of the addition product.

$$\overset{\displaystyle R''}{\underset{\displaystyle R''}{R'.CH_2.C:NOH}} + C_6H_5SO_2Cl \xrightarrow{-HCl} R'.CH_2.\overset{\displaystyle R''}{C}:NOSO_2C_6H_5$$

$$\overset{\displaystyle R''}{R'.CH_2C:NOSO_2C_6H_5} + (H_2O) \xrightarrow{C_2H_5OK} R'.CHNH_2COR'' + C_6H_5SO_3H.$$

pounds which are not greatly affected by ordinary hydrogen gas.

NASSE REAGENT FOR ALBUMIN. A solution of mercuric acetate to which sodium nitrite is added.

NATANSON TEST FOR IRON. Add some potassium thiocyanate to the slightly acid solution to be tested and extract with ether. A rose-red color indicates iron.

NATRIUM. Latin name for **sodium.**

NATURAL BASE. An organic substance, occurring in nature, which combines with an acid. The term is usually restricted to the **alkaloids.**

NEBULIZATION. Atomization (q.v.) of liquids in air.

NECKE - SCHMIDT - KLOSTERMANN REAGENT FOR LEAD. Tetramethyldiaminodiphenylmethane, which forms a blue color when its acetic acid solution is used to treat a lead dioxide precipitate.

NEEDLE. In general, a pointed rod, wire, or tube designed for use in puncturing or pointing.

NEEDLE, HYPODERMIC. A hollow needle, used for injections beneath the skin.

NEEDLE VALVE. See **valve, needle.**

NEF ALDEHYDE AND KETONE SYN-THESIS. Conversion of aliphatic nitro compounds to aldehydes or ketones by treatment of the *aci*-nitro compounds with mineral acids.

NEGATIVE RADICAL. See **radical, negative.**

NEGATRON. An **electron.** The term negatron emphasizes the negative charge

$$R'R''CHNO_2 + NaOH \rightarrow R'R''C{=}NO_2Na + H_2O$$

$$2R'R''C{=}NO_2Na + 2H_2SO_4 \rightarrow 2R'R''CO + 2NaHSO_4 + N_2O + H_2O.$$

NEF REACTION. A method of forming acetylenic hydroxy compounds from the action on ketones of sodium derivatives of acetylenic hydrocarbons.

on the electron and is used to avoid possible confusion because of some use of the term "positive electron" for the positron.

$$\overset{\displaystyle OH}{\underset{\displaystyle |}{R'COR''}} + NaC{:}CH \rightarrow R'R''C.C{:}CH + NaOH.$$

NEGATIVE ADSORPTION. See **adsorption, negative.**

NEGATIVE CATALYSIS. The retardation of the velocity of a reaction by a catalyst, e.g., alcohol markedly retards the oxidation of sulfites by free oxygen. (Also see **catalyst, negative.**)

NEGATIVE CRYSTAL. A **double-refracting** crystal in which the difference between the refraction of the ordinary ray and the extraordinary ray is negative, i.e., the **refractive index** of the latter is less than that of the former.

NEGATIVE ELEMENT. See **element, negative.**

NEGATIVE GROUP. (1) A group which readily forms compounds with electropositive atoms or groups like the metals. (2) A group which on introduction into a compound causes the latter to form compounds more readily with electro-positive atoms or groups. Negative groups often yield two electrons to form shared pairs, thus forming dative bonds (see **bond, dative**).

NEGATIVE ION. An **ion** having a negative charge.

NEGATIVE PRESSURE. See **pressure, negative.**

NELISSEN BLOWPIPE REAGENT. Sodium formate, used for reductions on charcoal.

NEMATIC PHASE. One of the forms of the **mesomorphic state,** the "liquid crystals." The characteristic appearance is that of mobile, thread-like structures, especially visible upon examination of thick specimens with **polarized light.** This form has a single **optical axis,** which takes the direction of an applied magnetic field. The liquid appears turbid but does not yield an x-ray diffraction pattern.

NENCKI REACTION. A condensation using ferric chloride as a catalyst; or the nuclear acylation of phenolic compounds by the catalytic action of zinc chloride and an acid.

NEO-. (Greek) *New;* a prefix designating a newer compound related in some way to an older one, as neoarsphenamine. Specifically, indicating a hydrocarbon in which at least one carbon atom is connected directly with four other carbon atoms, as neopentane, $(CH_3)_4C$.

NEODYMIUM. Rare earth metallic element. Symbol Nd. Atomic number 60. Atomic weight 144.27. Density 6.9563. Melting point 840° C. Valences 3 and 4. Oxides Nd_2O_3, NdO_2. Neodymium occurs in cerite and other rare minerals.

NEON. Gaseous element. Symbol Ne. Atomic number 10. Atomic weight 20.183. Density (g. per liter at S.T.P.) 0.9002. Melting point $-248.67°$ C. Boiling point $-245.9°$ C. Neon forms no known compounds. 10,000 volumes of air contain about 0.15 volume of neon.

NEPHELOMETER. A photometric instrument for determining the amount of light transmitted (or scattered) by a suspension of particles. Since this quantity is dependent upon the size and concentration of the particles, the method provides a means of determining particle size, if the number can be determined, or particle concentration, if the size can be controlled. As used in analytical procedures, one or more of the factors are eliminated by precipitating under standard conditions, or by comparison with a standard so that the instrument can be used in quantitative determinations.

NEPHELOMETRY. The measurement of the concentration, particle size, etc., of suspension by means of its light transmission or dispersion, etc., and the application of the results, especially in chemical analysis.

NEPTUNIUM. Transuranic radioactive element. Symbol Np. Atomic number 93. The atomic species of mass number 239 is produced by absorption of resonance neutrons by uranium atoms of mass number 238, followed by emission of an electron from the nucleus. The neptunium atoms of mass number 239, so formed, have a half-period of 2.3 days, emitting an electron and γ-radiation to yield plutonium ^{239}Pu. The neptunium isotope of mass number 237 is produced in the cyclotron by bombardment of uranium 238 with neutrons of such velocity that they cause the emission of two neutrons from each atom to form ^{237}U, an electron-emitter with a period of 6.63 days, which forms neptunium 237, which is a radioactive isotope (alpha-emitting) having a half-period of 2.22×10^6 years. Neptunium isotopes of mass number 231, 232, 233, 234, 235, 236, 238, 240, and 241 have also been reported. The chemical properties of neptunium, as far as determined, are similar to those of uranium.

Oxides, NpO_2, and Np_3O_8. Valences, 3, 4, 5, 6.

NEPTUNIUM SERIES. See **element, radioactive series.**

NERNST APPROXIMATION FORMULA. A formula for the **equilibrium constant** of a gas reaction derived from the **Nernst heat theorem** by certain simplifying approximations. This formula is expressed as:

$$\log K_p = -\frac{\Delta H}{4.57T}$$
$$+ \Sigma\nu 1.75 \log T + \frac{\beta}{4.57} T + \Sigma\nu I$$

where K_p is the equilibrium constant of the reaction, ΔH is its change in **heat content,** $\Sigma\nu$ is the algebraic sum of the number of moles of the gaseous reactants (or in other words, the change in number of moles of gaseous reactants due to the reaction), T is the absolute temperature, β is a constant, and I is the conventional chemical constant.

NERNST HEAT THEOREM. For a homogeneous system, the rate of change of the free energy with temperature, as well as the rate of change of heat content with temperature, approaches zero as the temperature approaches absolute zero.

NERNST, LAW OF. See **law of distribution.**

NESSLER REAGENT. An alkaline, aqueous solution of potassium mercuric iodide, used in the detection and determination of ammonia, various amines, and other substances. Yellow or brown colors or precipitates are obtained. A number of methods are available for the preparation of this reagent.

NESSLER REAGENT FOR WINE. A solution of 7 g. alum and 10 g. sodium acetate in 100 ml. water, used in detecting wine coloring.

NESSLER TEST. A test used to detect the presence of ammonia, certain amines, aldehydes, etc., by colorimetric estimation of the intensity of the reddish-brown color or precipitate formed with **Nessler reagent.**

NESSLER TUBE. A glass cylinder with a flat base, used in the **Nessler test** for ammonia, amines, aldehydes, etc., by colorimetric determination. The tube may be used generally in colorimetric measurements.

NET PLANES OR LATTICE PLANES. Any series of equidistant, parallel planes defined by the points in the **space lattice** of a crystal.

NEUBERG-BEHREN REAGENT FOR ISOLATING SUGARS. A solution of barium hydroxide in methanol.

NEUBERG-RAUCHWERGER TEST REACTION. An alcoholic solution of either cholesterol or phytosterol, containing a little methylfurfural solution, gives a raspberry-red ring test with concentrated sulfuric acid.

NEUBERG REACTION FOR FORMALDEHYDE. An aqueous solution of p-dihydrazinediphenyl hydrochloride gives a yellow color or precipitate with formaldehyde in solution, especially on warming.

NEUBERG REAGENT FOR ALIPHATIC ALCOHOLS AND AMINO ACIDS. α-Naphthylisocyanate, which forms crystalline compounds with aliphatic alcohols and amino acids.

NEUMANN REVERSION REACTION. The reaction between carbon monoxide and steam to produce carbon dioxide and hydrogen, as it occurs in the gaseous space above the fuel bed of a gas producer, according to the equation,

$$CO + H_2O \rightleftarrows CO_2 + H_2.$$

NEUTRAL. (1) Neither acid nor alkaline in reaction. (2) According to the **ionization** hypothesis a concentration of hydrogen ions equal to 1×10^{-7}. (The figure varies a little according to the temperature and the method of determining the degree of ionization of water.) Hydrogen ion concentrations greater than this figure confer acid properties; lower concentrations occur in alkaline systems. (3) Having no electric charge, or no net electric charge. (Thus, an atom, in which the total negative charge of the electrons is equal to the positive change of the nucleus which they surround, is a neutral atom.)

NEUTRAL ATOM. An atom in which the positive charge on the nucleus is equal to the total negative charge of the electrons which surround the nucleus. Therefore, the atom does not possess an electric charge.

NEUTRAL COMPOUND. A compound that is chemically neutral, i.e., neither acid nor alkaline.

NEUTRAL ELEMENTS. The rare gases of the atmosphere, together with helium and radon, constituting the zero group, or inactive **elements,** of the **periodic table.**

NEUTRAL MOLECULE. In general, a molecule without electrical charge; the term is applied often to a system of two ions of opposite but equal charge, in a solvent. The two ions comprising this system differ from solvated ions, which consist of complexes formed between molecules of solvent and ions.

NEUTRAL POINT. The point reached in the course of a titration or other chemical operation or process, at which the system contains equal concentrations of hydrogen and hydroxyl ions, each about 1×10^{-7} molar. In practice the neutral point will vary somewhat from this figure, depending upon the method of determining these **ionic concentrations.** If **indicators** are used, their tables of values must be consulted.

NEUTRAL PRINCIPLE. A substance isolated from plants, and more or less characteristic of them, i.e., neither acidic nor basic in reaction.

NEUTRAL REACTION. A reaction that does not involve a change in acidity or alkalinity.

NEUTRAL SALT. A salt which in solution, commonly aqueous solution, does not give an acidic or a basic reaction.

NEUTRAL SALT EFFECT. The diminution of the **ionization** of a weak acid or base on the addition of a salt that contains one of the ions of the ionized substance. This is a special case of the **common ion effect.**

NEUTRALITY. The condition of being neutral.

NEUTRALIZATION. The process of rendering a system neutral.

NEUTRALIZATION, HEAT OF. See **heat of neutralization.**

NEUTRALIZATION INDICATOR. See **indicator, neutralization.**

NEUTRALIZE. To bring into a **neutral** state.

NEUTRALIZER. Any agent capable of adjusting the **hydrogen-ion concentration** of a system to about 1×10^{-7}.

NEUTRETTO. See **meson.**

NEUTRINO. A hypothetical fundamental particle of zero charge, and a mass of about 6×10^{-30} gram. The existence of the neutrino is postulated on the basis of energy calculations.

NEUTRON. An elementary particle with no electric charge and with a mass of 1.00866 on the chemical scale of **atomic weights,** which is essentially the mass of the proton.

NEUTRON HOWITZER. A collimating apparatus for the production of a stream of **neutrons,** consisting of a source of neutrons, such as a mixture of beryllium filings and radon, contained in a block of paraffin, from which the stream of neutrons escapes by a circular passage, small in cross-sectional area and lined with cadmium.

NEWELL SOLUTION. A 10% aqueous solution of chromic acid to which hydrochloric acid is added. It is used in etching steels.

NEWLANDS OCTAVES. See **law of octaves.**

NEWTON EMISSION THEORY. The hypothesis advanced by Sir Isaac Newton that light was due to an emission of luminous corpuscles from a source.

NEWTON LAW OF COOLING. See **law of Newton for heat loss (cooling).**

NEWTON LAW OF GRAVITATION. See **law of Newton (gravitation).**

NEWTON LAWS OF MOTION. See **laws of Newton (motion).**

Ni Symbol for the element **nickel.**

NICHOLS-COOPER REAGENT. Dinitroresorcinol, used in aqueous solution to give a color or precipitate with a solution of copper, iron, or cobalt salts.

NICKEL. Metallic element. Symbol Ni. Atomic number 28. Atomic weight 58.69. Density 8.9. Specific heat 0.1034. Melting point 1455° C. Boiling point 2900° C. Nickel occurs in chalcopyrite, pentlandite, and other minerals. Valences 2 and 3. Oxides NiO, Ni_2O_3, Ni_3O_4.

NICKELATE (II). The anion $NiO_2^=$, or a compound containing it.

NICKELATE (VI). The anion $NiO_4^=$, or a compound containing it.

NICKELIC. Pertaining to or containing trivalent **nickel.**

NICKELOCYANIDE. See **cyanonickelate (II).**

NICKELONITRITE. See **nitronickelate (II).**

NICKELOUS. Pertaining to or containing bivalent **nickel.**

NICOL PRISM. A polarizing prism prepared by cutting down the end faces of the principal section of a crystal of calcite (Iceland spar) so that the face angles are reduced to 68°, then slicing the crystal in a plane perpendicular to the ends and the principal section, and cementing it together with Canada balsam, which has an index of refraction (see **refractive index**) less than that of calcite for the ordinary ray, and greater for the extraordinary ray. Thus the ordinary ray may be separated from the extraordinary ray, producing **plane polarized light.**

NIEMENTOWSKI QUINAZOLINE RE-ACTION. A method of formation of 4-keto, 3-4-dihydroquinazolines by the action of **amides** upon **anthranilic acids.**

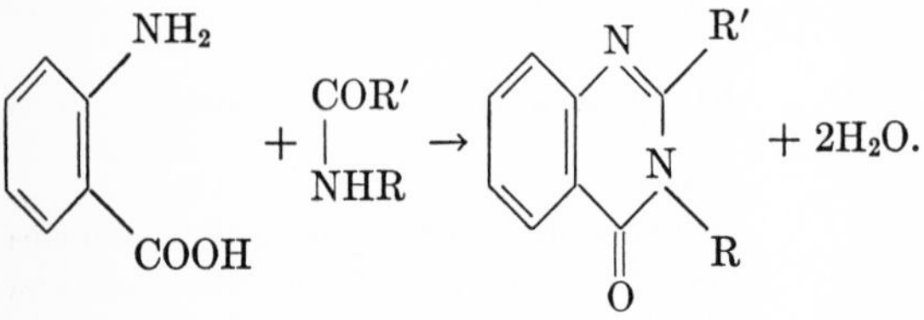

$$+ 2H_2O.$$

NIEMENTOWSKI QUINOLINE SYN-THESIS. A method of formation of γ-hydroxyquinoline derivatives from **anthranilic acids** and **ketones** (or other carbonyl compounds).

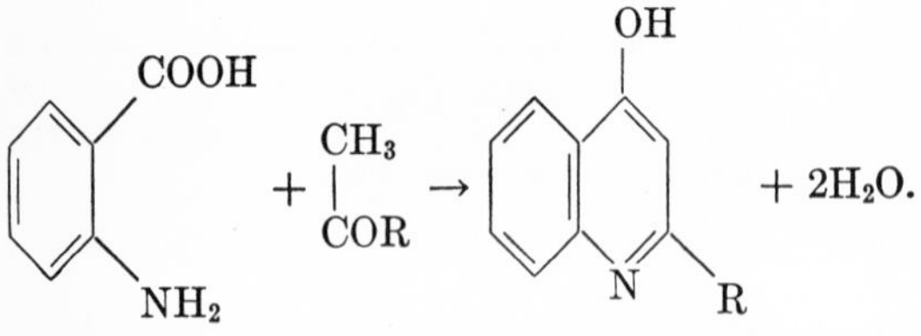

$$+ 2H_2O.$$

NIERENSTEIN REACTION. A reaction between an acid chloride (commonly aromatic) and diazomethane which yields the corresponding chloromethylketone.

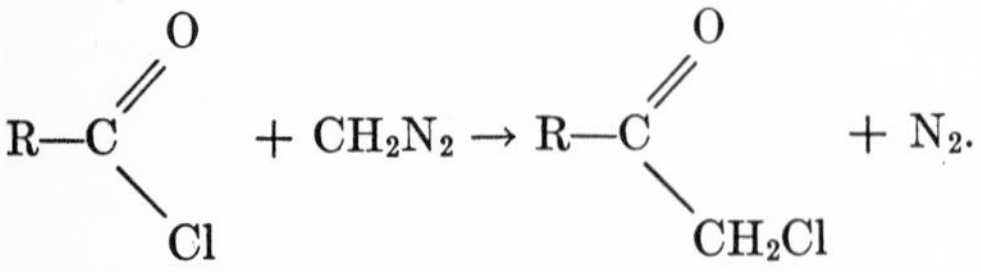

$$R—C \quad + CH_2N_2 \rightarrow R—C \quad + N_2.$$

NIERENSTEIN REAGENT FOR TAN-NINS. A 0.5% solution of diazobenzene chloride which gives precipitates on dropwise addition to cold solutions of pyrocatechol tannins. No precipitate is formed with pyrogallol tannins.

NIEUWENBURG-BROBBEL MICRO-TEST FOR MALIC ACID. The addition of solid brucine to one drop of either optical isomer of malic acid gives many microscopic crystals.

NIGYL MICRO-TEST FOR LIGNIN. On saturation with an aqueous solution of indole, and treatment with 20% sulfuric acid, lignin appears red to red-violet under the microscope.

NIKIFOROFF BORAX-CARMINE. A solution of 15 g. carmine in 500 ml. of a 5% aqueous solution of borax, alkalinized with ammonium hydroxide, then concentrated to 250 ml. and acidified until its red color disappears. It is a tissue stain.

NILSON TEST REACTION. Antimony is detected by a red opalescence with a bluish tinge which appears when a particle of an antimony salt is added to a mixture of a solution of 2 g. sodium thiosulfate in 5 ml. water and 5 ml. saturated sulfurous acid, followed by boiling.

NINHYDRIN REACTION. Ninhydrin (1,2,3-indantrione hydrate) in aqueous solution gives a deep blue to violet-pink or red color with protein degradation products, α-amino acids, or any substance containing an α-amino group. This reaction is used in the colorimetric determination of amino acids.

NIOBATE. The radical $NbO_3^=$ (no finite ion).

NIOBIC. Pertaining to or containing pentavalent **niobium.**

NIOBIUM. Metallic element. Symbol Nb. Atomic number 41. Atomic weight 92.91. Density variously given at 8.4 to 8.57. Melting point variously given at 2415° C., 2900° C., and other values. Boiling point variously given at 3300° C., 3700° C., and other values. Valences, 3, 4, 5. Oxide Nb_2O_5. Acid H_3NbO_4. Niobium was once called columbium.

NIOBOUS. Pertaining to or containing trivalent **niobium.**

NITON. A name for the element **radon.**

NITRAMIDE. (1) The compound NO_2NH_2. (2) One of many possible compounds derived from the compound NO_2NH_2 by replacement of hydrogen by a carboxy group, a substituted carboxy group, or a radical containing a carboxy or a substituted carboxy group.

NITRAMINE. One of many possible compounds derived from nitramide, NO_2NH_2, by replacement of one or both of its hydrogen atoms, commonly by alkyl or aryl radicals.

NITRAMINO. The radical $NO_2.NH—$.

NITRANILINE. (1) The compound

$$C_6H_4\begin{cases} NO_2 \\ NH_2 \end{cases}.$$

(2) One of a class of compounds, representing substitution of both amino- and nitro- groups in benzene and its derivatives.

NITRATE. (1) The anion NO_3^-, or a compound containing it. (2) A salt or ester of nitric acid (HNO_3).

NITRATE (ORTHO-). The anion NO_4^{3-}, or a compound containing it.

NITRATED. See **nitrate.**

NITRATION. The action or process of introducing the **nitro group** into an organic compound.

NITRATO. The radical

$$—O—N\begin{cases} O \\ O \end{cases}.$$

NITRATOCERATE. The anion $Ce(NO_3)_6^=$, or a compound containing it.

NITRATOR. An industrial apparatus used to carry out **nitration** processes, i.e., processes which introduce a nitro group into an organic compound.

NITRIC. (1) Related to nitric acid, HNO_3. (2) Containing nitrogen at a higher valence than nitrous, e.g., nitric oxide.

NITRIDATION. In its most common use, nitridation means simply the formation of **nitrides,** as of certain metals in industry. The term is also used sometimes to indicate the formation of a nitrogen compound by the action of ammonia, analogous to the use of the term oxidation.

NITRIDE, TRI-. See **azide.**

NITRIDO. The atom $N\!<$ in an inorganic compound.

NITRIFICATION. The formation of **nitrates** (or **nitrites**) by oxidation of ammonia and other nitrogen-containing compounds.

NITRIFIER. A nitrifying agent, i.e., an agent which oxidizes forms of nitrogen at lower valences, as in the form of ammonia and certain organic compounds, to nitrates or nitrites.

NITRIFY. To form nitrates or nitrites from ammonia.

NITRIFYING. Causing oxidation of combined nitrogen or ammonia to nitrates or nitrites, especially certain microorganisms in the soil.

-NITRILE. A suffix indicating a terminal —CN group.

NITRILE, ACID. See **nitrile.**

NITRILE BASE. One of the tertiary **amines** and **amides** as distinguished from the alkyl cyanides and acid nitriles.

NITRILO. The atom N< in an inorganic compound.

NITRITE. The anion NO_2^-, or a compound containing it.

NITRITE (ORTHO-). The anion NO_3^{3-}, or a compound containing it.

NITRITO. The group ONO—, in an inorganic compound.

NITRO. The radical O_2N—, constituting the nitro group.

NITRO GROUP. The radical

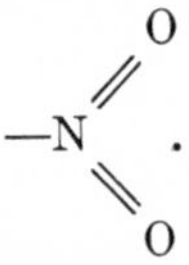

NITROACID. An organic acid (—COOH), which also contains a nitro group

NITROAMINE. See **nitramine.**

NITROBENZENE PROCESS. A process for the refining of lubricating oil, involving extraction with nitrobenzene.

NITROBENZOYL. The radical

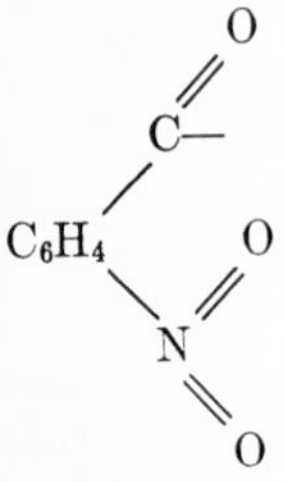

$$C_6H_4 \diagdown \begin{array}{c} C- \\ \diagup \\ O \diagup \\ N \\ \diagdown \\ O \end{array} \quad O \quad (3 \text{ isomers}).$$

NITROBENZYL. The radical

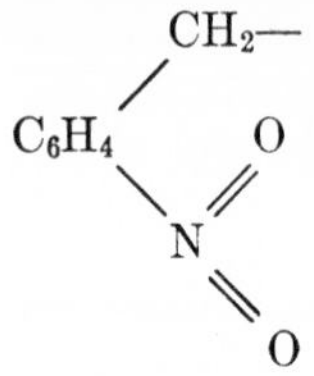

$$C_6H_4 \diagdown \begin{array}{c} CH_2- \\ \diagup \\ O \diagup \\ N \\ \diagdown \\ O \end{array} \quad O \quad (3 \text{ isomers}).$$

NITROCOBALTATE (II). See **cobaltonitrite.**

NITROCOBALTATE (III). See **cobaltinitrite.**

NITROCOMPOUND. A compound, of organic structure, containing the radical

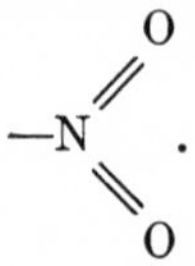

$$-N \diagup^{O}_{\diagdown O} \; .$$

NITROGEN. Gaseous element. Symbol N. Atomic number 7. Atomic weight 14.008. Boiling point −195.8° C. Melting point −209.86° C. Density (grams per liter at standard temperature) 1.2506. Valences 1, 2, 3, 4, and 5. Oxides, N_2O, NO, $NO_2(N_2O_4)$, N_2O_3, and N_2O_5. Acids; hydrazoic (HN_3), hyponitrous ($H_2N_2O_2$), nitrohydroxylamic ($H_2N_2O_3$), nitrous HNO_2 and nitric HNO_3.

NITROGEN CYCLE. The general biological series of changes in nature by which the elemental nitrogen of the atmosphere is converted into compounds, used in the nutrition of plants and animals, and ultimately liberated again as free elemental nitrogen. Major events in the natural cycle are the fixation of the atmospheric nitrogen by natural electrical discharges such as lightning, washing of the nitrogen compounds into the soil by rain, then their assimilation for plant use by bacteria, followed by their elaboration in the plant into a form available for animal nutrition. The animal produces nitrogenous wastes, and ultimately its body also is decomposed by bacteria; in both cases the nitrogenous end products return to the soil or the atmosphere to repeat the cycle.

NITROGEN FIXATION. A process by which the nitrogen in the atmosphere is converted into a compound. There are fixation processes carried out in nature, and also synthetic processes used in industry.

NITROGENATED. Having nitrogen, as in a compound.

NITROGENIZE. To combine or impregnate with nitrogen or nitrogenous compounds.

NITROGENOUS. Pertaining to or containing nitrogen. **Proteins** are nitrogenous foodstuffs.

NITROIC ACID. An acid containing the radical

$$-N\overset{\displaystyle O}{\underset{\displaystyle OH}{\Vert}}$$

—N—OH, which is a hydrated **nitro group.**

NITROIRIDATE (III). The anion $Ir(NO_2)_6^{3-}$, or a compound containing it.

NITROL. An organic compound having a **nitro group** and a **nitroso group** on the same carbon atom. The type-formula is

$$R_2C\overset{\displaystyle O}{\underset{\displaystyle N=O}{\diagdown N\diagdown O.}}$$

-NITROLIC. A suffix indicating a terminal $-C(:NOH)NO_2$ group.

NITROLIC ACID. An organic compound having a **nitro group** and an **oxime group** on the same carbon atom. The type-formula is

$$R-C\overset{\displaystyle O}{\underset{\displaystyle N-O-H}{\diagdown N\diagdown O}} .$$

NITROMETER. An apparatus in which nitrogen (or other gas) may be collected and measured. A special form of **eudiometer.** There are many forms of nitrometers. Some are arranged so that a nitrogen-evolving reaction may be conducted within the apparatus and the evolved nitrogen directly measured.

NITRONICKELATE (II). The anion $Ni(NO_2)_6^{4-}$, or a compound containing it.

NITROÖSMATE (III). The anion $Os(NO_2)_5^{=}$, or a compound containing it.

NITROPALLADATE (II). The anion $Pd(NO_2)_4^{=}$, or a compound containing it.

NITROPHENOL. An organic compound derived from phenol by substitution of **nitro group(s)** for one or more nuclear hydrogen atoms.

NITROPLATINATE (II). The anion $Pt(NO_2)_4^{=}$, or a compound containing it.

NITROPRUSSIDE. The anion

$$[Fe(NO)(CN)_5]^{=},$$

or a compound containing it.

NITRORHODATE (III). The anion $Rh(NO_2)_6^{3-}$, or a compound containing it.

NITRORUTHENATE (III). The anion $Ru(NO_2)_6^{3-}$, or a compound containing it.

NITROSATE. One of a series of organic nitrogen compounds, having an **oxime group** and a **nitrate group** on adjacent carbon atoms, as isoamylene nitrosate,

$$\begin{matrix} CH_3 & & O \\ & \diagdown & \diagup\!\!\Vert \\ & C-O-N & \\ & \diagup & \diagdown\!\!\Vert \\ CH_3 & | & O \\ CH_3 & -C=N-OH. \end{matrix}$$

NITROSITE. One of a series of organic nitrogen compounds, having an **oxime**

group and a **nitrite group** on adjacent carbon atoms, as isoamylene nitrosite.

$$CH_3$$
$$\diagdown$$
$$C{-}O{-}N{=}O$$
$$\diagup$$
$$H_3C$$
$$\mid$$
$$CH_3{-}C{=}N{-}OH.$$

NITROSO. The radical ON—, which forms nitroso compounds.

NITROSO COMPOUND. An organic compound that contains the **nitroso group** —N=O, as nitrosobenzene $C_6H_5N{=}O$.

NITROSO DYE. See **dye, nitroso.**

NITROSOAMINE. An organic compound containing both a **nitroso group** and an **amino group.**

NITROSOKETONE. An organic compound containing a **nitroso group** and a **carbonyl group,** or more commonly an **isonitroso group** on a carbon atom adjacent to a carbonyl group.

-NITROSOLIC. A suffix indicating a terminal —C(:NOH)NO group.

NITROSYL. The univalent radical —N=O in inorganic compounds, e.g., nitrosyl chloride, NOCl. Cf. **nitroso.**

NITROSYLIC. Pertaining to or containing **nitrosyl.**

NITROSYLSULFATE. The anion $O_2NSO_3^-$, or a compound containing it.

NITROUS. (1) Related to nitrous acid, HNO_2. (2) Containing trivalent nitrogen.

NITROXYL. The univalent radical —NO_2, when it occurs in inorganic compounds, such as nitroxyl chloride, NO_2Cl, or copper nitroxyl, $Cu(NO_2)_2$. Cf. **nitro.**

NITRYL. The univalent radical —NO_2, when it occurs in inorganic compounds. Thus, nitryl chloride is nitroxyl chloride. See **nitroxyl.**

NIXON REAGENT. A 1% aqueous solution of 2-naphthol-6,8-disulfonic acid, used in testing for nitrate and nitrite. A yellow to red color, on addition of sulfuric acid, shows the presence of nitrates or nitrites.

NOBLE GAS. One of the inert gases **helium, neon, argon, krypton, xenon,** and **radon,** so-called because of their chemical inertness. See **gas, inert.**

NOBLE METAL. See **metal, noble.**

NOMENCLATURE, CHEMICAL. See **chemical nomenclature.**

NOMENCLATURE, GENEVA. See **chemical nomenclature.**

NOMOGRAPH. Also called an alignment chart. It consists of two or more graphical scales, drawn and arranged so that results of calculations may be found quickly from the relation of points upon them. For example, three-scale charts of this type are usually constructed so that in a relationship involving three variables, the value in one variable is determined by a given set of values of the other two and may be found by locating the given values of the two known variables upon their proper scales, laying a straight-edge on the three scales, so that its edge cuts the two points, then the point at which it cuts the third scale is the value sought.

NONDECYLIC. Related to nondecylic acid, $C_{18}H_{37}COOH$.

NONDRYING OIL. See **oil, nondrying.**

NONLUMINOUS FLAME. See **flame, nonluminous.**

NONMETALLIC. Not of a metallic nature.

NON-METALS. Those elements which are not classified as metals.

NONPOLAR COMPOUND. See **compound, nonpolar.**

NONPOLAR LIQUID. See **liquid, normal.**

NONYL. The radical $CH_3(CH_2)_8$—.

NOR. From normal; a prefix (a) indicating the parent from which another compound may be theoretically derived, usually by the removal of one or more carbon atoms (and attached hydrogen), as norcamphane (of which camphane is a trimethyl derivative); (b) designating a compound of normal structure isomeric with the compound to which it is prefixed, as norleucine.

NORCAMPHANYL. The radical C_7H_{11}— (from norcamphane).

NORDLANDER TEST. Mercury vapor is detected by paper coated by a thin layer of selenium sulfide, which is colored black.

NORLEUCYL. The radical

$$CH_3CH_2CH_2CH_2CH(NH_2)CO—.$$

NORMAL ATOM. An atom which has all its electrons in their normal **orbitals,** as distinguished from an atom in which one or more electrons have been raised to higher energy levels by **excitation.**

NORMAL DENSITY. See **density, normal.**

NORMAL HYDROCARBON. See **hydrocarbon, normal.**

NORMALITY. The number of equivalent gram-molecular weights per unit volume of solution. Thus the normality of a solution is its concentration, in multiples or fractions of the number of equivalent gram-molecular weights of solute that it contains per liter.

NORMALITY FACTOR. The numerical value of the **normality** of a solution.

NORMALIZATION. A process for the heat treatment of alloys at lower temperatures ($500°–600°$ C.) by heating in a bath of fused salts.

NORMAL LIQUID. See **liquid, normal.**

NORMAL PRESSURE. The standard pressure to which measurements of volume, especially of gases, and other experimental work which may vary with pressure changes, are usually referred. It is the pressure of a column of mercury 760 millimeters high at sea-level at a latitude of 45°.

NORMAL SALT. A salt of a polybasic acid in which all of the replaceable hydrogen atoms have been replaced by other atoms or radicals, or a salt of a polyhydric base in which all the replaceable hydroxyl radicals have been replaced by other atoms or radicals.

NORMAL SOLUTION. (1) A solution containing one equivalent gram-molecular weight of solute per liter. (2) A physiologically normal solution, i.e., an isotonic solution. (See **solution, normal.**)

NORMAL TEMPERATURE. Average room temperature, to which a value of $20°$ C. is assigned.

NOVELLI REAGENT. A solution of 5 g. resorcinol in 150 ml. water, with the addition of 5 drops 20% ferric chloride solution, followed by boiling until the solution becomes yellow in color. It is used as a test reagent for nitrite. A green color in the presence of acetic acid is given by nitrite.

NOWOPOKROWSKY REAGENT. A solution prepared by dissolving 20 g. zinc chloride in 8.5 g. water and, after cooling, adding sufficient of a solution of 3 g. potassium iodide and 1.5 g. iodine in 60 ml. water to cause incipient precipitation. This solution imparts a blue color to cellulose.

Np Symbol for the element **neptunium.**

NU (N OR ν). The thirteenth letter in the Greek alphabet, used to denote the thirteenth carbon atom in a straight-chain compound or a derivative in which a substituent group is attached to that carbon atom (ν-). Symbol for frequency (ν). Symbol for reciprocal dispersive power (ν). Reciprocal permeability (reluctivity) (ν). Coefficient of kinematic viscosity (ν). Symbol for neutrino (ν).

NUCLEAR CHARGE. The positive charge on the atomic **nucleus** due to the **protons** it contains. The charge varies from 1 to 98 and corresponds to the **atomic number** of the element.

NUCLEAR COUNTER. See **counter.**

NUCLEAR ELECTRON. See **electron, nuclear.**

NUCLEAR ENERGY LEVELS. Differences in the energy of atomic nuclei. As in the case of atoms, nuclei can assume only a discrete number of **energy levels.**

NUCLEAR EQUATION. An equation showing the changes in composition, usually in terms of mass number and charge only, of an atomic **nucleus** during a nuclear reaction. The equation shows any particles captured, or radiations absorbed by the nucleus, and also the particles or radiations emitted. (See **equation, nuclear.**)

NUCLEAR EXCITATION FUNCTION. See **excitation function, nuclear.**

NUCLEAR ISOMERS. Two (or more) **nuclides** which have the same **mass number** and the same **atomic number,** but have different radioactive properties. They are believed to be composed ultimately of the same number of protons and the same number of neutrons, but to be different in their energy levels. Such isomeric nuclei are found among the naturally radioactive elements as well as among the artificially radioactive elements. Two examples of the latter are a radioactive zinc of mass number 69, which emits a gamma radiation to yield another radioactive zinc of mass number 69; and a radioactive krypton which has a mass number of 83 and is, therefore, a nuclear isotope of ordinary non-radioactive krypton.

NUCLEAR PARTICLE. A particle believed to exist as such in the nucleus of atoms or of certain atoms. (See **nuclear structure.**)

NUCLEAR REACTION. See **reaction, nuclear.**

NUCLEAR SPIN. The rotation of the nucleus of the atom.

NUCLEAR STRUCTURE. The arrangement of various particles in the nucleus of an atom. This subject is still in a de-velopmental stage, and one of the important questions to be answered is the role of the mesons which, together with the neutrons and protons, apparently make up the nuclei of the elements. (Hydrogen atoms of unit mass number have, of course, a nucleus consisting only of a single proton.) (Also see **meson.**)

NUCLEAR THEORY OF ATOMIC STRUCTURE. See **atomic structure.**

NUCLEI, CONDENSED. In organic chemistry, when two or more molecular nuclei (see **nucleus**) are linked together so that each nucleus has two carbon atoms in common with another nucleus, the condition is termed condensed nuclei, e.g., naphthalene contains a twin nuclei complex.

NUCLEI, TWIN. See **nuclei, condensed.**

NUCLEIC ACID. Also called nucleinic acid. One of a series of compounds in which phosphoric acid is combined with **carbohydrates** and with various bases derived from purine and pyrimidine. They are often conjugated with proteins to form nucleoproteins.

NUCLEIN. One of a series of phosphoproteins that are found in living organisms. (See **proteins.**)

NUCLEON. A general term for a **proton** or a **neutron,** regarded as primary particles of which atomic nuclei are composed.

NUCLEOPROTEIN. See **protein.**

NUCLEUS. The interior or central part, or the kernel. The term nucleus is widely used in science, as the nucleus of a **cell,** the nucleus of an **atom** or the nucleus of a **molecule.** The nucleus of an atom is the central part of the atom and contains all the protons and neutrons and most of the mass of the atom. The nucleus of a molecule is a group of atoms connected by valence bonds so that the atoms and their bonds form a ring or closed structure, which persists as a unit through a series of chemical changes.

NUCLEUS, ALICYCLIC. A molecular **nucleus** consisting of a closed ring of carbon atoms and their valence **bonds,** in which there is not more than one bond between any two carbon atoms, and in which none of the ring carbon atoms are bonded to more than two of the others.

NUCLEUS, ATOM. See **nucleus.**

NUCLEUS, BENZENE. See **benzene.**

NUCLEUS, COMPOUND. An atomic **nucleus** which has absorbed an incident particle, and (usually) is about to eject a particle and/or radiation.

NUCLEUS, CONDENSED. See **nuclei, condensed.**

NUCLEUS, HETEROCYCLIC. See **compound, heterocyclic.**

NUCLEUS, HOMOCYCLIC. See **compound, homocyclic.**

NUCLEUS, RECOIL. An atomic **nucleus** formed as a result of a nuclear reaction (see **reaction, nuclear**) in the course of which a particle and/or radiation has been ejected.

NUCLIDE. An atomic species characterized by the composition of its **nucleus,** as expressed by the number of **protons** and **neutrons** it contains, and its **energy level.**

NULL. Zero, or without action; or, in the case of an instrument, without giving a reading.

NULL ELECTRODE. An **electrode** having a **thermodynamic potential** of zero; i.e., an electrode in which there is actually no difference of potential between the metal and the ionic solution. It is believed, however, that no such electrodes have been prepared. Electrodes are known whereby, due to relative motion, it is possible to obtain an electrokinetic potential of zero, but it does not follow that their reversible potential is zero.

NUTRIANT. A drug which promotes nutritive processes; i.e., the metabolic processes by which living cells or organisms avail themselves of food.

NUTRIENT. A substance that acts as food for a living cell or organism.

NUTRITION. (1) The assimilation of food, from its entry into the organism through the entire series of processes in digestion and metabolism up to its final form as part of the materials composing the organism, as energy, heat, stored reserves, or waste products. (2) The science of the processes and reaction described in (1) with particular reference to the foods best suited for these purposes.

NYLANDER SOLUTION. A solution of 4 g. Rochelle salt, 2 g. bismuth subnitrate, and 8 g. sodium hydroxide in water to make 100 ml. of solution. This reagent is used in testing for glucose in urine. A black color on boiling indicates the presence of glucose.

O. Symbol for the element oxygen (O). Abbreviation for **ortho** (q.v.) when that prefix is used to denote the relation of the 1 and 2 positions in benzene, or a compound characterized by it as orthoxylene, abbreviated as o-xylene. The abbreviation o is also used for ortho when that prefix is used to designate the **ortho-state** of an element as o-H. Abbreviation for **orthohelium,** o-He. (See also **omicron** and **omega.**)

O-ELECTRON. An electron having an orbit of such dimensions that the electron constitutes part of the fifth **shell** of electrons surrounding the atomic **nucleus,** counting out from the nucleus (i.e., the K-shell is the first, the L-, the second, the M-, the third, the N-, the fourth, and the O-shell, the fifth).

O-SHELL. The collection of electrons characterized by the **quantum number** 5. The O-shell starts with the element rubidium (atomic number = 37), which has one electron in its O-shell, and the O-shell is finally completed (containing 18 electrons) with the element mercury (atomic number = 80). During the progression from rubidium to mercury, the difference between elements of consecutive atomic numbers is frequently not in the O-shell, but in an electron increment in the N-shell, or in the P-shell.

-OCANE. A suffix indicating an eight-membered ring.

OBERHAUSER TEST FOR SILICA. To the solution tested, add a large excess of ammonium molybdate solution, acidify slightly with acetic or hydrochloric acid, and add a 5% stannous chloride solution. A blue color indicates the presence of a soluble silicate.

OBERHOFFER SOLUTION. A solution of 30 g. ferric chloride, 0.5 g. stannous chloride and 1.0 g. cupric chloride in a mixture of 500 ml. water, 50 ml. concentrated hydrochloric acid, and 500 ml. alcohol. It is used in etching steel, for determining the primary distribution of phosphorus.

OBERMAYER SOLUTIONS FOR INDICAN. Two solutions: (1) a solution of 20 g. lead acetate in 80 ml. distilled water; and (2) a solution of 4 g. ferric chloride in 1 liter concentrated hydrochloric acid. This reagent is used to detect indican, as in urine, by the blue color produced in a chloroform extract by the successive addition of these solutions.

OCCLUDE. To contain by **occlusion.**

OCCLUSION. A condition of uniform molecular adhesion between a precipitate and a soluble substance, or between a gas and a metal, of such a nature that it is very difficult to separate the occluded substance by washing or other simple mechanical process. Occlusion in precipitates depends upon the distribution of a substance between solvent and solid and is, probably, due to **adsorption.**

-OCIN. A suffix indicating an eight-membered ring.

-OCINE. A suffix indicating an eight-membered ring.

OCTAD. An element, atom, or radical which is **octavalent.**

OCTAHEDRAL. Having eight faces, e.g., as of a crystal.

OCTANE RATING. Also called octane number. The percentage of a particular isooctane (2,2,4-trimethylpentane) which must be mixed with normal heptane to produce an internal-combustion engine fuel with the same combustion characteristics in a standard engine as those of the fuel under test. The combustion characteristics observed are those of knocking, i.e., premature combustion or pre-ignition, with resulting vibration and loss of power efficiency.

OCTAVALENT. An element, atom, or radical which has a valence of eight.

OCTET, ELECTRON. A group of eight valence **electrons** which constitutes the most stable configuration of the outermost, or valency, electron-shell of the atom, and hence the form which frequently results from electron transfer or sharing between two atoms in the course of a chemical reaction.

OCTOSE. A carbohydrate which contains a chain of eight carbon atoms.

OCTYL. The radical $CH_3(CH_2)_7$—.

OCULAR. The lens system in an optical instrument in the end through which the image is viewed by the eye.

ODD-ELECTRON LINKAGE. See **linkage, singlet.**

ODD MOLECULES. A few, unusual molecules that have an odd number of valence electrons.

ODDO-FERRARI TEST REACTION FOR ALDEHYDES. A modified **Fischer Reagent for Aldehydes and Ketones** (q.v.) whereby, in acetic acid solution containing fused sodium acetate, aldehydes condense with *sym*-diphenylcarbazide to give carbazoles plus aniline.

ODOR. The volatile part of a material as perceived by smell.

ODOR CLASSIFICATION. One of a number of schemes of classification of odors in terms commonly of substances which have different and distinctive odors.

ODORIMETER. An apparatus used in measuring the intensity of odors.

ODORIMETRY. Measurement of intensity of odors.

OFFICIAL. Recognized by law; a term applied in pharmacy to preparations listed in the U.S. Pharmacopoeia or the pharmacopoeias of other nations, or the National Formulary of the United States; or of analytical methods of an organization such as the Association of Official Agricultural Chemists.

OFFICINAL. Literally "of the shops." Applied to materials which are used in medicine or in the arts. Products, preparations or substances recognized by the United States or other pharmacopoeias or the National Formulary are termed "officinal."

OFFORD REAGENT. Ammonium thiocyanate paper used in testing for chlorate. A $3N$ solution of ammonium thiocyanate is used for treating the paper. A yellow color, shown after applying the unknown solution and drying under specified conditions, indicates the presence of chlorate.

OGBURN TEST REACTIONS FOR CERTAIN PLATINUM-GROUP METALS. Iridium salts give a deep blue solution on heating with aniline sulfate.

Potassium osmate gives a dark rose color with aniline sulfate; potassium chloroosmite gives a violet solution with aniline sulfate, and a blue solution with pyrocatechol or pyrogallol.

Platinum salts give a blood-red solution with pyrocatechol or pyrogallol; ammoniacal platinum solutions give the same color with resorcinol.

Ruthenium salts give a dark violet color on boiling with phloroglucinol in an alkaline potassium nitrite solution; ruthenium salts give a blue solution on heating with allyl thiourea.

OHM. An electrical unit of **resistance.** The international ohm is the resistance offered to an unvarying current by a column of mercury at the temperature of melting ice, 14.4521 grams in mass, of a constant cross-sectional area and of a length of 106.300 centimeters.

OHM LAW. See **law of Ohm.**

-OIC. A suffix indicating a terminal —COOH group.

OIL. A liquid that is immiscible with water, feels smooth and slippery when rubbed between the fingers, is soluble in most organic solvents, and usually is composed to a considerable extent, and in some cases entirely, of the elements carbon and hydrogen. Oils are usually combustible. There are many general groups and bases of classification, some of which are described in the following entries.

OIL BATH. (1) A body of oil used to heat chemical systems and apparatus uniformly and evenly. The volume of the bath minimizes variations in the temperature and facilitates control. (2) The container for a body of oil used as described in (1).

OIL, BLOWN. An oil which has become oxidized or partially polymerized (see **polymerization**) after air has been blown through it. Blown oils are used in manufacturing paints and other products.

OIL, BOILED. Linseed oil that has been heated with **catalysts** until it has become partly oxidized. It is used in paint manufacture because it dries more rapidly and uniformly than linseed oil which has not been treated in this way.

OIL COLOR. A pigment or mixture of pigments which have been ground in oil, and which are used in a mixture with the oil in which they are ground. In use, they require solvents in which the oil is soluble.

OIL, CRUDE. Oil obtained from mineral sources, i.e., petroleum.

OIL, CUTTING. An emulsion of soap, or alkali, and oil used in cutting metals to remove the heat generated by the cutting operation.

OIL, DRYING. An oil which combines readily with atmospheric oxygen, or can do so in the presence of a suitable catalyst, and which forms a permanent, adherent film by this process, whereby it is useful as a paint ingredient to form a protective or decorative coating on surfaces.

OIL, ESSENTIAL. One of a great group of oils of plant origin, which are derived from flowers, leaves, seeds, roots, and other parts of specific plants, or in some cases from the whole plant. Thier most general characteristic is their volatility; in fact, they are often called the volatile oils. Furthermore, they possess strong, usually pleasant, odors, and are used extensively in perfumery and in the manufacture of flavors.

OIL, EXPRESSED. An oil obtained by the application of pressure to seeds or other substances containing it; commonly an oil that is volatile.

OIL, FIXED. A nonvolatile oil of animal or vegetable origin, consisting usually largely of fatty acids and certain of their esters. Fixed oils may be solid, semi-solid or liquid at ordinary atmospheric temperature.

OIL, MINERAL. Petroleum, and oils distilled from it; or, more generally, any oil obtained from inorganic or mineral sources.

OIL, NONDRYING. This term is applied to an oil that does not possess the property of taking up oxygen from the air and solidifying in the process. A nondrying oil, therefore, remains liquid on exposure to the air.

OIL, VOLATILE. See **oil, essential.**

OINTMENT. A preparation for application to the skin or certain body membranes, which consists partly or largely of oil or fat.

-OL. A suffix indicating a terminal —OH group.

-OLANE. A suffix indicating a five-membered ring.

-OLE. A suffix indicating a five-membered ring.

OLEATE. An ester or other compound of oleic acid ($C_{17}H_{33}COOH$), a straight-chain acid containing one double bond.

OLEFINE. A member of the olefine series of unsaturated aliphatic hydrocarbons of the general formula C_nH_{2n}, e.g., ethene, C_2H_4. Olefines are named from the corresponding paraffin hydrocarbons by adding the suffix "ylene" to the stem or (Geneva plan) by changing the suffix "ane" to "ene." For example, the names ethylene and ethene are derived from ethane.

-OLENE. A suffix indicating a five-membered ring.

OLEOMETER. A **hydrometer** which is graduated to read the **specific gravity** of oils, or liquids in the specific-gravity range of oils.

OLEOPTENE. An **eleoptene.**

OLEORESIN. One of a class of plant products that consist of mixtures of **resins** and volatile oils, e.g., turpentine, oleoresin of aspidium, of ginger, etc.

OLEOYL. The radical $C_{17}H_{33}CO$— (from oleic acid).

OLEUM. (1) An oil. (2) Fuming sulfuric acid.

OLFACTOMETRY. See **odorimetry.**

OLFACTY. The unit of intensity of odor; being the minimum preceptible concentration in grams per cubic centimeter.

-OLIDINE. A suffix indicating a five-membered ring.

-OLINE. A suffix indicating a five-membered ring.

OLISTOMERISM. The sequence or study of reactions in which the same reactions yield the same final product by different intermediate phases.

-OLIUM. A suffix indicating a cation (of -ole base).

OLIVER REAGENT FOR BILE ACIDS IN URINE. A solution of 8.33 g. peptone and 1.12 g. salicylic acid in 1 liter water containing 2 drops acetic acid, used in testing for bile salts in urine. A turbidity, produced under test conditions, is given by bile salts.

OLIVIER TEST REACTION FOR NITRO COMPOUNDS. Aromatic nitro compounds dissolved in benzene give an orange-yellow color with anhydrous aluminum bromide.

OMEGA (Ω OR ω). The twenty-fourth letter in the Greek alphabet, used to denote the twenty-fourth carbon atom in a straight-chain compound, or a derivative in which the substituent group is attached to the twenty-fourth carbon atom (ω-). Symbol for solid angle (ω), prefix indicating substitution in a side chain (ω). Symbol for angular frequency (ω). Symbol for angular frequency with damping (ω′). Symbol for **dispersive power** (ω). Symbol for **resonance** periodicity (ω$_r$).

OMICRON (O OR o). The fifteenth letter in the Greek alphabet, used to denote (1) the fifteenth carbon atom in a straight-chain compound, or a derivative in which a substituent group is attached to that carbon atom.

-ONANE. A suffix indicating a nine-membered ring.

-ONE. A suffix indicating a **ketone.** (See also **alkone.**)

-ONIN. A suffix indicating a nine-membered ring.

-ONINE. A suffix indicating a nine-membered ring.

-ONIUM. A suffix indicating a cation.

ONIUM REACTION. See **reaction, onium.**

ONSAGER EQUATION. An equation expressing the relation between the measured equivalent **conductance** at a particular concentration to that at infinite dilution. It was based on the calculations of **Debye and Hückel.**

OPACIFIER. Any substance used to render transparent or translucent substances opaque.

OPACITY. Imperviousness to radiation, especially to light; the property of stopping the passage of light rays.

OPALESCENCE, CRITICAL. See **critical opalescence.**

OPEN-HEARTH PROCESS. A method of manufacturing steel in a shallow reverberatory furnace (lined with acidic or basic refractories that may combine with impurities in the metal), in which the charge of pig iron, scrap steel, and various fluxes, oxidizing substances, etc., is heated by combustion of gas above the surface of the charge.

OPL TOWER PROCESS. A process for the production of sulfuric acid by the **chamber process** in which the conversion of the SO_2 to H_2SO_4 takes place in packed towers, instead of lead chambers.

OPPENAUER REACTION. Oxidation of a secondary alcohol to the corresponding ketone by a lower aliphatic ketone, in the presence of aluminum tertiary-butoxide.

$$RR'CHOH + (CH_3)_2CO \xrightarrow{Al(OC(CH_3)_3)_3} RR'CO + (CH_3)_2CHOH.$$

OPPENHEIMER-PHILLIPS MECHANISM. An explanation of the role of deuterons in nuclear bombardment reactions, whereby the deuteron is thought of as behaving as a relatively loose combination of a neutron and a proton, since the binding energy is comparatively small. When the energy of the incident deuteron exceeds this binding energy, the proton portion will break off and be repelled, and the neutron will then enter the target nucleus.

OPPOSING REACTIONS. See **reactions, opposing.**

OPSONIC INDEX. The ratio between the number of bacteria destroyed by the **leucocytes** in a certain sample of blood and the number destroyed in a normal sample.

OPTICAL ACTIVITY. The power of a substance to rotate the plane of **polarized light** transmitted through it.

OPTICAL ANOMALY. The behavior of certain organic compounds, such as those whose molecules contain conjugated **double bonds,** in which the observed values of the **molar refraction** are not in accord with the values calculated from the known equivalents. When the observed values are higher than the calculated values, the substance is said to exhibit **optical exaltation.**

OPTICAL ANTIPODES. Two compounds composed of the same atoms and atomic **linkages,** which differ in their structural formulas only in that one is the mirror image of the other. The term is commonly applied to substances containing an asymmetric atom, or bond, in which the plane of polarized light is rotated to the right by one of the **optical antipodes,** and to the left by the other.

OPTICAL DENSITY. The negative logarithm of the relative transmittance of a photographic emulsion. $D = -\log_{10} T$, where D is the optical density and T is the relative **transmittance** (q.v.).

OPTICAL ELECTRON. See **valence electron.**

OPTICAL EXALTATION. The phenomenom whereby a compound possesses a **refraction** different from the value calculated from the various equivalents of the atoms and other structural units of which it is composed. This property is more strictly called optical anomaly, but since in most cases the difference is positive, i.e., the observed value exceeds the calculated one, the term exaltation is used.

OPTICAL ISOMERISM. The difference in **optical activity** among the isomers of compounds having asymmetric atoms or bonds.

OPTICAL ISOMERS. Two or more compounds which have the same chemical composition and the same two-dimensional structural formulas, but which differ in the spatial arrangement of the atoms or groups about one or more asymmetric atoms or bonds that are present, so that the plane of **polarized light** is rotated in a different direction (left or right) or to a different amount (if the substance has more than two optical isomers).

OPTICAL ROTATORY POWER. The ability of a substance to rotate the plane of **polarized light.**

OPTICAL SUPERPOSITION, PRINCIPLE OF. Van't Hoff's assumption that the optical **rotation** of a compound composed of two oppositely optically active radicals is the algebraic sum of the separate rotations of each radical. It does not hold in all cases.

OPTICALLY VOID LIQUIDS. Liquids that do not exhibit the **Tyndall effect,** e.g., liquids that contain no suspended solids.

-OR. A suffix meaning a device. For example, comparator, reflector, generator, and capacitor. (Other suffixes used to denote devices are -er, as in amplifier, and -ment, as in filament.)

ORBIT, ELECTRONIC. See **atomic structure.**

ORBITAL ELECTRON. See **electron, orbital.**

ORBITAL, MOLECULAR. See **molecular orbital.**

ORDER-DISORDER TRANSFORMATION. See **transformation, order-disorder.**

ORDER OF COMPOUNDS. One of a number of groups into which compounds may be classified by one or more of their structural properties, or modes of behavior. Thus, compounds may be classified into various orders based upon the number and arrangement of the atomic species they contain, or by their analytical reactions.

ORDER OF REACTION. See **reaction order.**

ORE. A mineral or combination of minerals found in nature, usually mixed with other substances.

ORFORD PROCESS. A method of separating copper and nickel based upon the settling out of Ni_3S_2 on cooling a mixture of the molten sulfides of nickel, copper, and sodium. Because the nickel is thus concentrated in the bottom of the chamber, and the copper in the top, the process is also called the "Top-and-Bottom" process.

ORGAN. Any part of an organism performing some definite function.

ORGANIC. (1) Pertaining to or derived from a carbon compound. (2) A product of a biochemical process.

ORGANIC ACID. A compound containing a carboxyl radical $\left[-C \diagup\diagdown \begin{matrix} O-H \\ O \end{matrix} \right]$.

ORGANIC BASE. An organic compound that has an alkaline reaction and often forms addition compounds with mineral acids. The chief organic bases are the **amines** and other compounds containing nitrogen atoms with readily-replaceable hydrogen atoms attached to them.

ORGANIC CHEMISTRY. See **chemistry, organic.**

ORGANIC COMPOUND. See **compound, organic.**

ORGANIC RADICAL. See **radical, organic.**

ORGANIZED FERMENTS. (Intracellular ferments) **Ferments** characterized by connection with living cells, as yeast. Formerly, organized and unorganized ferments were believed to have specific differences. This is known to be untrue, although certain fermentations are not known to take place in the absence of living matter.

ORGANOGEN. Any one of the four elements, carbon, hydrogen, nitrogen, and oxygen, and, by extension, sulfur, phosphorus, and chlorine, characteristic of organic products.

ORGANOLEPTIC. A property which may be perceived by a sense organ, as taste, odor, or color.

ORGANOMETALLIC COMPOUND. See **compound, organometallic.**

ORGANOSOL. A colloidal solution in which the continuous phase is an organic solvent such as alcohol, benzene, ether, amyl alcohol, pentane, etc.

ORIENTATION. From its general meaning of the assumption of a definite position with regard to existing points of reference, this term has acquired a number of specific uses in chemistry. It was applied first to denote the positions assumed by substituents in relation to the configuration of the parent substance and to each other. The term was then applied to the position assumed by a free particle in a field of force or other constraint, as the orientation of fatty-acid molecules in the surface of a polar solvent. The term orientation was also applied to the method of determination of the axial ratios of crystals, by assuming certain axes, and orienting the crystal faces with respect to them.

ORIENTATION EFFECT. A basis of calculating the attractive forces between molecules, or a component of such forces, from the interaction energy of molecular **dipoles** due to their relative orientation.

ORIENTATION, SURFACE. See **surface orientation.**

ORIFICE MIXER. See **mixer, orifice.**

ORLOSO TEST REACTION FOR PHENOLS. An aqueous solution of ceric sulfate gives a red color with phenol; brown with phloroglucinol; orange with pyrogallol; and other colors with other phenolic compounds.

ORLOW-HORST REACTION FOR AL-KALOIDS. A solution of ammonium persulfate in sulfuric acid gives characteristic color reactions with many alkaloids.

ORLOW-ORMONT REAGENT FOR MERCURY. A solution of 10 g. cobalt nitrate and 10 g. potassium thiocyanate in 30 ml. water. Two ml. of a dilute mercuric chloride solution, with 2 ml. of the reagent and 2 ml. concentrated nitric acid, give a blue ring or precipitate.

ORLOW TEST REACTION FOR RUTHENIUM. The element is converted to the tetroxide, which in its vapor phase blackens paper.

ORNITHYL. The radical

$$H_2NCH_2CH_2CH_2CH(NH_2)CO—.$$

ORSAT APPARATUS. A commonly-used apparatus for the analysis of gases, usually flue gases, to check combustion efficiency. It consists of a measuring burette provided with a leveling bottle and connected to a number of small glass chambers containing solutions for absorbing various gases.

ORTH FLUID. A solution of 4–10 ml. formaldehyde, 1.0 g. sodium sulfate, and 2.5 g. potassium dichromate in 100 ml. water, used as a fixative.

ORTHO-. (Greek, *straight, right, true*) A prefix meaning or designating: (1) the fully hydrated form of an acid, as, orthonitric acid, H_5NO_5; (2) sometimes, the highest-hydrated stable form, as orthophosphoric acid, H_3PO_4; (3) the common or symmetrical molecular form of an element, as ortho-hydrogen; (4) the group or system of terms in the spectrum of helium that is due to atoms in which the spin of the two electrons are parallel to each other; (5) the relation of the 1 and 2 positions in benzene, or a compound characterized by it, as ortho-xylene. Abbreviation (in this last sense) *o*, as *o*-xylene.

ORTHOANTIMONIC. Related to ortho-antimonic acid, H_3SbO_4.

ORTHOBARIC DENSITIES. The density of a liquid and of the saturated vapor in **equilibrium** with it at any temperature.

ORTHOCARBONATE. The anion CO_4^{4-}, or a compound containing it.

ORTHOHELIUM. One group or system of terms in the spectrum of helium that is due to atoms in which the spin of the two electrons are parallel to each other. Another group of spectral terms, the par-helium terms, is given by those helium atoms whose electrons have opposing spins.

ORTHOHYDROGEN. See **hydrogen, ortho.**

ORTHOPHOSPHORIC. Related to orthophosphoric acid, H_3PO_4.

ORTHOPHOSPHOROUS. Related to orthophosphorous acid, H_3PO_3.

ORTHOQUINOID GROUP. The atomic structure,

an important **chromophore.**

ORTHORHOMBIC SYSTEM. One of the seven fundamental systems of **crystallography;** in this system the axes are of unequal length, and intersect at right angles.

ORTHOSILICIC. Related to orthosilicic acid, H_4SiO_4.

ORTHO-STATE. (1) In diatomic molecules, such as hydrogen molecules, the ortho-state exists when the spin vectors of the two atomic nuclei are in the same direction (i.e., parallel), whereas the **para-state** is the one in which the nuclei are spinning in opposite directions. (2) In helium the ortho-state is characterized by a particular mode of coupling of the electron spins. (See **orthohelium.**)

ORTHOTITANIC. Related to orthotitanic acid, H_4TiO_4.

ORTODOSCU-RESSY MICRO-TEST FOR ANTIMONY AND TIN. The hydrochloric acid solution of antimony or tin is placed on a microscope slide, and the edge of the drop touched with a drop of 1.7% sodium chloride solution. Tin forms six-pointed stars, antimony four-pointed stars.

Os Symbol for the element **osmium.**

-OSAN. A suffix indicating a polysaccharide. (See **carbohydrate.**)

OSAZONE. A diphenylhydrazone. Osazones are often prepared because their crystalline forms and melting points aid in the identification of sugars. The reaction with phenylhydrazine involves the reaction of one molecule of the latter with a carbonyl group to form a phenylhydrazone, followed by oxidation with another molecule of phenylhydrazine of a —CHOH— group that was in the α-position to the carbonyl group, and then the reaction of a third molecule of phenylhydrazine with the carbonyl group formed by the oxidation. A typical osazone is glucosazone,

$$CH_2OH$$
$$|$$
$$(CHOH)_3$$
$$|$$
$$C{=}N{-}NH.C_6H_5$$
$$|$$
$$CH{=}N{-}NH.C_6H_5.$$

OSCILLATING DOUBLE BOND. See **tautomerism** and **phasotropy.**

-OSE. A suffix indicating a **carbohydrate** (specifically, a sugar).

-OSIDE. A suffix indicating a **glycoside.**

OSMATE (VI). The anion $OsO_4^{=}$, or a compound containing it.

OSMIC. Pertaining to or containing tetravalent **osmium.**

OSMIUM. Metallic element. Symbol Os. Atomic number 76. Atomic weight 190.2. Density 22.48. Specific heat 0.0311. Melting point 2700° C. Boiling point 5500° C. Valence 2, 3, 4, 5, 6, and 8. Oxides, OsO, Os_2O_3, OsO_2, OsO_4. Osmic acid, H_2OsO_4. Osmium occurs in platinum ores.

OSMOMETER. An instrument used to measure **osmotic pressure.**

OSMOPHOR. A group or radical that imparts odor to a compound, as a chromophore imparts color.

OSMOSIS. The passage of a fluid through a semipermeable membrane, due to **osmotic pressure.**

OSMOTIC COEFFICIENT. A factor introduced into equations for nonideal solutions to correct for their departure from ideal behavior, as in the equation:

$$\mu = \mu_x^0 + gRT \log_e X_1,$$

in which μ is the **chemical potential,** μ_x^0 is a constant, representing a standard value of the chemical potential, R is the **gas constant,** T the absolute temperature, X_1 is the **mole fraction** of solvent, and g is the osmotic coefficient.

OSMOTIC PRESSURE. Pressure that develops when a pure solvent is separated from a solution by a semipermeable membrane which allows only the solvent molecules to pass through it.

OSMOUS. Pertaining to or containing trivalent **osmium.**

OSMYL. The radical $OsO_4^{=}$.

OSONE. An α-ketone aldehyde, as for example

$$CH_2OH{-}CHOH{-}CHOH{-}CHOH{-}CO{-}CHO,$$

which is the osone formed by reduction of phenylglycosazone.

OSTROMISSLENSKY TEST REACTION FOR ETHYLENE COMPOUNDS. Ethylene compounds in neutral or acid solution give yellow, orange-yellow, or brown colors with tetranitro-methane.

OSTROMYSLENSKII REACTION. The direct condensation of alcohols and aldehydes to form diene hydrocarbons. Elevated temperatures and catalysts are required.

$$CH_3CHO + CH_3CH_2OH \xrightarrow[-2H_2O]{\Delta} CH_2{:}CH.CH{:}CH_2.$$

OSTWALD-FOLIN PIPETTE. See pipette, Ostwald-Folin.

OSTWALD LAW. See law of Ostwald.

OSTWALD PIPETTE. See **pipette, Ostwald.**

OSTWALD PROCESS. A method for the preparation of nitric acid from ammonia by its oxidation successively to nitric oxide, nitrogen dioxide, and finally nitric acid, using elevated temperatures and platinum gauze as a catalyst.

OSTWALD RULE. When a substance can exist in more than one form, reactions for its production usually yield the least stable modification, which subsequently undergoes a process of transformation until the most stable form is reached.

OSWALD THEORY OF INDICATORS. Indicators are weak acids or bases, in which the ion differs in color from the molecule.

OSZACKI REAGENT. A solution of 1.5 g. uranyl acetate in 100 ml. water, used to de-albuminate blood serum.

OTHMER PROCESS. A process for the production of pure acetic acid from crude pyroligneous acid; the crude liquor is distilled, and the vapor is passed through purifying columns, in which the methanol, acetone, tar, and other components are removed by absorption, adsorption, or solution. The vapors of acetic acid and water then pass to condensers.

OTTO COKE OVEN. A by-product coke oven for the production of coke by the regenerative heating and distillation of coal.

OUNCE. A unit of mass in the avoirdupois, apothecaries', and troy systems. The apothecaries' and troy ounces are identical.

1 avoirdupois ounce = 28.3495 grams
1 avoirdupois ounce = 437.5 grains
1 troy or apothe-
   caries' ounce   = 31.1035 grams
1 troy or apothe-
   caries' ounce   = 480 grains

OUNCE, FLUID. A unit of liquid measure in the English system.

1 U.S. fluid
   ounce   = 29.5729 milliliters
1 milliliter = 0.033815 U.S. fluid ounce

OVER-ALL PLATE EFFICIENCY. See **plate efficiency, over-all.**

OVERBECK TEST FOR COTTON. To detect cotton in wool, saturate the material three times with a solution of alloxanthine, drying each time, then place in dry ammonia gas. Wool fibers are colored red, fast to water, and cotton is not colored.

OVERCOOLING. See **supercooling.**

OVERHEATING. Raising the temperature of a liquid above its boiling point. Drops of water in oil may be overheated to 140° C. at atmospheric pressure without vaporizing.

OVERSATURATED. See **supersaturated.**

OVERVOLTAGE. See **excess voltage.**

OVERVOLTAGE, COUNTER. See **counter overvoltage.**

OXACID. See **oxyacid.**

OXALATE. The anions $C_2O_4^=$, $HC_2O_4^-$, or a compound containing one of these anions.

OXALATOALUMINATE. The anion $Al(C_2O_4)_3^{3-}$ or $Al(C_2O_4)_2^-$, or a compound containing one of these anions.

OXALATOCHROMATE (III). The anion $Cr(C_2O_4)_3^{3-}$, or a compound containing it.

OXALATOCOBALTATE (III). The anion $Co(C_2O_4)_3{}^{3-}$, or a compound containing it.

OXALATOFERRATE (II). The anion $Fe(C_2O_4)_2{}^{=}$, or a compound containing it.

OXALATOFERRATE (III). The anion $Fe(C_2O_4)_3{}^{3-}$ or $Fe_2(C_2O_4)_6{}^{6-}$, or a compound containing one of these anions.

OXALATOIRIDATE (III). The anion $Ir(C_2O_4)_3{}^{3-}$, or a compound containing it.

OXALATONICKELATE (II). The anion $Ni(C_2O_4)_2{}^{=}$, or a compound containing it.

OXALATOPALLADATE (II). The anion $Pd(C_2O_4)_2{}^{=}$, or a compound containing it.

OXALATOPLATINATE (II). The anion $Pt(C_2O_4)_2{}^{=}$, or a compound containing it.

OXALENE. The radical $-N:\overset{|}{C}-\overset{|}{C}:N-$.

OXALIC. (1) Related to oxalic acid, COOH.COOH. (2) Related to a group of acids of type-formula, $C_nH_{2n}(COOH)_2$.

OXALIC ACID SERIES OR OXALATE SERIES. A series of organic acids or their salts, of the general formula $C_nH_{2n-2}O_4$, having two carboxy groups (or their salts), one at each end of the molecule.

OXALYL. The radical $-OCCO-$ (from oxalic acid).

OXAMIDO. The radical $H_2NCOCONH-$.

OXAMINIC. Related to oxaminic acid, $NH_2.CO.COOH$.

OXAMYL. The radical $H_2NCOCO-$.

OXAZINE. One of a number of unsaturated 6-membered, ring compounds, containing one oxygen atom, one nitrogen atom, and four carbon atoms in the ring, and having the formula, C_4H_5ON.

OXAZOLE (C_3H_3ON). An unsaturated 5-membered ring compound, containing one oxygen atom, one nitrogen atom, and three carbon atoms in the ring.

OXAZOLYL. The radical C_3H_2NO- (from oxazole).

OXFORD PROCESS. A metallurgical process for the removal of copper from nickel by formation of the insoluble sulfide.

OXIDASE. One of the **enzymes** which catalyze the oxidation of many substances by free oxygen, e.g., tyrosinase, lactase, uricolase. Cf. **peroxidase.**

OXIDATION. In its original use, oxidation meant simply combination with oxygen. Its use has, however, been considerably widened to cover a great many processes similar to oxidation, such as chlorination, and other processes of combination with strongly nonmetallic elements, which add electrons readily. In fact, the term oxidation in its broadest sense means simply a chemical reaction whereby electrons are removed from one or more of the atoms of a substance. It is, of course, most frequently accompanied by a simultaneous process, in the same reaction, whereby another substance or substances gain the electrons and thus undergo reduction; therefore, calling the process oxidation, under these circumstances, simply means that it is this part (i.e., loss of electrons) of the particular process that is of greatest interest.

OXIDATION AND REDUCTION CELL. See **cell, oxidation and reduction.**

OXIDATION, FRACTIONAL. The separation of the components of a mixture by oxidizing under such conditions that only a part of the components are affected. Cf. **combustion, fractional.**

OXIDATION-REDUCTION INDICATOR. See **indicator, oxidation-reduction.**

OXIDATION-REDUCTION REACTION. See **reaction, electron-transfer.**

OXIDATION STATE. See **valence number.**

OXIDE. A binary compound of **oxygen.**

OXIDE, ACID. An oxide that forms an **acid** on combination with water.

OXIDE, AMPHOTERIC. An oxide that forms either a **base** or an **acid,** depending on the conditions, on combination with water.

OXIDE, BASIC. An oxide that forms a **base** on combination with water.

OXIDE, INERT. An oxide that forms neither a base nor an acid on combination with water.

OXIDIMETRY. An analysis, or method of analysis, based upon a **titration** with a solution of an oxidizing agent.

OXIDIZING AGENT. A substance that readily enters into chemical reactions by which it gains electrons; or, more specifically, a substance that readily yields oxygen to other substances, or reacts so that hydrogen is removed from them.

OXIDIZING FLAME. See **flame, oxidizing.**

OXIDIZING REACTION. See **oxidation** and **reaction, electron-transfer.**

OXIME. One of a number of compounds that result from the interaction of **aldehydes, ketones,** and other **carbonyl**-containing substances with hydroxylamine, e.g., acetone yields acetoxime

$$\begin{matrix} CH_3 \\ \quad \\ CH_3 \end{matrix}\!\!\!>\!C\!\!=\!\!O + H_2NOH \rightarrow \begin{matrix} CH_3 \\ \quad \\ CH_3 \end{matrix}\!\!\!>\!C\!\!=\!\!NOH + H_2O.$$

OXIMIDO. See **isonitroso.**

OXIRANE. The radical $-\!\overset{|}{C}\!-\!-\!\overset{|}{C}\!-$.

$\qquad\qquad\qquad\qquad\qquad \underset{O}{\diagdown\!\diagup}$

OXO. The radical $O\!\!=$ in organic compounds (both valence bonds joined to same atom).

OXONIUM COMPOUNDS. Coordination compounds, commonly of certain oxygen-containing organic substances, with mineral acids, of the general type

$$[R_2O]HCl.$$

They bear a strong resemblance to the "oxonium ion," H_3O+, which is a proton, in combination with an H_2O molecule, and is the form in which protons commonly exist in aqueous solutions.

OXOZONIDE. A compound containing the group $O\!\!=\!\!\overset{|}{O}\!-\!\overset{|}{O}\!\!=\!\!O$, which usually adds to an unsaturated organic compound at a double bond.

OXY. The radical $-O-$ in organic compounds (used as a connective; cf. **epoxy** and **oxo**).

OXYACID. An acid that contains oxygen, as chloric acid, $HClO_3$.

OXYAZO COMPOUNDS. Compounds of the type $RN\!\!=\!\!NC_6H_4OH$, containing both the **azo group** $-N\!\!=\!\!N-$, and the oxy group **(hydroxy group)** $-OH$, both attached to carbon atoms in the same ring. These compounds are commonly produced by the action of diazo compounds upon phenols in alkaline solution. They constitute a class of dyes.

OXYBENZOIC. Related to oxybenzoic acid, $HO.C_6H_4.COOH$.

OXYGEN. Gaseous element. Symbol O. Atomic number 8. Atomic weight 16.0000. Melting point $-218.4°$ C. Boiling point $-182.96°$ C. Density 1.429 (grams per liter at standard temperature and pressure). Density of liquid 1.14 at $-183°$ C. Density of solid 1.426 at $-252.5°$ C. An allotropic form of oxygen is ozone, which has a molecular weight of 48, corresponding to the formula O_3. It is highly reactive and has a density of 3.03 grams per liter at $-80°$ C. Oxygen occurs in air (about 20%), in oxides, etc. Valence 2.

OXYGEN ACID. An acid which contains **oxygen.**

OXYGEN TEST, ACTIVE. The volume of iodine liberated from an acidic solution of potassium iodide by an oil or fat. This test is used as an approximate measure of degree of **rancidity.**

OXYGENATE. (1) To impregnate with oxygen. (2) To **oxidize.**

OXYGENATION. (1) Impregnation with oxygen. (2) **Oxidation.**

OXYGENATOR. An apparatus for impregnating a liquid with oxygen.

OXYGENIC. Pertaining to or containing **oxygen.**

OXYGENIZABLE. Oxidizable.

OXYHYDROGEN. Employing or produced by a mixture of oxygen and hydrogen, as the oxyhydrogen blowpipe or oxyhydrogen flame.

OXYHYDROGEN BLOWPIPE. An apparatus for burning hydrogen and oxygen together at one jet. The combustion furnishes an intensely hot flame, so that platinum and the most refractory metals may be melted by it.

OXYHYDROGEN WELDING. Welding accomplished by the use of an oxyhydrogen torch which consists of a pair of tubes, to which oxygen and hydrogen are supplied in proper proportions to produce water by combustion. Temperatures as high as 2500° C. may be obtained.

-OYL. A suffix indicating an organic acid radical.

OZONATION. Impregnating or combining with ozone.

OZONE. Allotropic form of **oxygen.**

OZONIDE. A compound of ozone with certain unsaturated organic compounds produced by direct addition of ozone to the double bond, e.g.,

OZONIZE. To impregnate with ozone, as in a process for purifying water.

P. Symbol for phosphorus (P). Abbreviation for pressure (P or p), (pressure at constant volume P_v; pressure at constant temperature P_T). Abbreviation for power (P). Symbol for **principal series** of spectrum lines (p). Abbreviation for para, when that prefix is used to designate the relation of the 1 and 4 positions in benzene, or a compound characterized by it, as paraxylene (p-). Symbol for **parachor** (p). Abbreviation for **potential** (p). Symbol for **electric moment (p).** Symbol for momentum, generalized (p). **Electric polarization (P).** Partial potential coefficient (p). The abbreviation p is also used for para when that prefix is used to designate the **para-state** of an element, as p-H. Abbreviation for **parhelium** (p-He). See also **pi, phi** and **psi.**

P-ELECTRON. An electron having an orbit of such dimensions that the electron constitutes part of the sixth shell of electrons surrounding the atomic nucleus, counting out from the nucleus (i.e., the K-shell is the first; the L-, the second; the M-, the third; the N-, the fourth; the O-, the fifth; and the P-shell, the sixth).

P-SHELL. The collections of electrons characterized by the **principal quantum number** six. The P-shell is started with the element cesium (atomic number = 55), which has one electron in its P-shell, and the P-shell is not completed, as far as is known, even with the transuranic element californium (atomic number = 98). Many of the elements in the progression from cesium upward differ in an increment of electrons in the N-shell, or the O-shell, or the Q-shell.

Pa Symbol for the element **protactinium.**

PAAL-KNORR PYRROLE SYNTHESIS. A method of formation of pyrrole deriva-

$$R—CH=CH—R + O_3 \rightarrow R—\overset{\overset{\displaystyle H}{\displaystyle |}}{C}—O—O—O—\overset{\overset{\displaystyle H}{\displaystyle |}}{C}—R.$$

tives from 1,4-dicarbonyl compounds and amines (or ammonia).

0.1% aqueous solution of cupric sulfate, gives a blue color with cyanides.

$$\begin{matrix} RCO & COR' \\ | & | \\ CH_2 & CH_2 \end{matrix} + NH_2R'' \xrightarrow{-2H_2O} \qquad .$$

PACHUCA TANK. An apparatus for agitation of suspensions of solids (especially ores) in liquids. It consists of a vertical cylindrical tank, with an internal air lift placed on its axis.

PACINI-TARAS TEST FOR VITAMIN A IN OILS. One drop of the oil is treated with 1 drop guaiacol, 2 drops phenol, and 1 ml. of perchloric acid in 5 ml. chloroform. A purple color, changing to red, indicates the presence of vitamin A.

PACKING. The gathering or compression of material or material particles into a relatively confined space.

PACKING, ATOMIC. The compression of atoms into small space, such as one smaller than that required by considering their effective radii.

PACKING EFFECT. A difference between the observed mass of a nucleus and that calculated by adding the masses of the constituent elementary particles. (See **packing fraction.**)

PACKING FRACTION. An expression of the fraction by which the **atomic weight** of an **isotope** differs from its mass number (defined as the nearest whole number). The actual value of the packing fraction is found by dividing the difference between the isotopic atomic weight and mass number by the mass number, and multiplying by 10,000.

PACKING, NUCLEAR. The concentration of particles within the **nucleus** of an **atom.**

PAGENSTECHER-SCHÖNBEIN CYANIDE PAPER. Filter paper treated with guaiac tincture and, after drying, with a

PAGET-BERGER TEST. A test for oxalate in which 5 ml. of a solution believed to contain 0.01% oxalate is heated to boiling with zinc and 0.5 ml. concentrated hydrochloric acid. After standing 3 minutes it is decanted, and 5 drops 1% phenylhydrazine hydrochloric acid solution added. It is heated nearly to boiling and cooled. Then an equal volume concentrated hydrochloric acid and 5 drops 5% potassium ferricyanide solution are added. A bright-red color develops with oxalate. Iron interferes and requires the substitution of hydrogen peroxide or other oxidants for the potassium ferricyanide.

PAINT. A preparation for coating surfaces, for protection, decoration, etc., consisting commonly of finely ground particles of a solid substance or substances, chosen for their stability, color, and opacity, plus an oil or other substance which dries or oxidizes to form an adherent film; usually in the presence of ingredients such as solvents, driers, etc.

PAINT DRIER. See **drier, paint.**

PAINT REMOVER. A mixture of solvents and waxes, or other materials, used to remove paint, lacquer, and varnish finishes from a surface.

PAINT, WATER. A mixture of pigment with glue, casein, or other substances capable of forming with water a suspension which may be applied evenly to a surface.

PAIRED ELECTRON. See **electron, paired.**

PALLADIC. Containing or pertaining to tetravalent **palladium.**

PALLADIOUS. Containing or pertaining to divalent **palladium.**

PALLADIUM. Metallic element. Symbol Pd. Atomic number 46. Atomic weight 106.7. Density reported values range from 11.4 to 12.0. Specific heat 0.0586. Melting point 1555° C. Boiling point about 2200° C. Valences 2 and 4. Palladium occurs in platinum ores. Oxides PdO, Pd_2O.

PALLADOUS. Containing or pertaining to divalent **palladium.**

PALM REAGENT FOR ALKALOIDS A solution of lead chloride used as a precipitant for alkaloids.

PALMITIC. Related to palmitic acid, $C_{15}H_{31}COOH$.

PALMITOYL. The radical

$$CH_3(CH_2)_{14}CO—$$

(from palmitic acid).

PAMFIL-WONNESCH REAGENT. A solution of 14.3 g. freshly precipitated silver chloride in 300 ml. of a cold saturated solution of hexamethylenetetramine, 300 ml. of a cold, saturated aqueous solution of sodium chloride, and sufficient ammonium hydroxide for complete solution. The volume is made up with water to 1 liter, and the reagent is used for the determination of bromide and iodide.

PANASYNK SOLUTION. A solution of 35.4 g. ferrous sulfate in 120 ml. water, to which are added 10 g. tartaric acid and 45 ml. 25% ammonia. This solution is used as an absorbent for oxygen.

PANETH RULE. Adsorption of radio-elements is promoted by formation of an insoluble compound with the adsorbing substance, especially when the radio-element is present in a negative radical.

PANETH TECHNIQUE. A method for observing the action of **free radicals** or atoms of short life by using them to remove a metallic "mirror" by passing them over its surface. The metallic compounds can be analyzed.

PANTACHROMISM. The phenomenon of existing in two or more differently colored varieties. For example, salts of diphenylvioluric acid exhibit pantochromism.

PAPAFIL-CERNATESCO REAGENT. A solution of 1.5 g. tetramethyldiaminodiphenylmethane in 300 ml. water containing 10 ml. glacial acetic acid. The solution is filtered, and dilute ammonium hydroxide added drop-by-drop until an opalescence appears, at which time it is filtered again. This reagent gives a blue precipitate with molybdate solutions, a yellow precipitate turning green with a neutral vanadate solution. (For this vanadate test, the pH of the reagent should be about 3.5.)

PAR-. See **para-.**

PARA-. A prefix used to distinguish between isomers or nearly related compounds. Specifically, (1) in organic chemistry the derivatives of cyclic nuclei which contain substituents in the 1–4 position; (2) some polymers are designated by the prefix para-, as paraldehyde; (3) in certain acids which have several forms differing in water content, one of the forms may be designated by the prefix para-; and, more recently, (4) the prefix has been used to designate, in the case of gaseous elements having diatomic molecules, the form in which nuclei have anti-parallel spins, as distinguished from the **ortho-state,** in which the two nuclei have parallel spins. Para-molecules have even rotational levels in the ground state, whereas ortho-molecules have odd rotational levels. The two states are present in varying proportions, depending on the temperature, as exemplified by ortho- and para-states of hydrogen. (5) However in helium the ortho- and para-states are characterized by a particular mode of coupling of electron spins. See **parhelium** and **orthohelium.**

PARACHOR. A constant relationship, for a given substance, between **surface tension** and **density.** This relationship is of the form

$$[P] = \frac{M\sqrt[4]{\gamma}}{\rho_l - \rho_g}$$

in which $[P]$ is the parachor; M is the molecular weight; γ is the surface tension of the substance, in liquid form, at a given temperature; and ρ_l and ρ_g are the densities of the liquid and vapor at that same temperature.

From the formula above, it follows that the parachor of a substance is proportional to its molecular volume, an additive property.

PARAFFIN. A member of an homologous series of saturated aliphatic **hydrocarbons** of the general formula C_nH_{2n+2}. The first member is methane, CH_4. The lower members of the paraffin series are gases, those which contain 5 to 17 carbon atoms are liquid at 20° C., and the higher members are colorless solids. Most of the paraffins occur in petroleum. They are designated by the suffix "ane," and all but the first four members of the series are named from the Greek numerals corresponding to their straight-chain carbon content. The names of the first six members of the series are methane, ethane, propane, butane, pentane, and hexane.

PARAFFIN, ISO. A member of the paraffin series containing one side chain.

PARAFFIN, NEO. A member of the paraffin series containing a dimethylated carbon bonded to two other carbon atoms.

PARAFFIN, NORMAL. A member of the paraffin series having all its carbon atoms arranged in a single, straight chain.

PARAFLOW. A substance or mixture of substances added to lubricating oils to delay or inhibit the crystallization of solid paraffins.

PARAHYDROGEN. See **hydrogen, para.**

PARALLAX. The difference between the actual position of an object and its observed position, due to the position of the observer. An important consideration in obtaining correct readings of the position of indicator needles, levels of liquids measured against scales, etc.

PARALLELOSTERISM. A relationship between **analogous** and **isomorphous groups**

in which similar differences in chemical composition occur with similar differences in **molecular volume.** Thus the difference in the molar volumes of KCl and KBr is 6.9, between NaCl and NaBr, 6.7, and between AgCl and AgBr, 6.2.

PARALYZER. A name sometimes used for a catalytic poison.

PARAMAGNETIC. Offering less resistance to the passage of magnetic flux than does air, and hence capable of being attracted by a magnet. Paramagnetic substances have, in other words, **magnetic permeabilities** greater than 1.

PARAMAGNETIC ELEMENT. An element having a **magnetic moment** greater than unity, which is the value for air.

PARAMORPH. One of two or more forms of a substance which have the same chemical composition but differ in certain properties.

PARAQUINOID GROUP OR STRUCTURE. See **quinoid.**

PARASEMIDINE. See **semidine rearrangement.**

PARASITIC. Growing on and deriving nourishment from another organism.

PARASITICIDE. A substance which kills parisitic organisms.

PARA-STATE. (1) In diatomic molecules, such as hydrogen molecules, the para-state exists when the spin vectors of the two atomic nuclei are in opposite (i.e., antiparallel) directions, whereas the ortho-state is the one in which the nuclei are spinning in the same direction. (2) In helium, the para-state is a state characterized by a particular mode of coupling of the electron spins. (See **parhelium.**)

PARATARTARICS. **Racemic** forms (Pasteur).

PARHELIUM. One group or system of terms in the spectrum of helium that is due to atoms in which the **spin** of the two electrons are opposing each other. Another group of spectral terms, the **orthohelium**

terms, is given by those helium atoms whose two electrons have parallel spins.

PARKE PROCESS. A process for the separation of silver from lead. This process is used extensively in the recovery of silver in the refining of argentiferous lead ores. The process is based on the fact that silver is far more soluble in zinc than in lead, whereas zinc is but very slightly soluble in molten lead. Zinc is added to the silver-containing molten lead, thoroughly mixed, and allowed to stand, whereupon the zinc containing the silver floats to the surface of the molten lead, and is separated. Later the silver is separated from the zinc-silver by distilling off the zinc.

PARKES REAGENT. A solution of 10 g. butyric acid and 2 ml. water in 90 g. glacial acetic acid, used in testing for artificial dyes in fats. On acidification with dilute sulfuric acid, this reagent extracts the dye from the fat.

PARR APPARATUS. A calorimeter used for determining the calorific value of solid fuels, together with means for analysis of substances produced by the combustion.

PARRI ALCOHOL REAGENT. A solution of 3 g. phosphomolybdic acid and 0.3 g. ammonium vanadate in 100 ml. concentrated sulfuric acid, used in testing for the alcoholic hydroxy group. Various color reactions are obtained, as, for example, blue with the monohydric alcohols (except methanol).

PARRI TEST REACTION FOR ALKALOIDS. A solution of sodium cobaltinitrite gives yellow to chestnut-brown precipitates with alkaloids.

PARRI TEST REACTIONS FOR CINNAMIC, SUCCINIC, AND MALIC ACIDS. With Parri's phosphomolybdate-vanadate (see **Parri alcohol reagent**), characteristic color reactions are obtained with cold and hot solutions of cinnamic, succinic, and malic acids.

PARRI TEST REACTION FOR PHENOLS. On addition of an alcoholic solution of a phenol with a few drops concentrated sulfuric acid containing 0.5% ammonium vanadate, characteristic colors are produced, which give other colors, characteristic of the various phenols, on dilution with water, and again upon addition of sodium hydroxide solution.

PARRI REAGENT FOR METALS. A solution of ammonium dithiocarbamate prepared by warming 35 ml. concentrated ammonium hydroxide solution with 10 ml. carbon disulfide, or an alcoholic solution of the addition-product of 1 part carbon disulfide and 2 parts phenylhydrazine. It is used as a test reagent for lead, copper, silver, and other metals. Characteristic colors or precipitates are obtained.

PARTIAL CONDENSATION. See **condensation, partial.**

PARTIAL PRESSURE. The pressure exerted by each component in a mixture of gases. See **law of Dalton.**

PARTICLE. A small entity.

PARTICLE, ALPHA. See **helium nucleus**

PARTICLE, BETA. See **electron.**

PARTING. The wet process for separating silver from gold in the laboratory.

PARTITION COEFFICIENT. See **coefficient, distribution,** and **law, distribution.**

PARTITION FUNCTION. A quantity used mostly in **quantum** statistical calculations which is defined by the relation:

$$Q = \Sigma p_i e^{-\epsilon_i/kT}$$

in which Q is the partition function, p_i is the statistical weight of any given state, e is the logarithmic base, ϵ_i is the energy of the given state, k is the **Boltzmann constant,** and T is the absolute temperature; the summation Σ extends over all possible **energy levels.** This quantity serves to correlate macroscopic (thermodynamic) properties of a system and microscopic (atomic or molecular) properties of the constituent particles.

PASCAL LAW. See **law of Pascal.**

PASCHEN-BACK EFFECT. A type of splitting of **spectral lines** that takes place in magnetic fields of intermediate strength.

PASCHEN BOLOMETER. A very small **thermopile** with a triple junction of bismuth-cadmium, silver, and cadmium-antimony, so suspended that a current causes rotation in a magnetic field.

PASCHEN SERIES. A series of lines in the **infrared** region of the emission spectrum of atomic hydrogen. The wave numbers of the lines in this series are given by the relationship:

$$\bar{\nu} = R_H \left(\frac{1}{n_1{}^2} - \frac{1}{n_2{}^2} \right)$$

where $\bar{\nu}$ is the wave number in reciprocal centimeters, R_H is the **Rydberg constant,** n_1 is 3, and n_2 has various integral values.

PASSERINI REACTION. A method of synthesis of aromatic amides of α-acyloxy acids, using aromatic **isonitriles,** organic **acids,** and **carbonyl** compounds.

ionization due to the visible presence upon its surface of an oxide film, or other protective film, the phenomenon is called mechanical passivity, in recognition of the similarity of the phenomenon to chemical and electrochemical passivity which are probably due, in part at least, to similar protective effects of very thin films.

PASTEUR FLASK. A flask with spherical body, and two outlet tubes, one containing an enlarged portion. This flask is designed primarily for yeast cultures, or those of other organisms in which gas production is to be determined.

PASTEUR SALT SOLUTION. An aqueous solution of potassium phosphate, calcium phosphate, magnesium sulfate, and ammonium tartrate, used in fermentation research.

PASTEURIZATION. The process of heating a given material at a certain temperature for a definite length of time in order to kill pathogenic organisms; specifically milk;

$$\text{ArNC} + \text{R'COOH} + \text{R''COR'''} \rightarrow \text{Ar.HNOC.}\overset{\displaystyle \text{OOC.R'}}{\overset{\displaystyle |}{\text{CR''R'''}}}.$$

PASSIVE STATE. See **passivity.**

PASSIVITY, CHEMICAL. Certain metals, when treated by certain reagents, such as nitric acid and other oxidizing agents, undergo a marked decrease in their reactivity, even to the reagent causing this change. The phenomenon is called chemical passivity and is strikingly similar to **electrochemical passivity.**

PASSIVITY, ELECTROCHEMICAL. Certain metals, when used as anodes in electrolytic **cells,** exhibit a **polarization** so great that it must be attributed to an irreversibility in the **ionization** process. In fact, at certain values of current density, ionization of the metal ceases almost entirely. This has been called the passive state. It is more or less temporary, being lost rapidly under various conditions.

PASSIVITY, MECHANICAL. Where a metallic anode exhibits abnormally slow

in the holding method milk must be heated to 143° F., held at that temperature for 30 minutes and promptly cooled to 50° F.; in the high-temperature short-time method, milk must be heated to 160° F., held at that temperature for 15 seconds, and promptly cooled to 50° F.

PATEIN SOLUTION FOR MILK. A reagent used in milk analysis made by adding to 220 g. mercuric oxide and 300–400 ml. water, just enough nitric acid to produce a clear solution. Sodium hydroxide solution is added, after cooling, until a turbidity just forms, then the solution is made up to 1 liter and filtered; 10 ml. of this solution clears 100 ml. milk.

PATERA PROCESS. A metallurgical process for the recovery of silver from its ores by first converting the silver into the insoluble chloride by heating with chlorides, leaching out the soluble chlorides with water, removing the silver by leaching with a hyposulfite solution, and finally precipitating silver sulfide from that solution for reduction to the metal.

PATHOGEN. A **microorganism** that causes disease.

PATHOLOGICAL CHEMISTRY. See chemistry, pathological.

PATHOLOGY. A branch of medicine that treats of the course of disease and its causes and effects.

PATSCHOWSKY SOLUTION. A solution of 10 g. ferrous ammonium sulfate in 90 ml. water, acidified with acetic acid, used in testing for oxalate in plant substances. Green-yellow prisms indicate the presence of oxalate.

PATTINSON PROCESS. A method used in the separation of silver from lead, in which the mass is partially solidified and crystals of pure lead removed.

PAULI EXCLUSION PRINCIPLE. No two electrons in the same atom have their four **quantum numbers** identical. The four quantum numbers in question are the principal quantum number, the azimuthal quantum number, the spin quantum number, and the magnetic quantum number.

PAULING CONCENTRATOR. A nitric acid concentrator consisting of a packed tower, into which weak nitric acid with or without weak sulfuric acid is introduced at the top and live steam at the bottom. Nitric acid vapors leave at the top and are condensed to yield a nitric acid stronger than 90%.

PAULY-BUTTLAR TEST REACTION FOR ALCOHOLS. A little protocatechuic aldehyde is added to the alcohol tested, and hydrogen chloride is passed into it. Primary alcohols give colors that appear red by transmitted light, secondary alcohols appear green, and tertiary alcohols are not colored.

PAULY PROTEIN REACTION. A characteristic color reaction, due to the formation of an azo dye given by benzene diazoniumsulfonate with various proteins, as, for example, the red color with tyrosine.

PAVELKA-KOLMER TEST FOR CADMIUM. Cadmium salts in acetic acid solution give a yellow-white precipitate of long, narrow prismatic crystals on treatment with nitrophenylarsonic acid.

PAVELKA-MORTH REACTION FOR THALLIUM. On acidification with nitric acid, a thallous salt solution gives a yellow precipitate with phosphomolybdic acid.

PAVELKA SPOT TEST FOR TITANIUM, ZIRCONIUM, AND THORIUM. Treat filter paper with an alcoholic solution of alizarin. Place on it a drop of the solution tested, and expose to ammonia fumes. Titanium gives a red-violet color; zirconium, a raspberry-red; and thorium, violet. The colors deepen on drying.

PAVELKA SPOT TESTS FOR LEAD. (1) Apply to filter paper, previously soaked in a 0.5% ammoniacal solution of carminic acid, 1 drop of the solution tested (which should be nearly neutral) and treat with ammonia fumes and dry. A violet spot indicates lead.

(2) Place on filter paper 1 drop of the solution tested, add 1 drop pyridine solution, and then a 0.1% solution of gallocyanine. Wash with drops of 1% pyridine solution. A violet stain indicates lead.

PAVELKA TEST FOR FLUORIDE. Moisten filter paper with a solution of basic zirconium chloride to which an excess of an alcoholic alizarin solution has been added. Dry. In testing, the paper is moistened with 1 drop 50% acetic acid solution, then with 1 drop of the solution tested. A yellow stain on the red paper indicates fluoride.

PAVOLINI REAGENT FOR METALS. An alcoholic solution of 2,3-diaminophenazine, which gives a red precipitate with mercurous and cuprous ions on shaking a few drops of the reagent with the test solution neutralized with sodium hydroxide.

Bismuth, cadmium, and tin give yellow to orange precipitates, but the test is not so sensitive.

PAVOLINI TEST REACTION FOR FERROUS, CUPROUS, COBALT, AND NICKEL IONS. The monoxime (m.p. 154° C.) made from phenanthraquinone and hydroxylamine hydrochloride gives, in alcoholic solution, a blue-green color with ferrous ion, cochineal with cuprous, yellow-ochre with cobalt, and maroon with nickel.

PAVY SOLUTION. A test reagent for glucose, prepared either by adding an aqueous solution of sodium and ammonium hydroxides to **Fehling solution** (q.v.); or by mixing an aqueous solution of cupric sulfate with an aqueous solution of Rochelle salt, ammonium hydroxide, and potassium hydroxide; or (in a two-solution form), by preparing separate solutions of cupric sulfate, and of Rochelle salt, potassium hydroxide, and ammonium hydroxide.

PAYNE PROCESS. A process for the impregnation of wood with iron and calcium salts by treating it with solutions of ferrous sulfate and calcium chloride, commonly to render it resistant to attack by minute animals or fire.

Pb Symbol for the element **lead.**

Pd Symbol for the element **palladium.**

PEACHEY PROCESS. A **vulcanization** process in which rubber is treated successively with sulfur dioxide and hydrogen sulfide.

PEBBLE MILL. See **mill, pebble.**

PECHE TEST FOR CYANIDE. Mercurous nitrate is reduced to metallic mercury by cyanides.

PECHMANN CONDENSATION. The formation of coumarin derivatives by condensation of phenols with β-keto esters or similar compounds.

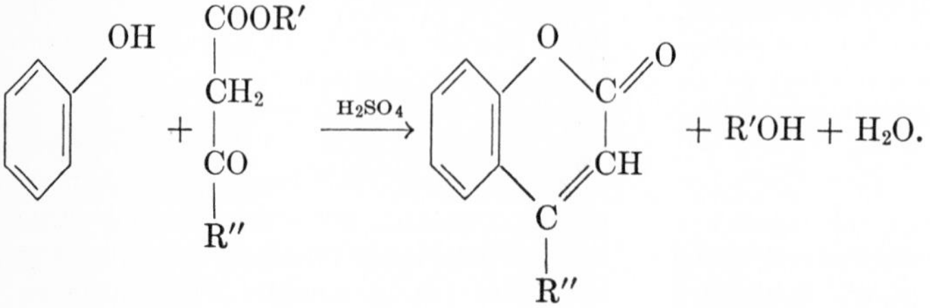

PECHMANN COUMARIN SYNTHESIS. See **Pechmann condensation.**

PECHMANN PYRAZOLE SYNTHESIS. Direct union of **acetylenes** and diazomethane to give **pyrazoles.**

$$CH{\equiv}CH + CH_2N_2 \rightarrow$$

PECTIC ACIDS. A term applied to pectic substances mostly composed of colloidal polygalacturonic acids and essentially free from methyl ester groups. The salts of pectic acids are either normal or acid pectates

PECTIC SUBSTANCES. A group designation for those complex, colloidal **carbohydrate** derivatives which occur in, or are prepared from, plants and contain a large proportion of anhydrogalacturonic acid units that are thought to exist in a chain-like combination. The **carboxyl** groups of polygalacturonic acids may be partly esterified by methyl groups and partly or completely neutralized by one or more bases.

PECTIN. A general term which designates those water-soluble pectinic acids of varying methyl ester content and degree of neutralization that are capable of forming gels with sugar and acid under suitable conditions.

PECTINIC ACIDS. A term used for colloidal polygalacturonic acids containing more than a negligible proportion of methyl ester groups. Pectinic acids, under suitable conditions, are capable of forming gels with sugar and acid, or, if suitably low in methoxyl content, with certain metallic ions. The salts of pectinic acids are either normal or acid pectinates.

PECTISE. To gelate or gelatinize. (See **gel.**)

PECTIZATION. Gelation or gelatinization. (See **gel.**)

PEDERSEN PROCESS. A process for producing alumina, in which bauxite, lime, iron ore, and coke are smelted to yield by-product iron and a low-silica calcium aluminate slag, which is leached with a dilute sodium carbonate solution, and the resulting sodium aluminate solution is carbonated with CO_2 to precipitate aluminum hydroxide (yielding alumina on dehydration) and to regenerate the sodium carbonate solution. The process has been modified by using, as raw materials, clay and limestone, which, on sintering, yield calcium aluminate and dicalcium silicate, and then recovering alumina from the sinter by a method similar to Pedersen's.

PEDRETTI TESTS FOR HAIR DYE INTERMEDIATES. Many of the intermediates used in hair dyes give characteristic colors with (1) dilute sodium nitrite solution followed by hydrochloric acid, and (2), potassium hypochlorite solution followed by hydrochloric acid.

PELARGONIC. Related to pelargonic acid, $C_8H_{17}.COOH$.

PELARGONYL. The radical

$$CH_3(CH_2)_7CO—$$

(from pelargonic acid).

PELLET SOLUTION. A solution made by dissolving in 700 ml. water, 200 g. Rochelle salt, 100 g. anhydrous sodium carbonate, 7 g. ammonium chloride, and 68.7 g. cupric sulfate; then diluting to 1 liter. This solution is used in testing for glucose.

PELOGGIO TEST. Very small traces of iodine can be detected on electrolysis with hydrochloric acid and starch solution. Blue streaks appear at the anode.

PELOUZE SYNTHESIS. A method of formation of nitriles from alkyl sulfates and potassium cyanide.

$$RSO_4K + KCN → RCN + K_2SO_4.$$

PELTIER EFFECT. If electric current is sent through a circuit consisting of two different metals, heat is generated at one junction and absorbed at the other. The heat developed at a junction of two metals is proportional to the first power of the current and depends on the direction of the current.

PENETRATING AGENTS. Substances used in formulating various mixtures in order to promote penetration into various solid media. For example, penetrating agents are added to certain pharmaceutical preparations used in treating skin diseases, in dye baths to promote "wetting-out" and to obtain better distribution of the dye in the fabric, and for many analogous purposes. Penetrating agents owe their action to their solvent qualities, to their effect upon **surface tension,** and to related properties.

PENETRATION. (1) In general, the process of entering, saturating or piercing. (2) The passage of particles or radiations through solids. (3) The consistency of a material in terms of the depth it is entered by a standard needle under standard conditions.

PENETROMETER. (1) An apparatus for determination of the penetration of solids by radiations. (2) An apparatus for determination of the consistency of a material in terms of the depth to which it is entered by a standard needle under standard conditions.

PENFIELD REAGENT. Silver thallium nitrate (m.p. 75° C.) which, on melting, has a specific gravity of 4.5 and is useful in separating minerals.

PENFIELD SCALE. A series of integral numbers used to designate materials, chiefly minerals, according to their fusibility—the higher numbers corresponding to higher fusing points. The substance whose fusing points (melting points) constitute the integral values in this scale are: (1) stibnite, (2) chalcopyrite, (3) almandite, (4) actinolite, (5) orthoclase, (6) bronzite, (7) infusible.

PENNYWEIGHT. A unit of weight in the troy system of weights and measures equal to 24 grains or about 1.56 grams.

PENTABASIC. Capable of furnishing five equivalents of monobasic acid; i.e., having five atoms of replaceable hydrogen per molecule and capable of neutralizing five equivalents of monohydroxy base.

PENTACID. Capable of neutralizing five equivalents of monobasic acid.

PENTACYCLIC. Containing a five-membered ring.

PENTAD. An element or radical which is pentavalent, e.g., nitrogen, phosphorus, or arsenic, in many of their compounds.

PENTADECANOIC. Related to pentadecanoic acid, $C_{14}H_{29}COOH$.

PENTAMETHYLENE. The radical $-CH_2(CH_2)_3CH_2-$.

PENTATHIONATE. The anion $S_5O_6^=$, or a compound containing it.

PENTATHIONIC. Related to pentathionic acid, $H_2S_5O_6$.

PENTATOMIC. Containing five atoms or, by extension, five radicals, as a molecule containing five atoms in all, or five atoms or radicals of one specified kind, as a ring containing five atoms, etc. (See **pentacyclic.**)

PENTAVALENT. Having a valence of five.

PENTAZOLYL. The radical

$$N=N-N=N-N-.$$

PENTENYL. The radical C_5H_9- (containing one double bond).

PENTITE. A pentahydroxy **alcohol**, as *l*-arabite, $C_5H_7(OH)_5$.

PENTOSAN. One of a group of **carbohydrates** which, on hydrolysis, yield pentoses, as cherry gum which yields *l*-arabinose. They are classed as polysaccharides.

PENTOSE. A sugar that contains five carbon atoms, as arabinose, $C_5H_{10}O_5$.

PENTYL. See **amyl.**

PENZOLDT-FISCHER TEST FOR ALDEHYDES AND PHENOL. One g. of diazobenzenesulfonic acid crystals is dissolved in 60 ml. water and a little sodium hydroxide solution. On addition of the substance to be tested and a few granules of amalgam, a red-violet color develops in 10–20 minutes if aldehyde is present. Phenol gives a dark red color with the diazobenzenesulfonate solution, without the violet cast given by aldehyde.

PEPTISE. See **peptize.**

PEPTIZATION. The liquefaction or transformation of a **colloidal system** from a **gel** to a **sol.**

PEPTIZE. To bring about **peptization.**

PEPTOLYSIS. The hydrolysis of peptides or peptones.

PEPTONE. A secondary **protein** derivative that is water-soluble, not coagulated by heat, and not precipitated on saturation of its solutions with ammonium sulfate.

PEPTONIZATION. Conversion into peptones.

PER-. (Latin) Complete, thorough, extreme; the prefix specifically denoting: (1) a compound containing an element in the highest (or a high) state of oxidation, as perchloric acid, manganese peroxide (better, dioxide); (2) presence of the $-O_2-$ group, as barium peroxide, perbenzoic acid, peracid (better, peroxy acid); (3) exhaustive substitution or addition, as perchloroethylene, C_2Cl_4; perhydronaphthalene, $C_{10}H_{18}$. In naming halogenated organic compounds or groups, the terms "per-bromo," "perchloro," "perfluoro," and "periodo" denote substitution of all hydrogen atoms attached to carbon atoms except those whose substitution would affect the nature of the functional groups present. "Per" may refer to the whole word or to part of the word to which it is attached, but not to more than one word. Parentheses are used where necessary to avoid ambiguity as to whether "per" refers to part of a name or to a whole name. Examples: $C_6F_{11}CF_3$, perfluoro(methylcyclohexane); C_3F_7CHO, perfluorobutyraldehyde; $C_2H_5CO_2C_4Cl_9$, perchlorobutyl propionate; $CBr_3CBr_2CH{=}NOH$, perbromopropionaldoxime;

$$(CCl_3)_2CCl(CCl_2)_3CCl_3,$$

perchloro(2-methylhexane); $C_6H_5C_5Cl_{11}$, (perchloropentyl)benzene.

Perfluoro(decahydro-1-methylnaphthalene)

It should be noted that this use of "per" excludes names in which "per " is preceded by other prefixes. Thus, $CF_3CClFCF_3$ would be called 2-chloroheptafluoropropane and not 2-chloroperfluoropropane. The reason for this limitation is to avoid the implication that some other atom rather than hydrogen has been substituted.

PERACETIC. Related to peracetic acid, $CH_3.CO.O.OH$.

PERACID. An acid containing a greater proportion of oxygen than the form of that acid bearing the simple name, as perchloric acid is $HClO_4$ while chloric acid is $HClO_3$. Many peracids yield hydrogen peroxide on acidification with mineral acids.

PERBORATE. The anion BO_3^-, or a compound containing it. ($NaBO_2.H_2O_2.3H_2O$ is also called perborate.)

PERBORIC. Related to the hypothetical metaperboric acid, HBO_3, from which the perborates are derived.

PERBROMIC. Related to perbromic acid, $HBrO_4$.

PERBROMO. In naming brominated organic compounds or groups, the term perbromo denotes substitution of all hydrogen atoms attached to carbon atoms except those whose substitution would affect the nature of the functional groups present. "Per" may refer to the whole word or to part of the word to which it is attached, but not to more than one word. Parentheses are used where necessary to avoid ambiguity as to whether "per" refers to part of a name or to a whole name. Example: $CBr_3CBr_2CH{=}NOH$, perbromopropionaldoxime.

PERCARBIDE. A carbide that contains more carbon than is necessary to saturate the highest valence of the metal with which it is combined.

PERCARBONATE. See **peroxycarbonate** and **peroxydicarbonate**.

PERCHLORATE. The anion ClO_4^-, or a compound containing it.

PERCHLORIC. Related to perchloric acid, $HClO_4$.

PERCHLORIDE. A chloride that contains a larger proportion of chlorine than any other chloride of the same element or radical.

PERCHLORO-. In naming chlorinated organic compounds or groups, the term perchloro denotes substitution of all hydrogen atoms attached to carbon atoms except those whose substitution would affect the nature of the functional groups present. "Per" may refer to the whole word or to part of the word to which it is attached, but not to more than one word. Parentheses are used where necessary to avoid ambiguity as to whether "per" refers to part of a name or to a whole name. Example: $C_2H_5CO_2C_4Cl_9$, perchlorobutyl propionate.

PERCHROMATE. See **peroxychromate.**

PERCOLATE. Literally, to strain through. To extract by **percolation.**

PERCOLATION. A process for the continuous extraction of soluble matter from its admixture with insoluble material by a suitable solvent, conducted in such a way that the solvent travels through the mass to be extracted, from one surface of which the partially saturated solution is removed while fresh solvent is admitted at the opposite surface.

PERCOLATION FILTRATION. See **filtration, percolation.**

PERCRYSTALLIZATION. The crystallization of a dissolved substance from a solution, during or after **dialysis.**

PERDISULFATE. See **peroxydisulfate.**

PEREIRA TEST FOR HYDROGEN. Heated hydrogen gas gives a blue color on passage through a mixture of 2 ml. saturated phosphomolybdic acid, 1 ml. 1% palladium chloride, and 3 ml. water.

PERFERRATE. The anion $FeO_5^=$, or a compound containing it.

PERFLUORO-. In naming fluorinated organic compounds or groups, the term perfluoro denotes substitution of all hydrogen atoms attached to carbon atoms except those whose substitution would affect the nature of the functional groups present. "Per" may refer to the whole word or to part of the word to which it is attached, but not to more than one word. Parentheses are used where necessary to avoid ambiguity as to whether "per" refers to part of a name or to a whole name. Example: C_3F_7CHO, perfluorobutyraldehyde.

PERI-. (Greek, around, about) A prefix indicating (1) the relation between positions 1 and 8 of naphthalene; (2) in polycyclic ring systems, fusion of a ring to two or more adjoining rings, as *peri*-dinitronaphthalene, *peri*-naphthindene.

PERICYCLO. A term proposed by Bredig for a valence bond extending partly around

a ring, as in the case of the position (or linkage) *a–b* in R-hexane derivatives, viz.

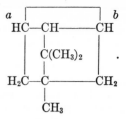

PERIMIDYL. The radical $C_{11}H_7N_2-$ (from perimidine, 8 isomers).

PERIOD. An interval, especially one established by repeated or regular recurrence, or the entities contained within such an interval. Specifically between stipulated elements in the **periodic table** and the elements, arranged in order of **atomic number,** which it contains.

PERIOD, HALF-LIFE. The time in which one-half of a given **radioactive element** undergoes **nuclear transformation.** This period is independent of the mass of the radioactive element that is present.

PERIOD, LONG. The third, fourth, or fifth periods of the **periodic table** and the elements they contain. The third period extends from argon (atomic number 18) to bromine (atomic number 35); the fourth period extends from krypton (atomic number 36) to iodine (atomic number 53); and the fifth period from xenon (atomic number 54) to astatine (atomic number 85).

PERIOD OF DECAY. See **period, half-life.**

PERIOD OF INDUCTION. The initial period of certain reactions which is characterized by an apparent quiescence.

PERIOD, RARE EARTH. The period (fifth) of the **periodic table** which includes the rare earth elements (the elements from atomic number 57 to atomic number 71, inclusive): lanthanum, cerium, praseodymium, neodymium, promethium, samarium, europium, gadolinium, terbium, dysprosium, holmium, erbium, thulium, ytterbium, and lutecium.

PERIOD, SHORT. The first or second periods of the **periodic table,** and the elements they contain. The first period extends from hydrogen (atomic number 1) to fluorine (atomic number 9); and the second period extends from neon (atomic number 10) to chlorine (atomic number 17).

PERIODATE. The anion (dimeso-) $I_2O_9{}^{4-}$, (meso-) $IO_5{}^{3-}$, (meta-) $IO_4{}^-$, (ortho- or para-) $IO_6{}^{5-}$, $(H_3IO_6)_n{}^{2n-}$, or a compound containing one of these anions.

PERIODIC ACID. The compound HIO_4 or H_5IO_6, in which iodine is heptavalent.

PERIODIC CHAIN. An arrangement of the **periodic system** in the form of a simple vertical listing of the elements in order of increasing **atomic numbers,** and divided by horizontal lines.

PERIODIC LAW. See **law, periodic.**

PERIODIC PROPERTY. A property which is related in its magnitude to the atomic weight or atomic number of an element, i.e., to the position of the element in the periodic table. (See **law of Moseley** and **law, periodic.**)

PERIODIC SPIRAL. An arrangement of the periodic system in the form of a spiral.

PERIODIC SYSTEM. An arrangement of the elements in a systematic grouping wherein elements having like properties occur in related positions, as in horizontal or vertical sequence, so that unknown

PERIODIC TABLE. An arrangement of the periodic system in the form of a table, which is the most common arrangement.

PERIODICITY. The recurrence of an event, phenomenon, or characteristic feature at regular intervals of time, distance, or other variable, specifically the variation of the physical or chemical properties of an element in relation to its **atomic number,** as shown by its position in the periodic system.

PERIODO-. In naming iodinated organic compounds or groups, the term periodo- denotes substitution of all hydrogen atoms attached to carbon atoms except those whose substitution would affect the nature of the functional groups present. "Per" may refer to the whole word or to part of the word to which it is attached, but not to more than one word. Parentheses are used where necessary to avoid ambiguity as to whether "per" refers to part of a name or to a whole name. Example: C_3I_7CHO, periodobutyraldehyde.

PERISPHERE. The volume surrounding an object in which the gravitational, magnetic, or electric fields of the object produce observable effects.

PERITECTIC POINT. See **melting point, incongruent.**

PERKIN METHOD FOR ALICYCLIC COMPOUNDS. A method of formation of **alicyclic** compounds from dihalogenated compounds and compounds containing active methylene groups.

$$\underset{\overset{\diagup}{\underset{\diagdown}{}}}{CH_2}\;\overset{CHBr.R'}{\underset{CHBr.R''}{}} + CH_2(COOC_2H_5)_2 + 2NaOC_2H_5 \rightarrow \underset{\overset{\diagup}{\underset{\diagdown}{}}}{CH_2}\;\overset{CHR'}{\underset{CHR''}{}}C(COOC_2H_5)_2 + 2NaBr + 2C_2H_5OH.$$

properties of known elements, and even properties of unknown elements, can be deduced from their positions in this arrangement. The arrangement of the elements of the system is based on the **atomic number** of each element.

PERKIN, JR., REACTION. A reaction between the sodium compound of either acetoacetic ester or malonic ester and a dibromide (as ethylene dibromide) which results in the formation of a cyclic compound, e.g.,

$$\begin{matrix} CH_2Br \\ | \\ CH_2Br \end{matrix} + Na_2C \begin{matrix} COOEt \\ \diagup \\ \diagdown \\ COOEt \end{matrix} \rightarrow \begin{matrix} CH_2 \\ | \\ CH_2 \end{matrix} \diagup C \diagup \begin{matrix} COOEt \\ \diagdown \\ COOEt \end{matrix} + 2NaBr.$$

PERKIN REACTION. A condensation reaction between sodium salts of **carboxylic acids** and **aldehydes,** usually in the presence of acid anhydrides, resulting in the formation of an unsaturated carboxylic acid, as, for example:

$$C_6H_5CHO + CH_2R\text{—}COONa \rightarrow C_6H_5CH=CR\text{—}COONa + H_2O.$$

This condensation is closely related to the **Knoevenagel reaction** and to the **Claisen condensation.**

PERKIN REARRANGEMENT. A reaction of 3-halocoumarins with alkali to yield benzofuran-2-carboxylic acids.

$$+ 2NaOH \rightarrow \qquad + NaBr + H_2O.$$

PERMANENT GASES. An historic classification that included those gases which are very difficult to liquefy and which were thought to be nonliquefiable. The distinction has vanished since all the gases have been liquefied because of the advance in low temperature techniques.

PERMANENT HARDNESS. See **hardness, permanent.**

PERMANGANATE. The anion MnO_4^-, or a compound containing it.

PERMANGANIC. Related to permanganic acid, $HMnO_4$.

PERMANGANYL. The radical $\text{—}MnO_3$, in which manganese is heptavalent.

PERMEABILITY. (1) The capacity of a **membrane** or other material to allow another substance to penetrate or pass

through it; or, specifically, the quantity of a specified gas or other substance which passes through under specified conditions. (2) **Magnetic permeability** is the value of the total **magnetic induction** in a unit field.

PERMEABILITY, MAGNETIC. See **magnetic permeability.**

PERMEATE. (1) To pass through a substance, as in the case of a gas or liquid which passes through small channels or pores in a membrane or other medium. (2) To pass into an object or substance as by traveling through minute openings or intermolecular spaces, so that the diffusing substance becomes more or less uniformly distributed throughout the medium into which it travels.

PERMONOSULFATE. See **peroxymonosulfate.**

PERMUTATION. A term used in some cases and by some writers as equivalent to **transmutation** and by others for chemical substitution (see **reaction, substitution**).

PERONNET-TRUHAUT REACTION FOR ALDEHYDES. Warm 5 ml. 0.1% alcoholic solution of m-dinitrobenzene with 1 ml. 10% sodium hydroxide solution. This pink solution becomes violet on addition of various aldehydes.

PERONNET-TRUHAUT REACTION FOR AMINO ACIDS AND URIC ACID.

On dissolving 0.1 g. of an amino acid in 2 ml. 10% sodium hydroxide solution, and superimposing 2 ml. of a 0.1% alcoholic *m*-dinitrobenzene solution, a violet ring appears. The same violet color is given by uric acid.

PEROSMIC. Containing octavalent **osmium.**

PEROXIDASE. One of a class of **enzymes** that activate hydrogen peroxide, and probably other peroxides, and catalyze oxidation reactions that do not proceed with appreciable velocity in their absence.

PEROXIDE. The anion $O_2^=$ or HO_2^-, or a compound containing one of these anions.

PEROXIDES, FALSE. Oxides into which the oxygen does not enter as whole molecules. See also **holoxides.**

PEROXIDATION. See **peroxidize.**

PEROXIDIZE. To oxidize to the highest degree so as to form a peroxide.

PEROXY-. A prefix denoting presence of the peroxide group, $—O_2—$, as peroxymonosulfuric acid, $HOSO_2OOH$ (now considered preferable to per- in this sense).

PEROXYBORATE. See **perborate.**

PEROXYCHROMATE. The anion CrO_6^-, $Cr_2O_{12}^=$, CrO_8^{3-} or $Cr_2O_{16}^{6-}$, or a compound containing one of these anions.

PEROXYDICARBONATE. The anion $C_2O_6^=$, or a compound containing it.

PEROXYDIPHOSPHATE. The anion $P_2O_8^{4-}$, or a compound containing it.

PEROXYDISULFATE. The anion $S_2O_8^=$, or a compound containing it.

PEROXYGERMANATE. The anion $GeO_5^=$ or $Ge_2O_7^=$, or a compound containing one of these anions.

PEROXYMOLYBDATE. The anion $MoO_5^=$, $MoO_6^=$, or $MoO_8^=$, or a compound containing one of these anions.

PEROXYMONOCARBONATE (META-). The anion $CO_4^=$ or $CO_5^=$, or a compound containing one of these anions.

PEROXYMONOPHOSPHATE. The anion PO_5^{3-}, or a compound containing it.

PEROXYMONOSULFATE. The anion $SO_5^=$, or a compound containing it.

PEROXYNIOBATE. The anion $NbO_4^=$ or $NbO_5^=$, or a compound containing one of these anions.

PEROXYNITRATE. The anion NO_4^-, or a compound containing it.

PEROXYTANTALATE. The anion TaO_4^- or TaO_8^{3-}, or a compound containing one of these anions.

PEROXYTUNGSTATE. The anion WO_4^-, $WO_5^=$, $WO_8^=$, or $W_2O_{11}^=$, or a compound containing one of these anions.

PEROXYURANATE. The anion $UO_5^=$, $UO_6^=$, UO_8^{4-}, $U_2O_{10}^=$, or $U_2O_{13}^{6-}$, or a compound containing one of these anions.

PEROXYVANADATE. The anion VO_4^- or VO_6^{3-}, or a compound containing one of these anions.

PERRHENATE. One of the anions ReO_4^- (meta-), or ReO_5^{3-} (meso-), or a compound containing one of them.

PERRIN DETERMINATION OF THE AVOGADRO NUMBER. A method of determination of the **Avogadro number,** based upon the distribution of colloidal particles, subject to the **Brownian movement,** of known mass and density, at two different levels in a suspension in equilibrium with gravity. From a series of experiments made with mastic and gamboge suspensions, over a wide range of particle sizes, values of Avogadro's number lying consistently between 6.5×10^{23} and 7.3×10^{23} were obtained.

PERRIN RULE. A generalization derived from certain results on **electroosmosis, to** the effect that ions of charge opposite **to**

that of the diaphragm have by far the greatest effect upon endosmosis, and that the higher their valence (if it is of opposite sign) the greater the reduction of electro-osmotic flow.

PERRUTHENATE. The anion RuO_4^-, or a compound containing it.

PERSALT. A salt having a negative radical or ion containing, commonly, oxygen and a metal and in which the metal is at a high, commonly its highest, state of oxidation.

PERSELENO. The radical $Se:Se=$.

PERSORPTION. An intimate mixture of a solid and a gas due to **sorption** processes.

PERSOZ REAGENT. A solution of 100 g. zinc chloride in 100 ml. water, to which 20 g. zinc oxide is added. This solution is used in differentiating silk and wool. At 45° C., the reagent dissolves silk but not wool.

PERSULFATE. See **peroxymonosulfate** and **peroxydisulfate**.

PERSULFIDE. A sulfide which contains a larger proportion of sulfur than is necessary to satisfy the highest normal valence of the associated element, as FeS_2.

PERSULFURIC. Related to persulfuric acid, $H_2S_2O_8$.

PERTHIO. The radical $S:S=$ (replacing O only).

PERTHIOCARBONATE. The anion (meta-) CS_4^-, or a compound containing it.

PERTUSI-GASTALDI REAGENT FOR CYANIDE. A mixture of 1 drop 3% cupric acetate solution, 5 drops saturated benzidine acetate solution, and 0.5 ml. water. This reagent colors cyanide solutions blue.

PERTUSI REACTION FOR FLUORIDE. A neutral or nearly neutral fluoride

solution gives a yellow, acid-soluble, precipitate with mercuric acetate and benzidine acetate solutions.

PERVAPORATION. Evaporation through a semi-permeable membrane.

PERVIOUS. Permitting the passage of radiations or substances, commonly liquids or gases. The negative term, impervious, is more frequently used.

PESET-BEUNDIA REAGENT. A solution of 1 g. tannic acid in 100 ml. sulfuric acid, used in testing for alkaloids. Characteristic color reactions are obtained.

PETERSON CONCENTRATOR. A nitric acid concentrator, consisting of a short packed tower. The dilute nitric acid enters at the top and meets a rising current of steam, supplied by a boiler. The action of the steam expels oxides of nitrogen, which are condensed by cooling outside the tower. This process owes its effectiveness to the small amount of water vapor carried by the oxides of nitrogen.

PETERSON REAGENT. Two solutions used in testing for tartrates and citrates. They are: (1) an aqueous solution of 0.116 g. sodium salicylate made up to 1 liter; and (2) a solution of 1 ml. 10% ferric chloride solution in 50 ml. water, alkalized with ammonium hydroxide until the precipitate just redissolves, then 1 drop acetic acid is added, and the volume made up to 100 ml. with water. On test with these solutions, citrates and tartrates give a violet color or, in small concentrations, an opalescence.

PETERSON TOWER PROCESS. A process for the production of sulfuric acid by the **chamber process** in which the conversion of the SO_2 to H_2SO_4 takes place in packed towers, instead of lead chambers.

PETRENKO-KRITSHENKO PIPERIDONE SYNTHESIS. A method of formation of piperidones by condensation of esters of acetone dicarboxylic acid with aldehydes and primary amines.

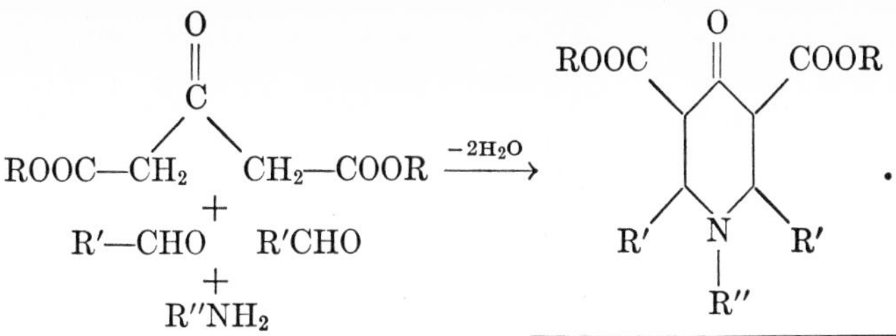

$$\underset{\underset{R''NH_2}{\overset{R'-CHO \quad R'CHO}{+}}}{\overset{\overset{O}{\parallel}}{\underset{ROOC-CH_2 \quad CH_2-COOR}{C}}} \xrightarrow{-2H_2O}$$

PETRI DISH. A small circular dish used for the incubation of **cultures** of microorganisms.

PETROCHEMICAL. A chemical obtained from petroleum. The rapid expansion of this industry dates from the period of development of the cracking processes, when large quantities of lower (gaseous) unsaturated hydrocarbons became available, with little use, in many instances, except for their value as fuel or illuminating gas. Their reactivity led to their use in producing a wide range of compounds of value in the chemical industry and elsewhere. The use of petroleum hydrocarbons as chemical starting materials has been vastly broadened in recent years, and the term petrochemical now applies to a great number of processes and products.

PETROFF MEDIUM. A culture medium for microorganisms prepared by the extraction of beef with glycerol-water solution followed by the addition of eggs beaten in a strong alcohol-water solution, the addition of crystal violet indicator, and coagulation by heating.

PETROVSKII TEST. To detect tungsten in ores, treat 0.1–0.2 g. of the powder with a small piece of lead and heat with concentrated hydrochloric acid for 1–2 minutes. A blue color indicates tungsten; a blue, green, or brown flocculent precipitate forms on dilution. The undiluted blue solution becomes yellow on evaporation.

PETTENKOFER REAGENT FOR FREE CARBON DIOXIDE IN WATER. A solution of 0.2 g. rosolic acid in 100 g. 80% alcohol neutralized with an aqueous solution of barium hydroxide, and used in testing for free carbon dioxide in water. A yellow color indicates the presence of free carbon dioxide, while combined carbon dioxide gives a red color.

PFAFF TEST REACTION FOR MALIC ACID. A solution of malic acid is colored green by the dropwise addition of ammoniacal copper solution.

PFEIFFER TEST FOR PHENOLS. Phenols, when present in phenolic ethers, give a yellow solution with a greenish tinge on treatment with **Michler ketone** (q.v.) or with p,p'-tetramethyldiaminodibenzalacetone.

PFEILRING REAGENT. A sulfonated mixture of glycerol and various hydrocarbons used as a catalyst in the hydrolysis of fats to yield glycerol and fatty acids.

PFIFFNER-MYERS REAGENT. A solution of 6 g. sodium nitroprusside and 8.5 g. sodium ferrocyanide in 100 ml. water, used in the colorimetric determination of methylguanidine.

PFITZINGER REACTION. A method of formation of quinoline carboxylic acids by condensation of isatic acid or isatins with α-methylenecarbonyl compounds.

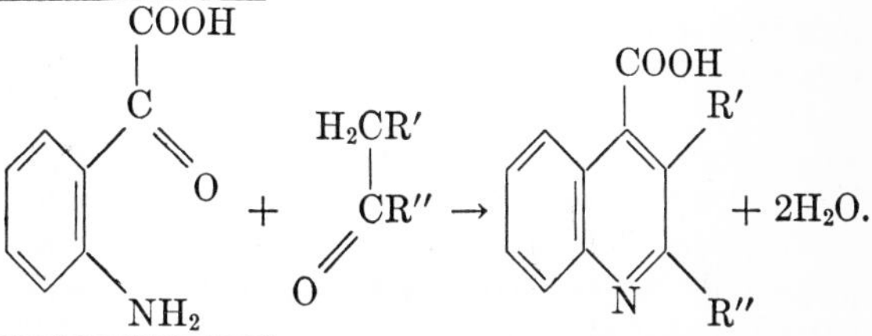

$$\underset{NH_2}{\overset{COOH}{\overset{|}{\underset{}{C}}}} \underset{O}{\overset{}{}} + \underset{\underset{O}{\overset{}{}}}{\overset{H_2CR'}{\overset{|}{CR''}}} \rightarrow \underset{N}{\overset{COOH}{\overset{|}{\underset{R''}{}}}} R' + 2H_2O.$$

PFUND SERIES. A series of lines in the **infrared** region of the emission **spectrum** of atomic hydrogen. The wave numbers of the lines in this series are given by the relationship.

$$\bar{\nu} = R_H \left(\frac{1}{n_1^2} - \frac{1}{n_2^2} \right)$$

where $\bar{\nu}$ is the wave number in reciprocal centimeters, R_H is the **Rydberg constant,** n_1 is 5, and n_2 has various integral values.

PH. Abbreviation for phenyl.

pH. The logarithm of the reciprocal of the **hydrogen-ion concentration:**

$$pH = \log \frac{1}{c_{H^+}}.$$

PHAGOCYTES. **Cells** that swallow or engulf foreign substances such as **bacteria.** They are divided into two classes, the "fixed" phagocytes which are cells of the connective tissue and endothelium, and "free" phagocytes. Not synonymous with leucocytes. The engulfing action is termed "phagocytosis."

PHAGOCYTOSIS. See **phagocytes.**

PHARMACEUTIC. Relating to the art of pharmacy.

PHARMACEUTICAL CHEMISTRY. See **chemistry, pharmaceutical.**

PHARMACODYNAMICS. The science that treats of the actions and relations of drugs within the organism.

PHARMACOLOGY. The entire body of scientific knowledge dealing with drugs, their source, composition, identification, and physiological action.

PHARMACOPHORE. A structural arrangement of atoms that is considered to impart pharmacological activity to a chemical substance.

PHARMACOPOEIA. An authoritative list of drugs and medicinal compounds with a description of each, tests for their identity and purity, and their average doses. Directions for compounding all mixtures contained in the list are also included. Substances listed in the pharmacopoeia are termed "official." The United States Pharmacopoeia is revised every five years. Many other countries of the world issue pharmacopoeias bearing the names of the respective countries.

PHARMACOPOEIAL. Pertaining to the pharmacopoeia. Conforming to the requirements of the pharmacopoeia.

PHARMACY. The art of selecting, preparing, and compounding medicinal agents.

PHASE. (1) In the chemical sense, a homogeneous, physically-distinct part of a system which is separated from other parts of a system by definite bounding surfaces. Thus a gas, a homogeneous liquid, or a homogeneous solid is a single phase, while, for example, a system of two insoluble or partly-soluble liquids which form separate layers has two phases, and a system of two solids in equilibrium with their solution has three phases.

(2) The term phase is used to express one of two more forms, appearances, or forms of behavior exhibited by the same entity, as the phases of the moon, of alternating electric current, of protoplasm, and of bacteria.

PHASE, CONTINUOUS. The enveloping phase in a system which contains one or more disperse phases. It is also called the dispersion medium.

PHASE DIAGRAM. A graph showing the condition of **equilibrium** between various phases of a substance or of different substances.

PHASE, DISPERSE. A system of one or more **components,** with definite boundaries, which is dispersed within another medium, called the continuous phase.

PHASE RULE, THE. A mathematical expression which shows the conditions of **equilibrium** in a system as a relationship between the number of **phases,** the number of **components,** and the **degrees of freedom** possible under the given conditions. If C represents the number of components, P, the number of phases, and F, the degrees of freedom, then $C + 2 - P = F$.

PHASINE. One of a group of nitrogenous substances found in seeds, barks, and probably other plant tissues, which agglutinate red blood corpuscles, although most of the phasines are nontoxic. They are found in beans (*Phaseolus vulgaris*), whence the name phasine. They act like strong bases and can be recovered from the agglutinate with dilute HCl. Phasines are digested and detoxicated in the intestinal tract; they lose their agglutinating powers on heating.

PHASOTROPY. (Virtual tautomerism) A phenomenon shown by certain **diazo-amino** compounds, **amidines,** and **formazyl** derivatives in which isomerism occurs through "oscillation" of a hydrogen atom and a double bond between nitrogen atoms, viz.,

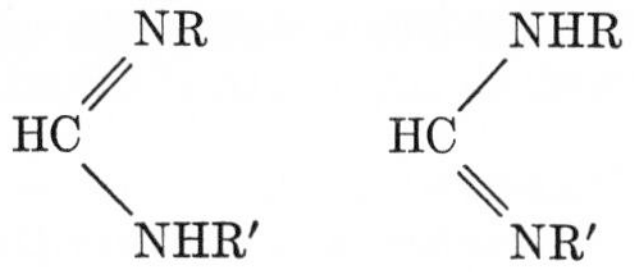

where R and R' are univalent radicals.

PHEN-. See **pheno-.**

PHENACYL. The radical $C_6H_5COCH_2$—

PHENACYLIDENE. The radical

$$C_6H_5COCH=.$$

PHENANTHROLINE. One of a number of compounds derived from phenanthrene

$C_{14}H_{10},$, by replacement of

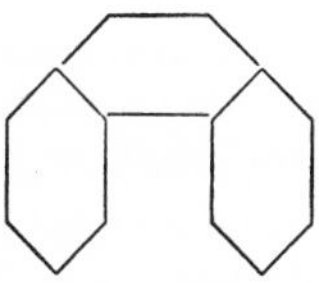

two ring carbon atoms (and their attached hydrogen atoms) by two nitrogen atoms. The phenanthrolenes have the formula, $C_{12}H_8N_2$.

PHENANTHRYL. The radical $C_{14}H_9$— (from phenanthrene, 5 isomers).

PHENANTHRYLENE. The radical —$C_{14}H_8$— (from phenanthrene).

PHENATE. A **phenol** in which a hydroxyl hydrogen atom is replaced by a positive radical, commonly a metal.

PHENENYL. The radical $C_6H_3\equiv$ (*s, as, v*).

PHENETHYL. The radical

$$C_6H_5CH_2CH_2—.$$

-PHENETIDE. A suffix indicating a terminal —$NHC_6H_4OC_2H_5$ group.

PHENETIDINO. The radical

$$C_2H_5OC_6H_4NH—.$$

PHENETYL. The radical

$$C_2H_5OC_6H_4— (o, m, \text{ or } p).$$

PHENMETHYL. See **benzyl.**

PHENO-, PHEN-. (From phene, benzene) The prefix meaning relation to phenyl or benzene, as phenacyl; specifically, denoting the presence of two benzene rings in a complex, as phenazine, phenothiazine.

PHENOL. An hydroxyl derivative of a carbocyclic compound in which the hydroxyl is directly united to a ring carbon atom (distinction from alcohols). E.g.,

carbolic acid, "phenol," 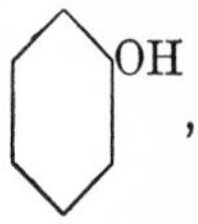 , or β-

naphthol, 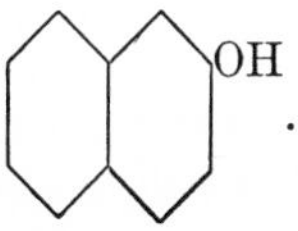 . Under the Geneva nomenclature, phenols are named from the hydrocarbon from which they are derived, followed by the suffix -ol. Polyhydric phenols are designated by the suffixes -diol, -triol, etc., depending upon the number of phenolic hydroxyl groups present. However, names universally adopted, such as "phenol" and β-naphthol above, and cresol, resorcinol and many others, are retained. Compounds containing more than one phenolic hydroxy group are also named as dihydroxy-, trihydroxy-, etc. compounds, so that the compound

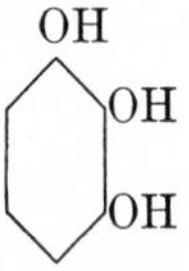

may be called 1,2,3-benzenetriol (Gen.), or pyrogallol, or 1,2,3-trihydroxybenzene.

PHENOL EXTRACTION PROCESS. A process for the refining of lubricating oil, involving extraction with phenol.

PHENOLATE. A **phenol** in which a hydroxyl hydrogen atom is replaced by a positive radical, commonly a metal.

-PHENONE. A suffix indicating a terminal —C_6H_5 group attached to **acyl,** a phenyl ketone.

PHENOXY. The radical C_6H_5O—.

PHENYL. The radical C_6H_5—.

PHENYLACETYL. The radical

$$C_6H_5.CH_2.CO—.$$

PHENYLAMINE. One of a group of compounds, which may be regarded structurally as substituted ammonias, in which one, two, or three of the hydrogen atoms of NH_3 have been substituted by phenyl (C_6H_5—) radicals.

PHENYLATE. (1) To introduce a phenyl radical into a compound. (2) A **phenolate** (q.v.).

PHENYLAZO. The radical $C_6H_5N:N$—.

PHENYLCARBAMIDO. See **phenylureido.**

.**PHENYLENE.** The radical —C_6H_4— (*o, m,* or *p*).

PHENYLENEDISAZO. The radical

$$—N:NC_6H_4N:N—$$

(*o, m,* or *p*).

PHENYLHYDRAZIDE. A substitution-product of phenylhydrazine

$$(C_6H_5NH—NH_2),$$

in which one of the hydrogen atoms attached to a nitrogen atom is substituted, commonly by an **acyl group.**

PHENYLHYDRAZONE. A substitution-product of phenylhydrazine

$$(C_6H_5NH—NH_2)$$

in which the hydrogen atoms of the —NH_2 group are replaced by alkyl- or aryl- substituted (or disubstituted) methylene group as $C_6H_5NH—N=CHR$ or

$$C_6H_5NH—N=CR_1R_2.$$

PHENYLIDENE. See **cyclohexadienylidene.**

PHENYLLACTIC. Related to phenyllactic acid, $C_6H_5.CH_2.CHOH.COOH.$

PHENYLPHOSPHONIC. Related to phenylphosphonic acid, $(HO)_2P(O)C_6H_5.$

PHENYLSULFAMYL. The radical

$$C_6H_5NHSO_2—.$$

PHENYLSULFONAMIDO. The radical $C_6H_5SO_2NH$—.

PHENYLSULFONYL. The radical

$$C_6H_5SO_2—.$$

PHENYLUREIDO. The radical

$$C_6H_5NHCONH—.$$

PHEO-, PHAEO-. (Greek: *phaios,* dun-colored) A prefix denoting a series of compounds related to **chlorophyll,** as pheophytin.

PHERON. The carrier of an **enzyme.** The pheron is **colloidal** in character and is the source of catalytic activity.

PHI (Φ, ϕ OR φ). The twenty-first letter in the Greek alphabet, used to denote the twenty-first carbon atom in a straight-chain compound, or a derivative in which the substituent group is attached to that carbon atom (ϕ-). Symbol for angle (ϕ). Symbol for **angle of incidence** (ϕ). Symbol for **angle of refraction** (ϕ'). Symbol for **critical angle** (ϕ_c). Symbol for function (of) (ϕ). Abbreviation for **phenyl** (ϕ). Symbol for **fluidity** (ϕ). Symbol for **electron affinity** or net **work function** per unit charge (ϕ). Symbol for gross electron affinity or gross work function per unit charge (ϕ_g). Symbol for **magnetic flux** or radiant flux (Φ). Symbol for velocity potential (ϕ).

PHILLIPS-WILLIAMS TEST FOR NICKEL. Five ml. of the solution to be tested, mixed with 5 ml. N ammonium hydroxide, are treated at once with 0.5 g. nitroaminoguanidine dissolved in 50 ml. hot water, and boiled gently for 15 minutes. Nickel gives a precipitate, which dissolves in sodium hydroxide to form a blue solution.

PHIPSON TEST FOR CINNAMIC ACID. On oxidation of cinnamic acid with potassium dichromate and sulfuric acid, benzaldehyde is formed.

PHLOGISTON. A name given by Stahl to an hypothetical "combustible principle" which was considered to be a component of all combustible substances and which conferred combustible properties upon them. This component was assumed to escape during combustion so that combustible substances were postulated as compounds of phlogiston and what we now call their oxidation products. E.g., sulfur was assumed to be a compound of phlogiston and sulfur dioxide. The researches of Lavoisier on combustion overthrew the phlogiston theory.

PHLORO-, PHLOR-. A preffix meaning relating to phlorizin, as phloroglucinol, phloretin.

PHLOROGLUCINOL TEST. A characteristic red color obtained by heating a pentose with phloroglucinol and hydrochloric acid.

PHONOCHEMICAL REACTION. See **reaction, phonochemical.**

PHOSPHARSENO. The radical

$$-P:As-,$$

in an organic compound.

PHOSPHATE. An anion consisting essentially of pentavalent phosphorus and oxygen (with, in some cases, hydrogen) or a compound containing such an anion, many of which are derived from **phosphoric acid,** $HP(OH)_3$ or H_3PO_4. There are a number of these anions and compounds, which are listed below with their special designations. The orthophosphates [see **phosphate (ortho)**] are often designated by the group name, which is presumed to refer to them when not otherwise indicated.

PHOSPHATE, ACID. A salt of **phosphoric** acid in which only one or two of the hydrogen atoms are neutralized (replaced by a metal or radical).

PHOSPHATE, DIBASIC. A salt of **phosphoric** acid in which two of its hydrogen atoms are replaced by a metal or radical.

PHOSPHATE, DIHYDRIC. A salt of **phosphoric** acid in which one of its hydrogen atoms is replaced by a metal or radical.

PHOSPHATE, HOLO-. See **holophosphate.**

PHOSPHATE, HYPO-. The anion $P_2O_6^{4-}$ (meta) or a compound containing it.

PHOSPHATE, META-. See **metaphosphate.**

PHOSPHATE, MONOBASIC. A salt of phosphoric acid in which one of its hydrogen atoms is replaced by a metal or radical.

PHOSPHATE, MONOHYDRIC. A salt of **phosphoric** acid in which two of its hydrogen atoms are replaced by a metal or radical.

PHOSPHATE, NORMAL. A salt of **phosphoric** acid containing no replaceable hydrogen atoms, because all have already been replaced.

PHOSPHATE (ORTHO). The anions PO_4^{3-}, $HPO_4^=$, or $(H_2PO_4)_n^{n-}$, or a compound containing one of these anions. These anions and compounds are often referred to simply as phosphates, the prefix ortho- being understood, and the other anions composed essentially of phosphorus and oxygen, and their compounds (holo-, meta-, poly-, pyro-, tetra-, and tri-) are always designated. In this book they are defined under holophosphate, metaphosphate, polyphosphate, pyrophosphate, and triphosphate.

PHOSPHATE, POLY-. See **polyphosphate.**

PHOSPHATE, PYRO-. See **pyrophosphate.**

PHOSPHATE, TETRA-. See **tetraphosphate.**

PHOSPHATE, TRI-. See **triphosphate.**

PHOSPHAZO. The radical —P:N—, in an organic compound.

PHOSPHENIC. Related to phosphenic acid, $HOP=O(O)$.

PHOSPHENIMIDIC. Related to phosphenimidic acid, $HOP=O(NH)$ or

$$HOP=NH(O).$$

PHOSPHENIMIDODITHIOIC. Related to phosphenimidodithioic acid,

$$HSP=S(NH)$$

or $HSP=NH(S)$.

PHOSPHENIMIDOTHIOIC. Related to phosphenimidothioic acid, $HPOS(NH)$.

PHOSPHENIMIDOTHIOLIC. Related to phosphenimidothiolic acid,

$$HSP=O(NH)$$

or $HSP=NH(O)$.

PHOSPHENIMIDOTHIONIC. Related to phosphenimidothionic acid,

$$HOP=S(NH)$$

or $HOP=NH(S)$.

PHOSPHENIMIDOTHIOUS. Related to phosphenimidothious acid $HSP=NH$.

PHOSPHENIMIDOUS. Related to phosphenimidous acid, $HOP=NH$.

PHOSPHENODIIMIDIC. Related to phosphenodiimidic acid, $HOP=NH(NH)$.

PHOSPHENODIIMIDOTHIOIC. Related to phosphenodiimidothioic acid,

$$HSP=NH(NH).$$

PHOSPHENODITHIOIC. Related to phosphenodithioic acid, $HPOS_2$.

PHOSPHENODITHIONIC. Related to phosphenodithionic acid, $HOP=S(S)$.

PHOSPHENODITHIOUS. Related to phosphenodithious acid, $HSP=S$.

PHOSPHENOTHIOIC. Related to phosphenothioic acid, HPO_2S.

PHOSPHENOTHIOLIC. Phosphenothiolic acid, $HSP=O(O)$.

PHOSPHENOTHIOLOTHIONIC. Related to phosphenothiolothionic acid,

$$HSP=O(S)$$

or $HSP=S(O)$.

PHOSPHENOTHIOLOUS. Related to phosphenothiolous acid, $HSP=O$.

PHOSPHENOTHIONIC. Related to phosphenothionic acid, $HOP=O(S)$ or

$$HOP=S(O).$$

PHOSPHENOTHIONOUS. Related to phosphenothionous acid, $HOP=S$.

PHOSPHENOTHIOUS. Related to phosphenothious acid, $HPOS$.

PHOSPHENOTRITHIOIC. Related to phosphenotrithioic acid, $HSP=S(S)$.

PHOSPHENYL. The radical $C_6H_5P<$.

PHOSPHIDE. A compound produced by replacing hydrogen atoms in phosphine by a metal, as calcium phosphide, Ca_3P_2. In other words, a binary, metallic compound of phosphorus.

PHOSPHINE. One of a group of organic compounds which are formed by replacing one or more of the hydrogen atoms of the parent substance phosphine (PH_3), commonly by **alkyl** or **aryl groups.**

-PHOSPHINIC. A suffix indicating a terminal $>P(:O)OH$ group in an organic compound, attached to two radicals, and derived from phosphinic acid, $H_2(O)POH$.

PHOSPHINICO. The radical $HO(O)P=$, in an organic compound (from phosphinic acid).

PHOSPHINIMIDIC. Related to phosphinimidic acid, $HOP(NH)H_2$.

PHOSPHINIMIDOTHIOIC. Related to phosphinimidothioic acid, $HSP(NH)H_2$.

PHOSPHINIMINE. An organic compound containing the type radical

$$>P=N-.$$

PHOSPHINO. The radical H_2P-, in an organic compound.

PHOSPHINODITHIOIC. Related to phosphinodithioic acid, $HSP(S)H_2$.

PHOSPHINOTHIOIC ACID. Related to phosphinothioic acid, H_3POS.

PHOSPHINOTHIOLIC. Related to phosphinothiolic acid, $HSP(O)H_2$.

PHOSPHINOTHIONIC. Related to phosphinothionic acid, $HOP(S)H_2$.

PHOSPHINOTHIOUS. Related to phosphinothious acid, $HSPH_2$.

-PHOSPHINOUS. A suffix indicating a terminal $>POH$ group, attached to two radicals, and related to phosphinous acid, H_2POH.

PHOSPHITE. An anion consisting essentially of trivalent phosphorus and oxy-

gen (with, in some cases, hydrogen) or a compound containing such an anion. There are a number of these anions and compounds, which are defined below under their special designations. Without special designation the ortho-form is generally understood. See also **phosphorous** acid.

PHOSPHITE, ACID. A salt of **phosphorous** acid in which two of its hydrogen atoms have been replaced by a metal.

PHOSPHITE, DIACID. A salt of **phosphorous** acid in which one of its hydrogen atoms has been replaced by a metal.

PHOSPHITE, HYPO-. A salt of hypophosphorous acid $\left(HP{<}{}^{OH}_{OH} \right)$.

PHOSPHITE, META-. See **metaphosphite.**

PHOSPHITE (ORTHO-). The anion $HPO_3^=$ or $H_2PO_3^-$, or a compound containing one of these anions.

PHOSPHITE, PYRO-. See **pyrophosphite.**

PHOSPHO. The radical O_2P-, in an organic compound.

PHOSPHOMOLYBDATE. The anion $PMo_{12}O_{40}^{3-}$, or a compound containing it.

PHOSPHONAMIDIC. Related to phosphonamidic acid, $(HO)(H_2N)P(O)H$.

PHOSPHONAMIDIMIDIC. Related to phosphonamidimidic acid,

$$(HO)(H_2N)P(NH)H.$$

PHOSPHONAMIDODITHIOIC. Related to phosphonamidodithioic acid,

$$(HS)(H_2N)P(S)H.$$

PHOSPHONAMIDIMIDOTHIOIC. Related to phosphonamidimidothioic acid, $(HS)(H_2N)P(NH)H.$

PHOSPHONAMIDODITHIO(THIOCY-ANATIDIC). Related to phosphonamidodithio(thiocyanatidic) acid,

$$(HS)(H_2N)(NCS)PS.$$

PHOSPHONAMIDOTHIOIC. Related to phosphonamidothioic acid, $H_2POS(NH_2)$.

PHOSPHONAMIDOTHIOLIC. Related to phosphonamidothiolic acid,

$$(HS)(H_2N)P(O)H.$$

PHOSPHONAMIDOTHIONIC. Related to phosphonamidothionic acid,

$$(HO)(H_2N)P(S)H.$$

PHOSPHONAMIDOTHIOUS. Related to phosphonamidothious acid,

$$(HS)(H_2N)PH.$$

PHOSPHONAMIDOUS. Related to phosphonamidous acid, $(HO)(H_2N)PH$.

-PHOSPHONIC. A suffix indicating a terminal $-P(:O)(OH)_2$ group, replacing H in an organic compound.

PHOSPHONIMIDIC. Related to phosphonimidic acid, $(HO)_2P(NH)H$.

PHOSPHONIMIDODITHIOIC. Related to phosphonimidodithioic acid,

$$(HS)_2P(NH)H.$$

PHOSPHONIMIDOTHIOIC. Related to phosphonimidothioic acid,

$$(HO)(HS)P(NH)H.$$

PHOSPHONITRYL. The radical

$$N{\equiv}P{=}.$$

PHOSPHONIUM COMPOUNDS. Compounds of phosphine, PH_3, which contain the radical $-PH_4$. They are analogous to ammonium compounds. E.g., PH_4Cl, PH_4Br.

PHOSPHONO. The radical $(HO)_2OP-$, in an organic compound (from phosphonic acid).

PHOSPHONOCHLORIDIC. Related to phosphonochloridic acid, $Cl(HO)P(O)H$.

PHOSPHONOCHLORIDIMIDIC. Related to phosphonochloridimidic acid, $Cl(HO)P(NH)H$.

PHOSPHONOCHLORIDIMIDOTHIOIC. Related to phosphonochloridimidothioic acid, $Cl(HS)P(NH)H$.

PHOSPHONOCHLORIDODITHIOIC. Related to phosphonochloridodithioic acid, $Cl(HS)P(S)H$.

PHOSPHONOCHLORIDOTHIOIC. Related to phosphonochloridothioic acid, H_2POSCl.

PHOSPHONOCHLORIDOTHIOLIC. Related to phosphonochloridothiolic acid, $Cl(HS)P(O)H$.

PHOSPHONOCHLORIDOTHIONIC. Related to phosphonochloridothionic acid, $Cl(HO)P(S)H$.

PHOSPHONOCHLORIDOTHIOUS. Related to phosphonochloridothious acid, $Cl(HS)PH$.

PHOSPHONOCHLORIDOUS. Related to phosphonochloridous acid, $Cl(HO)PH$.

PHOSPHONOCYANIDIC. Related to phosphonocyanidic acid, $(HO)(NC)P(O)H$.

PHOSPHONODITHIOIC. Related to phosphonodithioic acid, H_3POS_2.

PHOSPHONODITHIOLIC. Related to phosphonodithiolic acid, $(HS)_2P(O)H$.

PHOSPHONODITHIOUS. Related to phosphonodithious acid, $(HS)_2PH$.

PHOSPHONONITRIDIC. Related to phosphononitridic acid, $(HO)P(N)H$.

PHOSPHONONITRIDOTHIOIC. Related to phosphononitridothioic acid, $(HS)P(N)H$.

PHOSPHONOTHIOIC. Related to phosphonothioic acid, H_3PO_2S.

PHOSPHONOTHIOLIC. Related to phosphonothiolic acid, $(HO)(HS)P(O)H$.

PHOSPHONOTHIOLOTHIONIC. Related to phosphonothiolothionic acid, $(HO)(HS)P(S)H$.

PHOSPHONOTHIONIC. Related to phosphonothionic acid, $(HO)_2P(S)H$.

PHOSPHONOTHIOUS. Related to phosphonothious acid, $(HO)(HS)PH$.

PHOSPHONOTRITHIOIC. Related to phosphonotrithioic acid, $(HS)_2P(S)H$.

-PHOSPHONOUS. A suffix indicating a terminal $—P(OH)_2$ group in organic compounds (related to phosphonous acid, $HP(OH)_2$).

PHOSPHOPROTEIN. One of a group of conjugated proteins containing phosphorus. See **protein.**

PHOSPHORAMIDIC. Related to phosphoramidic acid, $H_2N(HO)_2PO$.

PHOSPHORAMIDIMIDIC. Related to phosphoramidimidic acid,

$$(HO)_2(H_2N)P(NH).$$

PHOSPHORAMIDIMIDODITHIOIC. Related to phosphoramidimidodithioic acid, $(HS)_2(H_2N)P(NH)$.

PHOSPHORAMIDIMIDOTHIOIC. Related to phosphoramidimidothioic acid, $(HO)(HS)(H_2N)P(NH)$.

PHOSPHORAMIDOCHLORIDIC. Related to phosphoramidochloridic acid, $Cl(HO)(H_2N)PO$.

PHOSPHORAMIDOCHLORIDIMIDIC. Related to phosphoramidochloridimidic acid, $Cl(HO)(H_2N)P(NH)$.

PHOSPHORAMIDOCHLORIDIMIDO-THIOIC. Related to phosphoramidochloridimidothioic acid, $Cl(HS)(H_2N)P(NH)$.

PHOSPHORAMIDOCHLORIDODITHI-OIC. Related to phosphoramidochloridodithioic acid, $Cl(HS)(H_2N)PS$.

PHOSPHORAMIDOCHLORIDOTHI-OIC. Related to phosphoramidochloridothioic acid, $HPClOS(NH_2)$.

PHOSPHORAMIDOCHLORIDOTHI-OLIC. Related to phosphoramidochloridothiolic acid, $Cl(HS)(H_2N)PO$.

PHOSPHORAMIDOCHLORIDOTHI-ONIC. Related to phosphoramidochloridothionic acid, $Cl(HO)(H_2N)PS$.

PHOSPHORAMIDOCHLORIDOTHI-OUS. Related to phosphoramidochloridothious acid, $Cl(HS)(H_2N)P$.

PHOSPHORAMIDOCHLORIDOUS. Related to phosphoramidochloridous acid, $Cl(HO)(H_2N)P$.

PHOSPHORAMIDODITHIOIC. Related to phosphoramidodithioic acid, $H_2POS_2(NH_2)$.

PHOSPHORAMIDODITHIOLIC. Related to phosphoramidodithiolic acid, $(HS)_2(H_2N)PO$.

PHOSPHORAMIDODITHIOUS. Related to phosphoramidodithious acid, $(HS)_2(H_2N)P$.

PHOSPHORAMIDONITRIDIC. Related to phosphoramidonitridic acid,

$$(HO)(H_2N)PN.$$

PHOSPHORAMIDONITRIDOTHIOIC. Related to phosphoramidonitridothioic acid, $(HS)(H_2N)PN$.

PHOSPHORAMIDOTHIOIC. Related to phosphoramidothioic acid, $H_2PO_2S(NH_2)$.

PHOSPHORAMIDOTHIOLIC. Related to phosphoramidothiolic acid,

$$(HO)(HS)(H_2N)PO.$$

PHOSPHORAMIDOTHIOLOTHIONIC. Related to phosphoramidothiolothionic acid, $(HO)(HS)(H_2N)PS$.

PHOSPHORAMIDOTHIONIC. Related to phosphoramidothionic acid,

$$(HO)_2(H_2N)PS.$$

PHOSPHORAMIDOTHIOUS. Related to phosphoramidothious acid,

$$(HO)(HS)(H_2N)P.$$

PHOSPHORAMIDOTRITHIOIC. Related to phosphoramidotrithioic acid, $(HS)_2(H_2N)PS.$

PHOSPHORAMIDOUS. Related to phosphoramidous acid, $(HO)_2(H_2N)P.$

PHOSPHORATO. The radical $O_4P{<}$ occurring in an inorganic compound.

PHOSPHORESCENCE. A term often applied to processes, commonly in living organisms, in which light is emitted without a rise in temperature. The phenomenon is exemplified by the light emitted by the element phosphorus (white or yellow variety) upon exposure to air, whereupon slow oxidation occurs. The luminosity of animals, such as fireflies and certain marine infusoria, is also probably a slow oxidation of certain organic substances. All these processes in living organisms probably do not comply rigidly with the physical definition of the process, which is the emission of energy obtained by the absorption of radiations of a different frequency. In this sense, phosphorescence differs from fluorescence merely in that in the latter the emission ceases as soon as the absorption of radiation does, whereas in phosphorescence the process continues for some time afterward.

PHOSPHORETTED. Combined with phosphorus, especially "phosphoretted hydrogen" or phosphine, PH_3.

PHOSPHORIC. (1) Containing pentavalent phosphorus. (2) Related to phosphoric acid (ortho), H_3PO_4, phosphoric acid (meta), HPO_3, or phosphoric acid (pyro), $H_4P_2O_7$.

PHOSPHORIMIDIC. Related to phosphorimidic acid, $(HO)_3P(NH).$

PHOSPHORIMIDODITHIOIC. Related to phosphorimidodithioic acid,

$$(HO)(HS)_2P(NH).$$

PHOSPHORIMIDOTHIOIC. Related to phosphorimidothioic acid,

$$(HO)_2(HS)P(NH).$$

PHOSPHORIMIDOTRITHIOIC. Related to phosphorimidotrithioic acid,

$$(HS)_3P(NH).$$

PHOSPHORIODIDIC. Related to phosphoriodidic acid, $I(HO)_2PO.$

PHOSPHORISOCYANATIDIC. Related to phosphorisocyanatidic acid,

$$(HO)_2(OCN)PO.$$

PHOSPHORISOCYANIDIC. Related to phosphorisocyanidic acid, $(HO)_2(CN)PO.$

PHOSPHORISOTHIOCYANATIDIC. Related to phosphorisothiocyanatidic acid, $(HO)_2(SCN)PO.$

PHOSPHORO. The radical $—P{:}P—$, in organic compounds.

PHOSPHOROBROMIDIC. Related to phosphorobromidic acid, $Br(HO)_2PO.$

PHOSPHOROCHLORIDIC. Related to phosphorochloridic acid, $Cl(HO)_2PO.$

PHOSPHOROCHLORIDIMIDIC. Related to phosphorochloridimidic acid,

$$Cl(HO)_2P(NH).$$

PHOSPHOROCHLORIDIMIDODITHIOIC. Related to phosphorochloridimidodithioic acid, $Cl(HS)_2P(NH).$

PHOSPHOROCHLORIDIMIDOTHIOIC. Related to phosphorochloridimidothioic acid, $Cl(HO)(HS)P(NH).$

PHOSPHOROCHLORIDODITHIOIC. Related to phosphorochloridodithioic acid, $H_2PClOS_2.$

PHOSPHOROCHLORIDODITHIOLIC. Related to phosphorochloridodithiolic acid, $Cl(HS)_2PO.$

PHOSPHOROCHLORIDODITHIOUS. Related to phosphorochloridodithious acid, $Cl(HS)_2P.$

PHOSPHOROCHLORIDOFLUORIDIC. Related to phosphorochloridofluoridic acid, ClF(HO)PO.

PHOSPHOROCHLORIDONITRIDIC. Related to phosphorochloridonitridic acid, Cl(HO)PN.

PHOSPHOROCHLORIDONITRIDO-THIOIC. Related to phosphorochloridonitridothioic acid, Cl(HS)PN.

PHOSPHOROCHLORIDOTHIOIC. Related to phosphorochloridothioic acid, H_2PClO_2S.

PHOSPHOROCHLORIDOTHIOLIC. Related to phosphorochloridothiolic acid, Cl(HO)(HS)PO.

PHOSPHOROCHLORIDOTHIONIC. Related to phosphorochloridothionic acid, Cl(HO)$_2$PS.

PHOSPHOROCHLORIDOTHIOLOTHI-ONIC. Related to phosphorochloridothiolothionic acid, Cl(HO)(HS)PS.

PHOSPHOROCHLORIDOTHIOUS. Related to phosphorochloridothious acid, Cl(HO)(HS)P.

PHOSPHOROCHLORIDOUS. Related to phosphorochloridous acid, Cl(HO)$_2$P.

PHOSPHOROCYANATIDIC. Related to phosphorocyanatidic acid,

$$(HO)_2(NCO)PO.$$

PHOSPHOROCYANIDIC. Related to phosphorocyanidic acid, $(HO)_2(NC)PO.$

PHOSPHORODIAMIDIC. Related to phosphorodiamidic acid, $(H_2N)_2(HO)PO.$

PHOSPHORODIAMIDIMIDOTHIOIC. Related to phosphorodiamidimidothioic acid, $(HS)(H_2N)_2P(NH).$

PHOSPHORODIAMIDODITHIOIC. Related to phosphorodiamidodithioic acid, $(HS)(H_2N)_2PS.$

PHOSPHORODIAMIDOTHIOIC. Related to phosphorodiamidothioic acid,

$$HPOS(NH_2)_2.$$

PHOSPHORODIAMIDOTHIOLIC. Related to phosphorodiamidothiolic acid,

$$(HS)(H_2N)_2PO.$$

PHOSPHORODIAMIDOTHIONIC. Related to phosphorodiamidothionic acid, $(HO)(H_2N)_2PS.$

PHOSPHORODIAMIDOTHIOUS. Related to phosphorodiamidothious acid, $(HS)(H_2N)_2P.$

PHOSPHORODIAMIDOUS. Related to phosphorodiamidous acid, $(HO)(H_2N)_2P.$

PHOSPHORODICHLORIDIC. Related to phosphorodichloridic acid, $Cl_2(HO)PO.$

PHOSPHORODICHLORIDIMIDIC. Related to phosphorodichloridimidic acid, $Cl_2(HO)P(NH).$

PHOSPHORODICHLORIDIMIDOTHI-OIC. Related to phosphorodichloridimidothioic acid, $Cl_2(HS)P(NH).$

PHOSPHORODICHLORIDODITHIOIC. Related to phosphorodichloridodithioic acid, $Cl_2(HS)PS.$

PHOSPHORODICHLORIDOTHIOIC. Related to phosphorodichloridothioic acid, HPCl$_2$OS.

PHOSPHORODICHLORIDOTHIOLIC. Related to phosphorodichloridothiolic acid, $Cl_2(HS)PO.$

PHOSPHORODICHLORIDOTHIONIC. Related to phosphorodichloridothionic acid, $Cl_2(HO)PS.$

PHOSPHORODICHLORIDOTHIOUS. Related to phosphorodichloridothious acid, $Cl_2(HS)P$

PHOSPHORODICHLORIDOUS. Related to phosphorodichloridous acid,

$$Cl_2(HO)P.$$

PHOSPHORODITHIOIC. Related to phosphorodithioic acid, $H_3PO_2S_2.$

PHOSPHORODITHIOLIC. Related to phosphorodithiolic acid, $(HO)(HS)_2PO.$

PHOSPHORODITHIOLOTHIONIC. Related to phosphorodithiolothionic acid, $(HO)(HS)_2PS$.

PHOSPHORODITHIOUS. Related to phosphorodithious acid, $(HO)(HS)_2P$.

PHOSPHOROFLUORIDIC. Related to phosphorofluoridic acid, $F(HO)_2PO$.

PHOSPHOROMETER. An instrument similar to a **radiometer** used for the measurement of **phosphorescence** phenomena.

PHOSPHORONITRIDIC. Related to phosphoronitridic acid, $(HO)_2PN$.

PHOSPHORONITRIDODITHIOIC. Related to phosphoronitridodithioic acid, $(HS)_2PN$.

PHOSPHORONITRIDOTHIOIC. Related to phosphoronitridothioic acid,

$$(HO)(HS)PN.$$

PHOSPHOROSO. The radical OP—, in organic compounds.

PHOSPHOROTETRATHIOIC. Related to phosphorotetrathioic acid, $(HS)_3PS$.

PHOSPHOROTHIOCYANATIDIC. Related to phosphorothiocyanatidic acid,

$$(HO)_2(NCS)PO.$$

PHOSPHOROTHIOIC. Related to phosphorothioic acid, H_3PO_3S.

PHOSPHOROTHIOLIC. Related to phosphorothiolic acid, $(HO)_2(HS)PO$.

PHOSPHOROTHIOLOTHIONIC. Related to phosphorothiolothionic acid,

$$(HO)_2(HS)PS.$$

PHOSPHOROTHIONIC. Related to phosphorothionic acid, $(HO)_3PS$.

PHOSPHOROTHIOUS. Related to phosphorothious acid, $(HO)_2(HS)P$.

PHOSPHOROTRITHIOIC. Related to phosphorotrithioic acid, H_3POS_3.

PHOSPHOROTRITHIOLIC. Related to phosphorotrithiolic acid, $(HS)_3PO$.

PHOSPHOROTRITHIOUS. Related to phosphorotrithious acid, $(HS)_3P$.

PHOSPHOROUS. (1) Containing or pertaining to trivalent phosphorus.
(2) Related to phosphorous acid (ortho), H_3PO_3, phosphorous acid (meta), HPO_2, or phosphorous acid (pyro), $H_4P_2O_5$.

PHOSPHORUS. Non-metallic element. Symbol P. Atomic number 15. Atomic weight 30.975. Phosphorus exists in several allotropic modifications: (1) Ordinary crystalline phosphorus (white or yellow). Density 1.82. Melting point 44° C. Boiling point 280° C. This form of phosphorus exists in alpha, beta, and gamma modifications, which differ slightly in melting point and other properties. The melting point of the gamma modification is 46° C. (2) Red phosphorus. Rhombohedral crystals. Density 2.34. Boiling point 590° C. (at 43 atmospheres), formed by heating white phosphorus. (3) Violet phosphorus (crystalline). Density 2.4. Melting point 590° C. (4) Black phosphorus (alpha). Density 2.69. A metallic substance, forming rhombohedral crystals, obtained by heating yellow phosphorus under pressure with molten lead. (5) Black (beta) phosphorus. Density 2.7. Melting point 588° C. It differs from black (alpha) phosphorus in being a fairly good conductor of electricity. Valences of phosphorus 1, 3, 4, and 5. Oxides P_2O_3, P_2O_4, and P_2O_5.

PHOSPHORYL. The radical $\equiv P{=}O$, as in phosphoryl bromide $POBr_3$.

PHOSPHOTUNGSTATE. The anion $PW_{12}O_{40}{}^{3-}$ or $P_2W_{16}O_{56}{}^{6-}$, or a compound containing one of these anions.

PHOT. A unit of illumination intensity. One phot is equal to one **lumen** per square centimeter.

PHOTOCATALYSIS. The **catalysis** of a chemical reaction achieved by irradiation with light, usually in the optical or the **ultraviolet** region of the spectrum.

PHOTOCATALYST. A substance which promotes a reaction that is catalyzed by light. The most universal reaction of this type is the **photosynthesis** of **carbohydrates** in green plants from carbon dioxide and water. It is accelerated by light in the presence of chlorophyll, the photocatalyst of the reaction.

PHOTOCHEMICAL. Related to the effects of radiation, commonly in the region of visible or ultraviolet light, upon a chemical reaction.

PHOTOCHEMICAL CATALYSIS. The same as **photocatalysis** (q.v.).

PHOTOCHEMICAL EQUILIBRIUM. See **equilibrium, photochemical.**

PHOTOCHEMICAL EQUIVALENT, LAW OF. See **law, Stark-Einstein.**

PHOTOCHEMICAL REACTION. See **reaction, photochemical.**

PHOTOCHEMISTRY. That branch of chemistry which is concerned with effects produced by radiant energy.

PHOTOCONDUCTIVITY. In general, the increase in electrical **conductivity** of a substance when illuminated, commonly by visible or ultraviolet light. Specifically, the effect is most marked in some crystals which show a substantial charge in conductivity when illuminated.

PHOTODISINTEGRATION REACTION. See **reaction, photodisintegration.**

PHOTOELECTRIC CELL. See **phototube.**

PHOTOELECTRON. See **electron, photo-.**

PHOTOISOMERIC CHANGE. The conversion of one **isomer** into another as a result of the action of light, e.g., *anti*nitrobenzaldoxime changes, when exposed to light, into the more stable *syn* form, and anthracene dimerizes to dianthracene.

PHOTOLYSIS. Photochemical **decomposition,** in other words a chemical decomposition resulting from the action of light.

PHOTOLYTIC. Pertaining to a reaction in which a substance is decomposed or split by radiant energy.

PHOTOMETER. An instrument for measuring relative **radiant power** or relative **luminous flux** or some function of these quantities.

PHOTOMETRIC. Relating to measurements or methods of measurement of intensity of light.

PHOTOMETRY. The measurement of luminous intensity, **luminous flux** density or illumination, and the physical princiiplse underlying such measurements.

PHOTOMICROGRAPH. A photograph of a microscopic object obtained by attaching a camera to a microscope.

PHOTON. The corpuscle which, according to the **de Broglie theory** of the duality of matter and radiation, is equivalent to radiant energy of amount $h\nu$, where h is **Planck's constant,** and ν is the frequency of the radiation.

PHOTOPOLYMERIZATION. The **polymerization** of a substance when it is exposed to light, e.g., of anthracene to dianthracene.

PHOTOSENSITIZATION. The initiation of a chemical reaction by irradiation of an intermediary substance. The intermediary absorbs the radiation, is excited to a state of high energy, and initiates the process by collisions with the reactants, thereby transferring part or all of its excess energy to the reactants.

PHOTOSTABLE. Not altered upon exposure to light.

PHOTOSYNTHESIS. (1) A synthesis of sugars from carbon dioxide and water by the action of **chlorophyll** which has been irradiated with sunlight. (2) More generally, any synthesis of sugars or starches by means of a biochemical **catalyst** exposed to radiation.

PHOTOTRANSMUTATION REACTION. The same as **reaction, photodisintegration.**

PHOTOTROPY. A reversible isomeric change in solid substances attributable to the influence of light energy and accompanied by a color change.

PHOTOTUBE. A photosensitive or light-actuated **electron tube,** consisting essentially of a cathode which is photosensitive, i.e., which will emit electrons when illuminated, and an anode for collecting the electrons emitted by the cathode. Phototubes are used in innumerable industrial and scientific control operations which are governed by variation in intensity, or complete interruption, of a beam of light.

PHTHAL-. See **phthalo-.**

PHTHALAL. See **phthalylidene.**

PHTHALATE. A compound containing the radical

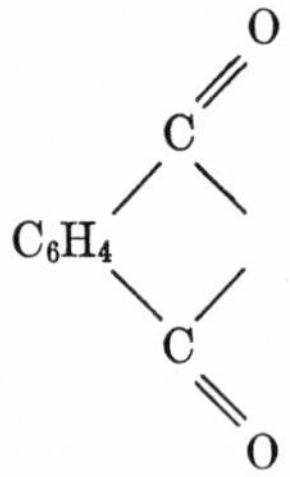

derived from phthalic acid.

PHTHALEIN. A derivative of phthalic anhydride containing two phenolic residues, as fluorescein (resorcinolphthalein) is formed by condensing one molecule of phthalic anhydride with two molecules of resorcinol.

PHTHALIC. Related to phthalic acid' $C_6H_4(COOH)_2$.

PHTHALIDE. The compound

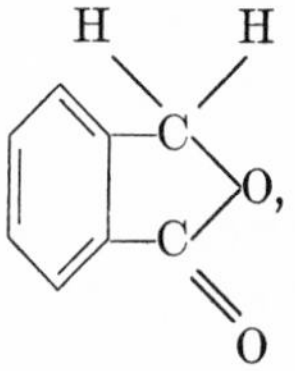

which can be produced by several methods, one of which is the reduction of phthalic anhydride with zinc and hydrochloric acid. Radicals derived from phthalide enter into many compounds.

PHTHALIDENE. See **phthalidylidene.**

PHTHALIDYL. The radical

$$C_6H_4.CO.O.CH—$$

(from **phthalide**).

PHTHALIDYLIDENE. The radical

$$C_6H_4.CO.O.C{=}$$

(from **phthalide**).

PHTHALIMIDO. The radical

$$C_6H_4(CO)_2N— \ (o).$$

PHTHALO-, PHTHAL-. A prefix relating to phthalic acid, as phthalocyanine, phthalide.

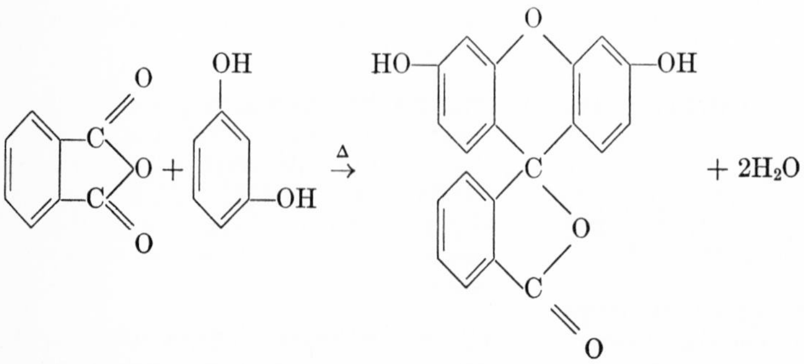

PHTHALOYL. The radical

$$-OCC_6H_4CO- \ (o).$$

PHTHALYLIDENE. The radical

$$=HCC_6H_4CH= \ (o).$$

PHYLLO-, PHYLL-. (Greek: **phyllos**, leaf) A prefix relating to leaves, as phylloporphyrin (a decomposition product of chlorophyll).

PHYSICOCHEMICAL. Pertaining to physical chemistry, see **chemistry, physical.**

PHYT-, PHYTO-. (Greek) A prefix relating to plants, as phytosterol, phytase.

PHYTOCHEMISTRY. The science that deals with the chemical changes occurring in vegetable organisms.

PHYTYL. The radical

$$(CH_3)_2CH(CH_2)_3CH(CH_3)(CH_2)_3CH(CH_3)(CH_2)_3C(CH_3):CHCH_2-.$$

PI (Π OR π). The sixteenth letter in the Greek alphabet, used to denote the sixteenth carbon atom in a straight-chain compound, or a derivative in which a substituent group is attached to that carbon atom (π-). Symbol for peri- (π). The constant 3.14159 ... the ratio of the circumference of a circle to the diameter (π). Peltier coefficient (π).

PICCARD TEST REACTION. Trivalent titanium gives a yellow to orange-yellow color with oxalic acid and with pyrocatechol.

PICCININI REAGENT FOR POTASSIUM AND SODIUM. A 2.5% solution of γ-methyldicyanodihydroxyhydropyridine, which precipitates long, fine needles with sodium salts, and prisms with potassium salts.

PICEAN RING. A four-membered ring which exists in certain **terpenes,** viz.,

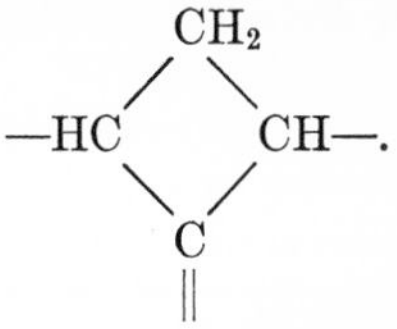

PICKLING. Immersion in acid, as for example in the cleaning of certain metal surfaces by washing them with dilute solutions of mineral acids.

PICON TEST REACTION. Thallium is detected by adding to 1–2 ml. of the solution tested 1 drop carbon disulfide, an excess of ammonium hydroxide and ammonium sulfide, and heating until the carbon disulfide boils. A black precipitate, turning red, indicates thallium.

PICR-, PICRO-. A prefix meaning bitter, as picrotoxin, picric acid.

PICRYL. The radical

$$2,4,6\text{-}(NO_2)_3C_6H_2-.$$

PICTET-GAMS ISOQUINOLINE SYNTHESIS. A method of formation of isoquinolines from acylated aminoethylphenyl alcohols or their ethers.

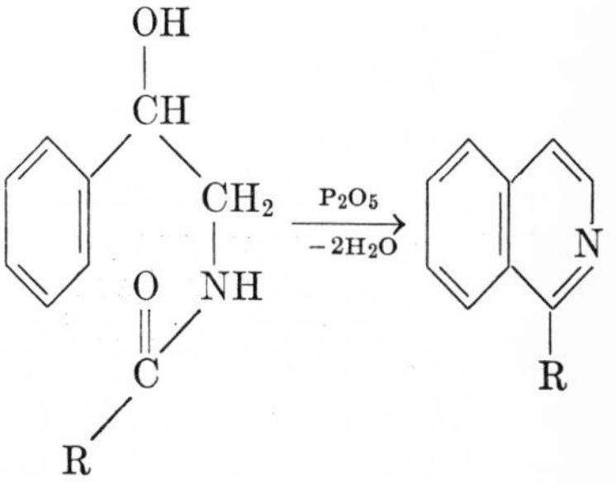

PICTET-HUBERT REACTION. A method of formation of phenanthridine derivatives by dehydration of acyl-ortho-xenylamines. The Pictet-Hubert method is heating at 250–300° C. with zinc chloride; the Morgan-Walls method is by treatment with $POCl_3$ in nitrobenzene.

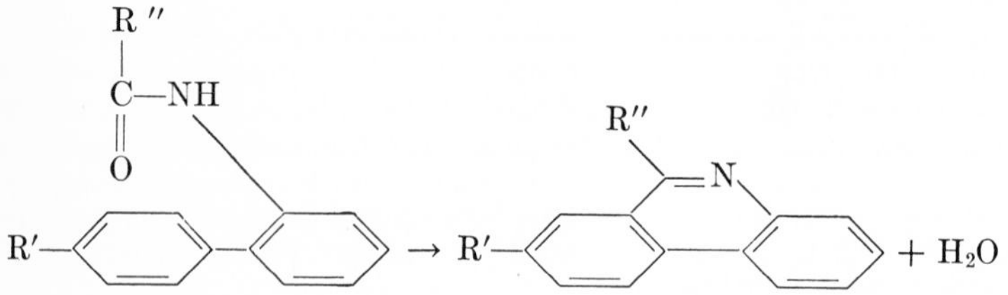

and 3 g. hydroxylamine hydrochloride, followed by dilution with water to a total volume of 50 ml. It is used in testing oils for sulfur and carbon disulfide. It gives a black precipitate or a dark colored solu-

PICTET-SPENGLER ISOQUINOLINE SYNTHESIS. A method of formation of tetrahydroisoquinoline derivatives from β aromatic ethylamines and aldehydes (and other carbonyl compounds).

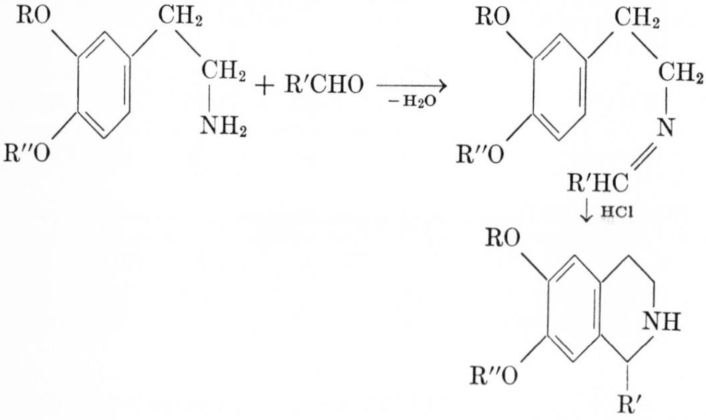

tion with oils containing sulfur or carbon disulfide.

PIETSCH-ROMAN REAGENT. A solution of 5 g. quinalizarin in 100 ml. ammo-

PIDGEON PROCESS. A process for the production of metallic magnesium from magnesium oxide by reduction with ferrosilicon, and volatilization of the magnesium.

PIER PROCESS. The utilization of bitumious coal instead of coke in generators during the manufacture of fuel and illuminating gases. The generator and fuel are arranged in such a manner as to insure the use of all the bituminous coal present.

PIERCE REAGENT. A solution of 1 g. cupric sulfate in 10–15 ml. water, to which is then added 4 ml. ammonium hydroxide

nium hydroxide, used as a test reagent for gallium, indium, and thallium. Characteristic precipitates are formed.

PIETTE COKE OVEN. A by-product coke oven for the production of coke by the regenerative heating and distillation of coal.

PIEZO-CHEMISTRY. Literally, "pressure chemistry," a term applied to chemical reactions and processes conducted under high pressure, and the effect of the pressure upon them.

PIEZO EFFECT. An electro-elastic property of certain crystals by means of which mechanical energy may be converted into electrical energy and vice versa.

PIEZO-ELECTRICITY. Electricity produced by pressure (elastic deformation). The phenomenon is observed in certain crystals, e.g., tourmaline, mica, calcite, and quartz, which become electrically charged when subjected to pressure. One end of the crystal becomes positively charged and the other negatively charged.

PIEZOMETER. An instrument for determining the compressibility of various substances, particularly at very high pressures.

PIEZOMETER RING. A hollow ring surrounding a pipe to which it is connected by several symmetrically spaced small holes so that the pressure in the ring is the average of the various values obtained at the holes in the pipe. A piezometer, or other pressure-measuring device, is connected to the ring to measure this average pressure.

PIGMENT. A coloring substance. The term originally connoted a paint pigment, a colored substance used in preparing surface coatings, and which was, therefore, insoluble in water and commonly applied to the surface in the form of a suspension of its particles. The use of the term has widened to include many other classes of colored substances, such as many substances elaborated by living organisms.

PILE, RADIOACTIVE. An apparatus for the controlled conduct of **nuclear fission** reactions, attended by the production of energy, by means of a self-maintained reaction of particles emitted by substances undergoing nuclear disintegration. The first pile was operated at the University of Chicago where masses of uranium metal and oxide were distributed among masses of graphite (in a graphite chamber) with removable rods of cadmium or boron steel to control the rate of reaction by shielding the uranium by their absorption of neutrons. The radioactive pile is preferably designated by the term nuclear reactor.

PILE, THERMO-. A series of **thermocouples,** i.e., junctions of two metals arranged so that their contact **potential difference** yields a measurable current, as by connecting them in a circuit which contains two contact points, at different temperatures, between the two metals.

PILHASHY TEST FOR FORMALDEHYDE. One g. phenylhydrazine hydrochloride and 1.5 g. sodium acetate are dissolved in 10 ml. water. Five drops of the solution tested, on heating with 5 drops of this reagent and 5 drops sulfuric acid for 1 minute and standing for a few minutes, give a green color if formaldehyde is present.

PILOT FLAME. A small flame that burns continuously and is used to ignite a larger flame that is operated intermittently, often by automatic control of its fuel supply.

PILOT PLANT. A small-scale industrial process operated to test the application of a chemical or other manufacturing process under conditions that will yield information useful in the design and operation of full-scale manufacturing equipment. Commonly, the pilot plant serves to disclose the special problems to be solved in adapting a method, which has proved successful in the laboratory, to the plant.

PILOTY ALLOXAZINE SYNTHESIS. A method of condensation of violuric acids and m-aromatic diamines to form alloxazine, isoalloxazine, or their derivatives.

PILOTY-ROBINSON PYRROLE SYN-THESIS. Ring closure to form pyrroles from azines of enolizable ketones.

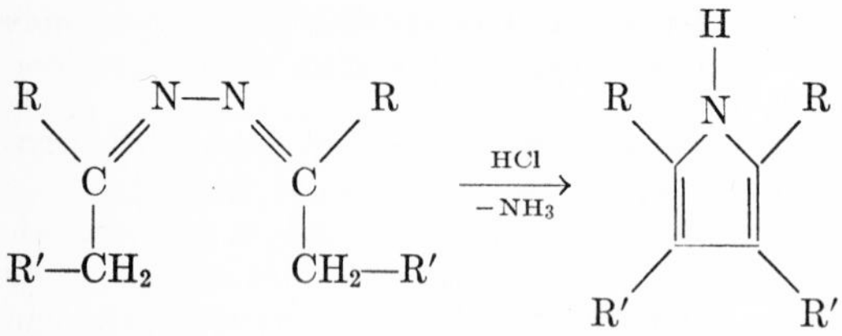

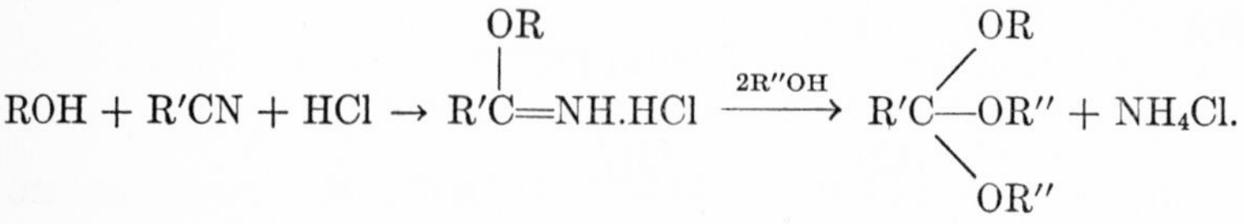

PINT. A measure of volume in the English system. Certain of its equivalent values in other units are given below:

$$
\begin{array}{c}
R \\ \diagdown \\ C \\ | \\ R'-CH_2
\end{array}
\begin{array}{c}
N-N \\ \diagup \quad \diagdown \\ \quad \quad C \\ \quad \quad | \\ \quad \quad CH_2-R'
\end{array}
\xrightarrow[-NH_3]{HCl}
\begin{array}{c}
H \\ | \\ N \\ R \diagup \diagdown R \\ | \quad | \\ R' \quad R'
\end{array}
$$

PIN-, PINO-. (Latin: *pinus*, pine) A prefix relating to pine or pinene, as pinic acid, pinocarvone.

PINACOLONE REARRANGEMENT. A rearrangement of pinacol compounds, in the presence of mineral acids or iodine, to yield **ketones** or **aldehydes**.

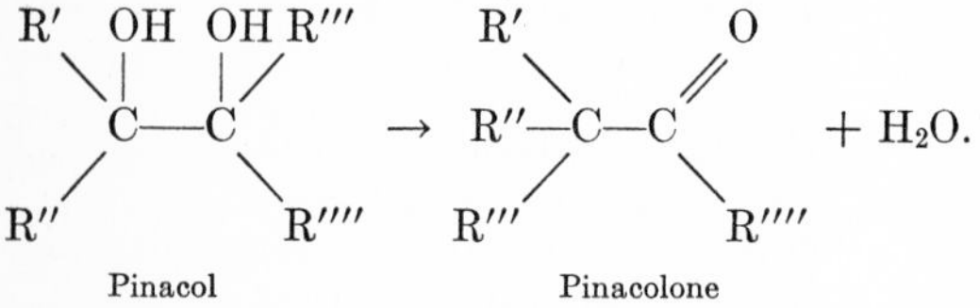

One U.S. pint, liquid	= 16 U.S. fluid ounces
One U.S. pint, liquid	= 473.18 cubic centimeters
One U.S. pint, dry	= 33.6003 cubic inches
One U.S. pint, dry	= 550.61 cubic centimeters

$$
\begin{array}{c}
R' \quad OH \quad OH \quad R''' \\
\diagdown \quad | \qquad | \quad \diagup \\
\quad C \!-\! C \\
\diagup \qquad \quad \diagdown \\
R'' \qquad \qquad R''''
\end{array}
\rightarrow
\begin{array}{c}
R' \qquad \qquad O \\
\diagdown \qquad \quad \diagup\!\!\diagup \\
R''\!-\!C\!-\!C \\
\diagup \qquad \quad \diagdown \\
R''' \qquad \qquad R''''
\end{array}
+ H_2O.
$$

     Pinacol   Pinacolone

PINNER AMIDINE SYNTHESIS. A method of formation of amidines from nitriles by treatment first with HCl and alcohol (to form the imidoester) and then with amines.

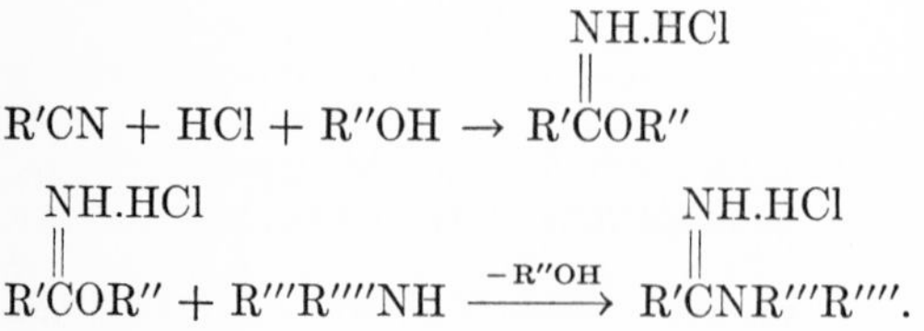

PINTSCH GAS. See **gas, Pintsch.**

PION. A π-meson.

PIOSCOPE. A milk **colorimeter,** cali-

$$
\begin{array}{c}
\qquad \quad NH.HCl \\
\qquad \quad \| \\
R'CN + HCl + R''OH \rightarrow R'COR''
\end{array}
$$

$$
\begin{array}{c}
NH.HCl \qquad \qquad \qquad NH.HCl \\
\| \qquad \qquad \qquad \qquad \| \\
R'COR'' + R'''R''''NH \xrightarrow{-R''OH} R'CNR'''R''''.
\end{array}
$$

PINNER METHOD. A method of producing orthoesters by the action of alcohols on imidoesters, which may be made by condensing an alcohol and a nitrile with HCl.

brated for reading the content of cream or butterfat.

PIPERIDINE. The compound hexahydro-pyridine, made by the strong reduction of

$$
\begin{array}{c}
\qquad \qquad OR \\
\qquad \qquad | \\
ROH + R'CN + HCl \rightarrow R'C\!\!=\!\!NH.HCl \xrightarrow{2R''OH}
\end{array}
\begin{array}{c}
OR \\
\diagup \\
R'C\!-\!OR'' + NH_4Cl. \\
\diagdown \\
OR''
\end{array}
$$

pyridine:

$$\text{Pyridine} \xrightarrow{[+6H]} \text{Piperidine}$$

PIPERIDYL. The radical $C_5H_{10}N-$ (from piperidine, 4 isomers).

PIPERONYL. The radical

$$3,4\text{-}(CH_2O_2)C_6H_3CH_2-.$$

PIPERONYLIDENE. The radical

$$3,4\text{-}(CH_2O_2)C_6H_3CH=.$$

PIPETTE. A glass vessel used to hold temporarily or to deliver a specified volume of liquid. The common form, especially in larger sizes, is a small-bore intake tube (commonly with a capillary tip to avoid loss of drops), which expands into a large-bore central portion, contracting again into a small-bore upper portion. Liquid is commonly drawn into the pipette by suction applied at the top until a graduated mark on the upper tube is reached, where a definite volume of liquid is contained or will be delivered in a specified time at a given temperature. These data on volume, time, and temperature are usually etched on the surface of the central part of the pipette.

Many pipettes, especially 1, 2, 5, and 10 ml. volumes, used commonly in bacteriological work, are straight-bore tubes drawn to a jet at the bottom end and to a narrower bore at the top end. They are generally calibrated at 0.1 ml. intervals.

PIPETTE, BABCOCK. A pipette used in milk analysis, usually calibrated to deliver 17.6 ml. in 5 to 8 seconds.

PIPETTE, DUDLEY. A pipette used in viscosity determinations. It is usually calibrated to deliver 100 ml. of water at 10° C. in 35 seconds.

PIPETTE, GAS. An apparatus used in gas analysis, consisting of bulbs for selective absorption, together with the necessary interconnecting tubing and stopcocks.

PIPETTE, MOHR. A pipette with a uniform bore, graduated in divisions as small as 0.01 ml., and ranging in capacity from 0.1 to 1.0 ml. Larger sizes reach 25 ml. in capacity, and commonly have 0.1 ml. graduations. Some types have a stopcock so that they can also be used as burettes.

PIPETTE, OSTWALD. A pipette used in viscosity determinations, usually by the Poiseuille method (q.v.).

PIPETTE, OSTWALD-FOLIN. A pipette used in milk determinations. It is commonly designed "to deliver" the total volume by blowing out the last drop. It is usually made of capillary tubing, with an enlarged central portion.

PIRIA REACTION. Sulfonation and reduction of an aromatic nitro-compound by treatment with a sulfite and a mineral acid, such as hydrochloric acid. For example, nitrobenzene gives sulfanilic acid, nitrotoluene gives the corresponding toluidine-sulfonic acid, and α-nitronaphthalene gives naphthionic acid.

$$\text{NO}_2\text{-benzene} \xrightarrow[\text{HCl}]{\text{Na}_2\text{SO}_3} \text{NH}_2\text{-benzene-SO}_3\text{H}$$

PITTARELLI TEST FOR ASCORBIC ACID (VITAMIN C). (1) A solution of ascorbic acid on addition of cupric sulfate solution, and dilute ammonium thiocyanate solution drop-by-drop gives a white precipitate and then a green color with more ammonium thiocyanate.

(2) A solution of ascorbic acid gives a white precipitate with mercuric chloride solutions.

PIVALYL. The radical $(CH_3)_3CCO-$ (from pivalic acid).

PLACE ISOMERISM. See isomerism, place.

PLAIT POINT. The point at which two **conjugate solutions** of partially miscible liquids have the same composition, so that the two layers become one.

PLANCK CONSTANT. The constant in the Planck equation $\epsilon = h\nu$, in which ϵ is the energy of the **quantum,** h is Planck's constant, and ν is the frequency of the radiation. Planck's constant is also called the constant of action. Its value is 6.6238×10^{-27} erg second.

PLANE OF SYMMETRY. An imaginary plane by which a body is divided into two parts, each of which is the exact mirror image of the other.

PLANE SYMMETRIC CONFIGURATION. The malenoid form. See **isomerism, geometric.**

PLANT HORMONE. One of a group of substances which is formed in plants, and which initiates, controls, or retards various **metabolic processes** within the plant, acting in the manner of, if not as, a positive or negative catalyst. Plant hormones include auxin a and b, traumatic acid, ethylene, and many other substances. In recent years, there has been a great expansion in the use of these substances, as, for instance, 2,4-dichlorophenoxyacetic acid, its sodium salt and its esters, for the control of weeds.

PLANT PIGMENTS. The distinctive green color of leaves and many other plant organs results from the presence in such organs of two pigments called chlorophyll a and chlorophyll b. In the higher plants these pigments occur only in the chloroplasts. The molecular formula for chlorophyll a is $C_{55}H_{72}O_5N_4Mg$; for chlorophyll b, $C_{55}H_{70}O_6N_4Mg$. The structural formulas for the molecules of the chlorophylls have also been worked out. The chlorophylls are not water-soluble but can readily be dissolved out of leaf tissues with alcohol, acetone, ether, or other organic solvents. The resulting solutions exhibit the phenomenon of fluorescence; they are deep green when held between an observer and the light, but deep red when viewed in reflected light. The chlorophylls play an indispensable biological role because their presence in plant cells is essential for the occurrence of **photosynthesis.**

Invariably associated with the chlorophylls in the chloroplasts are the yellow pigments carotene and the xanthophylls. These pigments are not, however, restricted in their occurrence to the chloroplasts, but may also be present in non-green parts of the plant where they commonly occur in chromoplasts. Collectively these pigments, together with certain others which are closely related chemically, are called the carotinoids.

Most of the red, blue, and purple pigments of plants belong to the group of anthocyanins. These pigments are chemically related to the **glycosides** and usually occur dissolved in the cell sap, being water-soluble. In general the anthocyanins are red in an acid solution and change in color through purple to blue as the solution becomes more alkaline.

Another group of cell-sap water-soluble pigments is the anthoxanthins. These pigments are also chemically related to the glycosides. Anthoxanthins often occur in the plant in a colorless form, but under suitable conditions their typical yellow or orange color becomes apparent.

PLASMA SUBSTITUTE. A product prepared from chemical substances for use in solutions for intravenous injection in shock or other conditions for which injections of natural plasma are indicated. One of the widely-used substances in formulating plasma substitutes is polyvinyl pyrrolidone.

PLASMOLYSIS. Abstraction of water from cells by bathing them in hypertonic solutions of salts, e.g., employing **osmotic pressure** to concentrate the cell sap. It is evident that, if the osmotic pressure of the cell is known, plasmolysis offers a means of approximately determining the osmotic pressure of "unknown" solutions.

PLASTICITY. A property of substances which expresses their ease of deformation without fracture, or, in other words, the ease with which they can be formed, or changed in shape, with a minimum of pressure.

PLASTICIZER. A substance added to an organic mixture or material to keep it soft and to avoid the cracking, checking and other undesirable effects of brittleness. Plasticizers are widely used in the plastics, lacquer, and synthetic fabric industries.

PLASTICS. Various materials, natural or synthetic, which exist in two states, soft and hard, so that they can be shaped while soft into a form desired of the finished hard, durable article. Plastic materials are of two major types: (1) those which are rigid at ordinary temperatures and, when subjected to increased temperature and pressure, become softened so as to permit bending and forming; and (2) those which in the process of working soften sufficiently—generally when subjected to increased temperature and pressure, so they can be made to fill molds or forms. Representative plastic materials are rubber, glass, and the various natural and synthetic plastics such as those made by polymerization of organic substances, such as cellulose acetate, phenol-formaldehyde, urea-formaldehyde, methyl methacrylate, glycerol-phthalic acid, etc.

PLASTOMETER. An apparatus for measuring plasticity, consisting essentially of a capillary tube, arranged so that the rate of flow of the material through successive increments of length of the tube may be determined.

PLATE. A flat object, commonly of circular shape, used to hold a relatively small amount of a solid or liquid. Many fractionating columns or towers consist of a number of plates, which are provided with means for permitting the flow of the vapors rising through the tower, and the flow of the descending condensed liquid with which the vapors are to be brought into contact.

PLATE EFFICIENCY, OVER-ALL. The ratio of the number of theoretical plates in a fractionating column to the number of actual plates required for the operation.

PLATEAU. A term used in the technology of counters to denote the more or less horizontal portion of the curve of counting rate as a function of voltage.

PLATINAMMINE. An ammonium compound of platinum of the general formula, $X_4(NH_3)_4$ Pt, in which X is a general symbol for univalent acid radicals.

PLATINATE (HYDROXO-). The anion Pt $(OH)_6^=$, or a compound containing it.

PLATINATE (META-). The anion $PtO_3^=$, or a compound containing it.

PLATING. See **electroplating.**

PLATINIC. Containing or relating to quadrivalent **platinum.**

PLATINIZE. To coat, plate, or combine with **platinum.**

PLATINOCYANIDE. See **cyanoplatinate (II).**

PLATINOUS. Containing or relating to bivalent **platinum.**

PLATINUM. Metallic element. Symbol Pt. Atomic number 78. Atomic weight 195.23. Density values range from 21.37 to 21.447. Specific heat 0.0292. Melting point 1773.5° C. (A value of 1755° C. is also reported.) Boiling point values of 4300° C. and 4530° C. reported. Valences 2 and 4. Oxides PtO, PtO_2. Platinum occurs native in sperrylite and in other minerals.

PLATINUM METAL. A metal of the platinum group, which commonly is considered to comprise the elements **platinum, iridium, osmium, palladium, rhodium,** and **ruthenium.**

PLATOSAMMINE. An ammonium compound of **platinum** of the general formula, $X_2(NH_3)_2$ Pt, in which X represents an univalent acid radical.

PLATTNER PROCESS. A metallurgical process for the recovery of gold as the trichloride by chlorination with gaseous chlorine and leaching.

PLAUSEN MILL. See **mill, Plausen.**

PLEOCHROMATISM. A phenomenon observed in the transmission of **polarized**

light by bi-axial **crystals,** whereby a polarized ray is observed at right angles to the axial ray, and is of a color complementary to it.

PLEOMORPHISM. The property of crystallizing in two or more forms. The term includes dimorphism and trimorphism. Cf. **polymorphism.**

PLEWS PROCESS. A method of recovery of antimony by volatilizing its oxide from sulfide ores by heating in a roasting furnace.

PLUGGE SOLUTION FOR GUM AMMONIAC. An aqueous solution formed by dissolving 3 g. sodium hydroxide and 2 g. bromine in water, and diluting with water to 100 ml. It is used in testing for gum ammoniac. A fugitive violet color, given with this reagent by an alcoholic extract of the specimen, indicates the presence of gum ammoniac.

PLUGGE TEST FOR CERIUM. The solution tested is alkalinized with sodium hydroxide solution, evaporated to dryness, and treated with a few drops of a solution of 1 g. strychnine sulfate in 1000 ml. concentrated sulfuric acid. A violet to blue color is given by cerous salts.

PLUGGE TEST FOR NITRITE. A nitrite-containing solution, on heating with mercurous nitrate and a dilute aqueous solution of phenol, gives a red color.

PLUGGE TEST FOR PHENOL. A phenol-containing solution, on boiling with a solution of mercurous nitrate containing a little nitrite, gives a red solution and a precipitate of metallic mercury.

PLUMBATE. An anion containing tetravalent lead and oxygen, or a compound containing such an anion.

PLUMBATE, HYDROXO-. The anion $Pb(OH)_6^=$, or a compound containing it.

PLUMBATE (META-). The anion $PbO_3^=$, or a compound containing it.

PLUMBATE (ORTHO-). The anion PbO_4^{4-}, or a compound containing it.

PLUMBIC. Containing or pertaining to quadrivalent lead.

PLUMBITE. The anion $PbO_2^=$, or a compound containing it.

PLUMBOUS. Containing or pertaining to bivalent **lead.**

PLUMBUM. The Latin name of **lead.**

PLUNKET REACTION FOR POTASSIUM. An aqueous solution of sodium bitartrate precipitates potassium bitartrate from a potassium solution, if concentrations are correct.

PLUTONIUM. Transuranic radioactive element of atomic number 94. Its isotope of mass-number 239 is produced by the emission of electrons from **neptunium 239,** (q.v.) which is another transuranic radioactive element produced from uranium 238 by absorption of resonance neutrons followed by electron emission from the nucleus. Plutonium has been given the symbol Pu. Plutonium 239 emits an α-particle from its nucleus in normal radioactive disintegration, for which it has a half life period of 24,300 years. However, by the action of slow neutrons, the nucleus of the plutonium atom disintegrates in an entirely different way to form a number of products consisting of elements having mass numbers on the order of one half that of plutonium. This process is attended by an over-all loss of mass which appears as energy. Since the amount of this energy is proportional to the product of the loss of mass by the square of the velocity of light, the amount of energy so obtained is huge. If the mass of plutonium present or of a mixture of plutonium and uranium 235 exceeds a certain critical size, then the reaction started by one or a few fast neutrons is self-accelerating, because the reacting molecules yield to the surrounding mass more fast neutrons than the number required to initiate the reaction in a corresponding number of other nuclei. Since the amount of material present is great enough to permit the capture by fissionable atoms of most of these neutrons, the reaction continues at a rapidly-increasing rate. As a result, a high proportion of the total number of plutonium and uranium

235 atoms present undergo fission, producing tremendous amounts of energy within a very small volume. This is the principle of the atomic bomb.

Plutonium is produced from uranium by means of a **radioactive pile** (q.v.). In the construction of a pile, masses of uranium or uranium oxide, containing both the 235 and the 238 isotopes, are distributed throughout a chamber in which they are separated by large amounts of light elements, such as carbon in the form of graphite. The function of the latter is to slow down the neutrons which are emitted by uranium 235 atoms that are undergoing fission (in a reaction initiated by a few resonance neutrons) to the point where the velocity of these neutrons becomes slow enough to permit their capture by atoms of uranium 238, resulting in the formation successively of uranium 239, neptunium 239, and plutonium 239. The plutonium is then separated from the other materials by chemical methods. Its chemistry is similar to that of uranium.

Plutonium has also been produced in other ways, e.g., in the form of Pu^{238}, by bombardment of U^{238} with deuterons, forming Np^{238} and 2 neutrons, and followed by the beta disintegration of the Np^{238} to yield Pu^{238}. Other plutonium isotopes have been reported with massnumbers of 232, 234, 235, 236, 237, 240, 241, 242 and 243. Valences, 3, 4, 5, 6.

PNEUMATIC. Related to, or pertaining to, air or derivatively to other gases. Thus, a pneumatic trough is a small tank, containing a shelf with small holes. It is used to collect gases in the laboratory, by pouring water into it to a level above the shelf, on which are placed inverted gas-collecting bottles filled with water, which is displaced from them by gas from tubes passing under the shelf and into the bottles through the holes in the shelf.

Po Symbol for the element **polonium.**

POCH TEST FOR CHLORATE. One ml. of the solution tested is evaporated to dryness with 1 ml. 0.5 N ammonium thiocyanate solution. On heating to 140–150° C., an orange-red color indicates the presence of chlorate.

POGGENDORF CELL. A voltaic cell, used as a standard in measurement of **electrical potential.** It consists of a mercury-zinc anode and carbon cathode in a dilute sulfuric acid solution of potassium dichromate.

POGGENDORFF COMPENSATION METHOD. A method of determining the **electromotive force** of a cell by balancing its potential against the voltage drop across a portion of a uniform resistance wire, and comparing that with the corresponding measurement for a standard cell.

POHL REAGENT FOR GLOBULINS. An ammoniacal saturated solution of ammonium sulfate.

POIDOMETER. An apparatus for determining large masses (weights) rapidly. It is used extensively in industry.

POINT GROUPS, CRYSTAL. See **crystal classes.**

POINT, LIQUEFACTION. (1) Melting point. (2) A temperature and pressure at which a gas condenses to a liquid. Cf. **critical point.**

POISE. The unit of **viscosity** in the centimeter-gram-second system, equal to one dyne per square centimeter per second.

POISEUILLE'S EQUATION. A relationship for determining the **viscosity** of a fluid by the use of a capillary tube. The form of this relationship is:

$$\eta = \frac{\pi p r^4 t}{8 V l}$$

in which η is the coefficient of viscosity, p is the pressure difference across the tube, r is its radius, t is the time required to deliver volume V, and l is the length of the tube.

POISON. A substance that causes a radical impairment in structure or function, or a complete destruction of the life or effectiveness, of an organism, an entity, or a substance. The original meaning of the term was restricted to those substances that caused death or disturbance in living organisms, but it has been extended to cover substances affecting substances with various specific functions. (See **catalyst poison.**)

POLAR. Having, or pertaining to, a pole, or one of two ends of an axis of rotation, and (derivatively) one of two regions of antithetical properties.

POLAR BOND. See **bond, polar.**

POLAR COMPOUND. See **compound, polar.**

POLAR LIQUID. See **liquid, polar.**

POLAR MOLECULE. A molecule that has an electrical **dipole moment,** because of the presence in its structure, commonly, of polar valence bonds, such as bonds between atoms which differ in their attraction for shared electrons.

POLAR NUMBER. See **valence number.**

POLARIMETRY. Measurement of the rotation of the plane of polarization of **polarized light.**

POLARISCOPE. An instrument used for the direct measurement of the angular rotation produced in a ray of polarized light by an optically active substance.

POLARITY. A partial separation of positive and negative charges exhibited by substances. This separation may persist in the natural state (as in dipolar molecules) or may be induced or maintained by the action of an external field.

POLARIZABILITY, MOLECULAR. The constant of proportionality between the **electrical moment** of the **dipole** induced in a molecule and the **field intensity,** as in the relationship

$$m = \alpha F$$

in which m is the electrical moment of the induced dipole, α is the molecular polarizability, and F is the field intensity.

POLARIZATION. (1) The process of confining the vibrations of the magnetic (or electric field) vector of light to one plane.

(2) The formation of localized regions near the electrodes of an electric cell during electrolysis, of products which modify (usually adversely) the further flow of current through the cell.

(3) The process of bringing about a partial separation of electrical charges of opposite sign in a body by the superposition of an external field.

POLARIZATION CURVE. The current-voltage relationship of an electrolytic system as plotted graphically, especially as it shows the progressive effect of the growth of a counterelectromotive force due to **polarization** phenomena.

POLARIZATION, INDUCED. An expression sometimes used for molar **polarization.**

POLARIZATION POTENTIAL. The total counterelectromotive force of an electrolytic (voltaic) cell, which increases as the process of **polarization** within the cell proceeds, in the course of many electrolytic processes.

POLARIZED IONIC BOND. See **bond, polarized ionic.**

POLARIZED LIGHT. Electromagnetic radiation, usually in the optical (visible) spectrum, which is characterized by the property that the vibrations of its electric (or magnetic) field vector are confined to a single plane.

POLARIZED LIGHT, CIRCULAR. Polarized light composed of vibrations of circular, rather than the common linear, motion in the plane normal to the direction of transmission.

POLARIZED LIGHT, ELLIPTICAL. Polarized light composed of vibrations of elliptical, rather than the common linear, motion in the plane normal to the direction of transmission.

POLARIZER. A device for producing polarized light usually by selective transmission of polarized rays, such as a **Nicol prism,** a **Polaroid sheet,** or other apparatus.

POLARIZING GLASS. See **glass, polarizing.**

POLARIZING MICROSCOPE. See **microscope, polarizing.**

POLAROGRAM. The record, obtained on a polarograph, of a variation in current, or current-voltage relation. These records are applied in many phases of analytical and research work concerned with inorganic compounds, cations, anions, complex ions, certain catalysts, capillary active substances, many organic compounds, etc.

POLAROGRAPH. An instrument used to register a current-voltage relationship, particularly of the polarized microelectrodes used in polarography. The basic circuit of this instrument, as developed by Heyrovsky and Shikata, consists of a uniform slide wire, carrying a steady current which can be varied by changing the e.m.f. (number of batteries in its circuit) and by varying a series resistance. The electrolytic cell containing the microelectrode is in the circuit of the moveable slide-wire contact; this circuit also having a sensitive galvanometer, commonly a recording galvanometer, to measure or record the values of current flowing through the electrolytic cell as the potential across it is varied by moving the slide-wire contact. Modern machines produce these records automatically.

POLAROGRAPHY. The methods of measurement of potential difference-current relationships in solutions by means of a polarized microelectrode; and the interpretation of data or records so obtained in terms of the nature and behavior of many substances and systems. In an electrolytic cell having one electrode large in area, and the other electrode very small, the polarization of the latter approaches a maximum, and variations in the electromotive force of the cell are due almost entirely to changes in the potential of this electrode. Consequently, this microelectrode can function as an indicator electrode to measure changes in potential while current is flowing.

Many types of microelectrodes have been used successfully in polarographic work.

The solid microelectrodes have been used extensively, both in stirred solutions, and by rotating the solid microelectrode in a stationary solution. Another important type is the dropping-mercury electrode, consisting of a slowly-growing drop of mercury issuing in small uniform drops from a glass capillary of small size (approximately 0.05 mm. in diameter).

POLENSKÉ NUMBER. A quantity which expresses the relative water-insoluble volatile fatty acid content of fats, soaps, and similar substances. The actual value of this quantity is the number of cubic centimeters of tenth-normal alkali required to neutralize an alcoholic solution of the water-insoluble volatile fatty acids obtained by saponifying a 5 g. sample.

POLLACCI SOLUTION FOR ALBUMIN. A solution of 5 g. mercuric chloride and 1 g. tartaric acid in 100 ml. water, with addition of 5 ml. 37% formaldehyde, used in testing for albumin in urine. A characteristic ring test is obtained.

POLLACCI TEST FOR IODIC ACID. Red phosphorus reduces iodic acid, liberating free iodine.

POLLARD TEST. Gold is detected in solution by acidifying 10 ml. of the solution with hydrochloric acid and adding 1 ml. of a solution of 0.1 g. o-toluidine in 100 ml. 1:10 hydrochloric acid. A yellow color appears if gold is present.

POLONIUM. Radioactive element. Symbol Po. Atomic number 84. Discovered in pitchblende residues (associated in small quantity with the extracted bismuth) by the Curies in their early work. Various radioactive atomic species of atomic number 84 are known. Among them are: (1) radium A which has a mass number of 218 and a half-period of 3.05 minutes; it is produced from radon by α-particle emission, and in turn emits another α-particle to form radium B; (2) radium F which has a mass number of 210 and a half-period of 138.3 days; it is produced from radium E by β-particle emission, and in turn emits an α-particle to form radium G which is a lead isotope of mass number 206 (radium F is the most stable natural isotope of polonium); (3) actinium A which has a mass number of 215 and a half-period of 1.83×10^{-3} second; it is produced from actinon by α-particle emission, and in turn emits another α-particle to form actinium B; (4) thorium A which has a mass number of 216 and a half-period of 0.158 second; it is formed from thoron by α-particle emission, and in turn emits another α-particle to form thorium B; (5) thorium C' which has a mass number of 212 and a half-period of 3×10^{-7} second; it is formed from thorium C by β-particle emission, and in turn emits an α-particle to form thorium C''.

Two other naturally-occurring radio-isotopes of polonium are known with mass numbers 211 and 214, in addition to the five listed above. There are also known twelve isotopes of polonium which have been produced artificially, directly or indirectly. They have mass numbers of 200, 201, 202, 203, 204, 205, 206, 207, 208, 209, 213 and 217.

POLUETKOV MICRO-TEST FOR RHENIUM. One drop 10% bromine in concentrated hydrobromic acid and 3 drops concentrated sulfuric acid are added to 1 drop of the solution tested and the mixture is distilled. Add 1 ml. concentrated hydrobromic acid to the distillate and evaporate to dryness at 100° C. Warm residue with hydrogen peroxide, add 1 drop water, 2 N tartaric acid and stannous chloride, then 1% sodium tellurate solution. A black turbidity or precipitate indicates rhenium.

POLUETKOV TEST FOR GALLIUM. (1) Gallium forms a light red lake with an alcoholic solution of alizarin, in the presence of ammonium chloride and ammonium hydroxide.

(2) One ml. of the neutral or weakly-acid solution tested is treated with 3 ml. 0.5% manganese chloride solution in 6–7 N hydrochloric acid, and 5 drops N potassium ferrocyanide solution containing a little potassium bromate. A red-brown precipitate or turbidity indicates the presence of gallium.

POLUETKOV TEST FOR GERMANIUM. A 0.01% solution of hydroxynaphthalenequinonesulfonic acid in con-centrated sulfuric acid produces a bright pink color with germanium when examined in blue light.

POLUETKOV TEST FOR POTASSIUM. Boil 0.2 g. auranita dye with 2 ml. N sodium carbonate and 20 ml. water until dissolved. This solution gives an orange-red crystalline precipitate and a red spot test with potassium salts.

POLUETKOV TEST FOR RHENIUM. One drop of the solution tested is mixed with 1 drop of a solution of 10 g. stannous chloride in 20 ml. hydrochloric acid. A black color or precipitate on addition of sodium tellurate indicates rhenium.

POLY-. (Greek, many, much) A prefix meaning more than one (or two, or three), as polymer, polysulfide, polysaccharide.

POLYACID BASE. See base, polyacid.

POLYAD. Having a valence of more than two, as applied to an atom, element, or radical.

POLYAMIDE. A polymer obtained from substances containing amino and carboxyl groups.

POLYATOMIC. Containing more than two atoms or, derivatively, containing more than two of a particular kind of atom, indicated by the term modified by the word polyatomic.

POLYBASIC ACID. See acid, polybasic.

POLYCHROMIC (POLYCHROMATIC). Having two or more colors.

POLYCYCLIC. Having two or more rings, as a compound having a structure containing two or more rings of atoms.

POLYDISPERSE SYSTEM. A colloidal system that consists of particles of different sizes. In centrifuging, the sedimentation constant has different values for a poly-disperse system.

POLYENE. A compound which contains more than two double bonds.

POLYFORM PROCESS. A method of petroleum **cracking** in which thermal cracking and naphtha reforming take place in the same reaction zone, specifically by preheating a mixture of naphtha and C_3 and C_4 hydrocarbons and passing them together through the heating coil.

POLYGEN. An element which can combine in two or more proportions, as chromium, iron, sulfur, oxygen, nitrogen, due to its having two or more valences.

POLYHYDRATE. A compound containing more than two associated molecules of water.

POLYHYDRIC. Containing more than two **hydroxyl groups.**

POLYMER. (1) A compound formed by two or more molecules of a simpler compound, as paraldehyde is formed by association of acetaldehyde, the relative amount of each element remaining the

POLYMERIZATION. In general, a reaction in which a complex molecule of relatively high molecular weight is produced from a number of simpler molecules. The reaction may proceed by mere addition of molecules of a single molecular species; it may include more than one species; or it may involve condensation, i.e., elimination of water, ammonia, or other simple substance, or their elements. The process was described by Carothers as consisting of "intermolecular combinations functionally capable of proceeding indefinitely."

POLYMERIZATION, ADDITION. A **polymerization** reaction which consists only of the addition of like or unlike molecules, without elimination of any atoms or molecules.

POLYMERIZATION, AROMATIC. The **polymerization** of an aliphatic substance to form a carbocyclic compound, as in the polymerization of crotonylene to hexamethylbenzene, viz.,

(3 molecules)   (1 molecule).

same. (2) Derivatively, the meaning of this term has been extended to denote any one of a number of compounds composed of the same elements or radicals and so related that the molecular formulas are in the relation of whole number multiples of each other.

POLYMERIC. The condition of being a polymer.

POLYMERID. A **polymer.**

POLYMERISM. **Isomerism** in which the isomers are of different molecular weights.

POLYMERIZATION, BULK. A term applied to **polymerization** reactions that take place without a solvent or other medium, directly between the reacting molecules.

POLYMERIZATION, CARBOHYDRATE. The **photosynthesis** of sugars from formaldehyde.

POLYMERIZATION, CO-. An addition polymerization (see **polymerization, addition**) which involves two or more distinct molecular species, each of which is capable of polymerizing alone. The molecule formed contains each molecular constituent, or an essential unit therefrom, as a distinct entity in its structure.

POLYMERIZATION, CONDENSATION. A polymerization reaction that is attended by the elimination of some simple substance, such as water, ammonia, etc., or its constituent elements, from the molecules undergoing the polymerization.

POLYMERIZATION, EMULSION. A polymerization reaction carried out in one of the phases of an emulsion, as synthetic rubbers are produced by polymerization in the disperse phase of an emulsion in which water is the continous phase.

POLYMERIZATION, GASEOUS. A polymerization reaction carried out in the gaseous or vapor phase.

POLYMERIZATION, HETERO-. An addition polymerization (see polymerization, addition) which involves two or more distinct molecular species, one of which does not polymerize by itself. It does, however, enter into the polymer molecule as a distinct structural entity.

POLYMERIZATION, MASS. A polymerization reaction carried out with liquid molecules without the addition of any diluent.

POLYMERIZATION, SIMPLE. An addition polymerization (see polymerization, addition) reaction that involves only a single molecular species.

POLYMERIZATION, SOLUTION. A polymerization reaction carried out by first dissolving the substance to be polymerized (or one of such substances) in a suitable solvent.

POLYMERIZE. To produce a polymer.

POLYMEROUS. (1) Polymeric. (2) Tending to polymerize.

POLYMORPH. A substance that exhibits two or more crystalline forms.

POLYMORPHIC. Existing in two or more crystalline forms.

POLYMORPHISM. A phenomenon in which a substance exhibits different forms. Dimorphic substances appear in two crystal forms, whereas trimorphic exist in three, as sulfur, carbon, tin, silver iodide, and calcium carbonate. Polymorphism is restricted to the solid state. Polymorphs yield identical solutions and vapors (if vaporizable). The relation between them has been termed "physical isomerism" and the polymorphs have been termed "physical isomers."

POLYPEPTIDE. A compound composed of two or more amino acids and similar in many properties to the natural peptones. The amino acids are joined by peptide

groups $-NH-C\overset{\displaystyle O}{\underset{\displaystyle \diagdown}{\diagup\diagup}}$ formed by the reaction between an $-NH_2$ group and a

$-C\overset{\displaystyle O}{\underset{\displaystyle \diagdown}{\diagup\diagup}}$ group, whereby there is elimination of a molecule of water, and formation

OH

of a valence bond. They may be termed di-, tri-, tetra-, etc., peptide according to the number of amino acids present in the molecule. See proteins.

POLYPHOSPHATE. The anion

$$P_nO_{3n+1}{}^{(n+2)-},$$

or a compound containing it.

POLYSACCHARIDE. (Polysaccharose) One of a class of carbohydrates characterized by amorphous, complex structure and lack of sweet taste, as starch, dextrin, inulin. On hydrolysis they yield, after a series of reactions, several molecules of monosaccharide.

POLYSULFIDE. A compound of sulfur with another element, in which the molecules contain a greater number of atoms of sulfur than calculated for bivalent sulfur and the common valence or valences of the other element.

POLYVALENT. Having two or more valences.

POMERANZ-FRITSCH REACTION. A method of formation of isoquinolines by condensing aryl aldehydes and amino acetals, followed by ring closure in the presence of acid.

or sodium naphthionate on the water bath, and add an alcoholic solution of the substance tested. A light yellow to red color, becoming more pronounced on evaporation, indicates an aromatic aldehyde.

See also **Schlittler-Müller reaction.**

PONDER STAIN. A solution of 0.02 toluidine blue in 1 ml. glacial acetic acid, 2 ml. alcohol, and 100 ml. distilled water. It is used as a stain for the microorganisms of diphtheria. Various modifications have been developed.

PONDERATOR. A term suggested by W. W. Hansen for a device used to produce high-energy particles, when the speed of the particles becomes so great, approaching that of light, that an increase of energy results in an appreciable increase in mass.

PONS REAGENT. A 1:1000 aqueous solution of the sodium salt of sulfochondroitic acid, used to precipitate albumin from dilute acetic acid solution.

PONZIO REACTION. Conversion of benzaldoximes to dinitrophenylmethanes by the action of nitrogen dioxide in ethereal solution.

POOTH TEST REACTION FOR ARO-MATIC ALDEHYDES. Heat 3–4 ml. of a 10% aqueous solution of sodium sulfanilate

POPOV TEST FOR CADMIUM. One ml. of the solution tested is heated with 0.5 g. ammonium bromide and 1 ml. concentrated sulfuric acid until sulfur trioxide is evolved, then the volume is made up to 8 ml. with water, and 0.5 g. iron powder added. Filter after 30 seconds, add to filtrate an equal volume phosphoric acid and pass in hydrogen sulfide. A yellow precipitate indicates cadmium.

POPOV TEST FOR NITRATE. One ml. of the solution tested is mixed with 1 ml. of a saturated aqueous solution of β-naphthylamine and superimposed on concentrated sulfuric acid. A violet-red ring indicates the presence of nitrate.

POROSIMETER. An instrument used to determine the porosity of solids to fluids, both liquids and gases.

POROSITY. (1) The property of containing pores, which are minute channels or open spaces in a solid. (2) The proportion of the total volume occupied by such pores.

PORPHIN RING. An important element in the structure of many compounds of wide occurrence in plants and animals including chlorophyll and hemoglobin. The porphin ring consists essentially of four **pyrrole** groups (five-membered unsaturated rings composed of four carbon atoms and one nitrogen atom), united by methylene groups, and usually coordinated by a metal atom.

POSITIVE ELECTRON. See positron.

POSITIVE ELEMENT. See element, positive.

POSITIVE GROUP. See positive radical.

POSITIVE NUCLEUS. The nucleus of an atom, which always carries a positive charge, of magnitude depending upon the particular atomic species. See atomic structure.

POSITIVE RADICAL. A group of atoms bearing a positive charge, resulting from the loss of an electron or electrons by one or more of its atoms.

POSITIVE RAYS. Rays originally observed in gas discharge tubes, which were deflected by a magnetic field along a path opposite to that of cathode rays. These positive rays were later shown to consist of positively charged ions. See mass spectrograph for methods of positive ray analysis.

POSITRON. An elementary particle of electronic mass and positive charge whose magnitude is the same as that of the electron. The life span of positrons is very short; positron-electron pairs appear momentarily upon the absorption of γ-rays or cosmic rays; positrons are also commonly emitted in many nuclear reactions.

POSITRONIUM. A positron and an electron which are revolving around each other like a double star, with their spin axes parallel. The half-life of positronium is very short, becasue the two particles disintegrate completely, and in their place two gamma-rays appear.

POSNER TEST. Chromium is detected by adding 1 ml. chlorine water and 0.5 ml. of the solution tested to 5 ml. 2 N silver nitrate, the mixture is boiled for 1 minute and made slightly ammoniacal with 2 N ammonium hydroxide. Filter and neutralize with 2 N nitric acid. A red precipitate appears at once if chromium is present.

POSOLOGY. The science of the dosage of drugs and their administration, a branch of pharmacology.

POTASSIC. Containing potassium.

POTASSIUM. Metallic element. Symbol K. Atomic number 19. Atomic weight 39.100. Density 0.86. Specific heat 0.170. Melting point 62.3° C. Boiling point 760° C. Valence 1. Oxides, K_2O, K_2O_4. Potassium occurs in sylvite, carnallite, and seawater.

POTENCY. In its original mathematical sense, this term connoted the power of a term, i.e., the number of times a number was multiplied by itself. It is used in the therapeutics to denote the power of a drug in the sense of its therapeutical activity.

POTENTIAL. Among its many meanings and connotations, this term is used commonly in science as an adjective with the meaning of available, rather than in action or use, as potential energy (energy of position or state) as opposed to kinetic energy. The term potential is also used as a substantive and in this sense designates the name of a number of different quantities used in physics, such as electric potential, magnetic potential and mass potential, the latter being defined at any point as the energy necessary to carry a unit mass from that point to a region of space infinitely removed from all matter. Electric potential and magnetic potential at a point are defined as the energy necessary to carry unit charge, or unit pole, respectively, from infinity to that point.

POTENTIAL BARRIER. The electrical repulsion of a nucleus for a positively-charged particle, e.g., an α-particle, computed by the law of Coulomb. Although by classical physics a particle must possess an energy exceeding this value to pass this barrier, the wave mechanical interpretation shows that there is a definite possibility that a particle with less energy may do so.

POTENTIAL, CONTACT. A difference of electrical potential existing between two substances in direct contact. All metals, electrolytic solutions, and other substances containing "free" ions or electrons, exhibit a difference of potential on direct contact.

POTENTIAL, CRITICAL. In general, the potential that must be applied to raise an electron in an atom from a lower **energy level** to a higher one. It is thus an energy quantity, equal to the product of potential and charge, which is stated in terms of potential because the electronic charge is unity.

Two specific types of critical potential are: (1) the resonance potential, which is the amount of energy necessary to raise an electron from its lowest energy level to any other level; and (2) the ionization potential, the amount of energy necessary to remove entirely an electron in the lowest energy level from the atom (to "infinite distance").

POTENTIAL, DIFFUSION. The difference of potential at the boundary of an electrical **"double layer."** This is also called the **liquid junction** potential.

POTENTIAL, DISCHARGE. A characteristic value of the **electrode potential,** observed in the electrode potential-current relationship determined for an electrode in contact with an ionic solution. The distinguishing feature of this value is that it marks a point of inflection, at which the current increases very rapidly with small increases in electrode potential. This high current value is marked by discharge of ions upon the electrode.

POTENTIAL, ELECTRIC. See **potential.**

POTENTIAL, ELECTRODE. See **electrode potential.**

POTENTIAL HEAD. See **head, potential.**

POTENTIAL, IONIZATION. See **potential, critical.**

POTENTIAL, MAGNETIC. See **potential.**

POTENTIAL, LIQUID JUNCTION. See **potential, diffusion.**

POTENTIAL, MASS. See **potential.**

POTENTIAL, RESONANCE. See **potential, critical.**

POTENTIAL, SPARKING. The difference in electrical **potential** necessary to

cause an electrical spark to pass between two given points in a given medium under a given temperature and other conditions.

POTENTIAL, STANDARD. The potential of an **electrode** composed of a substance in its **standard state,** in equilibrium with ions, which are all in their standard states.

POTENTIAL, STREAMING. See **streaming potential.**

POTENTIAL, THERMODYNAMIC. See **free energy.**

POTENTIOMETER. Any instrument used to measure or compare electric **potentials;** specifically, one of a number of circuits designed for the accurate measurement of small potentials, usually by balancing the unknown potential against the voltage drop across a portion of a uniform resistance wire, and comparing with the corresponding measurement for a standard cell.

POTENTIOMETRIC TITRATION. A method of titrating a **solution** by determining, after each addition of standard solution, the **potential** of a suitably-chosen **electrode** in **equilibrium** with that solution. If the system is properly arranged, a marked change in potential will be found at the end point of the **titration.** The method frequently uses a **potentiometer** to determine the changing values of the electrode potential.

POUGET-CHOUCHAK SOLUTION. A two-solution reagent used in the determination of phosphoric acid, which gives a blue-yellow turbidity, even in very low concentrations. The reagent consists of: (1) a solution prepared by dissolving 95 g. molybdenum trioxide and 30 g. sodium carbonate (anhydrous) in 600 ml. warm water adding 200 ml. nitric acid (36° Bé.) and diluting to 1 l.; and (2) a solution of 2 g. strychnine sulfate in 100 ml. water. The solutions are mixed (1:10) before using.

POULENC TEST FOR NITRATE. Mix 2 moles formic acid with 1 mole nitron.

This reagent, in 10% aqueous solution, gives precipitates with nitrate solutions.

POUND. A unit of weight or mass in the English system of weights and measures unless specified otherwise, it is understood to be the avoirdupois pound of 453.59 grams, rather than the troy pound of 373.24 grams. The equivalents are as follows:

1 pound avoirdupois = 16 av. ounces
1 pound avoirdupois = 7000 grains
1 pound avoirdupois = 0.45359 kilogram
1 pound avoirdupois = 453.59 grams
1 pound troy   = 373.24 grams
1 pound troy   = 12 ounces troy
1 pound troy   = 5760 grains

POUNDAL. The unit of force in the English system (the foot-pound-second system) defined as the force which, acting on a pound mass for one second, imparts to it a velocity of one foot per second. One poundal equals 13,825 dynes.

POUR POINT. (1) In the foundry, the temperature at which a charge of molten metal is cast. (2) In the laboratory, the lowest temperature at which a liquid will pour.

POWDER METALLURGY. A method of metal-working in which metals are produced in finely-divided form and are then pressed into finished shapes, or into shapes from which the finished articles are fabricated. The particles are caused to coalesce by a heating operation, commonly called **sintering,** which is done either before or after the pressing operation.

POWDER METHOD OF ANALYSIS. A method for the **x-ray analysis** of **crystals.** A beam of x-rays is directed on the finely-powdered crystalline material, by which it is diffracted. Many minute crystals in the powder are oriented in the correct direction for the **Bragg equation** to be applied to the determination. The diffracted x-rays are allowed to impinge on a film strip which surrounds the powder; characteristic ring patterns are then obtained. The x-ray photograph made in the process is characteristic of each crystalline material, and so can be used in identification.

POZZI-ESCOT-COUQUET TEST REACTION FOR PALLADIUM. Sodium nitrite and excess ammonium or sodium hydroxide precipitate from a solution of palladium chloride, rhombohedral crystals, usually colored.

POZZI-ESCOT MICRO-REAGENT FOR YTTRIUM, ERBIUM, NEODYMIUM, AND PRASEODYMIUM. A solution of ammonium chromate which forms definite crystals with yttrium, erbium, neodymium, and praseodymium ions.

POZZI-ESCOT MICRO-TEST FOR SULFATE. On treating a solution containing sulfate ion with p-diaminobiphenyl and formaldehyde, especially in presence of copper or manganese salts, an organic sulfate crystallizes in hexagonal plates.

POZZI-ESCOT TEST FOR BROMINE. Treatment of bromides with chromic and sulfuric acids liberates bromine, which is absorbed by a fresh aqueous solution of aniline with the formation of microscopic prisms of tribromoaniline.

POZZI-ESCOT TEST FOR NICKEL IN PRESENCE OF COBALT. A neutral or weakly-acid solution of cobalt and nickel chlorides, on addition of excess saturated ammonium molybdate solution, gives a greenish-white precipitate of the nickel, the cobalt remaining in solution.

POZZI-ESCOT TEST FOR THIOSULFATE. One ml. of the solution tested is mixed with 1 ml. 10% ammonium molybdate solution and superimposed on concentrated sulfuric acid. A blue ring appears in the presence of thiosulfate.

POZZI-ESCOT TEST FOR TUNGSTEN OR MOLYBDENUM. To the neutral solution tested, add 1 drop saturated mercurous nitrate solution, 1–1.5 ml. concentrated hydrochloric acid, and excess potassium iodide. Shake until any precipitate dissolves. A transitory blue color indicates the presence of tungsten or molybdenum.

POZZI-ESCOT TEST REACTION FOR CHLORATE. To 1 ml. of the solution tested add 2 drops 10% aniline sulfate solution and superimpose the mixture on 4 ml. concentrated sulfuric acid. A blue ring indicates chlorate. Using benzidine instead of aniline gives an orange-yellow ring and is more sensitive.

POZZI-ESCOT TEST REACTIONS FOR COBALT. A few drops of an alcoholic solution of phenyl- or β-naphthylthiohydantoic acid and 1 drop ammonium hydroxide give a carmine-red color with a dilute cobalt solution, and a brown-red precipitate with a concentrated solution. Nickel gives an ocher-yellow color or green precipitate, soluble in excess of ammonia.

POZZI-ESCOT TEST REACTION FOR COPPER. A solution of a copper salt alkalinized with diethanolamine gives a color reaction on saturation with carbon dioxide.

POZZI-ESCOT TEST REACTION FOR GOLD. A dilute gold solution, on addition of a solution of phenylhydrazine acetate, becomes blue by transmitted light and brown by reflected light. If excess citric acid is first added to the gold solution, a persistent violet color appears.

POZZI-ESCOT TEST REACTION FOR ROTENONE. A sulfuric acid solution of rotenone gives, with a sulfuric acid solution of mercuric oxide, a white precipitate, which dissolves on heating to form a deeply colored solution. This reaction is useful in colorimetric determination of rotenone.

Pr Symbol for the element **praseodymium**; abbreviation for propyl.

PRAGER-JACOBSON CLASSIFICATION. The system of classification of organic compounds used in the Beilstein *Handbuch der Organischen Chemie.*

PRANDTL NUMBER. The product of the **specific heat** and the **viscosity** of a fluid, divided by its **thermal conductivity.**

PRASEO-. A prefix from the Greek *praseos*, which denotes a green color.

PRASEODYMIUM. Rare earth metallic element. Symbol Pr. Atomic number 59.

Atomic weight 140.92. Density 6.4754. Melting point 940° C. Valences 3, 4. Oxides PrO_2, Pr_2O_3. Praseodymium occurs in cerite and other rare minerals.

PREBULA-McCOLLUM REACTION FOR VITAMIN B₁ (THIAMINE). Vitamin B_1 produces with a diazotized solution of *p*-aminoacetanilid or methyl-*p*-aminophenylketone a purple-red stable color, insoluble in water and soluble in xylene.

PRECIPITABLE. Capable of being precipitated.

PRECIPITANT. A reagent that may cause a precipitate.

PRECIPITATE. (1) A solid or liquid separated from a solution by a chemical or physical process that renders it insoluble. (2) To render a dissolved substance insoluble or to react on it in such a way as to produce an insoluble derivative. Precipitation may be due to altering the temperature or to lessening the volume of the solvent; to coagulation, as in the case of certain protein solutions; to driving off a gas which has held a substance in solution, as $CaCO_3$ in aqueous CO_2 solutions; by the addition of some substance in the presence of which a solute becomes insoluble, as the salting out of phenol; by adding some reagent which reacts with the solute producing an insoluble substance; and by adding a second solvent in which the solute is insoluble, as in adding alcohol to a saturated aqueous solution of sodium chloride. In the language of the ionization hypothesis, a precipitate occurs when an electrically neutral species of molecule exceeds the amount of its solubility product.

PRECIPITATION. The act of producing a precipitate in any system.

PRECIPITATION, ELECTROSTATIC. Precipitation by means of an electric discharge. The most widely-used electrostatic precipitation method is the separation of solid or liquid particles from gases by passage of a current through them, whereby the particles are charged and then attracted to the region (wire or surface) of opposite charge.

PRECIPITATION, FRACTIONAL. Separation of a mixture in solution by the addition of a reagent in sufficient quantity only to precipitate one component (the least soluble). By this method mixtures of the sodium salts of organic acids in water solution may be separated.

PRECURSOR. In general, a substance which occurs or is formed in a preliminary stage of a reaction or process, and which is subsequently transformed into another substance or system. Among the well-known examples of such substances are the precursors of **vitamins** and the precursors of **protoplasm.**

PREDISSOCIATION. A special process of molecular **dissociation.** Certain molecules, upon absorbing the appropriate radiations, are transferred into an excited electronic state; the excess energy then redistributes itself, and another **excited state** is attained in which the excess energy is available for dissociation of the molecule.

PRESSURE. Force per unit area. Commonly-used units of pressure are the dyne per square centimeter and the pound per square inch.

PRESSURE, ABSOLUTE. The term applied to the true pressure of a substance or system, commonly to distinguish it from partial pressure, gage pressure, etc.

PRESSURE, ATMOSPHERIC. The normal atmospheric pressure, or pressure of one atmosphere, is 1.013×10^6 dynes per square centimeter or about 14.7 pounds per square inch. This will support a column of mercury (in a barometer) 76 centimeters high at 0° C.

PRESSURE, COHESION. The correction applied to the pressure term in the **van der Waals' equation** to take care of the effect of **molecular attraction.** It is usually expressed as $\dfrac{a}{V^2}$, where a is a constant and V is the volume of the gas.

PRESSURE, CRITICAL. The pressure necessary to condense a gas at the critical temperature (see **temperature, critical**).

PRESSURE, FUGITIVE. (Transitory pressure) Local variation of pressure in the vicinity of an **explosion wave,** in rapidly burning mixtures, much greater than the mean pressure of the whole mass of gas, produced either in the compression wave or the explosion wave.

PRESSURE, GAGE. The pressure in a substance or system in excess of the pressure of the atmosphere.

PRESSURE, IMPACT. Pressure exerted by a moving fluid on a plane perpendicular to its direction of flow. In other words, it is measured *in* the direction of flow.

PRESSURE, NEGATIVE. A pressure that is less than atmospheric, or a pressure less than 760 millimeters of mercury at 0° C.

PRESSURE, PARTIAL. The pressure that is exerted by a single gaseous **component** of a mixture of gases.

PRESSURE, SOLUTION. See **solution pressure.**

PRESSURE, STANDARD. The pressure exerted by a column of mercury 760 millimeters high at 0° C.

PRESSURE, STATIC. Pressure in a fluid or system that is exerted normal to the surface on which it acts. In a moving fluid, the static pressure is measured at right angles to the direction of flow.

PRESSURE, VELOCITY. The component of the pressure of the moving fluid that is due to its velocity and is commonly equal to the difference between the impact pressure and the static pressure.

PRESSURES, LAW OF PARTIAL. See **law of Dalton.**

PRÉVOST REACTION. The production of α-glycol benzoates from olefins by the action of iodosilver benzoate, which can be obtained by direct action of iodine upon silver benzoate.

$$2C_6H_5COOAg + I_2 \rightarrow Ag(C_6H_5COO)_2I + AgI$$

$$R'CH{=}CHR'' + Ag(C_6H_5COO)_2I \rightarrow R'CH{-}CHR'' + AgI.$$
$$\begin{array}{cc} | & | \\ C_6H_5COO & OOCC_6H_5 \end{array}$$

PRILESCHAJEW REACTION. The action of **peracids** upon **alkenes** to yield **epoxides**.

$$RCOO.OH + R'CH{=}CHR'' \rightarrow R'CH\underset{O}{\overset{\displaystyle O}{\diagdown\diagup}}CHR'' + RCOOH.$$

PRILESCHAJEW REAGENT. Benzoylhydroperoxide, used as a reagent for unsaturated organic compounds.

PRIMARY ALCOHOL. See **alcohol, primary.**

PRIMARY AMINE. See **amine, primary.**

PRIMARY CELL. See **cell, primary.**

PRIMARY IONIZING EVENT. See **ionizing event, primary.**

PRIMARY NUCLEUS. A ring-structure of atoms in an organic compound, in which only hydrogen atoms are attached to the atoms of the ring.

PRIMER. A substance or material used to start an action, or used as the first stage in an operation. Thus, detonators for explosives are called primers. The term is also used to denote a coat of a finishing material that is applied to an uncoated surface before painting.

PRIMOT REAGENT FOR ANTIPYRINE AND CRYOGENINE. A solution of 1 g. vanillin and 6 g. hydrochloric acid in 100 g. alcohol, used as a test reagent for antipyrine and cryogenine. Antipyrine gives an orange-yellow color on evaporation with this reagent, and cryogenine a green-yellow color.

PRIMOT REAGENT FOR NITRITE. A solution of 1 g. of one of certain aryl amines, such as dianisidine, o-tolidine, or benzidine in 100 ml. 30–40% alcohol, used in detecting nitrites in water. Yellow or orange colors are obtained in acetic acid solution, in the absence of mineral acids.

PRINCIPAL AXIS. (1) The longest axis of a **crystal.** (2) The **optical axis** of a crystal.

PRINCIPAL QUANTUM NUMBER. See **quantum number, principal.**

PRINCIPAL SERIES. A series of lines in the spectra of many atoms which have one, two, or three electrons in their outer **shells,** either in their neutral state or as a result of **ionization.** (Excluded are the atoms which have only one electron in all, such as hydrogen, singly-ionized helium, doubly-ionized lithium, etc.) The principal series differs from the other series for such elements in having a somewhat distinctive physical appearance, and in having a characteristic formula,

$$\bar{\nu}_p = L - \frac{R}{(m+c)^2},$$

where $\bar{\nu}_p$ is the **wave number** of a line in the principal series, L and c are constants for the principal series, m is a variable integer, whose values give the various lines in the principal series, and R is the **Rydberg constant.**

PRINCIPAL VALENCE. See **valence, principal.**

PRINCIPLE OF ADDITIVITY. See **additivity, principle of.**

PRINS REACTION. A method of formation of **glycols** (1,3 position) and their derivatives from **olefins,** formaldehyde, and organic **acids** in the presence of mineral acid.

changed to red-violet by acids and to brown by oxidants.

PRODUCER. An apparatus for the manufacture of illuminating and fuel gas by the

$$RCH{:}CH_2 + HCHO + 2CH_3COOH \xrightarrow{\text{H}_2\text{SO}_4} R.CH.CH_2.CH_2.OOC.CH_3 + H_2O.$$
$$| $$
$$CH_3.COO$$

PRISM. A solid object, composed of glass or other transparent material, and having a shape suitable for various optical purposes. For example, the common triangular prism receives light upon one face and passes it out through another after two refractions, resulting in a total deviation dependent upon the angle of the prism (i.e., the angle between the face through which light enters and the face through which it emerges) and its refractive index for the frequency of light used.

PRISM, CONSTANT DEVIATION. A **prism** so constructed that the **deviation** by it of a light ray, entering through one face and leaving through another, is always equal to the angle between those two faces.

PRISM, NICOL. See **Nicol prism.**

PRO-. (Greek, before) A prefix denoting an antecedent substance, as proenzyme, provitamin.

PROBABILITY FACTOR. See **steric factor.**

PROCESS, UNIT. See **unit process.**

PROCKE-UZEL SOLUTION. A reagent for lithium, prepared by dissolving 2 g. potassium periodate in 10 ml. 2 N potassium hydroxide solution, diluting with water to 50 ml., adding 3 ml. 10% ferric chloride solution, and then diluting to 100 ml. with 2 N potassium hydroxide solution. This reagent gives a yellow color with lithium solutions.

PROCTOR TEST REACTION FOR TANNIC ACID. Tannic acid solutions give with potassium arsenate a green color,

reaction between air and steam and coal. The producer process differs from the "water gas" process in that the coal is kept at the proper high temperature by an air blast introduced with the steam instead of alternately. The product of the apparatus is known as producer gas, and consists chiefly of carbon monoxide and nitrogen, with some hydrogen, carbon dioxide, and other compounds. Mond gas is a special type of this gas.

PROENZYME. A **cell** substance or constituent from which **enzymes** are derived.

PROFERMENT. A **cell** substance or constituent from which **ferments** are derived.

PROLAMINE. (Glaidin) See **protein.**

PROLYL. The radical

$$\overline{NH.CH_2.CH_2.CH_2.CHCO}—$$

(from proline).

PROMETHIUM. Element of rare earth group whose existence in nature is still unconfirmed. Symbol Pm. Atomic number 61. Two radioactive isotopes were identified among the fission products of uranium by Marinsky, Glendenin, and Coryell. These two isotopes were also identified in the material obtained by bombardment of stable **neodymium** with slow neutrons in the **pile.** They are the isotope of mass number 147, which has a half-life of 2.6 years and 149 with a half-life of 55 hours. Both are β-emitters. Other isotopes of promethium have been reported with mass numbers of 141, 143, 144, 145 (2 isotopes), 146, 148, 150 and 151.

PROMOTER. A substance of little or no catalytic activity which increases the catalytic activity of a **catalyst;** the total catalytic activity of promoter and catalyst is greater than would be expected from their individual activities.

PROOF SPIRIT. A mixture of water and ethyl alcohol containing approximately 50% alcohol by volume. Such a solution is said to be 100 proof.

PROPANOLYSIS. Alcoholysis in which the alcohol split is propyl alcohol.

PROPARGYL. See **2-propynyl.**

PROPENYL. The radical $CH_3CH:CH$—.

PROPENYLIDENE. The radical

$$CH_3CH:C=.$$

PROPERTY. That which is inherently characteristic of a substance and naturally essential to it.

PROPERTY, ADDITIVE. A property of a system that is equal to the sum of the values of that property for the constituents of the system.

PROPERTY, COLLIGATIVE. A property that depends for the most part on the number of molecules involved and not on their nature.

PROPERTY, CONSTITUTIVE. A property that depends for the most part on the arrangement of the atoms in the molecule and, to a lesser degree, on their number and nature.

PROPERTY, EXTENSIVE. A property of a system that varies in its value with the quantity of material contained in the system.

PROPERTY, INTENSIVE. A property of a system that is independent of the quantity of material contained in the system.

PROPERTY, POLAR. A property of a system relating to a partial separation of electric charges of opposite sign.

PROPHYLACTIC. A substance or agent that aids in, or contributes to prevention of infection or of a disease.

PROPIOLYL. The radical $HC:CCO$—.

PROPIONATE. A compound containing the radical

$$CH_3-CH_2-C \overset{\displaystyle O}{\underset{\displaystyle O-}{\big\langle}}.$$

PROPIONIC. Related to propionic acid, $C_2H_5.COOH$.

PROPIONYL. The radical CH_3CH_2CO—.

PROPORTIONAL COUNTER. A **counter** designed to operate in the **proportional region.**

PROPORTIONAL REGION. A term used in **counter** technology to denote the part of the characteristic curve of **pulse size** versus voltage, in which the pulse size is proportional to the number of ions formed in the **initial ionizing event.**

PROPORTIONS, DEFINITE, LAW OF. See **law of definite proportions.**

PROPORTIONS, MULTIPLE, LAW OF. See **law of multiple proportions.**

PROPOXY. The radical $CH_3CH_2CH_2O$—.

PROPYL. The radical $CH_3CH_2CH_2$—.

PROPYLENE. The radical

$$-CH(CH_3)CH_2-.$$

PROPYLIDENE. The radical

$$CH_3CH_2CH=.$$

1-PROPYNYL. The radical $CH_3C:C$—.

2-PROPYNYL. The radical $CH:CCH_2$—.

PROS POSITION. In general, any nearby position; or specifically, the 2,3 position in the naphthalene ring and similar condensed rings.

PROSTHETIC GROUP. That portion of a **protein** molecule which is not protein in nature, e.g., **nucleic acids** in the nucleoproteins, or **carbohydrate** groups in the glycoproteins.

PROT-. See proto-.

PROT-, PROTO-. (Greek, first) A prefix specifically designating: (1) first in an inorganic series, as protoxide (now little used); (2) parent or immediate antecedent, as protoactinium, protochlorophyll.

PROTACTINIUM. Radioactive element. Symbol Pa. Atomic number 91. Mass number 231. Protactinium yields actinium by α-particle emission and has a half-life of 3.43×10^4 years. The oxides range in composition from PO_2 to P_2O_5. The element exists in aqueous solution largely as complex ions. Its other isotopes include two isomers of mass number 234, uranium X_2 with a half-life of 1.14 minutes, and uranium Z with a half-life of 6.7 hours. Other nuclear species have mass numbers 226–230, 232, 233 and 235. Valences 4, 5.

PROTAMINE. One of a class of simple **proteins.**

PROTEASE. An **enzyme** that catalyzes the **hydrolysis** of proteins, as pepsin.

PROTECTIVE ACTION. The effect of a substance which stabilizes a system of **colloidal** particles against **coagulation** by electrolytes or other means.

PROTECTIVE COLLOID. A **colloidal** substance that increases the stability of systems of colloidal particles to the coagulating action of electrolytes or other agencies.

PROTECTIVE FOOD. See **food, protective.**

PROTEIDIN. A generic term for a class of bacteriolytic enzymes "combined" with blood **albumins** which have immunizing and curative properties.

PROTEINATE. A protein compound, commonly formed by reaction with a metallic hydroxide or other base.

PROTEINOGENOUS. Produced by a **protein,** especially by the decomposition of a protein, as a proteinogenous amine, such as histamine or p-hydroxyphenylethylamine.

PROTEINS. (Proteids, albumins) A class of complex organic compounds of high molecular weight and their immediate derivatives, found associated with living matter, although some simple proteins have been prepared synthetically. They consist of carbon, hydrogen, nitrogen, and oxygen, with sulfur, phosphorus, iron, copper, chlorine, iodine, and a few other elements, in individuals. They are classified in several ways; the system adopted by the American Society of Biological Chemists is as follows:

I. Simple proteins. On hydrolysis these yield amino acids or their derivatives alone.

   A. Albumins. Soluble in water and dilute saline solutions, coagulable by heat. Egg albumin, serum albumin.

   B. Globulins. Insoluble in water, soluble in dilute saline solutions, coagulable by heat. Edestin, serum globulin.

   C. Glutelins. Insoluble in water or dilute salt solutions, soluble in very dilute acids or alkalies, coagulable by heat. Glutenin.

   D. Prolamines. Insoluble in water, soluble in 80% alcohol. Glaidin, hordein, zein.

   E. Albuminoids. Insoluble in dilute acid, alkali, water, or salt solutions. Elastin, keratin, collagen. (Also called scleroproteins.)

   F. Histones. Soluble in water and dilute acids, precipitated by ammonia, strongly basic, not coagulable by heat. Histone.

   G. Protamines. Soluble in ammonia, not coagulable by heat, strongly basic, yielding large amounts of diamino acids on hydrolysis. Sturnin, salmin, clupein.

II. Conjugated proteins, called proteides. Compounds of simple proteins with prosthetic groups.

A. Hemoglobins. (Chromoproteides.) The prosthetic group is colored. Hemoglobin, hemocyanin, phycoerythrin.

B. Glycoproteides. (Glucoproteides.) The prosthetic group contains a carbohydrate residue. Mucin, ichthulin.

C. Phosphoproteides. Proteins of cytoplasm. The prosthetic group contains phosphoric acid but neither nucleic acid nor a phospholipin. Casein, vitellin.

D. Nucleoproteides. The prosthetic group is nucleic acid. Nuclein, nucleohistone.

E. Lecithoproteides. The prosthetic group is lecithin or a phospholipin. Lecithoproteides are soluble in ether.

F. Lipoproteides. (Mathews.) The prosthetic group is a higher fatty acid.

III. Derived proteins. Decomposition products of the natural proteins and synthetic products.

A. Primary protein derivatives.
   a. Derived proteins, the first products of the action of acids, enzymes, or water. Insoluble in water. (Proteans.)
   b. Metaproteins, produced by further action of acids or alkalies. Insoluble in neutral solutions, soluble in weak acids and alkalies. Acid albumin.
   C. Coagulated proteins, produced by the action of heat or alcohol, insoluble.

B. Secondary protein derivatives.
   a. Proteoses. Hydrolytic decomposition products of proteins, soluble in water, not coagulable by heat, precipitated by saturating their solutions with ammonium sulfate.
   b. Peptones. Hydrolytic decomposition products of proteins, not coagulable by heat, soluble in water, not precipitated by saturation with ammonium sulfate.

c. Peptides. Compounds of amino acids of known composition. The synthetic polypeptides are included in this class.

The system of classification proposed by the English Society of Physiologists is:

I. Simple proteins.
   1. Protamines.
   2. Histones.
   3. Globulins.
   4. Albumins.
   5. Glutelins.
   6. Glaidins (prolamines).
   7. Scleroproteins.
   8. Phosphoproteins.
II. Conjugated proteins.
   1. Chromoproteins.
   2. Nucleoproteins.
   3. Glucoproteins.
III. Hydrolyzed proteins.
   1. Metaproteins.
   2. Albumoses or proteoses.
   3. Peptones.
   4. Polypeptides.

PROTEOCLASTIC. Proteolytic. See **enzymes, proteolytic.**

PROTEOLYSIS. Hydrolysis of **proteins** to form **peptones** and other products.

PROTIUM. The name sometimes given to the lighter isotope of **hydrogen,** which consists of a single proton and electron, has an atomic number of 1 and a mass number of 1, and constitutes about 99.98% of ordinary hydrogen.

PROTOLYSIS. A reaction in which a **proton** (hydrogen ion) is transferred.

PROTOLYTIC REACTIONS. See **protolysis.**

PROTON. An elementary particle that has a charge of positive electricity equal in size, but opposite in sign, to the negative charge on the **electron,** and a mass of 1.6722×10^{-24} g., or about 1836 times as great as that of the electron. The proton is the nucleus of a hydrogen atom, i.e., it is a hydrogen atom without its electron, and is one of the basic "building-blocks" of the nuclei of all atoms.

PROTONE. One of a class of substances intermediate between the **amino acids** and the protamines, prepared from the latter by mild hydrolysis. The protones bear to

plains many types of chemical behavior, as for example, the fact that glutaconic acid, unlike maleic acid, does not exhibit *cis*- and *trans*-isomerism

$$HOOC—CH_2—CH=CH—COOH \rightleftarrows HOOC—CH=CH—CH_2—COOH.$$

the protamines a relation similar to that which the peptones bear to the proteins.

PROTOPECTIN. A term applied to the water-insoluble parent pectic substance which occurs in plants and which upon restricted hydrolysis, yields **pectin** or **pectinic acids.**

PROTOPHILE. A substance which accepts (i.e., forms combinations with) **protons** (hydrogen ions) readily.

PROTOPLASM. The fundamental material of all living tissue, and the essential substance of all life. It is a colloidal material, of which water is the continuous phase, and it is composed of various carbohydrates, fats, proteins, and inorganic substances constantly reacting with each other and with various solutes or suspensoids in the water phase. Structurally, protoplasm consists of various characteristic parts, such as spongioplasm, hyaloplasm, nucleoplasm, and others.

PROTOTROPY. In general, the shifting of a proton or hydrogen atom in a compound to yield an isomeric substance. Thus, in β-dicarbonyl compounds, a prototropic change to the enol-form accounts for many of the reactions of these substances

$$\begin{array}{cc} \overset{O}{\underset{\|}{}} \overset{H}{\underset{|}{}} \overset{O}{\underset{\|}{}} & \overset{OH}{\underset{|}{}} \overset{O}{\underset{\|}{}} \\ —C—C—C— & \rightleftarrows \quad —C=C—C— \end{array}$$

especially those reactions in which the enol-form yields protons. Cf. **ionotropy.** Another example of this type of prototropic change is that of phenylnitromethane

$$C_6H_5—CH_2—NO_2 \rightleftarrows C_6H_5—CH=N(O)OH$$

A somewhat different type of situation is that of the three-carbon prototropic system

$$—CH=CH—CH_2— \rightleftarrows —CH_2—CH=CH—$$

The mobility of the H in this system ex-

PROUT HYPOTHESIS. An idea of atomic structure advanced in the early days of chemistry, to the effect that all elements were aggregations of hydrogen, or of some other very light substance. Prout's opinions anticipated, in many respects, current views of atomic structure, although he had little or no experimental basis for them.

PROVITAMIN. A substance which yields a **vitamin** by suitable processing or by metabolic change, as carotene yields a vitamin A, or certain sterols yield a vitamin D.

PROXIMATE ANALYSIS. See **analysis, proximate.**

PROXIMATE PRINCIPLE. In **phytochemistry,** an **alkaloid, glycoside,** or bitter principle upon which the properties, especially the medicinal properties, of a plant depend.

PRUD'HOMME REAGENT FOR ALDEHYDES. An acid solution of diazofuchsin decolorized by sodium hydrosulfide. It gives a violet color in presence of aldehydes.

PRUSSATE. A term used for various negative radicals derived from the **cyanide group,** as well as for the cyanide group itself.

PSCHORR REACTION. A method of formation of phenanthrene derivatives by ring closure of diazotized α-aryl-*o*-cinnamic acids, which may be prepared from *o*-nitrobenzaldehydes (or other aromatic nitrocarbonyl compounds) and aryl acetic acids, followed by reduction of the nitro group.

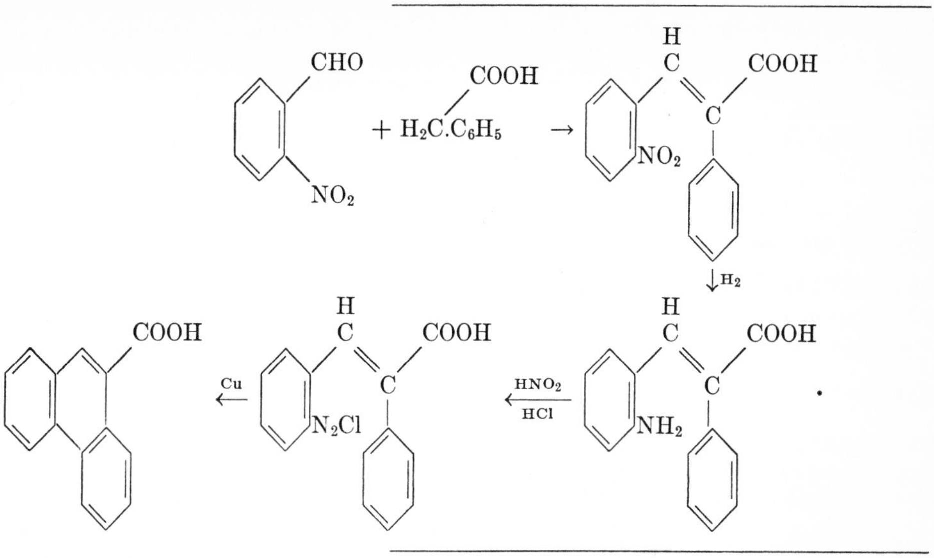

PSEUDO-, PSEUD-. (Greek, false) A prefix indicating resemblance to or relation (especially isomerism) with, as pseudo-cumene, pseudaconitine, pseudobase. Abbreviation: ψ or ps; as ψ-cumene.

PSEUDO-ACID. A substance that exhibits ionic isomerism (see **isomerism, ionic**), wherein one of the forms exhibits acidic properties. For example various compounds containing the group $-NO_2$ and which are neutral may become acid by the tautomeric change of the $-NO_2$ group to $=NO.OH$ and exhibit the characteristic properties of acids.

PSEUDOALLYL. See **isopropenyl.**

PSEUDO-ALUM. One of a series of double sulfates consisting of a double salt of a sulfate of a trivalent metal of the aluminum group and a sulfate of one of certain bivalent metals (manganese, ferrous iron, copper, zinc, and magnesium). Thus, a representative pseudo-alum is

$$Al_2(SO_4)_3.MnSO_4.24H_2O.$$

The pseudo-alums receive their name from their resemblance to the **alums.**

PSEUDO-ASYMMETRY. Asymmetry caused by a nonasymmetric carbon atom becoming asymmetric due to a change in the configuration of asymmetric groups

with which it is associated. Thus in an asymmetric compound of the type

$$X$$
$$|$$
$$(H)-C-(OH)$$
$$|$$
$$Z$$

where X and Z are asymmetric groups and C is inactive, as long as X and Z are of the same rotation C remains inactive; but let X and Z assume opposite rotations and C becomes asymmetric and, although it does not affect the optical rotation of the compound, it does produce two different inactive substances, viz.,

$$+X \qquad\qquad +X$$
$$| \qquad\qquad |$$
$$+C \quad \text{and} \quad -C.$$
$$| \qquad\qquad |$$
$$-Z \qquad\qquad -Z$$

PSEUDO-AZIMIDE. A derivative of the nucleus $C_6H_4 \diagup\!\!\!\diagdown NR$, such as n-phenyl-pseudoazimidobenzene,

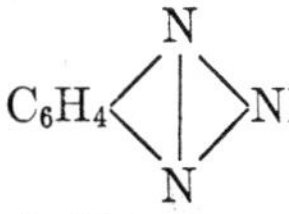

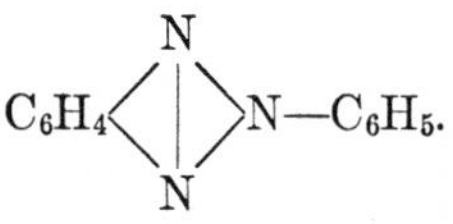

$$C_6H_4 \diagup\!\!\!\diagdown N-C_6H_5.$$

PSEUDO-BASE. A substance that exhibits ionic isomerism, (see **isomerism, ionic**) wherein one of the forms exhibits basic properties.

PSEUDO-CATALYSIS. (Catalysis by transvection, cyclic action) A type of cyclic action in which one of the reactants of a reaction appears among the products unchanged, although it has taken part in the reaction (distinction from true **catalysis**).

PSEUDO-CELLULOSE. (Reserve cellulose) Hemicellulose.

as-**PSEUDOCUMYL.** The radical

$2,3,5\text{-}(CH_3)_3C_6H_2\text{---}$.

s-**PSEUDOCUMYL.** The radical

$2,4,5\text{-}(CH_3)_3C_6H_2\text{---}$.

v-**PSEUDOCUMYL.** The radical

$2,3,6\text{-}(CH_3)_3C_6H_2\text{---}$.

PSEUDOINDOLYL. The radical $C_8H_6N\text{---}$ (from pseudoindole, 7 isomers).

PSEUDO-ISOMERISM. A term applied to tautomerism. See **isomerism, dynamic.**

PSEUDOMERISM. Tautomerism. See **isomerism, dynamic.**

PSEUDOMORPHISM. A phenomenon in which a substance exhibits an abnormal crystalline form. Substances which show this are termed pseudomorphous.

PSEUDO-SALT. A compound that has some of the normal characteristics of a salt, but lacks certain others, notably the ionic lattice in the solid state and the property of ionizing completely in solution. The absence of these properties is due to the fact that the bonds between the metallic and nonmetallic radicals are covalent or semi-covalent instead of polar. Because these salts do not ionize completely, they are also called weak salts.

PSEUDO-SOLUTION. A solution which does not obey the usual physical laws applying to solutions, as the **law of Raoult,** the **law of van't Hoff,** etc. **Colloidal solutions** are often spoken of as pseudo-solutions.

PSEUDO-SYMMETRY. (Compound symmetry, indirect symmetry) (1) The condition of certain inactive indivisible types of **asymmetric compounds** which contain two structurally similar asymmetric carbon atoms and are without a plane of symmetry, yet whose reflected image is identical with them, as a compound of the type

in which the *a-c-b* groups are assumed to be at right angles to the plane of the ring. One half of the compound must be rotated through an angle of 180° to make the configuration symmetrical. This type is not a *meso*-type. (2) In crystals, twins or fourlings which show forms that apparently belong to crystal systems of higher symmetry than the system of the single individual. These are termed pseudo-symmetric or mimetic.

PSEUDO-TANNIN. A tannoidal substance which cannot convert hide into leather, e.g., caffetannic acid, hop tannin, etc.

PSI (Ψ OR ψ). The twenty-third letter in the Greek alphabet, used to denote the twenty-third carbon atom in a straight-chain compound, or a derivative in which the substituent group is attached to that carbon (ψ). Symbol for function (of) (ψ). Symbol for **pseudo** (ψ). Symbol for total **dielectric flux** (Ψ). **Planck function** (Ψ). Symbol for **wave function,** time dependent (ψ).

PSYCHROMETER. A type of **hygrometer,** which consists of two thermometers mounted side by side, one of which has on its bulb a small cloth sleeve, which is thoroughly moistened with water before using. The apparatus is operated by whirling it in the air until the temperature of the wet bulb has reached a minimum value. Then the difference in temperature between the dry bulb and the wet bulb is a function of the rate of evaporation of water from the wet bulb, and hence an inverse function of the degree of saturation of the atmosphere with water vapor. Therefore, the readings of the instrument may be calibrated in terms of relative humidity (or absolute humidity) for the various temperatures of the range covered.

PSYLLIC. Related to psyllic acid,

$$C_{32}H_{65}COOH.$$

Pt Symbol for the element **platinum.**

PTOMAINE. (Cadaveric alkaloid, aporrhegma) Any one of a class of strong amine bases formed by the bacterial splitting of carbon dioxide from the amino acids. Formation:

requires a preliminary treatment to protect the reducing groups from oxidation, as by changing them into **glycosides.**

PURE CHEMISTRY. See **chemistry, pure.**

PURGATIVE. A drug that causes violent bowel evacuation.

PURGOTTI MOLYBDATE REAGENT. In 30 ml. water, dissolve 1.1 g. ammonium molybdate and 5 ml. sulfuric acid, and add slowly 4–5 g. zinc dust. Filter, make up the filtrate to 200 ml. with water, and add a solution of 2 ml. sulfuric acid and 4.2 g. ammonium molybdate in 800 ml. water. Then boil this green liquid until it turns blue. It is used in the volumetric determination of oxidizing substances.

PURINE. A nitrogenous cyclic compound, the parent of several important bases, uric

$$NH_2-CH_2-CH_2-CH_2-CH_2-CHNH_2-COOH \rightarrow NH_2-CH_2-CH_2-CH_2-CH_2-CH_2NH_2 + CO_2.$$
Lysine   Cadaverine (a ptomaine)

Pu Symbol for the element **plutonium.**

PUDDLING FURNACE. A furnace used at one time in the production of wrought iron from pig iron, cast iron, or similar material. It consisted essentially of a shallow, disc-shaped hearth, heated on the reverberatory principle, avoiding contact of the fuel with the charge. Hematite was charged, or used as a lining, to oxidize most of the carbon in the charge. Stirring was effected by long bars, or rabbles, which were also used to remove the impurities which floated to the surface of the molten metal.

PUMP. Any apparatus for moving fluids.

PUMP, AIR. See **air pump.**

PUMP, FILTER. See **filter pump.**

PUMP, VACUUM. See **vacuum pump.**

PURDIE METHYLATION. The use of methyl iodide and silver oxide as methylating agents for **carbohydrates**; this method

acid, etc. The purine complex is numbered as follows:

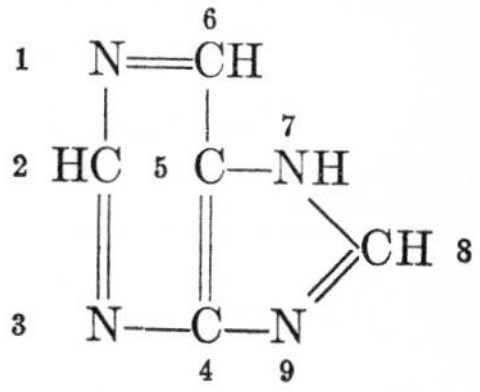

PURPURO-. (Latin: *purpura*, purple) A prefix indicating purple or red color, as purpuroxanthin.

PUTREFACTION. A form of **decomposition** of organic materials, especially **proteins**, brought about by microorganisms and characterized by complexity of process and by the offensive odor of the products.

Py. Abbreviation for **pyridine**, often used in designating positions of substituents in compounds containing a pyridine ring.

PY-. See **pyo-.**

PYCNOMETER. (Pyknometer) A standardized vessel used in determining the **specific gravity** of a liquid by weighing a definite volume at a specified temperature.

PYO-, PY-. (Greek) A prefix relating to pus, as pyoctanine, pyoflavine.

PYR-. See **pyro-**.

PYRAN. One of a group of cyclic compounds, which are the parent substances of a number of important compounds. The pyrans all have the formula C_5H_6O, and consist of six-membered rings, containing five carbons and one oxygen atom.

PYRANYL. The radical $C_5H_5O—$ (2-α, 2-γ, 3-α-, etc.).

PYRAZINYL. The radical $C_4H_3N_2—$ (from pyrazine).

PYRAZOLIDYL. The radical $C_3H_7N_2—$ (from pyrazolidine).

PYRAZOLONE. One of a group of cyclic compounds which are the parent substances of a number of compounds, especially drugs. The pyrazolones have the formula $C_3H_6N_2O$, and consist of five-membered rings, containing two nitrogen atoms and three carbon atoms, one of which has a doubly-bonded (carbonyl) oxygen atom.

PYRAZOLYL. The radical $C_3H_3N_2—$ (from pyrazole, 4 isomers).

PYRENYL. The radical $C_{16}H_9—$ (from pyrene).

"PYREX" GLASS. See **glass, "Pyrex."**

PYRIDINE DERIVATIVES. Derivatives of the heterocyclic substance pyridine, C_5H_5N. The isomerism of pyridine derivatives is similar to that of benzene derivatives. The pyridine ring is lettered or numbered thus,

PYRIDYL. The radical $C_5H_4N—$ (from pyridine, 3 isomers).

PYRIDYLIDENE. The radical [4(1)-form shown]
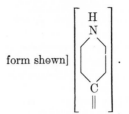
.

PYRIMIDYL. The radical $C_4H_3N_2—$ (from pyrimidine).

PYRO-, PYR-. (Greek: *pyr*, fire) A prefix indicating formation by heat, as pyrocinchonic acid, pyrene; specifically, designating an acid derived from two molecules of an "ortho" acid by loss of 1 H_2O, as pyrophosphoric acid, $H_4P_2O_7$ ($2H_3PO_4 - H_2O$).

PYROACID. An acid containing less water than the **orthoacid** of the same elemental name. Thus, pyroarsenic acid has the formula $H_4As_2O_7$, whereas orthoarsenic acid is H_3AsO_4.

PYROANTIMONIC. Related to pyroantimonic acid, $H_4Sb_2O_7$.

PYROBORIC. Related to pyroboric acid, $H_2B_4O_7$.

PYROELECTRIC EXCITEMENT. A phenomenon observed in certain **crystals,** e.g., tourmaline, which become electrically charged upon uniform, and in some cases uneven, heating or cooling (thermal deformation). One end of the crystal becomes positively charged and the other end negatively charged.

PYROELECTRICITY. Electricity produced by **pyroelectric excitement** (q.v.).

PYROGEN. Literally, producing of heat. A substance that produces fever, commonly when injected into the blood stream.

PYROGENIC. Literally, due to heat. A process, change, or reaction that is accelerated by higher temperatures.

PYROLYSIS. Thermal decomposition, a type of reaction important in coke manufacture, in petroleum cracking, and in many other industries.

PYROMETER. An instrument used for measuring high temperatures, usually those higher than can be indicated on the mercury thermometer, as the melting point of iron, the temperature of a blast furnace, etc.

PYROMETER, ELECTRICAL THERMOCOUPLE. A pyrometer which is actuated by the difference in contact potential between a junction of two metals or alloys at the temperature to be measured, and another junction of the same metals at a fixed or known temperature.

PYROMETER, OPTICAL. A pyrometer that is actuated by the variation with temperature of the energy in a given frequency range, radiated by a body.

PYROMETER, RADIATION. A pyrometer that is actuated by the variation with temperature of the energy radiated by a body.

PYROMETER, RESISTANCE. A pyrometer that is actuated by the change in electrical resistance with temperature of a standard length of metallic wire of standard cross-sectional area.

PYROMETRIC CONES. Small cones that differ in the temperatures at which they soften on heating. They are made of clay and other ceramic materials and are used in the ceramic industries to show furnace temperatures within ranges. In practice, three or four of the cones which have softening points at consecutive temperature ranges are used, and the increase in kiln temperature is judged from the progressive deformation of the cones.

PYROMETRY. The art of measuring high temperatures.

PYROMUCYL. See **2-furoyl.**

PYRONE. One of a class of heterocyclic oxygen compounds derived from α- and γ-pyrone, e.g.,

(α-pyrone)   (γ-pyrone)

The pyrone derivatives are important as possible basic compounds from which **alkaloids** are synthesized in plants. The so-called α, α- and α, γ-pyrones contain one more carbonyl oxygen atom than shown in the above formulas.

PYROPHORIC. (1) Igniting on contact with air. (2) Producing sparks when ground or abraded.

PYROPHORUS. Finely divided material that ignites on contact with the air. Finely divided iron, cobalt, nickel, and other substances show this phenomenon. The ratio of exposed surface to the mass to be heated is so great that the surface oxidation generates sufficient heat to raise the temperature to incandescence.

PYROPHOSPHATE. The anion $P_2O_7^{4-}$ or $H_2P_2O_7^=$, or a compound containing one of these anions.

PYROPHOSPHITE. The anion $P_2O_5^{4-}$, or a compound containing it.

PYROPHOSPHORIC. Related to pyrophosphoric acid, $H_4P_2O_7$.

PYROPHOSPHOROUS. Related to pyrophosphorous acid, $H_4P_2O_5$.

PYROPHOSPHORYL. The quadrivalent radical $P_2O_3\equiv$ derived from pyrophosphoric acid, e.g., pyrophosphoryl chloride, $P_2O_3Cl_4$.

PYROSULFATE. The anion $S_2O_7^=$, or a compound containing it.

PYROSULFITE. The anion $S_2O_5^=$, or a compound containing it.

PYROSULFURIC. Related to pyrosulfuric acid, $H_2S_2O_7$.

PYROSULFURYL. The radical S_2O_5=.

PYRR-. See **pyrrolo-**.

PYRRO-. See **pyrrolo-**.

PYRROLE. A nitrogenous cyclic compound, which is an essential element in the structure of many derivatives important in plant products as well as in organic synthesis. The pyrrole ring is numbered or lettered as follows:

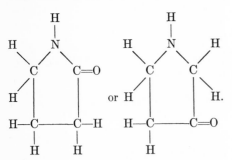

PYRROLIDINE. A saturated **pyrrole** (containing four added hydrogen atoms).

PYRROLIDONE. A saturated **pyrrole** (containing two added hydrogen atoms, and one added oxygen atom, attached to a ring carbon by a double bond).

PYRROLIDYL. The radical C_4H_8N— (from pyrrolidine, 3 isomers).

PYRROLO-, PYRRO-, PYRR-. A prefix relating to **pyrrole**, as pyrrolopyridine, pyrrocoline.

PYRROYL. The radical

$$\overline{CH:CH.CH:CH.NCO}-.$$

PYRRYL. The radical C_4H_4N— (from pyrrole, 3 isomers).

PYRUVIC. Related to pyruvic acid, $CH_3CO.COOH$.

Q. Symbol for quantity of electricity (Q). Symbol for quantity of heat (Q). Symbol for volumetric rate of flow (q). Symbol for rate of heat transfer (q). Symbol for luminous energy (Q). Symbol for heat entering system (q). Symbol for electric quadrupole moment (Q). Symbol for moment of area (Q).

Q-ELECTRON. An **electron** having an orbit of such dimensions that the electron constitutes part of the seventh shell (or **Q-shell**) of electrons surrounding the atomic nucleus, counting out from the nucleus (i.e., the K-shell is the first; the L-, the second; the M-, the third; the N-, the fourth; the O-, the fifth; the P-, the sixth; and the Q-, the seventh).

Q-SHELL. The seventh layer of electrons in motion about the nucleus of an atom; the first, or innermost, layer being the K-shell; the second, the L-shell; the third, the M-shell; the fourth, the N-shell; the fifth, the O-shell; and the sixth, the P-shell. The Q-shell is started, it is believed, with the element **francium** (atomic number = 87) and the elements of higher atomic number have electrons in Q-shells.

QUADRIBASIC. (1) Capable of neutralizing four molecules of monacid base, as pyrophosphoric acid. (2) Having four hydrogen atoms replaceable by bases.

QUADRIMOLECULAR. Involving, or pertaining to, four molecules. There are quadrimolecular reactions if the term is used in the sense of a reaction involving four molecules; but it is unlikely that there are quadrimolecular reactions in the sense of fourth-order reactions, i.e., reactions having a rate that depends upon four concentration terms.

QUADRIVALENCE. The condition of being **quadrivalent**.

QUADRIVALENT. The accepted meaning of this term is having four valencies. The term has also been used to mean having a valence of four, but the latter meaning is now more commonly expressed by the term tetravalent.

QUADRUPLE POINT. The temperature at which four **phases** are in **equilibrium.** An example is the case in which an anhydrous salt, a hydrate of the salt, its saturated solution, and its water vapor are in equilibrium in a salt-water system.

QUADRUPOLE. Let a collection of electric or magnetic charges be distributed around a point; for example, the center of mass of a system of atoms, molecules, or nuclei. The potential at a distance r from this point may be represented by an infinite series of terms in inverse powers of r. The term in the inverse first power is the **Coulomb potential,** the inverse second power term is the **dipole potential,** the inverse third power term is the quadrupole potential, etc. A typical example is an array of four charges of equal magnitude so spaced that they coincide with the vertices of a parallelogram. Charges located on opposite vertices are of the same sign; the distance of separation between charges is taken to be of the order of molecular or infinitesimal dimensions.

QUALITATIVE ANALYSIS. See **analysis, qualitative.**

QUALITY. A term used in chemistry to express the relative excellence, or, more commonly, the degree of purity.

QUANTITATIVE ANALYSIS. See **analysis, quantitative.**

QUANTITY. The amount of a substance or force, commonly expressed in the number of units of mass or of quantity of force present; or a distinct numerical entity or magnitude.

QUANTIVALENCE. Valence.

QUANTIZE. To restrict the possible values of a variable to a discrete number of possible values.

QUANTUM. A unit quantity of energy which is bound during absorption of radiation or set free during emission of radiation. It is symbolized by ϵ and is expressed by the formula, $\epsilon = h\nu$, where ν is the frequency number of the radiation (the quotient of the velocity of light divided by the wave length of the radiation), and h is the **Planck constant.**

QUANTUM EFFICIENCY. In a photochemical reaction (see **reaction, photochemical**), the ratio of the number of molecules transformed to the number of quanta of radiation absorbed.

QUANTUM MECHANICS. A branch of science dealing with the description of atomic and molecular properties, based on the dualistic relation between matter and wave radiation. It is characterized by the fact that many of the variables investigated by use of this theory can assume only discrete values.

QUANTUM NOTATION. One of various systems of symbols for indicating the quantum numbers (energy levels) of electrons, and sometimes the electronic transitions accompanying the emission of various radiation frequencies.

QUANTUM NUMBER. One of a set of integers which is used to characterize a particular value among the selection of discrete values that a quantized variable is allowed to assume.

QUANTUM NUMBER, AZIMUTHAL. (Obs.) A quantum number characterizing the angular momentum of an electron in the Bohr model of the atom. It is related to the ellipticity of the electronic orbit about the nucleus.

QUANTUM NUMBER, INNER. A term sometimes applied to the sum of the azimuthal quantum number and the spin quantum number, representing the resultant of the two corresponding contributions to the angular momentum of the electron.

QUANTUM NUMBER, MAGNETIC. A quantum number that determines the component of the angular momentum vector of an atomic electron or group of electrons along the externally applied magnetic field. The values of these components are restricted, i.e., quantized.

QUANTUM NUMBER, PRINCIPAL. A quantum number which, in the old Bohr model of the atom, determined the energy of an electron in one of the allowed orbits around the nucleus. In the theory of quantum mechanics the principal quantum number is used mostly to identify the electronic orbital of the electrons.

QUANTUM NUMBER, RADIAL. In the Bohr theory of the atom, the quantum number that characterized the momentum of an electron in the direction of the radius vector.

QUANTUM NUMBER, SPIN. An integral term in the expression for the contribution to the total angular momentum of the electron that is due to the rotation of the electron on its own axis. This contribution is quantized, having two values $\frac{1}{2}$ and $-\frac{1}{2}$, in terms of $h/2\pi$ units of angular momentum (h = **Planck's constant**). The spin quantum number gives a numerical basis for the occurrence of many multiplet lines in ordinary spectra.

QUANTUM STATISTICS. A method of statistical analysis of the behavior of the fundamental particles of matter, and their higher aggregates, such as atoms and molecules, from the standpoint of quantum mechanics. One of its basic postulates is that similar particles are not distinguishable. Two widely known systems of quantum statistics are the **Bose-Einstein statistics** and the **Fermi-Dirac statistics.**

QUANTUM THEORY. (Cf. **Quantum mechanics**) A theory concerning the behavior of atoms and molecules, characterized by the limitation that most of the variables discussed in the theory can assume only a restricted number of discrete values.

QUARENTOXIDE. An oxide in which the proportion of another element to oxygen is as four to one, e.g., Cu_4O.

QUART. A unit of dry and liquid measure in the English system.

1 U.S. liquid quart	=	0.94633 liter
1 U.S. liquid quart	=	2 U.S. pints
4 U.S. liquid quarts	=	1 U.S. gallon
1 Imperial quart	=	1.13650 liters
1 U.S. dry quart	=	1.1012 liters

QUARTATION. A method of assay of silver or gold ores, or other materials containing one of these precious metals. In order to effect this separation accurately, which is done by differential solution in nitric acid, the amount of gold present should be about one-quarter of the total gold and silver, and the ratio is adjusted by estimating the original concentrations and adding the calculated amount (usually of silver) before separating. Then the process is repeated by adjusting the amount of silver added to the results of the first analysis, and a closer approximation to the correct result is obtained. If necessary, the process of successive analyses is repeated until a sufficiently consistent result is obtained.

QUARTERING. The widely-accepted method of obtaining representative samples of bulk materials. The large original sample, or if necessary, the entire mass, is thoroughly mixed and then formed into a conical heap, which is then divided into quarters. Two diagonally-opposite quarters are rejected, and the other two are mixed again, and a new conical pile is formed from them. The process is continued until the volume of material has been reduced to the size desired for the sample.

QUATERNARY. A term having the general meaning of the fourth, or of the fourth order. It is used most commonly in chemistry to indicate certain compounds in which four hydrogen atoms are substituted, as a quaternary ammonium or a quaternary phosphonium compound; or to indicate a compound composed of four different atoms or radicals.

QUENCH. To cool suddenly, commonly by immersion in a liquid; a process applied in metallurgy to obtain (1) alloys and other metallic systems which retain certain of the characteristics of forms stable at higher temperatures, which would otherwise undergo complete **transition** on slow cooling, or (2) to obtain a metal structure of characteristic grain-size. The brittleness resulting from the sudden cooling is frequently modified by subsequent partial reheating.

QUENCHING. A term used in counter technology to denote the process of terminating the discharge in a counter. A quenching circuit is a circuit that causes the discharge to cease, and the term "self-quenching" as applied to counters refers to those in which the discharge ceases due to an internal (atomic) mechanism within the counter.

QUINAZOLYL. The radical $C_8H_5N_2-$ (from quinazoline).

QUINCK REAGENT FOR IRON. Ammonium sulfide solution used in histological or pathological work. It gives a black-green color with pigment granules that contain iron.

QUINHYDRONE. An equimolecular compound of p-benzoquinone and hydroquinone.

QUINHYDRONE ELECTRODE. An electrode of **quinhydrone,** which accepts protons (hydrogen ions) to yield hydroquinone, and donates protons to yield p-benzoquinone, and has, therefore, a definite relation between its potential and the **pH** of the solution. Its values have been recorded at definite temperatures, and it is used as a standard electrode in **pH** measurement.

QUINOCARBONIUM SALT. One of a group of salts of nonnitrogenous organic compounds with mineral acids in which the acid is combined with carbon (carbonium valence). A rearrangement of the molecule occurs with production of quinoid structure and development of color. They have the general structure

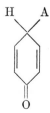

in which A is commonly an acid radical, and the remaining quinoid oxygen, shown above, is usually replaced by substituents.

QUINOGEN. An intermediate product in the condensation of aliphatic alpha diketones to quinones. General formula,

$$R-C(OH)-CO-CH_3$$
$$|$$
$$CH_2-CO-CO-R.$$

QUINOID FORM. The atomic grouping

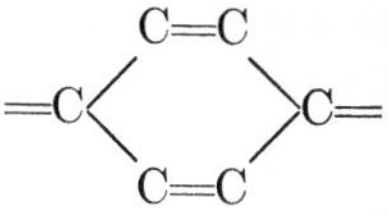

characteristic of quinones and believed to be the chromophore in certain colored benzene derivatives. Cf. **benzenoid.** Since the preparation of o-quinone derivatives it has been necessary to distinguish the above grouping as the "p-quinoid" to avoid confusion. The unqualified term "quinoid," however, always refers to the above group.

QUINOLE. One of a class of substances allied to p-benzoquinone, having the general type-formula

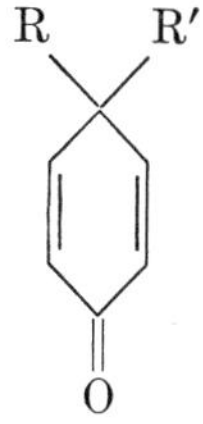

in which R is an alkyl group, and R′ a hydroxy or halogenated alkyl group.

QUINOLINE. A basic heterocyclic compound of the formula,

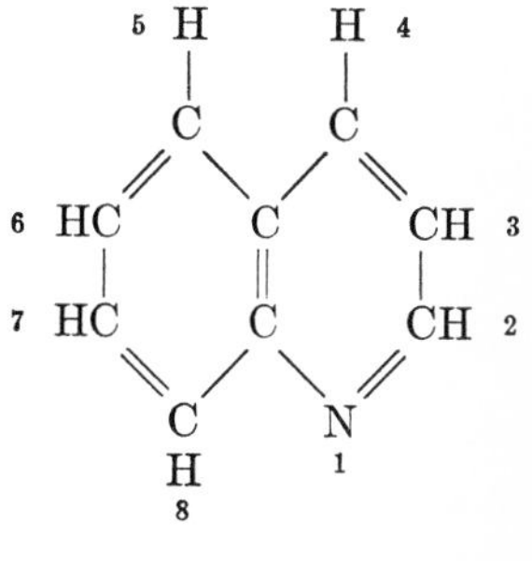

As is apparent from the formula, quinoline consists of a **benzene** nucleus (left side) joined to a **pyridine** nucleus (right side).

Instead of numbering the positions as shown, the carbon atoms of the pyridine nucleus may be designated by Greek letters and those of the benzene nucleus numbered. Carbon atom No. 5 is also known as the *ana* position, while carbon atoms Nos. 8, 7, and 6 may be termed *ortho*, *meta*, and *para*. Substitution in the pyridine nucleus may be distinguished by the notation Py 1, Py 2, or Py 3, instead of by the Greek letters, or the numbers.

QUINOLYL. The radical $C_9H_6N—$ (from quinoline, 7 isomers).

QUINONE. One of many dioxy derivatives of cyclic hydrocarbons having a characteristic arrangement of double bonds, e.g., *p*-benzoquinone,

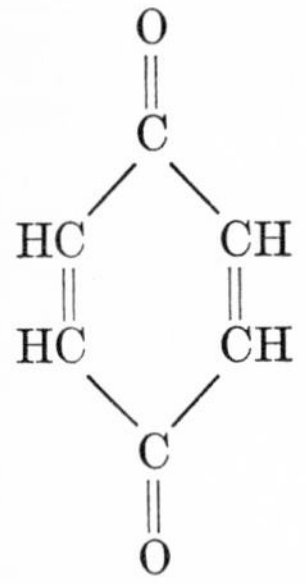

o-benzoquinone,

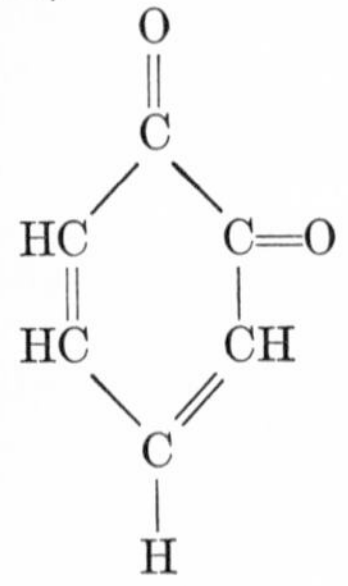

α-naphthaquinone,

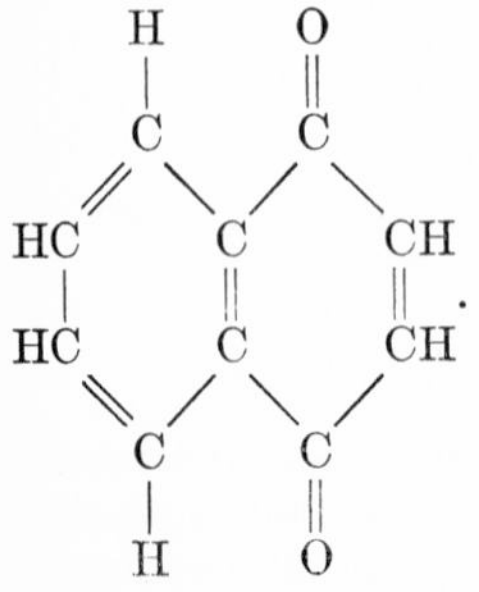

QUINONYL. The radical $C_6H_3O_2—$ (from quinone).

QUINOXALYL. The radical $C_8H_5N_2—$ (from quinoxaline).

QUINOYL. (1) A name originally applied to a radical derived from **quinone** by loss of a hydrogen atom. (2) A term used to designate the quinone group oxygen.

QUINQUEMOLECULAR. Containing or involving five molecules.

QUINQUEVALENT. The accepted meaning of this term is having five valencies. It has also been used to mean having a valence of five, but pentavalent is preferable for the latter meaning.

QUINTESSENCE. (1) An extract. (2) An essential oil.

QUINTUPLE POINT. The temperature at which five **phases** are in equilibrium.

R. Symbol for the **gas constant** (R). Abbreviation for radical, usually organic (R). Symbol for **Reamur temperature** (°R). Symbol for **Rankine temperature** (°R). Abbreviation for radius (r). Abbreviation for racemic (r). Symbol for equivalent resistance of cloth (r). Symbol for hydraulic radius (R_H). Symbol for production rate (R). Symbol for **reflux ratio** (R). Symbol for **roentgen** (r). Symbol for angle of reflection (r). Symbol for radial distance (r). Symbol for relative **humidity** (r). Symbol for **rotational quantum number** (R). Symbol for **radioactive range** (R). Symbol for electric **resistance** (R, r). Symbol for thermal resistance (R). **Rydberg constant** (R). Symbol for position vector (r). See also **rho.**

Ra Symbol for the element **radium.**

RABL CHROMO-FORMIC ACID. A solution of 0.3 g. chromium trioxide, and 2 drops formic acid in 100 ml. water, used as a fixative.

RABL FLUID. A fixative prepared by mixing 10 ml. of a saturated aqueous solution of mercuric chloride, 10 ml. of a saturated aqueous solution of picric acid, and 20 ml. distilled water.

RACEMATE. A racemic salt; see **raceme.**

RACEMATION. Racemization.

RACEME (RACEMIC FORM). An optically inactive compound which consists of equal quantities of the dextro and laevo forms of optical isomers. Racemic compounds crystallize in holohedral, not in hemihedral, crystals and may be resolved into the enantiomorphs by several methods; see **resolution** and **inactive compounds.**

RACEMIZATION. (Racemation) The rendering inactive of an optically active substance by converting it into the racemic form. Heating is the usual method of effecting the conversion. Some substances racemize spontaneously at ordinary temperatures (autoracemization); others are not completely racemized but sometimes only a single asymmetric group is affected (partial racemization).

RACEMIZATION, PARTIAL. Incomplete racemization of compounds that contain several asymmetric carbon atoms in which only a single asymmetric group is affected by the racemizing process.

RACEMIZED PROTEINS. Proteins that have been treated with concentrated alkali thereby diminishing their optical activity.

RADCLIFFE TESTS FOR CARBON TETRACHLORIDE. (1) Carbon tetrachloride reacts with phenylhydrazine to form a crystalline product, which melts at 198–200° C. and dissolves in alcohol, the solution giving a red color with sodium hydroxide solution.
(2) Carbon tetrachloride gives, with triethylphosphine in anhydrous ether, a rose-red color changing to a white precipitate.

RADIAL DISTRIBUTION METHOD. A statistical method for the analysis of data obtained by measuring the intensity of **x-ray diffraction** at various angles, in order to determine interatomic distances of liquids and gases, within certain limitations.

RADIANT. A term denoting motion on a radius or, more particularly, along a very great number of radii, as the emission of energy from a point source, which travels along the various radii of a sphere of constantly-increasing radius, so that the radiation-pattern at any instant occupies, in a perfectly homogeneous medium, the position of the surface of a sphere. From this original meaning, the term has been extended in its application to connote either particles of matter or electromagnetic energy emerging from a more or less sharply defined region, or the substance or entity which emits such particles or radiations.

RADIANT ENERGY. Energy transmitted as electromagnetic **radiation.**

RADIANT INTENSITY. The **radiant power** emitted per unit solid angle in a specified direction.

RADIANT POWER. The rate at which energy is transported in a beam of radiant energy. It is sometimes called the radiant flux. It is preferably expressed in watts or ergs per second. See **law of Beer.**

RADIATION. As described under the term radiant (above). the concept of radiation is basically that of the emission of electromagnetic energy or small material particles from a more or less sharply defined region. Electromagnetic energy is energy which in many of its manifestations exhibits the characteristics of waves. These waves range in wave length from 3×10^{-14} meter to 3×10^4 meters or more, and in frequency from 10^{22} to 10^4 vibrations per second. They comprise cosmic rays, gamma rays, x-rays, ultraviolet rays, visible light rays, infrared rays, heat rays, radio waves, and many intermediate frequencies not specifically named because they have not been encountered in any extended series of investigations or applications.

In addition to its primary use as the name of this characteristic form of energy, the word radiation is used to express the act of emitting energy in this way. Furthermore, it has been extended to include certain cases of the emission of material particles, whether or not such emissions are thought of (in accordance with the de Broglie concept) as having the properties of waves. The so-called **alpha radiations** and **beta radiations,** are, respectively, streams of helium nuclei and streams of electrons, which were discovered originally in the investigation of naturally-radioactive substances. The term corpuscular radiation is sometimes applied to such streams of particles.

RADIATION, ČERENKOV. Radiation emitted by a high-energy charged particle moving in a medium having an index of refraction considerably greater than unity. This radiation is due to the effect of the discrepancy between the high velocity of the particle, which may be close to that of light in a vacuum, and the lower velocity of its associated electric and magnetic fields, which have a velocity equal only to the velocity of light in a vacuum *divided by* the **refractive index** of the medium.

RADIATION, COSMIC. See **cosmic rays.**

RADIATION, ELECTROMAGNETIC. As described under **radiation** (above), a moving field of electromagnetic energy which exhibits, in many of its manifestations, the characteristics of waves. There is a periodic variation in intensity, which determines the wave length and the associated frequency. Radiations as diverse as cosmic rays, light rays, heat waves, and radio waves, are called electromagnetic radiations because they have all been shown to be characterized by a moving electrical field and an associated magnetic field.

RADIATION, INFRARED. The region of the electromagnetic spectrum extending from 0.78 micron to about 300 microns. For convenience, it may be divided into three parts as follows:

	Wave Length, μ	Wave Number, cm^{-1}	Frequency, f
Near infrared	0.78–3.0	12,800–3,333	385–100
Middle infra-red	3.0–30	3,333–333	100–10
Far infrared	30–300	333–33.3	10–1

in which the wave length is in microns, the wave number in cm^{-1}, and the frequency in **fresnels.** See also **light, ultraviolet,** and **microwave.**

RADIATION, MONOCHROMATIC. Electromagnetic radiation of one wave length and, hence, one frequency. It is called monochromatic because when it is within the wave length and frequency range of visible light, it consists of one color only. In practice, the term is often applied to a radiation of a narrow frequency range.

RADIATION PRESSURE. The pressure produced by impinging radiation on an absorbing body.

RADIATION, RECOIL. A term applied to radiations emitted during **nuclear disintegrations** which are attended by an observable recoil of the nucleus emitting the radiation.

RADIATION, RESONANCE. See **resonance radiation.**

RADIATION, STRAY. All radiation which reaches the detector at wave lengths that do not correspond to the spectral position under consideration.

RADIATION TEMPERATURE. See **law of Stefan.**

RADIATION ULTRAVIOLET. The region of the electromagnetic spectrum extending from 100 to 3800 Å. For convenience, it is divided into two parts as follows:

	Wave Length, $\overset{\circ}{A}$	Wave Number, cm^{-1}	Frequency, f
Far ultraviolet	100–2000	10^6–50,000	30,000–1,500
Near ultraviolet	2000–3800	50,000–26,300	1,500–790

in which the wave length is in Ångströms, the wave number in cm^{-1}, and the frequency in **fresnels**. See also **light** and **infrared**.

RADIATION, VISIBLE. Radiant energy which is perceived by the normal eye (approximately 3800 to 7800 Å). See also **infrared** and **ultraviolet**.

RADIATOR. In the broadest sense, a body emitting energy, although the term is applied most often to a body emitting electromagnetic energy.

RADICAL. A group of atoms which may enter into several combinations as a unit, and take part in reactions like an elementary substance, viz., NH_4—, CH_3—, C_6H_5—, C_6H_5CO—, $=SO_4$.

RADICAL, ACID. (1) A radical formed from an acid by loss of protons (hydrogen ions); or (2) a radical formed from an organic acid by loss of the **hydroxy group** from a **carboxy group**.

RADICAL, ALKOXY. See **alkoxy**. In all other cases of specific radicals, see the specific name of the radical.

RADICAL, DISSIMILATED. A radical which is combined in an atomic complex so that it no longer reacts in normal fashion. For example, in certain modifications of chromium sulfate in solution only a fraction of the total sulfate radicals present may be precipitated by barium chloride; the remainder is said to be dissimilated. See **sequestrating agent.**

RADICAL, FREE. A distinct molecular species in which one or more of the valence electrons of the atomic constituents do not contribute to the bonding and are free. These species have a very transitory existence.

RADICAL, HYPERCHROMIC. See **hyperchromic radical.**

RADICAL, NEGATIVE. A radical, or group of atoms, which behaves as a unit and carries a negative electric charge. Negative radicals may result by the sep-

aration of one or more hydrogen ions (protons) from an acid and are, therefore, usually synonymous with acid radicals.

RADICALS, MULTIVALENT. Radicals of valence greater than two, as the methine group.

RADIO-. A prefix which denotes a relationship with the phenomena of **radiant energy** or of **radioactivity.**

RADIOACTINIUM. A **thorium** isotope of mass number 227, produced naturally by β-decay of actinium 227. Radioactinium emits α-particles (half-period 18.8 days) to give radium 223 (actinium X).

RADIOACTIVE. Emitting **radiations** or particles of sub-atomic size.

RADIOACTIVE CAPTURE REACTION. See **reaction, radioactive capture.**

RADIOACTIVE CONSTANT. The proportionality constant which expresses the relationship between the rate of decay of the activity of a radioactive element, and its activity at any time. It is defined by the expression:

$$\lambda I = -\frac{dI}{dt}$$

where λ is the radioactive constant of an element, I is its instantaneous activity, and $-dI/dt$ is its rate of decay.

RADIOACTIVE DECAY. Loss of **activity** of a radioactive substance. Its rate is proportional to the activity of the substance at any instant. (See **radioactive constant**.)

RADIOACTIVE DISINTEGRATION. The disintegration of atoms of radioactive elements, with the emission of particles, such as **alpha** and **beta particles**, and of **gamma radiations**, and the formation of another element or elements. These may also be unstable, and the process continues as a series of transformations, each accompanied by characteristic emission of particles and/or radiations, until an element having a stable nucleus is reached.

RADIOACTIVE DISINTEGRATION, THEORY OF. The atoms of any radioactive element undergo spontaneous change, with the formation of atoms of a new element (which may also be radioactive), and with the emission of **alpha particles** (doubly-ionized helium atoms), or **beta particles** (electrons), and/or **gamma rays.** This theory was developed to explain the behavior of the natural radioactive elements. It is inadequate to explain many of the phenomena observed in the study of artificial radioactivity, where such additional events are encountered as, for example, **positron** emission, K-electron capture (capture of an electron in the K-shell by the nucleus), etc.

RADIOACTIVE ELEMENT. An element that undergoes a radioactive change spontaneously. This definition excludes the elements exhibiting radioactivity which are produced by bombardment with particles or radiations, and to which the term radioelement is more or less exclusively applied. The important radioactive elements are those which range in atomic number from 82 to 92, with certain of their various isotopes.

RADIOACTIVE EMANATIONS. Radioactive gases given off by certain radioactive elements. Thus, **radium, thorium,** and **actinium** give off the radioactive gaseous emanations, **radon, thoron,** and **actinon,** respectively.

RADIOACTIVE EQUILIBRIUM. See **equilibrium, radioactive.**

RADIOACTIVE INDICATOR. A radioactive substance which is used, because of the convenience and ease of its detection, to investigate chemical and biochemical processes, commonly those of a nonradioactive atomic species of the same atomic number, and hence the same chemical properties.

RADIOACTIVITY. The process of **radioactive disintegration.** This process is exhibited naturally by certain elements, which continue to do so as long as any of the element remains, and the process may, in fact, continue long afterward in the

event that the elements formed by it are themselves radioactive.

The process is also exhibited artificially when nonradioactive elements are changed, by bombardment with **neutrons, protons, deuterons, helium nuclei, gamma rays,** etc., into other species, many of which also have unstable nuclei, and hence undergo radioactive disintegration.

RADIOACTIVITY, ARTIFICIAL. Radioactivity induced in an element by bombarding it with particles or radiations or both. See **radioactivity** and **radioactivity, induced.**

RADIOACTIVITY, INDUCED. The production of radioactive elements by bombardment of other elements, commonly the stable ones, with **alpha particles, neutrons, protons,** and other particles or radiations. The artificial radioactive elements (commonly called radioelements) usually, but not always, have short life periods; they emit **electrons, positrons,** and other particles, as well as **gamma rays,** in their decomposition. See **reaction, nuclear.**

RADIOELEMENT OR RADIO-ELEMENT. A radioactive element, natural or artificial, although there is an increasing tendency to apply the term particularly to the latter.

RADIOMETER. An instrument used to measure the mechanical effects of radiant energy.

RADIOMICROMETER. A sensitive **thermopile** used to detect minute changes of radiant energy.

RADIOTHORIUM. A **thorium** isotope of mass number 228, produced naturally by β-decay of actinium 228 (mesothorium II). Radiothorium emits α-particles (half-period 1.90 years) to give radium 224 (thorium X).

RADIUM. Radioactive element. Symbol Ra. Atomic number 88. Atomic weight 226.05. Melting point 960°C. Boiling point 1140° C. Radium has a half-period of 1620 years. It is formed from ionium by **alpha-particle** emission, and radium in turn emits an alpha particle to form radon. Among the isotopes of radium are actinium X which has a mass number of 223 and a half-period of 11.2 days; mesothorium 1 which has a mass number of 228 and a half-period of 6.7 years; thorium X which has a mass number of 224 and a half-period of 3.64 days. Other isotopes of radium include those of mass numbers 219–222, 225, 227, 229 and 230. Radium is found in a number of ores, namely, pitchblende and carnotite. Valence 2. Chemical properties of radium are similar to those of barium.

RADIUM EMANATION. See **radon.**

RADON. Radioactive gaseous element. Symbol Rn. Atomic number 86. Mass number 222. Half-period 3.825 days. Emits **alpha particles** to yield radium A, an isotope of polonium. Radon is formed in turn by the emission of the alpha particles from the radium nucleus. Radon has been liquefied at $-65°$ C. and solidified at $-110°$ C. It has also been called niton and radium emanation. Among its isotopes are actinon which has a mass number of 219, a half-period of 3.93 seconds, and is a member of the actinium family; and also thoron which has a mass number of 220, a half-period of 54.4 seconds, and is a member of the thorium family. Other isotopes of radon include those of mass numbers 209–218 and 221.

RAFFINATE. (1) A refined petroleum product, produced by fractionation of a crude charge. (2) Any refined product obtained by fractional distillation.

RAIGH TEST FOR MAGNESIUM. Acidify the solution tested with hydrochloric acid, and add 1 drop 0.5% solution of o,p-dihydroxyazo-p-nitrobenzene in 1% sodium hydroxide solution, followed by slight excess sodium hydroxide. A sky-blue lake indicates magnesium. Nickel and cobalt interfere.

RAIKOW REAGENT FOR SULFUR. Paper treated with a solution of 1 g. phloroglucinol and 1 g. vanillin in 100 ml. ether. It is used in detecting sulfur in organic compounds. A red color, produced when the moist paper is held over the burning sample, indicates the presence of sulfur.

RAIKOW TEST FOR CALCIUM. On moderate ignition of precipitated alkaline-earth carbonates, and treatment of the residue with water, alkalinity to phenolphthalein indicates the presence of calcium, because calcium carbonate decomposes at a much lower temperature than barium or strontium carbonates.

RAIKOW TEST FOR METHANOL. The methanol is converted to nitromethane, which, on treatment with sodium nitroprusside in ammoniacal solution, gives a deep-blue color, changing to green, yellow, and red-yellow.

RAMAN EFFECT. The change in frequency of light on **scattering,** due to absorption of part of its energy by the scattering medium. The change in frequency is generally equal to the change in rotational and vibrational energy of the scattering molecules and is, therefore, useful in the study of molecular structure and behavior.

RAMAN SPECTRUM. A spectrum obtained by illuminating a substance with radiation of a single frequency, and obtaining from the radiations scattered at right angles a spectrum of those frequencies differing from the incident radiation.

RAMSAY-YOUNG RULE. An empirically derived relationship between two sets of temperatures at which two chemically-similar liquids have the same **vapor pressures** of the form:

$$T_1/T_2 = T_1'/T_2'$$

in which T_1 and T_2 are temperatures at which two similar liquids have the same vapor pressure P, and T_1' and T_2' are temperatures at which the substances have the same vapor pressure P'. This relationship is useful in comparing vapor pressures at different temperatures, and boiling points at different pressures, of similar compounds.

RANKINE TEMPERATURE SCALE. A **temperature scale** which corresponds to the Kelvin scale, but is based on the absolute zero of the Fahrenheit system, so that $0°$ Rankine $= -459.69°$ F.

RAOULT LAW. See **law of Raoult.**

RARE EARTH. An oxide of one of the rare earth metals (see **element, rare earth**) or a mixture of such oxides.

RARE GAS. See **gas, rare.**

RASCHIG PROCESS. The catalytic conversion of benzene to phenol, which takes place in two stages, as follows:

$$2C_6H_6 + 2HCl + O_2 \rightarrow 2C_6H_5Cl + 2H_2O$$

$$C_6H_5Cl + H_2O \rightarrow C_6H_5OH + HCl.$$

The hydrochloric acid is distilled off the water fraction obtained from the second stage, and is returned to the first stage. The first stage takes place, with the catalysts in use (c. 1948) at about 230° C., and the second stage at about 425° C. Although the percentage conversion in both reactions is only about 10%, giving the process the disadvantage of low operating capacity, it has a relatively high yield, because only a very small amount of by-products is obtained.

RASCHIG RINGS. Rings made of stoneware which are used in packing absorption towers. They are designed to provide a great surface of contact between gas and liquid per unit volume, and a small resistance to the flow of the gas.

RASPAIL TEST REACTION. Lecithin in concentrated sulfuric acid solution is colored purple-red by the addition of sugar.

RAST MOLECULAR WEIGHT METHOD. A micro method for the determination of **molecular weights.** The method consists of dissolving a small weighed amount of the substance in molten camphor and determining the depression of the freezing point of the camphor attributable to the substance. By conducting the test in a capillary tube attached to a thermometer, close temperature readings are obtained.

RATHGEN MICRO-CHEMICAL TEST FOR ALUMINA. The powdered sample is heated to dryness in a platinum crucible with ammonium fluoride and a few drops concentrated sulfuric acid, then heated to redness for a moment. Colorless, corundum-like, hexagonal crystals are seen under the microscope if aluminum is present.

RAY. In wave motion, a line from the center of disturbance at right angles to the wave front, everywhere indicating the direction of motion of the waves. Since electromagnetic **radiation** of any form (light, heat, x-rays, etc.) consists of a transmission of energy from a source in the form of a sphere of ever-increasing radius, a ray represents the energy traveling out along one of the radii of such a sphere, or a small area around such a radius. This description applies to a single, homogenous medium; if, however, part of the wave front is passed through a lens-system, or other concentrating device, then a more or less longitudinal beam may be obtained, which is also called a ray.

The term ray is also applied to beams of moving particles, such as alpha rays or other ions directed by magnetic or electric fields.

RAY, ACTINIC. An electromagnetic **radiation** or band of radiations having chemical or biological effects. The term is applied most commonly to **ultraviolet radiation.**

RAY, ALPHA. A stream of helium nuclei, which have two positive charges, since the **helium** atom has two electrons.

RAY, BECQUEREL. Radiation emitted by radioactive substances, discovered in early work on radioactivity by the action upon photographic plates. These rays were later named **gamma rays.**

RAY, BETA. A stream of **electrons.** The name beta rays was given them upon their discovery in the early investigation of radioactive elements.

RAY, CANAL. A stream of positive ions in the gas phase; the derivation of the name canal rays is due to the fact that such streams of particles were obtained by boring holes in the cathode of a gas-discharge tube.

RAY, CATHODE. A stream of electrons produced by passing a high-voltage electric current through a highly evacuated tube. The stream of electrons is luminous, passes from cathode to anode, and is deflected by a magnet placed in certain positions. Lenard rays are cathode rays extending a short distance outside the walls of the tube which contains the cathode rays.

RAY, COSMIC. A range of electromagnetic radiations of extremely short wave length (in the approximate range from 0.008 to 0.0003 Ångström units), which are known to reach the earth from distant space, and which do not seem to come from any particular direction in the universe.

RAY, GAMMA. A range of electromagnetic radiations of very short wave length, extending from 1.8 to 0.018 Ångström units. They are produced by radioactive disintegration, natural or artificial, as well as by the impact upon solid substances of very high-speed electrons.

RAY-GUPTA REAGENT FOR METALS. Dimercaptothiodiazole, which gives precipitates of characteristic color with most of the elements precipitated by hydrogen sulfide.

RAY, INFRARED. A range of electromagnetic radiations in a region of the spectrum, which begins at the end of the visible red and extends for some distance in the direction of increasing wave length.

RAY, LENARD. See ray, cathode.

RAY, MOLECULAR. See molecular ray.

RAY, ORDINARY. When light is incident obliquely on an anisotropic crystal or other double-refracting medium and is split into two components, the ray which is deviated at an index of refraction independent of the angle of incidence is the ordinary ray. The other ray, the extraordinary ray, has an index of refraction that varies with the angle of incidence.

RÂY-RAY REAGENT FOR COPPER. Rubeanic acid (dithiooxamide). A few drops of its alcoholic solution give a green-black precipitate or dull green color with neutral copper solutions to which $\frac{1}{10}$ volume of 5 N acetic acid has been added.

RAY, ROENTGEN. The familiar x-rays, a type of radiation produced whenever cathode rays (streams of high-speed electrons) impinge on any solid substance such as the walls of a gas-discharge tube or upon obstacles placed within their path. X-rays penetrate many substances through which the cathode rays do not pass, are not deflected by a magnet, excite phosphorescence in many substances and ionize gases. They occupy a range of the electromagnetic spectrum from about 20. to 0.04 Ångström units.

RAY, ULTRAVIOLET. A range of electromagnetic radiations in a region of the spectrum which begins at the end of the visible violet, and extends for some distance in the direction of decreasing wave length.

RAY, X-. See ray, Roentgen.

RAYBIN TEST REACTION FOR VITAMIN B₁ (THIAMINE). About 0.001 g. of vitamin B_1 is dissolved in several ml. of a borax solution of pH 9.6, and a drop added of an alcoholic solution of 2,6-dibromoquinonechloroimide. An orange color, soluble in chloroform and other organic solvents, forms at once.

RAYLEIGH EQUATION. An expression for the separation by distillation of one component of a liquid system. It is of the form:

$$\frac{dN}{N} = \frac{dx}{(y - x)}$$

where N is the total number of moles of liquid, dN is an infinitesimal amount distilled off, x is the composition of the original liquid with respect to one component, and y is the composition (determined as a function of x) of the distillate dN.

This expression has been integrated for a number of cases, i.e., for certain binary mixtures, dilute solutions, and others.

Rb Symbol for the element rubidium.

Re Symbol for the element rhenium.

REACT. To exhibit or participate in a reaction.

REACTANT. One of the chemical substances that take part in a chemical reaction. (See **reaction**.)

REACTING WEIGHT. The **equivalent weight.**

REACTION. (1) A chemical change. Specifically, a change by which one or more substances are transformed into one or more entirely new substances, the process being accompanied by a change in energy, but not, in most cases, by a change in the total mass of the system. Radioactive reactions, however, both natural and artificial, do involve a change of the mass of the system, which is accompanied by a change in energy, opposite in sign to the change in mass, and equal to its magnitude multiplied by the square of the velocity of light. (2) A particular chemical (or physical) change used in analysis to detect the presence or amount of a particular substance, e.g., a molecular or atomic species. (3) A particular analytical reaction, e.g., an acid reaction or an alkaline reaction. (4) In biology or physics, the term reaction is used in the general sense of a response, e.g., the

in a chemical compound.

REACTION, ACID. A chemical change which indicates that a substance or system has a **hydrogen-ion concentration** greater than some established standard, commonly greater than that of pure water, i.e., a **pH** lower than 7.0.

REACTION, ADDITION. When two or more molecules react to produce but one product, the reaction is termed "addition" or, less commonly, a synthetical reaction. The direct union of carbon and hydrogen to produce acetylene, or of sulfur and oxygen to produce sulfur dioxide, is an addition reaction.

REACTION, ALCOHOLYSIS. A chemical change analogous to hydrolysis in which an alcohol causes decomposition of another substance, with one part of the alcohol molecule combining with one fragment of the decomposed molecule, and the other part of the alcohol molecule combining with the other fragment of the decomposed molecule. For example,

$$CH_3\text{--}CHCl\text{--}CH_2\text{--}O\text{--}\overset{\displaystyle O}{\overset{\|}{C}}\text{--}CH_3 + CH_3OH \rightarrow CH_3\text{--}CHCl\text{--}CH_2\text{--}OH + CH_3\text{--}O\text{--}\overset{\displaystyle O}{\overset{\|}{C}}\text{--}CH_3.$$

response to a stimulus applied to a living entity or organism, or the equal and opposite force which, according to Newton's Third Law, results when a force is applied to a material system.

Various chemical changes and analytical reactions are listed below, under the term "reaction," followed by a descriptive adjective; reactions commonly designated by proper names are listed throughout this book under the name or names of the men to whom they are accredited.

REACTION, ACETYLATION. A reaction resulting in the addition or substitution of the acetyl radical,

REACTION, ALDOL CONDENSATION. See **condensation, aldol.**

REACTION, ALKALINE. A chemical change which indicates that a substance or system has a **hydrogen-ion concentration** less than some established standard, commonly less than that of pure water, i.e., a **pH** greater than 7.0.

REACTION, ALKYLATION. The introduction, as by substitution or addition, of an **alkyl group** into a chemical compound, commonly by treatment with the corresponding alcohol or ester in the presence of a catalyst. Alkylation processes in hydrocarbon systems, where the reactants are often all hydrocarbons, play an important part in the modern petroleum processing industries for the production of special hydrocarbons for use in fuels, etc.

REACTION, AMIDATION. Any chemical change which results in the formation of an **amide**. It can take place in many ways, depending upon the type of amide formed. Thus simple acid amides

$$\left[R-C \underset{NH_2}{\overset{O}{\Big\backslash}} \right]$$

may be formed by treatment of various acids or acid derivatives (**esters, acid halides, anhydrides,** etc.) with ammonia, by partial hydrolysis of certain organic **cyanides,** etc. Diamides and triamides have been prepared by heating organic **cyanides** with **acids** and **acid anhydrides,** respectively, as well as by other methods. N-substituted amides have been prepared from organic **isocyanides,** etc.

REACTION, AMINATION. Any chemical change which results in the formation of an **amine**. It can take place in many ways, depending on whether the amine is primary, secondary, tertiary, or quaternary, whether its organic radicals are alkyl or aryl, or whether they contain substituent groups. Primary amines may be prepared by hydrolysis of alkyl **isocyanates**

$$(R-N=C=O);$$

by treatment of an acid amide with a hypohalite (see **reaction, Hofmann**); by reduction of acid amides, organic cyanides, oximes, hydrazones, and other compounds; by conversion of an acid azide (see **reaction, Curtius**); by the reaction of an alkyl iodide with potassium phthalimide, followed by hydrolysis (see **Gabriel synthesis**); by the formation of a Grignard reagent of the alkyl halide, adding chloroamine ($ClNH_2$) and hydrolyzing; etc.

Secondary amines may be prepared by hydrolysis of an organic cyanamide (R_2NCN) formed from an organic halide and di-

sodium cyanamide; by hydrolysis of p-nitrosoanilines, whereupon the substituted N-group ($R_1R_2N—$) of the aniline forms the secondary amine; by reducing **Schiff's bases,** etc.

Tertiary amines may be prepared by certain Grignard reactions or from organic halides by reaction with ammonia in strongly alkaline solution. This reaction commonly yields mixtures of amines, but by using the alkyl halide in excess, good yields of the tertiary amine are often obtainable. Similarly, quaternary amines are best obtained by exhaustive alkylation.

REACTION, AMMONOLYSIS. In its most general use of the term, a chemical change analogous to **hydrolysis,** in which ammonia causes decomposition of another substance, with one part of the NH_3 molecule combining with one fragment of the decomposed molecule, and the other part of the ammonia molecule combining with the other fragment of the decomposed molecule. In ammonolysis reactions, the NH_3 molecule commonly divides into NH_2^- and H^+ radicals or ions, and this process itself is sometimes called ammonolysis.

REACTION, ANALYTICAL. A reaction used in a process of qualitative or quantitative **analysis.**

REACTION, AROMATIZATION. A reaction which results in the formation of an **aromatic** compound, i.e., a compound having a stable, unsaturated ring such as that present in benzene, its derivatives and compounds containing fused rings similar to that of **benzene,** such as naphthalene, anthracene, phenanthrene, etc. Such processes may start from straight-chain compounds, as exemplified by the **polymerization** of acetone to form mesitylene, or from saturated cyclic compounds by dehydrogenation. Selenium is an especially effective dehydrogenating agent for this purpose.

REACTION, ARSONATION. A chemical change in which the **arsonic acid** group is introduced into a molecule. The resulting compound may be one of several different types as

$$\underset{\underset{O}{\diagdown\!\diagdown}}{\overset{\overset{OH}{\diagup}}{RAs}}{-}OH \quad \text{or} \quad \underset{\underset{O}{\diagdown\!\diagdown}}{\overset{\overset{OR'}{\diagup}}{RAs}}{-}OH \quad \text{or} \quad \underset{\underset{O}{\diagdown\!\diagdown}}{\overset{\overset{OR'}{\diagup}}{RAs}}{-}OR'' \quad \text{or} \quad \underset{\underset{O}{\diagdown\!\diagdown}}{\overset{\overset{O}{\diagup\!\diagup}}{RAs}} \quad .$$

REACTION, ARYLATION. The introduction, as by substitution or addition, of an **aryl group** into a chemical compound.

REACTION, AUTOCATALYTIC. A reaction that is **catalyzed** by one of its own products.

REACTION, BALANCED. A reaction in which, under usual conditions, the products react to reform the initial reactants so that a state of **equilibrium** is finally reached in which, at any definite temperature, the concentrations of initial reactants and products are constant, e.g.,

REACTION, BI-FUNCTIONAL. A reaction in which each of two different reacting molecules has two groups that enter into the reaction, or are capable of doing so.

REACTION, BIMOLECULAR. Although originally used in its literal sense as meaning a reaction between two molecules as reactants, this expression is now used most commonly as a synonym for a **second-order reaction**, i.e., a reaction having a velocity that depends upon two concentration terms. Reactions involving two molecules as reactants are sometimes of the first order, and many reactions involving more

$$CH_3COOH + C_2H_5OH \rightleftarrows CH_3COOC_2H_5 + H_2O.$$

The reversed pointers $\rightleftarrows$ are used to denote that the reactions proceed from either side. At equilibrium the velocity of the esterification reaction in the example is equal to that of the hydrolysis, and, although the system is in continual reaction, the concentrations suffer no change. In such systems, the direction of the reaction may be controlled by variation in chemical or physical conditions.

REACTION, BENZOIN. See **condensation, benzoin.**

REACTION, BENZOLATION. A reaction resulting in the addition or substitution of the **benzoyl radical**

$$C_6H_5{-}\overset{\overset{O}{\diagup\!\diagup}}{C}\diagdown$$

in a chemical compound.

REACTION, BENZYLATION. A reaction resulting in the addition or substitution of the **benzyl radical,**

$$C_6H_5{-}CH_2{-}$$

in a chemical compound.

than two molecules (as where one is present in excess) are of the second order and hence are said to be bimolecular.

REACTION, BI-TRIFUNCTIONAL. A reaction in which one of the two different reacting molecules has two groups that can or do enter into the reaction, and the other of the reacting molecules has three groups that enter into the reaction, or are capable of doing so.

REACTION, BROMINATION. The introduction, as by substitution or addition, of **bromine** into a chemical compound.

REACTION, BUTYLATION. A reaction resulting in the addition or substitution of the **butyl radical,**

$$-C_4H_9,$$

in a chemical compound.

REACTION, CAPTURE. One of a number of **nuclear** processes in which a particle is captured by the **nucleus** of an atom.

REACTION, CARBONATION. A reaction in which carbon dioxide is one of the

reactants. The term carbonation is sometimes used incorrectly for reduction to free
carbon, which is correctly called **carbonization.**

REACTION, CARBOXYLATION. A reaction whereby a **carboxyl group**

$$\left[-C \begin{array}{c} \diagup\!\!\!\!\diagup O \\ \diagdown OH \end{array} \right]$$

is introduced into a chemical compound.
Among the various possible methods by
which this can be accomplished, there are,
for example, the treatment of a **Grignard**
reagent with carbon dioxide, followed by
hydrolysis; the substitution of the cyanide
group, followed by hydrolysis; the oxidation of side chains of phenyl compounds,
etc.

REACTION, CATALYTIC. A reaction in
which a **catalyst** is used to increase the **reaction rate.**

REACTION, CHAIN. A reaction which
becomes self-perpetuating through the formation as a product, of one of the same substances required for the initial reaction.
The chain initiator may be an activated
atom, molecule, radical, or even a thermal
neutron as in the case of nuclear chain reactions. A chain thus initiated will be
propagated until all of the reactants have
been used up or until some chain-breaking
mechanism occurs.

REACTION, CHLORINATION. The introduction, as by substitution or addition,
of **chlorine** into a chemical compound.

REACTION, CHLORINOLYSIS. See
chlorinolysis.

REACTION, COLOR. Any reaction that
is accompanied by a change of color, i.e.,
the color of the product(s) differs from that
of the initial reactant(s).

REACTION, COMBINATION. A reaction in which two or more elements or compounds combine to form a new compound.

REACTION, COMPLEX. Any reaction
having more than three molecules in its
chemical (stoichiometric) equation. Since
there is little evidence or probability of the
existence of reactions of higher order than
the third (other than that suggested by
certain ionic reactions), reactions of more
than three molecules must take place in
stages, and, therefore, the term complex
reaction is applied to them.

REACTION, COMPOSITE. The same as
reaction, complex.

REACTION, CONCURRENT. One of
two or more reactions which proceed together. Usually, the term concurrent reaction is restricted to those reactions that are
mutually interdependent, as the various
reactions by which chlorine and carbon act
upon chromic oxide to form chromic chloride and carbon dioxide. However, the
term concurrent reaction is also applied to
reactions that are merely simultaneous, as
the reactions which the chlorates undergo
on heating.

REACTION, CONDENSATION. In the
broadest sense, a reaction in which the
largest parts, constituting the essential
structural elements, of two or more molecules combine to form a new molecule, with
the elimination of minor elements, such as
the elements of water. In specific usage,
a condensation is a reaction in organic
chemistry in which carbon atoms are
joined. See various condensations listed
under the term **condensation,** and the
various condensations which are listed
under the names of the men who discovered
or developed them.

REACTION, CONSECUTIVE. One of
two or more reactions so related that one
or more of the products of one reaction
constitute one or more of the reactants of
the next reaction.

REACTION, COUNTER. See **reaction,
balanced.**

REACTION, COUPLED. One of two or
more reactions that are mutually interdependent, as in the case of the series of reactions by which chlorine and carbon act

upon chromic oxide to form chromic chloride and carbon dioxide.

REACTION   (REARRANGEMENT) CYANIC OR THIOCYANIC. See **rearrangement, cyanic or thiocyanic.**

REACTION, CYCLIZATION. A chemical transformation which results in the formation of a ring of atoms joined by their valence **bonds.** Examples of the process are the formation of mesitylene (s-trimethylbenzene) by the condensation of three molecules of acetone and loss of water; the formation of lactones from hydroxy acids, the formation of anhydrides of o-dicarboxy aromatic acids, etc.

REACTION, DEALKYLATION. Removal of an **alkyl group** from an organic compound. The most extensive development of this type of reaction has been encountered in the petroleum industry, where it occurs in a general way, in the course of thermal **cracking** to produce **hydrocarbons** of shorter carbon-chain structure, and hence lower boiling point; the more definite development of the dealkylation reaction has been in the various catalytic processes designed to produce reconstituted hydrocarbon molecules, with more desirable properties as fuels. See also **reaction, demethylation.**

REACTION, DEAMINATION. Removal of the **amino group** ($-NH_2$) from a chemical compound. This is accomplished for aliphatic amines by treatment with nitrous acid, leaving the alcohol, and for aromatic amines, by the same method, followed by heating, leaving the phenol. The amino group may also be removed in certain cases by oxidation or by reduction.

REACTION,   DECARBOXYLATION. Removal of the **carboxyl group**

$$\left[-C \begin{matrix} \nearrow O \\ \searrow OH \end{matrix} \right]$$

from a chemical compound usually leaving

a hydrogen atom in its place. This reaction is brought about by many **catalysts,** including such **enzymes** as the carboxylase in yeast. Many esters of higher orders and more complex nature, produced by condensation reactions, are decarboxylated merely by hydrolysis. A commonly used method of decarboxylation is by converting the carboxyl group to the amide and treating with a hypohalite. (See **rearrangement, Beckmann.**)

REACTION,   DECOMPOSITION. A chemical change in which a single chemical substance is broken up into two or more other substances, which differ from each other and from the parent substance in chemical identity.

REACTION, DEGRADATION. Reduction of the number of carbon atoms in an organic compound, usually an aliphatic compound. Among the specific methods used for this purpose has been the **Hofmann reaction,** treating an amide with a hypohalite; the conversion of fatty acids to methyl ketones, followed by oxidation; and the **Curtius reaction** for the conversion of an acid azide to the primary amine.

REACTION, DEHALOGENATION. Removal of **halogen** from a compound. The process may be accomplished simply by heating; as auric chloride, on ignition at 180° C., loses chlorine to form aurous chloride:

$$AuCl_3 \overset{\Delta}{\rightleftarrows} AuCl + Cl_2.$$

With many organic compounds, dehalogenation is conveniently accomplished by formation of the **Grignard reagent** followed by hydrolysis.

$$RI + Mg \rightarrow RMgI.$$

$$RMgI + H_2O \rightarrow RH + MgIOH.$$

The term dehalogenation also includes all the cases in which halogen and hydrogen are removed from an organic compound, as by treatment with metal hydroxides, with metals, with alkaline solutions, etc. For example,

$$CH_3-CH_2-CH_2Br + KOH \rightarrow CH_3-CH=CH_2 + KBr + H_2O.$$

REACTION, DEHYDRATION. A reaction which results in the removal of water or the elements of water, from a substance. The elements of water may be removed from a single molecule or from more than one molecule, as in the dehydration of alcohol, which may yield ethylene by loss of the elements of water from each molecule, or ethyl ether by loss of the elements of water from two molecules, which then join to form a new compound:

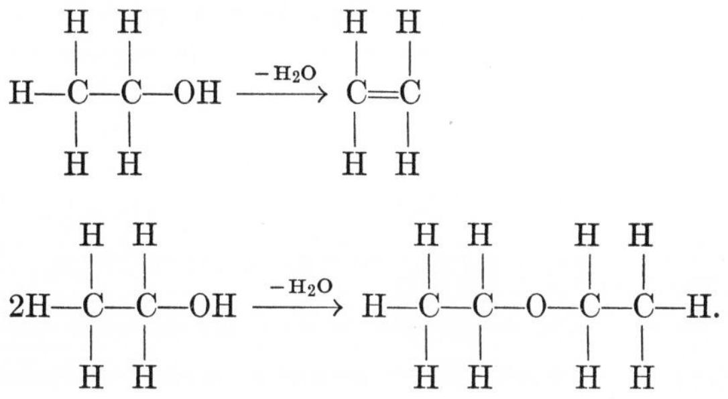

$$\underset{\substack{H\ H \\ | \ \ | \\ H-C-C-OH \\ | \ \ | \\ H\ H}}{} \xrightarrow{-H_2O} \underset{\substack{H\ H \\ | \ \ | \\ C=C \\ | \ \ | \\ H\ H}}{}$$

$$2\underset{\substack{H\ H \\ | \ \ | \\ H-C-C-OH \\ | \ \ | \\ H\ H}}{} \xrightarrow{-H_2O} \underset{\substack{H\ H \quad\ H\ H \\ | \ \ | \ \ \ \ \ | \ \ | \\ H-C-C-O-C-C-H. \\ | \ \ | \ \ \ \ \ | \ \ | \\ H\ H \quad\ H\ H}}{}$$

Many reactions known in chemistry under special names, such as **neutralization, esterification, etherification,** etc., are dehydration reactions.

REACTION, DEHYDROGENATION. A reaction which results in the removal of **hydrogen** from an organic compound or compounds. This process is brought about in many ways. Simple heating of hydrocarbons to high temperature, as in thermal **cracking,** causes some dehydrogenation, indicated by the presence of unsaturated compounds and free hydrogen. Catalytic processes often produce commercially-practicable yields of selected dehydrogenated products. The **enzyme** dehydrogenase is a selective catalyst of this character. There is considerable evidence to indicate that many reactions commonly classed as oxidations, e.g., the oxidation of methanol to formaldehyde, are actually dehydrogenations, i.e.,

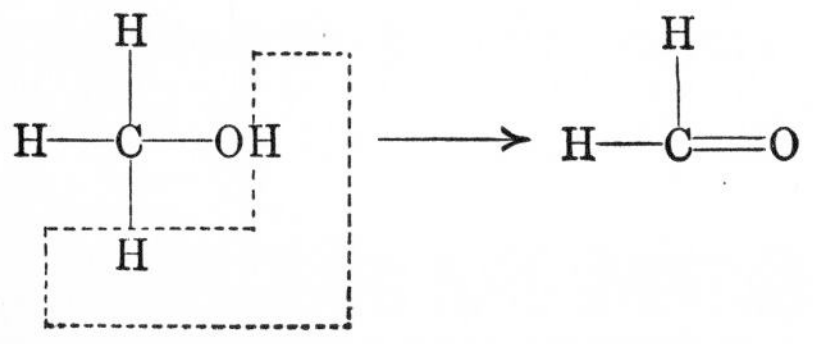

$$\underset{\substack{H \\ | \\ H-C-OH \\ | \\ H}}{} \longrightarrow \underset{\substack{H \\ | \\ H-C=O}}{}$$

REACTION, DEMETHYLATION. A special case of a dealkylation reaction (see **reaction, dealkylation**), in which one or more **methyl groups** are removed from an organic compound. An important application of this reaction in organic synthesis is the formation of methyl ethers with hydroxy groups to prevent their reaction during a step in the synthesis, and subsequently the methyl group is removed by hydrolysis to restore the hydroxyl group.

REACTION, DEPOLYMERIZATION. A **dissociation** of a compound consisting of two or more identical molecules that have condensed into a single structure, or two or more different molecules that have so condensed, forming commonly a long-chain pattern that regularly repeats the same molecular structure. Moreover, a depolymerization reaction commonly yields the same substances which participated in the original polymerization. Depolymerization reactions are exemplified by the depolymerization of paraldehyde, on heating with dilute acid, to give acetaldehyde again:

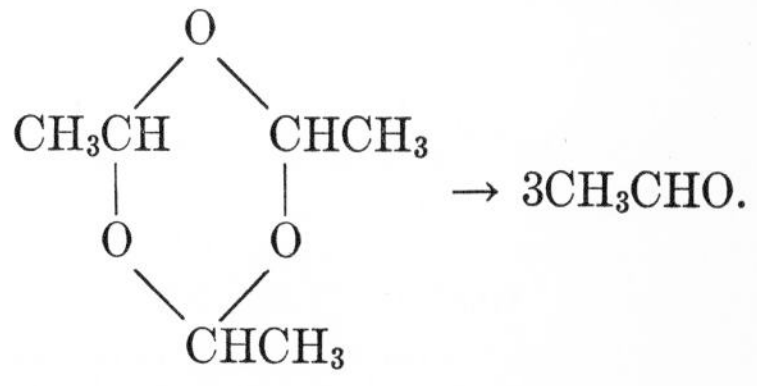

$$\underset{\substack{O \\ / \ \ \backslash \\ CH_3CH \quad CHCH_3 \\ | \qquad\quad | \\ O \qquad\quad O \\ \backslash \quad / \\ CHCH_3}}{} \rightarrow 3CH_3CHO.$$

Many of the reactions by which complex carbohydrates yield simpler carbohydrates on hydrolysis, enzymatic or otherwise, are essentially depolymerizations.

REACTION, DESULFURIZATION. A chemical process for the removal, or replacement, of **sulfur** from a chemical compound. Methods vary widely, as exemplified by the removal of sulfur atoms from organic compounds by replacement with hydrogen; and by the transformation of inorganic sulfides by precipitation of the sulfide ions by the addition of solutions of salts of metals having insoluble sulfides.

REACTION, DIAZO. A reaction characteristic of the primary aromatic **amines** whereby they yield, on treatment with sodium nitrite in strongly acid solution, compounds in which the amino nitrogen atom is joined to a second nitrogen atom. The reaction may be represented as follows:

REACTION, DISSOCIATION. A reversible **decomposition**, i.e., a decomposition in which the products may reunite to produce the original substance.

REACTION, DOUBLE DECOMPOSITION. See **reaction, metathetical.**

REACTION, ELECTRODE. A reaction that takes place at an **electrode** in a solution through which current is passing. Such reactions are commonly due to the discharge of ions, to the formation of ions by the charging of neutral atoms, to changes in the magnitude of ionic charges, etc.

$$C_6H_5NH_2 + NaNO_2 + 2HCl \rightarrow C_6H_5N{\overset{\displaystyle Cl}{\underset{\diagup}{\equiv}}}N + NaCl + 2H_2O.$$

See also **Diazo Reaction (Griess), Diazo Reaction (Knoevenagel),** and **Diazo Reaction (Witt).**

REACTION, DIENE. See **Diels-Alder reaction.**

REACTION, DISMUTATION. Although the derivation of this term would indicate that it could be applied to any decomposition of one substance into two others, it is restricted to cases in which both of the new substances are produced by modification of the arrangement, or state of oxidation, of the atoms in the original substance. Thus the self-oxidation and reduction of an aldehyde, as in the **Cannizzaro reaction,** furnishes the best example.

REACTION, ELECTRON-TRANSFER. A reaction in which one or more electrons move from one atom or group of atoms to another. Oxidation-reduction reactions are of this type.

REACTION, ENDOTHERMIC. A reaction accompanied by the absorption of heat.

REACTION, ENOLIZATION. The establishment of the equilibrium between the **ketone** (carbonyl) form of a compound and the **enol** form, as in acetaldehyde, for example

$$CH_3CHO \rightleftarrows CH_2{=}CHOH$$
(Unstable

$$2C_6H_5CHO \xrightarrow{+H_2O} C_6H_5CH_2OH + C_6H_5COOH.$$

REACTION, DISPLACEMENT. The replacement of a metal in a compound by a more electropositive metal, or the replacement of a non-metal in a compound by a more electronegative non-metal.

REACTION, DISPROPORTIONATION. An ionic self-oxidation reaction, in which a single ionic species gives rise to two (or more) others by gain and loss of electrons.

or in general,

$$R'COCH_2R'' \rightleftarrows R'COH{=}CHR''$$

or any addition or change that tends to displace this equilibrium to the right, i.e., in the direction of the enol form.

REACTION, ESTERIFICATION. A reaction which results in the formation of an

ester, an organic compound of the type formula

$$\left[R-C {\overset{\displaystyle O}{\overset{\displaystyle \|}{\underset{\displaystyle O-R'}{\diagdown}}}} \right].$$

Esters are the result of a dehydration reaction between an acid and an alcohol or phenol, although they are made in many other ways as well.

dium ions, which are not objectionable in the water. The use of these reactions, and the media by which they are accomplished, have been vastly extended in recent years. An important field of application has been that for the separation of elements which are similar in chemical behavior, such as the separation of the rare earth elements.

REACTION, EXOTHERMIC. A reaction accompanied by the liberation of heat.

$$R-C {\overset{O}{\underset{OH}{\diagdown}}} + HOR' \leftrightarrows R-C {\overset{O}{\underset{O-R'}{\diagdown}}} + H_2O$$

Organic acid   Alcohol   Ester
           or phenol

$$\overset{O}{\underset{O}{\diagdown}} \overset{OH}{\underset{OH}{\diagup}} S + HOR' \rightarrow \overset{O}{\underset{O}{\diagdown}} \overset{OH}{\underset{OR'}{\diagup}} S + HOR' \rightarrow \overset{O}{\underset{O}{\diagdown}} \overset{OR'}{\underset{OR'}{\diagup}} S .$$

Sulfuric acid   Alcohol   Alkyl sulfuric acid   Dialkyl sulfate

REACTION, ETHERIFICATION. A reaction that results in the formation of an **ether** (i.e., an organic compound of the type-formula, R—O—R', in which the oxygen atom is joined to two carbon atoms). Among the methods for conducting this reaction are the treatment of an alkyl halide with a sodium alkylate or arylate, the limited dehydration of an alcohol, etc.

REACTION, ETHYLATION. The introduction, as by substitution or addition, of an **ethyl group** into a chemical compound, commonly by treatment with an ethyl halide, or other ethyl ester, or ethyl alcohol, or other compound containing the ethyl radical, usually in the presence of a catalyst.

REACTION, EXCHANGE. A reaction involving an exchange of ions, as in the reversible reaction by which calcium ions, and other objectionable ions, are removed from water by treatment with zeolites, from which the calcium ions displace so-

REACTION, FERMENTATION. A chemical change that is catalyzed by an **enzyme** or **ferment.** Such reactions in most cases result in the change of organic substances to simpler molecular structures, as for example the hydrolysis of starches and the fermentation to the resultant sugars to produce alcohols, acids, etc., the fermentation of sugars to produce alcohols or acids, the fermentation of proteins to yield simpler products, etc. The most common fermentation reaction is hydrolysis, although there are many instances of oxidation, reduction, decarboxylation, and other reactions.

REACTION, FIRST-ORDER. A reaction in which the velocity, or reaction rate, is determined by the concentration of a single molecular or atomic species, as the rate of the decomposition of nitrogen pentoxide depends only upon the concentration of N_2O_5 molecules, or the rate of decomposition of acetone depends only upon the concentration of $CH_3.CO.CH_3$ molecules.

REACTION, FISSION. See fission.

REACTION, FLUORINATION. The introduction, as by substitution or addition, of **fluorine** into a chemical compound.

REACTION, FORMYLATION. A reaction resulting in the addition or substitution of the **formyl radical**

$$\left(HC \overset{O}{\underset{\diagdown}{\diagup\!\!\diagup}} \right)$$

in a chemical compound.

REACTION, FRACTIONAL ORDER. A reaction in which the rate is proportional to a fractional power (less than unity) of the concentration, or to a fractional power of some factor which is itself proportional to the concentration, such as pressure in a gaseous system. Frequently, the decomposition of gases upon surfaces is proportional to a fractional power of the pressure and, therefore, is of a fractional order.

REACTION, FUSION. A nuclear reaction (see **reaction, nuclear**) in which an isotope or isotopes of light elements react with each other to form heavier nuclides. The potential barriers of these reactions are quite high, and temperatures of the order of millions of degrees are usually necessary before they can occur.

REACTION, HALOFORM. A general reaction of primary and secondary **carbinols,** containing at least one methyl group, and of the corresponding carbonyl compounds. They react with alkaline hypohalides, giving as their probable first products substances like $Cl_3C.CHO$ or $Cl_3C.CO.CH_3$ which then react with the alkali present to give the haloform (CHX_3) and formate or acetate. See also **Lieben iodoform reaction.**

REACTION, HALOGENATION. The introduction, as by substitution or addition, of an element of the **halogen** family into an organic compound.

REACTION, HEAT OF. See **heat of reaction.**

REACTION, HETEROGENEOUS. A reaction in which the reactants are present in two or more **phases,** and the reaction takes place partly or entirely between phases.

REACTION, HIGHER ORDER. A term used to refer to reactions of higher order than third-order reactions. The actual occurrence of such processes of higher than third order has not been established, although it is suggested by certain ionic reactions.

REACTION, HOMOGENEOUS. A reaction in which all of the reactants are in one **phase,** and the reaction takes place in that phase.

REACTION, HYDROGENATION. In general, the introduction of **hydrogen** into a chemical compound, commonly by addition. Specific applications, of great industrial importance, are the hydrogenation of carbon monoxide to form methanol, the hydrogenation of nitrogen to form ammonia, the hydrogenation of certain vegetable oils high in their content of unsaturated compounds to form solid fats, and the hydrogenation of petroleum and coal to produce liquid lubricants and fuels of high purity.

REACTION, HYDROGENOLYSIS. The decomposition of a chemical compound brought about by reaction with **hydrogen,** usually by the formation of new compounds by addition of hydrogen atoms to the fragments of the decomposed compound.

REACTION, HYDROLYSIS. The decomposition of a chemical compound brought about by reaction with water, usually by formation of new compounds by addition of atoms from the H_2O molecule to one fragment of the decomposed compound, and by addition of the other atoms of the H_2O molecule to the other fragment or fragments of the decomposed compound. Commonly one fragment adds a hydrogen atom and the other a hydroxyl group, as in the hydrolysis of **salts** to form acids and **bases,** of esters to form **acids** and **alcohols,** of **acid anhydrides** to form **acids,** of **ethers** to form alcohols, etc.

REACTION, INCOMPLETE. See reaction, balanced.

REACTION, INTRAMOLECULAR. A reaction that takes place within a molecule, as, for example, the formation of a **lactone,**

$$CH_2OH(CH_2)_3COOH \rightarrow \overset{O\text{———}}{\underset{\delta\text{-valerolactone}}{CH_2(CH_2)_3C=O}} + H_2O.$$

δ-hydroxyvaleric acid   δ-valerolactone

REACTIONS, INDEPENDENCE OF. If in any system several simultaneous reactions are taking place, each reaction proceeds as if it were independent of all the rest and according to the law of mass action. At the establishment of equilibrium the condition of the system is the sum of all the changes in progress.

REACTION, INDUCED. (Sympathetic or coupled reaction) A chemical process in which a slow reaction between A and B is accelerated by a simultaneous rapid reaction between A and C. The fastest reaction is termed the primary reaction, the accelerated reaction is the secondary reaction. The substance which takes part in both reactions is the "actor," the second reactant in the primary reaction is termed the "inductor," and the second reactant in the secondary reaction is named the "acceptor."

REACTION, PERIOD OF APPARENT INDUCTION. A false period of **induction.** A reaction measured by the rate of evolution of a gas from a liquid frequently shows an apparent period of induction due to retention of gas by the liquid.

REACTION, INTERMOLECULAR. A reaction between molecules, or molecules and independent atoms, as distinguished from a reaction that occurs within a molecule, which is called an intramolecular reaction. Intermolecular reactions may involve only one kind of molecule, as long as the process takes place between two or more distinct particles. Thus the condensation of two molecules of ethyl acetate to form ethylacetoacetate is an intermolecular reaction:

REACTION, IODINATION. The addition or substitution of **iodine** in a chemical compound. It is accomplished in some cases by direct action of elementary iodine, and in others by treatment with iodine compounds, such as hydrogen iodide, phosphorus triiodide, etc., often in the presence of a catalyst.

REACTION, ION-EXCHANGE. See reaction, exchange.

REACTION, IONIC. A reaction between ions, commonly in solution.

REACTION, IRREVERSIBLE. (Complete reaction) A reaction that proceeds until one or all of the reactants have been exhausted, as the union of hydrogen and chlorine to form hydrochloric acid. In these reactions the products do not react to reform the initial reactants under the conditions of the main reaction. Cf. **reactions, balanced.**

REACTION ISOCHORE. An equation (or more strictly, the graph of the equation) which relates the variation with temperature of the equilibrium constant of a gaseous reaction. It is of the form:

$$\frac{d(\ln K_p)}{dT} = \frac{\Delta H}{RT^2}$$

where K_p is the equilibrium constant at constant pressure, T is temperature, ΔH is the change in heat content, and R is the gas constant.

REACTION, ISOLATED. A reaction that proceeds directly in accordance with a chemical equation, without any secondary

$$2CH_3COOC_2H_5 \rightarrow CH_3COCH_2COOC_2H_5 + C_2H_5OH.$$

effects, such as a reverse reaction by the reaction products, or a side reaction or simultaneous reaction involving the reactants or products, or both, or any other process tending to complicate the relationship between concentration of reactants and rate of reaction.

REACTION, ISOMERIZATION. Transformation of a compound into an isomeric form. Since there are many types of **isomerism,** there are a number of isomerization reactions. For example, fumaric acid on heating slowly changes to maleic acid (which then forms its volatile anhydride).

$$
\begin{array}{ccc}
\text{H—C—COOH} & & \text{H—C—COOH} \\
\parallel & \rightarrow & \parallel \\
\text{HOOC—C—H} & & \text{H—C—COOH} \\
\text{Fumaric acid} & & \text{Maleic acid}
\end{array}
$$

Isomerization reactions are used extensively in the production of special fuels and other products from hydrocarbons, being especially useful in bringing about a rearrangement of alkyl groups within the molecule. See **isomerization.**

REACTION ISOTHERM. A relationship (or more strictly, a graph of a relationship) expressing the change in free energy, in a chemical reaction that does not reach equilibrium, in terms of the difference between the logarithms of equilibrium **partial pressure** terms and the logarithms of the actual **partial pressure** terms. It is of the form:

$$-\Delta F = RT \ln K_p - RT \Sigma \nu_i \ln p_i$$

in which $-\Delta F$ is the decrease in **free energy,** R is the **gas constant,** T is the absolute temperature, K_p is the **equilibrium constant** at constant pressure, ν_i is the number of moles of each reactant, and p_i is the corresponding partial pressure.

REACTION, MAIN. That reaction among more than one simultaneous or consecutive reactions which is most important, because it controls the over-all rate, or because it yields the desired products, or for some other reason. Commonly, the term main reaction is used in contrast with side reaction (see **reaction, side**).

REACTION, MALONIC ESTER. See **synthesis, malonic ester.**

REACTION, MERCURIZATION. A reaction whereby the element **mercury,** or a radical containing it, is added to, or substituted in, a chemical compound.

REACTION, METATHETICAL. A chemical reaction that consists essentially of an exchange of atoms or radicals in two compounds. This reaction is also called a double decomposition and does not involve oxidation or reduction (transfer of electrons or change of valence). It may be represented by the general equation:

$$AB + CD \rightleftharpoons AD + BC.$$

REACTION, METHYLATION. The introduction, by substitution or addition, of a **methyl group** into a chemical compound. Among the most widely used methylating agents are the methyl halides, dimethyl sulfate, formaldehyde, diazomethane, dibromomethylal ($Br_2C(OCH_3)_2$), etc.

REACTION, MICRO-. (1) A chemical reaction conducted in the field of a microscope, as the interaction between a drop of a solution of an unknown substance and a drop of reagent. (2) A reaction conducted on a very small scale with **microchemical apparatus.**

REACTION, MOLECULAR. A chemical reaction that takes place between molecules, as distinguished from a reaction between atoms or ions.

REACTION, MONOMOLECULAR. Although originally used in its literal sense as meaning a reaction involving as reactant only one molecule, this expression is now used most commonly as a synonym for a **first-order reaction,** i.e., a reaction having a velocity that depends upon one concentration term. There are reactions involving two or more molecules, which have velocities dependent upon only one concentration term, that are therefore spoken of as monomolecular (see **reaction, pseudounimolecular**).

REACTION, NEUTRALIZATION. A chemical reaction between an **acid** and a base to form a **salt** and water. This statement assumes that the acid and base are present in equivalent quantities, but not that the resultant product or solution is necessarily neutral. The result of the neutralization of a weak base by a strong acid, or vice versa, is far from a neutral solution (pH = 7.0) if the process takes place in a **protophilic** solvent like water. In line with the modern definition of an acid as a proton donor and a base as a proton acceptor, the definition above may well be broadened to cover ionic reactions as follows:

$$NH_3 + H_3O^+ \leftrightarrows NH_4^+ + H_2O$$

$$CH_3COOH + OH^- \rightleftarrows CH_3COO^- + H_2O$$

$$OH^- + H_3O^+ \rightleftarrows 2H_2O.$$

REACTION, NITRATION. A chemical reaction which results in the introduction of a **nitro-group**

$$\left[-N \begin{array}{c} \nearrow O \\ \searrow O \end{array} \right]$$

into a compound, by addition or substitution. This may be accomplished, especially in the case of many aromatic compounds, by direct treatment with nitric acid, or mixed nitric and sulfuric acids. Among the many indirect methods of nitration are the treatment of an α-halogenated aliphatic acid (or its sodium salt) with sodium nitrite, the treatment of an organic halide with silver nitrite, the oxidation of amines, etc.

REACTION, NITROSATION. A chemical reaction that results in the introduction of a **nitroso-group**, $-N=O$, into a compound, by addition or substitution. Direct treatment with nitrous acid is frequently the most efficient means of nitrosation, as in the case of aromatic substances containing activating groups.

REACTION, NUCLEAR. A reaction in which the **nucleus** of an atom undergoes transformation. Although this term includes the disintegration of natural radioactive elements, it also denotes those trans-

formations of nuclei that are brought about "artificially," i.e., by bombardment with particles or radiations. The equations of these reactions are frequently written in a form illustrated by the following example:

$$Mg^{26}(d, \alpha)Na^{24}$$

This is a reaction for the transformation of the magnesium isotope of mass number 26 to yield radiosodium of mass number 24 upon bombardment by deuterons, with α-particles being emitted in the process. Subsequently, the radiosodium disintegrates in turn yielding a magnesium isotope of mass number 24, and an electron. These two nuclear reactions may be expressed in the following way:

$$_{12}Mg^{26} + {}_1H^2 \rightarrow {}_2He^4 + {}_{11}Na^{24},$$

$$_{11}Na^{24} \rightarrow {}_{12}Mg^{24} + {}_{-1}e^0.$$

(See **equation, nuclear.**)

REACTION, "ONIUM." A reaction resulting in the formation of an "onium" compound, a term used to designate compounds formed by molecular combinations in which there is an arithmetical increase in the total number of positive and negative charges on the atoms, but no algebraic change. Examples of such reactions are the formation of ammonium chloride from ammonia and hydrogen chloride, the formation of iodonium compounds, sulfonium compounds, etc.

REACTIONS, OPPOSING. Reversible reactions, i.e., two reactions so related that, under usual conditions, the products of the first reaction are the reactants of the second, and the products of the second reaction are the reactants of the first, so that a state of equilibrium is reached in which, under fixed conditions of temperature, pressure, etc., the concentrations of all substances in the system remain the same. (See **reaction, balanced.**)

REACTION, ORDER OF. The class to which a chemical reaction may be assigned according to the number of distinct molecular or atomic species that determine the rate of the reaction. Although in a few cases the order of a reaction is determined by the number of reacting molecules, it must be emphasized that this is by no means invariably the case. In fact, it is not considered likely that there are any reactions of higher than third order (with the possible exception of certain ionic reactions). Moreover, since the rate of a reaction may depend upon many complicating factors, it sometimes happens that the rate is not a direct function of concentration or its second or third power, but varies according to some fractional power of concentration, so that there are fractional orders of reaction. (See **reaction, fractional order**.)

REACTION, OXIDATION. See **oxidation** and **reaction**.

REACTION, PERIODIC. A chemical reaction which, during its course, varies periodically in rate, increasing and decreasing more than once. Such reactions are usually members of a group of interrelated successive reactions.

REACTION, PHOTOCHEMICAL. A reaction brought about or markedly accelerated by exposure to electromagnetic **radiations** in the **spectrum** of visible light, the ultraviolet, and (rarely) the near infrared. Such reactions include most, if not all, the major types—oxidation, reduction, decomposition, hydrolysis, synthesis, etc. The photosynthesis of **carbohydrates** from carbon dioxide and water in the presence of chlorophyll is a photochemical reaction of the most universal significance.

REACTION, PHOTODISINTEGRATION. A nuclear reaction (see **reaction, nuclear**) brought about by radiation, as, for example, the reaction $_4Be^9(\gamma,_0n^1)_4Be^8$, which is brought about by γ-rays of sufficiently high energy.

REACTION, PHOTOLYSIS. The decomposition of a chemical compound by light, usually of a highly selective frequency. Examples are the decomposition of silver chloride, ammonia, etc.

REACTION, PHOTOSENSITIZED. A reaction brought about by collision between a reacting molecule and an **excited particle** that has been excited by exposure to radia-

tion, commonly of highly characteristic frequency. Thus hydrogen reacts with various other gases, on exposure to radiation from a mercury vapor lamp, in the presence of mercury vapor. Similarly, the decomposition of ammonia is photosensitized by the presence of mercury vapor and the radiations of the mercury vapor lamp.

REACTION, PHOTOTRANSMUTATION. The same as **reaction, photodisintegration**.

REACTION, POLYMERIZATION. See **polymerization**.

REACTION, PRIMARY. See **reaction, induced**.

REACTION, PRINCIPAL. That reaction among more than one simultaneous or consecutive reactions which is most important, because it controls the over-all rate, or because it yields the desired products, or for some other reason. Commonly, the term principal reaction is used in contrast with side reaction (see **reaction, side**).

REACTION, PROTOLYTIC. See **protolysis**.

REACTION, PSEUDO-UNIMOLECULAR. A reaction in which more than one type of molecule participates, but which has a reaction rate that is dependent upon the concentration of only one of the molecules. One of the general cases in which this behavior is exhibited is in reactions between two molecules where one of the reactants is present in great excess, so that the concentration of the other determines the reaction rate, and hence the reaction is of the first order.

REACTION, PYROLYSIS. A decomposition reaction brought about by heat, with or without a catalyst. The thermal **cracking** of **hydrocarbons** is an outstanding example of this reaction, and a good illustration of its application to a single compound is in the heating of the calcium salts of the aliphatic acids, which yield chiefly ketones, or aldehydes if calcium formate is one of the salts present.

REACTION, RADIOACTIVE. A nuclear disintegration of a chemical substance, in which there is a transformation of the atomic nucleus into a nucleus differing in charge, mass or stability; the process being accompanied by the emission of particles, radiations, or both. The process may occur naturally, or as a result of bombardment with particles or radiations. See **reaction, nuclear.**

REACTION, RADIOACTIVE CAPTURE. A nuclear process in which a particle is captured and the excess energy is emitted as radiation.

REACTION RATE, SPECIFIC. A constant of proportionality in certain relationships between concentration of reacting substances and **rate of reaction.** For first-order reaction, it is defined by the expression

$$kc = -\frac{dc}{dt}$$

in which k is the specific reaction rate at the temperature at which the reaction has taken place, c is the concentration of the reacting substance, and $-\frac{dc}{dt}$ is the rate of change in concentration of the reacting substance or, in other words, the rate of reaction.

REACTION, REARRANGEMENT. A process that brings about a regrouping of atoms or radicals within a molecule, thus producing a substance having a different structure and different properties. See under **rearrangement** for the specific chemical changes of this type, and also see under proper names for rearrangements known by the names of the men who discovered or developed them.

REACTION, REPLACEMENT. A chemical reaction in which one atom or radical takes the place in a chemical compound of another atom or radical.

REACTION, RESINIFICATION. A reaction that results in the formation of a natural or synthetic **resin.** In plant **essential oils** there are present compounds containing reactive hydrogen atoms as well as **carbonyl** and other groups with which

they can readily condense to form complex **polymers** or **condensation** compounds. Resinification reactions important in the manufacture of plastics include such outstanding examples as those involving the condensation of phenol and formaldehyde, the condensation of casein and formaldehyde, the condensation of polyalcohols with phthalic anhydride, and various other condensations resulting in the formation of polyamides, vinyl polymers, acrylate polymers, and many other polymeric compounds.

REACTION, RESTITUTION. A reaction in which an **element** is one of the products of the interaction of two or more compounds. It is the reverse of substitution and is, in fact, also called reverse substitution. A reaction of this type accounts for the fact that iodine does not replace hydrogen on an aromatic nucleus—i.e., the reverse substitution by hydrogen iodide takes place more readily:

$$CH_3C_6H_4I + HI \rightleftarrows CH_3C_6H_5 + I_2.$$

REACTION, REVERSE SUBSTITUTION. See **reaction, restitution.**

REACTION, REVERSIBLE. A reaction in which, under usual conditions, the products react to reform the initial reactants so that a state of **equilibrium** is finally reached at which, at any definite temperature, the concentrations of all substances involved are constant, since the amounts being produced by the forward reaction are equal to the amounts being transformed by the reverse reaction. See **reaction, balanced.**

REACTION, SAPONIFICATION. The hydrolysis (see **reaction, hydrolysis**) of an ester by an alkali so that a free alcohol and an alkali salt of the ester acid result. The term was formerly restricted to the alkaline hydrolysis of fats, whereby soaps are formed, but has been extended to include a variety of hydrolyses, even those of alkyl esters of inorganic acids and hydrolysis by superheated steam.

REACTION, SECONDARY. A simultaneous reaction (see **reaction, simultaneous**) that does not consume the major portion of the substances present in a reacting system. The reaction so doing is termed the principal or main reaction; whereas the others are called secondary or side reactions (see reaction, side).

REACTION, SECOND-ORDER. A reaction in which the velocity, or the reaction rate (see rate of reaction), is determined by two concentration terms, as the rate of saponification of certain esters depends upon the concentration of both the unchanged ester and the unused saponifying agent.

REACTION, SEMIDINE. See rearrangement, semidine.

REACTION, SIDE. (Simultaneous reaction) When two or more reactions occurring simultaneously to the same reactant or reactants giving rise to different products, the predominating reaction is termed the main or principal reaction, the other, the secondary reaction. The term side reaction is often used in the sense of the secondary reaction.

REACTION, SIMULTANEOUS. One of two or more reactions occurring at the same time to the same reactant or reactants. (See reaction, side.)

REACTION, SPALLATION. See spallation.

REACTION, STAIRCASE. A reaction that consists of a number of chemical changes whereby the product of each successive change enters into the next one as a reactant. The term staircase reaction is applied to this entire process because the diagram of the substances produced (including both those that result from a particular stage which do not react further, and those which do enter into the next reaction) takes the form of a staircase.

REACTION, SUBSIDIARY. A special type of simultaneous reaction (see reaction, simultaneous) in which a transformation of one of the reaction products occurs concomitantly with, and dependently on, the main reaction which, in turn, is dependent upon this subsidiary reaction; e.g., if the reaction:

$$HBrO_3 + 6HI = HBr + 3H_2O + 3I_2$$

is written in its ionic form,

$$6H^+ + BrO_3^- + 6I^- \rightarrow Br^- + 3H_2O + 3I_2,$$

it may be dissected into two processes,

$$6H^+ + BrO_3^- + 6e \rightarrow Br^- + 3H_2O$$

and

$$6I^- \rightarrow 3I_2 + 6e,$$

in which the second of the two ionic reactions is the subsidiary one, since it furnishes the six electrons necessary to neutralize the hydrogen atoms in the main reaction. Although this breakdown of the reaction explains, in certain cases, some of the kinetic factors, there is far from complete evidence that it represents the actual mechanism.

REACTION, SUBSTITUTION. A reaction that results in the replacement of an atom or radical in a compound by another atom or radical. The displaced atom or radical often combines with the fragment, if any, left by the atom or radical which entered the compound.

REACTION, SUCCESSIVE. A reaction that involves as initial reactants one or more of the products of another reaction. See reaction, consecutive.

REACTION, SULFONATION. The introduction into a chemical compound of one or more sulfonic acid groups

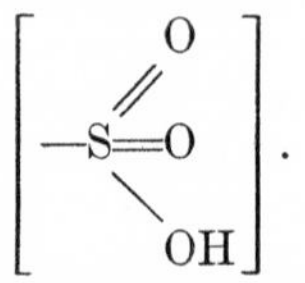

$$\left[-S \underset{\diagdown OH}{\overset{\diagup O}{\underset{=}{=}} O} \right].$$

This can often be done best by treatment with concentrated sulfuric acid or oleum. Among the other methods is the introduction of a mercaptan group (—SH), followed by oxidation, the action of an alkali sulfite on an alkyl halide, and the treatment of

Grignard reagents with SO_2, followed by oxidation.

REACTION, SULFURIZATION. To form a **sulfide,** or other compound containing one or more sulfur atoms combined directly, and solely (i.e., with both valences of the sulfur atom), to metallic atoms in inorganic compounds, to carbon atoms in carbon compounds, etc. Sulfurization is accomplished by heating directly with sulfur, by heating with **polysulfides,** etc.

REACTION, SYMPATHETIC. The same as an induced reaction. See **reaction, induced.**

REACTION, SYNTHETIC. The combining of elements or compounds to form products of one kind, e.g., $H_2 + Cl_2 = 2HCl$.

REACTION, TERMOLECULAR. (Trimolecular reaction) Although originally used in its literal sense as meaning a reaction between three molecules as reactants, this expression is now used most commonly as a synonym for a third-order reaction, i.e., a reaction having a velocity that depends upon three concentration terms. (See **reaction, third-order.**)

REACTION, THERMOLYSIS. The same as pyrolysis; a dissociation reaction or decomposition reaction caused by heating. (See **reaction, dissociation,** and **reaction, decomposition.**)

REACTION, THERMONUCLEAR. A nuclear reaction (see **reaction, nuclear**) in which the interacting nuclei acquire sufficient thermal kinetic energy to overcome their mutual electrostatic repulsion or coulomb barrier.

REACTION, THIRD-ORDER. A reaction in which the velocity, or the reaction rate, is determined by three concentration terms, as the rate of reaction of nitric oxide with hydrogen, oxygen, and the halogens is apparently dependent upon the square of the concentration of the nitric oxide, as well as upon the concentration of the other reactant.

REACTION, TRANSFORMATION. A term indicating a change in the internal composition or structure of an entity, usually applied only to the atomic nucleus. Any change in a natural or artificial atomic nucleus that results in the production of a nucleus differing in atomic number, or mass, or stability (i.e., forming a different **element,** or an **isotope** of the parent element, or an **isobaric isotope** of it). See **reaction, nuclear,** for examples of such transformations.

REACTION, TRANSMUTATION. The change of one element into another element. Since the common characteristic of the various isotopic species of a given element is their nuclear charge, or atomic number, transmutation is a change in the nuclear charge (atomic number) of an atom, whether brought about by natural radioactivity, by bombardment with particles or radiations, or by subsequent spontaneous changes in an unstable nucleus resulting from these processes. See **reaction, nuclear,** for examples of such transformations.

REACTION, TRI-TRIFUNCTIONAL. A reaction in which each of two different reacting molecules has three groups that enter into the reaction, or are capable of doing so.

REACTION, UNIMOLECULAR. Although originally used in its literal sense as meaning a reaction involving only one molecule, this expression is now often used as a synonym for a first-order reaction, i.e., a reaction having a velocity that depends upon one concentration term. (See **reaction, pseudo-unimolecular,** and **reaction, first-order.**)

REACTION, ZYMOLYTIC. A chemical reaction catalyzed by an **enzyme,** especially a reaction involving bond rupture or splitting, usually a hydrolysis.

REAGENT. In the original use of the term, a substance used to react with another substance or mixture of substances in order to dissolve them, to oxidize or to reduce them, etc., in order that they might be analyzed or utilized. The present meaning of the term is more closely limited to those substances that produce reactions of use in analysis, including all phases of analysis from solution of the sample to detection and determination of specific substances.

RÉAUMUR DEGREE. A degree on the Réaumur thermometric scale; see **thermometric scales.**

REARRANGEMENT. As used in chemistry, this term is most commonly limited to a regrouping of atoms or radicals within a molecule in order to produce a substance of different structure and properties. Various rearrangements are listed below, and others are listed throughout this book under the name or names of the men to whom they are accredited.

REARRANGEMENT, ALLYLIC. The essential characteristic of this rearrangement is the shifting of a double bond in a three carbon-atom system, from the 1,2-carbon position to the 2,3 position, with the migration of a substituent, or entering substituting group, from the third carbon atom to the first.

$$H_2C=CH-CHOH-CH_3 \xrightarrow{HX} XH_2C-CH=CH-CH_3 + H_2O.$$

REARRANGEMENT, BENZIDINE. The rearrangement of molecules of **hydrazo compounds,** usually caused by the presence of mineral acids, which result in the interchange of a group attached to nitrogen and a *para* hydrogen atom, with the formation of *p,p'*- diaminodiaryl compounds. The nature of the rearrangement of the reaction is:

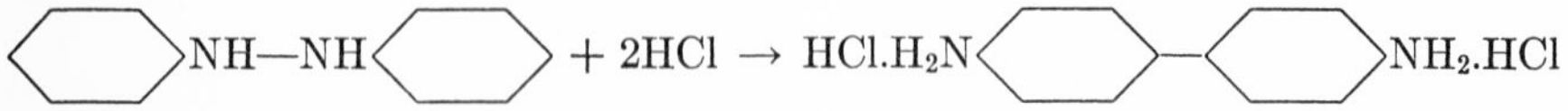

If the *para* position is blocked, the **semidine rearrangement** (q.v.) takes place.

REARRANGEMENT, BENZILIC ACID. The series of changes of the type resulting when *o*-diketones are fused with potassium hydroxide.

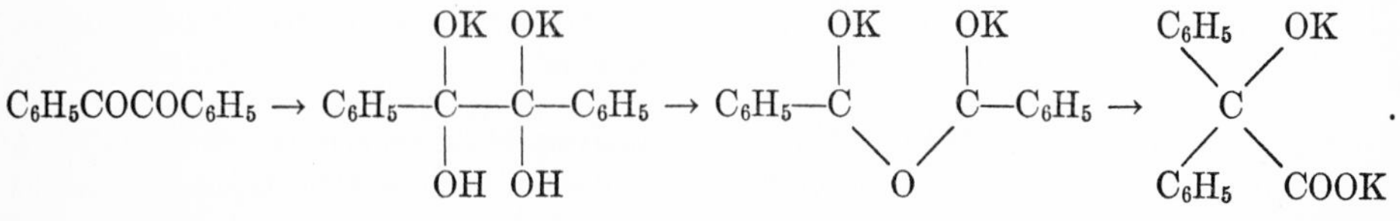

REARRANGEMENT, CYANIC OR THIOCYANIC. Transformations of ammonium cyanate to urea and ammonium thiocyanate to thiourea,

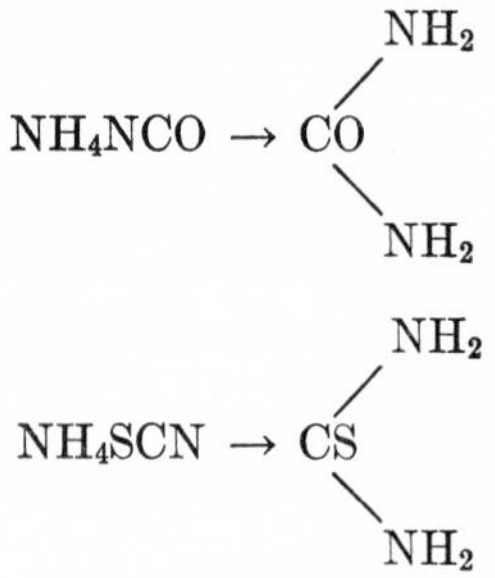

as well as many more complex transfers of valence bonds from carbon-nitrogen to carbon-sulfur, as exemplified by the formation of many isothiocyanates from thiocyanates. These rearrangements are usually brought about by heat.

REARRANGEMENT, MOLECULAR. See **molecular rearrangement.**

REARRANGEMENT, SEMIDINE. See **semidine rearrangement.**

REBELLO-ALVES REACTION FOR COPPER. Copper solutions give a blue color with a freshly-prepared hematoxylin solution.

REBER TEST REACTION FOR β-NAPHTHOL. One ml. of a 5% aqueous β-naphthol solution gives a carmine-red color, soluble in amyl alcohol, on heating to 55–60° C. with a mixture of 1 part 25% hydrochloric acid and 3 parts 25% nitric acid.

RECALESCENT POINT. A temperature at which a change in the **allotropic** form, or **solid solution,** occurs during the cooling of alloys, especially steel.

RECARBONIZE. To add carbon to a substance or system from which carbon has been removed. In various metallurgical processes, metals are purified by treatment which reduces the carbon content, as by oxidation, to a value below that desired in the finished product. Accordingly, the value is adjusted by the addition of carbon, a carbide, or other carbonaceous substance.

RECIPROCAL OHM. The **mho.**

RECIPROCAL SALT PAIR. Two salts which interact in a double decomposition reaction to produce two other salts, in which the ions or radicals have exchanged their molecular groupings. Thus, in the reaction

$$AB + CD \rightleftarrows AD + CB$$

if AB and CD are salts, then the pair AB and CD, and the pair AD and CB are reciprocal salt pairs.

RECIPROCITY LAW. The statement that in a photochemical reaction (see **reaction, photochemical**) a constant effect is produced if the product of time and **radiant power** is a constant.

RECOIL ATOM. See **atom, recoil.**

RECOIL RADIATION. See **radiation, recoil.**

RECOMBINATION COEFFICIENT. A quantity entering into calculations of the decrease in concentration of ionized pairs by recombinations of ions. In its simplest application, it is shown in the expression,

$$\beta N_1 N_2 = -\frac{dN_1}{dt} = -\frac{dN_2}{dt}$$

where N_1 and N_2 are the numbers of positive and negative ions per cubic centimeter, $-\frac{dN_1}{dt}$ and $-\frac{dN_2}{dt}$ are their respective rates of disappearance, and β is the recombination coefficient.

RECRYSTALLIZATION. Repeated **crystallization,** a process used to purify substances.

RECRYSTALLIZE. To subject to the process of **recrystallization.**

RECTIFICATION. (1) The interaction of a partial **condensate** with the vapor rising through a **fractionating column,** resulting in further enrichment of the vapor in the low boiling component. This specific use of the term rectification is commonly extended to cover the entire process of distillation, as used in the purification of liquids.
(2) The adjustment of alcoholic content, of alcoholic beverages, etc., to obtain a product of predetermined strength.

RECTIFY. To submit to the process of **rectification.**

RECTIFYING COLUMN. A **fractionating column** in which the direct interchange of heat, and consequent evaporation and condensation, takes place.

RECTILINEAR DIAMETERS, LAW OF. See **law of Cailletet and Mathias.**

RECUPERATIVE HEATING. The countercurrent flow of hot combustion gases from a furnace through flues on the other side of which cold gases pass to the furnace. This method accomplishes the interchange of heat without intermixture of incoming and outgoing gases.

REDDELIEN TEST REACTION. Unsaturated ketones dissolve in concentrated sulfuric acid to give colored solutions, which give characteristic color changes with nitric acid at various dilutions.

REDOX. A shortened expression for "reduction-oxidation" or "oxidation-reduction."

REDUCE. To submit to a process of **reduction.**

REDUCED EQUATION OF STATE. A generalized **equation of state** containing as variables the reduced pressure, reduced volume, and reduced temperature. In the case of **van der Waals'** equation, the form is:

$$\left(\pi + \frac{3}{\phi^2}\right)(3\phi - 1) = 8\theta$$

where π is the reduced pressure, defined as the ratio of the existing pressure to the **critical pressure**; ϕ is the reduced volume, defined as the ratio of the existing volume to the **critical volume**; and θ is the reduced temperature, defined as the ratio of the existing temperature to the **critical temperature**.

REDUCER. A substance or force that effects a reducing reaction (see **reducing agent** and **reaction, reduction**); or any form of apparatus used in laboratory or plant for conducting reducing reactions.

REDUCING AGENT. A compound, element, or force, that is capable of effecting a reduction reaction under the proper conditions. Hydrogen, hydriodic acid, stannous chloride, ferrous chloride, dextrose, iron, ammonium sulfide, sodium amalgam, electricity, and light, are among the common reducing agents.

REDUCING FLAME. A flame in which substances undergo reduction reactions, as the reduction of a metallic oxide to the free metal. The term is applied commonly to the luminous inner portion of the flame of gas burners, blowpipes, etc., which, because of its content of carbon monoxide and other reducing substances, has a marked reducing action.

REDUCTASE. An **enzyme** which catalyzes reduction reactions.

REDUCTION. (1) Addition of hydrogen to or subtraction of oxygen from a substance. (2) Lowering the valence of an element in combination, as reducing ferric chloride to ferrous chloride. (3) Both the preceding processes, and the complete reactions of which they are a part, involve an interchange of electrons between atoms, whereupon the atom gaining the electron or electrons is reduced, and the atom losing the electron or electrons is oxidized.

REDUCTION OF ESTERS, BOUVEAULT AND BLANC. See **Bouveault and Blanc reduction of esters.**

REDUCTION POTENTIAL. See **potential, reduction.**

REDUCTION RATIO. A term, used specifically in connection with milling and grinding processes, to indicate the ratio of particle sizes before and after crushing or grinding. The particle chosen from a given mass of material may be the average or mean of the aggregation of particles or, more commonly, the largest.

REDUCTION, WOLFF-KISHNER. See **Wolff-Kishner reduction.**

REDUCTOR. Various glass apparatus used in the laboratory for accomplishing reductions, commonly those made in the course of certain analytical determinations. (See **Jones reductor.**)

REDWOOD NUMBER. An integer expressing a **viscosity** value obtained by the **Redwood viscometer.**

REDWOOD VISCOMETER. An apparatus used in the determination of relative viscosities of various commercial products.

REED REACTION. Direct treatment of **paraffin** or **alicyclic hydrocarbons** with chlorine and sulfur dioxide to produce their sulfonyl chlorides.

$$RH + SO_2 + Cl_2 \rightarrow RSO_2Cl + HCl.$$

The reaction is catalyzed by light.

REED TEST FOR CERIUM. Place 50 ml. of the solution tested in a Nessler tube, and acidify by dropwise addition of 5 N sulfuric acid. Add 1 drop hydrogen peroxide and 1 drop 0.5% methylene blue solution, shake and alkalinize with 5 N sodium hydroxide. A blue color is obtained in the presence of cerium. Several other metals interfere.

REED-WITHROW TEST FOR POTASSIUM. Potassium salt solutions give, with a concentrated aqueous solution of zirconium sulfate, precipitates of zirconium potassium sulfate.

REFLECTION WAVE. In general, any wave-form which is reflected by a solid surface or other obstacle. Specifically, a wave of compression sent back through the burnt gas when an explosion wave is completely or partially stopped against a closed extremity or constricted portion of a tube.

REFLECTIVITY. The fraction of the incident **radiant energy** reflected by a surface that is exposed to uniform radiation from a source that fills its field of view.

REFLUX CONDENSER. (1) An ordinary condenser set so that the condensed vapor will flow back into the vessel which contains the boiling mixture. (2) A device to prevent evaporation during a heating process.

REFORMATSKY REACTION. The condensation reaction between an α-haloester and a carbonyl compound (such as an aldehyde, ketone, or ester) in the presence of zinc. This reaction is used in organic synthesis as a means of preparing β-hydroxy esters and the corresponding unsaturated acids and esters, as well as a means of adding two carbon atoms to the carbon chain.

$$RCOR' + BrCH_2COOCH_3 + Zn \xrightarrow{HBr} RR'COH{-}CH_2{-}COOCH_3 + ZnBr_2.$$

The further step is:

$$RR'COH{-}CH_2{-}COOCH_3 \xrightarrow{-H_2O} RR'C{=}CH{-}COOCH_3.$$

REFORMING PROCESS. A cracking process for transforming hydrocarbon mixtures of low octane number into fuels having high **octane numbers.** The process involves, to a greater or less degree, all three of the reactions; dehydrogenation, decomposition, and aromatization. The process is commonly carried out at temperatures of 500–600° C., and pressures of 250 to 1000 pounds per square inch.

REFRACTION. A physical phenomenon that consists of a change of direction of

a system of **electromagnetic waves** upon passage from one medium to another in which the velocity of the wave front is different.

REFRACTION, ATOMIC. The product of the **specific refraction** of an element by its **atomic weight.**

REFRACTION, DOUBLE. A characteristic property of various nonhomogeneous media by which they divide incident energy into two wave-trains or rays, which move at different speeds in different directions throughout the medium.

REFRACTION, INDEX OF. A constant characteristic of a homogeneous substance at a definite temperature: the ratio of the sine of the angle of an incident ray of light to the sine of the angle of the refracted ray. That is,

index of refraction

$$= \frac{\text{sine angle of incidence}}{\text{sine angle of refraction}}.$$

REFRACTION, MOLAR. The product of the specific refraction (see **refraction, specific**) by the **molecular weight.** The form of this relationship is

$$[R] = Mr$$

in which $[R]$ is the molar refraction, M is the molecular weight, and r is the specific refraction. The direct form of this relationship is

$$[R] = \left(\frac{n^2 - 1}{n^2 + 2}\right)\left(\frac{M}{\rho}\right)$$

in which $[R]$ is the molar refraction, n is the index of refraction for any chosen wave length, M is the molecular weight, and ρ is the density.

REFRACTION, SPECIFIC. A relationship between the refractive index of a medium at any definite wave length and its density, of the form

$$r = \left(\frac{n^2 - 1}{n^2 + 2}\right)\left(\frac{1}{\rho}\right)$$

in which r is the specific refraction of the medium, n is its index of refraction at any definite wave length, and ρ is its density.

REFRACTIVE. Having or exhibiting the property of **refraction.**

REFRACTIVE INDEX. See **refraction, index of.**

REFRACTIVE INDEX, MAXWELL'S RELATIONSHIP FOR. The **dielectric constant** of a nonpolar substance which has no permanent molecular **dipole moment** is equal to the square of its refractive index, when the latter is measured for a light radiation of long wave length.

REFRACTIVE POWER, MOLECULAR. The same as **refraction, molar.**

REFRACTIVE POWER, SPECIFIC. The same as **refraction, specific.**

REFRACTIVITY. In general, the property of **refraction,** or a quantitative relationship by which it is expressed, which is commonly some function of the index of refraction.

REFRACTIVITY, ATOMIC. The same as **refraction, atomic.**

REFRACTIVITY, MOLAR. The same as **refraction, molar.**

REFRACTIVITY, SPECIFIC. The same as **refraction, specific.**

REFRACTOMETER. An optical apparatus used in the determination of index of refraction (see **refraction, index of**). Most refractometers are designed for use with liquids or solutions.

REFRACTORY. Resistant to the action of heat, especially in the sense of having a high melting point, or any substance which possesses this property. Refractories are used extensively in the construction of furnaces and other apparatus which operates at high temperatures.

REFRIGERANT. Any substance or mixture used in the production of reduced temperatures. Refrigerants range from the various substances which are used as working media in refrigeration apparatus to substances or mixtures which are used without apparatus to produce reduced temperatures, such as solid carbon dioxide, liquid air, and other substances or materials of low boiling point (or low sublimation point) or mixtures of substances, such as ice and salt, which absorb heat on mixing, or more exactly, which exhibit an increase in heat content in their mixture.

REFRIGERATION. Any process, operation, or action for the production of lower temperatures (i.e., the absorption of heat), especially apparatus designed specifically to accomplish that purpose. In the laboratory, refrigeration is often accomplished by the use of volatile, low-boiling substances which are lost in the atmosphere after they have been allowed to evaporate in contact with the object or system to be cooled. All large-scale or regularly-operated refrigeration systems, however, are designed for the recovery and recirculation of the cooling medium.

REFRIGERATION TON. The American ton of refrigeration is a rate of heat absorption unit used to express the capacity of a cooling system. It is a rate of heat absorption equivalent to the freezing of one ton (2000 pounds) of water to ice in twenty-four hours.

REGELATION. The phenomenon that occurs when two pieces of ice are rubbed together, the pressure causing the ice to melt at the surfaces of contact while the temperature drops, and, on relieving the pressure, the two surfaces freeze together, producing one mass of ice. This phenomenon is due to reduction of the freezing point of water (melting point of ice) under increased pressure. At very high pressures, the relationship changes, and the melting point of ice increases steadily with increasing pressure.

REGENERATION. Restoration to initial condition or state.

REGENERATIVE. Possessing the property or characteristic of **regeneration.**

REGENERATIVE FURNACE. See **furnace, regenerative.**

REGENERATIVE HEATING. The preheating of fuel gases by passing them alternately through two "checkerwork" chambers which have been heated with the waste gases from a furnace in such a way that the waste gases are heating one series of chambers while the fuel gases are being heated in the other. When the second series of chambers has been cooled, the fuel gas and waste gases are shifted so that the fuel gas passes through the chambers which have just been heated, and the waste gases pass through and heat the cool chambers.

REGION OF LIMITED PROPORTIONALITY. See **limited proportionality, region of.**

REGNAULD TEST FOR CHLOROFORM. Chloroform, on heating with alcoholic potassium hydroxide solution, gives ethyl formate unless the potassium hydroxide is present in excess, when potassium formate is produced.

REGULAR SYSTEM. See **crystallographic systems.**

REICH TEST REACTION FOR OILS. A number of essential oils give a red, yellow-red or violet color on heating with hydrochloric acid and sesame oil; some essential oils give yellow-red to brown-red colors with hydrochloric acid alone, or with zinc chloride and vanillin hydrochloride.

REICHARD TEST REACTIONS FOR LACTIC ACID. In the presence of sulfuric acid, lactic acid gives color reactions with ammonium vanadate, titanic acid, tungstic acid, mercuric chloride, α-nitroso-β-naphthol, and α-naphthylamine.

REICHARD TEST REACTION FOR NICKEL. On heating an anhydrous nickel salt with dry methylamine hydrochloride, a dark blue color is obtained, which disappears on cooling and reappears on heating.

REICHARD TEST REACTION FOR STANNIC ION. A little powdered uric acid is moistened with 1 drop of the solution tested, then with strong sodium hydroxide solution, and heated. A gray to black spot is obtained if stannic ion (not stannous) is present.

REICHERT NUMBERS. Various methods of expressing the volatile water-soluble organic acids in a fat, which are usually determined by first saponifying the fat, distilling, and then titrating the liberated fatty acids. The specific Reichert numbers, which are designated usually by the name of Reichert and some other investigator, as the Reichert-Meissl or Reichert-Wollny numbers, are the volume in cubic centimeters of a standard alkali solution of specified concentration, (commonly 0.1 N NaOH) required to titrate the volatile, water-soluble fatty acids from a specified amount of fat (5 grams).

REICHL TEST REACTION FOR ALBUMIN. A mixture of ferric sulfate, dilute sulfuric acid and alcoholic benzaldehyde solution gives a blue color with albumin.

REICHL TEST REACTION FOR GLYCERIN. On heating equal parts glycerin, phenol, and concentrated sulfuric acid to 120° C., a brown-yellow mass separates which gives a carmine-red solution in water and ammonia.

REICHSTEIN REAGENTS. (1) 3,5-Dinitrobenzoylchloride, which forms crystalline esters of characteristic melting point with alcohols. These esters give deep-red to orange colors with α-naphthylamine. (2) Anthraquinone-β-carboxylic acid chloride gives characteristic compounds with primary and secondary alcohols. The reaction also takes place with many phenols, enolic compounds, mercaptans, amines, etc.

REID VAPOR PRESSURE. See **vapor pressure, Reid.**

REIMER-TIEMANN REACTION. The preparation of oxy-aldehydes by the interaction of a phenol, chloroform, and aqueous alkalies. The aldehyde group enters the *ortho* and *para* positions with respect to the **hydroxyl group.** Oxyacids are similarly produced from carbon tetrachloride.

$$C_6H_5OH + CHCl_3 + 3KOH \rightarrow C_6H_4(OH)CHO + 3KCl + 2H_2O.$$

$$C_6H_5OH + CCl_4 + 4KOH \rightarrow C_6H_4(OH)COOH + 4KCl + 2H_2O.$$

REINSCH TEST. A qualitative test for arsenic. The element is reduced, and deposited from a hydrochloric acid solution on a small piece of burnished copper as a characteristic black stain.

REISSERT REACTION. A method of synthesis of the "Reissert Compounds," which are 1-acyl-2-cyano-1,2 dihydroquinoline derivatives, by the direct action upon quinoline of acid chlorides and alkali cyanides.

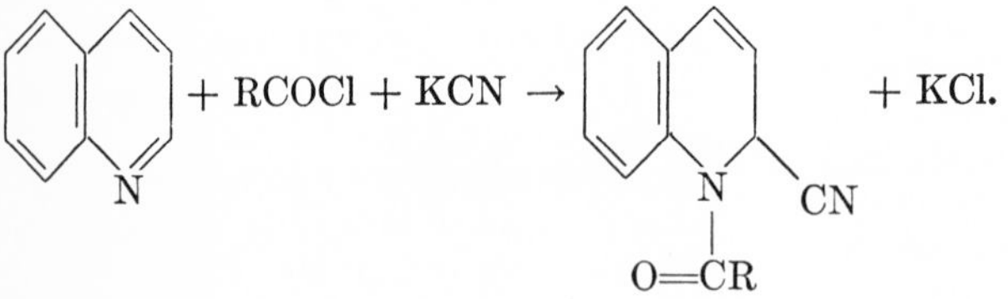

A useful reaction of these compounds is their hydrolysis to yield quinaldic acids and aldehydes.

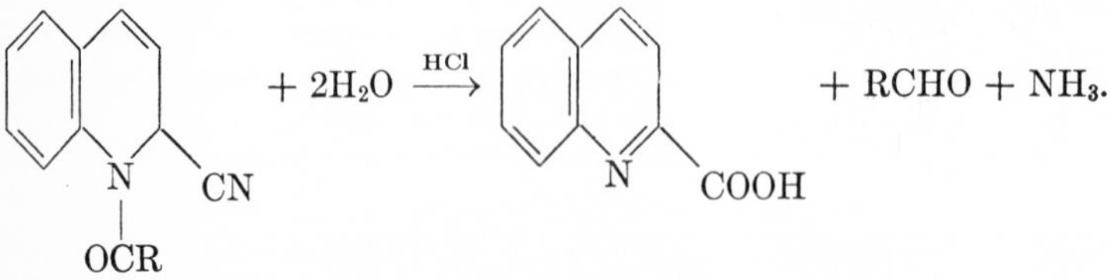

RELATIVE DENSITY. See **density, relative.**

RELATIVE STOPPING POWER. See **stopping power.**

RELATIVE WEIGHT. **Atomic weight.**

RELAXATION PHENOMENA. Any phenomenon in which a system requires an observable length of time in order to respond to sudden changes in conditions, forces, or effects which are applied to the system.

RELAXATION TIME. In relaxation phenomena, that time interval which is required for a predetermined portion of the system to respond to a sudden change in external conditions, forces, or effects.

REMY TEST. Ruthenium is detected by mixing the material tested with 1 ml. hydrochloric acid, and passing in chlorine. An intense blue color indicates the presence of ruthenium.

RENTELN SOLUTION. A solution of 3 g. sodium selenate in 80 ml. water, with 60 ml. concentrated sulfuric acid, used in testing for alkaloids. Characteristic color reactions are obtained.

RENZ TEST REACTION. Thallium salts, when in alcoholic solution, give a violet color or precipitate with α-naphthylamine. With β-naphthylamine a double compound with a silvery luster is obtained.

REPEATABILITY. A measure of **deviation** of test results from their mean value, all determinations being carried out by one operator without change of apparatus in those cases where the manner of handling apparatus can alter results.

REPLACE. To substitute one atom or radical for another atom or radical in any compound. See **reaction, replacement.**

REPLACEABLE. An atom or radical in a compound for which another atom or radical may be directly substituted, e.g., benzene has six replaceable hydrogen atoms. Acetic acid has one hydrogen atom replaceable by a metal and three replaceable by halogens.

REPLACEMENT, CHEMICAL. See chemical replacement.

REPPMANN TEST. Arsenic is detected by placing 1 drop of the solution tested on filter paper, moistening with hydrochloric acid and a 0.5% solution of N-ethyl-8-hydroxytetrahydroquinoline hydrochloride. Then 1 drop ferric chloride solution is added and the paper is warmed. A red-brown color indicates the presence of arsenic.

REPULSION FORCES. Forces between bodies which tend to move them apart. The existence of such forces between molecules is shown by their **collision diameters** and similar properties; while in the case of crystals these forces, in equilibrium with forces of attraction, result in the formation of a stable ionic system.

RES-. A prefix meaning relating to resorcinol, as resazurin. (See **reso-.**)

RESIDUAL ENTROPY. See **entropy, residual.**

RESIDUE. (1) In general, a remainder or partial product. (2) The insoluble matter left on a filter or from which a liquid has been removed. (3) A radical or a group, especially in carbon compounds, that remains after removal of a portion of a larger entity, such as a molecule.

RESIN. In the original and still most general meaning of the term, resins are a group of natural products of vegetable origin, commonly the solid exudation-products of plants, frequently formed by **polymerization** of **essential oil** constituents. Chemically, they are largely mixtures of oxygen derivatives of cyclic hydrocarbons, resin acids, and phenolic derivatives. Resins are characterized by lack of crystalline structure, low melting point, insolubility in water, solubility in alkalies, alcohol, and most organic solvents. On fusion with alkalies resins yield phenols (resorcinol, phloroglucinol, etc.) and on distillation with zinc dust they yield benzene, naphthalene, and similar hydrocarbons. Cf. **gum-resins.**

The term artificial resins is frequently used for many industrial polymerization products, although they are more generally known as **plastics** (q.v.).

RESINIFICATION. The formation of natural or artificial resins (see **resins** and **plastics**).

RESISTANCE, EXTERNAL. The resistance of that part of the electric circuit which lies outside the source of the current, e.g., the resistance of a wire and other apparatus connected externally between the poles of an electrolytic cell or cells.

RESISTANCE, INTERNAL. The resistance within the apparatus which is generating an electric current; e.g., in a **cell,** the resistance of the **electrodes** and the electrolyte **solution.**

RESISTANCE, SPECIFIC (RESISTIVITY). A proportionality factor characteristic of different substances equal to the **resistance** that a centimeter cube of the substance offers to the passage of electricity. It is defined by the expression:

$$R = \rho \, \frac{l}{A}$$

where R is the resistance of a uniform conductor, l is its length, A is its cross-sectional area, and ρ is its resistivity.

RESISTOR. An element of apparatus used to offer considerable **resistance** to the passage of an electric current and thus to produce heat.

RESISTS. In textile printing, substances printed on the cloth to prevent access of dye or mordant to certain portions.

RESO-. A prefix meaning relating to resorcinol, as resorufin. (See **res-.**)

RESOLUTION. A term used in a number of specific cases in science to denote the process of separating closely-related forms or entities. The term is most frequently used in optics to denote the smallest extension which a magnifying instrument is able to separate or the smallest change in wave length which a spectrometer can differentiate. In this last sense, it is defined as the ratio of the average wave length (wave number or frequency) of two spectral lines, which can just be detected as a doublet, to the difference in their wave lengths (wave numbers or frequencies). The term resolution is also applied to such varied processes as the separation of a racemic mixture into its optically-active components or as the breaking up of a vectorial quantity into components.

RESONANCE. A phenomenon in which a system subjected to external forces emits a sharp response as the magnitude of the external effect passes through one or more critical values. As an example, certain mechanical systems can be made to oscillate by periodic application of an external force. If the periodicity is made to coincide precisely with the natural frequency of the system, the amplitude of the oscillations increases enormously. This effect is known as the condition of resonance.

A most important application of the term resonance is to atomic or molecular systems which oscillate between two or more forms. For example, in benzene the electrons responsible for the double bonds are considered to shift easily between the two principal resonance forms, i.e., in one form the double bonds are between the 1–2, 3–4, and 5–6 carbon atoms; and in the other between the 2–3, 4–5, and 6–1 carbon atoms. The compound exists, therefore, not as a mobile equilibrium between the forms, but as a resonance hybrid of them,

and its chemical behavior (e.g., its stability and resistance to addition reactions) is in accordance with this structure.

RESONANCE FLUORESCENCE. Also called resonance radiation. The emission by an excited atom of a **radiation** of the same frequency as the exciting radiation.

RESONANCE POTENTIAL. See **potential, critical.**

RESONANCE RADIATION. Also called resonance fluorescence. The emission by an excited atom of a radiation of the same frequency as the exciting radiation.

RESONATOR. A group of atoms that absorbs characteristic optical and other **electromagnetic radiations.**

RESORPTION. The **absorption,** or less commonly, the **adsorption** by a body or system of material previously released from absorption or adsorption by that same body or system.

RESPIRATOR. A gas mask, or any protective mask designed to remove from inspired air either solid or liquid particles, or toxic or irritating components in the air.

RESPIRATORY QUOTIENT. The ratio of the volume of oxygen inhaled by an organism to the volume of carbon dioxide exhaled. This ratio is generally less than 1, due to the volume of expired carbon dioxide being less than the volume of inspired oxygen.

RESTITUTION. See **reaction, restitution.**

RESULTANT. An entity or quantity obtained by means of (as the result of) a given process. Thus, the resultant of a system of forces is the single force that has the same effect; whereas the resultants of a chemical reaction are the products yielded by it.

RETARDATION, CATALYTIC. Negative catalysis. (See **catalysis, negative.**)

RETARDER. A negative catalyst. (See **catalyst, negative.**)

RETGER, LAW OF. See law of Retger.

RETGER LIQUID. Methylene iodide (sp. gr. 3.3) which is miscible with benzene and suitable for specific gravity determinations and separations of minerals and other solids.

RETICULAR DENSITY. The number of points per unit area in a network, as in that of a plane in a crystal lattice.

RETICULATED. Having the form of a network.

RETONATION. The repetition of a detonation; an explosion-wave which travels again from the origin of the explosion through the substances that have already exploded.

RETORT. A distilling vessel.

RETROGRESSION OF IONIZATION. The old name for the "common ion effect" (q.v.).

RETROGRESSIVE SUBSTITUTION. See reverse substitution.

REVERBERATORY FURNACE. See furnace, reverberatory.

REVERDIN REARRANGEMENT. A migration of iodine that occurs during the nitration of iodophenolic ethers.

$$\text{(OR, I at bottom)} + \text{HNO}_3 \rightarrow \text{(OR, I at top, NO}_2\text{ at bottom)} + \text{H}_2\text{O}.$$

REVERSE SUBSTITUTION. A substitution reaction, in which the speed of reaction in one direction is less than that in the reverse direction; e.g., iodine does not replace aromatic hydrogen because the reverse substitution by hydrogen iodide takes place more readily:

$$CH_3C_6H_5 + I_2 \rightleftarrows CH_3C_6H_4I + HI.$$

REVERSIBLE CELL. A storage battery, or any electric cell in which the chemical reaction by which the cell produces its electromotive force and current is reversible by application to the cell terminals (emergent part of the electrodes) of an e.m.f. opposite in sign to that of the cell, and great enough in magnitude to force a current to flow through the cell in the opposite direction to that prevailing when the cell is producing current. The result of the process is to restore the electrodes and electrolyte to their original chemical condition.

REVERSIBLE ELECTRODE. An electrode which derives its electrochemical potential from a reaction that is reversible.

REVERSIBLE REACTION. See reaction, reversible.

REVIVIFICATION. The process of reviving.

REYNOLDS NUMBER. A numerical expression of the fluid flow in a pipe obtained by multiplying the velocity of flow by the cross-sectional area, and dividing by the coefficient of kinematic viscosity of the liquid.

Rh Symbol for the element rhodium.

rH. (1) The oxidation-reduction potential, expressed as the logarithm of the reciprocal of the hydrogen pressure (in atmospheres)

$$rH = \log\left(\frac{1}{p_{H_2}}\right),$$

where the partial pressure of the hydrogen is given in atmospheres.
(2) The term rH is used for a factor in human blood which has especially serious, or even fatal, results in offspring of parents in whom this factor is antagonistic.

RHAMNOGALACTOSIDE. One of a group of glycosides which, on hydrolysis, yield rhamnose and galactose, as robinin and xanthorhamnin.

RHAMNOGLUCOSIDE. One of a group of glycosides which yield rhamnose and glucose on hydrolysis, as hesperidin, rutin, sophorin.

RHAMNOMANNOSIDE. One of a group of **glycosides** which yield rhamnose and mannose on hydrolysis, as strophanthin.

RHAMNOSIDE. One of a group of **glycosides** which yield rhamnose upon hydrolysis, as quercitin, baptisin, frangulin, etc.

RHE. The absolute unit by which **fluidity** is measured or expressed. It is the reciprocal centipoise, which is in turn, one-hundredth of the poise, the c.g.s. unit of viscosity. One poise is equal to one dyne second per square centimeter.

RHEINBOLDT TEST FOR MERCAPTANS. The solution to be tested is poured on sodium nitrite, and dilute sulfuric acid or glacial acetic acid is added. Primary and secondary aliphatic mercaptans give a deep red color; tertiary aliphatic or aromatic mercaptans give a green color in dilute solution, and a dichroic green color in concentrated solution.

RHEINBOLDT TEST REACTION FOR OXIMES. An ethereal solution of an aldoxime or of most ketoximes gives a blue color with aqua regia.

RHENATE (IV). The anion $ReO_3^=$, or a compound containing it.

RHENATE (VI). The compound $ReO_4^=$, or a compound containing it.

RHENIUM. Metallic element. Symbol Re. Atomic number 75. Atomic weight 186.31. Density 20.53. Melting point values reported, 3000° C. and 3440° C. Specific heat 6.44. Compounds are known at all integral valences from 1 to 7. Rhenium heptoxide dissolves in water to give a solution of perrhenic acid, in which the element has a valence of 7. Rhenium occurs most frequently in molybdenum ores and residues.

RHEOLOGY. The science of flow, which deals with the phenomena of deformation under stress for all forms of matter, and the mathematical relationships which have been developed from these data.

RHEOMETER. A galvanometer.

RHEOPEXY. A property exhibited by certain **sols** containing rod-like or plate-like particles (such as bentonite and other clay suspensions), which consists in accelerated setting to the **gel** form brought about by any mechanical means that will facilitate the orientation of the particles.

RHEOSTAT. An instrument used to control the **resistance** through which an electric current must pass. It therefore furnishes a means of controlling the amount of current, according to the **law of Ohm.**

RHO (P, ρ OR ϱ). The seventeenth letter in the Greek alphabet, used to denote the sixteenth carbon atom in a straight-chain compound, or a derivative in which the substituent group is attached to that carbon atom (ρ-). Symbol for density (ρ). Symbol for the pros-position (2,3 in naphthalene) (ρ-). Symbol for the rhe (ρ). Symbol for volume **charge density** (ρ). Symbol for **radius of curvature** (ρ). Symbol for the **reflectance** (ρ). Symbol for **reflectivity** (ρ'). Symbol for **specific resistance** (resistivity) (ρ).

RHOD-. A prefix derived from the Greek, *rhodon*, rose (red), as rhodamine.

RHODANATE. The same as **thiocyanate.**

RHODATE. The anion $RhO_4^=$, or a compound containing it.

RHODES REAGENT. A solution of 20 g. mercuric iodide and 16 g. potassium iodide in 100 ml. water, to which is then added 1 liter 3 N sodium hydroxide solution. It is used in detecting oxycellulose in artificial silk. Characteristic dark stains are obtained under the test conditions.

RHODIUM. Metallic element. Symbol Rh. Atomic number 45. Atomic weight 102.91. Density 12.414. Specific heat 0.0580. Melting point values reported of 1955° C., 1966° C., 1985° C. Valence 3. Oxides RhO, Rh_2O_3, RhO_2. Rhodium occurs in platinum ores. Its sulfate forms a series of alums with the alkali metals.

RHODO-. A prefix derived from the Greek, *rhodon*, rose (red), as rhodoporphyrin.

RHOMBIC SYSTEM. See **crystallographic systems.**

RICE BROMINE SOLUTION. A solution of 12.5 g. bromine and 12.5 g. sodium bromide in water, dilute to a volume of 100 ml. and used in the determination of urea.

RICE-FOGG-JAMES REAGENT. A 10% solution of phenylarsonic acid, which precipitates zirconium quantitatively from acid solutions. This reagent has also been used to precipitate tin, and thorium in the presence of ammonium acetate and acetic acid.

RICE TEST FOR PHENOL. One g. potassium chlorate is added to 10 ml. concentrated hydrochloric acid and, after 15 minutes, 15 ml. water. The chlorine gas is blown out of the tube, and ammonium hydroxide superimposed. Then 1 drop of the liquid to be tested is added. A rose-red to red-brown color in the ammonia layer indicates phenol.

RICHARD TEST FOR MERCURY OXYCYANIDE. Mercury oxycyanide, unlike mercury cyanide, dissolves only partly in concentrated ammonium hydroxide, leaving a yellow residue.

RICHARDSON TEST FOR NAPHTHOLS. The reagent is a solution of

This reagent is added to a solution of 0.04 g. naphthol in 5 ml. 10% sodium hydroxide solution. A dark blood-red color is given by α-naphthol, with a dark brown precipitate on addition of dilute sulfuric acid; β-naphthol gives a red-yellow color, unchanged on dilution.

RICHAUD-BIDOT SOLUTION. A solution of 25 g. sodium phosphotungstate and 5 ml. hydrochloric acid in 250 ml. water, used in detecting ferrous iron in foods, etc. A blue color formed in alkaline solution is obtained if ferrous iron is present.

RICHMOND-BOSELY TEST FOR FORMALDEHYDE IN MILK. Equal volumes milk and water are mixed with 4 volumes concentrated sulfuric acid having in solution a little ferric sulfate. A violet color indicates formaldehyde.

RICHMOND-BOSELY TEST REACTION FOR FORMALDEHYDE. A solution of diphenylamine in water and sulfuric acid gives, with formaldehyde, a white precipitate, changing to a green color on addition of nitric acid.

RICHTER CINNOLINE SYNTHESIS. A method of formation of cinnoline derivatives from o-amino aromatic propiolic acids, by diazotization and ring closure.

0.05 g. sulfanilic acid in 5 ml. N sodium hydroxide solution which is added to 5 ml. N sulfuric acid, and followed by 0.02 g. sodium nitrite dissolved in a few drops of water.

RICHTER LAW. See **law of Richter.**

RIDEAL REAGENT FOR FORMALDE-HYDE. A 0.5% solution of fuchsin, decolorized by sulfurous acid, or by sodium bisulfite or sulfite and hydrochloric acid, gives a violet-red color with formaldehyde.

RIDENOUR TEST REACTION FOR SALICYLIC ACID.
A 3% hydrogen peroxide solution gives a cherry-red color with salicylic acid in the presence of ammonium carbonate.

RIEGLER REAGENTS FOR ALBUMIN, ALBUMOSES, AND PEPTONES.
(1) A 10% solution of asaprol containing hydrochloric acid, used as a precipitant for albumin and peptones.

(2) A solution of 8 g. asaprol and 8 g. citric acid in 200 ml. water, used to give a turbidity with albumin in urine.

(3) A solution of 5 g. β-naphthalenesulfonic acid in 100 ml. alcohol, used in detecting albumin in urine. A precipitate which does not dissolve on warming indicates albumin.

(4) A solution of 4 g. aluminum β-naphtholdisulfonate and 4 g. citric acid in 100 ml. water. A few drops gives a turbidity with either albumin or albumoses, but the latter (only) dissolves on heating.

(5) A solution of 2.5 g. p-nitroaniline and 5 ml. concentrated sulfuric acid in 25 ml. water, to which 30 drops 10% NaOH solution is added. It gives a red color with albumin, albumoses, or peptones.

RIEGLER REAGENT FOR AMMONIA.
A reagent prepared by dissolving (by warming) 1 g. p-nitroaniline and 2 ml. hydrochloric acid in 20 ml. water, then adding 160 ml. water, cooling, and finally adding a solution of 0.5 g. sodium nitrite in 20 ml. water. This reagent gives a red to yellow color with solutions containing ammonium ion, after addition of sodium hydroxide solution.

RIEGLER REAGENT FOR BILE PIGMENTS.
A two-solution reagent, consisting of: (1) a solution of 5 g. p-nitroaniline in 25 ml. water and 6 ml. concentrated sulfuric acid, to which is then added 100 ml. water; and (2) an aqueous solution of 3 g. sodium nitrite in a volume of 250 ml. A chloroform extract of the urine, an addition of absolute alcohol and these reagents, gives a red or red-yellow color in the presence of bile pigments.

RIEGLER REAGENT FOR BLOOD PIGMENTS.
A solution of 5 g. sodium hydroxide in 50 ml. water, to which is then added 2.5 g. hydrazine sulfate, followed by 50 ml. alcohol. A purple-red color is obtained with solutions of oxyhemoglobin, hemoglobin, or hematin.

RIEGLER REAGENT FOR NITRITES.
A solution of 1 g. β-naphthol and 2 g. sodium naphthionate in 200 ml. water. A pink to red color obtained under the test procedure at an ammonium hydroxide interface indicates the presence of nitrites. This is an extremely sensitive test.

RIEGLER REAGENT FOR SACCHARIN.
A solution of 2.5 g. p-nitroaniline in 25 ml. water, to which is added 5 ml. concentrated sulfuric acid, and 25 ml. water, then a solution of 1.5 g. sodium nitrite in 20 ml. water, and finally enough water to obtain a volume of 250 ml. A blue to green color, obtained upon alkalization of an ether extract of the reagent-sample mixture, indicates the presence of saccharin.

RIEGLER REAGENT FOR URIC ACID.
A mixture of 0.5 g. p-nitroaniline, 10 ml. water, and 15 drops concentrated sulfuric acid, which is diluted with 20 ml. water and cooled, and then diazotized with 10 ml. 2.5% sodium nitrite solution, and diluted with 60 ml. water. A red-yellow color, changing to blue or green, in alkaline solution, is given by this reagent with solutions containing uric acid.

RIEGLER TEST FOR FORMALDEHYDE IN MILK.
Shake 2 ml. milk and 2 ml. water with 0.1 g. phenylhydrazine hydrochloride until dissolved, add 10 ml. 10% sodium hydroxide solution and shake for 30 minutes. A rose-red color indicates formaldehyde.

RIEGLER TEST FOR LACTOSE IN MILK.
Heat to boiling 1 ml. milk and 2–3 ml. water with 0.1 g. phenylhydrazine hydrochloride. Add a little sodium acetate and 10 ml. 10% sodium hydroxide solution. A rose-red color, becoming red, is obtained if lactose is present.

RIEHM QUINOLINE SYNTHESIS.
A method of formation of quinoline derivatives by condensation of aniline hydro-

chloride (or other aromatic amine hydrochlorides) with ketones.

or more rings which have two or more atoms in common.

RIENISDIJK REAGENT. A mixture of 3 ml. 10% glucose solution, 1 drop N sodium hydroxide solution, and 1 drop 0.1% methylene blue solution. Gauze impregnated with this solution is decolorized in 1 minute at 37° C. if oxygen is present.

RILEY OXIDATION REACTION. The use of selenium dioxide in certain organic oxidations, especially the oxidation of active methylene groups to carbonyl groups.

RING. A number of atoms arranged in a ring, as the benzene ring, pyridine ring, etc. Ring-shaped compounds are termed cyclic.

RING, BENZENE. A homocyclic six-membered ring designed to represent the structure of **benzene.**

RING BREAKAGE. A chemical change by which a compound having some or all of its atoms connected by **valence bonds** to form a ring is changed so that one or more of those valence bonds are broken and the ring structure no longer exists.

RING CLOSURE. The change of the arrangement and/or the number of atoms in a chemical compound, or a portion of a chemical compound, from an open-chain linkage of atoms to a closed or ring structure.

RING, FUSED. A number of atoms connected by **valence bonds** so as to form two

RING, HETEROCYCLIC. A ring which contains more than one kind of atom, as the **pyridine** ring, **lactone** ring, **thiophene** ring, betaine ring and diazosulfide ring.

RING, HOMOCYCLIC. A ring in which all of the members are atoms of the same element.

RING, LIESEGANG. See **Liesegang rings.**

RING, NAPHTHALENE. The atomic complex which represents the structure of **naphthalene.**

RING OPENING. The change in the arrangement and/or the number of atoms in a chemical compound, or a portion of a chemical compound, from a closed-chain or ring linkage of atoms to an open-chain structure.

RING, PYRIDINE. A heterocyclic ring in which nitrogen takes the place of one of the carbons in benzene, thus

RING REACTION. See **reaction, ring.**

RING STRUCTURE. See **ring.**

RINGER ARTIFICIAL SERUM. A solution prepared by dissolving in 100 ml. water, 0.60 g. sodium chloride, 0.075 g. potassium chloride, 0.01 g. calcium chloride, and 0.01 g. sodium bicarbonate.

RINGER BLOOD DILUENT (EXTER-NAL). A solution used in laboratory work for diluting blood. It is prepared by dissolving in 1 liter water, 9 g. sodium chloride, 0.30 g. potassium chloride, and 0.26 g. calcium chloride.

RINGER CULTURE MEDIUM SOLUTION. A solution in 1 liter water of 10.0 g. sodium chloride, 0.2 g. calcium chloride, 0.1 g. sodium bicarbonate, 0.2 g. potassium chloride, and 1.0 g. glucose.

RIPAN REACTIONS FOR CYANATE.
(1) A hot solution of potassium cyanate precipitates aluminum hydroxide from aluminum chloride solutions.

(2) A hot solution of cyanate precipitates ferric hydroxide, with gas evolution, from a ferric chloride solution.

tion as zinc-pyridine-iodide. Cobalt, manganese, and nickel do not interfere.

RIPENING AGENT. A chemical substance (commonly ethylene) used to accelerate the internal changes in various fruits and vegetables so as to hasten ripening; one of the accelerated changes and probably the most important is the destruction of chlorophyll with the subsequent production of the ripe aspect of the fruit or vegetable.

RITTER REACTION. A method of formation of amides by introduction of a cyanide radical and hydrolysis. The reaction applies to a number of types of compounds, including alkenes and secondary and tertiary alcohols.

$$RHC{=}CH_2 + R'CN + H_2O \xrightarrow{H_2SO_4} RR'HC.CONH.CH_3$$

$$R_2CHOH + HCN + (H_2O) \xrightarrow{H_2SO_4} HCONH.CHR_2.$$

(3) On addition of 2–3 ml. dibenzylamine solution in amyl alcohol to the solution tested, followed by the addition of 2–3 ml. 1% cupric sulfate solution, a violet color in the alcohol layer indicates cyanate.

(4) On addition of 2–3 ml. 1% cadmium nitrate solution to the solution tested, then a few drops pyridine, a precipitate is given by cyanate.

RIPAN REAGENT FOR PHTHALIC AND TEREPHTHALIC ACIDS. A solution of 2 ml. pyridine in 100 ml. 4% cupric sulfate solution, used in differentiating phthalic and terephthalic acids. Both give a blue precipitate, the latter at once and the former only after standing for hours.

RIPAN TEST FOR COBALT. One or two ml. freshly-prepared 4% potassium cyanate solution is added to the solution tested, then 1 drop glacial acetic acid. A blue color, soluble in acetone, indicates the presence of cobalt.

RIPAN TEST FOR ZINC. An excess of pyridine and an excess of 15% potassium iodide solution precipitates zinc from solu-

RITZ COMBINATION PRINCIPLE. The Ritz combination principle states that the wave number of any spectral line for a given atom can be calculated by means of the formula:

$$\bar{\nu} = R\left(\frac{1}{x^2} - \frac{1}{y^2}\right)$$

in which $\bar{\nu}$ is the wave number, R is a constant, x is constant for a given series, and y varies from term to term in the series. (Also see **Lyman, Balmer, Paschen, Brackett,** and **Pfund series.**)

Rn Symbol for the element **radon.**

ROAST. The operation of **roasting.**

ROASTER, FLASH. See **flash roaster.**

ROASTING. Heating a solid or partially solid material in the presence of air. This process is used extensively in metallurgical processes, as a means of converting compounds of metals with sulfur, and certain other non-metals, to oxides. The non-metal is commonly driven off as its oxide, and is often recovered, e.g., the sulfur dioxide, obtained by roasting sulfide ores, is the source of a great tonnage of sulfuric acid.

ROBERTS COKE OVEN. A by-product coke oven for the production of coke by the regenerative heating and distillation of coal.

ROBERTS REAGENT. (1) A mixture of 250 ml. of a saturated aqueous solution of magnesium sulfate and 50 ml. nitric acid, used as a test reagent for albumin. A white ring test is given by this reagent with urine containing albumin.

(2) A solution of 10 g. sodium chloride in 25 ml. water, to which 5% hydrochloric acid has been added. A turbidity or precipitate forms with urine containing albumin or peptone.

ROCHAIX TEST FOR NITRITE IN WATER. Twenty ml. of a 0.02% aqueous solution of neutral red, and 1–3 ml. 20% sulfuric acid are added to 10 ml. of the water tested. A violet to blue color indicates nitrite. Many modifications of this test have been reported.

RODILLON REAGENT FOR NITRITE. A solution of 3 g. resorcinol in 50 ml. concentrated sulfuric acid. The water tested is superimposed on the reagent. A rose-red ring indicates nitrite.

ROE REACTION FOR VITAMIN C (ASCORBIC ACID). On boiling ascorbic acid with hydrochloric acid, carbon dioxide is evolved and furfural is formed. The latter gives colors with aniline, phloroglucinol, or orcin. Other substances yielding furfural interfere.

ROENTGEN RAY. See **ray, Roentgen.**

ROENTGEN UNIT. The amount of **radiation** which, on passage through dry air under standard conditions, produces an electrostatic unit of ions, of either plus or minus charge, per cubic centimeter.

ROESLER PROCESS. A metallurgical process for the separation of copper and silver from gold, by taking advantage of their greater reactivity with sulfur, so that copper and silver sulfides are formed by heating with sulfur, under conditions that leave the gold unaffected.

ROGAI TEST. Hydrogen peroxide is detected by adding the solution tested to a reagent prepared by shaking a freshly-prepared solution of ferrous sulfate and potassium thiocyanate with a peroxide-free ether. The ether is colored red in the presence of hydrogen peroxide.

ROGERS-CALAMARI TEST FOR ROTENONE. One to two ml. of the solution tested are brought up to 5 ml. with chloroform, 5 ml. 10% thymol solution in chloroform are added, followed by 3 ml. of a mixture of 0.2 ml. nitrous acid and 100 ml. hydrochloric acid, and the mixture is agitated for $\frac{1}{2}$ minute. A blue-green to blue color indicates rotenone.

ROGERS TEST REACTION FOR ALDEHYDES. A 1:1000 silver nitrate solution is added to the solution tested, followed by ammonium hydroxide. In the presence of aldehydes, metallic silver separates in the form of a mirror and becomes dark purple-green.

ROHRBACH SOLUTION. A high-density solution of mercuric chloride and barium chloride in water, used in the classification of minerals by their specific gravity.

RÖHRIG TUBE. A laboratory apparatus used in the extraction of fats, chiefly with ether.

ROMANI TEST FOR SUCROSE. Two drops of a 20% alcohol solution of β-naphthol and 3 ml. hydrochloric acid are added to a few drops of the sugar solution, and boiled for 3–4 seconds. Sucrose gives a red color, which becomes yellow on addition of chloroform; glucose and lactose give a pale yellow color which becomes colorless on addition of chloroform.

ROMIEU TEST FOR PROTEIN MATERIAL. On gentle boiling with syrupy phosphoric acid, protein material forms a garnet-red color, slowly turning purple.

ROMIJN REAGENT FOR GLUCOSE. An aqueous solution prepared by dissolving enough borax and iodine in water so that each 25 ml. of solution contains 1 g.

borax and an amount of iodine equivalent to 30–33 ml. 0.1 N sodium thiosulfate solution. This solution is used as a test reagent for glucose, which reduces it.

ROQUES BENZIDINE REAGENT. A solution prepared by dissolving 1 g. benzidine in 30 ml. water and 10 ml. acetic acid, boiling, and then diluting with water to 50 ml. It is used in detecting levulosans in plant tissues, on histological examination.

ROSE PROCESS. A metallurgical process for the recovery of gold involving precipitation, fusion, and atmospheric oxidation.

ROSENBLAT TEST FOR BORIC ACID. The substance tested is acidified with hydrochloric acid, placed with methanol in a Woulff flask, and treated with a stream of hydrogen or illuminating gas. The gas is ignited as it issues from the flask; a green flame indicates boron.

ROSENHAIN-HAUGHTON REAGENT. A solution for etching steel, consisting of 30 g. ferric chloride, 10 g. cupric chloride, 0.5 g. stannous chloride, and 100 ml. hydrochloric acid, dissolved in 1 liter water.

ROSENHEIM-CALLOW TEST REACTIONS FOR STEROLS. Dissolve 25 g. mercuric acetate in 100 ml. nitric acid (sp. gr. 1.42). Add to the chloroform solution of the sterol an equal volume of the reagent, and shake immediately. Characteristic colors are given by certain types of sterols.

ROSENHEIM-DRUMMOND TEST FOR VITAMIN A. One ml. arsenic trichloride is added to one drop of the oil to be tested, which is then dissolved in petroleum benzine and shaken. If vitamin A is present, the oil dissolves with a blue color, changing to purple, then becoming paler. The test can be used for the colorimetric determination of the vitamin.

ROSENHEIM REAGENT FOR CHOLINE. A solution of 2 g. iodine and 6 g. potassium iodide in 100 ml. water, used as a test reagent for choline. Characteristic dark brown crystals are obtained by adding

this reagent to choline platinic chloride solid (produced by evaporation of its solution in 15% alcohol).

ROSENMUND ARSONIC ACID REACTION. A reaction for the preparation of aromatic **arsonic acids** by the interaction of sodium or potassium arsenite with aryl halides.

$$ArX + K_3AsO_3 \rightarrow Ar.AsO(OK)_2 + KX.$$

ROSENMUND REDUCTION REACTION. A method for synthesizing aromatic and aliphatic aldehydes by the hydrogenation of a carboxylic acid chloride in the presence of a palladium-barium sulfate catalyst.

$$RCOCl + H_2 \rightarrow RCHO + HCl.$$

ROSENMUND-VON BRAUN SYNTHESIS. A method of formation of aryl nitriles from aryl bromides and cuprous cyanide.

$$RBr + CuCN \xrightarrow{250° C.} RCN + CuBr.$$

ROSENSTEIN PROCESS. A process for the reduction of chlorine to hydrochloric acid by carbon monoxide (from water gas). The complete equation is believed to be:

$$Cl_2 + CO + H_2O \rightarrow 2HCl + CO_2.$$

ROSENTHAL-ERDELYI REAGENT. A two-solution reagent, consisting of (1) a solution of 0.5 g. pyrocatechol in 100 g. absolute chloroform; and (2) a cold saturated solution of antimony trichloride in absolute chloroform. This reagent is used in estimating vitamin A, especially in oils. A pink to violet color indicates the presence of vitamin A.

ROSENTHALER-GÖRNER TEST REAGENTS FOR ALKALOIDS. Various aromatic nitro-compounds such as nitrophenols, nitrocresols, dinitro-α-naphthol, etc.

ROSENTHALER TEST REACTION FOR ASCORBIC ACID (VITAMIN C). On addition of 0.5 ml. N hydrochloric acid and several drops 0.2% aqueous solution of cacothelin to 4.5 ml. of a 1:1000 ascorbic acid solution, a lilac color appears.

ROSENTHALER TEST REACTION FOR DIFFERENTIATING ALCOHOLS. Nessler solution (q.v.), which is alkaline mercuric potassium iodide solution, is reduced on heating with primary and secondary alcohols, but not with tertiary alcohols.

ROSENTHALER TEST REACTION FOR HYDROXYL GROUP. Add to the solution tested a mixture of 4 parts 0.5% sulfanilic acid solution and 1 part 0.7% sodium nitrite solution, then add excess sodium hydroxide solution and heat in the boiling water bath. Red to red-violet colors are produced with many organic hydroxy-compounds.

ROSENTHALER TEST FOR NITROGEN IN ORGANIC COMPOUNDS. Heat the material with lead peroxide, and pass the gases evolved into 50 ml. water containing 5 drops of a solution of 0.5 g. sulfanilic acid and 5 g. hydrochloric acid in 100 ml. water. After a few minutes, add a little solid α-naphthol and alkalinize with sodium hydroxide. A red dye indicates nitrogen in organic combination.

ROSENTHALER TEST FOR SULFUR IN ORGANIC COMPOUNDS. Heat the material in a tube and pass the gases evolved into a 1% solution of iodic acid containing starch. A blue color indicates sulfur in organic combination.

ROSENTHALER TEST REACTION FOR LACTIC ACID. With excess sodium hydroxide solution and **Ehrlich diazo reagent** (q.v.) a lactic acid solution slowly forms a violet color.

ROSENTHALER-TURK REAGENT. A solution of 1 g. potassium arsenate in 100 g. concentrated sulfuric acid used in testing for various opium alkaloids. Characteristic color reactions are obtained.

ROSSI-CELSI MICROREAGENT. A mixture of equal parts formaldehyde and hydrochloric acid, which forms a microcrystalline solid with gallic acid, but an amorphous product with tannic acid.

ROSSI CHLORAL HYDRATE REAGENT. A solution of 2 g. chloral hydrate in 10 ml. alcohol to which is added 20 ml. concentrated sulfuric acid. This reagent is used in testing for yohimbine, which gives with it a blue color on warming.

ROSSI COINCIDENCE CIRCUIT. See **coincidence counting.**

ROSSI TEST REACTION FOR PHOSPHATES. Add 1 ml. of the solution tested and 1–5 drops hydrogen sulfide water to 1 ml. of a 5% solution of sodium nitroprusside. Primary phosphates give no color, secondary phosphates a violet color, and tertiary phosphates a red color.

ROTAMETER. An instrument for measuring the rate of flow of gases or liquids by the position of a float in a tube, either transparent or provided with a sight glass, and which is mounted vertically and carries a scale.

ROTARY CRUSHER. See **crusher, rotary.**

ROTARY DRIER. See **drier, rotary.**

ROTATE (LIGHT). To turn the plane of **polarized light** either to the right or left.

ROTATION, MAGNETIC. Optical activity developed in a liquid when placed between the poles of a magnet. (See **Faraday effect.**) Specific magnetic rotation is the ratio of the specific rotation of the substance to that of water under like conditions. The molecular magnetic rotation is calculated by multiplying the specific magnetic rotation of the substance by the molecular weight and dividing by the molecular weight of water.

ROTATION, MOLAR. Or molar rotatory power or molecular rotation. The product of the specific rotation by the molecular weight, divided by 100. The form of this relationship is

$$[M] = M[\alpha]/100$$

in which $[M]$ is the molar rotation, M is the molecular weight, and $[\alpha]$ is the specific rotation. The direct form of this relationship is

$$[M] = M\alpha/100l\rho$$

in which $[M]$ is the molar rotation, M is the molecular weight, α is the angle of rotation for a column of liquid of effective length l, and ρ is the density of the liquid.

ROTATION PHOTOGRAPH. A photograph of the **diffraction pattern** obtained by rotation of a single crystal in the beam of impinging x-rays.

ROTATION, SPECIFIC. An expression of the **optical rotatory power** of a substance or solution, as defined by the relationships:

For a pure substance $[\alpha] = \dfrac{\alpha}{l\rho}$

For a solution $[\alpha] = \dfrac{\alpha}{l\rho f}$,

in which $[\alpha]$ is the specific rotation, α is the observed rotation of a depth of substance or solution of l centimeters, ρ is the density of the substance or solution, and f is the weight fraction of the substance in the solution. The specific rotation varies with temperature and the wave length of light used.

ROTATIONAL ENERGY OF MOLECULES. That fraction of the total energy of a molecule which is associated with the rotation of the molecule about an internal axis.

ROTATIONAL PARTITION FUNCTION. A contribution to the total **partition function** of a system which arises from the rotational energy of the molecules. The summation occurring in the definition of the partition function is restricted to all rotational **energy levels.**

ROTATIONAL SPECTRA. Spectra in the far infrared portion of the spectrum that are caused by rotational transitions within a molecule.

ROTATORY. Optically active. Capable of rotating the plane of polarized light, distinguished as dextro-rotatory and levo-rotatory.

ROTATORY FILTER. See **filter, rotatory.**

ROTATORY POWER, OPTICAL. The ability of a substance to rotate the plane of polarization of **polarized light.**

ROTATORY POWER, SPECIFIC. See **rotation, specific.**

ROTATORY REFLECTION. A method for securing superposition in crystals of 2-, 4-, or 6-fold axes, consisting of rotation around an axis followed by reflection in a plane normal to the axis of rotation.

ROTH SOLUTION. Sulfuric acid saturated with nitrogen trioxide, used in testing fatty oils. This is the "elaidin" test for olive oil, and is based upon the time required for solidification after addition of the reagent.

ROTHENFUSSER TEST FOR FORMALDEHYDE. A little ammonium molybdate is dissolved in a mixture of 100 parts sulfuric acid and 20 parts water. Equal volumes of this reagent and the solution tested are heated with a little ammoniacal casein solution. A violet color indicates formaldehyde.

ROTHERA SOLUTION. A solution of 5 g. sodium nitroprusside in 100 ml. water, used in testing for acetone in urine. A red color formed in the area of contact with ammonium hydroxide, under test conditions, indicates the presence of acetone.

ROW LINES. Lines formed by the diffraction spots on a rotation photograph of a crystal as obtained by rotation of a crystal in a beam of x-rays, and photographing the **diffraction pattern.**

Ru Symbol for the element **ruthenium.**

RUBEFACIENT. A drug or other substance that produces a reddening of the skin, due to congestion with blood of the superficial capillaries.

RUBEL TEST FOR NITRITE. Add 0.5 ml. of a 0.1% solution of 2-ethoxy-6,9-diaminoacridine hydrochloride and 0.5 ml.

hydrochloric acid (sp. gr. 1.06) to 10 ml. of the diluted (2 to 100 times) solution to be tested. Nitrite gives a yellow-green to orange or red color.

RUBIDIC. Containing or pertaining to rubidium.

RUBIDIUM. Metallic element. Symbol Rb. Atomic number 37. Atomic weight 85.48. Density 1.53. Specific heat 0.0908. Melting point 38.5° C. Boiling point 700° C. Valence 1. Oxide Rb_2O. Rubidium occurs in lepidolite, triphylite, mineral waters, etc.

RUBNER TEST FOR DEXTROSE AND LACTOSE. Add lead acetate and ammonium hydroxide to the dilute solution tested until a permanent precipitate is formed, and boil for 20–25 seconds. A red color indicates dextrose. Lactose gives a pale red color only after 2–3 minutes boiling.

RUDISCH-BOROSCHEK REAGENT. A solution of 0.7175 g. silver chloride in 100 ml. of a 0.05 N sodium sulfite solution, used in testing for uric acid in urine. A light, flocculent precipitate indicates the presence of uric acid.

RUDOLPH TEST REACTION. Various polynitro compounds give characteristic color reactions if 0.5–1.0 ml. of the compound is dissolved in 10–15 ml. acetone and 2–3 ml. dilute sodium hydroxide solution added.

RUFF-FENTON DEGRADATION. A method of shortening the carbon chain of a sugar by oxidizing the aldonic acid or its calcium salt with hydrogen peroxide in the presence of ferric salts.

RULE OF MAXIMUM MULTIPLICITY. An empirical statement that the energy of interaction between the electrons in any one atom is at a minimum when their resultant spin is greatest.

RULE, SCHUTZ-BORRISOW. See Schutz-Borrisow rule.

RUPE-BECHERER REAGENT. A solution of 10 g. di-(1-naphthylmethyl)-amine acetate in 90 g. 50% acetic acid. It precipitates nitrate gravimetrically from a boiling solution acidified with sulfuric acid, if other mineral acids are absent.

RUPE REACTION. See Meyer-Schuster rearrangement.

RUPP-POGGENDORFF REAGENT. A solution of 5 g. cobalt nitrate in 2.1 g. glacial acetic acid and 1 g. water, to which a lukewarm solution of 10 g. sodium nitrite in 11 g. water is added. After aspirating with air for $\frac{1}{2}$ hour, standing for $\frac{1}{2}$ hour and filtering, the solution is mixed with 20 g. freshly-dehydrated sodium sulfate and placed in a vacuum desiccator for a day. It is a reagent for potassium.

RUSSELL-SAUNDERS COUPLING. One of the possible methods of calculating the total angular momentum of two or more optical electrons in an atom. According to this method the orbital angular momentum and the spin angular momentum vectors of the electrons are added separately to obtain a resultant **orbital** and a resultant **spin** angular momentum vector. The two resultants are then combined vectorially to obtain a series of allowed total angular momentum vectors.

RUTHENATE. The anion $RuO_4^=$, or a compound containing it.

$$R.CHOH.COOH + H_2O_2 \rightarrow R.CHO + CO_2 + 2H_2O.$$

RULE, HUDSON. See isorotation rule.

RULE, KONOWALOFF. See Konowaloff rule.

RULE, LE CHATELIER. See law of Le Chatelier.

RUTHENIC. Containing or pertaining to tetravalent ruthenium.

RUTHENIOUS. Containing or pertaining to trivalent ruthenium.

RUTHENITE. The anion $RuO_3^=$, or a compound containing it.

RUTHENIUM. Metallic element. Symbol Ru. Atomic number 44. Atomic weight 101.7. Density 12.2. Specific heat 0.061. Melting point 2450° C. Boiling point about 3700° C. Valences (chief) 2, 3, 4, 6, 7 and 8. Oxides, Ru_2O_3, RuO_2, RuO_4. Acids, ruthenic, H_2RuO_4, and perruthenic $HRuO_4$, known in their salts. Ruthenium occurs in platinum ores.

RUTHERFORD ATOM. See **atom, Rutherford.**

RUTHERFORD SOLUTION. A mixture of 20 ml. 9% hydrogen peroxide with 60 ml. glacial acetic acid, used in etching lead and its alloys.

RUZICKA LARGE RING SYNTHESIS. A method of formation of large-ring **alicyclic hydrocarbons,** in the form of their **ketones,** by ring closure on heating of the salts of the proper dicarboxy acids. Ruzicka used salts of metals of the third and fourth groups of the periodic system.

RUZICKA TEST REACTIONS FOR AROMATIC AMINES. A mixture of 1 ml. 3% potassium iodate solution and 1 ml. 10% potassium iodide solution gives a chocolate-brown color with naphthylamine, blue with tolidine and benzidine, and black with *m*-phenylenediamine; no colors with aniline, the toluidines, or xylidines.

RUSTIG TEST REACTION FOR COBALT. On addition of a few sodium thiosulfate crystals to a cobalt solution, followed by a potassium thiocyanate solution, and shaking with ether and alcohol, a deep blue color forms in the ether layer.

RYAZONOV TEST REACTION FOR COBALT. Furfural and a saturated ammonium nitrate solution give a green color with a cobalt nitrate solution.

RYDBERG CONSTANT OR RYDBERG FUNDAMENTAL CONSTANT. A constant used in various fundamental formulas which express the **wave number** of spectral lines in terms of differences of two numerical terms. Thus, for the lines in the various spectra of atomic hydrogen, this

general relationship becomes:

$$\frac{1}{\lambda} = R_H \left(\frac{1}{n_1{}^2} - \frac{1}{n_2{}^2} \right),$$

in which λ is the wave length of a given line, R_H is the Rydberg constant for hydrogen, 109,677.8 cm^{-1}, n_1 is the series term (its value is 1 in the **Lyman series** of spectral lines, 2 in the **Balmer series,** 3 in the **Paschen series,** 4 in the **Brackett series,** and 5 in the **Pfund series**). The term n_2 has various integral values for the lines within a given series.

The relationship applies to other atomic species, such as singly-ionized helium, sodium and potassium atoms, and others which have only one electron in the outer shell. In such cases the value of R_H increases slightly, reaching a magnitude of 109,737 cm^{-1} for elements of higher atomic weight. (See also **Ritz combination principle.**)

RYMSZA TEST REACTION FOR PICRIC ACID. On heating picric acid with potassium cyanide and sodium hydroxide solution, or on evaporating picric acid solution and adding potassium cyanide and ammonium hydroxide, a blood-red color is produced.

S. Symbol for the element **sulfur** (S). Abbreviation for second (s). Abbreviation for solubility (S or s). Abbreviation for **specific surface** (s). Abbreviation for area (S). Abbreviation for **compressibility** (exponential) (s). Abbreviation for **cross section** (s). Symbol for exponent of compressibility of cake (s). Abbreviation for symmetrical (s also *sym*-). Abbreviation for secondary (s or *sec*). Symbol for **action** (S). Symbol for **reciprocal capacitance,** or elastance (S). Symbol for displacement (s). Symbol for **entropy** per atom or molecule (s, s_m), per mole (s, S, S_M), per unit mass (s), total value (S). Symbol for length of arc or path (s). Symbol for **"spin" quantum number** (s), for total "spin" quantum number (S). **Scattering coefficient** (turbidity) (s). **Slip** (electric machinery) (s). See also **sigma.**

SA MICROREACTION FOR COBALT, COPPER, AND ZINC. Characteristic crystals are formed by the reaction of α-aminopyridine and ammonium thiocyanate with cobalt, copper, and zinc.

SA MICROTEST FOR BISMUTH, ANTIMONY, AND GOLD.

A small crystal of sodium bromide and a small crystal of potassium iodide are added to a drop of the acid solution to be tested and then α-aminopyridine is added. Bismuth produces a scarlet precipitate of lamellae and H-formed crystals; antimony an orange precipitate and larger crystals than those with bismuth, while gold produces yellow-red rectangular lamellae and H-formed crystals.

SABANIN-LASKOWSKY TEST REACTION.

A test for citric acid made by heating a little citric acid with ammonia in a sealed glass tube or small flask for several hours at 120° C. The mixture becomes blue or green upon standing exposed to the air.

SABATIER-SENDERENS REACTION.

The reduction of organic compounds by catalytic action of hydrogen in the vapor phase. The usual catalysts are finely-divided metals.

SABATIER-SENDERENS TEST.

A test for primary, secondary, and tertiary alcohols made by passing the vapors of the alcohol over finely divided copper heated to 300° C. Primary alcohols are decomposed into aldehydes and hydrogen; secondary into ketones and hydrogen, and tertiary into unsaturated hydrocarbons and water.

SABETAY REAGENT FOR DETECTING UNSATURATION.

A solution of 30 g. antimony chloride in 70 g. chloroform used in detecting unsaturation in organic substances. Many unsaturated compounds, chiefly those having double bonds, give characteristic color reactions.

SACCARDI TEST REAGENT.

A two-solution reagent, consisting of (1) a solution of 5 g. lead soap in 100 ml. benzene, and (2) a 30% alcoholic solution of potassium hydroxide. It is used in detecting sulfur oils in oil. A black precipitate on boiling is given by sulfur oils.

SACCHARIFY.

To convert into or impregnate with sugar or a sugar, especially to convert starches into maltose, as in the malting of grains.

SACCHARIMETER.

(1) A **polariscope** graduated to read directly in percentage of sugar (saccharose). (2) A **fermentation tube** designed to indicate the amount of sugar in a given sample by measuring the volume of carbon dioxide evolved by its fermentation.

SACHSSE SOLUTION.

An aqueous solution of 1.8 g. mercuric iodide, 2.5 g. potassium iodide, and 8 g. potassium hydroxide, diluted to a total volume of 100 ml. It is used in detecting and estimating glucose, which reduces it on boiling.

SACKUR-TETRODE EQUATION.

An equation giving the translational entropy of an ideal gas. With certain simplifying approximations, it becomes:

$$S_{tr} = R \left[\ln \frac{(2\pi mkT)^{3/2}}{h^3 N} V + \frac{5}{2} \right]$$

in which S_{tr} is the translational **entropy** of one mole of gas, R is the **gas constant,** m is the **molecular mass,** k is the **Boltzmann constant,** T is the absolute temperature, h is Planck's constant, N is the Avogadro number, and V is the molecular volume.

SAH-CHANG-LEI TEST REAGENT.

The compound, p-bromophenylisothiocyanate, used as a test reagent for aromatic amines. It condenses with aromatic amines to form substituted thioureas which have characteristic melting points.

SAH-LEI REAGENTS.

p-Tolylhydrazine and p-chlorophenylhydrazine, which are used to produce compounds of definite melting points with aldehydes and ketones.

SAHLI REAGENT.

A mixture of a 48% aqueous solution of potassium iodide, with an equal volume of an 8% aqueous solution of potassium iodate, used in determining free hydrochloric acid in stomach contents. The reagent is reduced by the hydrochloric acid, which can be determined by **titration** of the free iodine formed.

SAH-MA REAGENT FOR ALCOHOLS.
1-Nitroanthraquinone-2-carboxylic acid, which condenses with alcohols to form crystalline solids having definite melting points.

SAH-MA REAGENT FOR ORGANIC HALOGENS. Potassium-3-nitrophthalimide, which produces well-crystallized derivatives with sharp melting points on refluxing with the organic halide.

SAH-MA REAGENT FOR PHENOLS. The compound, 3,5-dinitrobenzazide. In boiling toluene, it forms with phenols 3,5-dinitrophenylurethans having definite melting points.

SAINT CLAIR-BLUE PROCESS. Molten zinc is used to treat a crude aluminum-silicon alloy, in order to dissolve the aluminum. The molten aluminum-zinc is filtered through crushed basalt, and the zinc removed by distillation.

SAINT PFAU-PLATTNER AZULENE SYNTHESIS. A method of formation of azulenes, starting from indanes and using diazoacetic ester.

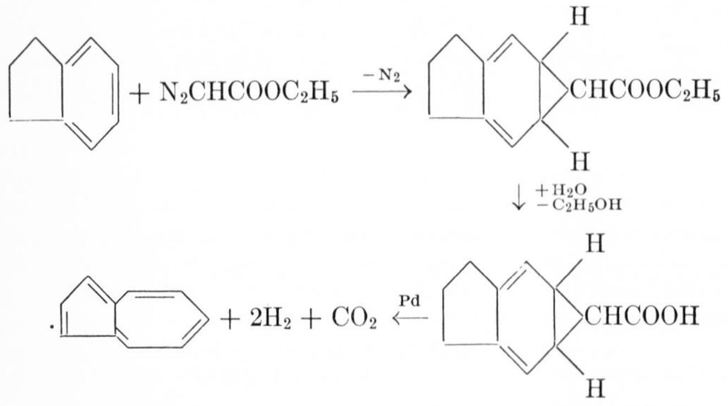

SALICYLATE. The radical

$$C_6H_4(OH)(COO—)$$

(ortho), or a compound containing it.

SALICYLIC. Related to salicylic acid,

$$HO.C_6H_4.COOH.$$

SALICYLIDENE. The radical

$$HOC_6H_4CH= (o).$$

SALICYLOYL. The radical

$$HOC_6H_4CO— (o).$$

SALIFY. To convert into a **salt,** as to salify a base. Substances which can react to form salts are termed salifiable, and the process is known as salification.

SALIMETER OR SALINIMETER. A type of **hydrometer** graduated to read the specific gravity of salt solutions.

SALINE. Of, pertaining to, or containing, a **salt.** Of the nature of a salt; salty, as saline substances, saline springs, etc.

SALINE SOLUTION. In general, a solution of a **salt,** commonly an aqueous solu-

SAL. A prefix that indicates a **salt,** as in sal ammoniac.

SALIC. Containing a substantial proportion of aluminum or, more commonly, aluminum oxide.

SALICYL. See o-hydroxyphenyl or o-hydroxybenzyl.

tion, and in many cases the meaning is restricted to an aqueous solution of sodium chloride.

SALINIMETER. See **salimeter.**

SALINOMETER. An apparatus which determines the electrical **conductivity** of a solution, originally a salt solution. This apparatus may be actuated by the conductivity to control the **concentration** or **pH** of the solution.

SALT. A compound formed by replacement of the hydrogen of an **acid** by an element or a radical which is essentially inorganic. Alkaloids, amines, pyridines, and other basic organic substances may be regarded as substituted ammonias in this connection. The halogen derivatives of **hydrocarbon** radicals and **esters** are not regarded as salts in the strict definition of the term.

SALT, ACID. A **salt** in which all the replaceable hydrogen of the acid has not been substituted by a radical or element. These salts, in ionizing, yield hydrogen ions and react like the acids. E.g., $NaHSO_4$, $KHCO_3$, Na_2HPO_4.

SALT, AMPHID. (Obs.) An old term for an oxy salt regarded as formed from two oxides, one of which is acid and the other basic, e.g., $K_2O.SO_3$ for K_2SO_4.

SALT, AMPHOTERIC. A **salt** which may ionize in solution either as an **acid** or a **base,** and react either with bases or acids, according to the conditions.

SALT, AMPHIPROTIC. The same as **salt, amphoteric.**

SALT, BASIC. A **salt** which contains combined **base** as $Pb(OH)_2.Pb(C_2H_3O_2)_2$, a basic acetate of lead. These salts may be regarded as formed from basic hydroxides by partial replacement of hydroxyl, e.g., $HO—Zn—Cl$. They react like bases and, when soluble, ionize to yield hydroxyl ions.

SALT, BINARY. A term used either as a synonym for a **double salt** or else for a salt consisting of two metal atoms, or other positive atoms or radicals, and one negative atom or radical.

SALT BRIDGE. A type of liquid junction used to connect electrically two electrolytic solutions. It consists commonly of a U-tube filled with a strong salt solution, and provided with porous plugs. It is used for such purposes as to connect electrolytic

half cells in making measurements of **electrode potential.**

SALT, COMPLEX. A saline compound formed by the combination of two or more salts and which is regarded as the normal salt of a complex acid. Complex salts do not split into a mixture of the constituent salts in solution but furnish a complex ion which contains one of the bases, e.g., potassium ferrocyanide, and potassium platinochloride.

SALT, CONNATE. A **salt** originally deposited by water left in the pores of sedimentary rocks that were laid down, during the geological process by which they were formed, in seas or lakes.

SALT, DOUBLE. Two simple **salts** that crystallize together in definite proportions but exist independently in solution (distinction from complex salts). The alums are representative double salts.

SALT EFFECT. (1) The tendency of ions of a strong **electrolyte** to increase the **degree of ionization** of a solution of a weak electrolyte, provided the ions of the strong electrolyte are not the same as those formed by the weak electrolyte.

(2) In regard to the kinetics of ionic reactions, and especially their catalysis, there are two types of salt effect, primary and secondary. The primary salt effect is the influence of concentration of the electrolyte on **activity coefficients** of reactions. The secondary salt effect refers to the change in the concentration of the reacting ions brought about by the addition of electrolytes, and derives from the definition (1).

SALT, HYDROXY. A salt containing one or more **hydroxyl radicals,** which may be considered to be derived from a poly-hydroxyl base, in which one or more of the hydroxyl groups have not been neutralized.

SALT, INNER COMPLEX. A member of a special class of **internal salts** in which an acid group and a neutral group coordinate with metals to form a cyclic complex. These salts occur widely in analytical chemistry, where they are formed between metallic ions and organic reagents, in dyestuffs, in life processes (chlorophyll and hematin belong to this class of compounds), and in many other fields.

SALT, INTERNAL. A compound in which the acidic or basic groups which react to produce the salt linkage (which may or may not entail the formation of water), are in the same molecule. This particular salt linkage may consist of a **polar** or a **nonpolar bond.**

SALT, MIXED. A **salt** of a polybasic acid, in which the hydrogen atoms are replaced by different metallic atoms or positive radicals.

SALT, NEUTRAL. A **salt** that has neither an acid nor a basic reaction in solution, understood to be an aqueous solution.

SALT, NORMAL. A **salt** in the formation of which the acid has been exactly neutralized by the base, as KCl, Na_2CO_3, $BaSO_4$, as distinguished from an acid salt, such as $NaHSO_4$ or a basic salt, such as $Pb(OH)_2.Pb(C_2H_3O_2)_2$.

SALT, OXY. A **salt** of an oxygen-containing acid, as $KClO_3$.

SALT PAIR, RECIPROCAL. See **reciprocal salt pair.**

SALT, PER. (Obs.) A **salt** supposed to be derived from a peroxide base.

SALT, PSEUDO. A compound which has some of the normal characteristics of a **salt,** but lacks certain others, notably the **ionic lattice** in the solid state, and the property of ionizing completely in solution. The absence of these properties is due to the fact that the **bonds** between the metallic and nonmetallic radicals are covalent or semi-covalent, instead of polar. Because these salts do not ionize completely, they are also called weak salts.

SALT, WEAK. See **salt, pseudo.**

SALTING OUT. Precipitating a substance from solution by adding a soluble salt in the presence of which the substance is insoluble or much less soluble. **Soaps**

are precipitated from aqueous solution by sodium chloride; many **dyestuffs** are insoluble in saline solutions and may be salted out; **proteins** may be separated by taking advantage of their varying solubility in saturated and partly saturated solutions of ammonium sulfate, sodium chloride, magnesium sulfate, and in pure water.

SALVADORI SOLUTION. A 20% solution of ammonium perchlorate in ammonium hydroxide, used as a test reagent for cadmium, which gives a crystalline precipitate.

SALZER TEST FOR PARAFFIN. A test for paraffin in fatty oils made by mixing 87 parts phenol and 13 parts water and adding an equal volume of olive oil, which will be dissolved. Any paraffin, however, will remain undissolved.

SAMARIC. Containing or pertaining to trivalent **samarium.**

SAMARIUM. Rare earth metallic element. Symbol Sm. Atomic number 62. Atomic weight 150.43. Density 7.7–7.8. Melting point values given range from 1300–1400° C. Valence 2 and 3. Oxide, Sm_2O_3. Samarium occurs in samarskite and other minerals.

SAMAROUS. Containing or pertaining to bivalent **samarium.**

SANCHEZ REAGENT FOR IRON. The compound, pyridine, which precipitates ferric salts, but not manganese salts.

SANCHEZ TEST FOR DIFFERENTIATING AMMONIUM SALTS, AMINES, AND AMIDES. An aqueous solution of an ammonium salt containing potassium iodide, added to a hypochlorite solution, darkens the solution and then nitrogen iodide, NI_3 precipitates. If an amide is used instead of an ammonium salt, the liquid merely turns yellow from free iodine dissolved by potassium iodide. If an amine is used, a yellow, red, or brown precipitate of varying composition is formed.

SANCHEZ TEST REACTION FOR ALDEHYDES. A solution of 0.5 g. piperazine in 10 ml. of 1% sodium nitroprusside solution produces a blue color with aldehydes.

SANCHEZ TEST REACTIONS FOR ALKALOIDS DERIVED FROM MORPHINE AND FOR EUCODAL. The reagent is made by dissolving 0.1 g. dimethylaminobenzaldehyde in 20 ml. of alcohol and 4 drops of sulfuric acid. The alkaloid to be tested is evaporated with 10 drops of the reagent. A red-violet residue, soluble in water and alcohol without any color, is given by morphine, codeine, ethylmorphine, and benzylmorphine. A red residue, soluble in water with a yellow color, is given by dilaudid, dicodid, and eucodal.

SANCHEZ TEST REACTION FOR PRIMARY CYCLIC AMINES. All compounds containing an amino group attached directly to the benzene ring, regardless of the other substituted groups, when treated with a saturated aqueous solution of furfural slightly acidified with acetic acid, produce immediately or after adding hydrochloric acid, a red, orange or purple color. Arsenic or antimony in the compound do not interfere; but if the amino group is on the carbon of the side chain, no color is produced.

SAND BATH. A mass of ordinary, coarse sand in an iron bowl, which is used to secure even, regulated heating. The vessel which contains the material to be heated is placed in the sand bath. The direct heat is applied to the sand bath, which transmits it evenly to the reaction vessel.

SANDELL-WISHNICK REAGENT. A solution of 1.0 g. β-naphthoquinoline in 100 g. 0.1 N sulfuric acid, to which enough 5% aqueous solution of potassium thiocyanate is added to produce a slight turbidity. This solution is used as a test reagent for zinc, which it precipitates.

SANDMEYER DIAZO REACTION. The preparation of halogen-substituted aromatic compounds from the corresponding diazonium compounds by treatment with cuprous salts and the appropriate halogen acid.

$$C_6H_5N_2Cl \xrightarrow[\text{HCl}]{\text{CuCl}} C_6H_5Cl + N_2.$$

Similarly, treatment with KCN and the cuprous salt yields the nitrile. See also **Gatterman reaction** and **Körner-Contardi reaction.**

SANDMEYER ISATIN SYNTHESIS. Methods of formation of isatin derivatives by ring closure of thioamides or isonitrosodiphenylamidines. The starting materials of this synthesis are aniline (or other arylamine) and carbon disulfide, or aniline and chloral hydrate.

SANIN REAGENT. A solution of 40 g. sodium acetate, 20 g. sodium chloride, 5 g. sodium bitartrate, and 20 g. potassium antimonyl tartrate in 100 ml. water, used as a precipitant for tannic acid.

SAPIPHORES. Atomic groups which bear to taste the same relation that an harmonic chord does to hearing. Substances which contain these groups are sweet.

SAPO-. (Latin, soap) Relating to soap, soap bark, or saponin, as sapogenin, sapotoxin.

SAPONIFICATION. The hydrolysis of an **ester** by an alkali so that a free alcohol and a compound of the ester acid portion result. The term was formerly restricted to the alkaline hydrolysis of fats whereby a soap is formed, but has been extended to include a variety of hydrolyses, even those of alkyl esters of inorganic acids and hydrolysis by superheated steam. A characteristic case of saponification is the action of caustic soda on tristearin:

$$C_3H_5(OOC\text{---}C_{17}H_{35})_3 + 3NaOH \rightarrow C_3H_5(OH)_3 + 3NaOOC\text{---}C_{17}H_{35}.$$

tristearin   glycerol   sodium stearate

SAPONIFICATION EQUIVALENT. The number of grams of a **fat** that would be saponified by 1 liter of normal alkali. It may be calculated from the **saponification number:** Saponification equivalent = 56108/ saponification number.

SAPONIFICATION NUMBER. (Koettstorfer number) The number of milligrams of potassium hydroxide consumed in the complete saponification of 1 gram of a **fat** or **wax.** A constant of a fat or wax.

SAPONIN. One of a class of glycosidal substances of high molecular weight characterized by (1) solubility in water and slight solubility in cold alcohol; (2) a persistent foaming of their aqueous solutions; (3) giving a greenish coloration with ferric chloride in the presence of alcoholic sulfuric acid; (4) production of strong irritation of mucous membranes; (5) producing hemolysis in the blood stream. They occur naturally in plants, e.g., *Quillaja saponaria.*

SARATA TEST REACTION. A test for copper made by adding *m*-benzaminosemicarbazide (cryogenine) to an aqueous solution of a cupric salt. A red color is produced; with concentrated copper solutions a precipitate is given.

SARGENT CURVES. Graphs obtained by plotting, for various β-particle-emitting radioelements, the logarithms of their **radioactive decay constants** against the corresponding values of the logarithms of their maximum β-particle energies. For the naturally-radioactive elements, most of the points fall on two roughly-parallel straight lines called, as stated above, Sargent curves; calculations using the artificial radioelements indicate the existence of other Sargent curves.

SARGENT RULE. An inverse proportionality between the **half-period** of a natural radioactive element and the fifth power of its maximum energy of β-radiation. It holds for many elements and can be extended to others by use of another proportionality constant.

SARVER REAGENT. The compound 2-nitro-1-naphthol-4-sulfonic acid, used as a reagent for cobalt, copper, and ferrous iron. Beautiful red, orange, and green color reactions are given with cobalt, copper, and ferrous iron, respectively.

SATURABLE. Capable of being saturated.

SATURATE. (1) To dissolve in a solvent all of a solute which the solvent can absorb, under equilibrium conditions, at the given temperature. (2) To dissolve under conditions as in (1) a gas in a solution of some compound which combines with it, as to saturate aqueous sodium hydroxide with hydrogen sulfide. (3) To cause a reaction to take place whereby one compound is completely converted into a product, as to saturate an acid with a base. (4) To neutralize. (5) To reduce completely an unsaturated compound, as to convert acetylene into ethane. The saturating agent may be called the saturant. The process is termed saturation.

SATURATED COMPOUND. An organic compound in which each carbon **valency** is combined with a distinct atom, except that double- or polylinkages between carbon and certain other elements (particularly nitrogen) do not cause unsaturation. If a carbon compound cannot be made to add hydrogen without splitting, it may be regarded as saturated.

SATURATED HYDROCARBON. A name applied to the paraffin **hydrocarbons,** although any hydrocarbon that does not contain a double or triple bond is saturated.

SATURATED SOLUTION. A solution containing the maximum proportion of solute to solvent at that temperature under equilibrium conditions; in other words, a solution that does not change in concentration when brought into contact with an excess of the undissolved solute.

SATURATED SOLUTION, INCONGRUENT. A solution of two or more components, which is unsaturated with respect to one solid phase present, and saturated with respect to a second solid phase present, with the added circumstance that there is a component in common to all three phases (i.e., the solution and the two solid phases). As the solution becomes more concentrated, one solid phase enters into solution, while the second solid phase (e.g., a double salt) separates from solution.

SATURATION. The condition of being saturated (see **saturate**).

SATURATION CURRENT. The maximum current that will pass through a gas under definite conditions of **ionization.** It is a measure of the charge carried by the ions produced in each second and hence may be used as a measure of the radioactivity of a substance.

SAUL-CRAWFORD TEST. A test and method for the separation of traces of copper in aqueous solutions made by dissolving 0.1% of the potassium salt of 8-hydroxyquinoline-5-sulfonic acid in the solution and permitting it to stand overnight. A yellowish precipitate of the copper salt, composed of flocculent masses of bundles of delicate needles, separates. This precipitate is soluble in dilute hydrochloric acid.

SAUL TEST REACTION FOR GOLD. A test for gold made by adding 1 volume of a 0.1% solution of p-phenylenediamine hydrochloride to 10 volumes of a solution containing 0.0005% gold trichloride. Due to the formation of colloidal gold, a distinct yellowish-green color appears.

SAUVEUR REAGENT. A mixture of 10 ml. concentrated hydrochloric acid, 20 ml. concentrated sulfuric acid, and 30 ml. water, used hot for etching metals.

SAVALLE TEST. A test for fusel oil in alcohol made by boiling together equal amounts of the sample and sulfuric acid. If a brown color develops, fusel oil is present.

SAYBOLT VISCOSIMETER. See **viscosimeter.**

SAYTZEFF RULE. A means of predicting the structure of the olefin formed on removal of the elements of water, or hydrogen halide, from a secondary or tertiary alkyl alcohol, or halide. The rule states that the hydrogen atom to be eliminated comes preferably from the carbon atom which has the least number of hydrogen atoms.

$$CH_3.CH_2.CHBr.CH_3 \rightarrow CH_3.CH:CH.CH_3 + HBr.$$

SAZERAC-POUZERGUES TESTS. Tests for bismuth. (1) Add several drops of nitric acid or sulfuric acid to a 2% aqueous solution of o-hydroxyquinoline. When the test is made, mix this solution with an equal volume of a 4% potassium iodide solution and pour this reagent into the solution to be tested. A flocculent orange precipitate indicates the presence of bismuth. (2) Shake 0.2 ml. of 2% aqueous solution of o-hydroxyquinoline and 1.5 ml. of a mixture of 2 volumes acetone and 1 volume amyl acetate with 2 ml. of the solution to be tested. A red-orange or red-violet color indicates the presence of bismuth.

Sb Symbol for the element **antimony.**

Sc Symbol for the element **scandium.**

SCALE. (1) A balance used for weighing; (2) a series of markings at regular intervals which are used for measurement or computation; (3) an incrustation, as of salts accumulated in a boiler, or of oxides on the surface of a metal.

SCALE, PENFIELD. See **Penfield scale.**

SCALE, VON KOBELL. See **Von Kobell scale.**

SCALPER. A coarse screen used to protect fine screens, especially from abnormally large particles.

SCANDIUM. Metallic element. Symbol Sc. Atomic number 21. Atomic weight 44.96. Melting point 1200° C. Valence 3. Oxide Sc_2O_3. Scandium occurs in euxenite and other minerals.

SCATTERING. In its general sense, this term means causing the random distribution of a group of entities, or bringing about a less orderly arrangement, either in position or direction. This type of process occurs very commonly in the case of radiations, that are scattered by encountering irregular surfaces or groups of particles, which cause mechanical scattering. The term has also been extended to include cases in which radiations encounter particles that contain vibrating systems (such as electrons) which are capable of reacting directly to the radiations, as by absorbing and re-radiating part or all of their energy, and not emitting a fundamental particle (e.g., an electron, neutron, or proton).

SCATTERING FACTOR. See **atomic scattering factor.**

SCAVENGER. A substance added to remove impurities, or to overcome the undesirable effects of one or more of the substances contained in a mixture. Vanadium is a well-known scavenger for steel, being added to remove nitrogen.

SCHACK TEST REACTION. A test for oil of peppermint which is based on the **Flückiger reaction** (q.v.). Add a sample of the material to be tested to fused salicylic acid. In the presence of oil of peppermint, a blue-green mass is immediately produced which, when dissolved in alcohol, is blood-red by reflected light but blue by transmitted light.

SCHAEFER TEST FOR OTHER CINCHONA ALKALOIDS IN QUININE SULFATE. In 60 ml. boiling water, dissolve 2 g. quinine sulfate, add a solution of 0.5 g. neutral potassium oxalate in 5 ml. water and make up the mixture with water to 67.5 g. Cool to 20° C., keep at this temperature for a half hour and shake frequently. Filter and add sodium hydroxide to the filtrate. A precipitate forms if the quinine sulfate contains more than 1% cinchonidine.

SCHAEFFER TEST FOR OTHER COCA ALKALOIDS IN COCAINE. In 20 ml. of water, dissolve 0.05 g of the cocaine salt, cool to 15° C. Add 5 ml. of 10% hydrochloric acid and 5 ml. of a 3% aqueous solution of chromic acid. The solution remains clear if the cocaine is pure but the more foreign coca bases that are present, the more pronounced is the resulting turbidity.

SCHAER REAGENT. A saturated alcoholic or aqueous solution of chloral hydrate, used as an extraction medium for investigation of alkaloids, resins, etc.

SCHAER TEST FOR BLOOD. Moisten the sample with glacial acetic acid and treat with a concentrated solution of chloral hydrate. Add guaiacol to a small portion of the extract and follow by adding hydrogen peroxide. A blue color indicates the presence of blood.

SCHAERGES TEST REACTION. A test for cocaine made by dissolving about 30 mg. of cocaine in a drop of water and a drop of sulfuric acid and adding a drop of potassium dichromate or chromate solution. A precipitate is formed which rapidly disappears. The yellowish-red liquid turns green when warmed and gives off fumes of benzoic acid on stronger heating.

SCHAPRINGER TEST FOR LIGNIN IN PAPER. This test is made by mixing 2 drops of aniline and a few drops of dilute sulfuric acid, and applying to the paper to be tested, which is colored yellow if it contains lignin.

SCHAPRINGER TEST FOR SHELLAC IN VARNISH. Add an excess of hydrochloric acid or of acetic acid to an alcoholic solution of the varnish and heat the liquid until the resin has formed a mass with a clear solution above it. Filter and add ammonia in excess to the filtrate. A red-violet color indicates the presence of shellac.

SCHAUDINN FLUID. A mixture of 20 ml. of a saturated aqueous solution of mercuric chloride, with 10 ml. alcohol, used as a fixative.

SCHEIBLER TEST. A test for alkaloids made by mixing 1 part of 25% phosphoric acid and 2 parts of 25% sodium tungstate solution, and adding this reagent to the solution to be tested. Precipitates are obtained if alkaloids (or albumin) are present.

SCHEMJAKIN-BELOKON MICRO-REACTIONS.
Micro-reactions for vanadates and molybdates. (1) With an alkaline solution of a vanadate, a saturated alcoholic solution of 1-nitroso-β-naphthol gives a dark green precipitate, with a solution acidified with hydrochloric acid, a brownish-red precipitate, and with a neutral solution, there is no precipitation. (2) With an acid solution of a molybdate, solutions of 1-nitroso-β-naphthol in acetic acid or alcohol form a red precipitate. If the test is made by "spotting" the reagent and the solution to be tested on paper, four rings, (inner) orange, lilac, yellow, and blue, may appear.

SCHEMJAKIN TEST REACTIONS.
Tests for rare earths as follows: (1) Cerium forms a dark or chocolate precipitate with a solution of morphine hydrochloride in aqueous ammonia. (2) Ceric ions form a stable pink color with a brucine solution in acetic acid. (3) Ceric ions form a dark brown precipitate in alkaline medium with a brucine solution. Cerous, lanthanum, and thorium ions form gelatinous precipitates.

SCHENK-BURMEISTER TEST.
A test for benzaldehyde or cinnamic acid. With phenol and sulfuric acid, traces of benzaldehyde produce a quince-yellow color. To test for cinnamic acid, the acid is first converted into benzaldehyde by alkaline permanganate solution.

SCHENK TEST FOR COPPER.
Add 1 drop of alkaline Rochelle salt solution (see **Fehling solution**) and 4–5 granules of glucose to 10 ml. of the solution to be tested and heat the mixture for 2–3 minutes in the boiling water bath. A precipitation of red cuprous oxide indicates the presence of copper. If the solution to be tested is acid, first add Rochelle salt solution until neutralization is nearly complete.

SCHERBATSCHEW TEST.
A test for silk and artificial silk made by boiling the sample with a 5% solution of mercurous and mercuric nitrate. True silk is colored rose, while a cellulose silk remains uncolored.

SCHERINGA TEST REACTION FOR NEOARSPHENAMINE.
A violet color is produced upon the addition of a concentrated ammonium persulfate solution to a 1:1000 aqueous solution of neoarsphenamine.

SCHEWKET TEST FOR GALLIC AND TANNIC ACIDS IN PLANT POWDERS.
Extract 3 g. of the sample with water, precipitate with 40 ml. of a solution of 10 g. zinc oxide dissolved in acetic acid to which 80 ml. of ammonia and enough water were added to make 1 liter. Suspend the precipitate in water and add 1–3 drops of sulfuric acid, then filter. Add 0.5 g. sodium acetate to the filtrate, then 1% iodine-potassium iodide solution until the color becomes orange-red, then dilute with 200 ml. of 0.5% sodium acetate solution. A red-violet color indicates the presence of gallic or tannic acid.

SCHEWKET TEST REACTION FOR DI- AND TRI-PHENOLS.
This test is made by adding a few drops of 1% iodine-potassium iodide solution to 1 ml. of the phenol solution, diluting with water and adding a few drops of 5% sodium hydroxide solution. Pyrocatechol (a diphenol) produces a green color which changes to brown when warmed, and back to green when shaken with a few drops of hydrogen peroxide. The return to green differentiates it from hydroquinone and resorcinol. Pyrogallol (a tri-phenol) produces a transitory blue-violet or red-violet color. Phloroglucinol produces a light brown color.

SCHEWKET TEST REACTION FOR LEAD.
Add sodium hydroxide to a 1% lead salt solution until the precipitate dissolves. Float on this solution 1–5 drops of 1% gallic acid solution, avoiding all motion. Two color zones form—one a green and the other a carmine-red. The liquid becomes carmine-red when mixed and, on adding 1–4 ml. gallic acid solution, a green color is produced.

SCHIEMANN REACTION.
A method of preparation of aryl fluorides by the reaction

of arylamines with nitrous and fluoboric acids, forming diazonium fluoborates, which decompose on heating to give the aryl fluorides.

been decolorized by sulfurous acid; the addition of these reagents to the solution containing aldehydes causes the color of the dye to reappear. Fuchsin, rosaniline,

$$Ar.NH_2 + HNO_2 + HBF_4 \rightarrow Ar.N_2BF_4 + 2H_2O$$

$$Ar.N_2BF_4 \xrightarrow{\Delta} ArF + N_2 + BF_3.$$

SCHIFF BASES. Compounds formed by the condensation of an **amine** and an **aldehyde,** with loss of water, and the formation of a double bond between the carbon atom of the aldehyde group and the nitrogen atom of the amine. Commonly, aromatic amines and aliphatic aldehydes are used in preparing Schiff bases, but there are also well-known cases in which both the reacting molecules are aromatic, as in the case of the benzylidene anilines,

and magenta are among the dyes used for this purpose.

SCHIFF TEST SOLUTION FOR ALLANTOIN OR UREA. A solution of furfural in hydrochloric acid, used to test for urea or allantoin with which it gives a yellow color, changing to violet.

SCHIFF TEST SOLUTION FOR HYDROGEN PEROXIDE. A titanium sul-

$$C_6H_5CHO + H_2NC_6H_5 \rightarrow C_6H_5CH{:}NC_6H_5 + H_2O.$$

SCHIFF TEST REACTION FOR CARBOHYDRATES. Mix equal parts of glacial acetic acid and xylidine in a little alcohol and saturate strips of paper with this mixture. Heat the sample with hydrochloric acid or sulfuric acid and expose the strips to the vapors. A red color indicates the presence of carbohydrates.

SCHIFF TEST REACTIONS FOR CHOLESTEROL. (1) With cholesterol, concentrated sulfuric acid and iodine produce a green color.

(2) A solution of cholesterol in concentrated sulfuric acid is colored red by ammonia.

(3) Cholesterol produces a red color when boiled with hydrochloric acid and ferric chloride.

(4) On evaporating cholesterol with nitric acid, the residue obtained is colored red by ammonia.

SCHIFF TEST REACTION FOR CHROMATE. With a 1:100 solution of guaiac in dilute alcohol, a solution of chromic acid or chromates weakly acidified with sulfuric acid produces an intense color.

SCHIFF TEST REAGENTS FOR ALDEHYDES. Various dyes which have

fate solution prepared by boiling titanium oxide with concentrated sulfuric acid, precipitating with ammonium hydroxide, and redissolving the precipitate in dilute sulfuric acid; it is used in testing for hydrogen peroxide, which gives a yellow color with it.

SCHINDELMEISER TEST REACTION. A test for nicotine made by adding 1 drop of 30% formaldehyde, free from formic acid, to the sample and then 1 drop of concentrated nitric acid. A rose to red color indicates the presence of nicotine. Coniine give no reaction.

SCHIRM REAGENT. A reagent for determining zinc, manganese, cobalt, nickel, copper, and cadmium. This reagent is prepared by dissolving 17 g. trimethylphenyl ammonium carbonate and 3 g. triethyl phenylammoniun iodide in 80 g. water.

SCHLAGDENHAUFFEN SOLUTION FOR ALKALOIDS. A mixture of 50 ml. of a saturated aqueous solution of mercuric chloride, with 50 ml. of a 3% alcoholic solution of guaiac, used in testing for alkaloids. A blue color is produced by many alkaloids.

SCHLAGDENHAUFFEN TEST. A test for magnesium in which the reagent is a gold-yellow solution of iodine in 2% sodium hydroxide solution, preferably freshly prepared. With magnesium salt solutions, brown-red precipitates are formed.

SCHLICKUM TEST FOR ARSENIC. Dissolve 0.2–0.4 g. stannous chloride in 3–4 ml. hydrochloric acid (sp. gr. 1.124) and add 0.01 g. sodium sulfide. Float the sample to be tested on this solution. Arsenious acid forms a yellow ring at the contact surfaces.

SCHLICKUM TEST FOR OTHER CINCHONA ALKALOIDS IN QUININE SULFATE. Add 0.5 g. quinine sulfate to 10 ml. water, bring to a boil, and add 0.15 g. powdered potassium chromate. Shake well, stir frequently for at least 4 hours, then filter, and to the filtrate add 1 drop of sodium hydroxide solution. No precipitate should form within 1 hour; a flocculent precipitate is produced with 0.5% cinchonine sulfate or with 1% quinidine or cinchonidine sulfate.

SCHLITTLER-MÜLLER REACTION. A method of formation of isoquinolines by condensing benzylamines with glyoxal semiacetal, followed by ring closure in the presence of acid.

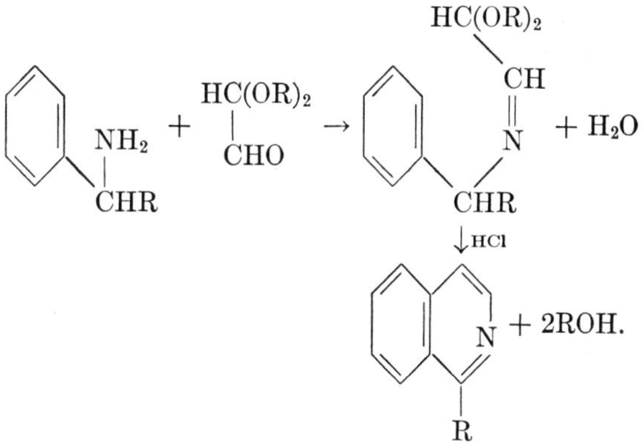

SCHLOSS REAGENT. A solution of 0.2 g. indole in 100 ml. water, used for testing for glyoxalic acid in urine. A red ring, formed with concentrated sulfuric acid under test conditions, indicates the presence of glyoxalic acid.

SCHLOSSBERGER TEST. A test for differentiating silk, wool, and cotton fibers made by adding the sample to a freshly precipitated solution of nickelous hydroxide in concentrated ammonia. Silk fibers are dissolved but not wool or cotton.

SCHLOTTERBECK REACTION. A reaction between diazoparaffins and aldehydes which results in the replacement of the aldehyde hydrogen atom by an alkyl group

$$RCHO + N_2CHR' \rightarrow RCOCH_2R' + N_2.$$

This reaction is most successful with the diazo derivatives of the lower paraffins, especially diazomethane.

SCHMATOLLA REACTION FOR TIN. Moisten a sample of the substance to be tested with hydrochloric acid and bring into the nonluminous Bunsen flame. If the latter becomes colored bluish-white, the test indicates the presence of tin.

See also **Pomeranz-Fritsch reaction.**

SCHLOSING TEST. A test for potassium made with perchloric acid and fairly strong solutions of potassium salts. A crystalline precipitate is formed.

SCHMATOLLA TEST FOR BENZOIC ACID. This test is a modification of the Jonescu test. At room temperature, add 5 ml. of hydrogen peroxide to 20 ml. of the sample to be tested, then add several drops of a solution of 5 g. ferrous sulfate and 5 g.

boric acid in 100 ml. of water. A blue color indicates the presence of benzoic acid. Hippuric acid gives the same reaction but the benzoic acid can be separated from it by shaking out with petroleum benzine.

SCHMATOLLA TEST FOR HYDROGEN PEROXIDE IN WATER. Add 5–10 drops of dilute sulfuric acid and 5–8 drops of 1% cobalt nitrate solution to 200 ml. of the sample to be tested, then add potassium hydroxide solution by drops. A distinct brown color indicates the presence of hydrogen peroxide.

SCHMIDLIN KETENE SYNTHESIS. Direct formation of ketene by decomposition of acetone vapor.

$$CH_3COCH_3 \xrightarrow{550° C.} CH_2{=}C{=}O + CH_4.$$

SCHMIDLIN-MASSINI TEST REACTION. A test for permonophosphoric acid, made by adding a dilute manganese sulfate solution to the acid. A pale violet color is produced slowly in the cold solution and rapidly when heated, if permonophosphoric acid is present.

SCHMIDT-HINDERER TEST FOR METALS. A test for zinc, cadmium, and copper, made by adding the sample to be tested to an aqueous solution of 2,7-diaminofluorene. White precipitates form with zinc and cadmium, and a blue precipitate and a blue-green solution with copper.

SCHMIDT-LUMPP REAGENT. A reagent for nitrate which is made by dissolving 0.1 g. di-(9,10-monohydroxyphenanthryl)amine in 1000 ml. concentrated sulfuric acid. The blue reagent is changed to blue-red and to wine-red by nitric acid, nitrates or their solutions in concentrated sulfuric acid.

SCHMIDT REACTION. A reaction between hydrazoic acid and carbonyl compounds that is catalyzed by mineral acids. The products depend upon the carbonyl compounds used; thus, **aldehydes** yield **nitriles, ketones** yield **amides, acids** yield **amines** (by loss of CO_2), and with excess hydrazoic acid, ring formation takes place

to yield compounds with several nitrogen atoms in the ring.

SCHMIDT TEST FOR EPHEDRINE. An aqueous solution of ephedrine, treated with sodium hydroxide solution and potassium ferricyanide solution, produces the odor of benzaldehyde at once.

SCHMIDT TEST REACTIONS FOR GELATIN. (1) Add ammonium molybdate solution to the sample. A white flocculent precipitate indicates the presence of gelatin. The precipitate dissolves partially on warming and reappears on cooling.
(2) Acidify some **Nessler reagent** with sulfuric acid and filter. This reagent produces a white precipitate, which dissolves in alkalies, if gelatin is present in the sample.

SCHMIEDEL PROCESS. A variation of the **chamber process** for the manufacture of sulfuric acid, in which nitrosylsulfuric acid is sprayed into the sulfur dioxide gases.

SCHMIEDEL TEST. A test for methanol which is based on the oxidation of methanol in alkaline solution with 30% hydrogen peroxide. The resulting formic acid is detected or determined by its reducing action on mercuric chloride.

SCHMIZ TEST. A test for ammonia or alkali made by mixing 1 ml. cupric sulfate solution with 1 ml. of 3% hydrogen peroxide and floating 0.5 ml. of the sample to be tested on the mixture. If ammonia or alkali is present, a brown-black precipitate forms; with weaker concentrations of ammonia or alkali (such as 0.001% or less), a yellow color appears.

SCHMOLUCHOWSKI EQUATION. See **equation, Schmoluchowski.**

SCHNEIDER ACETO-CARMINE SOLUTION. A saturated solution of carmine in 45% acetic acid, used as a stain.

SCHNEIDER TEST FOR LIGNIFIED PLANT TISSUE. Plant tissues, which have been immersed for a short time in acidulated water, and then treated with a

1% alcoholic solution of benzidine, become colored orange-yellow to yellow-red according to the degree of lignification.

SCHNEIDER TEST REACTION FOR ALKALOIDS. A test for alkaloids made by adding a few mg. of a mixture of 1 part of the alkaloid and 6–8 parts of sugar to a drop of sulfuric acid in a porcelain dish. Morphine or codeine turn to a pale purplered color which changes slowly to a blueviolet, dirty green, and finally to yellow. A large number of modifications and additions to this reaction have been developed.

SCHOENHERR PROCESS. One of the processes used for the production of nitrates directly from the air by the combination of oxygen and nitrogen under the action of an electric arc.

SCHOENTAL MICRO-TEST. A test for palladium made by adding an equal volume of *p*-amidoacetophenone solution to the sample to be tested. This solution is prepared by dissolving 1 g. of the solid in 40 ml. of warm 0.6 *N* hydrochloric acid and diluting when cold to 100 ml. A turbidity or yellow, voluminous precipitate indicates the presence of palladium.

SCHOLL REACTION. A method of ring closure of polynuclear ketones by heating with aluminum chloride.

SCHOLLER SACCHARIFICATION PROCESS. Hydrolysis of wood to form sugars by heating at 170–180° C. and 165–180 pounds per square inch pressure with $\frac{1}{2}$% aqueous sulfuric acid.

SCHOLVEIN TEST. A test for phosgene in chloroform, made by adding a solution of aniline in anhydrous benzene to the chloroform. A turbidity is produced if phosgene is present.

SCHÖNBEIN PYROGALLOL TEST FOR NITRITE AND NITRATE. An alkaline solution of pyrogallol, acidified with sulfuric acid, is colored brown by nitrite. Various modifications of this test have been developed; Horsley tested for nitrate by using a solution of pyrogallol in concentrated sulfuric acid, which gave a violet-blue color.

SCHÖNBEIN REAGENTS AND TEST FOR HYDROGEN PEROXIDE. (1) Potassium iodide-starch solution. (2) Potassium ferricyanide and ferric chloride. (3) Potassium permanganate. (4) Indigo tincture and ferrous sulfate. (5) Chromic acid. (6) Lead acetate. (7) Guaiac tincture.

Add ferrous sulfate followed by potassium iodide-starch paste, to the neutral or slightly acid solution. A blue color indicates the presence of hydrogen peroxide.

SCHÖNBEIN TEST FOR NITRITE IN THE PRESENCE OF NITRATE. Acidify with phosphoric acid a very dilute solution of the sample to be tested and add potassium iodide-starch paste. A blue color indicates the presence of nitrate. Several modifications of this test have been developed.

SCHÖNBEIN TEST FOR NITRITE IN NITRIC ACID. Add some of the nitric acid to be tested to the brown solution of potassium ferricyanide and ferric nitrate. Prussian blue forms if nitrite is present. This test must be made at room temperature.

SCHÖNBEIN TEST REACTION FOR COPPER. Copper salt solutions produce a blue color on paper which has been impregnated with guaiac tincture and dilute potassium cyanide solution. A number of modifications of this reaction have been developed.

SCHÖNBEIN TEST REACTION FOR OZONE. A blue color is formed by ozone on paper saturated with potassium iodide-starch paste, and a brown color is formed on paper saturated with thallous oxide.

SCHÖNBEIN TEST REAGENT FOR NITRITE, OZONE, AND HYDROGEN PEROXIDE.

This reagent is made by acidifying an aqueous indigo solution with hydrochloric acid and decolorizing with alkali sulfide. The blue color will return on treating it with nitrite, ozone, or hydrogen peroxide.

SCHÖNBERG-URBAN TEST.

A test for free sulfur made by heating a little of the substance to be tested with benzyl-imido-di(4-methoxyphenyl)methane in a melting-point tube for 5 minutes at 210° C. A blue substance is formed which can be extracted with benzene, if free sulfur is present.

SCHÖNN TEST REACTION FOR HYDROGEN PEROXIDE.

A yellow color is produced by reaction of hydrogen peroxide with titanic acid. Several modifications of this test have been developed.

SCHÖNN TEST REACTION FOR MOLYBDENUM.

Concentrated sulfuric acid is used to moisten the material to be tested, which is then carefully heated over an open flame until the acid has evaporated. The residue becomes an ultramarine-blue color if molybdenum is present.

SCHÖNVOGEL TEST.

A test for differentiating animal and vegetable oils which is made by shaking the sample with a saturated aqueous solution of borax. An emulsion is produced by vegetable oils; whereas animal oils, including butter and olive oil, produce no emulsion, but sharply separated layers.

SCHOORL TEST FOR DIFFERENTIATING CHLOROFORM AND CARBON TETRACHLORIDE.

Heat 1 drop of the liquid carefully in a loosely stoppered test tube. Carbon tetrachloride oxidizes with the formation of chlorine, which gives the starch-iodide test, but chloroform does not give this reaction. **Fehling solution** is not reduced by carbon tetrachloride but is by chloroform.

SCHOORL TEST FOR WATER IN GLACIAL ACETIC ACID.

Anhydrous glacial acetic acid is clearly soluble in carbon tetrachloride. If any water is present, two layers are formed and, on the addition of iodine, the lower layer becomes violet and the upper layer brown in color.

SCHOORL TEST REACTION FOR NAPHTHALENE.

Add a little of the sample to be tested to a mixture of concentrated sulfuric acid and yellow mercuric oxide and boil for several minutes. Then add a little resorcinol to the reaction product and heat. When cold, add this material to water and make alkaline with sodium hydroxide solution. If naphthalene is present, a green fluorescence will form, due to the oxidation of the naphthalene to phthalic anhydride.

SCHORIGIN REACTION.

A reaction involving a sodium-alkyl compound or other Grignard-type compound containing sodium in place of magnesium. See also **Wanklyn reaction.**

SCHORN REAGENT FOR ALOE.

A solution prepared by mixing 25 ml. 30% hydrogen peroxide with quinoline, drawing off the lower layer, drying it with anhydrous sodium sulfate, and adding more quinoline until the hydrogen peroxide concentration is 1%. It is used in testing for aloes, which gives color reactions on heating at 60° C.

SCHORN REAGENT FOR EUCALYPTOL.

A solution of 15 g. ammonium molybdate and 4.5 g. ammonium sulfate in 85 ml. dilute nitric acid. It gives a blue color on heating with eucalyptol.

SCHOSSBERGER TEST REACTION.

A test for sulfide made by supersaturating a dilute solution of sodium molybdate with hydrochloric acid. This solution is colored blue by hydrogen sulfide or by metal sulfides.

SCHOTT TEST REACTION.

A test for copper made by adding 5 drops of a 2% solution of potassium nitrite, 5 drops of 10% acetic acid, and 3 ml. of a 0.5% solution of salicylic acid in 10% alcohol, to

10 ml. of the solution to be tested, and then heating to boiling in a water bath for 45 minutes. A red color indicates the presence of copper.

SCHOTTEN-BAUMANN REACTION. Acylation with an acid chloride in alkaline solution. The compound to be acylated is dissolved in dilute alkali and the mixture shaken with the acid chloride until the odor of the latter is imperceptible. The reaction applies generally to **hydroxy** and **amino compounds** and to certain other **bases.** It is represented by the equation:

the amplitude function for the three co-ordinates of the particle, m is the mass of the particle, h is the **Planck constant,** E is the total energy of the particle, and V is its potential energy.

SCHRYVER TEST. A test for formaldehyde made by adding 1 ml. of 5% freshly prepared potassium ferricyanide solution and 2 ml. of 1% freshly prepared phenylhydrazine hydrochloride solution and 5 ml. of concentrated hydrochloric acid, to 10 ml. of the solution to be tested. A fuchsin-red color shows the presence of formaldehyde

$$ROH + C_6H_5COCl + NaOH \rightarrow C_6H_5C\overset{\displaystyle O}{\underset{\displaystyle OR}{\big\backslash\!\!\big/}} + NaCl + H_2O.$$

SCHREIBER REAGENT. A solution of 2 g. cupric sulfate, 2 g. sodium salicylate, and 2 g. sodium carbonate (crystalline), in 88 g. water, used in testing for glucose in urine. A dark green precipitate, or a yellow precipitate, on boiling shows the presence of glucose. A gray to black precipitate is negative.

SCHREINEMAKERS RESIDUE METHOD. A method of determining the true composition of a solid multi-component phase in **equilibrium** with the mother-liquid, from the analysis of the wet solid which separates. The liquid is also analyzed, and a line is extended through the two points plotted from these data. Then the process is repeated for another solution and the wet solid which has separated from it, and another line is drawn. The point of intersection of these two lines gives the true composition of the dry solid.

SCHRÖDINGER WAVE EQUATION. A partial differential equation whose solution yields the statistical charge density as well as the allowed **energy levels** of a particle moving in a given field. The equation is of the form:

$$\nabla^2 u + \frac{8\pi^2 m}{h^2}(E - V)u = 0$$

in which ∇^2 is the Laplacian operator, u is

SCHULEMAN-SCHÖNHÖFER-WINGLER TEST. A very sensitive test for plasmoquine (plasmochine) made by adding tetrachlorobenzoquinone to the solution to be tested. A blue color is produced even by very dilute solutions of plasmoquine.

SCHÜLTZE SOLUTION FOR ALKALOIDS. A solution of 20 g. antimony pentachloride in 80 g. phosphoric acid, used in precipitating alkaloids, chiefly when they are present as sulfates.

SCHULTZE SOLUTION FOR CELLULOSE. A solution of 250 g. zinc chloride, and 80 g. potassium iodide in 85 ml. water, which is then saturated with iodine. It is used in testing for cellulose, which it colors blue.

SCHULZ TEST REACTION FOR SALICYLIC ACID. A little cupric sulfate solution added to an aqueous solution of salicylic acid or of its sodium salt is colored emerald-green.

SCHULZE-HARDY RULE. A generalization derived from certain work on **colloidal** systems, to the effect that ions of sign opposite to that of a given colloidal particle are most effective in coagulating it, and that their coagulating power increases with increasing ionic charge.

SCHUMACHER-KOPP TEST REAC-TIONS FOR METHYL VIOLET AND TROPEOLIN. (1) Methyl violet turns green or blue in the presence of hydrochloric acid, sulfuric acid, nitric acid, or phosphoric acid. Oxalic, tartaric, and lactic acids give a bluish coloration. Citric acid gives a blue color. No change is produced by acetic or boric acid. (2) Tropeolin gives a reddish-violet color in the presence of hydrochloric, sulfuric, nitric, phosphoric, oxalic, or tartaric acids. Citric acid gives a yellowish-red, lactic acid a rose, acetic acid a cherry-red color. No change is produced by boric acid.

SCHUSTER TEST REACTION FOR URETHANE. Dissolve 0.04 g. urethane in 5 ml. water and add 5 ml. of sodium hydroxide and 2 ml. **Nessler solution.** A gelatinous, white precipitate is produced which becomes yellow on long standing. The precipitate turns brown on heating.

SCHÜTZ-BOURISON RULE. The rate of an **enzyme** reaction is directly proportional to the square root of the concentration of enzyme present. This rule holds only under very limited conditions, as in the determination of pepsin by Mott's method. This rule does not apply at all when the enzyme concentration is either very low or very high in proportion to the concentration of substrate.

SCHÜTZENBERGER TEST REAC-TION. A test for anthroquinone made by adding sodium hydrosulfite to an alkaline solution of anthroquinone. A red color is produced. On exposure of the solution to the air, the anthroquinone is regenerated.

SCHWALBE TEST. A test for distinguishing artificial silks, made by heating 0.2 g. of the sample to be tested in a test tube for 10 minutes with **Fehling solution** in the water bath and then filling the test tube with water. Copper-ammonia silk and viscose silk develop a blue-yellowish color, while on the threads of nitro-silk a precipitate of cuprous oxide forms and the solution becomes green. To distinguish between copper-ammonia and viscose silks, treat the samples briefly with zinc chloride-iodine solution and then wash with water.

Copper-ammonia silk becomes slightly brownish and rapidly loses this brown color on washing; viscose silk is colored blue-green and retains its color when washed.

SCHWARZ REACTION FOR NAPH-THALENE. When heated with anhydrous aluminum chloride, a chloroform solution of naphthalene becomes green-blue at the moment hydrochloric acid is evolved.

SCHWARZ REAGENT FOR BLOOD. Fifty ml. of a 2% alcoholic solution of benzidine, to which is added 1 ml. glacial acetic acid, and 1 drop quinoline or isoquinoline. It is a sensitive test reagent for blood, which it colors blue.

SCHWARZ TEST FOR LIME IN MAGNESITE. After calcination, the sample is placed on a watch glass or microscope slide and treated with a few drops of 0.33 N ammonium citrate, followed by a little thymolphthalein solution. If calcium is present, the material will be dyed blue.

SCHWEISSINGER TEST FOR ALKA-LIES. This test is made by adding an iodine-nutgall tincture to the sample to be tested. A rose-red color indicates the presence of alkalies.

SCHWEISSINGER TEST FOR PYR-IDINE. Add 10 drops of a saturated alcoholic solution of mercuric chloride to 10 ml. of the alcoholic liquid to be tested. If pyridine is present, a crystalline precipitate will form.

SCHWEITZER REAGENT FOR WOOL, COTTON, AND SILK. A solution used as a solvent or testing agent for cellulose, wool, cotton, and silk. (It does not dissolve wood.) It is prepared by dissolving 10 g. cupric sulfate in 100 ml. water, precipitating with sodium hydroxide solution, washing thoroughly, and forming a saturated solution of the precipitate in ammonium hydroxide (sp. gr. 0.90). This amount of cupric hydroxide is ample to saturate 10 ml. of the ammonium hydroxide.

SCHWEITZER TEST REACTION FOR QUININE. An infusion of nutgall produces a precipitate with quinine. This reaction is given by many other alkaloids, as it is based on the precipitation of the alkaloid by the tannic acid of the nutgall.

SCHWEIZER TEST REACTION. A test for xanthine made by heating a trace of xanthine with a few crystals of potassium chlorate and a few ml. hydrochloric acid, then evaporating to dryness on a watch glass. The alloxan formed gradually passes into its red modification, on prolonged heating of the residue on the water bath. If 1–2 drops of potassium hydroxide solution are added to the carmine-red residue, an intense ultramarine-blue color forms immediately.

SCISSION. A splitting or dividing of a molecule, especially the splitting off of one carbon atom from a chain.

SCLEROMETER. An apparatus for determining the hardness of a material by measuring the pressure on a standard point that is required to scratch the material.

SCLEROPROTEIN. One of a group of proteins which form the skeletal structure of animals (see **proteins**).

SCLEROSCOPE. An apparatus for determining the hardness of a material by measuring the rebound of a standard ball dropped on it from a fixed height.

-SCOPE. A suffix meaning an optical or viewing device, as in electroscope, microscope, and spectroscope.

SCOPOMETER. An instrument for making **turbidimetric** or **nephelometric** measurements by the contrast between a field of constant brightness and an illuminated line placed behind the solution under test.

SCOPOMETRY. A system of **turbidimetry** or **nephelometry** based on the use of the **scopometer** (q.v.).

-SCOPY. A suffix meaning observation, as in spectroscopy.

SCOTT-ADAMS REAGENT AND TEST. A reagent and test for cadmium. The reagent, 1(2-quinolyl)-4 allyl-thiosemicar-bazide, is prepared from 10 ml. allyl isothiocyanate and 16 g. of 2-quinolylhydrazine dissolved in ether. The test is made by adding a saturated solution of potassium iodide and a saturated solution of the reagent in 50% alcohol to the solution to be tested; then adding ammonia. The cadmium forms a yellow precipitate but any copper present is dissolved.

SCOTT FURNACE. A shaft furnace used for the production of mercury by heating its ores.

SCOTT-PLIMMER REAGENT. A solution of 20 g. ammonium chloride in 80 ml. of a 10% ammonium molybdate solution, to which are then added successively 12 ml. hydrochloric acid (sp. gr. 1.16) and 10 ml. of a saturated aqueous solution of potassium persulfate. It is used as a test for phosphate, especially in organic compounds.

SCOTT-WILSON REAGENT. A solution of 10 g. mercuric cyanide in 600 ml. water, to which is added a solution of 180 g. sodium hydroxide in 600 ml. water, and then a solution of 2.9 g. silver nitrate in 400 ml. water. This reagent is used in the detection of acetone. A white or dark-white precipitate or turbidity is given by acetone with this reagent.

SCOVILLE TEST. A test for differentiating benzoic and cinnamic acids in which some manganese sulfate is added, if the solution to be tested forms a yellow color with ferric chloride. A white crystalline precipitate develops within an hour if cinnamic acid is present. If this precipitate does not appear, the color developed by ferric chloride can be ascribed to the presence of benzoic acid.

SCREEN. A device used to classify (separate) materials or radiations, as a common wire screen separates particles small enough to pass through its apertures, from particles too large to pass through. Similarly a screen of colored glass passes certain wave lengths and absorbs others. The use of the term screen has been extended to include devices which absorb certain radiations and emit others, as in a fluorescent screen.

SCREEN ANALYSIS. The classification of material by size, accomplished by shaking it on screens of successively smaller sizes, and collecting separately the portions that fail to pass through the various screens.

SCREEN, FOURDRINIER. See **Fourdrinier screen.**

SCREENING CONSTANT. A quantity occurring in the relationship between the frequency of a line in a particular **x-ray series,** and the **atomic number** of the element emitting the rays, of the form:

$$\sqrt{\nu} = a(Z - \sigma)$$

in which ν is the frequency of the line, a is a constant, Z is the atomic number of the element, and σ is the screening constant, that is the same for all the lines in a given series. (See **screening effect.**)

SCREENING EFFECT. Since the orbital electrons surrounding an atomic nucleus are arranged in shells, it is logical that the attractive force of the nucleus for an electron in an outer shell is weakened by the presence of electrons in inner shells, whose negative charges act partly to "screen" the positive nucleus from the outer electrons, and thus to decrease the effective charge of the nucleus. It is assumed that this screening effect bears a definite relationship to the electrical charges involved, and is an inverse function of the distance of the screening electrons from the nucleus.

SCRIBA TEST. A test for water made by dipping strips of paper in a solution of 1 g. ferrous ammonium sulfate in 20 ml. water, drying and rubbing on the surface some finely powdered potassium ferricyanide. The slightest amount of water will color the strips blue.

SCRUBBER. An apparatus for separating components of gaseous systems by the action of a liquid. Scrubbers are used to remove solid or liquid impurities (such as dusts or droplets) from gases, to separate one gas from another by solution or chemical combination with the liquid, and to accomplish other purposes.

SCUDI-RATISH TEST. A method for detecting or determining ascorbic acid (vitamin C), carried out by adding 1 ml. of 0.05% sodium nitrite and 1 ml. of 20% sulfosalicyclic acid to 5 ml. of a 0.05 per cent solution of sulfanilamide. The solution is permitted to stand 1–3 minutes and 1 ml. of 1% urea is added. After 5 minutes, 10 ml. of a fresh 10% acetic acid solution of the vitamin is added. After 5 minutes, 7.4 ml. of 1-dimethylnaphthylamine solution (1 ml. diluted to 500 ml. with alcohol) are added and the solution is mixed. After 10 minutes, but within 50 minutes, the colors developed are compared with appropriate standards, prepared by diminishing the sulfanilamide concentration and replacing the vitamin solution by vitamin-free 10% acetic acid.

Se Symbol for the element **selenium.**

SEABOARD PURIFICATION PROCESS. A process for the purification of manufactured fuel gas, which consists of scrubbing with an aqueous solution of 2–3% sodium carbonate to absorb the hydrogen sulfide; the scrubbing solution is regenerated by spraying it in a tower against a current of air. A modification of the process uses for the scrubbing a sodium phenolate solution, which is regenerated by boiling.

SEBELIEN REAGENT. A reagent for albumin and peptone made by dissolving 10 g. crystalline phosphotungstic acid in 50 g. water and adding 1.2 g. concentrated sulfuric acid. On adding 1 ml. of this reagent to 10 ml. of the solution to be tested a precipitate develops if albumin or peptone is present.

SEC-. Abbreviation of secondary, as *sec*-butyl.

SECOND LAW OF THERMODYNAMICS. See **thermodynamics, second law of.**

SECOND-ORDER REACTION. See **reaction, second-order.**

SECONDARY COMPOUND. A term applied to one class of compounds to distinguish it from other generically similar compounds termed primary, tertiary, quaternary, etc. In organic chemistry, compounds that may be regarded as di-derivatives of the parent substance are often termed secondary. See secondary **alcohols, amines, bases,** etc.

SECTROMETER. A type of apparatus for **potentiometric titrations** in which the course of the reaction is followed by optical rather than electrical measurements. In the common form, the indicating method consists of a cathode-ray tube and a fluorescent screen.

SECULAR DETERMINANT. An equation in the form of a determinant whose solution yields the **eigenvalues** which the quantized system under consideration can assume.

SEDIMENTATION. The process of settling, commonly of solid particles from a liquid.

SEDIMENTATION CONSTANT. A quantity obtained in investigating the behavior of **colloidal particles** under the action of forces, chiefly centrifugal forces. This quantity for a given particle and medium is defined by the expression:

$$S = \frac{2r^2(p - p')}{9\eta}$$

in which S is the sedimentation constant, r is the radius of the particle, p and p' are the reciprocals of the partial specific volumes of particle and medium, respectively, and η is the viscosity of the medium.

SEEBECK EFFECT. When two wires of different materials are twisted or soldered together at their ends so as to form a complete circuit and one of the junctions is heated, an electric current flows in the circuit. If the junction is cooled, a current flows in the reverse direction.

SEELIGER REAGENT. A solution of 0.5 g. potassium iodide, 0.1 g. iodine, and 30 g. calcium nitrate (crystalline), in 25 ml. water, used in testing for lignin in paper. It colors cellulose light blue to dark blue, linen and half-linen wine red, and wood pulp and strongly-lignified fibers yellow brown.

SEGER CONES. Small cones used for indicating furnace temperatures, especially in the ceramic industries. They are prepared of mixtures of clay, salt, and other materials in various proportions, such that the softening points of the cones vary progressively in the series, so that they can be used to indicate temperatures through a considerable range.

SELENATE. The anion $SeO_4^=$, or a compound containing it.

SELENIC. (1) Containing or pertaining to tetravalent or hexavalent **selenium.** (2) Related to selenic acid, H_2SeO_4.

SELENIDE. A binary compound of **selenium.**

SELENIDO. The atom —Se—.

SELENINIC. The radical —Se(:O)OH.

SELENINO. The radical (HO)OSe—.

SELENINYL. The radical OSe=.

SELENIOUS. (1) Containing or pertaining to divalent or tetravalent **selenium.** (2) Related to selenious acid, H_2SeO_3.

SELENITE. The anion $SeO_3^=$ or $HSeO_3^-$, or a compound containing one of these anions.

SELENIUM. Nonmetallic element. Symbol Se. Atomic number 34. Atomic weight 78.96. Occurs in three allotropic forms: (1) Monoclinic (two varieties) red. Density 4.42. Melting point 144° C. (2) Hexagonal (gray). Density 4.84. Melting point 220° C. This form is called metallic selenium, has electrical conductivity varying with illumination and is used in photoelectric cells. It is formed by prolonged heating of other varieties of selenium. (3) Amorphous, a dark red to black powder. Density 4.28. Selenium is found in clausthalite, silver selenide, copper selenide, etc. Valence 1, 2, 4, and 6. Oxide SeO_2. Acids, H_2Se, H_2SeO_3, H_2SeO_4.

SELENO. The radical Se=.

SELENOCYANATE. The anion $SeCN^-$, or a compound containing it.

SELENOCYANO. The radical $NCSe$—.

SELENOL. The radical —SeH.

SELENONIC. The radical —$Se(:O)_2OH$.

SELENONO. The radical HO_3Se—.

SELENONYL. The radical —SeO_2—.

SELENOSULFATE. The anion $SSeO_3^=$, or a compoind containing it.

SELENYL. The radical HSe—.

SELF-ABSORPTION (SELF-REVERSAL). The reduction in **radiant power** at the center of emission lines, resulting from selective absorption of **radiation** emitted by the hot central core into the cooler outer vapor of the source envelope.

SELF-CONSISTENT FIELD METHOD. A method for calculation of the radial distribution of electron densities around a given nucleus, using approximation procedures.

SELF TEST. A test for salicylic acid made by moistening the substance to be tested with a cold mixture of equal parts of 37% formaldehyde and concentrated sulfuric acid. The mixture is brownish or colorless. If salicylic acid is present, the addition of a little ammonium vanadate will change the color of the solution to a Prussian blue shade immediately. This color will change rapidly to greenish-blue and then green.

SELIWANOFF REAGENT. A solution of 0.05 resorcinol in 100 ml. of a 1:2 aqueous solution of hydrochloric acid. It is used in testing for fructose, which gives a red color on boiling with it.

SELLMEIER EQUATION. An equation expressing the relationship between the refractive index of a medium and the wave length of the light; this variation of refractive index with wave length is known as refractive dispersion. The equation is of the form

$$n^2 = A + \frac{B}{\lambda^2} + \frac{C}{\lambda^4} + \cdots$$

in which n is the index of refraction, and λ is the wave length. This equation is the same as the **Cauchy formula** (q.v.).

SELMI REACTION FOR STRYCHNINE. A test made by slightly moistening the sample to be tested with a solution of iodic acid in sulfuric acid. A yellow color, becoming brick-red and slowly changing to violet-red is given by strychnine.

SELMI REAGENTS. Reagents for alkaloids in general, and for differentiating individual alkaloids, are the following: iodo-hydriodic acid, gold bromide, gold sodium thiosulfate, gold potassium iodide, lead tetrachloride, and manganese dioxide in sulfuric acid.

SEMET-SOLVAY COKE OVEN. A by-product coke oven for the production of coke by the regenerative heating and distillation of coal.

SEMI-. A prefix which means (1) "half," and (2) "imperfectly."

SEMICARBAZIDE. An organic compound having the formula,

$$\overset{\displaystyle O}{\overset{\|}{NH_2-NH-C-NH_2.}}$$

SEMICARBAZIDO. The radical

$$H_2NCONHNH—.$$

SEMICARBAZONE. A compound formed by reaction between **semicarbazide** and many carbonyl compounds, especially aldehydes and ketones. The general form of the reaction

$$\overset{\displaystyle O}{\overset{\|}{R-C-R'}} + \overset{\displaystyle O}{\overset{\|}{NH_2-NH-C-NH_2}} \rightarrow \overset{\displaystyle O}{\overset{\|}{RR'C=N-NH-C-NH_2}} + H_2O.$$

The semicarbazones are often solids which aid in identification of the parent **aldehyde** or **ketone** by means of melting-point determinations.

SEMI-COVALENT, BOND. See **bond, semi-covalent.**

SEMIDINE REARRANGEMENT. A special case of the **benzidine rearrangement** (q.v.) which occurs when one of the benzene nuclei in the hydrazobenzene is substituted in the para-position, so that the rearrangement to the *p,p'*-diamino-biphenyl compound is partly blocked. In this case, a para-aminodiphenylamine is formed (in the presence of strong acid).

acetate in 10 g. glycerol. It is used in testing for sugars in plant tissues.

SENSITIVENESS. In general, susceptibility to external action, as measured by readiness to respond to such action. Thus, the sensitiveness of an analytical method is the minimum quantity of substance it can detect, and the sensitiveness of a balance is the smallest mass to which it can respond.

SENSITIZATION. The process of rendering susceptible to the action of some force or state, as radiant energy, acidity, etc.

SENSITIZER. A catalytic agent whose presence in a chemical system initiates a

$$R-\langle\rangle-NH.NH-\langle\rangle \rightarrow R-\langle\rangle-NH-\langle\rangle-NH_2.$$

Some of the product may also be the ortho-aminodiphenylamine derivative.

SEMIPERMEABLE MEMBRANE. (Semipermeable diaphragm) A membrane or septum through which a solvent but not certain dissolved or colloidal substances may pass, used in **osmotic pressure** determinations. Many natural membranes are semipermeable, e.g., cell walls; other membranes may be made artificially, e.g., by precipitating copper ferrocyanide in the interstices of a porous cup, the cup serving as a frame to give the membrane stability.

SEMIPOLAR BOND. See **bond, dative.**

SENECIOYL. The radical

$$(CH_3)_2C:CHCO—$$

(from senecioic acid).

SENFT REACTION FOR COUMARIN. A test made by treating the sample with zinc chloride-iodine solution. If clusters of fine brown-violet needles form, coumarin is present.

SENFT REAGENT. This reagent consists of two solutions: (1) a solution of 1 g. phenylhydrazine hydrochloride in 10 g. glycerol; and (2) a solution of 1 g. sodium

reaction, under the influence of external excitation, which would not have occurred in the absence of the catalyzing material. (See **catalysis**.)

SEPARATION FACTOR. A relationship used to express the efficiency of any operation or process for the separation of **isotopes**; it is the ratio of the isotopic forms in the initial phase divided by their corresponding ratio in the final phase.

SEPARATION, HYDRAULIC. A process of hindered settling (see **settling, hindered**) by hydraulic, and sometimes also mechanical, means, which commonly follows a preliminary hydraulic **classification**.

SEPARATORY FUNNEL. A glass vessel, commonly pear-shaped, i.e., long and tapering toward the bottom, which consists of a stopcock and delivery tube. It is used for liquid phase extractions, by shaking a solution of a substance to be recovered with a solvent for that substance, this solvent being chosen for its insolubility in the other liquid medium. After shaking sufficiently, the two liquid layers are allowed to form, and the lower one is drawn off by means of the stopcock.

SEPTUM. A wall or partition separating two cavities.

SEQUESTERING AGENT. A substance which forms a complex compound, complex ion or other aggregate with a metal or a metallic compound, commonly with a metallic ion, and thereby modifies the action of the ion or compound. Many, but not all, sequestering agents owe their action to the formation of chelate compounds. Representative sequestering agents are ethylenediamine tetraacetic acid or its sodium salts, pyrophosphates, tripolyphosphates and citrates. Applications of sequestering agents are in analysis, in agriculture to stabilize solutions of dichlorphenoxyacetic acid (a herbicide) and other substances readily precipitated by metal ions, in detergents and food products to prevent precipitation by metal ions, and to restrain various undesirable reactions that are catalyzed by metal ions. Other applications of sequestering agents are in the technological separation of metals, in dyeing, and in the radioactive decontamination of surfaces exposed to debris from atomic explosions.

SERGER SOLUTION. A solution of 1 g. sodium molybdate in 100 ml. concentrated sulfuric acid, used in identifying vegetable oils, which give, in ethereal solution, characteristic color reactions with this reagent.

SERIES. A group of objects, numbers, or other entities of the same class arranged in accordance with a plan, commonly in the order of increasing or decreasing magnitude of a common property.

SERIES, ACTINIUM. See element, radioactive series.

SERIES, BALMER. See Balmer series.

SERIES, BRACKETT. See Brackett series.

SERIES, COLLATERAL. See element, collateral series.

SERIES, DIFFUSE. See diffuse series.

SERIES, DISPLACEMENT. See displacement series.

SERIES, FUNDAMENTAL. See fundamental series.

SERIES, HOMOLOGOUS. See homologous series.

SERIES, ISOLOGOUS. See isologous series.

SERIES, ISOMORPHOUS. See isomorphous series.

SERIES, K, L, M, N, ETC. See K series, L series, etc.

SERIES, NEPTUNIUM. See element, radioactive series.

SERIES OF COMPOUNDS. A series of any group of chemical compounds which are chosen and arranged in accordance with a fact or rule. Thus, the paraffin series of hydrocarbons consists of the saturated straight-chain compounds of carbon and hydrogen arranged in order of the number of carbon atoms contained in the successive compounds. For the various series of compounds, see under the series name, or name compound, as **alkane series** or **methane series.**

SERIES, PASCHEN. See Paschen series.

SERIES, PFUND. See Pfund series.

SERIES, PRINCIPAL. See principal series.

SERIES, RADIOACTIVE. See element, radioactive series.

SERIES, SHARP. See sharp series.

SERIES, THORIUM. See element, radioactive series.

SERIES, URANIUM. See element, radioactive series.

SERKE TEST. A test for purity of acetic acid (absence of aldehydes, empyreumatic substances, etc.) made by adding a pinch of benzidine to 5 ml. of the acetic acid, shaking until dissolved, and then heating to about 60° C. The solution must remain clear and colorless.

SERINI REACTION. A method of changing a secondary acetate or a secondary-tertiary 1,2, **glycol** into a **ketone,** by the action of zinc dust.

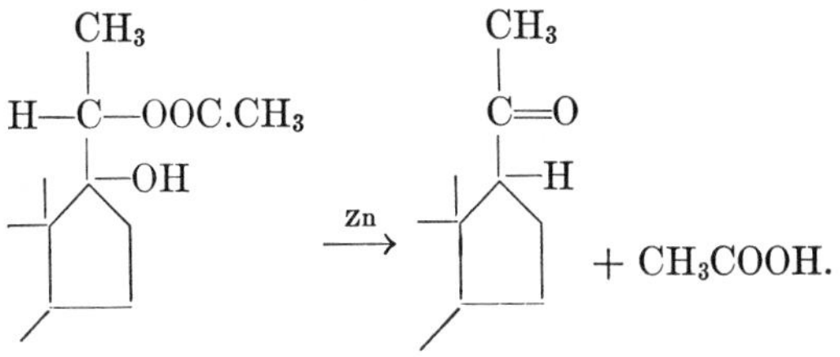

$$+ CH_3COOH.$$

This reaction is especially useful in steroid research.

SEROLOGY. In general, the science of sera, concerned largely with the reactions which occur in sera due to **immunization.**

SERULLAS REAGENTS FOR ALKALOIDS AND MORPHINE. Aqueous solutions of iodic acid or iodine chloride that produce crystalline precipitates with many alkaloids. With morphine, a brown color is formed with the liberation of iodine.

SERULLAS TEST FOR DIFFERENTIATING FORMIC AND ACETIC ACIDS. Formic acid reduces mercuric oxide to mercury, but acetic acid dissolves it.

SERUM. In its original connotation, this term is applied to the clear portion of any physiological fluid, free from particles. The term serum is commonly used to designate one particular fluid, that of the blood, which has been freed from hemoglobin and other cells by clotting, centrifuging, or other means. Blood serum is widely used in therapeutics by intravenous injection in the treatment of shock and related conditions.

SERYL. The radical

$$HOCH_2CH(NH_2)CO—.$$

SESQUI. A prefix which indicates a proportion of two to three, as a sesquioxide in which the atomic proportions of metal and oxygen are as two to three, e.g., Fe_2O_3.

The term is also used to indicate "half." Cf. **subsesqui-.**

SESQUIOXIDE. An oxide in which the ratio of metal to oxygen is as two to three' as in ferric oxide, chromic oxide, etc.

SESQUITERPENE. A **terpene** of the formula $C_{15}H_{24}$, as distinguished from the ordinary terpenes which have the formula, $C_{10}H_{16}$.

SETTLER. An apparatus in which solids are separated from liquids by deposition on standing, because of the action of gravity. A special type of settler is the classifier in which systems of particles are separated by gravity into two portions, differing in size, density, or both.

SETTLING. The separation of suspended solid particles from a liquid by the action of gravity or other force.

SETTLING, HINDERED. Any method for the application of forces to particles undergoing settling, which yields better or more rapid classification by size than can be obtained by free settling. For example, such forces may be applied by flow of fluids, by vibration, etc.

SEXAVALENT. A term meaning that an element or atom has six different valencies, or that it has a valence of six, although the term hexavalent is preferable for the latter meaning.

SEYDA TEST. A test for chromium in presence of iron in which the solution to be tested is made alkaline with sodium hydroxide and heated for 15 minutes with potassium permanganate and then the excess of permanganate is reduced with alcohol. The solution is colored yellow by the formation of chromate, if chromium is present.

SHAKHKELDIAN TEST. A test for zinc, made by adding 1 ml. of a 25% solution of cobalt sulfate and 1 ml. of a 5% potassium ferrocyanide solution to 1–2 drops of the solution to be tested. The mixture is shaken well and then 4–5 ml. of the 3:1 sulfuric acid are added along the side of the tube. If zinc is present, a greenbluish ring is produced. Copper, mercury, and nickel interfere. If any of these elements are present the solution is heated with sodium hydroxide, filtered, the filtrate acidified, and the zinc detected in the filtrate as above.

SHANER-WILLARD REACTIONS. Tests for yohimbine as follows: (1) To a solution of yohimbine in concentrated sulfuric acid, add a crystal of potassium dichromate. A violet streak is produced which changes quickly to slate-blue and finally to dirty green. (2) With p-dimethylaminobenzaldehyde and concentrated sulfuric acid, yohimbine gives a dark red-violet color which becomes dark violet after a short time.

SHANK SYSTEM. A method of extracting materials from solids by liquids, in which the solid is held in one tank throughout the entire process, but all the movement is made by the extracting liquid.

SHAPIRO-RUD TEST. A test for mercury, copper, silver, and for metals of the platinum group, made by adding 5 drops of 2% alcoholic solution of phenylthiocarbamide to 1 ml. of solution to be tested. With mercurous salts, a grayish turbidity and grayish-black precipitate are given. Mercuric ions react with formation of white turbidity; silver, with yellow solution and yellowish-brown precipitate; cupric, with white turbidity or precipitate; and auric, platinic, and palladous ions give a yellow turbidity or yellow precipitate.

SHAPIRO TEST. A test for antimony made by pouring 1 ml. of distilled water into one test tube and 1 ml. of the solution to be tested into another; then adding to each 0.5 ml. 1% potassium iodide solution, 1 ml. of 20% sodium hydroxide and 5 ml. of 0.01% gold trichloride solution and shaking. In the presence of antimony, the test solution is colored light pink immediately or within 2–3 minutes, but the blank is not colored until 5–6 minutes have passed.

SHARP SERIES. A series of lines in the **spectra** of many atoms which have one, two, or three electrons in their outer shells, either in their neutral state or as a result of ionization. (Excluded are the atoms which have only one electron in all, such as hydrogen, singly-ionized helium, doubly-ionized lithium, etc.) The sharp series differs from the other series for such elements in having a somewhat distinctive physical appearance, and being representable by the characteristic formula,

$$\bar{\nu}_s = L - \frac{R}{(m + c)^2},$$

where $\bar{\nu}_s$ is the wave number of a line in the sharp series, L and c are constants for the sharp series, m is a variable integer, whose values give the various lines in the sharp series, and R is the **Rydberg constant.**

SHARPLES PROCESS. One of a number of methods for the **dewaxing** of petroleum fractions by solvent extraction, centrifuging, and refrigeration.

SHAW TEST. A test for bleached flour made by extracting 1 kg. of the flour for 4 hours with 95% alcohol. The extract is evaporated, the residue treated with a mixture of equal parts alcohol and ether, filtered, and evaporated to dryness. A solution of diphenylamine in concentrated sulfuric acid is poured on the residue. A blue color develops with a flour bleached with nitrogen peroxide.

SHCHIGOL TEST. A test for mercury made by treating the solution with excess 10% potassium iodide solution and 30% sodium hydroxide, heating, filtering, and boiling the filtrate with 1 ml. glycerin and 2–3 ml. sodium hydroxide solution for several minutes. Formation of a black precipitate or darkening of the solution indicates the presence of mercury.

SHEAR REAGENT. A mixture of 45 ml. aniline and 3 ml. concentrated hydrochloric acid. It is used as a test reagent for vitamin D, which gives a red color with it.

SHEINKMAN TEST. A test for carbonate in the presence of sulfite made by heating the sample in a flask with water, adding sulfuric acid, and passing the gases evolved successively through a permanganate solution and through clear lime water. The presence of carbonates is indicated if turbidity appears in the lime water.

SHELL OF ELECTRONS. See **atomic structure.**

SHEMJAKIN REACTIONS. Reactions for detecting the presence of rare earths as follows: (1) If solutions of cerium, thorium, titanium, and lanthanum are treated with a little ammonia and 10 ml. of 1% pyrogallol solution, colored precipitates will be given, but solutions of iron, chromium, aluminum, manganese, cobalt, and nickel will not react. Cerium precipitates are violet or dark blue. Ethylenediamine may be substituted for ammonia. (2) Mix 3 ml. of 0.02% gallic acid solution and 3 ml. of the solution, add 2 ml. of ether, toluene, or mineral oil to form a protective layer, add a few drops of ammonia and mix carefully. A blue-violet color is given by cerium.

SHERARDIZING. A process for covering the surface of ferrous materials with a protective coating of zinc. The articles are treated with zinc dust in a closed vessel at a temperature of about 800° C.

SHIFT OF SPECTRAL LINE. A small displacement in the position of a spectral line that is caused by a corresponding change in frequency which is due, in turn, to one or more of a variety of causes, such as the **Doppler effect,** etc.

SHORE SCALE OF HARDNESS. A scale of relative hardness based on the elastic rebound of a heavy plummet, with a standard hard point, which is dropped on the surface of the specimen from a fixed height.

SHORT PERIOD. See **period, short.**

Si Symbol for the element **silicon.**

SICCATIVE. A drying agent.

SIDE CHAIN. See **chain, side.**

SIDE REACTION. See **reaction, side.**

SIELISCH TEST. A test for picrotoxin made by heating a trace of picrotoxin with sodium hydroxide solution to boiling, and cooling. A few drops of iodine solution are then added. Iodoform separates. (This test is not specific as many other substances give this reaction.)

SIEMENS FURNACE. See **furnace, Siemens.**

SIEMENS-HALSKE PROCESS. An electrolytic process for the metallurgical extraction of copper from its sulfide ores, in which the metal is dissolved in sulfuric acid and ferrous sulfate, and the solution electrolyzed.

SIEMENS-MARTIN PROCESS. An open-hearth process used for producing steel. It operates at high temperatures, and its charge usually consists of pig iron, scrap steel, and other materials, with iron oxide added to the slag to oxidize impurities.

SIEMENS PRODUCER. A variety of **gas producer.**

SIEMSSEN TEST REACTION FOR GOLD. Addition of a 5:1000 solution of *m*-phenylenediamine sulfate to a solution of gold, produces a yellow to dark brown color according to the quantity of gold present. Gold solutions as dilute as 0.005% form a violet color with the reagent.

SIEMSSEN TEST REACTIONS FOR URANIUM AND MERCURY. (1) When mixed with a solution of ethylenediamine, solutions of uranium salts immediately yield a bright yellow crystalline precipitate soluble in excess of the reagent. The precipitation is quantitative.

(2) Mercuric salts form, with ethylenediamine, a white, amorphous precipitate that is soluble in acids, in alkali solutions,

in an excess of ethylenediamine, and in potassium iodide solution. The precipitate is formed in dilute hydrochloric acid or nitric acid solutions containing mercury, but not in dilute sulfuric acid solutions of it.

SIGMA (Σ, σ, OR ς). The eighteenth letter in the Greek alphabet, used to denote: the eighteenth carbon atom in a straight-chain compound, or a derivative in which the substitutent group is attached to that carbon atom (σ-). Symbol for surface tension (σ). Mathematical symbol for summation (Σ). Symbol for millisecond (σ). Abbreviation for *syn*-position (**s**-). Symbol for stopping power (σ). Symbol for surface charge density (σ). Symbol for electric **conductivity** (σ). Symbol for **collision diameter** of molecule (σ). Symbol for **dispersion** (σ). **Surface tension** (σ or γ). **Thomson coefficient** (σ). Symbol for **wave number** (σ). **Stefan-Boltzmann constant** (σ).

SILANES. The compound SiH_4 is called silane; compounds having the general formula $H_3Si(SiH_2)_nSiH_3$ are called disilane, trisilane, etc., according to the number of silicon atoms present. (In disilane, n in the above formula has a value of 0, in trisilane n has a value of 1, etc.)

SILAZANES. Compounds having the general formula $H_3Si(NHSiH_2)_nNHSiH_3$ are called disilazane, trisilazane, etc., according to the number of silicon atoms present. They have the generic name *silazanes*. (In disilazane, n in the above formula has a value of 0; in trisilazane, a value of 1, etc.)

SILICANE. This term is used by different authorities to mean three entirely different compounds and types of compounds. It may denote (1) monosilane, SiH_4, which is discussed under **silane** (q.v.); (2) all compounds of silicon and hydrogen; (3) a compound of the general formula SiR_4 in which R_4 may denote four identical hydrocarbon radicals or any combination of hydrocarbon radicals.

SILICATE. An anion composed of silicon and oxygen, or a compound containing it.

Various silicate anions are listed below under the headings, **silicate, di-; silicate, hexa-;** etc.

SILICATE (DI-). The anion $Si_2O_5^=$ or $Si_2O_7^{6-}$, or a compound containing one of these anions.

SILICATE (HEXA-). The anion $Si_6O_{18}^{12-}$, or a compound containing it.

SILICATE (META-). The anion $(SiO_3)_n^{2n-}$, or a compound containing it.

SILICATE (ORTHO-). The anion SiO_4^{4-}, or a compound containing it.

SILICATE (TETRA-). The anion $Si_4O_{11}^{6-}$ or $Si_4O_{12}^{8-}$, or a compound containing one of these anions.

SILICATE (TRI-). The anion $Si_3O_7^=$, $Si_3O_8^{4-}$, or $Si_3O_{10}^{8-}$ or a compound containing one of these anions.

SILICEOUS. Containing silicon dioxide or one of its compounds.

SILICIC. (1) Containing or pertaining to **silicon**. (2) Containing silicic acid (ortho) H_4SiO_4; or silicic acid (meta) H_2SiO_3; or silicic acids of a higher degree of hydration (disilicic acids, trisilicic acids, etc.).

SILICIDE. A binary compound of **silicon.**

SILICO-. A combining term indicating content of silica or **silicon.**

SILICOMOLYBDATE. The anion $HSiMo_{12}O_{40}^{3-}$, or a compound containing it.

SILICON. Nonmetallic element. Symbol Si. Atomic number 14. Atomic weight 28.09. Exists in four varieties: (1) amorphous, density 2.00; (2) crystalline, density 2.42; (3) graphitoidal, and (4) adamantine. Melting point 1420° C. Boiling point 2600° C. Valence 4. Oxide SiO_2.

SILICONE. The term silicone is used in the literature to denote one of a series of organic compounds having the general formula

in which R and R' are alkyl or aryl radicals. These compounds are not usually produced in monomolecular form, but appear in the silicone resins, which consist of this type of compound that has been polymerized in straight chains, or cross-polymerized as well. A general method for their production is by treatment of **Grignard reagents** with silicon tetrachloride ($SiCl_4$), and then hydrolyzing and condensing the resulting organic silicon chlorides. In view of this trade usage of the term "silicone," the new American Chemical Society rule discontinued its use in systematic nomenclature.

SILICONIC. The radical $-Si(:O)OH$.

SILICOTUNGSTATE. The anion $SiW_{12}O_{40}^{4-}$, $HSiW_{12}O_{40}^{3-}$, or $H_2SiW_{12}O_{40}^{=}$, or a compound containing one of these anions.

SILOXANES. Compounds having the general formula $H_3Si(OSiH_2)_nOSiH_3$ are called disiloxane, trisiloxane, etc., according to the number of silicon atoms present. They have the generic name siloxanes. (In disiloxane, n in the above formula has a value of 0, in trisiloxane, a value of 1, etc.)

SILOXY. The radical H_3Si-O-.

SILTHIANES. Compounds having the general formula $H_3Si(SSiH_2)_nSSiH_3$ which are called disilthiane, trisilthiane, etc., according to the number of silicon atoms present. They have the generic name *silthianes*. (In disilthiane, n in the above formula has a value of 0, in trisilthiane, a value of 1, etc.)

SILVER. Metallic element. Symbol Ag (argentum). Atomic number 47. Atomic weight 107.880. Density 10.50. Specific heat 0.0544. Melting point 960.5° C. Boiling point 1950° C. Valence 1 and 2.

Oxides, Ag_2O, Ag_2O_2. Silver occurs native, in argentite, pyrargyrite, chlorargyrite (horn silver), etc.

SILYL. The radical H_3Si-.

SILYLAMINO. The radical $H_3Si-NH-$.

SILYLENE. The radical $H_2Si=$.

SILYLIDYNE. The radical $HSi\equiv$.

SILYLTHIO. The radical H_3Si-S-.

SIMON-CHAVAUNE TEST REACTIONS. (1) A test for ethyl glyoxylate made by heating the sample with ammonia. A black substance, soluble in water and insoluble in alcohol, is produced if glyoxalates are present; it dissolves in alkali hydroxides and carbonates with a deep red color.

(2) Ethylglyoxalate condenses with phenylhydrazine, hydroxylamine, or semicarbazide.

SIMON REACTION FOR PHENYLHYDRAZINE. Add a few drops of an aqueous solution of trimethylamine and of dilute sodium nitroprusside solution to a solution of phenylhydrazine and heat. The mixture becomes blue, and this color is darkened by potassium hydroxide and changed to sky-blue by acetic acid. The permanence of this color distinguishes it from the aldehyde reaction.

SIMON TEST FOR ALDEHYDES. Add to the liquid to be tested, a few drops of aqueous trimethylamine solution and some very dilute sodium nitroprusside solution. A blue color is given by aldehydes.

SIMON TEST FOR AMINES. A test for the differentiation of primary amines by the use of acetaldehyde and sodium nitroprusside. Primary amines give a red color, and other amines a blue one.

SIMON TEST REACTION FOR PYRUVIC ACID. The pyruvic acid solution is first treated with ammonia and then some sodium nitroprusside solution is added and the mixture is heated gently. A blue-violet color, changing to orange on long standing, is formed.

SIMONIS REACTION. A method of formation of chromones (or coumarins) by condensation of phenols with β-keto esters. The use of phosphorus pentoxide as a condensing agent favors the formation of chromones (as sulfuric acid favors coumarins).

point, provided only that the delivery point is below the starting point. It must be filled with liquid in order to start the flow.

SISLEY-FREHSE REAGENT. A mixture of 1.4 g. p-nitroaniline, 2.8 g. hydro-

See also **Pechmann condensation.**

SIMPLE. (1) Elementary. (2) Not complex, as a simple ether.

SIMPLE POLYMERIZATION. See **polymerization, simple.**

SIMULTANEOUS REACTION. See **reaction, simultaneous.**

SINGLET LINKAGE. See **linkage, singlet.**

SINGLETON TEST REACTIONS. Tests for osmium as follows: (1) Add thiocarbanilide to the sample and shake with ether. The ether layer becomes a deep red color if osmium is present. (2) If osmium is in the form of osmate, a red color is given with thiourea solution.

SINGULAR SOLUTION. See **solution, singular.**

SINTERING. A process for the production of pieces of larger size, such as lumps or briquettes, from small particles by the action of heat. This process, which is important in metallurgy, owes its action to recrystallization and crystal growth, accompanied in many cases by a change in the crystalline form.

SIPHON. A pipe, commonly in the shape of an inverted U, used for conducting liquids from one point to another. If the pipe is continuous it may rise to a height considerably higher than its starting

chloric acid and 10 ml. water, which is heated until a clear solution is obtained, diluted with 30 ml. water, and then diazotized with 8 ml. of a 10% sodium nitrite solution, then diluted to 100 ml. and used to determine the purity of olive oil. An orange or red color shows the presence of adulterating substances.

SIVADJIAN TEST FOR CARBON TETRACHLORIDE IN CHLOROFORM. Place some 1% pyrocatechol solution and 2 ml. of the chloroform in a test tube, then permit 0.5 ml. sodium hydroxide solution to flow in, avoiding mixing as much as possible. Add a pinch of copper powder, heat rapidly to boiling and boil for 8–10 seconds, cool rapidly in running water and filter. The resulting liquid is yellowish to brownish if the chloroform contains no more than 0.25% carbon tetrachloride; yellow-orange if it contains between 0.25% and 0.5%; and more or less purple-red if it contains more than 0.5%.

SIVADJIAN TEST REACTION FOR ALKALOIDS OF EPHEDRA. Render the salts alkaline with 0.1 N sodium hydroxide, then treat with hydrogen peroxide containing 4% sodium chloride. A red-violet to yellow color is given, if alkaloids of ephedra are present.

SIVADJIAN TEST REACTION FOR AMINES. With primary amines, chloranil produces a red color; with secondary amines, a violet color; and with tertiary amines, an emerald-green color.

SIZES. Materials such as starch or gum which are used to seal the pores of surfaces, to make them less penetrable by water, and to stiffen fabrics. Sizes are used extensively in the paper and textile industries.

SKELETON. The framework which indicates the atomic structure of a compound or a class of compounds. The benzene ring is the skeleton of many aromatic compounds. Cf. **nucleus.**

SKEY REAGENT. A reagent for alkaloids, which consists of a solution of potassium zinc thiocyanate or potassium thiocyanate in combination with a metal salt. Characteristic precipitates with the alkaloids are formed by this reagent.

SKEY TEST REACTION FOR COBALT. Add some citric or tartaric acid to the solution and follow with an excess of ammonia and some potassium ferricyanide. A dark red color indicates the presence of cobalt.

SKIOGRAPH. An apparatus which measures the intensity of x-rays.

SKRAUP REACTION. The preparation of quinoline and its derivatives from an aromatic amine (aniline and its derivatives), glycerol, sulfuric acid, and an oxidizer (nitrobenzene or arsenic oxide). The glycerol probably yields acrolein, which condenses with the aniline, and the acrolein-aniline thus produced condenses to quinoline.

flux that may have been used in the smelting. Slag usually floats on the molten metal and solidifies on cooling.

SLATER TEST. A test for arsenic and antimony spots made by placing the porcelain plate, which carries the arsenic or antimony spots obtained in the Marsh test, over a small receptacle containing 1 drop of bromine. Arsenic spots become lemon-yellow, but antimony spots color more rapidly and are orange-yellow. On exposure to the air, both spots become colorless.

SLAWIK TEST FOR VANADIUM IN STEEL. Add ammonium persulfate to steel turnings which have been dissolved in dilute nitric acid and heat until gas evolution ceases. Cool the mixture and add phosphoric acid to decolorize it, and then cautiously float hydrogen peroxide on the mixture. A red-brown zone is developed in the presence of vanadium.

SLAWIK TEST REACTION FOR FERROUS SALTS. Mix 1 ml. of a saturated alcoholic solution of dimethylglyoxime with 1 drop of a ferrous salt solution to which has been added a little tartaric acid, and then follow with an excess of ammonia. An intense red color forms.

SLIME. A solution of a solid in a liquid, or more commonly a suspension, which, because of the presence of gelatinous substances, **colloids,** or even very fine mineral

$$\text{(benzene ring with } NH_2) + \underset{\underset{CH_2OH}{|}}{\overset{\overset{CH_2OH}{|}}{CHOH}} \xrightarrow[\text{[O]}]{H_2SO_4} \text{(quinoline ring with } N) + 4H_2O.$$

SKRAUP TEST REACTION. A test for thalline solutions, which are colored green by oxidizers such as ferric chloride, chlorine, or chromic acid.

SLAG. The material which separates from the molten metal during the smelting of ores; it consists largely of the nonreduced portion of the ore, in combination with any

particles, often feels slippery to the touch. Mineral slimes are produced by the very fine grinding of rocks often necessary in the flotation process.

SLUDGE. A solid residue, usually containing liquid, which is often the end-product or waste-product of various processes.

SLUDGE, ACTIVATED. See **activated sludge.**

SLURRY. A thin, watery mixture.

Sm Symbol for the element **samarium.**

SMECTIC PHASE. One of the forms of the **mesomorphic state,** or the **"liquid crystals."** In the smectic phase, flow does not occur normally; the substance often forms drops which show a series of fine lines, especially on examination with polarized light. The liquid motion is more of a "gliding" than a flowing action, and x-ray diffraction patterns are obtained in one direction only.

SMELTING. In general, any method of obtaining metals from their ores, which includes fusion; or the fusion operation itself, in which the raw or partly-processed ore is heated in a furnace, with or without added fluxing agents, until the molten metal is separated.

SMILES REARRANGEMENT. A rearrangement of diaryl sulfones, sulfides, ethers, and similar compounds containing, in a position ortho to the groups named above, a hydroxy, amino, or similar group. The rearrangement results in the breaking of the bond between the sulfone, sulfide, etc., group and one of the aryl groups, and the formation of a new bond linking the aryl groups through the hydroxy, amino, or similar, group.

SMITH TEST FOR FORMIC ACID. Add ferric chloride to the neutral solution to be tested. If a red color is produced, add 5 ml. of alcohol per ml. of solution. A precipitate forms if formic acid is present.

SMITH TEST REACTION FOR ALKALOIDS. A few mg. of the alkaloid added to molten antimony trichloride produce the following reactions: brucine, dark red; veratrine, brick-red; aconitine, bronze; narcotine, dark green; narceine, yellow; morphine and codeine, green; thebaine, red.

SMITH TEST REACTIONS FOR CARBAZIDES. A red color develops which is fairly stable for several days, when carbazide or semicarbazide hydrochlorides and diacetylglyoxime are heated with hydrochloric acid. Heating with diacetyl produces a similar color. A bluish-violet color is produced by adding ammonia.

SMITH TEST REACTION FOR FLUORIDE. Fluorides change ferric thiocyanate solution from deep red to orange or yellow. The color is inversely proportional to the quantity of fluoride present and can be used for quantitative estimation of fluoride, provided interfering substances are not present.

SMOKE. In general, a system of solid particles dispersed in a gaseous medium. The gases resulting from combustion constitute a special case.

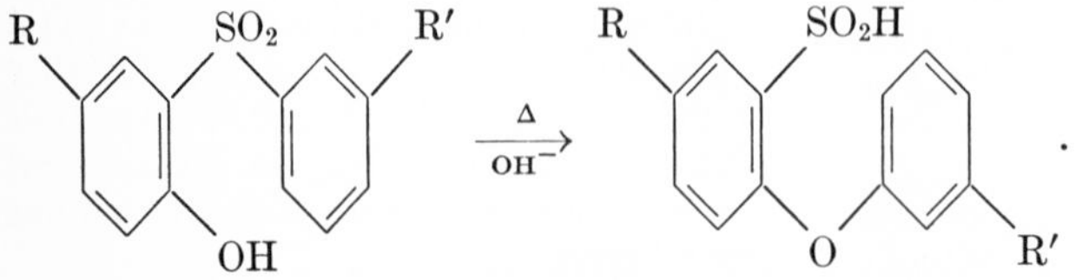

SMITH REAGENT FOR FREE ACIDS. Freshly precipitated silver chloride is dissolved in ammonia and a little of the silver chloride is left undissolved to be certain that the ammonia is fully saturated with silver chloride. This reagent forms precipitates with solutions containing free acids, even very weak acids.

SMOLUCHOWSKI EQUATION. See **equation, Schmoluchowski.**

Sn Symbol for the element **tin.**

SOAP. A compound of one of the higher **fatty acids** or a mixture of such compounds. The true soaps are salts of the alkali metals and are soluble in water but the term has been extended to include the salts of other metals, some of which are insoluble in water; combinations of fatty acids and certain organic bases, such as ethanolamine; mixtures of the foregoing substances with alkaline silicates, glycerol, and other additives. See also **detergent.**

SOAP, METALLIC. A compound formed by the reaction of a metal or metal oxide with an organic acid; in other words, a salt of a heavy metal and an organic acid. Metallic soaps are used as driers in the paint industry, and for other industrial purposes.

SOBOLEWA-ZALESKI TEST. A test for aldehydes made by acidifying the solution to be tested with 2–4% hydrochloric acid and adding a filtered aqueous solution of 1–2 g. pyrrol per liter. A turbidity is produced by small quantities of aldehydes, and a red color by larger quantities.

SODA NITRIC PROCESS. An old process (still operated in scattered small or local installations) for the production of oxides of nitrogen, or nitric acid itself, by treatment of sodium nitrate with sulfuric acid.

SODAIC, SODIC, SODIO-. Containing or pertaining to the metal **sodium.**

SODERBERG CELL. A cell for the production of aluminum by electrolysis of alumina dissolved in a bath of molten salts. This cell uses a large electrode, cylindrical in form, which originates as a carbonaceous mixture in a hopper above the cell, and becomes hard and conductive by heating as it moves down into the cell.

SODIUM. Metallic element. Symbol Na (natrium). Atomic number 11. Atomic weight 22.997. Density 0.97. Specific heat 0.253. Melting point 97.5° C. Boiling point 880° C. Valence 1. Oxides Na_2O, Na_2O_2. Sodium occurs in sea water, rock salt, cryolite, borax, etc.

SODYL. The radical—NaO.

SOFTENER. This term is widely used in chemical technology in its common meaning to denote a material or agent which is added to a product or process to increase the pliability or plasticity of any substance. A special usage is in the treatment of water, in which the term "water softener" is applied to a substance used to remove undesirable salts.

SOFTENING TEMPERATURE. A more or less definite physical constant of a substance that does not have a definite melting point, defined as the temperature at which viscous flow changes to plastic flow.

SOGASOID. A dispersed system of a solid in a gas (see **smoke**).

SOL. A **colloidal solution** in which the system is apparently liquid. If water is the continuous phase the system is termed a hydrosol. The term sol is also applied to the dispersion medium of a colloidal solution.

SOLATION. In colloidal nomenclature, the process of change from a **gel** to a **sol.** The gel is said to solate.

SOLDAINI SOLUTION. A solution of 41.6 g. potassium bicarbonate in 140 ml. water, in which 1.5 g. cupric carbonate are then dissolved; it is used as a test reagent for glucose, which reduces it.

SOLDER. An alloy which is applied in fused form to join two metallic surfaces.

SOLID. A state of aggregation in which the substance possesses both definite volume and definite shape. Solids possess elasticity both of shape and bulk, i.e., they resist any force that tends to alter their volume or form. Solids are characterized by very stable surfaces of distinct outline on all sides.

SOLID STRUCTURE. See **solution, solid.**

SOLIDIFY. To become solid. To change from the gaseous or liquid to the solid state.

SOLIDUS CURVE. A curve representing the **equilibrium** between the solid phase and the liquid phase in a **condensed system**

of two **components.** The relationship is reduced to a two-dimensional curve by disregarding the influence of the vapor phase. The points on the solidus curve are obtained by plotting the temperature at which the last of the liquid phase solidifies, against the composition, usually in terms of the percentage composition of one of the two components.

SOLIQUID. A dispersed system of a solid in a liquid. (See **colloid.**)

SOLM REAGENT. A solution of 0.5 g. ricin in 50 ml. of a 5% sodium chloride solution, to which 0.5 ml. 0.1 N hydrochloric acid is then added. It is used in testing for pepsin, which clarifies the solution.

SOLUBILITY. A property of a substance by virtue of which it forms mixtures with other substances which are chemically and physically homogeneous throughout. The degree of solubility (often spoken of as "solubility") is the concentration of a solute in a saturated solution at any given temperature. The degree of solubility of most substances increases with rise in temperature, but there are cases (notably the organic salts of calcium) where a substance is more soluble in cold than in hot solvents.

SOLUBILITY, APPARENT. The total amount of a salt present in unit volume of a solution (see **solubility, real**).

SOLUBILITY COEFFICIENT OF GASES. The volume of gas, under the experimental conditions of pressure and temperature, dissolved by unit volume of solvent.

SOLUBILITY CURVE. The graph showing the variation with temperature of the concentration by a substance in its **saturated solution** in a solvent.

SOLUBILITY PRODUCT. A numerical quantity dependent upon the temperature and the solvent, characteristic of electrolytes. It is the product of the concentration of ions in a saturated solution and defines the degree of solubility of the substance. When the product of the ion concentrations exceeds the solubility product, precipitation commonly results.

SOLUBILITY, REAL. The amount of nonionized dissolved salt that exists in unit volume of a solution, as distinguished from "apparent" solubility, which includes both the nonionized and ionized salt.

SOLUBILITY, RETROGRADE. Solubility which decreases with rise in temperature, as that of sodium sulfate above 34° C., and that of a number of organic calcium salts.

SOLUBLE. Capable of dissolving, i.e., of forming a single, homogeneous **phase** with a specified solid or liquid.

SOLUTE. The dissolved substance in a **solution.**

SOLUTIDE. A true **solution.**

SOLUTION. A homogeneous mixture of substances which forms a single **phase.** Gases are mutually soluble in all proportions; liquids may dissolve gases, other liquids, and solids; and solutions of solids in solids are known.

SOLUTION, ANISOTONIC. A solution that is not isotonic; see **solution, isotonic.**

SOLUTION, AQUEOUS. A solution in water.

SOLUTION, BUFFER. A solution whose **pH** is not notably altered upon addition of considerable quantities of **acid** or **base.** A buffer solution consists of a weak acid and a salt with the same anion as that of the acid, or of a weak base and a salt with the same cation as the base.

SOLUTION, CHEMICAL. A solution in which there is a chemical reaction between solvent and solute so that the solute cannot be recovered unchanged by physical processes.

SOLUTION, COLLOIDAL. (Disperse system) A heterogeneous system consisting of more than one **phase.** The solvent is termed the continuous phase and the suspended matter the disperse phase. The disperse phase consists of minute aggregated particles, each of which is very much larger than any of the constituent molecules. (This property distinguishes colloidal from real solutions.) If the disperse phase is a solid, the system is termed a colloid; if liquid, an emulsoid or emulsion (provided the particles of disperse phase are quite large).

SOLUTION, DIFFERENTIAL HEAT OF. See **heat of solution, differential.**

SOLUTION, GRAM-MOLECULAR. See **solution, molar.**

SOLUTION, HEAT OF. See **heat of solution, differential,** and **heat of solution, integral.**

SOLUTION, HYPERTONIC. A solution having an **osmotic pressure** greater than that of blood serum.

SOLUTION, HYPOTONIC. A solution having an **osmotic pressure** less than that of blood serum.

SOLUTION, IDEAL. A solution that conforms exactly to the **law of Raoult** over the entire range of composition and at all temperatures.

SOLUTION, INTEGRAL HEAT OF. See **heat of solution, integral.**

SOLUTION, ISOHYDRIC. See **isohydric solution.**

SOLUTION, ISOTONIC. A solution having the same **osmotic pressure** as that of blood serum.

SOLUTION, MOLAL. A solution that contains a mole of solute dissolved in one kilogram of solvent.

SOLUTION, MOLAR. A solution that contains a mole of solute dissolved in one liter of solution.

SOLUTION, NORMAL. A solution containing one gram equivalent of a particular **constituent** of the solute in a liter of solution.

SOLUTION, PHYSICAL. In distinction from a **solution, chemical** a physical solution is one in which there is no reaction between solute and solvent, so that recovery of both, in original composition, may be accomplished by physical processes.

SOLUTION, PHYSIOLOGICAL. See **solution, isotonic.**

SOLUTION POLYMERIZATION. See **polymerization, solution.**

SOLUTION PRESSURE. (1) The force impelling molecules or atoms to cross a **phase** boundary and enter into solution. (2) A term introduced by Nernst to denote the property possessed by metals, hydrogen, and certain non-metals, whereby they tend to pass into solution as ions. However, it has not been found possible to devise a method for the measurement of the absolute potential between an electrode and a solution of its ions.

SOLUTION PRESSURE, ELECTROLYTIC. See **electrolytic solution pressure.**

SOLUTION, SATURATED. A solution containing the maximum proportion of solute to solvent at that temperature under **equilibrium** conditions; in other words, a solution which does not change in concentration of solute as more solute is added.

SOLUTION, SINGULAR. A solution whose **vapor pressure** curve as a function of composition shows a maximum or minimum indicating the formation of a **constant boiling mixture,** as in aqueous solutions of alcohol.

SOLUTION, SOLID. A solid homogeneous complex of several substances the proportions of which may vary without affecting the homogeneity of the solid phase (van't Hoff). Isomorphous mixtures are solid solutions.

SOLUTION, STANDARD. Any solution of known, definite concentration.

SOLUTION, STANDARDIZED. A solution adjusted to contain a definite known concentration of solute.

SOLUTION, SUPERSATURATED. A solution which contains a greater quantity of dissolved solute than that which can exist at the given temperature in stable **equilibrium** with the solid solute. Supersaturated solutions are **metastable systems** in which a true equilibrium is not established. Addition of solid substance, stirring, friction, etc., cause the separation of the excess of solute.

SOLUTION VOLUME. See **molecular solution volume.**

SOLUTIONS, CONJUGATE. The two liquid **phases** of a partly-miscible, two-component system, in which one phase is a **saturated solution** of component A in component B, and the other phase is a saturated solution of component B in component A.

SOLUTIONS, ISOPIESTIC. Solutions that exert equal **vapor pressures.**

SOLVABLE. Soluble.

SOLVATE. A complex particle formed by combination of particles of solvent and solute, or a system containing such particles. Illustrations are complexes of the type $R(H_2O)_x$ formed in aqueous solution, where R is an ion, formed by **ionization** of the solute.

SOLVATION. The formation of a complex between solute and solvent in solution under certain circumstances.

SOLVAY PROCESS. A method for the production of sodium carbonate from sodium chloride and calcium carbonate. Ammonia is used as an intermediate agent, forming ammonium bicarbonate with the carbon dioxide from the calcium carbonate. The ammonium bicarbonate reacts with sodium chloride to form sodium bicarbonate and ammonium chloride, which returns its ammonia to the process on treatment with the calcium hydroxide formed from the calcium carbonate.

SOLVENT. Usually the term denotes a liquid which dissolves another compound to form a homogeneous one-phase liquid mixture. In a wider meaning, the term denotes that component of a gaseous, liquid, or solid mixture which is present in excess over all other components of the system.

SOLVENT, ACIDIC. See **acidic solvent.**

SOLVENT, AMPHIPROTIC. See **amphiprotic solvent.**

SOLVENT, ASSOCIATING. A solvent that undergoes **chemical association,** the formation of complexes between its molecules.

SOLVENT, BASIC. See **basic solvent.**

SOLVENT, CHEMICAL. A designation sometimes applied to solvents in cases where the process of solution is attended by a chemical reaction between solvent and solute.

SOLVENT, DISSOCIATING. A solvent in which solutes that associate in many other solvents enter into solution as single molecules. Thus, various carboxylic acids associate and hence give abnormal elevations of the boiling point, abnormal depressions of the freezing point, etc., in many organic solvents; in water, however, they do not associate. Therefore, water is called a dissociating solvent for such solutes.

SOLVENT, IMMISCIBLE. A liquid that dissolves or extracts a substance from solution in another solvent without mixing with the other solvent.

SOLVENT, NONPOLAR. A solvent whose constituent molecules do not possess permanent **dipole moments** and which do not form ionized solutions.

SOLVENT, NORMAL. A solvent that does not undergo **chemical association,** the formation of complexes between its molecules.

SOLVENT, PHYSICAL. A solvent that does not react with the solute in the process of solution. (Contrast **solvent, chemical.**)

SOLVENT, POLAR. A solvent consisting of polar molecules, i.e., molecules that exert local electrical forces. In such solvents **electrolytes** (salts, acids, and bases) dissociate into ions, and form electrically-conducting solutions. Water, ammonia, and sulfur dioxide are representative polar solvents.

SOLVENT, PROTOGENIC. An acidic solvent; one that is a **proton** donor.

SOLVOLYSIS. A generalized conception of the relation between a solvent and a solute (i.e., a relation between two components of a single-phase homogeneous system) whereby the solvent molecule donates a proton to, or accepts a proton from a molecule of solute, or both, forming one or more different molecules. A particular case of special interest occurs when water is used as solvent, in which case the interaction between solute and solvent is called **hydrolysis.**

SOMMELET REACTION. A method of obtaining **aldehydes** from organic **halides** by forming the hexamethylenetetramine addition product, and hydrolyzing it with hot water.

$$RCH_2X + C_6H_{12}N_4 \rightarrow RCH_2(C_6H_{12}N_4)X \xrightarrow{H_2O} RCHO.$$

See **Delépine reaction.**

SOMMELET REARRANGEMENT. The acid-catalyzed rearrangement of benzhydryltrimethylammonium hydroxide to o-benzylbenzyldimethylamine

$$(C_6H_5)_2CH.N(CH_3)_3OH \xrightarrow{H_2SO_4} C_6H_5.CH_2.C_6H_4.CH_2.N(CH_3)_2 + H_2O.$$

SÖNN-MULLER METHOD. A method of conversion of **amides** to **aldehydes,** involving dehydration to imidochlorides, followed by reduction to imines and hydrolysis to the aldehydes.

$$RCO.NH_2 \xrightarrow{SOCl_2} RCCl:NH \xrightarrow{SnCl_2+HCl} RCH:NH.HCl \xrightarrow{H_2O} RCHO + NH_4Cl.$$

SONNENSCHEIN REAGENTS FOR ALKALOIDS. (1) A preparation of ammonium phosphomolybdate which is dissolved

in nitric acid, evaporated, and redissolved in dilute nitric acid; or a similar solution evaporated with aqua regia and dissolved in dilute nitric acid; and (2) sulfuric acid solution of ceroceric oxide. These reagents are used to identify and separate alkaloids.

SOPORIFIC. A drug that produces deep sleep.

SORBED. See **sorption.**

SORBIC. Related to sorbic acid,

$$CH_3.CH:CH.CH:CH.COOH.$$

SØRENSEN NOMENCLATURE. See **hydrogen ion concentration.**

SØRENSEN STANDARD PHOSPHATE SOLUTIONS. Aqueous solutions ($M/15$ in strength) of (1) disodium hydrogen phosphate, and (2) potassium dihydrogen phosphate, used in pH adjustment in culture media.

SORPTION. A generalized term for the many phenomena commonly included under the terms **adsorption** and **absorption** when the nature of the phenomenon involved in a particular case is unknown or indefinite.

SOSOLOID. A dispersed system of a solid phase in a solid phase.

SOULE TEST REACTION. A test for nickel made by adding an aqueous solution of α-furildioxime to weakly ammoniacal solutions of nickel. It gives an insoluble precipitate of nickel-furildioxime.

SOXHLET EXTRACTION APPARATUS. Laboratory apparatus used in the extraction of solids, consisting of a boiling flask for the solvent, a condenser for the vapor so produced, and between the two a special glass apparatus in which the solid to be extracted is placed, usually held in a porous cup. Special features of this glass extraction apparatus are an integral by-pass glass tube for the vapor ascending from boiling flask to condenser and a siphon for the return of the extracting solvent to the boiling flask.

SOYER TEST. A test for phosphine in hydrogen made by bubbling the hydrogen through water, passing it through a plug of glass wool, and then through a glass tube with a platinum tip. It is ignited and a porcelain cover held over the flame. A green coloration indicates phosphine.

SPACE FORMULA. A structural formula, or more commonly a group of structural formulas grouped to show differences between stereoisomers, or compounds identical in composition but differing in spatial arrangement. A simple space formula is that showing the two stereoisomers of lactic acid:

$$\begin{array}{ccc} & \text{H} & \text{OH} & \text{O} \\ & | & | & \diagup\!\diagup \\ \text{H}-\text{C}-\text{C}-\text{C} \\ & | & | & \diagdown \\ & \text{H} & \text{H} & \text{OH} \end{array} \qquad \begin{array}{ccc} & \text{H} & \text{H} & \text{O} \\ & | & | & \diagup\!\diagup \\ \text{H}-\text{C}-\text{C}-\text{C} \\ & | & | & \diagdown \\ & \text{H} & \text{OH} & \text{OH} \end{array} \;.$$

SPACE GROUP. One of the 230 different arrangements produced by the application of the possible **symmetry elements** to the points of the space **lattice,** which is the spatial distribution of the atoms or groups of atoms in a crystal, using purely geometric methods.

SPACE LATTICE. In general, an arrangement of particles in space; specifically the arrangement in a **crystal** of the constituent atoms or radicals which is determined from the **diffraction patterns** obtained by x-ray photography and other methods.

SPACU-KURAS REAGENT. The compound mercaptobenzothiazole, which is used as a reagent for metals. Characteristic colors are given by this reagent with many metals.

SPACU-SPACU TEST FOR IODATE. To a solution of 0.03 mg. or more of iodate, add a few drops of 0.1 molar mercurous nitrate. A white precipitate of mercurous iodate is formed. The precipitate will dissolve if an excess of mercurous nitrate is not avoided.

SPACU-SPACU TEST FOR THIOSULFATE. The reagent is made by adding ethylenediamine to a solution of nickel nitrate until the solution has a violet color. A violet, crystalline precipitate is obtained by treating a cold, neutral or slightly alkaline solution of thiosulfate with an excess of the reagent. This precipitate is not soluble in cold water, alcohol, methanol, ether, acetone, or chloroform.

SPACU TEST REACTION FOR CADMIUM. An aqueous solution of a cadmium salt in the presence of pyridine forms a white, crystalline precipitate upon the addition of potassium thiocyanate. This precipitate is soluble in excess of pyridine and decomposed by acids.

SPACU TEST REACTIONS FOR COPPER. (1) Add a few drops of an alkali thiocyanate solution and 2 drops of freshly prepared 2% alcoholic tolidine solution to a very dilute copper solution. A blue flocculent precipitate forms.

(2) When an aqueous solution of copper salt is treated with pyridine and alkali thiocyanate, a compound insoluble in water but soluble in chloroform is formed. A green color is produced in chloroform. Several modifications of these reactions have been developed.

SPACU TEST REACTION FOR ZINC. Pyridine and ammonium thiocyanate solution added to a solution of a zinc salt produces zinc pyrodino-thiocyanate which is insoluble in water. This reaction takes place in neutral solution or with a slight excess of pyridine. The precipitate is dissolved in a great excess of pyridine.

SPALLATION. A nuclear reaction resulting from bombardment of atoms with high energy projectiles, such as 200 m.e.v. **protons** and 400 m.e.v. **alpha particles,** whereby nuclei having atomic numbers 10 to 20 lower than the bombarded nucleus are obtained. The difference is largely in the form of ejected protons and alpha particles. Spallations differ from ordinary nuclear reactions in that the latter rarely yield, at first instance, atoms differing in atomic number by more than 2, from the bombarded nucleus. Spallations differ from nuclear fission processes in that the reaction is not self-sustaining and that the changes in nuclear mass in spallation are not as large as usually encountered in fission.

SPALLING. The splitting-off portions of solids as a result of internal thermal or mechanical stresses.

SPARK LINE (ION LINE). A spectral line produced by radiation from ions (a loose term; see **arc line**).

SPARK SPECTRUM. See **spectrum, spark.**

SPARKING POTENTIAL. See **potential, sparking.**

SPECIFIC. (1) Related to a particular class or entity. (2) A drug that has a direct action, or a specially effective action, toward the treatment or cure of a particular disease.

SPECIFIC CATALYSIS. See **catalysis, specific.**

SPECIFIC CONDUCTANCE. See **conductance, specific.**

SPECIFIC DISPERSIVITY. See **dispersivity, specific.**

SPECIFIC GRAVITY. The ratio between the **density** of a substance at a given temperature and the density of some substance assumed as standard. For liquids and solids the standard assumed is either the density of distilled water at $4°$ C., or the density of distilled water at $60°$ F. (This value is often used in calibrating industrial **hydrometers**.) For gases the standards are air, hydrogen, or oxygen at $0°$ C., and a pressure of 760 millimeters of mercury, or distilled water at $4°$ C. The specific

gravity is a relative property that varies with the temperature.

SPECIFIC HEAT. The quantity of heat required to raise the temperature of unit mass of a substance one degree of temperature. Two figures are obtained for the specific heat of any gas according to whether the volume or the pressure is kept constant during the determination. The specific heat at constant pressure is greater than the specific heat at constant volume, by the amount of heat needed to produce expansion.

SPECIFIC HEATS, DEBYE THEORY OF. See **Debye theory of specific heats.**

SPECIFIC INDUCTIVE CAPACITY. The **dielectric constant.**

SPECIFIC REACTION RATE. See **reaction rate, specific.**

SPECIFIC REFRACTION. See **refraction, specific.**

SPECIFIC RESISTANCE. See **resistivity.**

SPECIFIC ROTATION. See **rotation, specific.**

SPECIFIC SURFACE. The surface, or area, of a substance or entity per unit volume; obtained by dividing the area by the volume, and expressed in reciprocal units of length.

SPECIFIC VISCOSITY. See **viscosity, specific.**

SPECIFIC VOLUME. The volume of a substance or entity per unit mass, obtained by dividing the volume by the mass; and expressed in units of length to the third power and reciprocal units of mass.

SPECIFIC WEIGHT. Specific gravity.

SPECTRA. Plural of **spectrum.**

SPECTRAL DISTRIBUTION CURVE (OF A SOURCE). The curve showing the **radiant power** emitted by a source as a function of **wave length** or **frequency.**

SPECTRAL POSITION. The effective wave length or frequency of an essentially monochromatic beam.

SPECTROGRAM. A record produced by a spectrograph, i.e., a record of a spectroscopic process, commonly one obtained by photographic methods.

SPECTROGRAPH. An instrument used to produce a record of a **spectrum.** It may be considered to include the apparatus for producing the radiations or particles to be investigated; and includes the other necessary apparatus, i.e., that for selecting a desired portion of the radiations or particles; that for arranging them in a uniform beam; that for separating the beam into a spectrum; and that for recording the spectrum by photographic or other means.

SPECTROGRAPH, QUARTZ. A spectrograph designed to detect radiations in the ultraviolet region of the electromagnetic spectrum. The optical system is constructed of quartz because ordinary glass is opaque over most of the ultraviolet spectral region.

SPECTROGRAPH, MASS. An instrument used to determine the relative masses of atoms or molecules, which are first **ionized** by electron bombardment, then accelerated by an electric field, and finally sent through a magnetic field. Ionized particles traversing the magnetic field experience an angular deflection whose magnitude depends on the mass of the particle. Atoms or molecules of different masses may be separated in this manner and their relative masses and concentrations determined by collecting the ions at the end of their trajectories.

SPECTROLOGY. Spectrum analysis.

SPECTROMETER. An instrument used to measure spectra or to determine **wave lengths** of the various radiations.

SPECTROPHOTOMETER. An instrument used to determine the intensity of radiations of various **wave lengths** in a **spectrum.**

SPECTROPHOTOMETRY, REFLECTANCE. Measurements of the intensity of various spectral frequencies, or narrow bands, of light reflected from surfaces, especially as applied to the specification of color, to problems in optical microchemistry, to uses in cytochemistry and histochemistry, and for other purposes.

SPECTROSCOPE. An instrument that disperses **radiation** into a **spectrum** for visual observation.

SPECTROSCOPE, COMPARISON. An instrument for comparing spectra, as used, for example, to compare the absorption lines in the spectra of stars and other astronomical objects, with the spectra of elements whose presence in the star is under investigation.

SPECTROSCOPE, DIRECT-VISION. A spectroscope without deflection of light, i.e., in which all components lie along one axis.

SPECTROSCOPE, GRATING. A spectroscope in which the resolving element for light of different wave lengths is a **diffraction grating.**

SPECTROSCOPE, PRISM. A spectroscope in which the resolving element for light of different wave lengths is a **prism.**

SPECTROSCOPE, MASS. See **spectrograph, mass.**

SPECTROSCOPIC ANALYSIS. Analysis of the conposition of substances through the use of the spectroscope.

SPECTROSCOPY. The branch of physical science treating the theory and interpretation of spectra.

SPECTRUM. (1) The resolution pattern of a group of radiations into its component parts over a surface or region in which radiation of any given wave length is physically separate from radiations of neighboring wave lengths. (2) The resolution pattern of a group of masses over a region according to increasing mass, in which particles of a given mass are physically isolated from those of neighboring masses. (3) A mathematical concept denoting the types of solutions which are associated with a given partial differential equation.

SPECTRUM, ABSORPTION. A band of light or other radiation produced from a composite train of light **frequencies,** or frequencies of other **radiations,** after it has passed through an absorbing medium, by which certain frequencies are absorbed, and after the remaining frequencies have been spread out into a band by means of a prism, grating, or other diffraction apparatus. Such spectra are characterized by dark lines, or bands, which appear at points where the absorbed frequencies would normally occur.

SPECTRUM, ANALYSIS. See **analysis, spectrum.**

SPECTRUM, ARC. A spectrum produced at the temperature of the **electric arc.** The element or compound under investigation is placed between the electrodes forming the arc, or is applied to them as a coating; and the light emitted from the arc is examined spectroscopically.

SPECTRUM, ATOMIC. When gases or vapors are heated to incandescence they produce spectra containing, commonly, lines and/or bands occupying definite positions in the electromagnetic spectrum corresponding to definite wave lengths. The line spectra produced by excitation of atomic valence electrons are called atomic spectra. The method of heating, or excitation, of the material may be by means of a flame, an electric arc, or an electric spark.

SPECTRUM, BAND. See **spectrum, molecular.**

SPECTRUM, CHANNELED. A spectrum in which there are interference bands, usually produced by the interaction of light rays approximately one half wave length apart in phase, as those resulting from reflection from parallel surfaces.

SPECTRUM, COMPARISON. A spectrum used as a standard for comparison to other spectra in spectrographic work, commonly by photographic methods.

SPECTRUM, CONTINUOUS. A spectrum without dark lines or bands caused by the absence of radiations of certain frequencies. A well-known example is the spectrum of white light that contains all the colors from red to violet and shows no discontinuities at any point. The spectra from incandescent bodies, molten metals, and incandescent lamps are often continuous.

SPECTRUM, DIFFRACTION. The spectrum produced by **diffraction,** as may be produced by a **diffraction grating.**

SPECTRUM, EMISSION. A spectrum of the type produced by an incandescent gas, which shows definite lines or bands at various frequencies. If these frequencies lie within the visible range, then their corresponding lines or bands are of characteristic colors.

SPECTRUM, FINE. The resolution of lines in atomic emission spectra, by high-power spectroscopes, into two or more fine lines situated close together. The fine lines in atomic spectra arise from so-called term **multiplicities,** i.e., from transition between groups of higher, to groups of lower, levels, the levels comprising each group lying close together. Groups of close-lying levels are obtained by coupling the **orbital angular momentum vector** with the **spin angular momentum vector** of the atom in a variety of possible combinations.

SPECTRUM, FLAME. A spectrum of a substance obtained at the temperature of flame, commonly by maintaining a supply of the substance in the Bunsen flame.

SPECTRUM, FLASH. (1) An atomic emission spectrum obtained in solar spectrophotography of the sun's corona. It shows the characteristic lines of many elements known to be present in the sun from the ordinary Fraunhofer absorption spectrum. (2) A spectrum obtained by irradiating the material under study with a very intense but short flash of exciting radiation.

SPECTRUM, HYPERFINE. In the case of atomic emission spectra, there is, in addition to the fine structure (see **spectrum, fine**) of the spectral lines attributable to term multiplicities a hyperfine structure (fine lines very close together), which is now believed to be due to an isotope effect or the **spin** of the atomic nucleus. This spin couples with the total **angular** or **orbital momentum** of the nucleus and yields a series of resulting vectors representative of closely spaced **energy levels.**

SPECTRUM, INFRARED. That region of the electromagnetic spectrum comprising radiations having wave lengths extending from the end of the visible red, at about 7.8×10^{-5} centimeters, to about 3×10^{-2} centimeters. The term infrared spectrum is also applied to a series of lines in this region obtained from a particular substance by resolution of its radiation, or by resolution of radiation transmitted through it, whereby dark lines are produced by absorption. The latter is called an infrared absorption spectrum.

SPECTRUM, INFRARED ABSORPTION (MOLECULAR). A spectrum produced by molecular absorption of radiations having wave lengths in the infrared region. These spectra depend, for their character and position, upon the energy changes involved, whether in vibrational energy, in rotational energy, or in combination. Their study furnishes considerable information about the groups and linkages in the molecule.

SPECTRUM, LINE. A spectrum consisting of various bright lines, separated by dark areas, such as the emission spectrum of an atom.

SPECTRUM, MOLECULAR. A spectrum emitted by molecules. Unlike the line spectra of atoms, molecular spectra usually appear as bands and are therefore called band spectra, although upon further analysis the bands are often shown to consist of many closely spaced lines.

SPECTRUM, NORMAL. A term applied to the diffraction **spectrum** (q.v.), because its dispersion is linear which is not the case in a spectrum obtained from a prism.

SPECTRUM, PRIMARY. The first-order spectrum produced by a **diffraction grating.**

SPECTRUM, RAMAN. Certain radiations, comprising the light scattered at right angles by a substance, which are characteristic of the substance itself. The change in frequency from that of the incident radiation is a function of the internal molecular energy and is useful in studies of structure.

SPECTRUM, ROENTGEN. See **spectrum, x-ray.**

SPECTRUM, SPARK. A spectrum produced by the passage of an electrical discharge, i.e., an electrical spark, commonly through a gas or vapor. (Spark discharges from metallic electrodes, at suitable potential, yield the spark spectra of the metallic vapors.) Variation of the applied potential has been found to change the character of the spark spectra obtained; the new series of lines observed at definite values of increasing potential are designated respectively as the first spark spectrum, the second spark spectrum, etc., those of higher numbers consisting of shorter wave lengths. It is believed that these successive spectra represent progressive stages in the ionization of the atoms emitting them.

SPECTRUM, ULTRAVIOLET. The portion of the electromagnetic **spectrum** that begins at the end of the violet portion of the visible spectrum, at a wave length of about 3900–4000 Ångström units, and consists of the radiations of decreasing wave length extending down toward the x-ray region to a wave length of about 200 Ångström units.

SPECTRUM, X-RAY. See **crystal analysis.**

SPEHL SOLUTION. A mixture of 4 ml. freshly prepared tincture of guaiac with 1 ml. 20% sodium carbonate solution, 4 ml. 3% hydrogen peroxide, and 1 ml. alcohol. This reagent is used in testing for blood. After acidification of the sample with acetic acid and extraction with ether, a blue color with the reagent indicates the presence of blood.

SPERRY PROCESS. An electrolytic method for the production of white lead, litharge, lead borate, copper carbonate, lead chromate, and similar compounds. As used for white lead, the apparatus consists of a concrete tank containing lead anodes and insoluble iron cathodes. The cathodes are suspended in porous fabric envelopes which separate the electrolytes. The catholyte is an aqueous solution of 1–3% sodium acetate, 7–14% sodium carbonate, and 5% sodium hydroxide. The anolyte is an aqueous solution of 3–5% sodium acetate, and very little of the other salts. The complex ionic interaction results in the precipitation of the lead ions dissolved from the anode as a complex compound in the proportions of basic lead carbonate, which are those of white lead.

SPHERE OF ATTRACTION OF MOLECULAR FORCES. The distance within which the mutual attraction of the molecules begins to have a "noticeable value."

SPHERICAL ABERRATION. See **aberration, spherical.**

SPHEROIDAL. Shaped like a sphere.

SPICULAR. Shaped like a needle.

SPIEGEL-MAASS TEST. A test for molybdenum. The reagent is made by adding 1 g. of freshly distilled phenylhydrazine to 70 ml. of 50% acetic acid. Add 5 ml. of the reagent to 10 ml. of the solution to be tested and heat to boiling for 1–2 minutes. A red color shows the presence of molybdenum.

SPIEGLER REAGENT. A solution used to precipitate albumin from urine when a ring test is made. This solution may be prepared by dissolving 4 g. mercuric chloride, 2 g. tartaric acid, and 10 g. sucrose in 100 ml. water; or by dissolving 4 g. mercuric chloride, 2 g. tartaric acid, 10 g. glycerol, and 5 g. sodium chloride in 100 ml. water.

SPIN. To rotate about an axis.

SPINNERET. A device for producing threads which consists of a die, tube, or other shape containing fine holes, through which a solution is forced under pressure into a coagulating bath.

SPINTHARISCOPE. An instrument used for the detection of radioactive rays, consisting essentially of a screen coated with zinc sulfide or other fluorescent material, and a tube carrying a lens for observing the screen. When radioactive material is placed near the screen, scintillations are observed.

SPIRAN. See **spiro-compound.**

SPIRIT. In chemistry a term applied to ethyl alcohol, or to solutions in ethyl alcohol of volatile substances, or (less commonly) to any distillate.

SPIRIT COLOR. A color that is soluble in alcohol. This term is used in the paint industry, and also in connection with silk dyeing and fur staining. Most spirit colors are aniline dyes which are more soluble in water than in alcohol.

SPIRO-COMPOUND. An organic compound in which two ring structures have one carbon atom in common.

SPIRO TEST REACTION. A test for hydrogen peroxide made by mixing a dilute phenol solution with a few drops of approximately 0.1 N hydrogen peroxide and then adding some freshly prepared approximately 0.01 N ferrous sulfate. The liquid is green but turns to red-violet upon the addition of dilute sodium carbonate solution. The green color is restored upon the addition of an acid.

SPITZKASTEN. A hydraulic separating device consisting of a series of inverted boxes (of conical shape, or other shape that decreases in cross-sectional area from top to bottom) which increase in size and depth in sequence. A mixture of solids with water or other fluid flows through the system, overflowing from each box into the next, so that settling takes place in each box, with resulting separation of particles of different sizes.

SPLASH HEAD. A baffle element used in distilling apparatus to prevent droplets of liquid from being carried over with the vapor from the still into the condenser by means of splash, entrainment, or other mechanical means.

SPLITTING. (Scission) The chemical divison of a molecule into two or more new molecules, especially in such processes as **hydrolysis, alcoholysis, saponification,** etc.

SPONGY METAL. Finely divided, porous metals, frequently employed as catalytic agents in chemical reactions. For example, spongy platinum is used in oxidation reactions, because of its ability to condense large quantities of oxygen. It may be prepared by gently heating ammonium chloroplatinate.

SPONTANEOUS. Occurring by virtue of inherent properties or energy as distinguished from processes carried out by deliberate application of external force, as spontaneous evaporation, combustion, oxidation, etc.

SPOT TEST. A small-scale analytical test, commonly conducted by placing a drop of sample and a drop of reagent together on a filter paper, flat porcelain plate, or "spot-plate" (a porcelain plate with many small depressions). Sometimes the test is made by "spotting" the drops so that their peripheries just meet.

SPRAY. (1) A distribution of small droplets of liquid throughout a gas. (2) A solution of one or more substances used for spray application, as in medicine or agriculture.

SPRAY DRYING. A method of evaporating a solution by heating a gas in which the solution has been introduced as a **spray.**

SPREADING COEFFICIENT. A thermodynamic expression for the work done in the spreading of one liquid on another. It is the difference between the work of adhesion between the two liquids and the work of cohesion of the liquid spreading, which may be expressed by the equation

$$K_s = \gamma_B - \gamma_A - \gamma_{AB}$$

where K_s is the spreading coefficient, γ_B is the **surface tension** of the stationary liquid, γ_A is the surface tension of the spreading liquid, and γ_{AB} is the interfacial tension between the liquids.

SPRENGEL PUMP. A form of mercury pump used to obtain high vacua.

SPUTTER. A method of producing systems containing very small particles of metals, as, e.g., metal sols, by passing an electrical arc between two metallic electrodes placed beneath the surface of a liquid or, sometimes, in a gas.

Sr Symbol for the element **strontium.**

SSOLONINA TEST REACTION. A test for ketones. A dark red color is produced by the action of vanillin-hydrochloric acid on ketones. This color changes to a dark green or dark blue, disappearing on adding an alkali but not on diluting with water or alcohol.

STABILIZER. A substance that renders another substance or system more stable. Thus, **antioxidants** stabilize the product in which they are contained by rendering it more resistant to oxidation, because they act as negative catalysts for reactions of the other components with oxygen, or because the stabilizers undergo preferential oxidation. Another use of the term "stabilizer" is to denote a substance used to render an emulsion more permanent, or more resistant to changes in temperature, pH, or other conditions.

STADDON TEST. A test for arsenic and antimony made by dissolving 0.5–2 g. of the sample to be tested in about 5 ml. water and adding 0.5–2 g. sodium hydrosulfite and warming the solution. If arsenic and antimony are present, a precipitate, varying in color from light to dark brown, forms in proportion to the amount present.

STADLIN TEST. A test for benzoic acid in fats which is made by spreading 20–30 g. of the half-melted fat on the parchment diaphragm of a Kreis dialyzer and covering with water and alcohol (mixed in equal volumes). About 70 ml. of the same alcohol are placed in the outer compartment. The alcohol is made alkaline if it reacts acid after standing for at least 24 hours, then evaporated on the water bath and the evaporated alcohol replaced with water. It is slightly acidified, cooled, extracted twice with ether, the ether extract washed twice with water, the ether evaporated at ordinary or slightly elevated temperatures, and the residue dissolved in water. Add 3 drops of ferric chloride solution, 3 drops of hydrogen peroxide and 3 drops of 3% ferrous sulfate solution to 10 ml. of the solution. The test shows the presence of benzoic acid if a violet color appears after 30 seconds.

STADLINGER TEST REACTIONS. Tests for artificial silk as follows: (1) ruthenium chloride solution colors copper cellulose light red; viscose silk, rose-red; dinitro-cellulose, strong red. Cellulose and nitro-cellulose are not colored. (2) A 2% methylene blue solution colors copper cellulose light blue; viscose silk, darker blue; and nitro-cellulose silk, marine blue.

STAEDEL-RÜGHEIMER PYRAZINE SYNTHESIS. A method of formation of pyrazines by condensation of α-halogenated ketones with ammonia

in moist air or when moistened with fluid containing water.

STAHL TEST FOR PYROGALLOL. Traces of pyrogallol give a blue color with a mixture of ferric chloride and potassium ferricyanide solutions.

STÄHLER TEST REACTION. Stannous chloride or titanium trichloride immediately form a deep violet color with gold solutions.

STAIN. A colored solution used for imparting decorative coloring, especially to wood. In biology or bacteriology, a colored solution used to color tissues or organisms so that they may be seen or differentiated.

STAIN, ACID. See **acid stain.**

STAINING, VITAL. The coloring of living organisms, or tissues, as by the administration or application of dyes, so that their structure can be differentiated when examined microscopically.

STALAGMOMETER. An apparatus for determining the mass of a drop of a liquid, by weighing a known number of drops, or by counting the number of drops obtained from a given volume of liquid. The stalagmometer is widely used in determining

$$2R'CHBrCOR + 4NH_3 \xrightarrow{[O]} \underset{\substack{R' \\ \diagup \\ N}}{\overset{\substack{N \\ R}}{\bigcirc}} + 3H_2O + 2NH_4Br.$$

STAHL REACTION FOR ORIENTATION OF HYDROXYL GROUP. Aromatic compounds having a hydroxyl group in the ortho position (e.g., pyrocatechol) reduce molybdic acid or ammonium molybdate solution. However, the isomers with the group in the meta or para position (e.g., hydroquinone and resorcinol) exert no reducing effect.

STAHL TEST FOR MOISTURE. Paper, moistened with cobalt chloride solution and dried at 100° C. until it becomes blue, forms the reagent. The paper becomes red

the surface tension of a liquid by comparing the weight of its drops with those of a liquid of known surface tension.

STAMM REACTION FOR BORIC ACID. (1) With 1 drop of 0.1% congo-red solution, a 4% boric acid solution produces a brown-violet color. With a 1% boric acid solution, there is no change. A blue residue is obtained, however, on evaporating the solutions. (2) On cautiously drying a strip of congo paper moistened with a 4% boric acid solution, a blue color develops.

STAMM REAGENT FOR CYANIDE.
A reagent for the cyanide radical, prepared
by mixing a solution of 0.01 g. fluorescein
in 5 ml. alcohol, with 2 ml. of a 33%
aqueous sodium hydroxide solution and
5 ml. water. It is then heated with powdered zinc until decolorized, and diluted
with 100 ml. water and 100 ml. alcohol.
On test, an intense fluorescence indicates
cyanide, or certain oxidizing substances.

**STAMM TEST FOR DECOMPOSI-
TION IN OILS AND FATS.** The reagent is prepared by mixing 0.1 g. diphenylcarbazide in 10 ml. pure Vaseline oil.
Mix 10 drops of the oil or a little of the
melted fat with Vaseline and add 5 drops
of the reagent and heat for 3 minutes.
Fresh oils give no coloration. One to 1.5%
free acidity produces a faint pink color.
Rancidity is present or will soon develop if
a red color is given.

STANDARD CANDLE. See **candle,
standard.**

STANDARD CELL. See **cell, cadmium,**
and **cell, Clarke.**

STANDARD CONDITIONS. For a gas,
a temperature of 0° C. (32° F.) and a pressure of 760 millimeters of mercury. For a
solid element, the allotropic form in which
it most commonly occurs, and at ordinary
temperatures, and at one atmosphere
pressure.

STANDARD ELECTRODE POTENTIAL.
The potential of a given **electrode** relative
to the hydrogen electrode when all the elements in both electrodes are in their
standard states.

STANDARD ENTROPY. See **entropy,
standard.**

STANDARD FREE ENERGY CHANGE.
The value of the **free energy** change of a
reaction existing when all the substances
taking part in it are in their standard
states of unit activity.

STANDARD POTENTIAL. See **potential, standard.**

STANDARD PRESSURE. See **pressure,
standard.**

STANDARD SAMPLE. A material of
known composition which closely resembles
in chemical and physical nature the materials with which the analyst expects to deal
and which is employed for calibration.

STANDARD SAMPLE, PRIMARY. A
standard sample whose composition is
certified by a recognized standardizing
agency or group as the weighted result of
the work of two or more independent
laboratories, and whose reliability and
limitations for the intended analytical
procedure have been established.

STANDARD SOLUTION. A solution of
definite or known concentration for which
(1) the **concentration factor** has been determined by analysis or method of preparation, or (2) the concentration has been
adjusted, after its determination, to a
simple value, as normal, decimolar, etc.

STANDARD STATE. The stable form of
a substance at unit activity. The stable
state for each substance of a gaseous system is the ideal gas at 1 atmosphere pressure; for a solution it is taken at unit mole
fraction; and for a solid or liquid element it
is taken at 1 atmosphere pressure and
ordinary temperature.

STANDARD SUBSTANCE. A substance
of accurately known composition and
purity, used for the preparation or analysis
of standard solutions.

STANDARD TEMPERATURE. See **temperature, standard.**

STANDARD VOLUME. The volume of
one mole of a substance, in the form of a
gas at a temperature of 0° C., and a pressure of 760 millimeters of mercury.

STANDARDIZATION. The process of
determining the precise assay of a complex
substance, or the composition of a solution,
which may then be used with the factor so
determined, or adjusted to the desired
value.

STANDARDIZED APPARATUS. Apparatus which has been checked to ascertain that its **deviation** from its specified capacity or weight lies within allowable limits. In many cases, the observed deviation is marked upon the apparatus, or certified for it.

STANLEY TEST. A test for cassiterite in which the sample tested is placed in contact with metallic zinc and covered with fairly strong hydrochloric acid. If the sample becomes coated in a few minutes with a thin layer of metallic tin, it is cassiterite.

STANNANE. One of various compounds of **tin** with hydrogen or with organic radicals, in which the metal usually has a valence of four.

STANNATE. See **stannate, hydroxo-,** or **stannate, meta-.** When not specified, the latter is usually intended.

STANNATE, HYDROXO-. The anion $Sn(OH)_6^=$, or a compound containing it.

STANNATE (META-). The anion $SnO_3^=$, or a compound containing it.

STANNIC. Containing or pertaining to tetravalent **tin.**

STANNITE. The anion $SnO_2^=$, or a compound containing it.

STANNITE, HYDROXO-. The anion $Sn(OH)_3^-$ or $Sn_2O(OH)_4^=$, or a compound containing one of these anions.

STANNO-. A prefix that indicates divalent **tin.**

STANNONIC. The radical $—Sn(:O)OH$.

STANNOSO. Same as **stanno-.**

STANNOUS. Containing or pertaining to bivalent **tin.**

STANNUM. Latin name of **tin.**

STANNYL. The radical H_3Sn—in organic compounds.

STARCH. Carbohydrate substances, found widely in nature, which form the chief nutritional element in plant foods. The chemistry of the starch from various sources is complex as is indicated by the formula

$$(C_6H_{10}O_5)_x.$$

All starches have certain properties in common, notably their hydrolysis under the action of acids and enzymes, and their characteristic blue color (in some cases violet) with iodine.

STARK EFFECT. The resolution, due to the action of an electric field, of a line in an optical **spectrum.** The line may be broken up to appear as two or more closely spaced "fine" lines.

STARK-EINSTEIN EQUATION. This equation, which is based on the **law of Stark-Einstein,** gives the amount of energy absorbed in a photochemical reaction. It is of the form

$$E = Nh\nu$$

in which E is the amount of energy absorbed by one mole reacting, N is the **Avogadro number,** h is the **Planck constant,** and ν is the frequency of the radiation. Since N and h are constants, E is a function only of the frequency. This quantity E for a given wave length is frequently referred to as one einstein of radiation.

STARK-EINSTEIN LAW. See **law of Stark-Einstein.**

STARK TEST REACTION. A test for antipyrine made by mixing sulfuric acid and a little dilute potassium nitrate solution and adding the solution to be tested. A characteristic green color is produced if antipyrine is present.

STARTING POTENTIAL, COUNTER. See **counter starting potential.**

STATE. In its fundamental connotation, this term refers to the condition of a substance, as its state of aggregation, which may be solid, liquid, or gaseous—massive or dispersed. As extended to a particle, the state may denote its condition of **oxidation,** as the state of oxidation of an atom, or its energy level, as the orbit of an electron about the atomic nucleus, or in fact, the energy level of any other particle possessing rotational or vibrational energy.

STATE, AMORPHOUS. See amorphous.

STATE, COLLOIDAL. See colloid.

STATE, CRYSTALLINE. See crystal.

STATE, EQUATION OF. See equation of state, general.

STATE, EXCITED. See excitation.

STATE, GASEOUS. See gas.

STATE, LIQUID. See liquid.

STATE, NASCENT. See nascent.

STATE, SOLID. See solid.

STATE, STEADY. A condition of dynamic balance, as in an **equilibrium** reaction, where at equilibrium the concentration of each of the reactants remains constant. In such cases the loss of reactants to form products just balances the formation of reactants from the products in the reverse reaction.

STATHIS TEST. A test for mercury made by adding 0.5 ml. of 1% potassium iodide solution, 1 ml. of 20% potassium hydroxide, and 5 ml. of 0.01% gold chloride solution to 1 ml. of the solution to be tested. A violet color is formed immediately, if mercury is present.

STATIC HEAD. See head, static.

STATIC PRESSURE. See pressure, static.

STATIONARY STATE. The same as steady state (see state, steady).

STATISTICS, BOSE-EINSTEIN. See Bose-Einstein statistics.

STATISTICS, FERMI-DIRAC. See Fermi-Dirac statistics.

STATMETRIC (STATHMETOMETRIC). See analysis, quantitative.

STEAD REAGENT. A solution of 40 g. magnesium chloride and 10 g. cupric chloride in the minimum volume of hot water, to which 20 ml. hydrochloric acid are added, and then the solution is made up to 1 liter with alcohol. It is used for etching steel to show phosphorus segregation.

STEAM. (1) Water vapor, especially when at a temperature at or above the boiling point of water. (2) By analogy, the vapor of any liquid at or above the boiling point of the liquid.

STEARATE. A compound containing the straight chain, aliphatic acid radical

STEARIC. Related to stearic acid,

$$C_{17}H_{35}COOH.$$

STEAROYL. The radical

$$CH_3(CH_2)_{16}CO-$$

(from stearic acid).

STEENHAUER MICROTEST. A microtest for organic acids made with a reagent composed of 4 ml. of 10% cupric sulfate solution, 1 ml. pyridine, and 5 ml. water, with which anisic, anthranilic, benzoic, fumaric, cinnamic, salicylic, and acetylsalicylic acids give crystalline compounds. The test distinguishes between salicyclic acid and acetylsalicylic acid, forming greenish-blue and violet-blue crystals, respectively.

STEENSMA REAGENT. A solution of 2 g. phloridzin and 1 g. vanillin in 30 ml. absolute alcohol, used in testing for hydrochloric acid in gastric contents.

STEENSMA TEST REACTION FOR ANTIPYRINE. A test for antipyrine, the reagent for which is a solution of 1 g. p-dimethylaminobenzaldehyde in 5 ml. of hydrochloric acid (sp. gr. 1.124), and 95 ml. absolute alcohol. A trace of antipyrine is evaporated with a few ml. of the reagent to dryness on the steam bath. A red spot remains.

STEFAN-BOLTZMANN EQUATION. An equation expressing the **law of Stefan and Boltzmann** which states that the total energy radiated from a black body is proportional to its absolute temperature raised to the fourth power:

$$E = \sigma(T^4 - T_o{}^4)$$

in which E is the total energy radiated expressed in ergs, T is the absolute temperature of the source, T_o is the absolute temperature of the surroundings, and σ is the Stefan-Boltzmann constant, which is 1.36×10^{-12} calories per second per square centimeter of black-body surface.

STEFAN-BOLTZMANN LAW. See **law of Stefan and Boltzmann.**

STEFANELLI TEST. A test for alcohol in ether made by shaking the sample with a little aniline violet. If alcohol is present, the ether becomes colored, but if no alcohol is present it remains colorless.

STEFFENS PROCESS. A series of operations used to recover the sugar from beet molasses. The molasses is treated with lime which reacts with sucrose to form saccharates of calcium. These are then extracted and treated with carbon dioxide which releases the sucrose and precipitates calcium carbonate. The sucrose is then purified.

STEIGER TEST. A test for fluoride in which small amounts of fluoride can be detected and estimated by the bleaching action of fluorine on the yellow color produced by oxidizing a titanium solution with hydrogen peroxide.

STEIN TEST FOR FREE ALKALI IN SOAPS. An alkali soap solution forms a yellow-red precipitate with an aqueous solution of mercuric chloride. A white precipitate is formed with neutral soap solutions.

STEIN TEST FOR IODINE IN NITRIC ACID OR NITRATES. Acidify the acid or the nitrite with nitric acid and digest with tin sticks until red vapors no longer are produced. Then shake the liquid with carbon disulfide. If iodine is present, the carbon disulfide becomes red.

STEINLE-KAHLENBERG TEST REACTION. A test for cholesterol. A chloroform solution of antimony pentachloride with a dilute solution of cholesterol forms a muddy brown precipitate. In more chloroform, the precipitate dissolves and forms a clear, purple liquid which rapidly changes to cobalt-blue on exposure to light.

STEM CORRECTION. A correction to be made in the reading of a thermometer which has part of its stem containing a portion of the thermometric-fluid column outside the region at the temperature being measured, so that amount of the thermometric fluid is not at the correct temperature.

STEPHEN PREPARATION OF ALDEHYDES. A method of preparing certain higher aldehydes, such as n-octyl, myristic, and stearic aldehydes, from the corresponding nitriles, by a process of reduction, followed by hydrolysis, using hydrochloric acid, stannous chloride, and ether containing a trace of water.

$$C_7H_{15}CN + SnCl_2 + 3HCl \rightarrow C_7H_{15}CH:NH.HCl + SnCl_4$$

$$C_7H_{15}CH:NH.HCl + H_2O \rightarrow C_7H_{15}CHO + NH_4Cl.$$

STEIGMANN TEST REACTIONS. Tests for solid irradiated ergosterol (vitamin D). (1) Add fuchsin-sulfurous acid to the sample to be tested. A violet color shows the presence of irradiated ergosterol. (2) Heat the sample to be tested with ammoniacal silver oxide. A stable silver sol is formed if irradiated ergosterol is present.

STEREO-. A prefix that indicates "solid" or "three-dimensional."

STEREOCHEMISTRY. See **chemistry, stereo.**

STEREOISOMERISM. **Isomerism** due to stereochemical differences. (See **chemistry, stereo.**)

STEREOISOMERS. Isomers which differ only in the relative spatial positions of their constituent atoms. See **isomerism, optical** and **geometric.**

STEREOSPECTROGRAM. A method of representing spectral data in which the three variables, concentration of solute, **optical density,** and wave length of light, are plotted in three dimensions to produce a three-dimensional figure; or else in two dimensions by choosing an oblique axis in addition to the customary x-axis and y-axis.

STERIC-FACTOR OR PROBABILITY FACTOR. A correction factor applied, in cases of many "slow" reactions, to correct the values calculated for the reaction rates by the collision theory. It is believed that the reason for the discrepancy, or, in other words, the physical meaning of the steric factor, may be the large number of **degrees of freedom** in which energy transformations must occur, in certain reactions, to form the **activated complex.**

STERIC HINDRANCE. The effect of the spatial arrangement of the atoms in the structure of a molecule in retarding a chemical reaction or process.

STERILE. Free from living **microorganisms.**

STERILIZE. To render free from living **microorganisms.**

STERKIN-HELFGAT SOLUTION. A mixture of 25 ml. of a 0.12% aqueous solution of sodium arsenate, 25 ml. of a 2% aqueous solution of ammonium molybdate, and 25 ml. of 2% hydrochloric acid, used as a test reagent for quinine. A permanent opalescence is formed with acidified quinine solutions.

STERN-GERLACH EXPERIMENT. An experiment verifying the hypothesis that the electronic spin angular momentum is quantized. A stream of atoms is passed through a powerful inhomogeneous magnetic field; during passage the beam is split into two or more portions which were focused onto a plate. From the splitting produced, information concerning space quantization of **orbital** and **spin** angular **momenta** with respect to a magnetic field can be obtained.

STEROID COMPOUND. One of a large number of complex compounds related in structure, which contain sterol groups as part of their molecules. They are of wide occurrence in plants and animals, both in relation to normal and pathological metabolic processes.

STEROL. One of a group of unsaturated alcohols that are of wide occurrence in nature, both free and in combination. They are chiefly solid alcohols, as, e.g., cholesterol, the phytosterols, etc.

STEUDEL REACTION FOR NUCLEIC ACID. Doubly refractive crystals, consisting of the nitrates of the purine bases, are obtained if nucleic acid is treated on a slide with concentrated nitric acid. Concentrated hydrochloric acid acts similarly.

STEVENS α-METHOXYKETONE SYNTHESIS. A method of formation of α-methoxyketones by treatment of α-bromoketones with sodium methylate to form epoxy ethers, which are rearranged by catalysts to give the α-methoxyketones:

$$R'.CO.CBrR_2 + NaOCH_3 \rightarrow R'-\overset{\displaystyle O}{\overset{\displaystyle /\backslash}{\underset{\displaystyle |}{C}}}-CR_2 + NaBr$$
$$OCH_3$$

$$\downarrow Cat.$$

$$R'-\underset{\displaystyle |}{\overset{\displaystyle R}{\underset{\displaystyle OCH_3}{C}}}-\overset{\displaystyle O}{\overset{\displaystyle \|}{C}}-R$$

The radical R′ is phenyl or a phenyl derivative. If R is aryl, an acid yielding protons will catalyze the rearrangement; if R is hydrogen, compounds such as $MgBr_2$ are needed as catalysts; while if R is alkyl, heat is also necessary for the rearrangement.

STEVENS REARRANGEMENT. In a quaternary ammonium salt, the shifting of a **benzyl group** from a nitrogen atom to an adjacent carbon atom.

$$R.CH_2\overset{\displaystyle Cl}{\underset{\displaystyle CH_2.C_6H_5}{\vert\,\,}}N(CH_3)_2 + NaOR' \rightarrow R\underset{\displaystyle CH_2.C_6H_5}{\overset{\vert}{C}H}N(CH_3)_2 + NaCl + R'OH.$$

STEVENSEN-RESUGGAN REAGENT. A reagent consisting of two solutions: (1) a solution of 5 g. aniline in 13 ml. concentrated hydrochloric acid and 26 ml. water; and (2) a solution of 4.5 g. sodium nitrite in 20 ml. water. This reagent is used in detecting p-hydroxybenzoic acid. A red color is obtained on test if that acid is present.

STEWARTS SOLUTION. A solution of 20 g. citric acid, 10 g. picric acid, and 400 g. magnesium sulfate in 1500 ml. water, used in testing for albumin.

STIBARSENO. The radical —Sb:As—.

STIBIC. Containing or pertaining to pentavalent **antimony.**

STIBINIC. The radical >Sb(:O)OH, (attached to 2 radicals).

STIBIOUS. Containing or pertaining to trivalent **antimony.**

STIBIUM. Latin name for **antimony.**

STIBO. The radical O_2Sb—.

STIBONIC. The radical —Sb(:O)(OH)$_2$.

STIBONIUM RADICAL. The radical —SbH$_4$.

STIBONO. The radical (HO)$_2$OSb—.

STIBONOUS. The radical —Sb(OH)$_2$.

STIBOSO. The radical O:Sb—.

STIBYL. See **stibino.**

STIBYLENE. The radical HSb=.

STICK TEST. A test for phosphorus in oil made by diluting 1 ml. of the oil with a mixture of 40 ml. of ether, 20 ml. alcohol, and 5 ml. acetone. Then 0.2 ml. of a solution of 0.25 g. silver nitrate in 100 ml. acetone is added. A brown color is given if phosphorus is present.

STIEGLITZ REARRANGEMENT. The course of this rearrangement of triphenylmethyl hydroxylamines and related compounds is such that there is possible the existence of intermediate univalent nitrogen compounds.

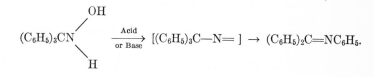

STIBINICO. The radical HOOSb=.

STIBINO. The radical H$_2$Sb—.

STIBINOUS. The radical >Sb(OH), (attached to two radicals).

Instead of hydroxylamines, haloamines, dihaloamines, or other compounds may be used.

STIFFNESS. A property of materials, defined as their resistence to deformation.

STILL. An apparatus for conducting distillation. It consists of the still proper (evaporator, vaporizer) which is a vessel of refractory materials used to contain the mixture to be vaporized, a condenser to condense the vapors, and a receiver to collect the distillate. Other appliances, such as fractionating columns, preheaters, dephlegmators, etc., are frequently incorporated in the apparatus. A vacuum still is a form of this apparatus constructed especially to allow distillation to be conducted under reduced pressure and to withstand high (external) air pressure.

STILL, BARNSTEAD. A still for producing distilled water, commonly of small (laboratory) size, in which the incoming water flows around the condenser tubes to recover as much as possible of the heat used.

STILL HEAD. A fractionating column.

STILL, STOKES. A small still for producing distilled water, in which the boiling chamber has a large cross-sectional area so that the water boils gently, with little tendency to be carried as spray into the condenser.

STILL, VACUUM. A still connected, usually through its condensing system, to a **vacuum pump,** so that distillation takes place at lower temperatures.

STIMULANT. A drug or other substance that increases functional activity.

STOBBE CONDENSATION. This condensation of aldehydes or ketones with esters of succinic acid takes place in the presence of sodium alkoxide, which usually acts to replace one of the ester groups with sodium.

oxide, a reddish-brown color develops which gradually becomes darker until it is almost black. Cod-liver oil gives this reaction also.

STOICHIOMETRY. The science which deals with the numerical relationships of chemical elements and compounds and the mathematical proportions of reactants and products in chemical transformations.

STOKE(S). The unit of kinematic viscosity; a fluid has a kinematic viscosity of unity when its dynamic viscosity is one poise and its density is one g. per cm.^{3}

STOKES LAW. See **law of Stokes.**

STOKES REAGENT. A reducing agent consisting of a solution of 3 g. ferrous sulfate and 2 g. tartaric acid in 100 ml. water.

STOKES REAGENT FOR GUMS. An aqueous solution of mercuric nitrate, prepared by dissolving mercury in twice its weight of nitric acid, and making up the resulting solution with water to 25 times its volume. Characteristic precipitates are obtained with gums.

STOLBA TEST REACTION FOR CESIUM. Tin chloride with cesium chloride, forms a compound which is difficultly soluble.

STOLBA TEST REACTION FOR POTASSIUM. Crystalline precipitates are formed by a concentrated solution of sodium borofluoride with potassium salt solutions.

STOLBA TEST REACTION FOR TELLURITES AND SELENITES. On heat-

$$R'CHO + CH_2.COOR'' + NaOR''' \rightarrow R'CH{:}C.COOR'' + R''OH + R'''OH.$$
$$| \qquad\qquad\qquad\qquad |$$
$$CH_2.COOR'' \qquad\qquad\qquad CH_2.COONa$$

STOELTZNER TEST. A characteristic test reaction for vitamin D. If an oil, such as olive oil, containing about 1% of vitamin D, is treated with phosphorus pent-

ing tellurous acid in alkaline solution with glucose, metallic tellurium is precipitated as a black powder. The same reaction is given by selenious acid.

STOLLÉ SYNTHESIS. A method of formation of indole derivatives from aromatic amines or diamines by the action of oxalyl chloride (or α-haloacid chlorides).

STOPCOCK TENSION CLIP. A spring-actuated device for the pressure-tight seating of stopcocks, used to prevent loosening, especially for apparatus requiring shaking.

STOLLÉ TEST REACTION. A test for trichloroacetic acid in which 1 g. trichloroacetic acid is boiled with 0.5 g. antipyrine and 2–3 ml. water for half a minute. A chloroform odor develops, and carbon dioxide is evolved.

STONE TEST FOR MAGNESIUM. An adaptation of the **Suitsu-Okuma reaction** made by dipping filter paper in a 0.01% alcohol solution of *p*-nitrosobenzeneazoresorcinol (Magneson) and drying. A drop of the solution to be tested is then placed on the test paper, which is dried and then immersed in 1% sodium hydroxide solution. A blue spot on a reddish field is given if magnesium is present. If the original solution contains much acid, the color is yellow at first.

STONE TEST FOR MERCURY IN ORGANIC COMPOUNDS. Mix 0.5 g. sodium carbonate with 5–10 mg. of the sample, heat in a dry test tube containing a glass rod coated with a suspension of cuprous iodide mixed with an equal amount of water. The vapors cause the cuprous iodide suspension to turn from white to a salmon or pink color, if mercury is present.

STOPPING POWER. The rate of loss of energy by an α-**particle** as it travels through a given medium. The relative stopping power is the ratio of the range of an α-particle in air to its range in a given material, the same source of α-particles being used in both instances. While the relative stopping power depends to some extent on the source of the α-particles, an approximate average value is generally used.

STORCH-MORAWSKI TEST. A test for rosin or rosin oil made by gently heating a little of the substance to be tested in acetic anhydride, cooling, and then adding a drop of concentrated sulfuric acid. A transitory blue-violet or red color, becoming brown-yellow and fluorescent, is given by rosin or rosin oil. Several modifications of this test have been developed.

STORFER REAGENT. A solution obtained by dissolving 51 g. cupric chloride in an aqueous solution of 7.6 g. thiourea at 70° C. After recrystallization, a saturated solution of the product is used to prepare a test paper for ferricyanide, which gives with it a red to violet color. This is a very sensitive test.

STÖRMER TEST REACTION. A test for thymol. When a little thymol, dissolved in concentrated potassium hydroxide solution, is heated with a few drops of chloroform, a violet color forms immediately. On shaking, the color becomes violet-red.

STRACHAN TEST. A test for free alum in paper in which 1 drop of 20% potassium iodide solution is placed on a small piece of the paper, covered with a watch glass, and allowed to stand in an atmosphere free from acid or ammonia. The moistened spot is colored reddish- to violet-brown, if uncombined alum and starch are present. Alum without starch gives only a yellow spot.

STRAIN THEORY. A theory according to which five- or six-membered carbon rings are the most stable. Rings comprising a larger or smaller number of carbon atoms may be formed, but are not as stable, since the structure of such a ring is strained.

STRAUB TEST FOR PHOSPHORUS. A test for phosphorus in phosphorated oils made by shaking 5 ml. of 5% aqueous copper sulfate solution with 10 ml. of the sample. If phosphorus is present, the emulsion becomes brown to black, im-

nitric acid, 20 g. chromic acid, and 30 ml. water; or from 5 ml. nitric acid, 20 g. chromic acid, and 75 ml. water.

STRAY RADIATION. See **radiation, stray.**

STREAK. This term is used in mineralogy to denote the more or less characteristic line produced by rubbing a mineral across a surface. Examination of the streak for color and other characteristic qualities frequently gives valuable clues to the nature of the mineral. For best results, the testing surface should be clean and absorbent, such as that provided by unglazed porcelain.

STREAMING POTENTIAL. A difference of **electrical potential** between a porous diaphragm, or other permeable solid, and a liquid which is passing through it.

STRECHER DEGRADATION. The reaction of **α-amino acids** with **carbonyl compounds** to give **aldehydes** or **ketones** containing one less carbon atom, and carbon dioxide. Under certain conditions, as when ninhydrin is the carbonyl compound used, the evolution of carbon dioxide can be determined quantitatively, and used to determine the α-amino acid content.

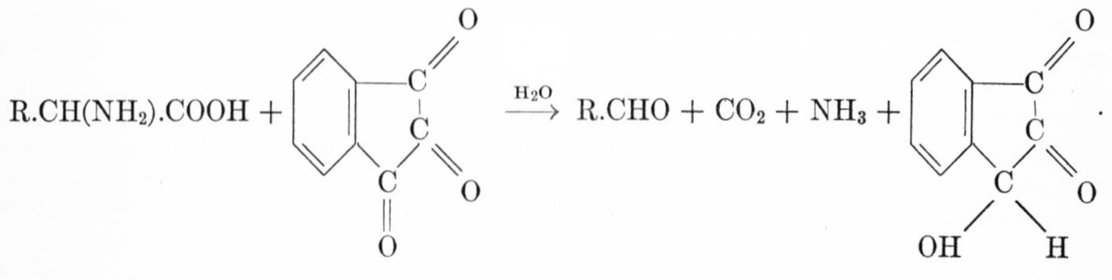

mediately or later, according to the quantity of phosphorus present.

STRAUSS SOLUTION. An aqueous solution of nitric acid and chromic acid, used in etching bronzes, especially aluminum bronzes. It may be prepared from 50 ml.

STRECKER AMINO ACID SYNTHESIS. A method of synthesizing α-amino acids from aldehydes (or ketones) by treatment with a cyanide and ammonia (or an amine), followed by hydrolysis. The course of the reaction is believed to be as follows:

$$RCHO + HCN + NH_3 \rightarrow RCH(NH_2)CN \xrightarrow{3H_2O} RCH(NH_2)COOH + NH_4OH.$$

The use of an alkali cyanide and ammonium chloride (instead of hydrogen cyanide and ammonia) is the Zelinsky-Stadnikoff synthesis.

STRECKER SYNTHESIS. A method of formation of alkyl sulfonates from alkyl halides and alkali sulfites.

$$RBr + Na_2SO_3 \rightarrow RSO_3Na + NaBr.$$

STRENG TEST REACTIONS. Tests for sodium as follows: (1) With sodium salts, uranyl acetate forms sodium uranyl acetate which appears as small tetrahedra, under the microscope. (2) With sodium salts, a solution of magnesium uranyl acetate in dilute acetic acid forms difficultly soluble sodium magnesium uranyl acetate in the form of rhombohedral crystals.

STRIPPED ATOM. See **atom, stripped.**

STRIPPING. The treatment of a liquid by a gas or vapor in order to remove a volatile **component.**

STROBOSCOPE. A device for producing a flashing light of high frequency. It consists commonly of a gas discharge tube or other light source capable of rapid fluctuation, connected to a source of electrical energy, which also can be varied in the frequency of its "make and break." The stroboscope is useful in observing rapidly moving objects because, in accordance with the well-known optical principle, such objects seem to stand still when the frequency of the light source equals or approaches their own frequency.

STROHMEYER TEST REACTION. A test for xanthine made by adding mercuric chloride solution to the sample to be tested. A distinct turbidity is produced if xanthine is present.

STRONTIC, STRONTITIC. Containing or pertaining to **strontium.**

STRONTIUM. Metallic element. Symbol Sr. Atomic number 38. Atomic weight 87.63. Density values reported of 2.54 and 2.6. Specific heat 0.0550. Melting point

757° C. Boiling point 1366° C. Valence 2. Oxides SrO and SrO_2. Strontium occurs in celestite, strontianite, etc.

STROUP TEST. A test for differentiating caffeine and theobromine made by triturating a sample in a porcelain dish and adding 1 drop of a 5:100 solution of potassium dichromate in sulfuric acid. Caffeine gives a light blue-green color; theobromine gives a dark purple color which gradually changes to purple-green, olive-green, then to blue-green.

STRUCTURAL FORMULA. See **formula, structural.**

STRUCTURAL THEORY. Any theory of the constitution of chemical compounds.

STRUCTURE. The grouping of the various parts of an assembled entity, and the points at which, or the means by which, they are held together.

STRUCTURE, ATOMIC. The internal structure of the **atom,** comprising its nucleus and the electrons which surround it.

STRUCTURE, HYPERFINE. See **hyperfine structure.**

STRUCTURE, MOLECULAR. The internal structure of the **molecule,** comprising the various **atoms,** and the valence **bond** structure which holds them together.

STRUCTURE, NUCLEAR. The internal structure of the atomic **nucleus,** which is at present a subject of active investigation.

STRUCTURE OF CHEMICAL COMPOUNDS. See **constitution** and **configuration.**

STRUVE TEST REACTION FOR MORPHINE. A test for morphine made by adding phosphomolybdic acid to a morphine solution. On adding concentrated sulfuric acid to the precipitate so produced, it is colored blue, and on heating it becomes brown.

STUBENRAUCH TEST REACTION. A test for iodoform made with 1–2 ml. of an aqueous iodoform solution, by adding a drop of fuming nitric acid and a little starch solution. No blue color is produced. However, if the solution is heated first with a little zinc dust and 1 drop of acetic acid, an immediate blue color is formed upon adding 1 drop of nitric acid and some starch solution.

STUFFER RULE. Gamma disulfones are split by alkali into a sulfinate and an alcohol. Other disulfones do not undergo this reaction.

greater than the atmospheric pressure the solid vaporizes completely at constant pressure. The temperature at the point where the vapor pressure of a solid equals the atmospheric pressure is its sublimation temperature.

SUBLIMATION CURVE. The graphical representation of the variation with temperature of the **vapor pressure** of a solid.

SUBLIMATION, HEAT OF. See **heat of sublimation.**

$$RSO_2.CH_2.CH_2.SO_2R + NaOH \rightarrow RSO_2.CH_2.CH_2OH + RSO_2Na.$$

STUTZER REAGENT. A reagent used for separating proteins from other nitrogenous compounds. It is an aqueous paste of cupric hydroxide free from alkali hydroxide.

STYRENE. (1) The radical

$$-CH(C_6H_5)CH_2-.$$

(2) The compound

$$C_6H_5CH:CH_2.$$

STYROLENE. See **styrene.**

STYRYL. The radical $C_6H_5CH:CH-$.

SUB-. (Latin) Under, below. Denoting (a) a low, or the lowest, proportion, as subiodide, suboxide; (b) any of certain "basic salts," as aluminum subacetate.

SUBATOMIC. Pertaining to processes or reactions in which atoms undergo **disintegration,** as in natural or artificial **radioactivity;** or to particles or radiations yielded by such reactions, such as **electrons, positrons, protons, neutrons, helium nuclei,** and nuclear fragments of larger size.

SUBLIMATE. The condensed vapor from the process of **sublimation,** analogous to the distillate from distillation.

SUBLIMATION. The transformation of a solid directly to the gaseous condition without passing through the liquid state. When the vapor pressure of a solid becomes

SUBLIME. To pass from the solid directly to the gaseous state without melting.

SUBMICRON. In Zsigmondy's nomenclature, submicrons are particles between 5×10^{-9} and 10^{-7} meters in diameter (50–1000 Ångström units).

SUBSESQUI-. (Obs.) A prefix indicating combination in the proportion of two to three, particularly where the acidic radical is in the proportion of two. In "sesqui" compounds the acidic radical is in the proportion of three to two of base.

SUBSTANCE. A term used to designate a pure chemical compound or a definite mixture of such compounds. The term substance should not be used as an equivalent to the term "body" which refers to a definite mass of material, i.e., two different masses of the same substance would constitute two "bodies" but not two substances.

SUBSTANTIVE DYEING. Dyeing fabrics with dyestuffs which do not require mordanting. See **dyeing.**

SUBSTANTIVE DYES. Dyes that color fabrics directly without requiring previous mordanting. See **dyes.**

SUBSTITUENT. An atom or group which replaces another in a compound during the course of a substitution reaction. (See **reaction, substitution.**)

SUBSTITUTE. To replace one atom or group in a compound by another.

SUBSTITUTED COMPOUND. A compound derived from a parent by **substitution**, e.g., toluene from benzene by substitution of methyl for hydrogen. Derivatives of this type are often spoken of as substituted benzenes, substituted naphthalenes, substituted phenols, substituted amines, etc.

SUBSTITUTION. The replacement of one element or group in a compound by another, e.g., in the preparation of chlorobenzene one atom of chlorine is substituted for one of hydrogen in benzene.

$$C_6H_6 + Cl_2 = C_6H_5Cl + HCl.$$

SUBSTITUTION, RETROGRESSIVE. The replacing of substituents by hydrogen, i.e., the reverse of **substitution.**

SUBSTRATE. The substance modified by the action of an **enzyme** or by the growing upon it of **microorganisms.**

SUCCINAMYL. The radical

$$H_2NCOCH_2CH_2CO—.$$

SUCCINIMIDO. The radical

$$(CH_2CO)_2N—.$$

SUCCINYL. The radical

$$—OCCH_2CH_2CO—.$$

SUCHIER REAGENT. A mixture of equal volumes of a 20% alcoholic solution of diphenylamine and a 20% alcoholic solution of p-dimethyl-p-aminobenzaldehyde, which is used to impregnate paper for testing for phosgene. A brown color is obtained if phosgene is present.

SUDBOROUGH-HIBBERT TEST REACTION. A test for primary and secondary amines in which the amine is treated with a solution of methylmagnesium iodide at room temperature. One mole of methane is evolved. On heating to 120–125° C., the secondary amine reacts further, giving off another mole of methane. This reaction is not given by tertiary amines.

SUGAR. (1) A generic term for a member of a class of **carbohydrates** characterized by solubility in water, a sweet taste, and crystallinity. (2) A term used synonymously for sucrose.

SUGAR, REDUCING. Any mono- or disaccharide, such as glucose or fructose, which reduces silver or copper salts in alkaline solution, because of the presence of free aldehyde or ketone groups.

SUIDA PROCESS. A method of recovering the acetic acid from the crude pyroligneous acid obtained in wood distillation. The material is distilled, and the acetic acid is absorbed in a stream of heavy tar oil circulating down a fractionating column. The other volatile components of the pyroligneous acid, such as water and methanol, are not absorbed, and pass out at the top of the column.

SUIDA TEST REACTION. A test for aspartic acid. Basic dyes, such as crystal violet, Nile blue, and safranine precipitate the hydrochloride of the acid from an aqueous solution.

SUITSU-OKUMA TEST REACTION. A test for magnesium made by alkalinizing the solution to be tested with sodium hydroxide and adding a few drops of a 0.5% solution of o-dihydroxyazo-p-nitrobenzene (Magneson) in 1% sodium hydroxide solution. A sky-blue lake forms if magnesium is present.

SULFAMATE. The anion $H_2NO_3S^-$, or a compound containing it.

SULFAMIC ACID. An organic sulfur acid of the general formula:

SULFAMIDE. A sulfone-containing derivative of one of the secondary amines, e.g., tetramethylsulfamide,

$$(CH_3)_2N—SO_2—N(CH_3)_2.$$

SULFAMINE. A compound of the general

formula R—S—NH$_2$, where R is an organic

radical.

SULFAMINO. The radical HO$_3$SNH—.

SULFAMYL. The radical H$_2$NO$_2$S—.

SULFANILAMIDO. The radical

$$p\text{-}H_2NC_6H_4SO_2NH—$$

(from sulfanilamide).

SULFANILIC. Related to sulfanilic acid p-H$_2$N.C$_6$H$_4$.SO$_3$H.

SULFANILYL. The radical

$$p—H_2NC_6H_4SO_2—$$

(from sulfanilic acid).

SULFATE. A compound containing the radical

e.g., sodium sulfate, Na$_2$SO$_4$; ethyl sulfate, (C$_2$H$_5$)$_2$SO$_4$. They are derivatives of sulfuric acid.

SULFATE, ACID. A derivative of sulfuric acid in which only one of the two acid hydrogen atoms is replaced, i.e., a compound containing the radical

SULFATE, BI-. See **sulfate, acid.**

SULFATE, HYPO-. A **dithionate.**

SULFATE (META-). The anion SO$_4$= or HSO$_4$$^-$, or compounds containing one of these anions.

SULFATE, ̄NORMAL. A derivative of sulfuric acid in which both of the two acid hydrogen atoms are replaced, i.e., a compound containing the radical

SULFATE PROCESS. A procedure for obtaining strong wood pulp by treating wood with a solution of sodium sulfide, containing some sulfate and carbonate. The cooking liquid used is alkalized with sodium hydroxide and the pulp is intentionally undercooled to make it stronger. The woods used in the process are long-fibered pine woods. The pulp made by the sulfate process is called kraft pulp.

SULFATE, PYRO-. A compound containing the radical, $=S_2O_7$, i.e., a derivative of pyrosulfuric acid.

SULFATE, THIO-. A **thionate.**

SULFATE, TRI-. See **trisulfate.**

SULFATO. The radical O$_4$S<.

SULFATORHODATE (III). The anion Rh(SO$_4$)$_2$$^-$, or a compound containing it.

SULFATOXIDE. A **sulfate.**

SULFAZIDE. A sulfone derivative of a hydrazo compound of the general formula R.NH.NH.SO$_2$.R′, e.g., phenylbenzenesulfazide, C$_6$H$_5$NH.NH.SO$_2$.C$_6$H$_5$.

SULFENIC. The radical —SOH.

SULFHYDRATE. A hydrosulfide (see **sulfide**).

SULFHYDRYL. See **thiol.**

SULFIDE. A salt of hydrosulfuric acid, H$_2$S, e.g., sodium sulfide, Na$_2$S, or a binary compound of sulfur in which that element is divalent. The inorganic acid sulfides, (NaSH) are termed hydrosulfides; the organic compounds (CH$_3$SH) being termed thiols.

SULFIDE (HYDRO-). The anion SH^-, or a compound containing it.

SULFIDIC SULFUR. Sulfur combined as salts of hydrosulfuric acid, H_2S, to distinguish it from sulfur in other combinations.

SULFIMIDE RADICAL. A sulfate radical, in which one of the hydroxy groups of sulfuric acid has been replaced by an imino group

$$-\underset{\displaystyle\overset{\displaystyle O}{\|}}{\overset{\displaystyle O}{\|}}{S}-NH-\,.$$

SULFINATE, CYCLIC. (Thetine) A sulfur analogue of the betaines, e.g., compounds of the general formula

$$\underset{H_2C-S}{\overset{O=C-O\ \ R}{|\ \ \ \ |/}}\,.$$
$$\diagdown R'$$

SULFINATE, NONCYCLIC. A derivative of sulfinic acid of the general formula

$$R-\underset{\displaystyle\overset{\displaystyle O}{\backslash\!\backslash}}{\overset{\displaystyle OH}{/}}S$$

or a tetravalent sulfur compound of several possible types.

SULFINE COMPOUND. (Sulfonium compound) An addition compound of an alkyl sulfide with an alkyl halide, halogen, a mercuric salt, etc. For example, dimethyl sulfide forms with methyl iodide the compound, trimethylsulfonium iodide $(CH_3)_3SI$.

SULFINIC. Related to a sulfinic acid, which has the type-formula $R.SO.OH$, in which R is an organic radical.

SULFINO. The radical HO_2S- in organic compounds.

SULFINYL. The radical $OS=$ in organic compounds.

SULFITE. The anion $SO_3^=$ or HSO_3^-, or a compound containing one of these anions.

SULFITE, ACID. A salt of sulfurous acid in which only one of the two acid hydrogen atoms is replaced, i.e., a salt containing the radical

$$O=\underset{\displaystyle\overset{\displaystyle\diagdown}{O-}}{\overset{\displaystyle OH}{/}}S\quad.$$

SULFITE, BI-. See **sulfite, acid.**

SULFITE, HYPO-. A **thionate** or a **dithionite.**

SULFITE, METABI-. See **pyrosulfite.**

SULFITE, PYRO-. See **pyrosulfite.**

SULFITO. The radical $O_3S<$.

SULFITOCOBALTATE (III). The anion $Co(SO_3)_3^{3-}$, or a compound containing it.

SULFITOMERCURATE (II). The anion $Hg(SO_3)_2^=$, or a compound containing it.

SULFITORHODATE (II). The anion $Rh(SO_3)_2^=$, or a compound containing it.

SULFITOSTANNATE (IV). The anion $Sn(SO_3)_4^{4-}$, or a compound containing it.

SULFO. The radical HO_3S- in organic compounds.

SULFOACETIC. Related to sulfoacetic acid $HSO_3.CH_2COOH$.

SULFO-ACID. See **sulfonic acid.**

SULFO GROUP. The univalent group

$$-\underset{\displaystyle\overset{\displaystyle O}{\backslash\!\backslash}}{\overset{\displaystyle O}{\|}}{S}-OH$$

characteristic of the **sulfonic** acids.

SULFOCYAN GROUP. The group $N\equiv C-S-$ which occurs in **thiocyanates.**

SULFOCYANIDE. See **thiocyanate.**

SULFONAMIDO. The radical

—SO₂NH—.

SULFONATE. A derivative of sulfuric acid; or a compound containing a sulfonic acid group, commonly an ester, general formula

$$R—S\!\!=\!\!O$$
with O double-bonded and O—H

or the action of conducting a sulfonation reaction. (See **reaction, sulfonation,** and **sulfonator.**)

SULFONATION. See **reaction, sulfonation.**

SULFONATOR. An apparatus for conducting sulfonations. By far the most common type is the sulfonating kettle used in manufacturing organic chemicals, which consists of a cast-iron vessel, provided with means for heating its contents and for stirring them vigorously over long periods of time.

SULFONE. An organic sulfur derivative of the type R—SO₂—R'.

SULFONIC. The radical —S(:O)₂OH.

SULFONIC ACID. A member of an important class of organic acids characterized by the presence of the group

$$R—S\!\!=\!\!O$$
with O double-bonded and OH

the "sulfonic acid" group. Sulfonic acids are formed by digesting certain hydrocarbons or other compounds with either concentrated or fuming sulfuric acid, and they react as acids. They are usually very soluble in water and alcohol and only slightly soluble in ether and nonoxygenated solvents.

SULFONIUM COMPOUND. See **sulfine compound.**

SULFONYL. The radical —SO₂— in organic compounds.

SULFOXIDE. A sulfur analogue of a **ketone,** e.g., dimethyl sulfoxide $(CH_3)_2S\!\!=\!\!O$.

SULFOXYLATE. The anion $SO_2^=$, or a compound containing it.

SULFUR. Nonmetallic element. Symbol S. Atomic number 16. Atomic weight 32.066. Boiling point 444.6° C. Exists in five solid allotropic forms: (1) Amorphous (soft). Density 1.9556. Melting point above 120° C. (2) Amorphous (yellow). Density 2.046. (3) Rhombic. Density 2.07. Melting point 112.8° C. Rhombic sulfur is the stable form at temperatures below 96° C. (4) Monoclinic. Density 1.957. Melting point 119.25° C. Monoclinic sulfur is the stable form at temperatures from 96° C. up to its melting point. (5) Plastic (probably supercooled liquid sulfur). Density 1.92. Liquid sulfur exists in two forms: Sλ which is a pale yellow mobile liquid, and Sμ which has a dark brown viscous form obtained on further heating. At higher temperatures, the two forms exists in equilibrium. Occurs native and as sulfides and sulfates. Valence 2, 4, and 6. Oxides, SO_2, SO_3, S_2O_3, S_2O_7. Acids: hydrosulfuric, H_2S; hydrogen persulfide, $H_2S_5(?)$; hyposulfurous, $H_2S_2O_4$; persulfuric, $H_2S_2O_6$; Caro's acid, $H_2S_2O_5$; thiosulfuric, $H_2S_2O_3$; dithionic, $H_2S_2O_6$; trithionic, $H_2S_3O_6$; tetrathionic, $H_2S_4O_6$; pentathionic, $H_2S_5O_6$; hexathionic, $H_2S_6O_6$; sulfurous, H_2SO_3; and sulfuric, H_2SO_4.

SULFURETTED. Combined with sulfidic sulfur.

SULFURIC. (1) Containing hexavalent sulfur. (2) Related to sulfuric acid, H_2SO_4 or $(HO)_2SO_2$. (3) Related to a number of acids of the type formula $H_xS_yO_z$, such as persulfuric acid, metasulfuric acid, etc., which are listed under the corresponding adjectives.

SULFURIZE. To combine with **sulfur.**

SULFUROUS. (1) Containing tetravalent **sulfur.** (2) Containing **sulfur.**

SULFURYL. See **sulfonyl.**

SULTAM. A derivative of 1–8 naphthyl-aminesulfonic acid formed by loss of one molecule of water.

$$O_2S\!\!-\!\!NH$$

SULTONE. A derivative of 1–8 naphthol-sulfonic acid produced in the same way as the sultams, e.g., naphsultone,

$$O_2S\!\!-\!\!O$$

SUPER-. (Latin) Above, over. Denoting a high, or the highest, proportion; as superoxide (peroxide) (now little used). (See also **superphosphate.**)

SUPERACID SOLUTIONS. Solutions which have some of the properties of extremely strong acids, but which are only weakly ionized. Solutions of mineral acids in acetic acid are good examples of super-acids. They are poor conductors of electricity, but good catalysts. Their properties are related to the fact that acetic acid is a poor **proton** acceptor and that strong acids cannot readily ionize (donate protons) in such a medium.

SUPERCOOLING. The cooling of a liquid below its freezing point without the separation of the solid phase. This is a condition of **metastable equilibrium,** as is shown by solidification of the supercooled liquid upon the addition of the solid phase, or the application of certain stresses, or simply upon prolonged standing.

SUPERHEATING. See **overheating.**

SUPERIMPOSITION APPROXIMATION. The assumption that in any system comprising molecules in fixed positions, the force on any molecule is the sum of the forces which would be exerted on the given molecule by all other molecules in turn acting as if all the remaining molecules were not present.

SUPERLATTICE. A type of arrangement of atoms in a multi-component solid system, in which the atoms of an element occupy certain regular positions in the **atomic lattice** of another element, even though no compound between the two elements of that composition can be separated or otherwise identified.

SUPERNATANT LIQUOR. The liquid standing above a precipitate or sediment.

SUPEROXIDE. The anion $O_2{}^-$, or a compound containing it.

SUPERPHOSPHATE. A long established process for the production of chemical fertilizers is the treatment of phosphate rock with concentrated sulfuric acid. The product of this reaction, as practiced in industry, is a mixture of calcium sulfates and calcium phosphates containing more or less of the acid salts, which is called superphosphate. Derivatively, this term is also applied to an acid phosphate.

SUPERPOLYMER. A **polymer** having molecules of very high molecular weight. In most usages the term is restricted to substances having molecular weights greater than 10,000.

SUPERPOSITION, PRINCIPLE OF. (1) (Nernst's principle of. . . .) The **potential difference** between **junctions** in similar pairs of solutions which have the same ratio of concentrations are the same even if the absolute concentrations are different, e.g., the same potential difference exists between normal solutions of HCl and KCl as exists between tenth-normal solutions of HCl and KCl. (2) A mathematical principle stating that two or more solutions of a differential or partial differential equation, when added, also form a solution.

SUPERPOSITION, PRINCIPLE OF OPTICAL. See **optical superposition, principle of.**

SUPERPOTENTIAL. See **excess voltage.**

SUPERSATURATE. To carry a process beyond **saturation,** as to supersaturate a solution.

SUPERSATURATION. The condition of containing an excess of some material or force over the amount required for **saturation.**

SUPERSTRUCTURE. See **superlattice.**

SUPERTENSION. See **excess voltage.**

SURFACE. (1) Mathematically, a two-dimensional entity, a figure having length and width but no thickness. (2) The exterior or limiting region of any object, which may be considered as an outer envelope of its substance, having for many practical purposes, a "zero" thickness or a negligible thickness.

SURFACE CONDENSER. See **condenser, surface.**

SURFACE ENERGY, FREE. The work necessary to increase the area of the surface of a liquid by unit area.

SURFACE ENERGY, INTERFACIAL. The work necessary to increase the surface of separation between two liquids by unit area.

SURFACE FILM, CONDENSED. A film of an insoluble substance, on the surface of a liquid, and consisting of a monolayer of closely packed molecules, at or near the point at which further compression of the film causes the formation of additional layers.

SURFACE ORIENTATION. The occupation of such positions by certain molecules in the surface of a liquid that one part of the molecule is turned toward the liquid; as, e.g., on the air-liquid interface of an aqueous system, molecules containing polar and nonpolar groups arrange themselves with the polar groups directed toward the water.

SURFACE TENSION. A property of fluid surfaces whereby they exhibit certain features resembling the properties of a stretched elastic membrane. One of those features is the tendency of the liquid surface to contract to a minimum. In general, whenever two dissimilar substances make contact at an interface, the inequalities of molecular attraction, together with other forces in action, tend to change the shape of the interface until the potential energy of the whole molecular system attains a minimum value. If both substances are fluid, the surface can readily adjust itself to this condition.

SURFACE TENSION EFFECT. A correction applied to computations of nuclear attractive energy, based on the fact that **nucleons** at the surface of the **nucleus** are less tightly bound by attraction of other nuclei than those in the interior. This effect is proportional to the surface area of the nucleus.

SURFUSION. Undercooling.

SUROXIDE. A peroxide.

SUSPENDED TRANSFORMATION. The cessation of action before true **equilibrium** has been reached, or the failure of a system to readjust itself immediately when conditions are changed. **Metastable equilibrium, supercooling,** etc., are examples.

SUSPENSION. (1) A means of supporting from above any object, such as a part of an instrument, commonly by attaching it to a wire. (2) A system of particles dispersed in a liquid, which do not separate because of their small size, the motion imparted to them by collision with water molecules, etc. Such a system is also called a suspensoid, or a colloidal suspension.

SUSPENSION, COLLOIDAL. See **suspension.**

SUSPENSOID. See **suspension.**

SÜSS TEST FOR SALICYLIC ACID IN MILK. Coagulate 100 ml. of the milk by warming at 80° C. with 1.5 ml. of a 20% solution of calcium chloride, filter, and allow the filtrate to drop through 50 ml. of ether. Separate and evaporate in a porcelain dish and test by running in from the edge 1–2 drops of dilute ferric chloride solution diluted with 10 ml. of water. A violet color indicates the presence of salicylic acid.

SÜSS TEST FOR SODIUM CARBONATE IN MILK. Add a 0.2% alcoholic solution of alizarin to 100 ml. of the milk to be tested. A rose-red color indicates the presence of sodium carbonate.

SUTHERLAND CONSTANT. A constant in an equation for the variation of the **viscosity** of a gas with temperature, of the form:

$$\eta = \eta_0 \frac{\sqrt{T}}{1 + C/T}$$

in which η is the viscosity, η_0 is a constant for the particular gas, T is the absolute temperature, and C is the Sutherland constant.

SUTHERLAND EQUATION. A relationship between the mean free path of a molecule and the molecular diameter. This relationship is expressed in the following equation:

$$d \propto \frac{1}{nl\sqrt{1 + C/T}}$$

in which d is the molecular diameter, n is

which exhibits Brownian movement and its period of vibration. The generalized form of this relationship is of the form: $a \propto t$, in which a is the amplitude of vibration, and t is the period.

SWAMINATHAN TEST. A test for nicotinic acid in foodstuffs made by precipitating the proteins from a hot aqueous extract of the sample to be tested by treating with lead acetate solution. The excess lead is removed with sulfuric acid, the solution is adjusted to pH 10 and any color present removed with charcoal. The clear, colorless extract is adjusted to pH 7.5 and made up to volume. An aliquot is diluted with water to 20–30 ml. in a 100 ml. separatory funnel, 4 ml. of freshly prepared cyanogen bromide solution are added; the solution shaken and let stand for a half hour. Four ml. of a saturated aqueous aniline solution are added and shaken. The yellowish-green color is extracted 3 times with 10 ml., 5 ml., and 5 ml. portions of purified amyl alcohol. It is then compared with a standard run on a known nicotinic acid solution.

SWARTS REACTION. A method of partial replacement by fluorine of other halogens in polyhalo compounds by the action of certain metallic fluorides.

$$CCl_2:CCl.CHCl_2 + SbF_3 \xrightarrow[\text{(Trace)}]{SbCl_5} CHCl:CClCF_3 + SbCl_3.$$

the number of molecules per unit volume, l is the mean free path, T is the absolute temperature, and C is the Sutherland constant.

SVANBERG-STRUVE TEST REACTION. A test for phosphate, made by adding strong nitric acid solutions of ammonium molybdate to phosphoric acid or its salts. A yellow precipitate of ammonium phosphomolybdate forms. This is soluble in ammonia and other alkalies and forms more rapidly on warming. Several modifications of this reaction have been developed.

SVEDBERG EQUATION. A relationship between the amplitude of a particle

SWELLING. In general, increasing in volume; used specifically for a change exhibited by certain substances or systems whereby they add water to form a **colloidal gel.**

SYM-. Abbreviation of **symmetric(al),** as *sym*-dichloroethylene.

SYMBIONS. See **symbiosis.**

SYMBIOSIS. A condition in which the simultaneous presence of two organic species in the same environment favors the development of both species, as the symbiosis of leguminous plants and nitrifying bacteria. The microorganisms which are found in symbiosis are termed symbions.

SYMBOL. A letter or mark used to represent an element, radical, compound, property, or mathematical quantity.

SYMMETRIC (SYMMETRICAL). Arranged in accordance with a certain similarity with reference to a certain geometrical entity or position, which may be a point (center or point of symmetry), a line (axis of symmetry) or a plane (plane symmetry), etc. The term is applied to that one of several isomers which possesses a symmetrical constitution, i.e., whose constitutional formula has a plane of symmetry, as the meso forms of optical isomers. Symmetrical tri-derivatives of benzene are those substituted in the 1-3-5 positions. Cf. **benzene.** The correlative term is asymmetrical.

SYMMETRY, ELEMENTS. See **crystal elements.**

SYMMETRY, GROUPS. See **crystallographic point groups** and **space groups.**

SYMMETRY, INDIRECT. See **pseudosymmetry.**

SYMPATHETIC REACTION. Induced reaction (see **reaction, induced**).

field. This voltage may be produced by passage of the ions repeatedly through a cavity resonator.

SYNERESIS. The contraction of a **gel** with accompanying pressing out of the interstitial solution or serum. Observed in the clotting of blood, with silicic acid gels, etc.

SYNTHESIS. The combination of elements or compounds to produce compounds of one kind, e.g., $H_2 + Cl_2 = 2HCl$ is a synthesis or synthetic reaction. In organic chemistry the term synthesis was originally applied to the process of preparing a compound from its elements or from other compounds which can be synthesized from their elements, nothing being used that is a product of a living organism. Various syntheses are listed throughout this book under the name or names of the men to whom they are accredited.

SYNTHESIS, ACETOACETIC ESTER. The substitution in the active methylene group of acetoacetic ester by reactive halides. Usually the sodium salt of the ester is used, and the condensation is followed by decarboxylation with dilute alkali, or deacylation with concentrated alkali.

$$CH_3.CO.CHNa.COOC_2H_5 + RI \rightarrow CH_3.CO.CHR.COOC_2H_5 + NaI$$

$$CH_3.CO.CHR.COOC_2H_5 \xrightarrow[\text{Dilute alkali}]{H_2O} CH_3.CO.CH_2R + C_2H_5OH + CO_2$$

$$CH_3.CO.CHR.COOC_2H_5 \xrightarrow[\substack{\text{Concentrated} \\ \text{alkali}}]{2H_2O} HOOC.CH_2.R + C_2H_5OH + CH_3COOH.$$

SYN-. (Greek) With, together. Equivalent to **cis**, as *syn*-benzaldoxime.

SYNALDOXIME. See **isomerism, geometrical.**

SYNCHROTRON. A modified **betatron** in which the acceleration of the electrons is accomplished more rapidly and effectively by the application of a high-frequency voltage, in addition to the magnetic

SYNTHESIS, MALONIC ESTER. An addition reaction involving malonic ester, which is diethyl malonate,

$$CH_2(COOC_2H_5)_2.$$

Either or both of the hydrogen atoms on the methylene carbon atom may be replaced by sodium, and these sodium compounds react with alkyl halides to form a wide variety of mono- and di-substituted compounds.

$$\underset{\underset{COOC_2H_5}{\diagdown}}{\overset{\overset{COOC_2H_5}{\diagup}}{CH_2}} + NaOC_2H_5 \rightarrow \underset{\underset{COOC_2H_5}{\diagdown}}{\overset{\overset{COOC_2H_5}{\diagup}}{CHNa}} + C_2H_5OH$$

$$\underset{\underset{COOC_2H_5}{\diagdown}}{\overset{\overset{COOC_2H_5}{\diagup}}{CHNa}} + RBr \rightarrow \underset{\underset{COOC_2H_5}{\diagdown}}{\overset{\overset{COOC_2H_5}{\diagup}}{CHR}} + NaBr.$$

The ester formed usually undergoes at least partial decarboxylation upon hydrolysis.

SYNTHESIZE. To prepare a compound from its constituent elements or from other compounds that can be prepared from their constituent elements.

SYNTHETIC. Artificial. Produced outside the organism.

SYNTHETIC FIBER. In its broadest sense, the term denotes any fiber made by man. This broad definition includes (1) the cellulose-base fibers, comprising those consisting of (A) cellulose itself, usually produced by regenerating cellulose from a solution or compound (as in the viscose and cuprammonium processes), and (B) those fibers which are utilized as cellulose compounds, such as cellulose acetate and ethyl cellulose; (2) the protein-base fibers, commonly consisting of formaldehyde polymers of casein (milk protein), soybean protein, and protein from other naturally-occurring materials; (3) the fibers prepared from glass, metals, rubber and other industrial products; and (4) the fibers produced from chemical substances which are, or can be, readily synthesized from the elements. The term synthetic fiber is more appropriately restricted to this fourth group, which includes polyamides (polymers of diamines with dibasic acids or their amide-forming derivatives), various acrylic fibers (including polymers of vinyl chloride or itaconic esters with vinyl cyanide (acrylonitrile)), the polyethylene fibers, the polystyrene fibers, and many others.

SYRUP. A viscous, heavy, aqueous solution of a carbohydrate, especially of cane sugar. Official syrup of the United States Pharmacopoeia is made by dissolving 850 grams of cane sugar in enough water to make one liter. The official syrup so prepared has a composition of approximately 65% cane sugar and 35% water.

SYSTEM. (1) A specified region, or portion of matter, containing a definite amount of a substance or substances, arranged in one or more phases. (2) A plan of arrangement of terms or entities, especially those composing a larger aggregate.

SYSTEM, CONDENSED. A system from which the gaseous phase is absent or, more commonly, is disregarded because of its very slight effect upon the processes under consideration.

SYSTEM, HETEROGENEOUS. A system having more than one **phase**.

SYSTEM, HOMOGENEOUS. A system having only one **phase**.

SYSTEM, RING. See **ring system**.

SYSTEM, STABLE. A system that can undergo considerable variation in external conditions, such as temperature, pressure, etc., without fundamental change.

SYSTEMS, BINARY, TERTIARY. . . . Systems composed of, respectively, two, three . . . **components**.

SYSTEMS, NONVARIANT, MONO-VARIANT, DIVARIANT. . . . Systems having, respectively, zero, one, two . . . **degrees of freedom.**

SZEBELLEDY-AJTAI TEST. A test for iron made by adding the following to a drop of the neutral solution: 0.1 ml. of 0.01% *p*-phenetidine-hydrochloric acid solution, 1 drop of 2% alcoholic solution of 2,2'-dipyridyl, and 0.1 ml. of 0.2% hydrogen peroxide. If iron is present, the solution is colored red either immediately or after heating on a water bath for 1–5 minutes. A blank remains colorless or is only faintly pink.

SZEBELLEDY-BARTFAY TEST. A test for manganese made by using two white test tubes, and in one placing 4.5 ml. of the solution to be tested and in the other an equal amount of water. To each is added 0.5 ml. of 20% potassium iodate solution, and from a burette, which delivers a fine stream, 0.1 ml. of 0.1% solution of *p*-phenetidine hydrochloride solution is added to each tube and the contents shaken. If the solution contains manganese, a violet color appears which constantly grows deeper during 2–3 minutes. The blank test remains colorless for about 10 minutes.

SZEBELLEDY-JONAS TEST. A test for molybdate made by adding tincture of cochineal to the acid solution. A fire-red fluorescence indicates the presence of molybdate.

SZEBELLEDY-TANAY TEST. A test for zinc made by mixing, on a spot plate, 6 drops of freshly prepared 2% potassium ferricyanide solution with 2 drops of N sulfuric acid and 12 drops of 1% phenetidine hydrochloride solution. To another cavity on the spot plate, transfer 0.1 ml. of the mixture and add carefully about 0.01 ml. of the solution to be tested. A blue precipitate or color is formed at the zone of contact if zinc is present.

SZENT-GYORGYI TEST REACTION. A reaction for ascorbic acid, made by mixing a slightly alkaline 1% solution of ascorbic acid with some ferrous sulfate solu-tion. Allow to stand exposed to the air. A dark violet color develops rapidly if ascorbic acid is present.

T. Abbreviation for absolute temperature (T). Abbreviation for temperature on centigrade or Fahrenheit scales (t). Symbol for **critical temperature** (t_c or T_c). Symbol for time (T, t or τ). Symbol for triple bond (T). Symbol for **transport number** (T). Symbol for **radioactive half-life** (T). Symbol for **ice point** (t_0 or T_0). Symbol for **oscillation period** (T). See also **tau** and **theta.**

Ta Symbol for the element **tantalum.**

TACHIRCH-EDNER REAGENT. A solution of 5 g. *p*-nitroaniline and 6 ml. sulfuric acid in 25 ml. of water is diazotized by addition of a solution of 3 g. of sodium nitrite in 25 ml. water, and finally made up with water to 500 ml. This reagent gives characteristic colors with certain vegetable drugs, such as rhubarb.

TACHOMETER. An instrument used to measure angular velocity, as of a shaft, either by registering the number of rotations during the period of contact, or by indicating directly the number of rotations per minute. The term is also applied to a biological instrument which indicates the rate of flow of a moving fluid, such as the blood in a living animal.

TAFEL REACTION FOR ANILIDES. The substance to be tested is dissolved in concentrated sulfuric acid and some potassium dichromate added. Acetanilide produces a red-violet color; benzanilide, violet; and propionanilide, blood-red.

TAFEL REACTION FOR STRYCHNINE. If a strychnine salt solution is treated with zinc dust or sodium amalgam, products are formed that produce a characteristic yellow color with ferric chloride.

TAFEL REARRANGEMENT. A rearrangement of substituted **acetoacetic esters** during electrolytic reduction to hydrocarbons in alcoholic sulfuric acid solution at a lead cathode. Some unrearranged hydrocarbon is also formed.

$$CH_3.CH_2.CH_2.CH_2.CH_2.CH_2.CH_3.$$

$$CH_3.CO.CH.COOR \overset{CH_2.CH_2.CH_3}{\underset{CH_3.CH_2.CH.CH_3}{\Big\langle}} \quad CH_2.CH_2.CH_3$$

TAGLIAVINI TEST REACTION. A test for tartaric acid in which the solution of free acid is heated with minium (Pb_3O_4) and filtered, a little potassium thiocyanate is added to the filtrate and boiled. There is an evolution of hydrogen sulfide. The appearance of a black color (due to lead sulfide) shows the presence of tartaric acid in the solution tested.

TAKAHASHI REAGENT FOR ALIPHATIC ALCOHOLS AND ETHERS. A solution of 1 g. vanillin in 200 ml. concentrated sulfuric acid. It gives characteristic colors with many alcohols and esters, especially the aliphatic alcohols and esters.

TAKAHASHI TEST REACTION FOR METHYL LACTATE. A test for methyl lactate made by adding to a few ml. of methyl lactate, 3–4 drops of a 1% alcoholic anisaldehyde solution. An intense blue-green color develops.

TAKAYAMA REAGENTS FOR BLOOD. Reagents used in blood analysis, prepared by mixing (1) 10 ml. 10% aqueous solution of glucose, 20 ml. 10% aqueous solution of sodium hydroxide, 40 ml. pyridine, and 130 ml. water; or (2) 3 ml. 10% aqueous solution of glucose, 3 ml. 10% aqueous solution of sodium hydroxide, 3 ml. pyridine, and 7 ml. water. These reagents, upon addition to blood, produce crystals of hemoglobin.

TAKEUCHI SOLUTION FOR INDICAN. A solution of 8.3 g. potassium iodide, 8.0 g. iodine, and 6.0 ml. potassium bromide in enough water to yield 100 ml. of solution. This solution is used in testing for indican in urine.

TALLERMAN REAGENT. A solution of 0.1 gram safranine in 100 ml. water, used in testing for fructose in urine. The sample is alkalinized with dilute sodium hydroxide solution, and warmed after addition of the reagent. In the presence of fructose the solution is decolorized.

TALLQUIST SCALE. A scale of shades of red corresponding to the color produced by blood of varying hemoglobin content when applied to the same surface, which is usually that of an absorbing paper.

TAMM TEST REACTION. A test for copper made by adding sodium bisulfite solution and potassium thiocyanate solution to a cupric salt solution. A white precipitate of cuprous thiocyanate is produced.

TANANAEV-DOLGOV TESTS FOR GOLD, PALLADIUM, AND PLATINUM. (1) Gold: A drop of the solution to be tested is placed on a strip of filter paper and a drop of a solution of benzidine in acetic acid is added. A blue or green color indicates gold. (2) Palladium: A filter paper is moistened with a drop of saturated thallium nitrate solution and gold chloride solution added, followed by the solution to be tested. The spot darkens if palladium is present. (3) Platinum: A drop of thallium nitrate is placed on a filter paper, followed with a drop of the solution to be tested, and another drop of thallium nitrate. Any free acid is neutralized with a drop of dilute ammonia applied to the center of the spot. Then stannous chloride is added. An orange or yellow color indicates the presence of platinum.

TANANAEV-PANCHENKO TESTS FOR TITANIUM AND URANIUM. A drop of titanium sulfate solution is placed on a filter paper and a drop of chromotropic acid added to the same spot. An intense brown color is obtained. Addition of stannous chloride weakens the color slightly by preventing interference by ferric iron or uranyl ions. To test for uranyl ions, the brown color formed with potassium ferrocyanide is a suitable test.

TANANAEV-PANCHENKO TEST FOR TUNGSTATE. A drop of the solution to be tested is placed on a filter paper moistened with concentrated hydrochloric acid. A yellow stain appears if tungstate is present. On the addition of ammonium thiocyanate and stannous chloride, this stain becomes blue and is intensified by the addition of concentrated hydrochloric acid.

TANANAEV-PANCHENKO TEST FOR VANADIUM. The solution to be tested is oxidized by concentrated nitric acid and a drop is placed on a filter paper which was previously moistened with aniline hydrochloride. A greenish-blue ring is formed in the presence of vanadium. The solution must first be boiled with concentrated hydrochloric acid if it contains chromate, chlorate, hypochlorite, or permanganate.

TANANAEV-RABINOVICH TEST FOR ANTIMONY (ANTIMONOUS). The solution to be tested is treated with sodium hydroxide to a slight turbidity and then with 2 drops of concentrated mercuric chloride solution, followed with an excess of sodium hydroxide. A brown solution and a gray-black precipitate of metallic mercury form in the presence of antimony.

TANANAEV REACTION FOR MERCUROUS SALTS. An excess of potassium nitrate solution is added to a solution of a mercurous salt in dilute nitric acid and shaken vigorously. A dark gray precipitate or a light to dark gray color of metallic mercury forms, according to the concentration of mercurous ion.

TANANAEV REAGENT FOR BISMUTH. A test reagent for bismuth, prepared by mixing 25 ml. saturated aqueous solution of potassium cyanide with enough 10% aqueous solution of manganous sulfate so that the precipitate barely dissolves. The solution to be tested is strongly acidified (to 10% HCl) with hydrochloric acid and poured down the side of a test tube containing the reagent. A dark ring indicates the presence of bismuth.

TANANAEV-ROMANINK TEST FOR OSMIUM. One to 2 ml. of the solution to be tested are placed in a small test tube and a stopper inserted which carries tubing with a short narrow opening at the outside end. Filter paper is moistened with either potassium ferrocyanide solution or with benzidine in acetic acid solution and the end of the tubing brought against the moistened part of the filter paper. The solution is then heated in the test tube and observed for coloration of the paper for 30 seconds. With ferrocyanide, osmium gives a green color, and with benzidine, a violet color.

TANANAEV SPOT REACTIONS FOR CESIUM, RUBIDIUM, AND THALLIUM. Solutions of cesium, rubidium, and thallium yield brown to black precipitates when added to a solution of equimolecular amounts of palladium chloride and gold chloride in dilute hydrochloric acid. Red to brown precipitates are produced by thallium and cesium with potassium bismuth iodide, but rubidium gives no precipitate.

TANANAEV SPOT REACTION FOR MAGNESIUM. (1) A drop of a magnesium solution is placed on a filter paper, a drop of ammonia added, and in the middle of the spot a drop of silver nitrate solution added. A brown spot is formed. Interference by calcium, barium, and strontium is prevented if the excess of ammonia is removed by heating before adding the silver nitrate. (2) A strip of paper is moistened with phenolphthalein indicator solution and a drop of a neutral magnesium solution (free from ammonium salt) and a drop of dilute ammonia is added to the middle of the spot. A red color is produced. When the paper is dried over a flame, it becomes colorless, but the red color is restored by moistening with water. If the original solution of magnesium contains ammonium salts, it is acidified with sulfuric acid, evaporated to dryness and carefully ignited before the test is made.

TANANAEV SPOT TEST FOR LEAD. A drop of dilute sulfuric acid is placed on a filter paper, and then a drop of the solution to be tested is applied to the same spot.

Lead sulfate forms in the presence of lead. All other substances are washed out with dilute sulfuric acid and the spot touched with a solution containing stannous chloride, potassium iodide and cadmium nitrate. An orange-red spot forms if lead is present.

TANANAEV TEST FOR CADMIUM AND ZINC. A test for cadmium and zinc made by adding 1.2 ml. of concentrated ammonia to the solution to be tested and heating. A little potassium iodide and some hydrogen peroxide are added to precipitate silver and manganese and the solution is heated again, filtered and to half of the filtrate an excess of potassium thiocyanate and some sodium sulfide are added. In the presence of cadmium, a yellow precipitate is formed. To the other half of the filtrate 20% sodium hydroxide solution and sufficient formaldehyde to remove the ammonia odor are added. The solution is then boiled to precipitate copper, nickel and cadmium, and the hot solution filtered. An excess of sodium sulfide is added to the filtrate and it is boiled a short time. A precipitate indicates zinc.

TANANAEV TESTS FOR TIN AND MERCURY. (1) Tin: A drop of the solution to be tested is placed on a strip of filter paper which has been moistened with mercuric chloride solution and dried. A drop of aniline is added. A dark stain indicates the presence of tin. Stannic tin must be reduced with magnesium in acid solution before the test is made. (2) Mercury: A drop of stannous chloride solution is placed on a strip of filter paper and a drop of the solution to be tested and a drop of aniline added. Mercury produces a dark stain.

TANANAEV-TRANANAEV MICRO-TESTS FOR CHROMIUM AND MANGANESE. Chromium: Oxidize chromic salts by warming with silver nitrate and sodium hydroxide and add ammonium nitrate to dissolve silver oxide and convert the sodium hydroxide to sodium nitrate. The chromate is detected with either silver nitrate (red precipitate) or with an acetic acid solution of benzidine, the latter producing a blue color. Manganese: Add ammoniacal silver nitrate solution to the solu-

tion to be tested. An intesne black color indicates manganese. This reaction does not take place with cobalt, nickel, lead, or chromium.

TANANAEV-YUNITZKAYA TEST FOR MERCURY. A little silver sulfide suspension in water is added to a little of the neutral solution to be tested and the mixture is heated with shaking for 10–20 seconds. It is filtered and 3 N nitric acid added to the precipitate. The sulfide precipitate dissolves easily in the nitric acid, if no mercury is present.

TANATAR-PETROFF TEST REACTION. A test for thallium in slightly acid solution, for which sodium cobaltinitrite serves as a very sensitive reagent. A red, crystalline precipitate is formed which is insoluble in hot water or in cold dilute acid. The precipitate dissolves with evolution of oxides of nitrogen, on boiling with acids. The thallium and cobalt pass into solution.

TANKAGE. Processed nitrogenous waste materials of animal origin, used largely as fertilizer or in the feeding of animals. The waste materials are the carcasses of animals, or the blood and other by-products of the meat-packing industry, and the processing operations consist of heating, drying and grinding.

TANNIC. Related: (1) to tannic acid, $C_{14}H_{10}O_5$; or (2) to tannic acid of commerce, which is a penta-digalloyl ester-like compound of glucose of the formula, $C_{76}H_{52}O_{46}$.

TANNIN. One of a group of naturally occurring carbon compounds characterized by the following properties; they are amorphous and astringent; they precipitate gelatin from solution, convert hide into leather, precipitate many alkaloids and glycosides from solution, form insoluble compounds with lead and copper, react with ferric salts to produce deep blue or green colors. In alkaline solution they absorb oxygen, and produce a deep red color with ammonia and aqueous potassium ferricyanide. The chemistry of the tannins is very incomplete, but some of them appear to be **glycosides.**

TANNING. The process of converting hides into leather. The agents used are tannins, metallic hydroxides (formed in the process from metallic salts, usually of chromium or aluminum) and oils (cod liver and whale oils). The mechanism of the process is considered to involve an absorption of the tanning agent on the surface of the fiber.

TANNING PROCESS, ALUM. A process for producing leather from skins or hides of animals by treatment with aluminum sulfate, or various double salts containing aluminum (alums).

TANNING PROCESS, CHROME. A process for producing leather from skins or hides of animals by treatment with chromium salts, such as chromium sulfate or chromates.

TANRET REAGENT FOR ALBUMIN. A solution which gives a white precipitate with albumin and some alkaloids. It is prepared by mixing a solution of 3.3 g. potassium iodide in 25 ml. water, with a solution of 1.35 of mercuric chloride in 25 ml. water, adding 20 ml. of glacial acetic acid, and then adding water until the volume of the solution reaches 60 ml.

TANRET REAGENT FOR ALKALOIDS. A reagent which precipitates alkaloids from acidified solution. It is an aqueous solution of 13.55 g. mercuric chloride and 50 g. potassium iodide, made up to one liter.

TANTALATE. An anion consisting essentially of tantalum and oxygen, or a compound containing it. Individual tantalate anions are discussed below.

TANTALATE (HEXA-). The anion

$$Ta_6O_{19}{}^{8-},$$

or a compound containing it.

TANTALATE (META-). The anion

$$TaO_3{}^-,$$

or a compound containing it.

TANTALATE (ORTHO-). The anion $TaO_4{}^{3-}$, or a compound containing it.

TANTALATE (PYRO-). The anion

$$Ta_2O_7{}^{4-},$$

or a compound containing it.

TANTALIC. Containing or pertaining to pentavalent **tantalum.**

TANTALOUS. Containing or pertaining to trivalent **tantalum.**

TANTALUM. Metallic element. Symbol Ta. Atomic number 73. Atomic weight 180.88. Density 16.6. Specific heat 0.033. Melting point 2850° C. Boiling point ca. 4100° C. Valence 2, 3, 4, 5, and 7. Oxides TaO_2, Ta_2O_5. Tantalic acid $HTaO_3$. Tantalum occurs in yttrotantalite, fergusonite, and other minerals.

TARE. The weight of a weighing bottle or other container in which liquids or other substances are weighed; or a mass of that magnitude, which is added to the masses on the scale, in order to balance the container.

TARGET. Any object or substance subjected to bombardment, as by neutrons, protons, helium nuclei (He^{++}), radiations, etc., or specifically the metal plate (anticathode) in an x-ray tube which, upon bombardment with electrons (β-rays) yields x-rays.

TARTARIC. Related to tartaric acid, HOOC.CHOH.CHOH.COOH.

TARTRATE. A salt of the general formula, MOOC.CHOH.CHOH.COOM; related to tartaric acid in that both of the carboxy hydrogen atoms have been replaced by metals, or inorganic radicals. If only one of the hydrogen atoms has been so replaced, the compound is called an acid tartrate or a bitartrate.

TARTRONIC. Related to tartronic acid, HOOC.CHOH.COOH.

TARUGI-LENCI REACTION FOR AMINO AND IMINO GROUPS. Treat about 0.5 g. of the substance to be tested with an excess of phenol crystals and add, drop by drop, a solution of sodium hypochlorite (containing about 3% active chlorine and of an alkalinity equivalent to 4% of sodium hydroxide). Amino acids, amino aldehydes, and, in general, all substances containing the groups —NH$_2$ or =NH give an intense blue color.

TARUGI-LENCI REACTION FOR p-BENZOQUINONE AND 2,6-DIBRO-MOQUINONE. An aqueous suspension of p-benzoquinone is treated with a solution of ammonia, then with a solution of sodium hypochlorite, and finally with a little zinc chloride; and the whole heated for 15 minutes on the water bath. A yellow, crystalline compound is produced which melts at 85° C. After evaporation, this compound can be extracted with alcohol. 2,6-Dibromoquinone, when treated in the same way, yields a dark yellow, crystalline substance, melting at 78° C. A blue coloration is given by both the above products with alkaline phenol solution.

TASSINARI-PIAZZA TEST. A test for nitrate made by heating the substance to be tested with potassium hydroxide solution and zinc dust. If nitrate is present, ammonia is evolved. Several modifications of this test have been developed.

TATTERSALL REACTION FOR CO-BALT. Add potassium cyanide to the solution of cobalt until the precipitate which forms is dissolved. On the addition of yellow ammonium sulfide, the yellow solution becomes blood-red. Copper salts impair the reaction, but nickel salts do not.

TATTERSALL REACTION FOR DEL-PHININE. The delphinine is triturated with an equal amount of malic acid, a few drops of concentrated sulfuric acid are added and mixed. An orange-red color forms, changing to rose, then gradually the mixture becomes blue-violet and finally dirty cobalt-blue.

TATTERSALL REACTION FOR MOR-PHINE. Add a little concentrated sulfuric acid and some sodium arsenate to a little morphine. The mixture becomes dirty violet and then sea-green.

TATTERSALL REACTION FOR PA-PAVERINE AND CODEINE. Add a few drops of concentrated sulfuric acid to the sample to be tested and heat in a porcelain dish. Add a little sodium arsenate and continue heating over a small flame, distributing the liquid over the dish as much as possible. A wine-red to violet color, which becomes orange on dilution with 10 ml. water and black on addition of sodium hydroxide, indicates the presence of papaverine or codeine.

TAU (T OR τ). The nineteenth letter in the Greek alphabet, used to denote the nineteenth carbon atom in a straight-chain compound, or a derivative in which a substituent group is attached to that carbon atom (τ-). Symbol for **radioactive mean life** (τ). Symbol for time (when t is used for temperature) (τ). Symbol for **transmittance** (τ). Symbol for unit vector tangent to path (τ).

TAUBER BENZIDINE REAGENT. A solution of 4 g. benzidine in 100 ml. glacial acetic acid. It is used in testing for pentoses, by boiling 0.5 ml. of the unknown solution with 1 drop of the reagent. A red color on cooling indicates the presence of pentoses.

TAUBER REAGENT FOR VITAMIN C. A reagent prepared by dissolving 1 ml. ferric sulfate in 80 ml. water and 18 ml. phosphoric acid (85%), and oxidizing with 1% potassium permanganate solution. In conducting the test, 5 g. of sample are ground with 15 ml. 8% acetic acid, then filtered, and the filtrate is spot tested on filter paper with the reagent. A blue color indicates the presence of vitamin C (ascorbic acid).

TAUBER REAGENTS FOR MONOSE SUGARS. There are two Tauber reagents for monose sugars. One is an aqueous solution of lactic acid and cupric acetate; and the other is prepared by dissolving molybdenum trioxide in an aqueous sodium carbonate solution, and then adding phosphoric acid (85%). A blue color, obtained under test conditions, shows the presence of monose sugars.

TAUBER TEST REACTION FOR VI-TAMIN B$_1$ (THIAMINE). A test for vitamin B$_1$ made by placing several mg.

of the vitamin and about 5 mg. *p*-dimethyl-aminobenzaldehyde in a small crucible, adding 0.1 ml. glacial acetic acid, evaporating, then cooling and adding 1 drop glacial acetic acid. A deep brick-red color is produced immediately. Amino acids and proteins interfere.

TAUFEL-THALER TEST REACTION. A test for glycerin made by converting the glycerin by way of acraldehyde into epi-hydrinaldehyde, which is then recognized by the formation of a red color with phloro-glucinol.

TAURO-. (Latin, *taurus*, bull) Relating to bulls or to taurine, as taurocholic acid, taurocyamine.

TAURYL. The radical

$$H_2NCH_2CH_2SO_2—.$$

TAUTOMERISM. A phenomenon whereby a substance exists in two isomeric forms, which are in equilibrium and exhibit characteristic reactions. Thus the substance may react in accordance with either structure, depending upon the conditions

and the other substances present. Most of the examples studied during the early history of tautomerism were keto-enol systems, i.e., certain triad prototropic systems containing oxygen, of the general type:

$$[H]C—C{=}O \rightleftarrows C{=}C—O[H]$$

as represented by ethyl acetoacetate, commonly called merely acetoacetic ester,

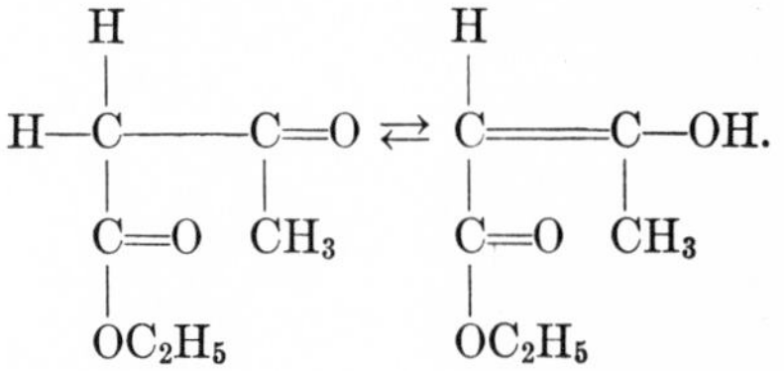

$$H—C\!\!-\!\!-\!\!-C{=}O \rightleftarrows C\!\!=\!\!=\!\!C—OH.$$

Keto form   Enol form

There are many types of tautomeric systems in addition to the triad prototropic carbon-carbon-oxygen system represented above. Thus, a partial list of the triad (three-atom) prototropic (proton-shifting) tautomeric systems consists of the following:

Some Triad Prototropic Tautomeric Systems

Name Commonly Used	Tautomeric System
Three carbon	$[H]C—C{=}C \rightleftarrows C{=}C—C[H]$
Keto-enol	$[H]C—C{=}O \rightleftarrows C{=}C—O[H]$
Imino-enamine	$[H]C—C{=}N \rightleftarrows C{=}C—N[H]$
Methylene-azomethine	$[H]C—N{=}C \rightleftarrows C{=}N—C[H]$
Azo-hydrazone	$[H]C—N{=}N \rightleftarrows C{=}N—N[H]$
Nitroso-oximino	$[H]C—N{=}O \rightleftarrows C{=}N—O[H]$

Some Triad Prototropic Tautomeric Systems—*Continued*

Name Commonly Used	*Tautomeric System*
Amide-imidol	$[H]N—C{=}O \rightleftarrows N{=}C—O[H]$
Amidine	$[H]N—C{=}N \rightleftarrows N{=}C—N[H]$
Diazoamino	$[H]N—N{=}N \rightleftarrows N{=}N—N[H]$
Nitrosoaminodiazohydrate	$[H]N—N{=}O \rightleftarrows N{=}N—O[H]$
Carboxyl group	$[H]O—C{=}O \rightleftarrows O{=}C—O[H]$
Nitro-acinitro	$[H]C—N{=}O \rightleftarrows C{=}N—O[H]$

Tautomeric changes are by no means confined to the triad prototropic systems shown above, but may also be exhibited by groups containing more or less atoms, such as dyads (two atoms), pentads (five atoms), etc. Furthermore, the entity which shifts may be some other positive ion than a proton; the term cationotropy being used to designate tautomerism in which the entity that shifts is any positive ion. The corresponding term anionotropy is used when the entity that shifts is a negative ion.

Tautomeric changes may result in the formation or the disruption of a ring, a phenomenon called ring-chain tautomerism; in a tautomeric change within a ring (transannular tautomerism), or by group migrations typical of the **pinacol rearrangement**.

The simplest approach to the mechanism of tautomerism is that of cationotropy, where the process may be considered to consist of (1) the separation of a positive ion, such as a proton, (2) the redistribution of the negative charge by electromeric rearrangement in the residual anion, and finally (3), the re-coordination of the positive ion at the new seat of the negative charge.

TAUTOMERISM, ELECTROLYTIC. A type of tautomerism in which a substance exhibits differences in electronic configura-

tion, often resulting in differences in chemical behavior, corresponding to changes in the electric character of the environment. This type of tautomerism is shown by **amphiprotic** substances which are capable of acting as proton donors or proton acceptors.

TAUTOMERISM, FUNCTIONAL. A type of tautomerism in which the **isomers** possess different chemical functions, as keto-enol, amide-imido, etc., tautomerism.

TAUTOMERISM, VIRTUAL. A type of tautomerism in which the **isomers** possess similar chemical properties or functions, e.g., the amidine type,

$$RNH—C{=}NR' \rightleftarrows RN{=}C—NHR'.$$

TAUTOROTATION. Mutarotation.

TAWING. A **tanning process** in which mineral agents, as alum or chromium salts, are employed to convert the hide into leather.

Tb Symbol for the element **terbium**.

Tc Symbol for the element **technetium**.

Te Symbol for the element **tellurium**.

TECHNETIUM. Radioactive element, not of natural occurrence. Symbol Tc. Atomic number 43. The known isotopes of this element have been produced by artificial radioactive processes, including occurrence among the fission products of uranium 235. Isotopes have been reported with the mass numbers 92 (two isomers), 93, 94, 95 (two isomers), 96 (two isomers), 97 (two isomers), 98, 99 (two isomers), 100, 101, 102 and 105. This element was formerly called masurium.

TELLERA TEST. A test for petrolatum in lanolin in which 1 g. of the lanolin is dissolved in 15 ml. ether with the aid of heat, allowed to cool, the precipitate stearin filtered off and 5 ml. absolute alcohol added to the filtrate. A flocculent precipitate indicates the presence of petrolatum.

TELLURATE. The anion $TeO_5{}^{4-}$ or $Te_4O_{13}{}^=$, or the various anions listed below as meta-, ortho-, and pyrotellurates; or a compound containing one of these anions.

TELLURATE (META-). The anion $(TeO_4)_n{}^{2n-}$ or $HTeO_4{}^-$, or a compound containing one of these anions.

TELLURATE (ORTHO-). The anion $TeO_6{}^{6-}$, $H_4TeO_6{}^=$, or $TeO_2(OH)_4{}^=$, or a compound containing one of these anions.

TELLURATE (PYRO-). The anion $Te_2O_7{}^=$, or a compound containing it.

TELLURIC. (1) Containing or pertaining to hexavalent tellurium. (2) Related to telluric acid, H_2TeO_4.

TELLURIDE. A binary compound of **tellurium,** usually one in which that element is bivalent.

TELLURINIC. The radical $-Te(:O)OH$.

TELLURITE. The anion $TeO_3{}^=$, $Te_2O_5{}^=$, or $Te_4O_9{}^=$, or a compound containing one of these anions.

TELLURIUM. Nonmetallic element. Symbol Te. Atomic number 52. Atomic weight 127.61. Exists in two allotropic forms: amorphous—density 6.00; crystal-line—density 6.25. Melting point 449.8° C. Boiling point 1390° C. Valence 2, 4, and 6. Oxides TeO, TeO_2, TeO_3. Acids H_2Te, H_2TeO_3, H_2TeO_4. Tellurium occurs in sylvanite, tetradymite, silver telluride, etc.

TELLURO-. The radical $Te=$ in organic compounds.

TELLUROCYANATE. The anion $TeCN^-$, or a compound containing it.

TELLURONIC. The radical $-Te(:O)_2OH$.

TELLUROUS. Containing or pertaining to tetravalent **tellurium.**

TELOMERIZATION. A **polymerization** reaction between two substances in which one substance breaks up, commonly into two parts which constitute the terminal groups of the new polymer molecule, while the other substances furnish the unsaturated groups or structural elements which form the links that constitute the interior of the polymer chain.

TEMPERATURE. The intensity factor of heat energy. The temperature of a body is its condition of thermal intensity, referred to an arbitrary standard.

TEMPERATURE, ABSOLUTE. (1) The temperature measured on the thermodynamic scale. (2) The temperature measured from the absolute zero ($-273.16°$ C.); which is the temperature at which the volume of an ideal gas becomes zero. Degrees centigrade $+ 273.16 =$ degrees absolute. See **temperature scale, Kelvin,** and **temperature scale, absolute.**

TEMPERATURE COLOR SCALE. The relationship between the temperature of an incandescent body or substance, and the color of the light emitted. Thus, when metals are heated, a faint red glow becomes perceptible at 500° C., or slightly higher, becoming bright red at around 800°–900° C., and reaching white heat at about 1500° C.

TEMPERATURE, CONSOLUTE. See **critical composition.**

TEMPERATURE, CRITICAL. That temperature above which a gas cannot be liquefied by application of any pressure, however great. The following are the critical temperatures of some common substances (in degrees centigrade):

Carbon Dioxide..	31.1
Ammonia.......	132.9
Ether..........	190.
Water..........	374.
Nitrogen........	−147.1
Oxygen.........	−118.8

TEMPERATURE, CRITICAL SOLUTION. See critical composition.

TEMPERATURE GRADIENT. The temperature difference between two points, divided by the distance between them, or $\dfrac{t_1 - t_2}{l}$. The temperature gradient is, therefore, the average fall in temperature per unit distance between the two points.

TEMPERATURE, KINDLING. The minimum temperature to which a substance, or mixture of substances in specified proportions, must be heated in order to cause them to burn continuously. In this definition, to burn means to undergo vigorous oxidation accompanied by the production of heat and light.

TEMPERATURE OF EXPLOSION. (Ignition or kindling temperature. Flash point) The minimum temperature at a given pressure at which an explosion will take place.

TEMPERATURE OF INVERSION. The temperature at which a substance undergoes a change in optical rotatory power due to a change in chemical structure; or, in general, the temperature at which a substance undergoes a change to an isomeric form. For inversion temperature, see **Joule-Thomson Inversion Temperature.** For the thermoelectric temperature of inversion, see discussion of **temperature, neutral.**

TEMPERATURE, NEUTRAL. The temperature at which the electromotive force produced by heating one junction of a thermocouple reaches a maximum. Above this temperature the electromotive force steadily decreases until it reaches a zero value. The latter point is called the temperature of inversion. For an iron-copper couple the neutral temperature is 275° C. and the temperature of inversion 550° C.

TEMPERATURE SCALE, ABSOLUTE. A temperature scale which has its zero point at that temperature at which the volume of an ideal gas becomes zero, and which has its degree of the same magnitude as the centigrade degree. Since the temperature at which the volume of an ideal gas becomes zero is −273.16° C., then temperatures on the absolute scale may be obtained from centigrade temperatures by adding 273.16°, and centigrade temperatures may be obtained from absolute ones by subtracting 273.16°. There is also a Fahrenheit absolute scale (called the Rankine scale) which bears the same relation to the absolute temperature scale that the Fahrenheit scale does to the centigrade scale. However, by the use of the term absolute scale or temperature absolute, the absolute scale based on the centigrade scale, as described above, is understood.

TEMPERATURE SCALE, KELVIN. A temperature scale independent of any particular substance, which defines the ratio of two temperatures as those of two heat reservoirs at constant, though different, temperatures, with an ideal reversible machine operating between them. It can be shown to follow from this definition that the Kelvin scale and the ideal gas scale have the same zero point and, by suitable definition of the degree, have the same values throughout. Therefore, a temperature has the same numerical value when expressed in degrees Kelvin (°K.) as in the absolute temperature scale.

TEMPERATURE, STANDARD. In general, a standard temperature established by some unvarying process, such as a melting or boiling point or pressure or volume of a substance under fully-defined conditions. In common use, the term is applied to the temperature of a mixture of pure ice and water when the pressure on the water surface is one atmosphere. This is the temperature of 0° on the centigrade scale, or 273.16° on the absolute scale.

TEMPERATURE, TRANSITION. (Transition point) That temperature at which one phase of a complete heterogeneous **equilibrium** disappears, and another phase takes its place. Thus the melting point of a homogeneous solid or the boiling or freezing points of a homogeneous liquid, are transition points. The term is most widely used, however, for the particular case of transition between two solid states of a **polymorphic** substance. It is the temperature at which two forms, commonly crystalline, can coexist in equilibrium, whereas above or below that temperature only one form or the other, respectively, are stable. A few transition temperatures are:

Rhombic to monoclinic sulfur, 95.6° C.

$Na_2SO_4.10H_2O$ to Na_2SO_4 + solution, 32.383° C.

$NaBr.2H_2O$ to $NaBr$ + solution, 50.674° C.

$MnCl_2.4H_2O$ to $MnCl_2.2H_2O$ + solution, 58.089° C.

$SrCl_2.6H_2O$ to $SrCl_2.2H_2O$ + solution, 61.341° C.

TEMPERING. In general, the process of rendering a material more suitable for its purpose. The tempering of metals is a process of heating or reheating, followed by cooling, at predetermined rates and temperatures to obtain a desired degree of toughness and hardness. The tempering of clays or plastics is a process of mixing, to obtain a more uniform product. The tempering of sugar solutions is a treatment with lime for clarification.

TEMPORARY HARDNESS. See **hardness, temporary.**

TENDENCY. The effect of a difference in intensity in a system, when equalization is restrained by a counter force. Equalization of intensities tends to take place; it will take place when the opposing force is withdrawn.

TENSILE STRENGTH. The resistance offered by a material to tensile stresses, as

measured by the tensile force per unit cross-sectional area required to break it.

TENSIMETER. An apparatus used to determine transition points (see **temperature, transition**) indirectly by measuring small changes in vapor pressure.

TENSIOMETER. An apparatus used for the "direct" measurement of **surface tension**. It operates by registering the force necessary to lift a metal ring from the surface of a liquid. This force is shown by the angle of torsion imparted to a fine wire.

TENSION CLIP. See **stopcock tension clip.**

TENSION, SOLUTION. See **solution tension.**

TENSION, SURFACE. See **surface tension.**

TENSION, VAPOR. See **vapor tension.**

TENTELEW PROCESS. A **contact** process for the manufacture of sulfuric acid, in which the burner gases containing the sulfur dioxide are purified by dry filtration and scrubbing with water.

TERBIUM. Rare earth metallic element. Symbol Tb. Atomic number 65. Atomic weight 159.2. Valence 3 and 4. Terbium occurs in gadolinite, monazite, etc. Oxides Tb_2O_3, Tb_4O_7.

TERE-. (Latin, *terebinthus, terebinth*) Relating to terebene or to terpenes, as terephthalic, teresantalic.

TEREPHTHALAL. See **terephthalylidene.**

TEREPHTHALOYL. The radical

$$-OCC_6H_4CO-(p).$$

TEREPHTHALYLIDENE. The radical

$$=HCC_6H_4CH=(p).$$

TERMOLECULAR REACTION. See reaction, trimolecular.

TERNARY COMPOUND. A compound having a molecular formula consisting of three types of atoms or radicals.

TERPENE. One of a class of unsaturated hydrocarbons of the formula $C_{10}H_{16}$. They and their derivatives occur in essential oils and related substances of vegetable origin. Sesquiterpenes, camphors, thymol, and menthol are closely related substances. Terpenes are classified as monocyclic and bicyclic according to whether they may be regarded as derivatives of *p*- or *m*-cymene or of a nucleus which contains a bridged ring. The first group, menthadienes, are represented by dipentene, terpinolene, and phellandrene; the second by pinene, camphene, and fenchene. There are also noncyclic terpenes. Camphene is the only solid terpene. See **sesquiterpene** and **hemiterpene.**

TERT-. Abbreviation of **tertiary,** as *tert*-butyl.

TERTIARY. A term meaning literally "of the third order," which has two important meanings in chemistry. It is applied to compounds of tribasic acids, such as phosphoric or arsenic acids, to denote the replacement of all three acidic hydrogen atoms by metals or radicals. It is also applied to classes of organic compounds in which the characteristic group is bound to three nonelementary radicals, as tertiary alcohols, which are compounds of the general formula,

$$R_1R_2R_3COH$$

tertiary amines, which are compounds of the general formula,

$$R_1R_2R_3N, \text{ etc.}$$

TERVALENT. A term meaning having three different valences. This term is occasionally used for trivalent, which means having a valence of three.

TEST. A trial or criterion of a decisive kind by which the chemical character, i.e., composition or properties of a substance, is determined.

TEST PAPER. A paper usually in the form of strips, which has been impregnated with an indicator or reagent for use in testing.

TEST SOLUTION. A solution used in the determination of the properties or composition of a substance or sample. A great variety of test solutions are used in qualitative and quantitative analysis and other chemical laboratory work. Many of them are known by the names of the investigators who first suggested them, and a great many of these solutions are defined in this book under the names of various investigators.

TEST TUBE. A small glass container, relatively long and of circular cross-section. It is closed at one end, and is used in the chemical laboratory for many tests and other operations.

TETRA-. A prefix which signifies four, as tetravalent, tetratomic, tetramethyl.

TETRABASIC ACID. An acid that contains four replaceable hydrogen atoms, e.g., $H_4P_2O_7$ (pyrophosphoric acid).

TETRACHROMATE. The anion

$$Cr_4O_{13}^=,$$

or a compound containing it.

TETRACID BASE. A base that contains four replaceable, hydroxyl groups, e.g., titanic hydroxide, $Ti(OH)_4$.

TETRAD. A tetravalent element, e.g., manganese, sulfur, carbon; or a crystal exhibiting four similar faces on rotation.

TETRAGONAL CRYSTAL. See **crystal, tetragonal.**

TETRAHEDRAL ATOM. A configuration of atoms with a valence of 4 in which the valence bonds are directed from the center of a regular tetrahedron, representing the location of the atom under consideration, to the four corners, representing the location of the nearest neighbors.

TETRAMETHYLENE. The radical

$$-CH_2CH_2CH_2CH_2-.$$

TETRAMIDO COMPOUND. See **tetramine.**

TETRAMINE. A compound that contains four **amino groups** ($-NH_2$). These compounds are also called tetramino or tetramido compounds, as tetraminobenzene, $C_6H_2(NH_2)_4$.

TETRAMINO COMPOUND. See **tetramine.**

TETRAMMINE. A coordination compound (q.v.) in which four molecules of ammonia (NH_3) are coordinated around a metal ion. Each ammonia molecule donates a pair of electrons to form a **semipolar** valence bond with the metal ion, of the general type,

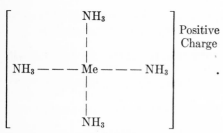

Investigation of the spatial configuration of such compounds has shown that they may be either tetrahedral or planar

TETRAMORPHIC SUBSTANCE. A substance capable of existing in four distinct solid forms.

TETRAPHOSPHATE. The anion

$$P_4O_{13}^{6-},$$

or a compound containing it.

TETRATHIONATE. The anion $S_4O_6^=$, or a compound containing it.

TETRATOMIC. Containing four atoms, as of a molecule; or containing four atoms or radicals of the same kind. The term was once used chiefly to indicate the presence of four hydroxyl groups.

TETRAVALENT. Having a **valence** of four.

TETRAZINE. One of three isomeric compounds having the formula $C_2H_2N_4$, and having a ring structure consisting of two carbon atoms and four nitrogen atoms.

TETRAZO COMPOUND. A compound containing four nitrogen atoms arranged in two **azo groups.**

TETRAZOLE. One of two isomeric compounds having the formula CH_2N_4, and having a ring structure consisting of one carbon atom and four nitrogen atoms.

TETRAZOLYL. The radical CHN_4- (from tetrazole, 2 isomers).

TETRAZONES. Derivatives of the hypothetical compound

$$NH_2-N{=}N-NH_2$$

as dimethyldiphenyl tetrazone,

$$(C_6H_5)(CH_3)N-N{=}N-N(C_6H_5)(CH_3).$$

TETROXIDE. An oxide that contains four oxygen atoms, as nitrogen tetroxide, N_2O_4.

TETTAMANZI REAGENT. A solution used to separate arsenic and phosphoric acids, by precipitating the latter in the presence of the former. The solution is prepared by adding 50 ml. triethanolamine to an aqueous solution of 15 ml. ammonium molybdate in 50 ml. water, and then adding 20 ml. of 6% nitric acid and 100 ml. of 10% citric acid.

TEXTURE. The character of the structure of a substance, apparent to the eye and touch.

Th Symbol for the element **thorium.**

THALLEIOQUIN TEST REACTION. A test for quinine, discovered by André, who found that a solution of quinine is colored green when treated with chlorine and then with ammonia. When this solution is neutralized with an acid, the color changes to blue, and on further addition of acid the color becomes red. A number of modifications of this reaction have been developed, in one (Winograd) the quinine is dissolved in chloroform, and treated with bromine water and ammonia, yielding an emerald-green color.

THALLIC. Containing or pertaining to trivalent **thallium.**

THALLIUM. Metallic element. Symbol Tl. Atomic number 81. Atomic weight 204.39. Density 11.85. Specific heat 0.0326. Melting point 303.5° C. Boiling point 1650° C. Valence 1 and 3. Oxides Tl_2O, Tl_2O_3. Thallium occurs in certain iron and copper pyrites, crookesite, lorandite, etc.

THALLOUS. Containing or pertaining to univalent **thallium.**

THAW-MELT METHOD. A method of obtaining accurate thermal data needed in the study of equilibria between solid and liquid phases of systems containing two or more components. The finely-divided solid of known composition is heated slowly in a glass tube and is pressed from time to time to expel the first drops of liquid as soon as they are formed, giving the "thaw point" or the temperature at which fusion commences (the point on the solidus curve). Then slow heating is continued until the solid melts completely, giving the "melt point," or the temperature at which the solid phase disappears (the point on the liquidus curve).

THÉNARD BLUE. A blue fusion-product, consisting chiefly of cobalt aluminate, obtained by heating aluminum salts which have been moistened with cobalt nitrate. This reaction is used as a test for aluminum.

THENOYL. The radical $C_4H_3SCO—$, which has two isomers and is derived from thiophenecarboxylic acid

or

THENYL. The radical $C_4H_3SCH_2—$ (2 isomers).

THENYLIDENE. The radical

$$C_4H_3SCH=$$

(2 isomers).

THEOREM. An established principle; a rule.

THEORETICAL CHEMISTRY. See **chemistry, theoretical.**

THEORY. (1) The collected principles which underlie and govern the phenomena of science. (2) A scientific doctrine that is confirmed by experiments designed to test the predictions based upon the theory.

THEORY, ATOMIC. See **atom, atomic structure,** etc.

THEORY, DUALISTIC. Berzelius' hypothesis that each element possesses a definite quantity of positive or negative electricity which causes the exhibition of affinity and leads to chemical combination.

THEORY OF TYPES. A generalization that played an important part in the early work on the organization of the characteristic chemical properties of substances. This theory postulated that, among organic compounds, there exist certain types which persist through derivatives formed by substitution of halogens, etc., for the hydrogen of the type compounds. Chemical types were found in those cases where derivative and parent possess the same general properties, as chloroacetic and acetic acids; mechanical types in cases where substitution produces a dissimilar compound, as acetic acid and alcohol.

THEORY OF VALENCY. The theory that atoms combine with other atoms in proportions which are determined by a property known as valence, the standard of which is the valence of hydrogen taken as one, or, better, of oxygen taken as two. This conception has been extended to include combinations entered into by groups of atoms as well as individual atoms. The present conception of the mechanism of the process is by the transfer or sharing of electrons between atoms. (See **valence,** and various entries under the term **atom.**)

THEORY, QUANTUM. See **quantum, atomic structure,** etc.

THERM. A unit of heat equivalent to 1,000 large **calories** used in expressing the calorific value of feeds.

THERMAL. Of or pertaining to heat, as thermal capacity, thermal conductivity.

THERMAL CAPACITY. See **heat capacity.**

THERMAL CONDUCTANCE. The ability to conduct heat in an unequally heated system from a region of high to one of lower temperature. The coefficient of thermal conductivity is the time rate of heat conduction per unit area per unit temperature gradient.

THERMAL DEFORMATION. See **pyroelectric excitement.**

THERMAL ENERGY. See **heat energy.**

THERMAL EXCITATION. The acquisition of excess energy by atoms or molecules by collision processes with other particles.

THERMAL SEPARATING TOWER. A vertical cylindrical tower, whose axis is strongly heated so that the horizontal flow of heat sets up convection currents which are used to separate components, differing in mass, of the fluid within the tower. The process was developed for the separation of **isotopes.**

THERMALIZATION (OF NEUTRONS). Reduction of the kinetic energy of neutrons, as by repeated collisions with other particles, to a point where they have approximately the same kinetic energy as the atoms or molecules of the medium in which the neutrons are undergoing elastic scattering. Since this atomic or molecular energy is thermal in origin, being a direct temperature function, the neutrons whose energies have been so reduced are called thermal neutrons, and the process thermalization.

THERMIONIC EFFECT. The emission of electrons by a heated **cathode,** i.e., by a heated substance maintained at a negative electrical potential. The term thermionic effect is also applied to the **ionization** of a gas in contact with a heated cathode.

THERMIONIC WORK FUNCTION. The energy required to release an electron from the metal in the **photoelectric effect.** It is equal to the difference between the energy of the photon of incident radiation and the kinetic energy of the emitted electron.

THERMITE PROCESS. See **Goldschmidt process.**

THERMOCHEMISTRY. See **chemistry, thermo-.**

THERMOCOUPLE. A device for the measurement of temperature, which is based upon the principle that an **electromotive force** exists at the junction of two dissimilar metals. In the practical construction of such instruments, the two dissimilar metals or alloys are joined at two points: the hot junction, which, with the necessary mechanical protection, is placed in the furnace or other point at which the temperature is to be measured; and the cold junction, which sets up its own electromotive force, so that the differential electromotive force of the circuit, which is measured by a sensitive voltmeter or ammeter, corresponds to the thermoelectric difference in potential between the hot Junction and cold junction.

THERMODYNAMIC EQUATION OF STATE. See **equation of state, thermodynamic.**

THERMODYNAMIC POTENTIAL. An extensive property of a system, defined as the difference between the **heat content** and the product of the **entropy** and temperature. The thermodynamic potential is also called the **free energy,** or the Gibbs function.

THERMODYNAMIC TEMPERATURE SCALE. See **temperature scale, Kelvin.**

THERMODYNAMIC WORK FUNCTION. The difference between the **intrinsic energy** of a system, and the product of the **entropy** and the temperature; it is called the work function because in an **isothermal** system it is equal to the maximum work done on the system.

THERMODYNAMICS. That branch of physics which deals with the relationships between heat and other forms of energy and the laws which govern their interconversion.

THERMODYNAMICS, FIRST LAW OF. One of the many forms of statement of this law is that energy cannot be created or destroyed, but can only be converted from one form to an equivalent quantity of another form. The discovery of the equivalence of mass and energy, based on the relativity theory, and its application in the conversion of mass into energy in nuclear reactions, has become the basis for a broader generalization, combining the first law of thermodynamics with the law of conservation of matter, in the statement that the total mass and energy of a system, whether expressed in terms of equivalent total mass or equivalent total energy, is constant.

THERMODYNAMICS, SECOND LAW OF. One of the many forms of statement of this law is that heat cannot pass from a colder to a hotter body without the intervention of some external force, medium, or agency. It follows from this law that all natural or isolated processes which occur spontaneously are irreversible.

THERMODYNAMICS, THIRD LAW OF. Every substance has a finite positive **entropy** which may become zero at a temperature of absolute zero, as it does in the case of crystalline substances.

THERMOELECTROMOTIVE FORCE. **Electromotive force** produced by differences in temperature between two dissimilar metals. Specifically, the total electromotive force that arises from a temperature difference at the junction of two dissimilar metals, as in a thermocouple.

THERMOELEMENT. See **thermocouple.**

THERMOFOR CATALYTIC CRACKING PROCESS. A continuous, catalytic **cracking** process for petroleum, consisting of a moving bed in which one chamber serves as reactor and another to regenerate the **catalyst.**

THERMOLABILE. Destroyed or greatly altered by moderate heating. Coagulable **proteins, microorganisms,** bacterial **toxins,** and certain **isomers** are examples.

THERMOLUMINESCENCE. See **luminescence.**

THERMOMETER. An instrument used to measure the intensity of the heat in a body, i.e., its temperature, usually constructed so that the expansion of matter caused by heat furnishes the measure of the temperature. Instruments for measuring high temperatures are termed **pyrometers,** and are based upon measurements of the amount of radiation emitted by the hot body, or by measurement of the amount of radiation of a particular frequency or narrow band of frequencies, or by measurement of the change in resistance of a standard length of wire, or by the use of a **thermocouple.**

THERMOMETER, HYDROGEN. A **gas thermometer** using hydrogen.

THERMOMETRIC SCALES. On the absolute scale (see **temperature scale, absolute**) $0° =$ absolute zero ($-273.16°$ C.).

The degree on the absolute scale is equal in magnitude to the degree on the centigrade scale. On the centigrade scale (q.v.) 0°= freezing point of water (temperature of melting ice) 100° = boiling point of water, both under standard conditions. On the **Fahrenheit scale** (q.v.) 32° = temperature of melting ice, 212° = boiling point of water. There is also a Fahrenheit absolute scale (called the Rankine scale) which bears the same relation to the absolute temperature scale that the Fahrenheit scale does to the centigrade scale. On the Réaumur scale, 0° = temperature of melting ice, 80° = boiling point of water. On the obsolete DeLisle scale, 0° = boiling point of water, 100° = temperature of melting ice.

THERMONEUTRALITY, LAW OF. There is no heat effect observed when the solutions of two soluble salts are mixed, provided that they do not form a weak salt, a slightly soluble precipitate, or a complex ion.

THERMOPILE. In effect, a series of **thermocouples,** consisting of a series of thin sheets of two different metals, connected in series, so that the thermoelectric potentials of all the pairs are additive. Apparatus containing such elements are extremely sensitive to small changes in temperature.

THERMOPLASTIC SUBSTANCE. A substance that becomes soft and pliable under the application of heat. An important class of the synthetic **resins** exhibits this property, and their technology has been developed accordingly.

THERMOSETTING SUBSTANCE. A substance that becomes hard and durable under the application of heat. An important class of the synthetic **resins** exhibits this property, and their technology has been developed accordingly.

THERMOSTABLE. Neither destroyed nor altered by moderate heating.

THERMOSTAT. An apparatus arranged so that it may be adjusted to maintain and keep constant any practicable temperature.

A system enclosed in a thermostat is thus kept at a definite constant temperature. This is usually accomplished by actuating controls which turn the heating mechanism on when an upper temperature limit is reached and which turn it off when a lower temperature limit is reached.

THETA (Θ, θ OR ϑ). The eighth letter of the Greek alphabet, used to denote the eighth carbon atom in a straight-chain compound, or a derivative in which a substituent group is attached to that carbon atom (θ-). Symbol for time (θ). Symbol for **thermodynamic temperature** (θ). Symbol for plane angle (θ). Symbol for glancing angle (θ). Symbol for **angle of contact** (θ). Symbol for **angle of diffraction** (θ). Symbol for **angle of optical rotation** (θ). Symbol for angular displacement (θ).

THETINE. A cyclic **sulfinate.**

THÉVENON TEST FOR NITRITE IN WATER. This is an adaptation of Denigès test. Add 2–3 ml. of a freshly prepared solution of 0.5 g. p-aminophenol hydrochloride in 100 ml. of water and 6–8 drops of 33% acetic acid to 10–100 ml. of the water to be tested. If nitrites are present, a deep garnet-red color is formed. Nitrates do not interfere.

THÉVENON TEST REACTION FOR SACCHARIN. Add 10 ml. of 10% sodium nitrite and 6 drops of 30% sulfuric acid to a solution of 0.1 g. saccharin in 25 ml. water. A diazonium chloride is formed which gives a red coloring matter by coupling with 0.1 g. β-naphthol.

THIAZINE. A heterocyclic compound having a ring containing one sulfur atom and one nitrogen atom.

THIAZOLE. One of two isomeric compounds having the formula C_3H_3NS, and having a ring structure consisting of three carbon atoms, one nitrogen atom, and one sulfur atom.

THIAZOLIDINE. One of two isomeric compounds having the formula C_3H_7NS, and having a ring structure consisting of three carbon atoms, one nitrogen atom and one sulfur atom.

THIAZOLIDYL. The radical C_3H_6NS— (from thiazolidine, 2 isomers).

THIAZOLYL. The radical C_3H_2NS— (from thiazole, 3 isomers).

THICKENER, DORR. See **Dorr thickener.**

THIEL-STOLL SOLUTION. A saturated solution of lead perchlorate, used in mineralogy to determine densities of minerals.

THIELE-BAILEY TEST REACTION. A test for formaldehyde made by adding a 4% solution of formaldehyde to an aqueous solution of semicarbazide hydrochloride. A gelatinous precipitate, which melts at 95° C., is formed.

THIELE-DRALLE REAGENT. Amidoguanidine. Characteristic crystalline compounds of definite melting points are formed when this substance is treated with an aliphatic aldehyde or ketone and permitted to evaporate over sulfuric acid.

THIELE REACTION. An acetylation of **quinones** with acetic anhydride that forms the triacetoxy compounds. Sulfuric acid or boron fluoride catalyze the reaction.

water to produce a faint turbidity and then adding 20 g. sodium hydroxide. The solution is decolorized by adding aluminum powder, a little at a time, and diluted to 150 ml. with boiled and cooled water and then filtered. The test for cyanide is made by steeping strips of paper in a 0.05% cupric sulfate solution and drying. These are moistened with a few drops of the reagent and immersed in the solution to be tested. A red color shows the presence of cyanide.

THINNER. A diluent used to reduce the viscosity or consistency of a liquid product, such as a paint.

THIO. A prefix denoting the divalent sulfur atom, especially but not necessarily, when it replaces oxygen.

THIOACETIC. Related to thioacetic acid, CH_3COSH.

THIOACID. An organic acid in which one or more of the oxygen atoms have been replaced by divalent sulfur atoms. If the hydroxyl oxygen has been replaced by sulfur, as R—COSH, the compound is a thiolic acid. If the carbonyl oxygen has been replaced (as, R—CSOH), the compound is a thionic acid. When both have

$$\text{(quinone)} + 2(CH_3CO)_2O \rightarrow \text{(triacetoxy)} + CH_3COOH.$$

THIELE STRUCTURE OF BENZENE. See **benzene, formulas.**

THIELE TUBE. See **tube, Thiele.**

THIENYL. The radical C_4H_3S— (from thiophene, 2 isomers).

THIÉRY TEST FOR CYANIDE. A test for cyanide, the reagent for which is prepared by dissolving 0.5 g. phenolphthalein in 30 ml. absolute alcohol, adding sufficient

been replaced (as, R—CSSH), a dithionic or thionthiolic acid results.

THIOALCOHOL. See **thiol.**

THIOANILINE. A sulfur derivative of the cyclic amines of the general type

$$NH_2C_6H_4—S—C_6H_4NH_2$$

in which one or more of the hydrogen atoms may be substituted by radicals or atoms.

THIOANTIMONATE. The anion SbS_4^{3-}, or a compound containing it.

THIOANTIMONITE. The anion SbS_3^{3-}, or a compound containing it.

THIOARSENATE. The anion $AsSO_3^{3-}$, $AsS_2O_2^{3-}$, AsS_3O^{3-}, or AsS_4^{3-}, or a compound containing one of these anions. There are also meta-thioarsenates and pyro-thioarsenates. (See below.)

THIOARSENATE (META-). The anion AsS_3^{-}, or a compound containing it.

THIOARSENATE (PYRO-). The anion $As_2S_7^{4-}$, or a compound containing it.

THIOARSENITE. The anion AsS_3^{3-}, or a compound containing it. There are also meta-thioarsenites, pyro-thioarsenites, and tetra-thioarsenites. (See below.)

THIOARSENITE (META-). The anion AsS_2^{-}, or a compound containing it.

THIOARSENITE (PYRO-). The anion $As_2S_5^{4-}$, or a compound containing it.

THIOARSENITE (TETRA-). The anion $As_4S_9^{6-}$, or a compound containing it.

THIOCARBAMYL. The radical

$$H_2NCS—.$$

THIOCARBONATE. The anion $CS_2O^{=}$ or $CS_3^{=}$, or a compound containing one of these anions.

THIOCARBONYL. The radical $SC{=}$.

THIOCYANATE. The anion SCN^{-}, or a compound containing it.

THIOCYANATOAURATE (III). The anion $Au(SCN)_4^{-}$, or a compound containing it.

THIOCYANATOCHROMATE (III). The anion $Cr(SCN)_6^{3-}$, or a compound containing it.

THIOCYANATOCOBALTATE (II). The anion $Co(SCN)_4^{=}$, or a compound containing it.

THIOCYANATOCUPRATE (II). The anion $Cu(SCN)_3^{-}$ or $Cu(SCN)_4^{=}$, or a compound containing one of these anions.

THIOCYANATOFERRATE (III). The anion $Fe(SCN)_6^{3-}$, or a compound containing it.

THIOCYANATOMOLYBDATE (III). The anion $Mo(SCN)_6^{3-}$, or a compound containing it.

THIOCYANATONICKELATE (II). The anion $Ni(SCN)_6^{4-}$, or a compound containing it.

THIOCYANATOPALLADATE (II). The anion $Pd(SCN)_4^{=}$, or a compound containing it.

THIOCYANATOPLATINATE (II). The anion $Pt(SCN)_4^{=}$, or a compound containing it.

THIOCYANATOPLATINATE (IV). The anion $Pt(SCN)_6^{=}$, or a compound containing it.

THIOCYANATORHODATE (III). The anion $Rh(SCN)_6^{3-}$, or a compound containing it.

THIOCYANATOTITANATE (III). The anion $Ti(SCN)_6^{3-}$, or a compound containing it.

THIOCYANATOTUNGSTATE. The anion $WO_2(SCN)_3^{=}$, $WO(SCN)_4^{-}$, or $WO(SCN)_5^{=}$, or a compound containing one of these anions.

THIOCYANATOVANADATE (III). The anion $V(SCN)_6^{3-}$, or a compound containing it.

THIOCYANIC, REARRANGEMENT. See **rearrangement, cyanic,** or **rearrangement, thiocyanic.**

THIOCYANO-. The radical $NCS—$.

THIOCYANOGEN VALUE. The quantity of a **thiocyanate** solution calculated as thiocyanogen $(SCN)_2$, required in a given titration, or equivalent to the iodine (which is titrated with thiocyanate solution) that is absorbed by unit mass of an organic compound or product.

THIODIAZINE. One of two isomeric compounds having the formula $C_3H_4N_2S$, and having a ring structure consisting of three carbon atoms, two nitrogen atoms, and one sulfur atom.

THIODIAZOLE. One of four isomeric compounds having the formula $C_2H_2N_2S$, and having a ring structure consisting of two carbon atoms, two nitrogen atoms, and one sulfur atom.

THIOHYDROXY. See **mercapto.**

THIOHYPOPHOSPHATE. The anion $P_2S_6^{4-}$, or a compound containing it.

THIOL. The radical —SH. The use of the term "thiol" commonly indicates the replacement of the oxygen in a —OH group by sulfur.

THIOLIC ACID. See **thioacid.**

THION. Containing divalent **sulfur.**

THIONATE, DI-. See **dithionate.**

THIONATE, POLY-. The anion $S_nO_6^=$, or a compound containing it. See **trithionate,** etc.

-THIONE. A suffix for a thioketone, $R_1C(:S)R_2$.

THIONIC ACID. See **thioacid.**

THIONO. The radical =CS. The use of the term thiono commonly indicates the replacement of the oxygen in a **carbonyl group** by sulfur.

THIONTHIOLIC ACID. See **thioacid.**

THIONYL. See **sulfinyl.**

THIOÖXALATE. The anion $C_2S_2O_2^-$, or a compound containing it.

THIOÖXALATONICKELATE (II). The anion $Ni(C_2S_2O_2)_2^=$, or a compound containing it.

THIOPERRHENATE. The anion $ReSO_3^-$ or ReS_4^-, or a compound containing one of these anions.

THIOPHENE. A heterocyclic sulfur compound, the parent of numerous derivatives

All thiophene derivatives give an intense blue color with isatin and concentrated sulfuric acid. Cf. **thienyl.**

THIOPHENOL. A phenol in which the hydroxyl oxygen has been replaced by sulfur, as benzenethiol (phenylmercaptan, thiophenol, phenthiol), C_6H_5SH.

THIOPHOSPHATE. The anion PSO_3^{3-}, $PS_2O_2^{3-}$, PS_3O^{3-}, or PS_4^{3-}, or a compound containing one of these anions.

THIOPHOSPHITE. The anion PS_3^{3-}, or a compound containing it.

THIOSTANNATE (META-). The anion $SnS_3^=$, or a compound containing it.

THIOSULFATE. The anion $S_2O_3^=$, or a compound containing it.

THIOSULFATOARGENTATE (I). The anion $Ag(S_2O_3)^-$, $Ag_2(S_2O_3)_3^{4-}$, $Ag(S_2O_3)_2^{3-}$, or $Ag(S_2O_3)_3^{5-}$, or a compound containing one of these anions.

THIOSULFATOAURATE (I). The anion $Au(S_2O_3)_2^{3-}$, or a compound containing it.

THIOSULFITE. The anion $S_2O_2^=$, or a compound containing it.

THIOSULFURIC. Related to thiosulfuric acid, $H_2S_2O_3$.

THIOSULFUROUS. See **dithionous.**

THIOTETRAZOLINE. A heterocyclic compound containing a five-membered ring composed of four nitrogen atoms, and one carbon atom to which a sulfur atom is attached, having the formula CH_2SN_4, known in its derivatives.

THIOTRIAZOLE. One of two heterocyclic compounds containing a five-membered ring composed of one carbon atom, three nitrogen atoms, and one sulfur atom, having the formula $CHSN_3$.

THIOVANADATE. The anion $VS_4{}^{3-}$, or a compound containing it.

THIOXENE. A dimethyl **thiophene.**

THIOXO. The $>CS$ radical. The use of the term thioxo commonly indicates the formation of the $>CS$ group by replacement of the hydrogen in a $>CH_2$ group.

THIOZONIDE. A member of a class of sulfur compounds analogous to the **ozonides** and formed from **thiozone.**

THIRD-ORDER REACTION. See **reaction, third-order.**

THISTLE TUBE. A glass tube terminating in a small glass receptacle which is roughly hemispherical in shape. The thistle tube is commonly used in the laboratory for the addition of liquids, which are poured into the receptacle, whence they discharge through the tube at a rate determined by its bore, and by the nature and height of the liquid.

THIURAM. See **thiocarbamyl.**

THIVOLLE REAGENT. A solution prepared by mixing an aqueous solution of ammonium molybdate and tartaric acid with concentrated nitric acid, followed by the addition of ammonium nitrate. It is used in the determination of free phosphate radicals in biological media.

THIXOTROPY. The property exhibited by certain **gels** of liquefying when subjected to the action of vibratory forces, such as **ultrasonic waves** or even simple shaking, and then setting again on standing. Gels of this type may be formed by the addition of small quantities of electrolyte to concentrated sols of certain metallic oxides, such as ferric oxide, aluminum trioxide, zirconium dioxide, etc., and also other sols, including those of the bentonite clays, and certain gelatin preparations.

THOMAS-CARPENTIER REAGENT. A reagent for copper, which consists of sodium or potassium phenolphthalein, decolorized by zinc. A pink color is produced with copper solutions.

THOMAS METER. An instrument for measuring the rate of flow of a gas in terms of the increase in temperature of the gas produced by a known quantity of heat.

THOMAS-MICSA TEST. A test for polyhydroxyl alcohols made by oxidizing the sample of alcohol by heating 1 part of a 5% solution with 10 parts of bromine water. The excess bromine is removed by an air current, and there is added a solution of 1 part β-naphthol-3,6-disulfonic acid in 300 parts sulfuric acid. Ethylene glycol produces a blue color surmounted by a yellow ring; glycerol, a greenish-blue surmounted by a yellow ring; propylene glycol, a red-brown ring; and butylene glycol, an intense brown-red ring.

THOMAS PROCESS. A **Bessemer process** modified by lining the convertor with dolomite, which aids in the removal of acidic impurities, notably phosphorus, by combining with them to form a slag.

THOMPSON-BEAMISH-SCOTT TESTS FOR OSMIUM. (1) Add a drop of hydrochloric acid to the solution to be tested, follow by a drop of concentrated pyrogallol solution. A distinct blue color indicates the presence of osmium. (2) Add a drop of a saturated aqueous solution of ephedrine hydrochloride to a solution of sodium osmate, and alkalinize with sodium hydroxide. An orange color is obtained.

THOMPSON-BEAMISH-SCOTT TEST REACTIONS FOR PLATINUM. (1) With solutions containing platinum, a 40% solution by weight of stannous chloride in concentrated hydrochloric acid gives an orange or yellow color. Gold and palladium interfere and must be removed. (2) A drop of 10% potassium iodide solution added to a solution of platinum in hydrochloric acid produces a red-brown color.

THOMPSON-HURST TEST. A test for paraffin in lard made by heating 3 ml. of the fat with 10 ml. of a 1:1 mixture of absolute alcohol and chloroform. The mixture becomes turbid, when cooled, if paraffin is present.

THOMPSON-STEWART PROCESS. A process for the production of white lead, consisting, first, of the preparation of a mixture of finely divided lead oxide and metallic lead, by agitating molten lead in the presence of air; and second, the formation of a slurry of this material with water containing a little acetic acid; and finally, the aeration and carbonation of this suspension to produce the white lead.

THOMS REACTION FOR g-STROPHANTHIN. A solution of 0.01 g. g-strophanthin in 1 ml. water is superimposed on concentrated sulfuric acid. The aqueous liquid assumes a dirty green color and the acid is colored rose or red.

THOMS REAGENT FOR COPPER. This reagent, which is potassium iodide solution, is used by itself or with starch solution. A cupric sulfate solution turns yellow when this reagent is added. A distinct violet color forms on adding a few drops of starch solution.

THOMS TEST FOR DIETHYLPHTHALATE IN ESSENTIAL OILS. Evaporate the oil to dryness on a water bath with alcohol and sodium hydroxide solution. Extract the residue with water and evaporate the extract to dryness. The residue is then tested with sulfuric acid and resorcinol. A brown or red color on heating,

THOMSON ISOTHERM. An S-shaped **isotherm** showing the continuous transition from the gaseous to the liquid state.

THORATE. The anion $ThO_3{}^{2-}$, or a compound containing it.

THORIUM. Metallic radioactive element. Symbol Th. Atomic number 90. Atomic weight 232.12. Density 11.2. Specific heat 0.406. Melting point 1845° C. Boiling point >3000° C. Valence 2, 3, 4. Half-period of 1.39×10^{10} years. It emits an α-particle and forms mesothorium 1, which is also radioactive having a half-period of 6.7 years, emitting a β-particle. There is a series of elements, called the thorium family (see **radioactive elements**) which are formed by the successive decomposition by each preceding element in the series. There are at least twelve members of the thorium family which are various isotopes of thorium, radium, actinium, polonium, radon, bismuth, thallium, and lead.

THORIUM SERIES. See **element, radioactive series.**

THORON. Thorium emanation, an isotope of radon (see **radioactive elements**).

THORPE REACTION. In general, the reaction between active **methylene groups** and **nitrile groups;** sometimes denoting specifically the reaction between a compound containing a nitrile group, and a compound in which the methylene group is activated by a nearby nitrile group. The reaction is catalyzed by bases.

$$R'CH_2CN + R''CH_2CN \xrightarrow{\text{KOH}} R'CH(CN).C(:NH)CH_2R''.$$

giving a yellow-green fluorescence with water and ammonium hydroxide, indicates the presence of diethylphthalate.

THOMSEN PROCESS. An old process for the manufacture of alumina from cryolite. The powdered cryolite is heated with lime to produce sodium aluminate, which is then decomposed into $Al(OH)_3$ and Na_2CO_3 by the action of carbon dioxide.

THOULET SOLUTION. A concentrated aqueous solution of potassium iodide and mercuric iodide. It has a specific gravity of 3.17 at 15° C., and is used in mineralogy in determining the specific gravity of minerals.

THRESH REAGENT. A reagent prepared by (1) adding 2.4 g. of bismuth citrate to a little water, adding enough ammonium hydroxide to dissolve the precipitate, and bringing the volume to 30 ml. with water and enough ammonium hydroxide to prevent reprecipitation; and (2) then adding a solution of 2 g. of potassium iodide in concentrated hydrochloric acid. This reagent gives precipitates with alkaloids (and albumin) in acid solution.

THRESH TEST REACTION. A test for bismuth made by adding an excess of potassium iodide to slightly acid bismuth solutions. An orange-red color is formed.

THRESHOLD VOLTAGE FOR GEIGER COUNTING ACTION. The lowest voltage at which all **pulses** produced in the **counter** by any **ionizing event** are of the same size, regardless of the size of the **primary ionizing event.**

THROWING POWER. A term used to denote the relative effectiveness of various electrolytic **cells** for the deposition of metal at the **cathode.** It is commonly determined by means of two half-cathodes which give the values for the relation between the distance from the anode and the weight of metal deposited.

THRUN TEST REACTION. A test for magnesium made by adding curcumin to the solutions to be tested. A yellow to orange lake is formed if magnesium is present.

THUJYL. The radical

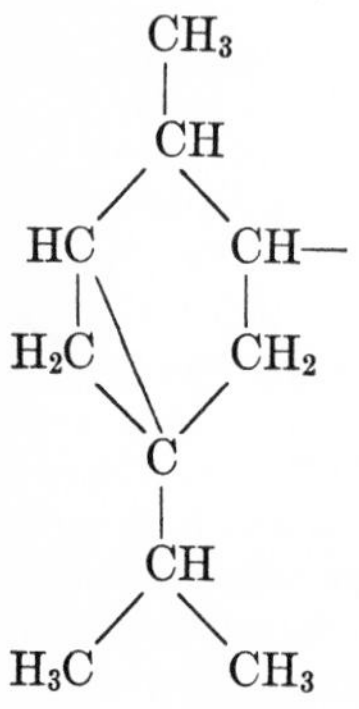

$$CH_3$$
$$|$$
$$CH$$
$$HC \quad CH-$$
$$H_2C \quad CH_2$$
$$C$$
$$|$$
$$CH$$
$$H_3C \quad CH_3$$

(from sabinane, attached at 2-position).

THULIUM. Rare earth metallic element. Symbol Tm. Atomic number 69. Atomic

weight 169.4. Valence 3. Oxide Tm_2O_3. Thulium occurs in gadolinite.

THYLOX PROCESS. A method for the purification of manufactured fuel gases. A solution of sodium or ammonium thioarsonate is used as an absorbing agent to remove hydrogen sulfide from the gas. After use, the solution is desulfurized for return to the system by bubbling air through it.

THYMO-, THYM-. (1) Relating to thyme, as thymoquinone, thymol. (2) Relating to the thymus, as thymonucleic.

THYMYL. The radical $C_{10}H_{13}$—, derived by loss of the hydroxyl group from thymol

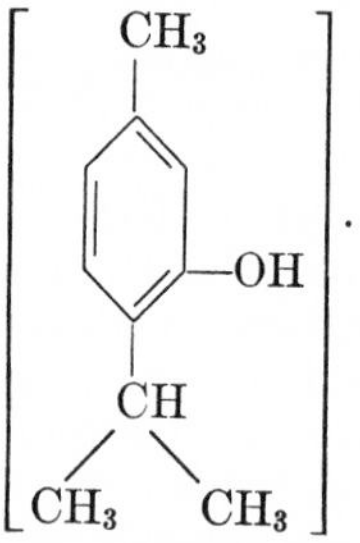

$$CH_3$$
$$OH$$
$$CH$$
$$CH_3 \quad CH_3$$

THYRONYL. The radical

p-(p-HOC$_6$H$_4$O)C$_6$H$_4$CH$_2$CH(NH$_2$)CO—.

Ti Symbol for the element **titanium.**

TIE LINE. On an **equilibrium diagram,** a line joining two points which represent the compositions of systems in equilibrium.

TIEDEMANN-GMELIN TEST REACTION FOR ACETATE. A red color is produced by the addition of ferric chloride or ferric sulfate to alkali acetates in aqueous solution.

TIEDEMANN-GMELIN TEST REACTION FOR TRYPTOPHANE. A violet-red color is produced by reaction of bromine water with tryptophane.

TIEGS REAGENT AND TEST. A test for guanidine bases, the reagent for which is made by exposing a moderately concentrated solution of sodium nitroprusside in a thin layer to direct sunlight for 1–2 days. The solution has a dirty brown color at the end of that time. The liquid to be tested is made $\frac{1}{30}$ N alkaline and 5 drops of reagent added to 1 ml. of the liquid. Creatine, creatinine, and free guanidines produce a red or red-brown color. Guanidine is recognized by the fact that it gives the test in neutral solution; creatinine by the fact that if the solution being tested is allowed to stand for 2 hours and then made $\frac{1}{30}$ N alkaline, the red color disappears and the solution turns a dirty green color.

TIEMANN REACTION. A rearrangement of amidoximes by treatment with benzenesulfonyl chloride and water, successively, to yield asymmetric ureas.

$$RC{:}NOH \xrightarrow[\text{H}_2\text{O}]{\text{C}_6\text{H}_5\text{SO}_2\text{Cl}} RNH.CONH_2.$$

with NH₂ group attached to RC:NOH

TIFFENAU REACTION. A rearrangement reaction whereby amino alcohols having their amino and hydroxy groups attached to adjacent carbon atoms are converted to carbonyl compounds by nitrous acid. As in the reaction shown, changes in the ring often accompany the reaction.

color, which is not characteristic in alkaline solution.

TIME, UNIT OF. The unit of time in all physicochemical measurements is the second.

TIN. Metallic element. Symbol Sn (Stannum). Atomic number 50. Atomic weight 118.70. Exists in three forms: (1) Cubic (gray or beta tin). Density (at 18° C.) 5.75. Transition point to rhombic tin 18° C. (2) Rhombic (alpha tin). Density (at 161° C.) 7.28. Transition point 161° C. (3) Tetragonal (gamma tin). Density 6.56. Melting point 231.9° C. Boiling point 2270° C. Occurs native and in cassiterite. Valence 2 and 4. Forms two series of salts, the stannous salts in which it is divalent and the stannic salts in which it is tetravalent. Oxides, SnO, SnO_2. Acids, stannic H_2SnO_3, metastannic $H_{10}Sn_5O_{15}$, perstannic $HSnO_4$.

TINCTURE. An alcoholic liquid containing a soluble extract of a drug, as Tincture Nux Vomica, or a dissolved compound or element, such as Tincture Ferric Chloride or Tincture Iodine. Tinctures are more dilute than fluid extracts and differ

$$\text{(amino alcohol)} + HNO_2 \rightarrow \text{(ketone)} + 2H_2O + N_2.$$

TILLMANS-ALT TEST REACTION FOR TRYPTOPHANE. A test for tryptophane made by adding a little formaldehyde and a large excess of 66% sulfuric acid to a solution to be tested. A distinct wine-yellow color develops gradually if tryptophane is present.

TILLMANS-HIRSCH TEST REACTIONS FOR ASCORBIC ACID. (1) Ascorbic acid reduces 2,6-dichlorophenolindophenol to a leuko-dye. (2) With naturally acid lemon juice, a 10% phosphomolybdic acid solution can be used as a reagent. The ascorbic acid produces a blue

from spirits in not being wholly volatile· Most tinctures used in medicine contain a concentration of the drug obtained by extracting thoroughly 10 grams of the drug with 100 cubic centimeters of ethyl alcohol.

TINTOMETER. A widely used type of **colorimeter,** in which the intensity of color, and hence the concentration of the colored substance in a colored solution, is determined by comparison with colored glass slides or standard solutions.

TISCHLER TEST. A test for carbon disulfide made by adding 5 drops of 0.05%

cupric sulfate solution in absolute alcohol and 1 ml. of 1% (by volume) diethylamine in absolute alcohol to 1 ml. of the solution to be tested. A yellow color is given by colorless solutions of carbon disulfide in acetone, chloroform, or alcohol. A precipitate is obtained in aqueous solutions.

TISHCHENKO REACTION. The formation of an **ester** from two molecules of an **aldehyde** in the presence of an **alcoholate**

$$2RCHO \xrightarrow{M(OR)_x} RCOO.CH_2R.$$

M represents a metal atom, and R is an **alkyl radical.**

TITANATE. The anion $TiO_3^=$ (meta-) or TiO_4^{4-}, or a compound containing one of these anions.

TITANATE (META-). The anion $TiO_3^=$, or a compound containing it.

TITANIC. (1) Containing tetravalent **titanium.** (2) Related to titanic acid (ortho-), H_4TiO_4; or to titanic acid (meta-), H_2TiO_3.

TITANIUM. Metallic element. Symbol Ti. Atomic number 22. Atomic weight 47.90. Density 4.5. Specific heat 0.142. Melting point 1725° C. Boiling point > 3000° C. Valence 2, 3, and 4. Oxides TiO_2, Ti_2O_3, TiO_3, TiO. Acids, orthotitanic, H_4TiO_4, metatitanic H_2TiO_3. Titanium occurs in ilmenite, rutile, brookite, and other minerals.

TITANO-. Containing titanium or pertaining to a compound of **titanium.**

TITANOUS. Containing or pertaining to trivalent **titanium.**

TITER. With one exception, the various meanings of this term all relate directly to the process of titration. Thus, titer means (1) the normality of a solution; (2) the number of grams of an element, ion, or compound per unit volume of solution; (3) the number of cubic centimeters per liter by which a normal solution differs from a true solution. The meaning of titer that relates only indirectly to the process of titration is its use in oil and fat analysis, where it

means the melting point of the **fatty acids** obtained by **saponification.** (See **titer test.**)

TITER TEST. A test used in the identification, analysis, and investigation of oils, fats, and waxes. The sample is saponified with alkaline hydroxide, the fatty acids are separated, washed, and fused, and the temperature at which crystallization begins on cooling is observed. Its value is the **titer.**

TITRATE. To determine the quantity of some component in a material or solution by adding a reagent of known concentration which reacts with it, under conditions, such as in the presence of an indicator, whereby the completion of the reaction is shown. From the known composition and concentration of the reagent, and the known identity of the substance to be determined, the quantity present may be calculated. (See **analysis, quantitative.**)

TITRATION. The process of determining the quantity of an element or compound by measuring the quantity of some reagent (liquid or solution) which reacts quantitatively with it.

TITRATION, AMPEROMETRIC. A method of **titration** involving the determination of the end point by observation of a steady **diffusion current** due to an excess of the reactant from the titrating solution. One of these methods is the titration of styrene with potassium bromate, using a mercury-mercuric iodide half-cell (instead of the customary calomel cell) and a rotating platinum wire electrode.

TITRATION, CONDUCTOMETRIC. A titration in which **electrical conductance** measurements are applied in the determination of the end point of the titration reaction.

TITRATION PRECIPITATION. A solution of one ion is titrated with a solution of another ion with which it forms a compound that is not soluble. The concentration of the first ion decreases rapidly near the equivalence point. The end points of precipitation titrations are determined by conductometric methods, by presence in the solution of an indicator, such as an ion which forms a colored product with excess of the precipitant, and in other ways.

TITRIMETER. An electric device that is used for potentiometric titrations in which the potential changes are followed on a microammeter automatically and continuously.

Tl Symbol for the element **thallium.**

Tm Symbol for the element **thulium.**

TOCHER TEST REACTIONS. Tests for tartaric, citric, and malic acids as follows: (1) The acid is heated with concentrated sulfuric acid. Tartaric acid gives a carbonaceous mass; citric acid, a yellow solution; malic acid, a dark solution. (2) Cobalt nitrate colors tartaric acid solution red. On the addition of sodium hydroxide solution, the liquid becomes colorless, then blue on boiling and colorless on cooling. Citric acid solution and malic acid solution are colored deep blue by cobalt nitrate and sodium hydroxide solutions. (3) A fruity odor is evolved when malic acid is heated with dilute sulfuric acid and potassium dichromate.

TOISSON FLUID. A reagent used in diluting blood for microscopic examination, especially for counting erythrocytes. It is prepared by dissolving 2 g. sodium chloride, 0.05 g. methyl violet 5B, 16 g. sodium sulfate, and 60 ml. glycerol in 320 ml. water.

TOLERANCE. This term has different meanings in science, in medicine, in technology, and in regulatory work (specifications). (1) In physical science, tolerance means the maximum error allowable in the graduation of instruments, such as scales, burettes, pipettes, etc. (2) In medicine tolerance means the ability of an organism to withstand the cumulative effect of repeated doses of a drug. (3) In the lacquer industry, and related industries, tolerance expresses the amount of a diluent that can be added to a product without causing precipitation or "clouding." (4) In regulatory work and in specifications, tolerance means the maximum amount of a substance permitted in a given product or material, as,

for example, the maximum amount of arsenic or lead permitted on fruits sold for human consumption, or of sulfur compounds in a petroleum product, etc.

TOLLENS REAGENT FOR ALDEHYDES. A solution of 10 g. silver nitrate in 60 ml. concentrated ammonium hydroxide and 40 ml. water; a small quantity of this solution is mixed immediately before using with an equal quantity of a 10% aqueous solution of sodium hydroxide. It is used as a test reagent for aldehydes, being mixed with the sample in a test tube. The formation of a silver mirror in the test tube indicates the presence of aldehydes.

TOLLENS-OSHIMA TEST. A test for methylfurfural made by adding an equal volume of hydrochloric acid to the solution to be tested and 0.1 volume of a 0.1% solution of phloroglucinol in 12.5% hydrochloric acid, filtering, and after 5 minutes, examining spectroscopically. The solution shows an absorption spectrum between green and blue if methylfurfural is present.

TOLLENS TEST FOR GALACTOSE. A test based on the oxidation of the sugar by nitric acid (sp. gr. 1.15), to mucic acid melting at 211–212° C.

TOLLENS TEST FOR GLYCURONIC ACID. A granule of the substance to be tested is boiled with 5 ml. water, 1 ml. of 1% alcoholic naphthoresorcinol solution, and 6 ml. hydrochloric acid for 1 minute, then cooled and shaken with ether. The ether becomes red to blue-red in the presence of glycuronic acid.

TOLOXY. The radical $CH_3C_6H_4O—$ (o, m or p).

TOLUINO. The radical $CH_3C_6H_4NH—$ (o, m or p).

TOLUYL. The radical

$$CH_3C_6H_4CO—\ (o,\ m\ \text{or}\ p).$$

α-TOLUYL. The radical $C_6H_5CH_2CO—$, preferably termed phenylacetyl.

TOLYL. The radical $CH_3C_6H_4—$ (o, m or p).

α-TOLYL. See **benzyl**.

TOLYLENE. The radical $CH_3C_6H_3=$ (6 isomers).

α-TOLYLENE. See **benzylidene**.

TOMICEK TEST REACTION. A test for tellurium based on the decomposition of tellurates in the presence of acetate or acetic acid by titanium trichloride. Malodorous tellurium hydride is evolved.

TOMMILA REACTION FOR ALDEHYDES. To the liquid to be tested, add 5 ml. of hydrochloric acid and a crystal of naphthoresorcinol, heat for a few minutes on a water bath, cool, dilute with an equal volume of water, and extract with ether. Glycolaldehyde produces a blue-green color; glyoxal, a red color with blue fluorescence, changing to cherry-red on addition of alkali; dihydroxyacetone, a yellow to pale violet, changing to deep violet on addition of ammonia.

TOMMILA TEST FOR BISMUTH. Treat the solution to be tested with fairly concentrated hydrochloric acid, dilute, and add a large excess of potassium thiocyanate either as a concentrated solution or as the solid salt. A distinct yellow color is given by bismuth. The color is easily extracted by ethyl acetate and amyl alcohol.

TON. In the United States, a unit of weight equal to 2000 pounds (short ton). The long ton is equal to 2240 pounds and is more widely used in England. The metric ton is equal to 1000 kilograms.

TON, REFRIGERATION. See **refrigeration ton**.

TONEGUTTI TEST. A test for differentiating coal tar and wood tar by use of alcohol, chloroform, or benzene. Wood tar is completely soluble in these substances, but coal tar is incompletely soluble. A greenish fluorescence is given by the coal tar constituents which do dissolve.

TONER. A coloring material added to a paint or lacquer to modify the color of the pigment or pigments. The use of dyes for this purpose, which is possible if such dyes are selected or treated so as to be insoluble in the vehicle or solvents used, gives the paint manufacturer the advantage of all the color tones available in the great variety of dye colors.

TONIC. A drug or other substance that restores or increases the vigor or "tone" of an organism.

TOP-AND-BOTTOM PROCESS. See **Orford process**.

TÖPFER REAGENT. A solution of 0.5 g. methyl yellow (dimethylaminoazobenzene) in 100 ml. 95% ethyl alcohol. It is a pH indicator, changing from red to yellow with increasing pH in the pH range 3–4. It is used specifically in the determination of hydrochloric acid in gastric juice.

TORRANCE MIXER. A vertical kneader, with rotating pan and two sets of rotating knives.

TORTELLI-GAFFE TEST. A test for liver oils and ergosterol made by mixing 1 ml. of the oil with 6 ml. chloroform and 1 ml. ice-cold glacial acetic acid, then adding 4 drops of a 10% solution of bromine in chloroform. The color changes from a reddish tint into green within a minute if the liver oil is from a sea animal. Hydrogenated fish oils give a similar reaction, but more strongly. The reaction is not given by fats and oils from land animals. Ergosterol gives a similar reaction.

TORTELLI-RUGGERI TEST FOR PEANUT OIL. A test for peanut oil made by separating the fatty acids after saponification, purifying and then dissolving in just enough 90% alcohol at 60° C. Fine silvery needles of lignoceric acid and pearly leaflets of arachic acid crystallize on cooling if peanut oil is present.

TOSCHI-ANGIOLANI REAGENT. 4,4'-Diphenylsemicarbazide, a reagent for carbonyl derivatives with which it gives difficultly-soluble compounds.

TOSYL. See **tolylsulfonyl**.

TOTAL EMISSIVE POWER. See emissive power, total.

TOTAL HEAT OF DILUTION. See heat of dilution, integral.

TOTAL HEAT OF SOLUTION. See heat of solution, integral.

TOUGARINOFF REAGENT FOR TIN. This reagent is nitrophenylarsonic acid. The tin present is converted, by evaporating with nitric acid, to the insoluble stannic oxide, which can be dissolved in dilute hydrochloric acid. A precipitate is formed when the reagent is added to the hydrochloric acid solution.

TOUGARINOFF TEST FOR RHENIUM. In the presence of stannous chloride, rhenium is detected in an acid solution by addition of a ferrocyanide or dimethylglyoxime. The former produces a red color, the latter a yellow color which changes to green on further heating.

TOWER, SPRAY. A chamber used to bring about intimate contact between a gas and a liquid. The liquid is distributed in finely-divided form throughout the chamber as by a spray system, so that there is a large surface of contact between the liquid phase and the gas passing through the chamber. A special application of the spray tower is to systems of water and air where the object is to cool the water or to humidify the air.

TOWNSEND AVALANCHE. A phenomenon of cumulative ionization occurring in an electronic and nuclear counter. When the field voltage or, more accurately, its differential with respect to the radial distance, is sufficient so that the incoming electron gains an amount of energy, in its free path between collisions, equal to the ionization potential of the gas, then the incoming electron can produce more ions by collision. The process is cumulative, and an "avalanche" of electrons is produced.

TOXALBUMIN. A toxic substance of protein nature similar to the bacterial toxins, but not produced by microorganisms. Representative toxalbumins are the toxins of rattlesnake and cobra venom, and the plant toxalbumins ricin, abrin, and robin.

TOXIC. Poisonous.

TOXIC DOSE. The minimum dose that gives characteristic symptoms of poisoning.

TOXICOLOGY. The science that studies the nature, actions, and relations of poisonous substances and the methods for detecting and treating poisoning.

TOXIN. (1) Any poisonous substance. (2) A plant poison of unknown composition. (3) A bacterial toxin, i.e., a poisonous substance produced by microorganisms. (4) A **toxalbumin** or venin.

TOXOPHORE GROUPS. (Toxophore molecule) The portion of a bacterial toxin which has the specific poisonous properties shown by the toxin.

TRACER COMPOUND. See **compound, tracer.**

TRANS-. (Latin, across) Indicating that one of two geometrical **isomers** in which certain atoms or groups are on opposite sides of a plane, as *trans*-cinnamic acid,

$$C_6H_5CH$$
$$\|$$
$$HCCOOH$$

TRANSFERENCE NUMBER OR TRANSPORT NUMBER. The fraction of the total current carried by each of the ionic species of an **electrolyte.** Thus, in the simple case of an electrolyte having two ions, such as sodium chloride solution, the transport number of the sodium ion is the ratio of the current it carries to the total current carried by both ions, while the transport number of the chloride ion is the ratio of the current it carries to the total current carried by both ions.

TRANS FORM. The fumaroid or axially symmetric form of geometrical isomers. See **isomerism, geometrical.**

TRANSFORMATION. A term having the general meaning of a change in structure or arrangement. It is applied most commonly to certain **rearrangements** of organic structures, such as the **Beckmann rearrangement** (they are defined in this book under their specific names), and to changes among and within atoms, especially within atomic nuclei.

TRANSFORMATION CONSTANT. The **rate of disintegration** of a radioactive substance, expressed as the fraction which disintegrates per unit time.

TRANSFORMATION,   ORDER-DISORDER. A change in the arrangement of the atoms in the **lattice** of certain alloys from a random distribution of the atoms of the metals to an ordered arrangement in which certain regularly chosen positions are regularly occupied by the atoms of each metal. (See **super lattice.**) The random arrangement results on quenching, or sudden cooling, whereas annealing causes the transformation to the ordered arrangement.

TRANSFORMATION SERIES. This term is commonly used in reference to radioactive elements to denote a series of elements which are produced by successive radioactive disintegrations from the parent element to their successors. See **element, radioactive,** for details of the various series.

TRANSITION. A change of form or external appearance, as a change of **allotropic form** or a **change of state.**

TRANSITION CELL. An electrolytic cell containing an electrolyte which is undergoing a definite change in valence of one of the ions present, or of other nature, with a corresponding change in **electromotive force.**

TRANSITION, HEAT OF. The increase in heat content when one **mole** of a substance changes to an **allotropic** form, at the transition temperature.

TRANSITION INTERVAL. In general, a range of values of a variable over which a process occurs. Two well-known transition intervals in chemistry are: the **pH** range over which the color change of an **indicator** occurs; and the temperature range over which the separation of a double salt from solution occurs, this range extending from the transition point, at which the three solid phases and the solution are in equilibrium, to the temperature at which the double salt is stable in contact with water.

TRANSITION POINT. See **temperature, transition.**

TRANSITION STATE. In the theory of **reaction rates,** the transition state, which is also called the activated complex, is an entity formed momentarily by the coming together of reactant molecules, which have the necessary activation energy; this entity decomposes at a specific rate to form the products of the reaction.

TRANSITORY PRESSURE. See **pressure, fugitive.**

TRANSLATIONAL ENTROPY. See **entropy, translational.**

TRANSLATIONAL PARTITION FUNCTION. See **entropy, translational.**

TRANSMITTANCE. The ratio of the **radiant power** transmitted by a sample to the radiant power incident on the sample, both being measured at the same spectral position and with the same slit width. The beam is understood to be parallel radiation and incident at right angles to plane parallel surfaces of the sample.

TRANSMUTATION. (1) The conversion of one element into another. (See **atomic transmutation.**) (2) A change in the configuration of a labile **stereoisomer** to the more stable form, as the transmutation of maleic into fumaric acid.

TRANSPORT NUMBER. See **transference number.**

TRANSPOSITION, ATOMIC. An intramolecular **rearrangement** wherein two or more atoms exchange places.

TRANSURANIC ELEMENTS. Elements with atomic numbers higher than uranium, which has an atomic number of 92. The six next in order have been made synthetically and given the names **neptunium, plutonium, americium, curium, berkelium,** and **californium.**

TRAPANI REAGENT. A solution of 2.5 g. mercuric cyanide and 5 g. potassium hydroxide in 100 ml. water. It is used as a test reagent for bilirubin, giving a red color that is discharged by acetic acid.

TRAUBE PURINE SYNTHESIS. A method of formation of purines by the action of formic acid or chlorocarbonic ester on 5,6-diaminopyridimines, which may be prepared from urea and α-nitrile esters.

the amount of distention of a cavity in a lead block in which a test explosion occurs.

TRAVERS TEST REACTION. A test for tungstate based on the reduction of tungstic acid by titanium trichloride. A blue oxide that remains in colloidal suspension under certain conditions is obtained.

TREE, LEAD. See **lead tree.**

$$
\begin{array}{ccc}
\overset{\displaystyle NH_2}{\underset{\displaystyle NH_2}{\overset{|}{\underset{|}{O=C}}}} + \overset{\displaystyle COOR}{\underset{\displaystyle CN}{\overset{|}{\underset{|}{CH_2}}}} & \xrightarrow{-ROH} & \overset{\displaystyle NH-C=O}{\underset{\displaystyle NH-C=NH}{\overset{|}{\underset{|}{O=C}}\quad\overset{|}{\underset{|}{CH_2}}}} & \xrightarrow{HNO_2} & \overset{\displaystyle NH-C=O}{\underset{\displaystyle NH-C-NH_2}{\overset{|}{\underset{|}{O=C}}\quad\overset{|}{\underset{\|}{C-NO}}}} + H_2O
\end{array}
$$

$$\downarrow 2H_2$$

$$
\overset{\displaystyle NH-C}{\underset{\displaystyle HN-C-NH}{\overset{|}{\underset{|}{O=C}}\quad\overset{|}{\underset{\|}{C-NH}}}}\!\!\!\Big\rangle C=O \quad + HCl + C_2H_5OH \xleftarrow{C_2H_5OOCCl} \overset{\displaystyle NH-C=O}{\underset{\displaystyle NH-C-NH_2}{\overset{|}{\underset{|}{O=C}}\quad\overset{|}{\underset{\|}{C-NH_2}}}} + H_2O.
$$

TRAUBE RULE. A relationship between the effects upon the **surface tension** of water produced by the addition of organic substances in various **homologous series.** In dilute solutions, the effect of each additional—CH_2— group in a given series is to decrease by three times the concentration at which equal lowering of surface tension is obtained.

TRAUBE TEST FOR HYDROGEN PEROXIDE. A test for hydrogen peroxide made by adding a little sulfuric acid and zinc iodide-starch solution to 8 ml. of the solution to be tested, then adding no more than 4 drops of cupric sulfate solution and a little of 0.5% ferrous sulfate solution. A blue color indicates the presence of hydrogen peroxide.

TRAUZL TEST. A test for determining the strength of an explosive by measuring

TREMAIN TEST. A test for free halogens in water, the reagent for which is made by adding 5 g. of purified p-aminodimethylaniline to 100 ml. absolute alcohol. The test is performed by adding 2–3 drops of the reagent to 5 ml. water and adding the solution to be tested slowly, adding only sufficient to produce a clear pink color. Confusing colors may result if too much is added.

TRI-. A prefix which indicates three. Cf. **ter-.**

TRIACID. A **base** capable of neutralizing three equivalents of monobasic acid.

TRIAD. (1) A class of **tautomeric** compounds in which the shifting hydrogen atom is supposed to travel from one polyvalent atom past a second to a third in a chain of three such atoms. For example, in the conversion of eugenol into isoeugenol,

$$
\underset{OCH_3}{\overset{CH_2.CH:CH_2}{HO\hexagon}} \quad \xrightarrow{\quad} \quad \underset{OCH_3}{\overset{CH:CH.CH_3.}{HO\hexagon}}
$$

Cf. **dyads.** (2) Trivalent elements, as nitrogen, chromium, or aluminum. (3) (Obs.) A molecule which contains three atoms. (4) A group of three elements having similar properties. (5) A crystal having three faces the same.

TRIADS OF DÖBEREINER. Certain groups of three elements which show similar chemical properties and nearly constant differences in physical properties, atomic weights, etc., as chlorine, bromine, and iodine; calcium, strontium, and barium; etc.

TRIAMIDO COMPOUND. See **triamine.**

TRIAMINE. A compound which contains three amino (—NH_2) groups, as triamino-benzene, $C_6H_3(NH_2)_3$.

TRIATOMIC. (1) Containing three atoms. (2) Containing three hydroxyl groups, as glycerol and pyrogallol. (3) Containing three acid hydrogen atoms.

TRIAZENO. The radical $NH_2N:N—$.

TRIAZINE. One of three isomeric compounds having the formula $C_3H_3N_3$, and having a ring structure consisting of three carbon atoms and three nitrogen atoms.

TRIAZINYL. The radical $C_3H_2N_3—$ (from triazine).

TRIAZO. See **azido.**

TRIAZOLE. One of six isomeric compounds having the formula $C_2H_3N_3$, and having a ring structure consisting of two carbon atoms and three nitrogen atoms. Two of these compounds are named iso-triazoles.

TRIAZOLYL. The radical $C_2H_2N_3—$ (from triazole).

TRIBO-. A prefix meaning friction or rubbing.

TRIBOLUMINESCENCE. Luminescence attributable to friction. It occurs usually in crystalline substances.

TRIBROMIDE. See **bromide.**

TRICHROISM. The property of exhibiting three different colors when viewed in as many different directions.

TRICHROMATE. The anion $Cr_3O_{10}^{=}$, or a compound containing it.

TRICLINIC CRYSTAL SYSTEM. See **crystallographic systems.**

TRICYCLIC. (1) A ring composed of three atoms. (2) A molecule containing three rings of atoms.

TRIDECOIC. Related to tridecoic acid, $C_{12}H_{25}COOH$.

TRIENTOXIDE. An oxide in which the proportion of metal to oxygen is as three to one, e.g., Cu_3O.

TRIER TEST REACTION. A reaction for differentiating aminoethylalcohol (colamin) and choline by use of mercuric chloride or potassium bismuth iodide solution. An aqueous solution of aminoethylalcohol hydrochloride produces no precipitate, but a solution of choline hydrochloride does.

TRIHYDROXYGLUTARIC. Related to trihydroxyglutaric acid,

$$HOOC(CHOH)_3COOH.$$

TRIIODIDE. See **iodide.**

TRILLAT TESTS FOR FORMALDE-HYDE. (1) To the solution to be tested, add 0.5 ml. dimethylaniline, acidify with sulfuric acid, and then heat for half an hour on the steam bath. Make alkaline with sodium hydroxide, boil until the odor of dimethylaniline has disappeared and then filter. Place the filtrate on a porcelain dish, moisten with acetic acid, and sprinkle with powdered lead dioxide. A blue color is given if formaldehyde is present. (2) To a dilute solution of formaldehyde, add a 3:1000 aqueous solution of aniline. A white turbidity or precipitate is formed.

TRILLAT TEST FOR LEAD AND MANGANESE DIOXIDES. In 100 ml. of 10% acetic acid, dissolve 5 g. of tetra-methyldiaminodiphenylmethane. A blue color should not develop in the cold solution or if it is heated to boiling. This reagent should be protected from light. It produces an intense blue color with lead peroxide and manganese dioxide, permitting the detection of small quantities of lead and manganese after conversion into the dioxide.

TRILLAT-TURCHET TEST. A test for ammonia in water made by adding 3 drops of a 10% potassium iodide solution to 20–30 ml. of the water and then adding 2 drops of concentrated sodium hypochlorite solution. If ammonia is present a dark color develops.

TRIMETHYLENE. The radical

$$-CH_2CH_2CH_2-.$$

TRIMOLECULAR REACTION. See reaction, termolecular.

TRIMORPHIC. Crystallizing in three forms, as titanium dioxide.

TRIMORPHISM. The property of crystallizing in three forms.

TRINITRIDE. See azide.

TRIOSE. A monosaccharide which contains three carbon atoms, as glyceric aldehyde, $CH_2OH—CHOH—CHO$.

TRIOXAZOLE. One of two isomeric compounds having the formula CHO_3N, and having a ring structure consisting of one carbon atom, one nitrogen atom, and three oxygen atoms.

TRIOXIDE. A binary compound having three oxygen atoms in its molecule, as, e.g., chromium trioxide, CrO_3, sulfur trioxide, SO_3, and arsenic trioxide, As_2O_3.

TRIPHOSPHATE. The anion $P_3O_{10}^{5-}$, or a compound containing it.

TRIPLE POINT. A definite condition of temperature and pressure where three **phases** can co-exist in **equilibrium.** For the system water, water vapor, and ice the triple point coordinates are: pressure 4.57 millimeters, temperature, $-0.0076°$ C. If either temperature or pressure is varied, one phase disappears.

TRISILANYL. The radical

$$H_3Si—SiH_2—SiH_2—.$$

TRISILANYLENE. The radical

$$—SiH_2—SiH_2—SiH_2—.$$

TRISULFATE. The anion $S_3O_{10}^=$, or a compound containing it.

TRITHIAZOLE. One of two isomeric compounds having the formula $CHNS_3$, and having a ring structure consisting of one carbon atom, one nitrogen atom, and three sulfur atoms.

TRITHIONATE. The anion $S_3O_6^=$, or a compound containing it.

TRITHIONIC. Related to trithionic acid, $H_2S_3O_6$.

TRITIUM. See hydrogen isotopes.

TRITON. A hydrogen nucleus of mass number 3, the term being derived from tritium, the hydrogen isotope of mass number 3.

TRI-TRIFUNCTIONAL REACTION. See reaction, tri-trifunctional.

TRITURATE. To grind finely with the aid of a liquid.

TRITYL. See triphenylmethyl.

TRIVALENCE. The state of being trivalent.

TRIVALENT. Having a valence of three, as exemplified by the elements aluminum, chromium, and nitrogen.

TROMMEL. A rotary screen used to classify materials by size.

TROPIC. Related to tropic acid,

$$C_6H_5.CH(COOH)CH_2OH.$$

TROTARELLI TEST. A test for ptomaines which is based on the color reactions obtained with palladium nitrate and sodium nitroprusside.

TROUTON LAW. See **law of Trouton.**

TROY SYSTEM. A system of weights and measures in which the ounce is identical with that in the **apothecaries' system.**

Troy System

24 grains = 1 pennyweight
20 pennyweights = 1 ounce
12 ounces = 1 pound
1 pound (Troy) = 373.25 grams
1 pound (Troy) = 0.823 pounds
    (avoirdupois)

TRUCHOT REAGENT. A solution of 0.2 g. diphenylamine in 100 ml. concentrated sulfuric acid. It is used in the identification of nitrocellulose silk, which dissolves in it with the formation of a blue solution.

TRYPTOPHYL. The radical $C_{11}H_{11}N_2O$— (from tryptophan).

TSALAPATANI REACTION FOR QUININE. Add a 20% trichloroacetic acid solution to an aqueous solution of quinine hydrochloride. This forms a white precipitate which, when dried and heated to 95–110° C. for 5–10 minutes, evolves chloroform and becomes red.

TSALAPATANI TEST FOR ACROLEIN. Add 1 to 2 ml. of an aqueous solution of resorcinol and several drops of a 10% sodium hydroxide to the liquid to be tested and heat the mixture. A bluish-green to red color is produced after about 2 minutes, depending upon the amount of acrolein present.

TSALAPATANI TEST FOR AMYL ALCOHOL AND METHYLAMINES. Amyl alcohol: Add about 50 mg. chloranil (tetrachloroquinone) to the liquid to be tested and heat on the steam bath. An orange-red color is produced in the presence of amyl alcohol. On cooling, an orange-red precipitate forms. Methylamines: The liquid to be tested is neutralized with hydrochloric acid and evaporated to dryness.

The residue is dissolved in 95% alcohol and 5 ml. of this mixture heated with about 50 mg. chloranil to 70–75° C. A violet color forms if mono-, di-, or trimethylamine is present.

TSCHIRCH REACTION FOR ERGOT. On 1 g. of the solid to be tested, pour 20 ml. ether, then add 10 drops ammonia and 20 ml. water. A red solution results, if ergot is present. To confirm, swirl the solution several times and let stand for 2 hours, then separate and evaporate the ether. Take up the residue with acetic acid and, after filtering, carefully float the solution on concentrated sulfuric acid containing some ferric chloride. A blue-violet zone must form at the contact surface of the liquid but only a very slight, yellow color, if any; while the acetic acid layer should show a green fluorescence.

TSCHIRCH TEST FOR SHELLAC AND ITS SUBSTITUTES. The shellac is dissolved in alcohol, allowed to settle, filtered, and then ether added to the filtrate. A yellow solution is obtained which, when shaken with dilute sodium carbonate, causes the yellow coloring matter to pass into the soda solution and impart a red-violet color. Subsequently, the aqueous solution is acidified, and it again becomes yellow. When shaken, the coloring matter dissolves in the ether with a yellow color. No coloring matter is obtained with shellac substitutes.

TSCHUGAEV-ORELKIN TEST FOR FERROUS IRON. Add 1 g. hydrazine sulfate and 5 ml. of a saturated alcoholic solution of dimethylglyoxime to 50 ml. of the sample to be tested and heat to boiling. Add 10 ml. of concentrated ammonia and boil for 1 minute. A red color indicates the presence of iron.

TSCHUGAEV REAGENT AND TEST FOR NICKEL. The reagent is α-dimethylglyoxime. The liquid to be tested is made strongly ammoniacal, shaken, and the powdered reagent added, then the mixture is heated to boiling. A scarlet precipitate forms in the presence of nickel. Several modifications of this test have been developed.

**TSCHUGAEV TESTS FOR DIFFEREN-
TIATING BORNEOL AND ISOBOR-
NEOL.** Nitrous gases are evolved on
treating borneol at ordinary temperatures
with concentrated nitric acid but isoborneol, when similarly treated remains unchanged. If the reaction mixture is
diluted with water, borneol produces crystals and isoborneol a thick oil.

TSEOU-CHOW TEST REACTION. A
reaction for differentiating acetals from
ethers conducted by adding 4 drops of the
solution to be tested to 5 ml. of 10% alcoholic resorcinol solution and then pouring
1 ml. of 20% sulfuric acid down the side of
the inclined tube. Acetals form a precipitate, usually red in color, at the junction
of the two layers and show a further change
of color on the addition of 6 N sodium hydroxide or ammonia. Ethers do not give
this reaction.

TUBE. A hollow cylinder.

TUBE, ABSORPTION. See **absorption
tube.**

TUBE-AND-TANK PROCESS. A petroleum **cracking** process operated at temperatures of about 450° C. and reaction
pressures around 350 pounds per square
inch. The pressure in the vaporizing and
fractionating unit is as low as 60 pounds
per square inch.

TUBE, CALCIUM CHLORIDE. A glass
tube, packed with calcium chloride, and
placed in a train of apparatus to absorb
water.

TUBE, CAPILLARY. (1) A tube of small
bore. (2) A tube of such small internal
diameter that the effect of surface tension
is to cause liquids to rise or fall visibly
above or below the liquid level in a liquid
container to which the capillary tube may
be connected. (See **capillarity.**)

TUBE, COMBUSTION. A tube of heat-
resistant material, such as special glass,
porcelain, etc., used in organic combus-
tions.

TUBE, CONDENSER. When a glass
condenser is assembled from two glass

tubes, the inner tube, through which the
vapors to be condensed pass, is called the
condenser tube.

TUBE, COOLIDGE. A type of **x-ray tube.**

TUBE, CROOKES. A tube used in the
investigation of the phenomena associated
with the conduction of electricity through
gases at low pressures; especially the study
of the emission by the cathode of radiations
which were, therefore, called **cathode rays,**
and were found to be streams of electrons.
Later the positive rays, i.e., streams of
positively charged ions, were found to be
produced in modified tubes of this type.

TUBE, DRYING. A tube used in the
laboratory to dry gases. It is usually filled
with calcium chloride, soda-lime, phosphorus pentoxide, or other drying agent.

TUBE, FERMENTATION. A tube used
in the laboratory study of a **fermentation**
process. The gases are collected for measurement in fermentation tubes.

TUBE, MELTING POINT. A thin-
glass tube which is used in the determination of melting points. A solid sample is
placed in the tube which is then attached
to a thermometer, and heated slowly in a
suitable bath until the contents of the tube
melt.

TUBE MILL. A mill used for fine grinding, consisting essentially of a long rotating
cylinder through which the material
passes, and in which it is ground by the
impact of pebbles or metal balls.

TUBE, THIELE. A tube whose lower
portion is formed in the shape of an irregular ring, so that liquid can circulate under
the action of heat. It is used in cases where
uniformity of heating is important, such
as in melting point determinations.

TUCKER SOLUTION. A reagent used in
metallography for etching aluminum. It
is a mixture of 9 parts by volume of concentrated hydrochloric acid, 3 parts concentrated hydrofluoric acid, 3 parts concentrated nitric acid, and 5 parts water.

TUNG-KAO-SAH REAGENT. A reagent for amines, m-nitrobenzoylisothiocyanate, which forms compounds with definite melting points.

TUNGSTATE (VI). The anion $WO_4^=$, WO_5^{4-}, or WO_6^{6-}, or a compound containing one of these anions. There are also ditungstates, hexatungstates, metatungstates, octatungstates, paratungstates, and pentatungstates (see below).

TUNGSTATE (VI) (DI-). The anion $W_2O_7^=$, or a compound containing it.

TUNGSTATE (VI) (HEXA-). The anion $W_6O_{19}^=$, or a compound containing it.

TUNGSTATE (VI) (META-). The anion $W_4O_{13}^=$, or a compound containing it.

TUNGSTATE (VI) (OCTA-). The anion $W_8O_{25}^=$, or a compound containing it.

TUNGSTATE (VI) (PARA-). The anion $W_7O_{24}^{6-}$, or a compound containing it.

TUNGSTATE (VI) (PENTA-). The anion $W_5O_{16}^=$, or a compound containing it.

TUNGSTEN. Metallic element. Symbol W. Atomic number 74. Atomic weight 183.92. Density 19.3. Specific heat 0.036. Melting point 3370° C. Boiling point 5900° C. Valence 2, 4, 5, and 6. Oxides, WO_2, WO_3. Acids, tungstic H_2WO_4, metatungstic $H_2W_4O_{13}$. Tungsten occurs in scheelite and wolframite.

TUNGSTIC. Containing or pertaining to hexavalent or pentavalent **tungsten.**

TUNGSTICYANIDE. See **cyanotungstate (V).**

TUNGSTOARSENATE. The anion $AsW_6O_{24}^{7-}$ or $AsW_{12}O_{40}^{3-}$, or a compound containing one of these anions.

TUNGSTOBORATE. The anion $BW_{12}O_{40}^{5-}$ or $H_2BW_{12}O_{40}^{3-}$, or a compound containing one of these anions.

TUNGSTOCYANIDE. See **cyanotungstate (IV).**

TUNGSTOPHOSPHATE. See **phosphotungstate.**

TUNMANN TEST REACTION FOR NICOTINE. A test for nicotine made by permitting a solution of p-dimethylaminobenzaldehyde in fuming hydrochloric acid to come in contact with a drop of nicotine on a slide. A violet color is given.

TUNNEL, DRYING. See **drying tunnel.**

TURBIDIMETER. An instrument which measures the reduction in **transmission** of light that is caused by interposing a solution containing solid particles between the light source and the eye. By using a known volume of solution in comparison with a standard, this instrument makes it possible to determine the mass effect, attributable to the number and size of the particles in the solution, and thus the quantitative amount of material present.

TURBIDIMETRY. The methods of analysis and measurement made by means of the **turbidimeter.**

TURBIDITY. The cloudiness in a liquid caused by the presence of finely-divided, suspended material.

TWADDELL SCALE. See **hydrometer scales.**

TWIN CRYSTALS. See **crystals, twin.**

TWIN ELECTRONS. See **bond, electron.**

TWIN NUCLEI. See **nuclei, twin.**

TWITCHELL REAGENT. A reagent for **hydrolysis of fats** made by treating a mixture of oleic acid and naphthalene with an excess of concentrated sulfuric acid. Any excessive rise in temperature is avoided by cooling the mixture and by adding the acid slowly. Ether is used to dissolve the crude naphthalenestearosulfonic acid formed; the ethereal solution is then washed several times with dilute hydrochloric acid and then extracted with water. Finally, the aqueous extract is diluted to contain about 10% naphthalenestearosulfonic acid.

TYNDALL EFFECT. A phenomenon first noticed by Faraday (1857). When a powerful beam of light is sent through a **colloidal solution** of high **dispersity,** the sol appears fluorescent and the light is polarized, the amount of polarization depending upon the size of the particles of the colloid. The polarization is complete if the particles are less than $100\mu\mu$ in diameter.

TYPE COMPOUNDS. Chemical compounds classified according to similarity in structure as a result of similarity in properties, especially chemical properties. Thus, compounds of the same type are those that undergo the same reactions, since they are, for example, respectively acids, or bases, or salts, or contain the same groups, as **alcohol groups,** or **aldehyde groups,** or **acid groups,** etc., or even have more than one such group in common.

TYRER PROCESS. The direct **sulfonation** of benzene with sulfuric acid to produce benzenesulfonic acid.

TYROSYL. The radical

$$p\text{-}HOC_6H_4CH_2CH(NH_2)CO\text{---}$$

(from tyrosine).

TZONI REAGENT. Two solutions used in the detection and colorimetric determination of vitamin D. (1) A solution of 0.1 g. of pyrogallol in 100 g. absolute alcohol. (2) A solution of 10 g. anhydrous aluminum chloride in 90 g. absolute alcohol. The test is made by dissolving or extracting the substance analyzed in benzene or chloroform, and adding 0.5 ml. of the first solution, and 0.25 ml. of the second. The mixture is then heated to boiling, and a few drops of an aluminum chloride solution are added. A red color indicates the presence of vitamin D.

U Symbol for the element uranium (U). Abbreviation for unit (u). Symbol for over-all **coefficient of heat transfer** (U). Symbol for density of **radiant energy** (u). Symbol for internal energy per atom or molecule (u or U_m). Symbol for internal energy per mole (u, U, U_M). Symbol for internal energy, total (U), per unit mass

(u). Symbol for spectral radiant energy (U_λ). Symbol for **reaction velocity** (u). Symbol for speed, linear or particle (u). Symbol for speed, average ($\bar{u}$ or u_{av}). Symbol for velocity (**u**). Symbol for velocity, average ($\bar{\mathbf{u}}$ or $\mathbf{u}_{av}$). Symbol for velocity, group (**u** or $\mathbf{u}_g$). Symbol for velocity, ionic (u). Symbol for **wave function,** time independent (u). See also **upsilon.**

UDRÁNSZKY TEST REACTION FOR CHOLESTEROL. A test for cholesterol made by adding 5 drops of 0.5% aqueous furfural solution to 5 ml. of the alcoholic solution to be tested, mixing, and then floating the mixture on 5 ml. of concentrated sulfuric acid. An intense red color, gradually changing to blue, is given by cholesterol.

UFFELMANN REAGENT FOR LACTIC ACID. A solution of 0.4 g. phenol and 1 drop of a saturated aqueous solution of ferric chloride in 50 ml. water. This reagent is used in testing for lactic acid in gastric juice. A color change from blue to yellow indicates the presence of lactic acid.

UFFELMANN TEST FOR CORN MEAL IN FLOUR. This test is made by boiling the flour with a dilute alcoholic solution of sodium hydroxide. A yellow, then a red color forms, if corn meal is present.

UFFELMANN TESTS FOR FUSEL OIL IN ALCOHOL AND IN ALCOHOLIC LIQUORS. (1) The alcohol is diluted with water to 20%, and then 200 ml. of it shaken with 20 ml. chloroform. The chloroform is separated and evaporated on the water bath. No residue having a fusel oil odor should remain. (2) The alcoholic liquid is extracted with chloroform and powdered diaminobenzene added to the chloroform extract. The presence of fusel oil is indicated if a yellow color appears. (3) A freshly prepared solution of methyl violet, rendered green with hydrochloric acid, is added to the residue obtained from the chloroform extract. A reddish-blue color is formed in the presence of fusel oil. (4) 1–2 drops of water are added to the residue, and then a glass rod dipped in bromine is passed over it. If fusel oil is present, the drops floating on the water become an intense yellow color.

UHLENHUT TEST. A test for copper made by adding a solution of 0.5 g. 1,2-diaminoanthraquinone-3-sulfonic acid in 500 ml. water and 40 ml. of 35% sodium hydroxide to a solution to be tested. If copper is present, an intense blue color is produced.

ULLMANN REACTION. A reaction of an aryl halide with certain metals to form compounds of the type RMgX, which are Grignard reagents and give coupling reactions. The Ullmann reaction relates particularly to their coupling with other halides, other molecules of the same halide, or metal phenolates. Thus, chlorobenzene on heating with copper powder yields diphenyl,

$$2C_6H_5Cl + Cu \rightarrow C_6H_5.C_6H_5 + CuCl_2.$$

ULTEE CYANHYDRIN METHOD. A method of forming cyanhydrins of ketones or aldehydes by treatment with anhydrous hydrogen cyanide containing a trace of alkali cyanide at 0° C.

ULTIMATE ANALYSIS. See **analysis, ultimate.**

ULTRA. A prefix meaning beyond.

ULTRACENTRIFUGE. A **centrifuge** that is operated at extremely high speed and is widely used in research in colloid chemistry and biochemistry.

ULTRAFILTRATION. The separation, by a special method of filtration, of highly dispersed substances in **colloidal solutions,** from the **dispersion medium.** Ultrafilters differ from ordinary filters only in the fineness of the pores through which the liquid must pass. By using a series of filters of graduated fineness it is possible to prepare a series of sols in which the sizes of the disperse phase particles progressively decrease.

ULTRAMICROSCOPE. See **ultramicroscopy.**

ULTRAMICROSCOPY. A method for extending the range of vision of the or-

dinary microscope in which a powerful beam of light is focused into a liquid under examination in such a way that the direction of the light is at right angles to the line of vision in the instrument. The ultramicroscopic particles, i.e., those smaller than 0.25μ in diameter, are then surrounded by visible diffraction rings and may thus be perceived. Particles as small as 1.7 $\mu\mu$ in diameter have been observed in this way. The arrangement of the apparatus for ultramicroscopy is called the ultramicroscope.

ULTRAPHOTIC RAYS. Rays beyond the visible region of the **spectrum.** This term is used as a general expression for **ultraviolet** and **infrared rays.**

ULTRAVIOLET RAYS. Radiations in that region of the spectrum of lower wave length (higher frequency) than the visible violet, extending from the end of the visible violet about 3900–4000 Ångström units in wave length, down to about 200 Ångström units.

ULTRAVIOLET SPECTRUM. See **spectrum, ultraviolet.**

UNARY SUBSTANCES. Substances whose molecules are all physically as well as chemically identical. Substances whose molecules all give an identical **ultimate analysis** but which show two sorts of physical properties are termed pseudobinary.

UNCERTAINTY PRINCIPLE. For a small, rapidly-moving object, accurate determination of velocity and instantaneous position cannot be made at the same time; the errors or, more exactly, the uncertainties in the determination of these two quantities vary inversely, so that the greater the certainty of one determination, the less will be that of the other. This specification is a basic consequence of the wave-particle duality of the particles in the universe, and is not due to limitations on the precision of measurements. In the case of the electron, the product of the uncertainty of position and the uncertainty of velocity is proportional to the **Planck constant.**

UNDECYL. See **hendecyl.**

UNDECYLIC. Related to the aliphatic acid, undecylic acid, $C_{10}H_{21}COOH$. See also **hendecylic.**

UNDERCOOLING. (Supercooling) The phenomenon which occurs when a substance is cooled without change of state below the temperature at which its state of aggregation normally changes. The system is then in a **metastable** condition, and a small disturbance often will cause the change in state to take place with evolution of heat and a temperature rise in the system to the normal temperature of the change.

UNIAXIAL. Characteristic of or by a single axis, as an object which has only one axis, or a flow of energy that travels only along one axis of a crystal or other medium.

UNIMOLECULAR LAYER. Layers having the thickness of a single molecule, such as those of **fatty acids** and **oils** upon water used in the study of **surface tension** phenomena and other properties of surface films.

UNIMOLECULAR REACTION. See **reaction, unimolecular.**

UNIT. (1) A single entity, as one element of apparatus in an industrial plant. (2) A standard of measurement as a unit of length, capacity, electromotive force, radiation intensity, etc.

UNIT ABSOLUTE. The ultimate units in any system of measurements, from which all others in that system may be derived. Absolute units are defined in terms of arbitrarily chosen fixed standards, e.g., the units of length in the **English system** and **metric system** are defined as the length of bars of metal maintained in England and France, respectively.

UNIT, ÅNGSTRÖM. A unit of length of 10^{-10} meter, used extensively to express wave lengths of radiations, and distances of intermolecular and interatomic orders.

UNIT, BRITISH THERMAL. The amount of heat required to raise one pound of water through one degree Fahrenheit (from 39° F. to 40° F.).

UNIT, c.g.s. See **c.g.s. system.**

UNIT, CONCRETE. A unit applied to or associated with a particular magnitude, as one gram.

UNIT, DERIVED. A nonfundamental unit which, however, may be expressed in terms of fundamental units. For example, area, volume, density, etc.

UNIT, e.m.u. One of the electromagnetic system of electric units which is based upon the unit pole as a fundamental unit, i.e., the unit of magnetic strength of the pole which repels a like pole one centimeter away in vacuo with a force of one dyne.

UNIT, e.s.u. One of the electrostatic system of electric units which is based upon the unit charge as a fundamental unit, i.e., the unit of electrical quantity is the charge which repels a like charge one centimeter away in vacuo with a force of one dyne.

UNIT, FUNDAMENTAL. One of a group of units for physical quantities which are chosen so that they bear the same relations to each other as their corresponding physical magnitudes bear to each other. In the c.g.s. system these units are the absolute units, the centimeter, gram, and second, plus certain constants such as the dielectric constant and the gravitational constant, from which complete dimensional equations may be written.

UNIT, METRIC. See **metric system.**

UNIT, m.k.h. A unit in the modification of the metric system which has as its absolute units the meter, kilogram, and hour.

UNIT OPERATION. The various physical operations which are common in industrial organic processes. The term includes the various kinds of information which have been accumulated about these processes in their application to practical manufacturing problems, extending from the fundamental investigation of process mechanisms, to the final construction of large-scale apparatus for conducting the processes, with all the intermediate steps, such as calculation of size, general principles of construction and details of design. The most common of the unit operations are fluid flow, heat transfer (heating and cooling), vaporization, distillation, filtration, crystallization, gas absorption and desorption, air conditioning, crushing and grinding, and separation of solid materials.

UNIT PROCESS. Certain chemical reactions, commonly organic reactions, which are so widely used that their general characteristics have been studied by chemists and chemical engineers. Among these important general reactions are halogenation, hydrolysis, esterification, nitration, amination, diazotization, coupling, oxidation, hydrogenation, sulfonation, Friedel-Crafts reaction, alkylation, polymerization, pyrolysis, cracking, isomerization, and cyclization. All these processes and a large number of others are described in this book together with many less commonly-used reactions, under the term **reaction,** followed by the specific name, or under the name of the discoverer or investigator to whom the reaction is attributed.

UNIT, ROENTGEN. See **Roentgen unit.**

UNITARY THERMAL PROCESS. A process for the **polymerization** of cracked or paraffin hydrocarbon gases made up of propane and propene, butanes and butenes, etc., in order to polymerize them to produce such liquid products as gasoline and gas oil. This process is conducted at temperatures of 500–585° C., and pressures of 1000 to 4500 pounds per square inch, and no catalysts are used.

U.S. BUREAU OF MINES PROCESS. A process for the production of alumina (chiefly for aluminum manufacture) by baking the clay with ammonium sulfate and water to form the ammonium alum, leaching with water to dissolve this alum, reducing iron present to ferrous state with sulfur dioxide, recrystallizing the alum, dissolving it and precipitating aluminum hydroxide, and calcining to alumina.

U.S. PHARMACOPOEIA OR U.S.P. An authoritative publication listing a large number of drugs, chemicals, biological materials, and other substances used in medicine, with directions for their preparation, assay, and use. The letters U.S.P. upon a label are the producer's warranty that the chemical or other material contained therein complies with the stipulated standards of purity.

UNITS, SYSTEM OF. A series of units for measuring various physical magnitudes of size, mass, force, rate, time, surface tension, magnetic permeability which are related in that certain ones (commonly three) are defined arbitrarily, and the others are derived from them by known relationships between the quantities they represent. Thus, in the c.g.s. system, which is derived from the arbitrary (absolute) units of length (the centimeter) of mass (the gram) and of time (the second), the unit of energy has the dimensions of (grams) (centimeters)^2 (seconds)$^{-2}$, from the formula: kinetic energy $= \frac{1}{2}mv^2$.

UNIVALENCE. The state of being **univalent.**

UNIVALENT. In its most common use, this term indicates an element or radical having only one valence, as, e.g., calcium. However, the term is also used to indicate an element or radical having a valence of 1, although the term monovalent is preferable for this meaning.

UNIVARIANT SYSTEM. According to the **phase rule,** a system which has but one **degree of freedom,** e.g., the system liquid water $\rightleftharpoons$ water vapor.

UNIVERSAL INDICATOR. See **indicator, universal.**

UNNA-GOLODETZ TEST REACTION. A test for many proteins, based on their reducing power, whereby sulfur suspended in water is converted into hydrogen sulfide, detectable by its odor or with lead paper.

UNNA SOLUTION. A stain prepared by dissolving 1 g. methylene blue and 1 g. potassium carbonate in 100 ml. distilled water.

UNORGANIZED. A term used frequently in chemistry or biology to express the absence of a definite structure, as to be without a definite crystallographic structure or a definite cellular structure.

UNORGANIZED FERMENT. An **enzyme** unconnected with living cells and capable of acting in sterile media.

UNS-, UNSYM-. Abbreviations of unsymmetrical; as, *uns*-dichloroethane, CH_3CHCl_2.

UNSATISFIED VALENCE. An atom, radical, or compound having a free valence **available** to form a bond with another atom or radical.

UNSATURATED COMPOUND. A substance that contains one or more elements of which the total valence is either not satisfied or is satisfied by union with another atom of the same element. $C=O$ is an example of the first class; $H_2C=CH_2$, an example of the second. Unsaturated compounds usually add hydrogen, halogens, ozone, halogen acids, and other compounds directly producing saturated compounds, viz.,

$$C=O + Cl_2 \rightarrow COCl_2$$

$$HC\equiv CH + 2HCl \rightarrow CHCl_2-CH_3.$$

UNSATURATED SOLUTION. A solution that can dissolve more solute under the given conditions of temperature and pressure, before reaching **equilibrium** with the **solid phase.**

UNSTABLE. A substance or system which assumes an entirely new condition or arrangement when disturbed from its initial state. Thus, unstable systems readily revert to a condition of greater **entropy.**

UNSYMMETRICAL. Asymmetrical, or not symmetrical. (1) Of a crystal, having no plane of symmetry. (2) Of a tetravalent atom, having four dissimilar atoms or groups bonded to it. (See **isomerism, optical.**) (3) Of a derivative of a benzene having three substituents which do not occupy the 1, 3, 5 (i.e., symmetrical) position.

UNVERHAU TEST REACTIONS. Reactions for strophanthin as follows: (1) Heating strophanthin with concentrated nitric acid produces a red to violet color which suddenly changes to light yellow. (2) Strophanthin with sodium nitroprusside and sodium hydroxide produces a red color. (3) Strophanthin dissolved in concentrated hydrochloric acid containing phenol, and then heated, produces a violet color which changes to green.

UPSILON (Υ OR υ). The twentieth letter in the Greek alphabet, used to denote the twentieth carbon atom in a straight-chain compound, or a derivative in which the substituent group is attached to the twentieth carbon atom.

UR-ACID. A hydrolytic product of a cyclic **ureide,** as oxaluric acid,

$$NH-CO-COOH$$
$$|$$
$$C-NH_2$$
$$\|$$
$$O$$
.

URAMINO-. See **ureido-.**

URANATE (DI- OR PYRO-). The anion $U_2O_7^{=}$, or a compound containing it.

URANATE (ORTHO- OR META-). The anion $UO_4^{=}$, or a compound containing it.

URANIC. Containing or pertaining to hexavalent **uranium.**

URANIUM. Metallic element. Symbol U. Atomic number 92. Atomic weight 238.07. Density 18.7. Specific heat 0.062. Melting point $> 1850°$ C. Valence 2, 3, 4, 5, and 6. Oxides UO, U_2O_5, UO_2, U_3O_8, UO_3. Acid H_2UO_4, analogous to chromic acid. Ore, pitchblende. Uranium is radioactive. The naturally-occurring element has three radioactive isotopes of mass numbers $234(U_{II})$, $235(AcU)$, and $238(U_I)$; while the reported artificially-produced isotopes include those with mass numbers 227, 228, 229, 230, 231, 232, 233, 236, 237, 239 and 240. (See **elements, radioactive.**)

URANIUM, DISINTEGRATION. See **radioactive disintegration.**

URANIUM SERIES. See **element, radioactive series.**

URANOUS. Containing or pertaining to tetravalent uranium.

URANYL. The radical $=UO_2$ found in some **uranic** salts, as UO_2Cl_2, and in uranic acid, $UO_2(OH)_2$.

URATE. A compound of **uric acid.**

URE TEST REACTION. A test for meconic acid made by adding ferric chloride solution to a solution of the acid. A red color is produced if meconic acid is present.

UREA. The parent substance of a great number of derivatives and synthetics, including many hypnotics. It is also a product of animal metabolism. It has the formula.

$$C=O \begin{matrix} NH_2 \\ \\ NH_2 \end{matrix} \ .$$

UREAMETER. A ureometer.

URECH CYANHYDRIN METHOD. A method of forming **cyanhydrins** of **ketones** by treatment of a mixture in equivalent proportions of the ketone and an alkali cyanide, with acetic or sulfuric acid.

URECH HYDANTOIN SYNTHESIS. A method of formation of hydantoins by addition of α-amino acids to potassium cyanate, followed by ring closure.

sometimes restricted to derivatives of urea with acid radicals, especially radicals of carboxy acids.

UREIDO. The radical $H_2NCONH-$ (sometimes used synonymously with ureylene).

UREOMETER. An apparatus for determining the amount of **urea** in a sample of urine by decomposing the urea with sodium hypobromite in sodium hydroxide solution and measuring the evolved nitrogen.

URETHANE. An ester of carbamic acid of the general form

$$H_2N-C \begin{matrix} O \\ \\ OR \end{matrix} \ .$$

UREYLENE. The radical $-HNCONH-$.

URIC ACID DERIVATIVES. The position of substituents in uric acid derivatives is defined by numbering the skeleton atoms in the basic purine structure as follows:

Cf. **purine derivatives.**

$$RCH(NH_2)COOH + KOCN \rightarrow \begin{bmatrix} R-CH-COOK \\ NH \quad NH_2 \\ C \\ O \end{bmatrix} \xrightarrow[\Delta]{HCl} \begin{matrix} R \quad O \\ HN \quad NH \\ O \end{matrix} + KCl + H_2O.$$

UREIDE. In general a derivative of **urea,** either by substituting for one or more of its hydrogen atoms, as for one of its NH_2 groups, or for its carbonyl oxygen atom, as for more than one of these. The term is

URICOLYSIS. The conversion of **uric acid** to **urea** in the organism.

URICOLYTIC ENZYME. An **enzyme** that catalyzes the destruction of **uric acid.**

URINE ANALYSIS. The clinical analysis of urine for indications of pathological conditions in the body. Samples of urine are tested particularly for specific gravity, color, presence of proteins, reducing sugars, acetone, hydroxybutyric acid; and quantitative determinations of ammonia, urea, phosphates, and sugars (if present) are made. Other substances are determined only in special cases. The microscopic examination of the sediment is an integral part of the analysis.

URINOMETER. A hydrometer used to take the specific gravity of samples of urine. Any hydrometer for liquids heavier than water will serve.

URO-, UR-. (Greek: *ouro-, our-*) Relating to urine, or urea, as urobilin, urethan.

URSO-, URS-. (Latin: *ursus*, bear) Relating to bears, or the bearberry, as ursolic acid.

USAMI REAGENT. A mixture of 1 ml. of a saturated alcoholic solution of methyl violet 6B or 0.2 ml. of a saturated alcoholic solution of fuchsin, with 16 ml. glacial acetic acid and 64 ml. absolute alcohol, which is then decolorized by shaking with 8 g. zinc dust. This reagent is used with hydrogen peroxide for testing for blood in feces.

UTZ REAGENT FOR COTTONSEED OIL. A solution of 1 g. sulfur in 100 g. pentachloroethane, used in testing for cottonseed oil. A red color on heating a sample with the reagent and amyl alcohol indicates the presence of cottonseed oil.

UTZ TEST FOR DIFFERENTIATING ARSPHENAMINE AND NEOARSPHENAMINE. When 0.1 ml. dilute hydrochloric acid is added to 5 ml. of a 1:1000 solution of neoarsphenamine, an immediate precipitate is formed. This reaction is not given by arsphenamine. Inasmuch as formaldehyde is formed in this reaction, adding 2.5 ml. Schiff's reagent for aldehydes produces a violet color, and the subsequent addition of 1 ml. hydrochloric acid a blue color. This reaction is not given by arsphenamine.

UTZ TEST FOR FORMALDEHYDE IN MILK. Equal volumes of milk and concentrated hydrochloric acid are heated with a few granules of vanillin. A pale violet color is produced if the milk is free from formaldehyde; if formaldehyde is present, a yellow color forms.

UTZ TEST FOR MINERAL ACIDS IN VINEGAR. To 10 ml. of the vinegar, add 4 g. of cane sugar and invert in the usual manner. Shake out 3 times with ether; and, after filtering the ether solution, evaporate it. Dry the residue on the steam bath and add a few drops of 1:100 resorcinol-hydrochloric acid. A rose to red color is given if mineral acids are present.

V Symbol for the element **vanadium** (V). Abbreviation for volume (V or v). Abbreviation for specific volume (v). Symbol for humid volume (V_H). Abbreviation for volt (v). Abbreviation for **vicinal** (V-). Symbol for vapor rate (V). Symbol for atomic volume (V). Symbol for shearing force in beam (V). Symbol for **Peltier potential** (V_π). Symbol for **potential difference** (V), for instantaneous potential difference (v), for average potential difference (V_{av}), for maximum potential difference (V_{max}), for inner potential or **ionization potential** (V_i). Symbol for vibrational **quantum number** (v). Symbol for specific magnetic rotation (**Verdet constant**) (V). Symbol for speed, linear or particle (v). Symbol for speed (average) ($\bar{v}$ or v_{av}). Symbol for velocity (**v**). Symbol for velocity (average) ($\bar{V}$ or V_{av}). Symbol for velocity (group) (V or V_g).

VACCINE. This term was applied originally to the preparation obtained by Jenner from lymph exuded from lesions developed by cows suffering from cow pox and which represented the pioneer work on immunization for smallpox. The term vaccine has been extended to cover any bacterial suspension used to confer immunity against a disease.

VACUUM. Theoretically a space devoid of matter; practically a region of space in which the atmospheric pressure has been reduced as much as possible with present pumping systems.

VACUUM DISTILLATION. A distillation in which a partial vacuum is produced and maintained over the liquid under distillation. The effect is to reduce the boiling point and to permit distillation at a lower temperature.

VACUUM DRYING. Drying under reduced pressure.

VACUUM EVAPORATION. Evaporation under reduced pressure.

VACUUM FILTER. See **filter, vacuum.**

VACUUM PAN. An element of equipment, commonly in the form of a large, strongly-reinforced vessel of circular section, used in performing evaporations or distillations under vacuum, commonly with the use of steam as a heating medium.

VACUUM PUMP. An apparatus that removes air or gas from an enclosed space, as, e.g., to conduct **distillations** or other processes under reduced pressure and thus at a lower temperature.

VACUUM TUBE. A highly-evacuated glass tube used for emission of electrons or radiations from metals by action of heat or radiations, or for the **ionization** of atoms, or for many related phenomena.

VAGELER EQUATION. An expression relating the degree of exchange and the **concentration** in an **ion exchange** system, of the form:

$$X = \frac{Sa}{a + c}$$

where X = amount exchange, a = electrolyte added, and S and c are constants.

VALDIGUIÉ TEST REACTION. A test for aminopyrine made by adding several drops of **Schiff reagent** (q.v.) to an aqueous or alcoholic solution to be tested. A more or less intense red coloration is produced if aminopyrine is present.

VALENCE. The property of an atom or radical to combine with other atoms or radicals in definite proportions, or a number representing the proportion in which a given atom or radical combines. The standard of reference is hydrogen, which is assigned a valence of 1, and the valence of any given atom or radical is then the number of hydrogen atoms, or their equivalent, with which the given atom or radical combines. Many elements have more than one valence, and their compounds are classified and designated accordingly.

VALENCE, ACTIVE. The valence which an element exhibits in any particular compound, e.g., the active valence of iron in the ferrous salts is two.

VALENCE ANGLES. Angles between the successive valence **bonds** of an atom.

VALENCE, ANOMALOUS. An exceptional valence that an element has in certain compounds.

VALENCE, AUXILIARY. (Secondary or supplementary valence) The valence that would enable molecules to form stable unions just as if these molecules were radicals. Werner represented this auxiliary valence by a dotted line, i.e., NH_3 . . . HCl. This concept is now obsolete.

VALENCE BOND. See **bond.**

VALENCE, CHIEF. (Primary valence) A term used by Werner to specify that valence of an element which can be expressed in terms of bonds with hydrogen atoms or their equivalents (or, if the compound has more than one such valence, then the valence occurring most commonly, or in the greatest number of compounds), as the chief valence of nitrogen is three. Cf. **auxiliary valence.**

VALENCE, CONTRA-. See **contravalence.**

VALENCE, ELECTRO-. A valence that is due to the transfer of an electron or electrons from one atom to another.

VALENCE, CO-. A valence that is due to the sharing of electrons between atoms.

VALENCE, DATIVE. A covalence in which one of the two atoms joined by the valence bond furnishes both of the shared electrons.

VALENCE ELECTRON. An electron in the outer shell of an atom. Such electrons are called valence electrons because, by gaining, losing, or sharing these outer-shell electrons, atoms combine to form molecules. Therefore, the number of these outer-shell electrons determines the valence or valences of the atom. (See **atomic structure.**)

VALENCE FORCE FIELD. An assumed force field utilized in order to solve the equation in which the potential energy of vibration of a polyatomic molecule is expressed in terms of the energies of the restoring forces of each atom and the energies of their interaction terms. This simplifying assumption is that a force constant is associated with every valence bond and every valence angle, representing their resistance to change in length or magnitude.

VALENCE, FREE. A valence that does not appear to be satisfied, as the valence of a free radical.

VALENCE ISOMERISM. Isomerism attributable to difference in linkage of primary and auxiliary **valencies.**

VALENCE, MAXIMUM. The highest valence shown by an element in any of its compounds. With chromium it is six; potassium, one; nitrogen, five; etc.

VALENCE, NEGATIVE. An electrovalence possessed by an atom because it has become ionized by addition of an electron or electrons.

VALENCE, NORMAL. The valence that an element exhibits in a majority of its compounds.

VALENCE, NULL. According to the electronic conception of valence, a condition in which an element has no valence because, in its normal state, it has a complete outer electronic shell, as in the case of the inert gases of the atmosphere and radon.

VALENCE NUMBER. A number assigned to an atom or ion that is equal to its valence, preceded by a plus or minus sign to indicate whether the ion is positive or negative, or whether the atom, in reaching the state of oxidation under consideration, has lost or gained electrons from its normal state. The basis of this computation of positive and negative numbers is the assignment to hydrogen ions or combined atoms (except in metallic hydrides) of a value of +1. The other elements are then assigned valence numbers such that in any stable molecule the sum of the valence numbers is zero.

VALENCE, PARTIAL. Thiele's assumption that atoms which are doubly linked possess extra valence by which union with other elements is first effected. It was represented thus, the dotted lines indicating the partial valence,

$$\text{R—C=CH—CH=C—R.}$$

Cf. **conjugated double bonds.**

VALENCE, POSITIVE. A valence state of an atom in which the **valence number** is positive.

VALENCE, PRIMARY. See **valence, chief.**

VALENCE RULES. See the **Perrin rule** and the **Schulze-Hardy rule.**

VALENCE, SECONDARY. See **valence, auxiliary.**

VALENCE SHELL. The group of electrons constituting the outer electronic shell of an atom. See **valence electron.**

VALENCE, SUPPLEMENTARY. A residual valence connecting atoms, groups, or molecules in which the ordinary valences are already saturated. Supplementary valences are found in **coordination compounds** and often in **associated molecules.**

VALENCY. (1) Valence. (2) The numerical value of the valence. (3) The symbols used to represent valence.

VALENTA REAGENT FOR DIFFERENTIATING ALIPHATIC AND AROMATIC HYDROCARBONS. This reagent is dimethyl sulfate, which dissolves aromatic hydrocarbons in the cold, but not aliphatic hydrocarbons.

VALENTA REAGENT FOR FATS. This reagent is glacial acetic acid, which produces clear solutions with fats and fatty oils at various temperatures.

VALENTA TEST FOR PINE OIL IN TURPENTINE OIL. An equal volume of the turpentine oil is shaken with a 1% aqueous gold chloride solution, then heated for 1 minute on the water bath, and shaken again. If pine oil (or pinoline) is present, the gold solution becomes decolorized completely. Pure turpentine oil will show a separation of gold only in the oily layer, while the solution itself will not be decolorized.

VALERIC. Related to valeric acid,

$$C_4H_9.COOH.$$

VALERYL. The radical $CH_3(CH_2)_3CO—$.

VALSER SOLUTION. A 10% aqueous solution of potassium iodide which is saturated with mercuric iodide and used as a test reagent for alkaloids. A white precipitate is given by most alkaloids.

VALTON TEST. A test for methylamine in the presence of ammonia made by pouring the solution to be tested into a 250-ml. flask and adding 30 ml. N sodium hydroxide and enough water to make 80 ml. Using a Kjeldahl apparatus, the mixture is distilled into 10 ml. of a 0.5% alcoholic solution of 2,4-dinitrochlorobenzene. When 10 ml. have distilled, the resulting mixture is allowed to stand for 20 hours. The presence of methylamine is indicated by a precipitate of crystalline dinitromethylaniline.

VALUE. The amount or magnitude of a quantity or property.

VALVE. An externally-operated device for regulating or controlling the flow of a gas, liquid, or form of energy.

VALVE, ANGLE. A globe valve which has one of its pipe connections at the bottom instead of the side.

VALVE, BALL CHECK. A check valve having a control element consisting of a ball seated on an aperture in the direction of flow. Reversal of flow seats the ball and cuts off the flow.

VALVE, CHECK. A valve designed to permit flow in one direction only.

VALVE, DIAPHRAGM. A valve having a control element consisting of a diaphragm which is closed by pressure of the valve stem against it.

VALVE, GATE. A valve having a control element that moves in or out of the stream of fluid from an upper or lateral chamber that is an integral part of the valve.

VALVE, GLOBE. A valve that has a globular body and a disc that seats on an orifice perpendicular to the line of flow.

VALVE, NEEDLE. A valve having a needle, or semi-pointed control element, that seats in a small orifice in the line of flow.

VALVE, SWING CHECK. A check valve having a control element consisting of a disc or plate pivoted at one end, which is swung by reverse flow of fluid into closed position against a seat.

VALYL. The radical

$$(CH_3)_2CHCH(NH_2)CO—$$

(from valine).

VAMVAKAS TEST. A test for gelatin (in starch syrup). On boiling a 10% gelatin solution with **Nessler solution** (q.v.), an immediate, lustrous, lead-gray precipitate is formed. The precipitate is duller in color with more dilute solutions.

VANADATE. Various anions consisting of vanadium and oxygen (see **vanadate, meta-; vanadate, ortho-;** and **vanadate, pyro-**) or a compound containing one of them.

VANADATE (META-). The anion VO_3^-, or a compound containing it.

VANADATE (ORTHO-). The anion $VO_4{}^{3-}$, or a compound containing it.

VANADATE (PYRO-). The anion $V_2O_7{}^{4-}$, or a compound containing it.

VANADIC. Containing or pertaining to trivalent or pentavalent **vanadium.**

VANADITE. The anion $V_4O_9{}^=$, or a compound containing it.

VANADIUM. Metallic element. Symbol V. Atomic number 23. Atomic weight 50.95. Density 5.87. Specific heat 0.1153. Melting point 1720° C. Boiling point 3000° C. Valence 2, 3, 4, and 5. Ore, vanadinite. Oxides V_2O, V_2O_2, V_2O_3, V_2O_4, V_2O_5. The higher oxides exhibit acidic properties.

VANADOUS. Containing or pertaining to divalent or trivalent vanadium.

VANADYLIC. Containing the radical $\equiv VO$.

VANADYLOUS. Containing the radical $-VO$.

VAN DEEN TEST REACTION. A test for blood made by adding several drops of tincture of guaiac resin and red (ozonized) turpentine oil to the sample to be tested. A blue color indicates the presence of blood.

VAN DER WAALS EQUATION. A form of the **equation of state,** relating the pressure, volume, and temperature of a gas, and the gas constant. Van der Waals applied corrections for the reduction of total pressure by the attraction of molecules (effective at boundary surfaces) and for the reduction of total volume by the volume of the molecules. The equation takes the form

$$\left(P + \frac{a}{V^2} \right)(V - b) = RT$$

in which P is the pressure of the gas, V is the volume, T is the absolute temperature, R is the gas constant, and a and b are correction terms which have been evaluated and reported for many gases.

VAN DER WAALS FORCES. Interatomic or intermolecular forces of attraction due to the interaction between fluctuating **dipole moments** associated with molecules not possessing permanent dipole moments. These dipoles result from momentary dissymmetry in the positive and negative charges of the atom or molecule, and on neighboring atoms or molecules. These dipoles tend to align in antiparallel direction and thus result in a net attractive force. This force varies inversely as the seventh power of the distance between ions.

VAN ECK REAGENT. A solution of 0.5 g. α-naphthylamine and 50 g. tartaric acid in 100 ml. water, used as a test reagent for chromic acid. A blue color indicates the presence of chromic acid.

VAN ECK TEST REACTION. A color reaction for aldehydes performed by adding a solution of benzidine in glacial acetic acid to the substance to be tested. Characteristic colors are given by the various aldehydes.

VAN EKENSTEIN-BLANKSMA TEST REACTION. A test for furfural performed by adding albumin and concentrated hydrochloric acid to the solution to be tested. A dirty red to brown color indicates the presence of furfural.

VANILLAL. See **vanillylidene.**

VANILLOYL. The radical

$$3,4\text{-}(CH_3O)(HO)C_6H_3CO\text{---}.$$

VANILLYL. The radical

$$3,4\text{-}(CH_3O)(HO)C_6H_3CH_2\text{---}.$$

VANILLYLIDENE. The radical

$$3,4\text{-}(CH_3O)(HO)C_6H_3CH\text{==}.$$

VANINO-GUYOT REAGENT. Citarin (sodium anhydromethylene citrate), by which gold and silver are quantitatively precipitated from their solutions.

VANINO-HARTL TEST REACTION. A test for bismuth in which hypophosphorus acid is added to the solution to be tested. A white precipitate which turns gray slowly in the cold, and more rapidly on heating, indicates the presence of bismuth.

VANINO TEST. A test for colloidal metal solutions in which barium sulfate precipitates and decolorizes colloidal solutions of gold, silver, etc. Dissolved substances, like aniline dyes, are not disturbed.

VAN ITALLIE-STEENHAUER TEST REACTION FOR ALKALOIDS. The substance is dissolved in 1 ml. of alcohol, some vanillin or piperonal and 2 drops of 0.5 N sulfuric acid added and then the mixture is evaporated on a steam bath. A red to red-violet or blue-violet color is given by apomorphine, aspidospermine, cevadine, codeine, and morphine.

VAN ITALLIE TEST FOR DIFFERENTIATING PHENOL AND RESORCINOL FROM SALICYLIC ACID. To 100 ml. of a saturated aqueous solution of salicylic acid, add 2 drops of ferric chloride solution. A blue-violet color is produced which does not change when 10 drops of lactic acid are added. Resorcinol and phenol give this same reaction but the color is changed to yellow-green on the addition of 1 drop of lactic acid.

VAN ITALLIE TEST FOR HYDROGEN SULFIDE. A yellow to reddish-brown color is produced when a freshly prepared solution of p-diazobenzenesulfonic acid is added to an alkaline solution of hydrogen sulfide.

VAN ITALLIE TEST REACTION FOR ANTIPYRINE. Heat the solution to be tested with nitric acid. A cherry-red color is given by antipyrine.

VAN ITALLIE TEST REACTION FOR THYMOL. Add 1 drop potassium hydroxide solution to a solution containing thymol and enough iodine-potassium iodide solution to color the liquid yellowish. A red color is given on gentle warming.

VAN KLOOSTER TEST. A test for cobalt made by adding 1 g. of powdered sodium acetate to 2 ml. of the dilute solution to be tested and then adding 2 ml. of a solution of 0.5 g. nitroso-R-salt in 100 ml. water. The mixture is then heated to boiling, about 1 ml. concentrated nitric acid added gradually, and the boiling continued for at least one minute. A red color, which remains permanent, indicates the presence of cobalt.

VAN RUYMBEKE PROCESS. A process used in refining glycerol, in which the crude glycerol is steam-distilled and fractionally condensed.

VAN SLYKE CARBON MONOXIDE REAGENT. An aqueous solution of potassium ferricyanide, caprylic alcohol, lactic acid, and saponin, used in determining carbon monoxide in blood.

VAN SLYKE METHOD. A method for determination of primary amines, and hence compounds which yield primary amines on hydrolysis, such as proteins, by reaction with nitrous acid and warming. The evolved nitrogen is measured. The reaction is:

$$RNH_2 + HNO_2 \rightarrow N_2 + ROH + H_2O.$$

VAN'T HOFF EQUATION. A relationship representing the variation with temperature (at constant pressure) of the equilibrium constant of a gaseous reaction in terms of the change in **heat content,** i.e., of the heat of reaction (at constant pressure). It has the form:

$$\frac{d \ln K_p}{dT} = \frac{\Delta H}{RT^2}$$

in which K_p is the equilibrium constant at constant pressure, T is absolute temperature, R is the gas constant, and ΔH is the standard change in heat content, or, for ideal gases, the change in heat content.

VAN'T HOFF FACTOR. A factor which expresses the ratio of the observed **osmotic pressure** of a solution to the value calculated upon the basis of ideal behavior, i.e., direct proportionality of the osmotic pressure to the product of the temperature and the gas constant, divided by the volume.

VAN'T HOFF ISOTHERM. See **reaction isotherm.**

VAN'T HOFF, LAW OF. See law of Van't Hoff.

VAN'T HOFF LAW OF MOBILE EQUILIBRIUM. See law of mobile equilibrium.

VAN URK REACTIONS FOR ARSPHENAMINE AND NEOARSPHENAMINE. (1) The substance is added to a 1% solution of o-nitrobenzaldehyde in dilute alcohol and enough sulfuric acid added to make its concentration 2%. The solution is then evaporated on a steam bath. A yellow color is given by arsphenamine and a fiery red by neoarsphenamine. (2) The substance is warmed with sulfuric acid containing a few drops of 1% furfural solution. A yellow-red color is produced by arsphenamine and a brown-yellow color by neoarsphenamine.

VAN URK REACTION FOR ERGOTAMINE, ERGOTOXINE, AND ERGOTONINE. On evaporation to dryness with a 1% alcoholic solution of p-dimethylaminobenzaldehyde, solutions of ergotamine, ergotoxine, and ergotonine give red-violet residues.

VAN URK TESTS FOR DIFFERENTIATING CHLORAMINE-T FROM HYPOCHLORITES. (1) With a resorcinol solution, hypochlorites give a purplered color immediately while chloramine-T gives a green and then a yellow color which becomes red on heating. (2) Hypochlorite gives a blue-green color with β-naphthol on boiling while chloramine-T gives a yellow color. (3) With reduced indigo solution, hypochlorite bleaches out the blue color while chloramine-T does not.

VAN URK TEST FOR ORGANIC DRUGS. A small amount of the substance to be tested is placed in a porcelain dish, 5–10 drops of a 1% alcoholic solution of p-dimethylaminobenzaldehyde and sufficient 12% sulfuric acid added to give an acid concentration of about 2% by volume. It is then evaporated, the residue shaken with water, and the color noted. Characteristic colors are obtained with many compounds, especially phenols, amines, etc.

VAN ZIJP TEST FOR CHOLESTEROL. A test for cholesterol made by exposing, for 1–4 hours, a thin layer of cholesterol (such as the evaporation residue from a solution in chloroform) to the vapors of concentrated hydiodic acid containing iodine. Blue or bluish-black crystals are obtained. This reaction is not given by ergosterol and phytosterols.

VAPOR. A term applied to a gas that is at a temperature below its critical temperature, which can, therefore, be condensed by pressure alone.

VAPOR BATH. A steam bath.

VAPOR DENSITY. The density of a gas referred to the density of hydrogen or air as unity. If the density of hydrogen is taken as 2, the vapor density is approximately the molecular weight; if it is taken as one, the vapor density equals half the molecular weight.

VAPOR PRESSURE. The pressure at which a liquid or liquid system and its vapor are at **equilibrium** at a given temperature.

VAPOR PRESSURE, REID. The vapor pressure of a liquid determined at 100° F. and expressed in pounds per square inch.

VAPOR, SATURATED. A vapor that is in **equilibrium** with its liquid at a given temperature.

VAPOR TENSION. The tendency of a liquid to enter the vapor state, balanced by, and numerically equal to, the **vapor pressure.**

VAPORIMETER. An instrument used to determine the vapor tension of a substance, particularly that of alcoholic liquids, whereby their content of alcohol may be estimated.

VAPORIZATION. The change of a substance from the liquid or solid state to the gaseous state.

VAPORIZATION, HEAT OF. (Latent heat of vaporization, heat of evaporation)

The amount of heat required to convert a unit mass of a substance into its vapor at the vapor pressure of the system and without temperature change. The amount of heat required varies with the temperature at which the evaporation is carried on, generally decreasing as the temperature increases. Thus for water,

Temperature	Heat of Vaporization
0° C.	596.3 calories per gram
25° C.	582.5
75° C.	553.3
100° C.	538.0

The heat of vaporization of a solid is termed its **heat of sublimation.**

VAPORIZATION, MOLAR INTERNAL LATENT HEAT OF. The amount of heat required to convert one gram-molecule of a substance into its vapor at constant temperature and constant volume.

VAPORIZATION, MOLAR LATENT HEAT OF. (Molecular heat of vaporization) The amount of heat required to convert one gram-molecule of substance into its vapor at a constant temperature and at the vapor pressure of the system; numerically this quantity is equal to the product of the heat of vaporization and the gram-molecular weight. Thus at 100° C., the molecular heat of vaporization of water is:

538 calories (Heat of Vaporization)

$\times$ 18.016 (Molecular Weight)

= 9692.6 calories

(Molar Heat of Vaporization).

VARIABILITY. The property of departing from an established value or standard, or the amount of such departure.

VARIANCE. Either the number of **degrees of freedom** possessed by a system, or the degrees of freedom themselves. (See also **phase rule.**)

VARNISH. A solution of a resin or a drying oil in a volatile solvent or in a drying oil. Varnishes are classified as spirit, turpentine, and linseed oil varnishes, according to the solvent used.

VASEY ACETALDEHYDE SOLUTION. An alcoholic solution prepared by mixing 1.386 g. of purified acetaldehyde ammonia, dissolved in 50 ml. alcohol, with 22.7 ml. N alcoholic sulfuric acid solution, and filtering. It is used as a standard aldehyde solution.

VASIL'EV TEST REACTION. A test for nitrate and nitrite made by adding 3 drops of 0.1% solution of β-methyl-umbelliferone in concentrated sulfuric acid to 2 drops of a N nitrate (or nitrite) solution. The nitrogen oxide which is evolved forms a yellow crystalline compound with β-methyl-umbelliferone. This compound is soluble in water. The acid solution is neutralized with ammonia, and the greenish lemon-yellow color of the liquid changes to dark straw-yellow. When diluted to 2 liters with water, the color changes to lemon-yellow.

VASMER TEST REACTION. A test for veratrine in which fuming sulfuric acid is added to the solution to be tested. An amethyst to dark red color indicates the presence of veratrine.

VASOCONSTRICTOR. A drug which causes constriction of blood vessels, or which causes the effect upon the circulatory system which results from such constriction, i.e., increased arterial pressure.

VASODILATOR. A drug which causes dilation of blood vessels, or which causes the effect upon the circulatory system which results from such dilation, i.e., decreased arterial pressure.

VASSALLO TEST REACTION. A test for tin and bismuth made by heating 50 g. hematoxylone wood with 100 g. alcohol for 3 hours under a reflux condenser and filtering. Strips of filter paper are then dipped into the extract and dried. Under certain conditions, tin and bismuth salt solutions produce a violet color.

VAVILOV TEST REACTION. A test for bismuth made by treating a drop of the solution to be tested with an alcoholic solution of thio-acetamide. A yellow color indicates the presence of bismuth.

VECTOR. A quantity that has both magnitude and direction.

VEGETABLE CHEMISTRY. See **phytochemistry.**

VEHICLE. A **component** of a mixture or system which has the primary function of acting as a carrier or diluent for other substances. For example, catalysts are often prepared by distributing an active substance over the surface of a vehicle or carrier.

VELARDI TEST. A test for aldehyde in volatile oils made by heating a few drops of the oil with some alcoholic potassium hydroxide and a trace of benzenesulfhydroxamic acid. The solution is then cooled, diluted with water and a little ether added. It is then neutralized with hydrochloric acid and a little ferric chloride solution added. A red to yellow color is produced if aldehyde is present.

VELOCITY. (1) The time rate of change of a variable or variables. (See **reaction velocity.**) (2) In mechanics, the term velocity is used with the specific meaning of the time rate of change of displacement or position.

VELOCITY COEFFICIENT. See **coefficient, velocity.**

VELOCITY CONSTANT. See **constant, velocity.**

VELOCITY HEAD. See **head, velocity.**

VELOCITY PRESSURE. See **pressure, velocity.**

VENABLE TEST REACTION. A test for ferric iron made by adding the sample to be tested to a cobalt nitrate solution which has been colored blue by adding concentrated hydrochloric acid. Traces of ferric salts will turn the solution green.

VENTRE TEST REACTION. A method for detecting sugar, the reagents for which are (a) a mixture of equal parts alcohol and nitrobenzene; (b) a saturated aqueous solution of ammonium molybdate. Ten ml. of the solution to be tested are boiled for 3 minutes with 5 drops of solution (a), 20 drops of solution (b), and 12 drops of concentrated sulfuric acid. If sugar is present, a blue color develops, the intensity of which is proportional to the sugar content.

VENTURI METER. A **flow meter** for liquids or gases utilizing the Venturi principle. A tapered constriction is placed in the pipe, and the pressure difference taken between a point in the pipe before the constriction begins, and a point in the throat, or the narrowest part of the constriction. The observed pressure difference is a function of the rate of flow and may be calibrated or calculated to obtain flow rates.

VENTUROLI TESTS. Tests for nitrite in water. (1) Add some sulfur, hydrocyanic acid, and hydrochloric acid to the water. A red color forms if nitrite is present. (2) The water is concentrated by evaporation, and 1 drop is brought into contact with 1 drop dilute hydrobromic or hydriodic acid on a polished silver foil. A black spot forms if nitrite is present.

VERATRAL. See **veratrylidene.**

VERATROYL. The radical

$$3,4\text{-}(CH_3O)_2C_6H_3CO\text{—}.$$

VERATRYL. The radical

$$3,4\text{-}(CH_3O)_2C_6H_3CH_2\text{—}.$$

VERATRYLIDENE. The radical

$$3,4\text{-}(CH_3O)_2C_6H_3CH\text{=}.$$

VERDA REAGENT FOR SAFFRON. A solution of 25 g. sodium phosphomolybdate in 90 ml. water and 20 ml. concentrated sulfuric acid, used in testing saffron. A characteristic green color is obtained with saffron.

VERDET CONSTANT. A proportionality factor in an equation of the **Faraday effect,** the rotation of the plane of polarization of light by transparent substances in a magnetic field. In the relationship:

$$\alpha = \omega l H$$

α is the angle of rotation, l is the depth of the medium transversed by the light, H is the intensity of the magnetic field, and ω is the Verdet constant.

VERDO-. (French *verd, vert,* green) Indicating green color, as verdoporphyrin.

VERHASSEL TEST REACTIONS. Reactions for α- and β-naphthols. (1) Chlorinated lime solution added to an aqueous solution of α-naphthol gives a violet color, added to β-naphthol a green-yellow color. (2) Potassium ferrocyanide added to an aqueous solution of α-naphthol gives a violet color, added to β-naphthol a light yellow color. (3) Potassium ferricyanide added to an aqueous solution of α-naphthol gives a brown color, added to β-naphthol a green-yellow color. (4) Ferric chloride added to an alcoholic solution of α-naphthol gives a violet precipitate, added to β-naphthol a greenish precipitate.

VERMANDE MICROCHEMICAL REAGENTS. The Vermande microchemical reagents are rubidium and cesium chlorides, which give characteristic crystals of double salts with silver, copper, lead, cobalt, zinc, magnesium, aluminum, and manganese.

VERMICIDE. A drug that kills worms and related organisms, commonly in the intestinal tract.

VERMIFUGE. A drug that expels worms and related organisms, commonly from the intestinal tract.

VERVEN SOLUTION. A solution of 5 g. cadmium iodide and 10 g. potassium iodide in 100 ml. water, used in precipitating alkaloids from sulfuric acid solution.

VESICANT. A drug or other substance that produces blistering.

VIBRATION. The original meaning of a to-and-fro motion has been extended to any projection of such motion, as to a rotation, and further, to any periodic physical process, such, for example, as a cyclic variation in electric or magnetic field intensity, or the vibrations of electrons within atoms, atoms in molecules, etc.

VIBRATION-ROTATION SPECTRUM. A spectrum in the infrared portion of the electromagnetic spectrum which is produced by vibrational and rotational transitions within a molecule. Such spectra are useful in calculating force constants, and other molecular constants.

VIBRATIONAL ENERGY OF MOLECULES. Diatomic molecules may possess vibrational energy, produced by relative oscillation of the two constituent atoms. Polyatomic molecules exhibit vibrational energy by oscillations in the directions of the valence bonds and by oscillations perpendicular to that direction; a molecule of n atoms usually has $3n - 6$ modes of vibration, increasing to $3n - 5$ modes in the case of a linear molecule.

VIBRATIONAL PARTITION FUNCTION. The contribution to the total partition function of molecules associated with their vibrational energy.

VIBRATIONS, THEORY OF SYNCHRONOUS. Abel's theory that there is a synchronism between the vibrations induced in air by detonators and the natural period of vibration of the molecules of certain explosives, to explain the fact that mercury fulminate is superior to nitroglycerin as a detonator for guncotton.

VIBRATORY VOLUME. See co-volume, molecular.

VIC-. Abbreviation of vicinal, as *vic*-triazine.

VICARIO TEST. A test for abrastol made by adding syrupy phosphoric acid and formaldehyde to the sample to be tested. A green fluorescence develops if abrastol is present.

VICINAL POSITION. A position "in the vicinity," used specifically for the 1, 2, 3, position of substituents on the benzene ring.

VICTOR MEYER ESTERIFICATION LAW. See law, esterification.

VICTOR MEYER SYNTHESIS. A method of formation of aliphatic **nitro** derivatives (and nitrites) by action of metallic **nitrites** on aliphatic halides.

$$RCl + MNO_2 \rightarrow RNO_2 \text{ (or } RONO) + MCl.$$

VIEHOVER TEST. A test for marijuana made by placing at least 0.1 g. of the material or $\frac{1}{3}$ or more of the suspected cigarette (without the wrapper) in a glass-stoppered flask and adding 3 ml. of iso-propyl alcohol containing 0.05% sodium hydroxide and 0.05 g. of activated char-coal. An almost immediate color change from practically colorless to pinkish is positive for marijuana. The color deepens on standing a short time. If evaporated, the residue obtained is pinkish to violet and dissolves in concentrated ammonia giving an orange-red color, and dissolves in acetone giving a violet to blue-violet color.

VIEL REAGENT. A solution of 40 g. potassium iodide and 5 g. antimony penta-chloride in 100 ml. water and 20 ml. con-centrated hydrochloric acid, used in testing for alkaloids. A precipitate is obtained with alkaloids in the presence of sodium sulfite.

VIGNON TEST. A test for free phos-phorus in phosphorus sulfide made by passing hydrogen over the phosphorus sulfide. If white free phosphorus is present, the hydrogen becomes phosphorescent and burns with a green flame.

VILELLA ETCH FOR ALUMINUM. A mixture of 10 ml. concentrated nitric acid, 20 ml. concentrated hydrofluoric acid, and 30 ml. glycerol.

VILELLA ETCH FOR LEAD. A mix-ture of 20 ml. concentrated nitric acid, 20 ml. glacial acetic acid, and 80 ml. glyc-erol.

VILLAVECCHIA REAGENT. A solution of 2 ml. C.P. furfural in 100 ml. alcohol used in testing oils for the presence of sesame oil. A pink to red color, in the presence of hydrochloric acid, is obtained if sesame oil is present.

VILLIERS-FAYOLLE REAGENT FOR FREE CHLORINE. A mixture of 20 ml. of a saturated aqueous solution of o-tolui-dine, 100 ml. of a saturated aqueous solu-tion of aniline, and 30 ml. acetic acid, used in detecting free chlorine. A blue color is obtained if free chlorine is present.

VILTER-SPIES-MATHEWS TEST RE-ACTION. A test for nicotinic acid and nicotinamide made by mixing the unknown substance with about twice its weight of 2,4-dinitrochlorobenzene and heating over a flame until melted, and then adding some alcoholic potassium hydroxide. A brilliant purple color is produced by nicotinic acid and nicotinamide.

VINCENT TEST REACTION FOR α- AND β-NAPHTHOL. A reaction of α-naphthol and β-naphthol with iodic acid. α-Naphthol gives a yellowish, flocculent precipitate which soon becomes violet. β-Naphthol gives a precipitate which gradually becomes red, and after a short time the solution turns reddish and the precipitate red-brown.

VINOUS FERMENTATION. See **alco-holic fermentation.**

VINTILESCU-POPESCU TEST. A test for rancid fats made by adding 4–5 drops of 5% blood or hemoglobin solution, 10 drops freshly prepared guaiac resin tincture, and 100 ml. of 3% hydrogen peroxide to 10 g. of the liquefied fat. A blue color, produced on shaking for a minute, indi-cates rancidity.

VINYL. The radical $H_2C:CH-$.

VINYLENE. The radical $-CH:CH-$.

VINYLIDENE. The radical $H_2C:C=$.

VIRGINIUM. The name that was assigned to element of atomic number 87 when its discovery was claimed by the magneto-optic method. (See **francium.**)

VIRIAL COEFFICIENTS. The coeffi-cients of ascending powers of one (or more) variables in an equation containing such a power series. Thus, the virial **equation of state** has the form:

$$PV = RT \left[1 + \frac{B}{V} + \frac{C}{V^2} \cdots \right]$$

in which B, C, . . . are virial coefficients.

VIRIAL EQUATION OF STATE. See **equation of state, general.**

VIRTUAL ENTROPY. See **entropy, virtual.**

VIRUS. A submicroscopic organism, or **toxin** from an organism, capable of transmitting disease.

VISCOSE PROCESS. A method for the manufacture of rayon. Purified sulfite pulp and cotton linters are used as raw material. Sheets of this material are dipped in sodium hydroxide, then shredded. The shredded material is treated with carbon disulfide, then dissolved in sodium hydroxide solution. This solution is forced through spinnerettes and comes in contact with a coagulating bath which hardens each jet into a filament. The fibers are then washed, desulfurized, and bleached.

VISCOSIMETER. An apparatus for determining the **viscosity** of a liquid. Various types of these instruments are based upon different effects of viscosity. Thus the Engler or Saybolt viscosimeters measure the rate of flow of a liquid through an orifice, the torsion viscosimeter measures the force required to twist an object immersed in the liquid; and another type measures the rate of rotation of a vane immersed in the liquid.

VISCOSITY. The internal friction or resistance to flow shown by liquids. Viscosity diminishes with rise of temperature and increases slightly with increased pressure.

VISCOSITY COEFFICIENT. The force per unit area necessary to sustain unit difference of velocity between parallel layers of fluid unit distance apart.

VISCOSITY COEFFICIENT, STOKES' LAW EVALUATION. An expression for the value of the viscosity coefficient of a liquid, which is obtained from the limiting, or maximum velocity of fall of a small sphere under free gravitational fall. It has the form:

$$\eta = \frac{2gr^2(\rho - \rho_l)}{9u}$$

where η is the coefficient of viscosity, g is the gravitational constant, r is the radius of the sphere, ρ is its density, ρ_l is the density of the liquid, and u is the maximum velocity of fall of the sphere in the liquid.

VISCOSITY, INTRINSIC. The value obtained by extrapolating, to zero concentration, the ratio of the specific viscosity of a solution to the concentration of the solute.

VISCOSITY, POISEUILLE('S) EQUATION FOR. An expression for the coefficient of **viscosity** of a liquid flowing through a narrow tube. It has the form:

$$\eta = \frac{\pi p r^4 t}{8vl}$$

where η is the coefficient of viscosity, p is the pressure on the liquid, r is the radius of the tube, t is the time in which a volume v flows through the tube, and l is the length of the tube.

VISCOSITY, SPECIFIC. A relationship between the viscosity of a solution having a given concentration of solute, and the viscosity of the pure solvent, of the form:

$$\text{Specific viscosity} = \frac{\eta - \eta_0}{\eta_0}$$

where η is the viscosity of the solution, and η_0 is the viscosity of the pure solvent.

VITAGEN. One of a group of substances essential not only for transformation of energy or regulation of the **metabolism** of structural units, but also in that they supply energy and/or structural building units. The last two properties, i.e., the function of supplying energy and structural units, are not possessed by **vitamins,** which are thus differentiated from vitagens. Examples of vitagens are the essential **amino acids, carbohydrates, fatty acids,** sulfur-containing compounds, and transferable methyl compounds.

VITALI TESTS FOR ALKALOIDS.
(1) The alkaloid is evaporated to dryness on the steam bath with fuming nitric acid and alcoholic potassium hydroxide added. Various characteristic colors and odors result. (2) With a number of aqueous alkaloidal solutions, the addition of a solution of 1 g. sodium monomethylarsenate in 100 ml. water produces characteristic crystalline precipitates.

VITALI TEST FOR DIFFERENTIATING ATROPINE AND STRYCHNINE.
The alkaloid and fuming nitric acid are evaporated to dryness on the steam bath, cooled, and a few ml. 4% alcoholic potassium hydroxide solution added. A violet color is produced which soon changes to red if the solution contains strychnine. Atropine gives a violet color which does not change.

VITALI TEST FOR ETHYL ALCOHOL.
The solution to be tested is treated with carbon disulfide, ammonium molybdate, potassium hydroxide, and excess dilute sulfuric acid. A red color is produced, due to the formation of molybdenum xanthogenate, if ethyl alcohol is present.

VITALI TEST FOR MORPHINE AND CODEINE. (1) This test is a modification of the Tattersall reaction. This test is made by heating morphine or codeine with concentrated sulfuric acid and sodium arsenate. If morphine or codeine is present, a blue-violet color forms which changes to bright green on standing. On addition of water the color changes, first to rose-red and then to blue. If ammonia is then added, the color becomes green. (2) If morphine is heated with sulfuric acid and sodium sulfide, the solution becomes flesh-red, changing to violet and finally to dark green. Upon adding a solution of potassium chlorate in sulfuric acid after the addition of sodium sulfide, the solution turns green and then changes to violet. If an excess of potassium chlorate is added, the final color is yellow.

VITALI TEST REACTIONS FOR ACETANILID. (1) A trace of acetanilid treated with a few drops of chlorinated lime solution and a crystal of phenol, produces a blue color. (2) Acetanilid added to a solution of potassium chlorate in sulfuric acid produces a red mixture, which changes to yellow when diluted with water and blood-red when heated. (3) On adding a trace of acetanilid to a solution of potassium nitrite in hydrochloric acid, a yellow color is produced which on heating changes to green and finally to blue.

VITALI TEST REACTIONS FOR ATROPINE AND DATURINE. (1) If potassium chlorate solution is poured over atropine, blue-green striae develop and a bright green solution finally results. (2) If a little atropine or daturine is evaporated with fuming nitric acid to dryness and some alcoholic potassium hydroxide solution added, a violet color is produced which changes to red in a short time.

VITALI TEST REACTION FOR BROMIDE. An adaptation of Cresti's test for copper, made by adding a little sulfuric acid and copper sulfate to a very dilute solution of hydrobromic acid or of a bromide and evaporating. As the mixture becomes concentrated, it becomes violet-brown and turbid; however, the turbidity disappears on dilution.

VITALI TEST REACTION FOR CHLORATE. An intense blue color is produced by chlorate with aniline sulfate and concentrated sulfuric acid.

VITALI TEST REACTION FOR FORMALDEHYDE. A modification of the Fischer test made by adding a not too concentrated solution of phenylhydrazine to the solution to be tested. A whitish, milky turbidity indicates the presence of formaldehyde.

VITALI TEST REACTION FOR IODOFORM. When iododorm is fused with a little potassium hydroxide and thymol, a violet mass forms which dissolves in alcohol. Upon addition of sulfuric acid to the alcoholic solution, the violet color is changed to scarlet.

VITALI TEST REACTION FOR PHENOL. Traces of phenol added to a solution of potassium chlorate in concentrated sulfuric acid will color the solution green for a few minutes; it then changes to blue.

VITALI TEST REACTION FOR QUININE. A modification of the Thalleioquin reaction made by rubbing 0.01 g. quinine salt with an equal amount of potassium chlorate, adding a few drops of water and 1 drop of concentrated sulfuric acid, and then an excess of ammonia. A green color is obtained.

VITAMIN. One of a group of organic compounds which are required for the normal growth and maintenance of the lives of animals, including man, which, as a rule, are unable to synthesize these compounds by **anabolic** processes independent of environment other than air. These compounds are effective in small amounts, do not furnish energy, and are not utilized as building units for the structure of the organism, but are essential for the transformation of energy and for the regulation of the metabolism of structural units.

It is well known that in the absence, or serious deficiency, of vitamins or **vitagens** clinical deficiency symptoms may occur or borderline deficiency may result. In any event one suffers abnormal development or uneasiness, or illness because of lack of vitamins in the diet.

Among the known vitamins there are: vitamin A and its precursors or provitamins A; the vitamin B complex, consisting of thiamine or vitamin B_1, riboflavin or vitamin B_2, niacin and niacin amide (nicotinic acid and nicotinic acid amide), pyridoxine or vitamin B_6, pantothenic acid, inositol, biotin or vitamin H, p-aminobenzoic acid; vitamin C or ascorbic acid; the vitamins D and their provitamins; the vitamins E; the vitamins K; vitamin P; folic acid.

The vitamins recognized as most important in human nutrition are vitamin A and its precursors; vitamin B_1 or thiamine, vitamin B_2 or riboflavin, niacin, and niacin amide; vitamin C or ascorbic acid; and the vitamins D.

VITAZYME. A compound term, indicating a substance possessing certain characteristics or properties of both a **vitamin**

and an **enzyme,** commonly an enzyme which has a vitamin as a prosthetic group.

VITREOUS. Like glass, one of the kinds of luster (or manner of reflection of light) used in describing minerals and other solids.

VITRIFY. To bring into a state which resembles glass; as in ceramics, to vitrify by firing at a temperature high enough to induce semi-fusion.

VITRIOL. A name applied to sulfuric acid, also known as oil of vitriol. Certain sulfates which crystallize in the rhombic system with seven molecules of water (or form isomorphous crystals with those that do, as $CuSO_4$) are termed vitriols. Thus ferrous sulfate (green vitriol), zinc sulfate (white vitriol), copper sulfate (blue vitriol), magnesium sulfate, manganous sulfate, cobalt sulfate and nickel sulfates, all crystallized with water, constitute the vitriols.

VITTE MICROCHEMICAL TEST FOR BARBITAL AND PHENOBARBITAL IN BRAIN TISSUE. A microchemical test for barbital and phenobarbital made by grinding pulped cerebral substance to homogeneity with 5 ml. of 20% trichloracetic acid and adding further quantities of acid until the total solution is about 100 ml. After a half hour, 50 ml. water are added and the mixture stirred for a half hour. It is then filtered, extracted with ether, the extract filtered, the ether evaporated and the residue dissolved in dilute ammonia and heated for 15 minutes on the water bath with a little animal charcoal. The residue is taken up with dilute ammonia, slightly acidified with hydrochloric acid, again extracted with ether, and evaporated. The residue is then treated under the microscope with 1 drop of 1:10 ammonia and 1 drop 1:15 sulfuric acid. Diethyl- and phenylethyl-barbituric acid crystals are readily distinguishable.

VOGEL MICRO-TEST FOR SPOILED FLOUR. Starch granules of spoiled flour are stained by an aniline violet solution, but granules of good flour are not stained at all or only slightly stained.

VOGEL TEST FOR ALCOHOL IN CHLOROFORM. Add a little dry potassium hydroxide to the chloroform, then pour off the chloroform. Some of the potassium hydroxide is dissolved if alcohol is present and, on adding a little pyrogallol, a yellow to brown color develops in the chloroform.

VOGEL TEST FOR NITRATE IN WATER. To 10–15 ml. of the water to be tested, add a little gold leaf and a few ml. hydrochloric acid and evaporate to a volume of a few ml. The solution becomes yellowish and, on adding stannous chloride solution, more or less red, if nitrate is present.

VOGEL TEST REACTION FOR NARCEINE. If chlorine water is poured on narceine on a watch glass and ammonia then added, a blood-red color develops. Tannin gives a similar reaction.

VOGET TEST REACTIONS. Color reactions given by a number of salts, glucosides, alkaloids, camphor, sugar, etc., on a dry trituration with iodine.

VOIGT REACTION. The addition of **amines** to **benzoins** to form aminodesoxybenzoins.

tested and distill. Reject the first 5 ml. of the distillate, and to the remainder of the distillate, add (a) and (b). A blue color shows the presence of methenamine.

VOLATILE. Having a low boiling or subliming temperature at ordinary pressure; in other words, having a high **vapor pressure,** as ether, camphor, naphthalene, iodine, chloroform, benzene, or methyl chloride.

VOLATILE OIL. Essential oil.

VOLATILITY PRODUCT. The product of the concentrations of two or more ions or molecules that react to produce a volatile substance. The volatility product is analogous to the **solubility product,** except that, when it is exceeded, the substance escapes from the system by volatilization rather than precipitation. As with the solubility product, if any of the reacting ions or molecules have a numerical coefficient greater than one, then the concentration term of that ion or molecule is raised to the corresponding power.

VOLATILIZE. To convert into vapor; to evaporate.

VOLCY-BOUCHER-GIRARD TEST. A

$$\underset{\text{R}'-\text{C}-\text{CH}-\text{R}''}{\overset{\text{O} \quad \text{OH}}{\overset{\parallel \quad |}{}}} + \text{R}'''\text{NH}_2 \xrightarrow{\text{P}_2\text{O}_5} \underset{\text{R}'-\text{CH}——\text{CR}''}{\overset{\text{NHR}''' \quad \text{O}}{\overset{| \qquad \parallel}{}}} + \text{H}_2\text{O}.$$

VOISENET TEST REACTION. A reaction for acrolein, formaldehyde, and methenamine, the reagents for which are (a) 0.5 ml. of a 3.6% potassium nitrite solution, added to a liter of concentrated hydrochloric acid, and (b) a solution containing 0.05 g. albumin per ml. Formaldehyde: Add 1 drop of the liquid to be tested to 2–3 ml. of (b) and then add 3 times the volume of (a). A rose color, changing to violet after 5 minutes, is given if formaldehyde is present. Acrolein: Add 2 ml. of (b) and several ml. (a) to a few ml. of 1:500–2000 solution of acrolein. A green to greenish-blue color is produced. Methenamine: Add a few drops of hydrochloric acid to 25 ml. of the liquid to be

test for resorcinol made by adding a few drops of 10% cupric sulfate solution to the neutral or slightly acid solution to be tested and then adding an equal quantity of 10% potassium cyanide solution, shaking vigorously, and diluting to a reddish-yellow color. In the presence of resorcinol, a distinct green fluorescence is produced.

VOLCY-BOUCHER TEST REACTION FOR α- AND β-NAPHTHOL. A reaction for α- and β-naphthol made by dissolving 0.5 g. of the naphthol in a very small quantity of alcohol and adding 2 ml. of 10% cupric sulfate solution and 4 ml. freshly prepared 10% potassium cyanide solution. A violet precipitate is given by α-naphthol and a yellow precipitate by β-naphthol.

VOLHARD-ERDMANN THIOPHENE SYNTHESIS. A reaction of sodium succinate (or related compounds) with phosphorus sulfides, yielding thiophene (or related compounds).

$$\underset{\underset{\text{COONa}}{|}}{\text{H}_2\text{C}}\text{------}\underset{\underset{\text{COONa}}{|}}{\text{CH}_2} \xrightarrow{\text{P}_2\text{S}_3} \underset{S}{\bigcup} .$$

VOLLAND TEST. A test for cod liver oil made by adding concentrated sulfuric acid. True cod liver oil is colored first violet, then brown-red, and finally black.

VOLMAR-LEBER REAGENT. Picrolonic acid, used in aqueous solution as a reagent for alkali and alkaline earth metals. In aqueous solution with salts of the alkaline earth metals and with salts of potassium, sodium, and ammonium, but not of lithium, yellow precipitates are formed.

VOLT. The unit of the intensity factor of electrical energy defined as the electric pressure which, when steadily applied to a conductor whose resistance is one ohm, will produce a current of one ampere. The volt has also been termed the unit of the intensity factor of chemical energy. It is somewhat lesser than the potential developed by the Weston standard cell (1.0183 volts) at 20° C. One volt equals 10^8 electromagnetic c.g.s. units.

VOLTAGE. Electromotive force or difference of potential measured in volts.

VOLTAGE, DECOMPOSITION. (Discharge potential) The minimum e.m.f. required to cause steady electrolysis in a solution. In normal solutions of sulfuric acid and zinc sulfate it is 1.67 volts and 2.35 volts, respectively.

VOLTAIC. Furnishing an electric current.

VOLTAIC CELL. See cell, voltaic.

VOLTAIC CURRENT. (Voltaic electricity. Voltaism) Terms formerly used to designate the electricity furnished by the voltaic cell, before the identity of the electricity from different sources was recognized.

VOLTAMETER. A coulometer. Cf. voltmeter.

VOLTMETER. An instrument used to measure difference of potential.

VOLUME. The space occupied by any body. It is definite for any specific temperature and pressure. The metric units of volume are the cubic centimeter and the liter. The volume of one gram molecule of a gas at standard temperature and pressure is about 22.4 liters.

VOLUME, ATOMIC. See atomic volume.

VOLUME, CRITICAL. The volume occupied by one gram of a liquid or gaseous substance at its critical temperature and critical pressure.

VOLUME, INCOMPRESSIBLE. See incompressible volume.

VOLUME, MOLAR. See volume, molecular.

VOLUME, MOLECULAR. (Gram-molecular volume) The volume occupied by a gram molecule of any substance. It is equal to the product of the specific volume by the molecular weight.

VOLUME, SPECIFIC. The volume occupied by unit mass (as one gram) of a substance.

VOLUME, STANDARD. The volume occupied by one gram molecular weight of a gas at 0° C. and a pressure of 760 millimeters of mercury.

VOLUME VALENCY. See valency, volume.

VOLUMETRIC ANALYSIS. See analysis, volumetric.

VOLUMETRIC FACTOR. See factor, volumetric.

VON BITTO TEST FOR MONOHYDRIC ALCOHOLS. A solution of 0.5 g. methyl violet in 1 liter water is the reagent used. One ml. of an alkali polysulfide solution and 1–2 ml. of the reagent are shaken with the liquid to be tested. If the liquid becomes cherry-red to violet-red and remains clear, a monohydric alcohol is present.

VON BITTO TEST REACTIONS FOR ALDEHYDES AND KETONES. (1) Add 1 ml. freshly prepared 0.3–0.5% aqueous sodium nitroprusside solution to the aldehyde or ketone solution and make alkaline with sodium hydroxide solution. A red-yellow to violet-red color forms which is characteristic of the aldehyde or ketone in question.

(2) In the liquid aldehyde or ketone or its alcoholic solution, dissolve a few crystals of *m*-dinitrobenzene. On addition of a few drops sodium hydroxide solution, a blue color develops which is changed to violet-red by acetic acid.

VON BITTO TEST REACTION FOR CREATININE. Creatinine gives a violet-red color with *m*-dinitrobenzene and sodium hydroxide solution, in the presence of acetone. On the addition of metaphosphoric acid the color changes to cherry-red.

VON BRAUN BENZAMIDE REACTION. A method of converting a primary amine to a halogen derivative by first converting it to a benzoyl derivative, then treating with phosphorus pentahalide.

$$RNH_2 + C_6H_5COCl \rightarrow RNH—CO—C_6H_5 + HCl.$$

$$RNH—CO—C_6H_5 + PCl_5 \rightarrow RCl + POCl_3 + C_6H_5CN + HCl.$$

VON BRAUN DEGRADATION REACTIONS. These two reactions are used for the degradation of amines and for the opening of nitrogen-containing ring compounds. In the first reaction, *N*-substituted benzamides are converted into organic halides and benzonitriles by a phosphorous halide.

$$C_6H_5CONR_2 + PX_5 \rightarrow 2RX + C_6H_5CN + POX_3.$$

In the second reaction, tertiary amines are converted into organic halides and substituted cyanamides by cyanogen halide.

$$R_3N + XCN \rightarrow RX + R_2NCN.$$

VON BRAUN REAGENT FOR CARBONYL COMPOUNDS. The compound diphenylmethanedimethylhydrazine, made by reduction with zinc dust, dilute acetic acid, and alcohol, of dinitrosodimethyldiaminodiphenylmethane. It forms condensation products with aldehydes and ketones, useful in their identification.

VON HEVESY-LÖGSTRUP TEST REACTION. To detect zirconium or hafnium, prepare their acetylacetonates by reaction of acetylacetone and sodium carbonate with zirconium oxynitrate or hafnium oxychloride. A carbon disulfide solution of the acetylacetonates becomes red on standing.

VON KOBELL SCALE. A series of integral numbers used to designate materials, chiefly minerals, according to their fusibility—the higher numbers corresponding to higher fusing points. The substances whose fusing points (melting points) constitute the integral values in this scale are: (1) stibnite; (2) natrolite; (3) garnet, lime-alumina variety; (4) hornblende; (5) orthoclase; (6) bronzite; (7) (infusible).

VON NEUREITHER MICRO-TEST FOR CYANIDE. Mix the material tested with concentrated oxalic acid solution in a beaker. Cover with a watch glass having a hanging drop of 1% silver nitrate solution colored by methylene blue. A turbidity (consisting of microscopic blue needles) indicates the presence of cyanide.

VON RICHTER REACTION. The action upon aromatic nitro compounds of potassium cyanide in alcoholic solution, whereby the nitro group is eliminated, and a carboxy group is joined to the ring in a position ortho to that occupied by the nitro group.

VON WEIMARN EQUATION. An expression for the rate of formation of particles of **colloidal** size from smaller particles such as ions and molecules. It has the form:

$$V_i = k\frac{P_1}{P_2},$$

in which V_i is the initial rate of "condensation" or coalescence, k is a constant, P_1 is the condensation pressure, and P_2 is the condensation resistance.

VORCE CELL. A diaphragm electrolytic **cell,** of circular type, used for the production of chlorine and sodium hydroxide solution by electrolysis of sodium chloride solution.

VORLÄNDER REAGENT FOR ALDE-HYDES. Dimethylhydroresorcinol gives difficultly-soluble condensation products with aldehydes, the melting points being characteristic for the aldehydes in question.

VORLÄNDER TEST FOR DIFFER-ENTIATING ALLYL- AND PRO-PENYLPHENOL ETHERS. Propenyl-phenol ether produces a red to brown color within a few minutes with hydrobromic acid dissolved in glacial acetic acid, but allylphenol ether does not give the reaction until several hours have passed.

VORLÄNDER TEST FOR HYDRO-CHLORIC ACID IN CHLOROFORM. Add about 0.01 mg. powdered p-dimethyl-aminoazobenzene to 10 ml. of the chloroform. A violet-red color shows the presence of hydrochloric acid.

VORTMAN TEST FOR CYANIDE. Add a few drops of potassium nitrite solution and 2–4 drops of ferric chloride solution to the liquid to be tested, then add dilute sulfuric acid until the yellow-brown color changes to bright yellow. Heat the solution to boiling, cool, precipitate the excess of iron with ammonia, filter, and add 1–2 drops of a very dilute colorless ammonium sulfide solution to the filtrate. The solution will become violet, then blue, then green, and finally yellow if cyanide is present. If the quantity of cyanide is very small, only a bluish color forms.

VORTMANN-BINDER SOLUTION. A solution used in the determination of iron, manganese, and other metals. It is prepared by dissolving 50 g. uranium sulfate in 200 ml. water, acidifying with sulfuric acid, heating with granulated zinc, and diluting to 0.1 N.

VORTMANN TEST REACTION FOR PHENOL. A dark red precipitate forms on heating phenol with iodine and sodium hydroxide to 50–60° C.

VOTOCEK TEST FOR KETOSES. Mix 2 ml. of glacial acetic acid, a small quantity of carbazole and 1 drop of fuming hydrochloric acid in an evaporating dish, add a drop of the sugar to be tested and place on the water bath for 10 minutes. A cherry-red color shows the presence of ketoses.

VOTOCEK TEST FOR SULFITE IN THE PRESENCE OF THIOSULFATE. A solution of 0.075 g. fuchsin in 300 ml. water is mixed with a solution of 0.025 g. malachite green in 100 ml. water. A few drops of this solution are added to 2–3 ml. of the liquid to be tested. Sulfites effect immediate decolorization but thiosulfates or thionates do not.

VOTOCEK TEST FOR WOOD PULP IN PAPER. Slightly acidify a decoction of tea leaves with hydrochloric acid. On contact with paper containing wood cellulose, a violet-blue color is given. Paper made from rags or similar materials does not give this reaction. This reaction is also given by the tannin obtained from the barks of trees, especially oak and birch.

VOTOCEK TEST REACTION FOR METHYLFURFURAL. A red substance soluble in alcohol is obtained when methylfurfural is added to a solution of phloroglucinol in hydrochloric acid (sp. gr. 1.126). The reaction is not given by furfural.

VOURNASOS REAGENT. A solution of 0.5 g. potassium iodide, 1 g. iodine, and 5 g. methylamine in 50 ml. water. It is used in testing for lactic acid in gastric secretion and acetone in urine. Characteristic odors of isonitriles or iodoform are given if lactic acid is present.

VOURNASOS TEST FOR ARSENIC AND PHOSPHORUS. A test for arsenic and phosphorus which is based on the formation of arsine or phosphine when arsenic or phosphorus is heated with sodium formate in the dry state.

VREVEN TEST FOR COD LIVER OIL. Five ml. of oil are mixed with 5 ml. of ether and then with 5 ml. of 92–98% alcohol. The mixture is allowed to settle, the upper layer poured off into a small dish and fuming nitric acid is cautiously added to it. A transitory sky-blue color forms if cod liver oil is present.

VREVEN TEST FOR DIFFERENTIATING CREOSOTE AND GUAIACOL. One drop of the liquid to be tested is shaken with 3 drops of ether, 2 drops of concentrated nitric acid, and 2 drops hydrochloric acid. The ether is allowed to evaporate spontaneously. Creosote forms oily drops, whereas guaiacol forms acicular crystals.

VREVEN TEST REACTION FOR FATS. Fats and oils treated with cane sugar and sulfuric acid, produce a yellow to brown color which changes to rose in 10 minutes, and then to a persistent lilac color. Heat must be used with solid fats.

VULCANIZATION. A process for improvement of the properties of rubber, especially its strength, resiliency and freedom from stickiness and odor, by combining it with sulfur. The method used by the discoverer of the process, Goodyear, consists of heating with sulfur and auxiliary substances. Other processes use sulfur compounds, such as S_2Cl_2, in some cases at ordinary temperatures. As vulcanizing processes have developed, the use of various adjunct substances, to expedite the processes and modify the finished rubber, has been greatly extended. (See **accelerators.**)

VULKOLLAN PROCESS. A method of producing synthetic **elastomers** by reaction of ethylene glycol and adipic acid to yield a polyester, which on subsequent treatments with (1) a diisocyanate, and (2) water or ethylene glycol, yields the desired elastomer.

VULPIUS TEST FOR TARTARIC ACID IN CITRIC ACID. Add 1 ml. of the 1:2 aqueous citric acid solution to 2 ml. of a solution of 1 g. potassium acetate in 20 g. of 90% alcohol. If the citric acid is pure, at first a precipitate forms and the solution becomes clear. A crystalline precipitate of potassium bitartrate forms immediately, if tartaric acid is present to the extent of 2%; the precipitate forms after vigorous shaking with 1% tartaric acid.

VULPIUS TEST FOR ACETANILID. Add 0.05 g. acetanilid to 1 ml. potassium hydroxide solution and boil. Then pass over the mixture a glass rod moistened with a drop of chlorinated lime solution. The latter becomes yellow and, on further heating, violet.

VULPIUS TEST REACTION FOR LANOLIN. A solution of 0.02–0.03 g. of lanolin in chloroform is floated on concentrated sulfuric acid. A fiery brown-red color develops at the contact surfaces which attains its maximum intensity in 24 hours.

VULPIUS TEST REACTION FOR MORPHINE. At least 0.25 mg. of morphine is heated with 6 drops of concentrated sulfuric acid and 0.03–0.05 g. of sodium phosphate until white vapors evolve. The mixture becomes violet and often, when cooled rapidly, violet-blue. On addition of water, the color becomes bright red, and with more water, dirty green.

VULPIUS TEST REACTION FOR SULFONAL. The odor of a mercaptan is produced on heating sulfonal with potassium cyanide.

W Symbol for the element **tungsten** (W). Symbol for **work** (W or W_k) (external work, W_e). Abbreviation for **watt** (w). Symbol for waste, bottoms, or residue (W). Symbol for weight, as quantity of matter (w). Symbol for free moisture content (W). Symbol for mass flow rate (w). Symbol for radiant **flux density** (W). Symbol for mixing ratio (w). Symbol for **work function,** net (w). Symbol for work function, gross (w_g).

WACHSMITH TEST. A test for nitrogen bases made by adding 0.5 ml. of 15% cupric sulfate solution and 1–2 drops of 1% potassium cyanide solution to 10 ml. of a very dilute solution of the substance to be tested. A color is produced immediately if nitrogen bases are present. If the solution is too concentrated, a turbidity may form and an excess of potassium cyanide is undesirable. The colors given are: animopyrine, violet; epinephrine, red; apomorphine, a red color which passes through rose to brown to gray and finally to green; morphine and codeine, yellow-green.

WACKENRODER REACTION. The reaction between sulfur dioxide and hydrogen sulfide, in the presence of water, which results in the formation of various polythionic acids ($H_2S_xO_x$), as, e.g.,

$$3SO_2 + H_2S \rightarrow H_2S_4O_6.$$

WACKER REAGENT FOR ALCOHOLS, ALDEHYDES, OR CARBOHYDRATES. A solution of p-phenylhydrazinesulfonic acid. This reagent must be well shaken. It gives a red color with aldehydes, alcohols, or carbohydrates in the presence of air and an excess of sodium hydroxide solution. Other hydrazine compounds may be used in this test.

WADA-NAKAZONO REAGENT. A reagent for separating iridium and rhodium which is made by adding a 1.5–2 N solution of titanium sesquisulfate, to 2 N sulfuric acid. Rhodium salts are reduced to the metal by it, but iridium salts remain in solution.

WADA TEST. A test for rhenium which is based on the reactions with stannous chloride, potassium thiocyanate, and hydrogen sulfide.

WAEGNER REAGENT. A reagent for absorption of carbon monoxide (a modification of the Winkler reagent) which is made by dissolving 5 g. cuprous chloride in 25 ml. of water and 10 g. concentrated hydrochloric acid, heating to boiling, and, after removing the flame but while swirling, adding sodium hypophosphite in small portions until the mixture has become colorless. It is cooled rapidly, concentrated ammonia in excess is added, and then ammonia (sp. gr. 0.96) is added to the desired volume.

WAGENAAR TEST FOR CITRIC ACID. Add a drop of 0.1 N iodine in potassium iodide to a drop of the citrate or citric acid solution and follow with some 30% acetic acid, heat, and add a drop of 3% potassium permanganate solution. Needle-like crystals form which can be increased in size by adding a drop of ether or ethyl acetate.

WAGENAAR TEST FOR DISTINGUISHING CITRIC, OXALIC AND TARTARIC ACIDS. Add 0.3 g. aminopyrine and 0.03 g. resorcinol to a mixture of a few drops of ferric chloride solution and 20 drops of water. Then add 0.05 g. of the acid to be tested and 3 ml. of concentrated sulfuric acid and warm over a small flame. Citric acid gives a yellowish-brown color; oxalic acid a dark green, changing to pale green on standing; and tartaric acid gives a deep red color, changing to raspberry-red on standing.

WAGENAAR TEST FOR NICKEL IN HARDENED FATS. A wick made from a roll of filter paper (20 × 2.5 cm) is placed in 30 g. of the melted fat contained in a dish and the wick ignited. After the fat has been burned, the wick is incinerated and the ash moistened with hydrochloric acid or nitric acid, made alkaline with ammonia and tested with dimethylgly-oxime. A red color is given if nickel is present.

WAGENAAR TEST REACTION FOR CAFFEINE. Add a little cesium chloride, a drop of potassium iodide solution, and a drop of sulfuric acid to a solution to be tested. Deep brown crystals are formed if caffeine is present.

WAGGONER SOLUTION. A solution of 50 ml. 85–90% C.P. formic acid in 35 ml. distilled water. It is mixed with an aqueous solution of sodium citrate, and the mixture is used to decalcify bones.

WAGNER-JAUREGG REACTION. A method of synthesis of aromatic ring systems by the addition of maleic anhydride to substituted arylethylenes. The initial products of the addition are *bis*-adducts which are decarboxylated to yield the aromatic ring systems.

WAGNER REAGENT FOR ALKALOIDS. A solution of 1.27 g. iodine and 2 g. potassium iodide in 100 ml. water, used as a precipitant for alkaloids.

WAGNER REAGENT FOR DIFFERENTIATING TEXTILE FIBERS. A solution used to differentiate between various textile fibers, giving characteristic colors with various synthetic fibers, as well as with silk and cotton. It is prepared by dissolving 5 g. picrocarmine, 1 g. sodium carbonate, and 4 g. disodium ammonium phosphate in 100 ml. water.

WAGNER REARRANGEMENT. A rearrangement of the carbon skeleton in an organic substance following the formation of a **carbonium ion** from a monoalcohol or halide. Where a change in ring size occurs, the process is called the Wagner-Meerwein rearrangement; the Nametkin rearrangement is the case involving an alicyclic system where the ring size remains unchanged.

WAGNER SOLUTION FOR PHOSPHATE ANALYSIS. A solution prepared by dissolving 25 g. citric acid and 1 g. salicylic acid in enough water to give 1 liter of solution. It is used in the analysis of phosphate rock.

WAIT TEST REACTION. A test for vitamins A, C, and D made by adding a 1% solution of phosphomolybdic acid in acetic acid to the sample to be tested. Vitamins A and C give a blue color, and vitamin D gives a green color. Substances containing both vitamins A and D yield first a green color and then a blue color.

WALDEN INVERSION. A change in configuration which occurs in many **metathetical** reactions involving atoms or radicals attached to asymmetric atoms. The concept of rearward attack mechanism gives experimental evidence that in most metathetical reactions the entering group attaches itself to the back face of the atom from that occupied by the displaced group, although the process is not readily detectable except in optically active substances.

$$
\begin{array}{ccc}
\underset{\text{l-malic acid}}{\begin{array}{c} CH_2-COOH \\ | \\ H-C-OH \\ | \\ COOH \end{array}}
& \xrightarrow{PCl_5} &
\underset{\text{d-chlorosuccinic acid}}{\begin{array}{c} CH_2-COOH \\ | \\ Cl-C-H \\ | \\ COOH \end{array}}
\end{array}
$$

$\uparrow$ Ag$_2$O + H$_2$O $\downarrow$ Ag$_2$O + H$_2$O

$$
\begin{array}{ccc}
\underset{\text{l-chlorosuccinic acid}}{\begin{array}{c} CH_2-COOH \\ | \\ H-C-Cl \\ | \\ COOH \end{array}}
& \xleftarrow{PCl_5} &
\underset{\text{d-malic acid}}{\begin{array}{c} CH_2-COOH \\ | \\ HO-C-H \\ | \\ COOH \end{array}}
\end{array}
$$

WALDEN RULE. The product of ion conductance and **viscosity** of a solvent is constant. The ion conductance must be taken as the **equivalent conductance** at infinite dilution. This rule assumes that an ion has the same radius in various solvents, and does not include the effect of combination between ion and molecules of solvent; it has, therefore, only limited application.

WALLACH DEGRADATION REACTION. A rearrangement of dihalocyclohexanones (with halogen atoms on the carbon atoms adjacent to the carbonyl group) to give 1-hydroxy cyclopentano-carboxylic acids, which yield cyclopentanone on oxidation. (Usually the dibromo-compounds are used.)

color noted, and then 1 ml. of it is added to excess of 10% ammonia. Characteristic colors are given.

$$
\begin{array}{c}
CH_2\!-\!CH_2\!-\!CHX \\
|\qquad\qquad| \\
CH_2\!-\!CHX\!-\!CO
\end{array}
\xrightarrow{2KOH}
\begin{array}{c}
\qquad\qquad OH \\
\qquad\qquad| \\
CH_2\!-\!CH_2\!-\!C\!-\!COOH \\
|\qquad\qquad\diagup \\
CH_2\!-\!\!-\!CH_2
\end{array}
+ 2KX
$$

$$
\downarrow O
$$

$$
\begin{array}{c}
CH_2\!-\!CH_2\!-\!CO \\
|\qquad\qquad\diagup \\
CH_2\!-\!\!-\!CH_2
\end{array}
+ CO_2 + H_2O.
$$

WALLACH REARRANGEMENT. The rearrangement of azoxybenzenes brought about by concentrated sulfuric acid.

$$
\begin{array}{c}
\qquad\quad O \\
\qquad\quad || \\
C_6H_5\!-\!N\!=\!N\!-\!C_6H_5
\end{array}
\xrightarrow{H_2SO_4}
C_6H_5\!-\!N\!=\!N\!-\!C_6H_4\!-\!OH(p).
$$

WANG-KAO-SAK REAGENT. *p*-Bromobenzohydrazide, which forms condensation products of definite melting point with aldehydes and ketones.

WANKLYN REACTION. The synthesis of salts of monobasic acids from sodium **alkyls** and carbon dioxide,

$$RNa + CO_2 \rightarrow RCOONa.$$

See also **Schorigin reaction.**

WARE TEST FOR NITRATE. Mix 50 mg. *o*-cresol and 0.2 g. sodium nitrite with 10–100 mg. of the substance to be tested. Then add rapidly 10 ml. concentrated hydrochloric acid, mix for 2 minutes, and allow to stand for about 5 minutes. If nitrate is present, a dichroic solution results which is deep green by reflected light and purple-red by transmitted light.

WARE TEST FOR PHENOL, CRESOL, NAPHTHOL, AND THYMOL. Fifty mg. of the substance to be tested are triturated with 10 ml. concentrated hydrochloric acid and 0.5 g. of a mixture of 1 part sodium nitrite, 1 part sodium nitrate and 2 parts anhydrous sodium sulfate. The mixture is let stand for 5 minutes and the

WARREN TEST REACTION FOR OILS. A test for drying and nondrying oils made by mixing equal volumes of sulfur chloride and carbon disulfide with the sample to be tested. Drying oils produce an insoluble mass, but nondrying oils remain dissolved.

WASHBURN CELL. A conductivity cell (see **cell, conductivity**).

WASICKY REAGENT. A solution of 2 g. *p*-dimethylaminobenzaldehyde in 6 g. concentrated sulfuric acid to which 0.4 g. of water has been added, which gives characteristic colors with alkaloids; some require heating.

WATER BATH. A vessel filled with water used to transfer heat uniformly and at temperatures below the boling point of water.

WATER, CONDUCTIVITY. Water of exceptional purity, prepared by repeated distillation, and used in electrical conductivity measurements of aqueous solutions.

WATER, CONSTANTS OF. Dielectric constant, 81.1; temperature of maximum density 4° C.; ionization constant (25°), 1.2×10^{-14}; concentration of hydrogen ions (25°), 1×10^{-7}; conductivity (18°),

0.04 $\times$ 10^{-6}; conductivity of absolutely pure water at 25° (calc.) 0.054 $\times$ 10^{-6}.

WATER, DISTILLED. Water which has been distilled to reach a suitable degree of purity for use in most laboratory operations. It is relatively free from solids, but contains dissolved gases, such as air and carbon dioxide.

WATER GAS. The product of the action of steam on incandescent carbon (coal) used as a fuel and illuminant. Its composition varies with the temperature at which the reaction is run. At 1000° C. it is 49.51% CO, 49.93% H, 0.35% H_2O, 0.21% CO_2. In practice the product contains much more carbon dioxide, nitrogen, water, etc.

WATER, HARD. A water obtained from the surface of the ground or below it, which contains various salts which cause trouble in boilers by deposition of scale, and in washing, by precipitation of soap, etc. (See **hardness**.)

WATER, HEAVY. See **heavy water.**

WATER OF CRYSTALLIZATION. A form in which water molecules are present in chemical compounds, whereby the H_2O molecule retains it structural identity. Commonly, such H_2O molecules are tetrahedrally or octahedrally coordinated around the cations in the crystal **lattice.**

WATER OF DELIQUESCENCE. See **deliquescence, water of.**

WATERPROOFING. Rendering a substance impervious to water, or resistant to its action.

WATER SOFTENING. Removal of salts from water, especially those that cause hardness, by heating, chemical precipitation, **base exchange,** or other processes.

WATER, STERILIZED. Water that is free from living microorganisms.

WATT. The unit of power in the **c.g.s. system.** It is the energy that delivers one **joule** in one second, or the power of an electric current of one **ampere** with an intensity of one **volt.**

1 watt = 1 volt-ampere
1 watt-hour = 3600 joules
746 watts = 1 horsepower

WAVE FUNCTION. The solution of a differential or partial differential equation for wave propagation through a medium. See **Schrödinger wave-equation.**

WAVE LENGTH. The distance, measured along the line of propagation, between two points which are in **phase** on adjacent **waves.**

WAVE LENGTH, DOMINANT. The **monochromatic** equivalent of a polychromatic beam of radiant energy, commonly light; in other words, that wavelength which, upon lightening or darkening in shade (addition of white or partial absorption), yields the same **color** as that of the light beam under investigation.

WAVE NUMBER. The number of waves per unit length in a vacuum, the reciprocal of λ_{vac}. (The usual unit of wave number is the reciprocal centimeter, cm^{-1}.)

WAVES, MATTER. See **deBroglie matter waves.**

WAXES. Liquids and solid mixtures of **fatty acid esters** of higher monohydric aliphatic and phytosterol alcohols, as cetyl palmitate (spermaceti), myricyl palmitate beeswax), ceryl certotate (in chinese wax). All plants appear to contain small amounts of waxes. Waxes are distinguished from fats in that they are esters of monohydric alcohols.

WAYNE SOLUTION. A solution of 10 g. cupric sulfate in 80 ml. water, to which is added 325 ml. of a 16.3% aqueous solution of potassium hydroxide and the solution is then diluted to one liter. It is used in testing for glucose.

WEAK SALT. See **salt, weak.**

WEATHEROMETER. An instrument used to determine rapidly the ability of a material to withstand prolonged exposure to weather conditions of heat, moisture, and others.

WEAVER TEST. A test for water which is based on the evolution of acetylene from calcium carbide by traces of water. Calcium carbide in the presence of an anhydrous solvent for acetylene is added to the sample to be tested. Any acetylene formed is detected by adding or distilling the resultant solution into an ammoniacal solution of cuprous chloride solution with which acetylene forms a red color or precipitate.

WEBER-KOCH TEST. A test for propyl, butyl, isobutyl, and isoamyl alcohols, made by gently heating 1 ml. of the alcohol with 2–8 drops of **Beckmann chromic acid mixture** (q.v.). The corresponding aldehyde is formed. After any precipitate has settled, the clear centrifuged solution is treated with sodium hydroxide and a little *o*-nitrobenzaldehyde. Characteristics colors are given by the various alcohols.

WEBER-TOLLENS TEST REACTION. A test for formaldehyde or hexamethylenetetramine that gives, on treatment with hydrochloric acid and phloroglucinol, a whitish flocculent precipitate, which becomes yellowish-red on standing.

WEEHUIZEN TEST FOR CYANIDE. A test for cyanide made by adding a few drops of alkaline phenolphthalein solution to the solution to be tested and then adding a little 1:200 cupric sulfate solution. If cyanide is present, a red color is obtained.

WEERMAN DEGRADATION. A method of formation of aldose sugars with one less carbon atom from aldonic acids by treating their amides with sodium hypohalite; the reaction is applicable to many α-hydroxy amides.

WEGSCHEIDER TEST FOR SIDE REACTIONS. A method of calculation for determining the existence of simultaneous, or side reactions. It is based upon the fact, demonstrable by reaction rate calculations, that the ratio of the concentrations of the products of side reactions is a constant for any system, independent of time.

WEIGHING. See **weight.**

WEIGHT. The force with which a body is attracted toward the earth; the product of the mass of a body and the acceleration attributable to gravity. The force of 980 dynes is the weight of one gram. The value of the acceleration due to gravity increases slightly from equator to pole so that the weight of a body varies according to its geographical location. The mass of a body, however, is constant.

In view of the difficulty, under most circumstances, of determining mass directly, masses are commonly determined in chemical operations by comparison of the weight of the unknown mass with the weight of known masses, a process called weighing, which involves, in very accurate work, certain corrections or methods to avoid the necessity for those corrections.

(1) One correction which arises when masses are determined by comparison with standard masses is the differential effect of the buoyancy of air. That is, the difference in density between the substance whose mass is being determined and the material of which the standard masses are composed results in a greater buoyancy of air on the less dense material, with a consequent error. Weighings corrected for this error are said to be *reduced to vacua.*

(2) If the masses are compared (the substance is weighed) on a beam balance, which is the widely-used laboratory method, errors may result from small differences in the length of the two "arms," i.e., the distances from the fulcrum of the beam to the

$$\begin{array}{c} CONH_2 \\ | \\ CHOH \\ | \\ R \end{array} + NaOCl + NaOH \rightarrow \begin{bmatrix} NCO \\ | \\ CHOH \\ | \\ R \end{bmatrix} \rightarrow RCHO + NaCNO + NaCl + 2H_2O.$$

point at which the lines of force of the compared masses intersect the beam. The methods used to cancel this error include "double weighing" which consists simply of weighing the object twice, exchanging the positions of object and standard masses, from one pan of the balance to the other between weighings, and taking the mean of the two values by multiplying them and extracting the square root of the product.

(3) Since the diameter of the earth varies somewhat with geographical location, its gravitational attraction also varies. This variation may cause error (which is usually very small) in masses compared by gravitational methods.

WEIGHT, ATOMIC. See **atomic weight.**

WEIGHT, COMBINING. (Equivalent, reacting, or symbol weights) The number of parts by weight of any element which can enter into combination with one part, by weight, of hydrogen or eight parts, by weight, of oxygen, or the atomic weight divided by the valence. Where an element possesses more than one valence the equivalent weight will depend upon the sense in which the element is reacting. In ferrous salts the equivalent weight of iron is 27.925 (55.85 ÷ 2) and in ferric salts it is 18.613 (55.85 ÷ 3). The equivalent weight of a compound is its molecular weight divided by the valence of its principal element.

WEIGHT, EQUIVALENT. See **weight, combining.**

WEIGHT, ISOTOPIC. See **isotopic weight.**

WEIGHT, MOLECULAR. The weight of a molecule of any substance referred to a standard. By international agreement the base for this standard is the **atomic weight** of natural oxygen taken as 16. (However, in the so-called "physical" atomic weight the basis is the oxygen isotope of mass number 16, and not natural oxygen, which consists of isotopes of mass numbers 16, 17, and 18.) The molecular weight may be calculated by taking the sum of the atomic weights of the constituent elements, each

atomic weight being multiplied by the number of atoms of that particular element present in the compound, thus

Mol. Wt. of NaCl,

$$22.997 + 35.457 = 58.454$$

Mol. Wt. of P_2O_5,

$$(30.975 \times 2) + (16 \times 5) = 141.950.$$

WEIGHT, REACTING. See **weight, combining.**

WEIGHT, SYSTEM OF. See **English system** and **metric system.**

WEIL TEST REACTION. A reaction for cobalt and nickel obtained by treating the solution to be tested with potassium chromate. Cobalt solutions give a brownish-red precipitate of basic cobaltous chromate, whereas nickel solutions react only slowly in the cold but, on boiling, a chocolate-brown precipitate of the basic chromate forms.

WEINGÄRTNER SOLUTION. A solution of 10 g. tannin and 10 g. sodium acetate in 100 m. water, used as a precipitant for basic coal-tar dyes.

WEINLAND-DÖTTINGER TEST REACTION. A reaction for cobalt in which ammonia is added to an aqueous solution containing catechol and a suitable cobalt salt in the necessary proportions. A red precipitate is obtained.

WEINLAND-HEINZLER REAGENT. Dissolve 27 g. arsenic acid in 70 ml. boiling water, add 44 g. pyrocatechol and filter when hot. Within a day, pyrocatechol-arsenic acid crystallizes as a voluminous precipitate. This substance in concentrated solution precipitates many bases and alkaloids, as well as albumin and peptone.

WEITBRECHT REAGENT. A solution of 5 g. *o*-nitrophenylpropiolic acid in 8 ml. of a 10% sodium hydroxide solution, which is then diluted to 1 liter. It is used in detecting sugar in urine. A deep blue color on heating is given if sugar is present.

WELDON PROCESS. A method for manufacturing chlorine from hydrochloric acid by the action of manganese dioxide, which is reduced in the process to manganous chloride. The latter is in turn reconverted to manganese dioxide, for re-use in the process, by treatment with lime, and oxidation.

WELMANS SOLUTION. A 5% aqueous solution of sodium phosphomolybdate, acidified with nitric acid, and used in testing for vegetable oils. The oil to be tested is dissolved in chloroform, and treated with the reagent. The formation of a green color changed to blue by addition of ammonium hydroxide, shows the presence of vegetable oils.

WELTER RULE. A method for approximating the heat of combustion of carbon compounds which contain hydrogen and oxygen. The rule is to subtract the oxygen with as much hydrogen as is necessary to form water with it, then the heats of combustion of the residual carbon and hydrogen give an approximate value of the heat of combustion of the whole compound. This rule gives results about 10% low.

WENGER-DUCKERT-BLANCPAIN REAGENT. Methyl-9-hydroxy-2,3,7-fluorone-6 in 0.4–0.5% alcoholic solution, which gives a copious red precipitate with antimony ions.

WERNER TEST REACTION. A test reaction for zinc, in which the sulfide precipitate obtained on analysis is dissolved in hydrochloric acid, precipitated with potassium ferrocyanide, and then treated with bromine water. An oxidation product, deep yellow in color, forms immediately if zinc is present.

WERNER THEORY. Also known as the coordination theory. It explained the formation of coordination compounds by postulating that, even when the combining power of certain atoms is exhausted (as judged by the valence number), such atoms still possess, in some instances, the ability of constructing complex molecules by the formation of definite atomic linkages. This action was attributed to the fact that atoms have in addition to their principal valences, the ability to form other bonds which are termed auxiliary valences.

WESTBERG TEST REACTIONS. Reactions for carbon disulfide: (1) The carbon disulfide is mixed with 5 volumes 10% ammonia and evaporated to about $\frac{1}{2}$ ml. Then 2–3 drops of ferric chloride solution are added to the residue. A red color is produced. (2) The carbon disulfide is permitted to evaporate in a desiccator with alcoholic potassium hydroxide at room temperature. Potassium xanthogenate is formed. This is colored red by the addition of molybdosulfuric acid. (3) The carbon disulfide is mixed with an alcoholic solution of lead acetate. Due to the formation of lead sulfide, the mixture becomes black after standing for some time.

WESTON CELL. See **cadmium cell.**

WESTPHAL BALANCE. A balance which reads directly the **specific gravity** of liquids. It is designed to operate by suspension from the end of the balance arm of a standard plunger which is immersed in a liquid. Then weights are adjusted on the balance arm until it balances, i.e., occupies a horizontal position, when the plunger is fully submerged. The weights are often calibrated in multiples of ten, so that their position in notches numbered from 1 to 9 on the balance arm, gives the various decimal-place figures for the specific gravity. The plunger often contains a small thermometer.

WETTING AGENT. A substance that causes a liquid to spread more readily upon a solid surface, owing its action chiefly to its effect in reducing the **surface tension.** Specific wetting agents have been developed in many industries.

WHEATSTONE BRIDGE. A combination of instruments used primarily for measuring electrical resistance. It consists essentially of a system of conductors in which a current is divided into two parts, each fork consisting of two sets of resistance in series. If a conductor (bridge) is now placed so that it connects between the two resistances in each fork and these resistances are so adjusted that no current crosses the bridge, the ratio of the resistances in one fork is equal to the ratio of those in the other fork. If three resistances are known, or one ratio and one other resistance, the fourth resistance may be calculated.

WHEELER-TOLLENS TEST. A test for pentoses made by heating a 20% hydrochloric acid solution and phloroglucinol with xylose, arabinose, or any substance that splits off a pentose. A cherry-red color is produced which shows an absorption spectrum between 5200 and 5900 A.

WHITBY TEST. A test for silver in very dilute solution which is based on the brown color it produces with sodium hydroxide solution and organic substances like dex-

organic bases not only from aqueous solutions but also from solutions in organic solvents.

WHITING CELL. A modified **Castner cell** for the electrolysis of sodium chloride brine, in which the mercury that constitutes the cathode is stationary during electrolysis, but is removed periodically for recovery of its sodium content by reaction with water to form sodium hydroxide, after which it is returned to the cell.

WHOLE NUMBER RULE. See the **Prout hypothesis.**

WIDMAN-STOERMER SYNTHESIS. A method of formation of cinnoline derivatives by **diazotization** and **cyclization** of *o*-aminoaryl ethylenes.

trin, starch, acacia, cane sugar, glycerin, etc.

WHITE MICRO-TEST. A micro-test for free lime in Portland cement made by mixing 5 g. phenol and 5 g. nitrobenzene, and adding 1 drop of this mixture and 2 drops of water to 3 mg. of the cement on a slide, rubbing slightly with the cover glass, and observing under a polarizing microscope with crossed Nicol prisms. Characteristic crystals of calcium phenate are observed if free lime is present.

WHITEHORN REAGENT. Permutit (a sodium aluminum silicate), which takes up

WIDMANSTÄTTEN STRUCTURE. A microstructure seen in many steels and other alloys. It is a duplex structure in which one **phase** forms sets of parallel plates embedded in the **matrix.**

WIEDEMANN-FRANZ LAW. See **law of Wiedemann-Franz-Lorenz.**

WIEN EFFECT. The increase in **conductance** of an **electrolyte** at high **potential gradients.**

WIEN EQUATION. A relationship between the intensity of radiation of any wave length yielded by a perfect radiator (black body) at a given temperature, of the form:

$$I \equiv a\lambda^{-5}e^{C/\lambda T}$$

in which I is the intensity of radiation at wave length λ, T is the absolute temperature, a and C are constants, and e is the logarithmic base (natural).

WIESNER SOLUTION FOR LIGNIN. A solution of 0.5 g. phloroglucinol in 122 ml. alcohol used in detecting lignin in paper. A red color, obtained on application of the reagent, followed by hydrochloric acid, shows the presence of lignin.

WIJS IODINE MONOCHLORIDE SOLUTION. An acetic acid solution of iodine monochloride and iodine, used in determining the iodine numbers of oils.

WIJS SPECIAL IODIDE SOLUTION. A solution prepared by dissolving dichloramine T in 200 ml. glacial acetic acid, then adding slowly 16.6 g. potassium iodide, finally diluting to 1 liter with glacial acetic acid. This solution is used in determining the iodine numbers of oils.

WILDENSTEIN REAGENT. A decoction of logwood, used as a reagent for chromic acid.

WILLARD-HALL REAGENT. A solution of phenylthiohydantoic acid, used to precipitate cobalt quantitatively from slightly ammoniacal solutions.

WILLGERODT REACTION. A reaction of a substituted **ketone,** commonly a substituted alkyl aryl ketone, with a solution of ammonium polysulfide to form an aliphatic **acid amide,** containing the aryl group. The effect of the reaction is to reduce the carbonyl group and oxidize a terminal methyl group. In the Kindler variation, a dry amine and sulfur, in equimolecular proportions, replace the ammonium polysulfide, giving a thioamide.

WILLIAMSON REACTION. A general reaction for the synthesis of an **ether** from an **alkoxide** and an **alkyl halide.**

$$ROK + R'Br \rightarrow ROR' + KBr.$$

WILLSTAEDT TEST REACTION. A test for vitamin B_1 made by adding 2,4-dichlorobenzenediazonium chloride to the sample to be tested. A yellow-red coloring matter is produced which can be extracted quantitatively from the aqueous solution by ether. Filtering the ether solution through a column of calcium hydroxide and then eluting the calcium hydroxide with alcohol, separates the coloring matter from other ether-soluble azo dyes.

WILPUTTE COKE OVEN. A by-product coke oven for the production of coke by the regenerative heating and distillation of coal.

WILSON CLOUD CHAMBER. An enclosure containing air or other gas saturated with water vapor, the cooling of which by a sudden expansion results in the formation of fog droplets upon particles of dust or other nuclei. That ions in the gas are capable of serving as condensation nuclei, even when no dust is present, was demonstrated by the experiments of C. T. R. Wilson. Thus the clouds produced are much more dense if the gas is traversed by some ionizing emission like **x-rays** or **alpha rays.** Sir J. J. Thomson utilized this effect in his early measurements of the electronic charge. One of the most striking phenomena of the Wilson cloud chamber is exhibited when single ionizing particles, such as **alpha** or **beta particles,** are allowed to traverse it just before the expansion. The path of each particle is marked by a visible white streak or "track" of mist, sometimes several centimeters in length, which soon diffuses and disappears. The study of photographs of such cloud tracks has in recent years afforded much information as to the nature and the movements of the particles producing them.

$$C_6H_5.CO.CH_3 \xrightarrow[H_2O]{(NH_4)_2S_x} C_6H_5.CH_2.CO.NH_2$$

$$C_6H_5.CO.CH_3 + R'R''NH + S \rightarrow C_6H_5.CH_2.CS.NR'R'' + H_2O.$$

WILSON REAGENTS FOR DETERMINING THE HARDNESS OF WATER. (1) A solution of soap in 56% (by volume) alcohol. Each ml. of the reagent used gives one-half degree of hardness with 100 ml. of the water as a sample. (2) 0.215 g. calcium carbonate is dissolved in dilute hydrochloric acid and made up with distilled water to 1 liter. This is used to standardize the soap solution for water analysis.

WILSON TEST FOR FLUORINE. Add 1 part of a borosilicate (e.g., axinite) to about 2 parts of potassium bisulfate, pulverize finely, and mix well. Mix about 3 parts of the above flux with 1 part of the substance to be tested on a watch glass. Then, make a semifused bead of this mixture on a platinum loop and hold the bead just outside the lower margin of the Bunsen flame. The presence of fluorine is indicated by a transient green flame coloration.

WILSON TEST FOR NITRITE. A test for nitrous acid made by diluting 1 ml. of the acid solution to be tested with 5 ml. water, cooling, and adding sulfuric acid and a minute amount of resorcinol. A more or less intense yellow color is produced by nitrite, according to the quantity of nitrous acid present.

WINDAUS TEST REACTION FOR CHOLESTEROL. Reactions for cholesterol: (1) To cholesterol dissolved in as little ether as possible, add a solution of bromine in glacial acetic acid until a distinct yellow-brown color results. A crystalline precipitate of cholesterol dibromide, melting at 123–124° C., is produced immediately.
(2) Cholesterol in alcoholic solution is precipitated almost quantitatively, as the double compound, by addition of an alcoholic solution of digitonin.

WINDISCH TEST FOR LACTIC ACID. A test for detecting slight quantities of lactic acid is made by distilling the material with potassium dichromate and sulfuric acid and receiving the distillate in **Nessler reagent.** A color, due to the aldehyde formed, is produced in the presence of lactic acid.

WINKLER REAGENT FOR AMMONIA. A substitute for **Nessler reagent,** prepared by dissolving 1 g. mercuric iodide, 5 g. potassium bromide and 2.5 g. sodium hydroxide in 25 ml. of natural water. It is let stand overnight and the clear supernatant liquid removed. The following solution is used to prevent the formation of a precipitate when natural waters are being tested: In 200 ml. water, dissolve 100 g. Rochelle salt, filter, add 1 g. sodium hydroxide, boil 10 minutes, cool and dilute to 250 ml., then add 0.2 g. mercuric iodide, shake, let settle, and use the supernatant liquid.

WINKLER REAGENT FOR ARSENIC, ANTIMONY, AND PHOSPHORUS HYDRIDES. An aqueous solution of silver nitrate, through which are passed the gases to be tested. A dark precipitate forms if a hydride of phosphorus, arsenic, or antimony is present.

WINKLER REAGENT FOR CARBON MONOXIDE. A solution of 20 g. cuprous chloride and 25 g. ammonium chloride in 75 ml. water, to which ammonium hydroxide is then added until the solution is clear. This reagent is used to absorb carbon monoxide.

WINKLER REAGENTS FOR DETERMINING HARDNESS IN WATER. Two reagents, consisting of: (1) a solution of 6 g. potassium hydroxide and 100 g. Rochelle salt in 250 ml. water, to which are then added 100 ml. 10% ammonium hydroxide solution, and the volume brought up to 500 ml. by addition of water; and (2) a solution of 15 g. oleic acid in 600 ml. 90–95% alcohol and 400 ml. water, to which 4 g. potassium hydroxide is added, and the solution standardized against barium chloride solution (4.363 g./l.).

WINKLER REAGENT FOR IODINE. A solution of nitrous acid (or an acidified solution of a nitrite), which liberates iodine from alkali iodides.

WINKLER REAGENT FOR NITRIC OXIDE GAS. A concentrated aqueous solution of ferrous chloride or sulfate which, with nitric oxide, produces a brown to black color.

WINKLER REAGENT FOR OXYGEN.
Fifty g. pyrogallol are dissolved in 1 liter
potassium hydroxide solution to form a
reagent which absorbs oxygen from gas
mixtures and is so used in gas analysis.

**WINKLER TEST FOR DISSOLVED
OXYGEN IN WATER.** A manganese
chloride solution, and a sodium hydroxide
solution containing potassium iodide, are
added to the sample to be tested. The precipitate of manganous oxide is oxidized
by any oxygen present to mangano-man-
ganite. On dissolving the precipitate by
addition of acid, iodine is liberated which
can be determined with 0.01 N thiosulfate.

**WINKLER TEST FOR HYPOCHLO-
RITE IN DRINKING WATER.** Add
1–2 drops of 1:5000 methyl orange solution
and 2–3 ml. of 10% hydrochloric acid to
250 ml. of the water to be tested and to a
blank of 250 ml. of distilled water. The
blank is colored pale rose-red, but water
containing hypochlorite is decolorized almost immediately.

**WINKLER TEST REACTION FOR
GERMANIUM.** A little ammonium sulfide and then an excess of hydrochloric
acid is added to an alkaline solution.
White germanium sulfide precipitates if
germanium is present.

WIRTH TEST. A test for cerous salts
which is an adaptation of the Hartley
reaction. Add 5 ml. of 10% ammonium
tartrate solution and 5 ml. of dilute ammonia to the neutral solution and boil.
The solution becomes yellow to yellow-
brown if cerous salts are present.

WISCHO REAGENT FOR ALOIN. A
solution of 0.4 g. of vanadium pentoxide in
4 ml. concentrated sulfuric acid to which
water to make 100 ml. is then added. This
reagent gives a red color with aloin solution.

WISCHO REAGENTS FOR PHENOLS.
Solutions of vanadium pentoxide in dilute
hydrochloric acid, or in dilute phosphoric
acid, or in dilute oxalic acid, or in dilute
sulfuric acid. They give color reactions
with some phenols, especially the *o*-phenols
or trihydroxyphenols.

**WISCHO TEST FOR DIFFERENTIA-
TING HYPOCHLORITE AND CHLO-
RATE.** A test for differentiating hypochlorite and chlorate made by adding 50 mg.
brucine and 5 drops dilute hydrochloric acid
to 5 ml. of a 0.5% solution of sodium hypochlorite. A yellow color, changing to
cherry-red on boiling, is produced. This
latter color is unchanged when boiled with
10 ml. dilute hydrochloric acid. A chlorate
solution, on similar treatment, is not
colored in the cold; when boiled the solution becomes yellow and later cherry-red,
but the color is discharged when boiling is
continued after the addition of 10 ml. of
dilute hydrochloric acid.

**WISLICENUS-KAUFMANN TEST RE-
ACTION.** A test for mercury made by
bringing metallic aluminum into contact
with a mercury salt solution. A grayish-
white layer of alumina develops on the
aluminum.

**WISLICENUS REAGENT FOR TAN-
NINS.** Aluminum hydroxide obtained by
the action of water on an aluminum
amalgam. It is used in the quantitative
determination of tannins.

WITHERS AND RAY SOLUTION. A
solution of 0.7 g. diphenylamine in 60 ml.
concentrated sulfuric acid and 28.8 ml.
water, to which, after cooling, 11.3 ml. concentrated hydrochloric acid are added.
This reagent is used in testing for nitrates
and nitrites. A blue color, formed on gentle
heating on the surface of concentrated sulfuric acid, shows the presence of nitrites or
nitrates.

WITNESS. A tube placed in a train of
laboratory apparatus, such as a combustion train, to trap any liquid carried
out of the other apparatus in the gas
stream.

WITT COLOR THEORY. A theory to
account for phenomena of color, and the
formation of dyestuffs. Certain radicals
and linkages (called chromophores) impart
color to a compound; others (called auxo-
chromes) impart the power to adhere to
fibers.

WITT DIAZO REACTION. See **diazo reaction (Witt).**

WITT TEST REACTIONS FOR *p*-DIAMINES. (1) An intense blue color is produced by diamines with an alkaline phenol solution and calcium hypochlorite. (2) A blue or green color, changing to red on boiling with water, is produced by diamines with aniline and ferric chloride.

WITTMACK TEST. A test for differentiating wheat and rye flours made by immersing the grains in water at 62.5° C. Rye starch grains swell, but wheat starch grains remain unchanged.

WOHL ALDOSE DEGRADATION. The method for obtaining a lower **aldose** from a higher one by treating the acetylated aldose oxime with ammoniacal silver oxide solution. The course of the reaction is as follows:

WÖHLER-METZ TEST REACTIONS. Ruthenium solutions, heated a short time with thiourea and concentrated hydrochloric acid, give a blue color. A more sensitive reaction can be made by substituting thiocarbanilide for thiourea. A blue-green color forms which can be shaken out with ether. Osmium solutions in concentrated hydrochloric acid, heated for 2 minutes with thiocarbanilide, give a red coloration which can be shaken out with ether to increase the sensitiveness. When metals of the iron and platinum groups are treated with trithiocarbonate in hydrochloric acid solution and shaken out with ether, characteristic colors are obtained. Osmium gives an olive-green color.

WÖHLER REACTION FOR CYANURIC ACID. A solution of cyanuric acid in very dilute ammonia is added to a solution of cupric sulfate in very dilute ammonia and

---

$$CH_2OH.(CHOH)_4.CHO + NH_2OH \rightarrow CH_2OH.(CHOH)_4.CH{:}NOH + H_2O.$$

$$CH_2OH.(CHOH)_4.CH{:}NOH + 3(CH_3CO)_2O \rightarrow CH_2OAc.(CHOAc)_4.CN + 3H_2O$$

$$+ CH_3COOH.$$

$$CH_2OAc.(CHOAc)_4.CN + 5NH_3 \xrightarrow{\text{AgOH}} CH_2OH.(CHOH)_3.CH(NHCOCH_3)_2$$

$$+ 3CH_3CONH_2 + HCN + H_2O.$$

$$CH_2OH.(CHOH)_3.CH(NHCOCH_3)_2 + H_2O \rightarrow CH_2OH(CHOH)_3.CHO + 2CH_3CONH_2.$$

In the Zemplen modification of this reaction, sodium alkoxides are used instead of the ammoniacal silver oxide.

The symbol Ac, used above, denotes the

$$\text{acetyl group} \left[CH_3.C \diagup^{\displaystyle \overset{O}{\diagup}}_{\diagdown} \right].$$

WOHL-ZIEGLER REACTION. A method of halogenation by the use of *N*-haloamides, used especially in such special cases as the substitution of a halogen atom in an unsaturated compound without affecting the unsaturated linkage.

heated. An amethyst precipitate is produced.

WÖHLER REACTION FOR PLATINUM. Stannous chloride added to a platinum solution produces a red color which may be extracted with ether or ethyl acetate. The red solution, when diluted with water, produces a chocolate-brown precipitate. The red solution becomes dark red to black on being heated.

WÖHLER SYNTHESIS. The pioneer organic synthesis (really a **rearrangement**)

$$\overset{\displaystyle \overset{\text{NBr}}{\rule{2cm}{0.4pt}}}{R.CH{:}CH.CH_3 + OC.CH_2.CH_2.CO} \rightarrow RCH{:}CH.CH_2Br + \overset{\displaystyle \overset{\text{NH}}{\rule{2cm}{0.4pt}}}{OC.CH_2.CH_2.CO.}$$

in which urea was obtained by heating ammonium cyanate.

$$NH_4OCN \xrightarrow{\Delta} \begin{array}{c} H_2N \\ \\ H_2N \end{array}\!\!\!\!>C{=}O.$$

WOLESKY SOLUTION. A solution of 1 g. diphenylamine in 50 ml. alcohol, to which is then added 5–6 ml. concentrated hydrochloric acid, used in testing for lignin in paper. An orange-red spot indicates the presence of lignin.

WOLF-HEYMANN TEST. A test for nitrate, for which the reagent is an aqueous solution of 2,4-diamino-6-hydroxy pyrimidine. One ml. of the liquid to be tested and 1 ml. of the reagent are mixed and floated on sulfuric acid. If nitrate is present, a raspberry-colored ring forms in $\frac{1}{2}$ to 1 minute.

WOLFF-KISHNER REDUCTION. A method for converting aldehydes and ketones to their corresponding hydrocarbons by heating their hydrazones, phenylhydrazones, or semicarbazones with dry sodium ethoxide (Wolff) or by heating the carbonyl compound with hydrazine sulfate and excess sodium ethoxide (Kishner).

WOLFF REACTION FOR BENZIDINE AND TOLIDINE. A very small quantity of the substance is dissolved in glacial acetic acid, diluted with water and lead peroxide added. A blue color, disappearing on heating, is produced in the presence of benzidine or tolidine.

WOLFF REACTION FOR THIOCYANATE. An excess of an alcoholic ammonium thiocyanate solution added to a very dilute neutral or nearly neutral alcoholic cobaltous salt solution produces a blue color which shows a characteristic absorption spectrum.

WOLFF REARRANGEMENT. A rearrangement of diazoketones, on reaction with alcohols or amines or water, to form esters or amides or acids, and free nitrogen, in the presence of a metallic catalyst.

WOLFF TEST FOR METHANOL. Oxidize the methanol with potassium permanganate to formaldehyde and float the oxidized solution on a mixture of apomorphine in concentrated sulfuric acid. A blue-violet color shows the presence of methanol.

WÖLFFENSTEIN-BÖTERS REACTION. A method of production of certain nitrophenols from aromatic compounds (chiefly hydrocarbons) by simultaneous oxidation and nitration. A well-known application of this reaction is in the production of picric acid by heating benzene with nitric acid in the presence of a mercury salt.

WOLFRAM (WOLFRAMIUM). Tungsten.

WOLFRAMIC. Tungstic.

WOLKOW-BAUMANN TEST REACTION. A test for hydroquinone made by adding **Millon reagent** (q.v.) to the solution to be tested. An amorphous yellow precipitate forming in the cold and a brick-red precipitate on heating is given by hydroquinone.

WOLTERING REAGENT. A reagent for alkaloids which is an aqueous 2% furfural solution. In 0.5 ml. of the reagent, dissolve a trace of the substance to be tested and float the solution carefully over cold, concentrated sulfuric acid. A characteristic colored ring is formed at the contact surface if alkaloids are present.

WOODALL-DUCKHAM COKING RETORT. A vertical retort for the distillation of coal to form coke. It is continuous in operation; coal enters at the top and coke is periodically withdrawn at the

$$R.CO.CHN_2 + R'OH \rightarrow R.CH_2.COOR' + N_2.$$

bottom; gas, tar, and ammonia are obtained from the distillate.

WORK. Work may be regarded as the transfer of energy from one body to another, or, in a slightly different sense, as energy in process of transfer. While there are numerous instances of energy transfer whose mechanism is unknown (by radiation, for example), in all cases open to direct observation the process appears to involve two essential factors: (1) the exertion of a force by one body A upon another body B, and (2) the motion or displacement of B in a direction in which the force has an effective component (not necessarily in the direction of the force itself).

WORK FUNCTION, THERMIONIC. See **thermionic work function.**

WORK FUNCTION, THERMODYNAMIC. See **thermodynamic work function.**

WORK HEAD. See **head, work.**

WÖRNER TEST REACTION. A test for potassium made by adding a solution of 1 g. phosphotungstic acid in 10 ml. water to solutions of neutral or acid potassium salts. A white precipitate is produced.

WOULFF BOTTLE. A type of bottle used in the laboratory for special purposes, especially in organic synthesis. It commonly has two or three necks, for convenience in connecting inlet and outlet tubes, and may have an opening in the bottom. One neck, usually the center, is used for stirring, and the others for the addition of reagents, etc.

WOYNOFF TEST FOR COBALT. A strip of filter paper is dipped into the solution to be tested, dried, a drop of 20–30% antipyrine solution added and dried again. A blue-green or pale green ring appears after a few minutes if cobalt is present.

WOYNOFF TEST REACTIONS FOR VANADIUM CHLORIDE. (1) An aqueous or alcoholic solution of vanadium chloride with salicylic acid gives a violet color; with sodium salicylate, a reddish-brown color. Vanadium chloride, with a hot aqueous solution of meconic acid, gives a red color.

WULLNER LAW. See **law of Wullner.**

WÜRTZ REACTION. The synthesis of aliphatic hydrocarbons by treatment of halogen-substituted alkyl compounds with metallic sodium. Thus ethyl iodide yields butane,

$$2C_2H_5I + 2Na \rightarrow C_2H_5{-}C_2H_5 + 2NaI.$$

WÜRTZ-FITTIG REACTION. The synthesis of mixed alkyl-aryl hydrocarbons by treatment of halogen-substituted alkyl and aryl compounds with metallic sodium. Thus bromobenzene and methyl bromide yield toluene:

$$C_6H_5Br + CH_3Br + 2Na \rightarrow C_6H_5CH_3 + 2NaBr.$$

The yield is reduced by the reaction of two molecules of the bromobenzene to form biphenyl, and the reaction of two molecules of the methyl bromide to form ethane.

WYSS TEST FOR AMYL ALCOHOL. Add 4 drops of a solution of 4.5 g. α-naphthol in 100 ml. 50% alcohol, 4 drops of a solution of 4.5 g. p-phenylenediamine in 100 ml. absolute alcohol, and 4 drops of 4.5% solution of sodium carbonate to 2 ml. of the liquid to be tested. A dark blue-violet color is produced if amyl alcohol is present.

WYSS TEST FOR INSULIN. This test is based on the fact that the oxidation of glucose or of phenols by hydrogen peroxide is retarded or prevented in the presence of insulin.

X. Symbol for a **radical** (X). Symbol for **mole fraction** in liquid (x). Symbol for distance above datum plane in direction of flow (x). Symbol for **volume fraction** (x_V). Symbol for **weight fraction** (x_w). Symbol for mole ratio in liquid (X). Symbol for **reactance** (X), for capacitative reactance (X_c), for inductive reactance (X_L). (See also **xi.**)

XANTHATE. A salt of xanthic acid of the general form

$$\begin{array}{c} \quad\quad OR \\ \quad\quad / \\ C{=}S \\ \quad\quad \backslash \\ \quad\quad SX \end{array}$$

in which R is commonly an alkyl or aryl radical, and X is a metal atom. In xanthic acid, R is an ethyl group, and X is a hydrogen atom.

XANTHINE BASE. One of a number of proximate principles of plants, formerly classed as **alkaloids,** and some products of the animal economy derived from xanthine. Representative xanthine compounds are caffeine, theobromine, theophylline, heteroxanthine, paraxanthine. Xanthine is 2,6-dihydroxypurine, having the formula

$$\begin{array}{c} N{=}C{-}OH \\ |\quad\quad | \\ HO{-}C\quad C{-}N{-}H \\ ||\quad\quad\quad\quad\backslash \\ ||\quad\quad\quad\quad\quad C{-}H \\ |\quad\quad\quad\quad\quad / \\ N{-}C{-}N \end{array}$$

or the di-keto form of this structure.

XANTHO-, XANTH-. (Greek) Yellow, as xanthocobaltic, xanthoprotein, xanthine.

XANTHYL. The radical $C_{13}H_9O{-}$, derived by loss of a hydrogen atom, from xanthene,

$$\begin{array}{c} \quad\quad O \\ \quad / \quad \backslash \\ C_6H_4 \quad\quad C_6H_4. \\ \quad \backslash \quad / \\ \quad\quad CH_2 \end{array}$$

X-RAY(S). Electromagnetic radiations ranging in wave length from approximately 0.006 millimicron to 0.2 millimicron $(6 \times 10^{-12}$ to 2×10^{-10} meters). They are commonly produced by directing a stream of **cathode rays** upon a metal target, in an x-ray tube. (See **ray, Roentgen.**)

X-RAY(S), CHARACTERISTIC. X-rays of frequency characteristic of the element by which they are emitted. Commonly, such x-rays are obtained most conveniently by secondary **excitation** of screens composed of particular elements, or by passing x-rays emitted by **anticathodes** through screens of the same material. Such x-ray spectra consist of various series of different frequencies but in all series the frequencies change regularly with the atomic number of the element.

X-RAY DETECTION. There are three principal means of detecting x-rays: the fluorescent effect, the photographic effect, and the ionizing effect. The only method at first available for distinguishing radiations of different wave length was to measure their penetration or their **absorption coefficient** in various substances. The discovery of the x-ray diffraction or grating effect of crystals, by von Laue, Friedrich, and Knipping, made it possible to analyze the rays and measure their wave lengths very much as light is studied with the **spectroscope.** When x-rays of given wave length are incident upon a crystal turned in various directions, the layers of atoms, at certain angles of incidence, reflect wave trains in phase with each other and produce a characteristic reflection pattern. While the matter is not as simple as in the case of light incident on a diffraction grating, it is nevertheless possible to interpret such patterns in somewhat the same way as a line spectrum and to deduce the wave length from it. A unit convenient for expressing x-ray wave lengths is the "x-unit," which is 10^{-11} cm. or 0.001 Ångström.

X-RAY DIFFRACTION. The sub-microscope structure of substances may be investigated by the **diffraction patterns** formed by x-rays upon passage through them. In general, gases yield merely a fog, or corona effect; liquids or amorphous solids (in which there is random distribution of particles) give a diffraction pattern in the form of a halo; while systems of solids consisting of molecules oriented in one direction usually yield diffraction patterns of concentric rings; and substances, such as crystals, in which the particles are arranged in a regular lattice, give point patterns.

X-RAY HARDNESS. The penetrating power of x-rays, which is an inverse function of the **wave length.**

X-RAY(S), HETEROGENEOUS. X-rays of a broad range or considerable number of frequencies.

X-RAY(S), HOMOGENEOUS. X-rays of a single frequency or of a narrow band of frequencies.

X-RAY(S), MONOCHROMATIC. See **x-rays, homogeneous.**

X-RAY(S), POLYCHROMATIC. See **x-rays, heterogeneous.**

X-RAY SPECTRA. When **cathode rays** of sufficient energy fall upon a specimen of some element, as the metal "target" of an x-ray tube, the resulting x-rays, thus analyzed, are in general found to consist of a continuous **spectrum** (somewhat analogous to the radiation from a heated solid) with an intensity maximum and an upper frequency limit at frequencies dependent upon the speed of the cathode rays. Upon this may be superposed certain groups of much sharper maxima, which may be regarded as rather diffuse spectrum lines. These are characteristic of the material of the target, not of the incident cathode rays; except that if the cathode rays are produced below a certain voltage, some groups of lines do not appear at all.

X-RAY SPECTROGRAM. A record of an x-ray diffraction pattern.

X-RAY SPECTROGRAPH. An apparatus used to record **x-ray diffraction** patterns, such as an **x-ray spectrometer** equipped with photographic or other recording apparatus.

X-RAY SPECTROMETER. An apparatus used to produce **x-ray diffraction** patterns by passing a beam of x-rays through a substance, such as a crystal, placed so that its space lattice acts as a diffraction grating. The resulting patterns are analyzed to determine either the structure of the crystal, or the wave lengths of the beam of x-rays.

X-RAY STRUCTURE. The **atomic** or ionic **structure** of substances as determined by **x-ray diffraction** patterns obtained by the passage through it of x-rays.

X-RAY UNIT. See **x-ray detection.**

Xe Symbol for the element **xenon.**

XENON. Gaseous element. Symbol Xe. Atomic number 54. Atomic weight 131.3. Density (grams per liter at S.T.P.) 5.851. Melting point $-112°$ C. Boiling point $-107.1°$ C. Xenon is one of the rare gases of the atmosphere. It forms no known compounds.

XENYL. See **biphenylyl.**

Xi (Ξ **OR** ξ). The fourteenth letter of the Greek alphabet, used to denote the fourteenth carbon atom in a straight-chain compound, or a derivative in which the substituent group is attached to the fourteenth carbon atom (ξ-). Symbol for propagation **flux density** (Ξ).

XYLO-, XYL-. (Greek, *xylon*, wood) Relating to wood, xylene, or xylose, as xyloidin, xylidine, xyloquinone, xylonic.

XYLOYL. The radical $(CH_3)_2C_6H_3CO-$ (from xylic acid, 7 isomers).

XYLYL. The radical $(CH_3)_2C_6H_3-$.

XYLYLENE. The radical

$$-H_2CC_6H_4CH_2-.$$

Y Symbol for the element **yttrium** (Y, also Yt). Symbol for depth (y). Symbol for **mole fraction** in vapor (y). Symbol for **mole fraction** in vapor, equilibrium value (y^*). Symbol for **mole ratio** in vapor (Y). Symbol for **admittance** (reciprocal impedance) (Y). Symbol for height of object (y). Symbol for height of image (y').

YAGODA TEST. A test for rhenium made by fusing a small quantity of sodium rhenate with sodium carbonate. The bead becomes a black color which persists for about 1 minute after being removed from the flame, changes to yellow, and fades entirely in about 10 minutes. The same color changes take place if the bead is reheated.

YANOWSKI-HYNES MICROREAGENT. A microreagent for anions which is chloropentammino-cobaltic chloride (purpureo-cobaltic chloride). The reaction between the reagent and bromate, chromate, silicofluoride, oxalate, thiosalicylate, and xanthate ions produces characteristic crystals.

YARD. A unit of length in the English system. The U.S. standard yard is the 3600/3937 part of the international meter and is slightly longer than the English legal standard.

1 yard	$= 0.9144$ meter
1.0936 yard	$= 1.0000$ meter
1 cubic yard	$= 0.7645$ cubic meter
1.3079 cubic yard	$= 1.0000$ cubic meter

Yb Symbol for the element **ytterbium.**

YEASTS. (*Blastomycetes, saccharomycetes*) Unicellular microorganisms characterized essentially by their method of multiplication, by budding. They are classed with the nonchlorophyll-containing fungi. The genus *saccharomyces* includes practically all of the yeasts of economic importance. *S. cerevisiae* is the special beer ferment; *S. cerevisiae var. ellipsoideus,* the wine ferment. Yeasts are grouped as top yeasts which are carried to the surface of the vat by the carbon dioxide they produce, and bottom yeasts, which remain on the bottom of the vat and act at lower temperature than the top yeasts. Compressed yeasts are made by collecting the yeast plants by filtration, mixing with 25 to 50% of starch and pressing. Wild yeasts are yeast plants about which little is known and which are often detrimental in their actions. Forulae are also industrially important yeasts, but they are not *saccharomyces*; and they do not have spores.

YIELD. The quantity of product obtained as the result of a process or reaction or series of processes or reactions; or the percentage so obtained of that theoretically obtainable from the quantity of one of the chemical compounds initially present.

YOE REAGENT. A saturated aqueous solution of 7-iodo-8-hydroxyquinoline-5-sulfonic acid. With ferric iron solutions, a green color is given, the depth of which is proportional to the concentration.

YOUNG TEST FOR COCAINE IN THE PRESENCE OF NOVOCAIN. Four to 5 drops of 2% cobalt thiocyanate solution are poured over a small sample of the solid substance. Dark blue flocks form, if only cocaine is present. If novocain is present also, the entire solution becomes blue. Four to 5 drops of a stannous chloride solution, freshly prepared by dissolving 10 g. stannous chloride and 5 g. metallic tin in 100 ml. of 1:1 hydrochloric acid, are added. The precipitate dissolves immediately leaving a clear rose-colored solution, if only novocain is present. The blue flocks undergo no change on the addition of the stannous chloride solution, if only cocaine is present.

YOUNG TEST FOR GALLIC ACID IN TANNIN. A carmine-red color is given by potassium cyanide with gallic acid solutions, but no color with tannin solutions.

YTTERBIC. Containing **ytterbium.**

YTTERBIUM. Rare earth metallic element. Symbol Yb. Atomic number 70. Atomic weight 173.04. Valence 3. Oxide Yb_2O_3. Ore, gadolinite.

YTTRIC. Containing **yttrium.**

YTTRIUM. Rare metallic element. Symbol Y or Yt. Atomic number 39. Atomic weight 88.92. Valence 3. Oxide Y_2O_3. Ore, gadolinite.

YVON REAGENTS FOR α- AND β-NAPHTHOL. (1) Two ml. nitric acid, 2 ml. alcohol, and 10 drops nitrate solution. (2) Two ml. alcohol, 3 drops concentrated potassium nitrate solution, and 10 drops sulfuric acid. On adding the reagents to 10 ml. of the aqueous naphthol solution, color reactions are obtained.

YVON REAGENT FOR WATER IN ALCOHOL. Calcium carbide; when it is added to alcohol containing traces of water, acetylene is evolved.

YVON TEST FOR ALCOHOL IN CHLOROFORM. Add a solution of 1 g. potassium permanganate and 10 g. potassium hydroxide in 250 ml. water to the solution to be tested and shake. If the violet color changes to green, the presence of alcohol is indicated.

Z. Symbol for **gram-equivalent weight** (Z). Symbol for **atomic number** (Z). Symbol for **ionic valency** (z). Symbol for **compressibility factor** (z). Symbol for distance above datum plane (Z). Symbol for height (Z). Symbol for molecular collision frequency (Z). Symbol for **impedance** (Z). Symbol for section modulus (z). (See also **zeta**.)

ZAFFUTO TEST REACTION. A test for molybdenum made by acidifying the solution with nitric acid, adding ammonium nitrate and 1 ml. of alcohol and shaking; then some crystals of sodium hydrosulfite ($Na_2S_2O_4$) are added. The solution turns brown, then greenish-blue and, when shaken and heated at 50–60° C., dark blue, if molybdenum is present.

ZAGORSKIKH SOLUTION. A solution of 1 g. ammonium molybdate in 100 ml. concentrated sulfuric acid, used as a test reagent for various salicylates. Characteristic color reactions are obtained.

ZAMBELLI TEST. A test for nitrite made by adding to 200 ml. of the water to be tested, a solution of sulfanilic acid in dilute sulfuric acid, and after 10 minutes adding a little aqueous α-naphthol solution and alkalinizing with ammonia. The solution is colored rose to deep red if nitrite is present. Several modifications of this test have been developed.

ZAMPARO REACTION FOR RESORCINOL AND PHLOROGLUCINOL. In 3 ml. of alcohol, dissolve 0.1 g. of the substance to be tested, add 2 ml. formaldehyde, and then 3 ml. concentrated hydrochloric acid. If colored precipitates are given immediately in the cold, resorcinol and phloroglucinol are present.

ZAMPARO TESTS FOR THE DIFFERENTIATION OF THE NAPHTHOLS. (1) Sulfuric acid in alcohol containing hydrogen peroxide and (2) formaldehyde and hydrochloric acid are used to differentiate the two naphthols by means of color reactions.

ZANFROGNINI REAGENT. A solution of 3 g. potassium permanganate in 240 ml. water, to which 8 ml. lactic acid are added slowly. This reagent is used as a test reagent for adrenaline, which gives a red color in the presence of hydrogen peroxide.

ZAPARANICK TEST. A test for triethanolamine made by decomposing oils, emulsions, etc., by boiling with an excess of mineral acid. The substance is then cooled, the fatty matter extracted with ether, the water layer strongly alkalinized with sodium hydroxide solution, and the ammonia boiled off, if present. The presence of ethanolamine is indicated if, upon the addition of cupric sulfate solution, a blue color develops.

ZEEMAN EFFECT. When a source of light is placed in an intense magnetic field, its spectral lines are broken up into two or more components, and these components are polarized. *In the simplest case,* when viewed in a direction perpendicular to the field, three lines appear, the central one being plane polarized at right angles to the field and having the same wave length as the original line, the other two components being plane polarized parallel to the field, and being, respectively, of shorter and longer wave length than the original line, the difference in wave length being the same in both cases. In this simplest case, when viewed in a direction parallel to the magnetic field, two components are seen, having the same wave lengths as the outside components previously mentioned, but being circularly polarized in opposite directions.

However, most spectral lines show a much more complex resolution than the simplest case. Instead of three components in a transverse magnetic field, there are observed a larger number, some having the same state of polarization as the central component mentioned above, and others similar to the outer components, the number of each class varying with the spectral type of the line. Since it was observed in the simplest case that the change in frequency of each outer component could be calculated by the relationship

$$\Delta \nu_n = \frac{eH}{4m_0} = 1.400 \times 10^6 H$$

where H is the magnetic field intensity, the designation of *normal* Zeeman effect was applied to cases for which this relationship held, while the more complex types of resolution were called the *anomalous* Zeeman effect.

ZEISBERG CONCENTRATOR. A nitric acid concentrator, consisting of a packed tower, into which weak nitric acid vapors are introduced. Some steam is admitted into the bottom, and strong nitric acid vapors are discharged from the top to a condenser.

ZEISEL METHOD. A method of determination of **methoxy groups** in organic compounds by means of hydriodic acid, whereby the methyl group is replaced by hydrogen, leaving a hydroxy group in place of the methoxy group, and forming methyl iodide, which can be determined in various ways.

ZEISEL REACTION. The demethylation of an organic compound by treatment with hydriodic acid, which leaves a hydroxy group in place of the methoxy group, and forms methyl iodide, which may readily be determined quantitatively, as in the study of the amount of methoxy groups present.

ZENGER TEST. A test for arsenic made by distilling the unknown substance with hydrochloric acid or with sodium chloride and sulfuric acid. The arsenic in the distillate is then precipitated as the trisulfide, removed by filtration, after which it is redissolved, oxidized with nitric acid and precipitated with magnesia mixture.

ZENGHELIS REAGENT AND TEST FOR AMMONIA. A mixture of 1 volume of 20% silver nitrate solution with 3 volumes of 37% formaldehyde solution is the reagent. The solution to be tested is made strongly alkaline with sodium carbonate or with sodium hydroxide, 1 ml. of the solution placed in a test tube, covered with a watch glass from the under surface of which is hung a drop of the reagent and the test tube heated in a sand bath. Ammonia forms a ring-shaped silver mirror.

ZENGHELIS REAGENT AND TEST FOR HYDROGEN AND TIN. A solution of 1 g. molybdic acid in dilute sodium hydroxide solution, acidulated with hydrochloric acid and then made up to 200 ml. with water, is the reagent. A blue color is produced on passing hydrogen through the warmed reagent. The same reduction phenomenon, accompanied by the formation of a blue color, is used as the basis of a test for stannous salts.

ZENKER FLUID. An aqueous solution of sodium sulfate, potassium dichromate, glacial acetic acid, and mercuric chloride, used as a fixative.

ZEREVITINOV DETERMINATION. A method of analysis of organic compounds containing active hydrogen atoms, as in **hydroxy, carboxy,** or **imino groups,** by reaction with methyl magnesium halide to yield methane quantitatively.

$$ROH + CH_3MgX \rightarrow CH_4 + ROMgX.$$

ZERO, ABSOLUTE. See **absolute zero,** and **temperature scale, absolute.**

ZERO-ORDER REACTION. A reaction which has a constant rate, as in the case of certain gases reacting on the surface of a solid when it is almost entirely covered. Under such conditions the **reaction rate** may be independent of pressure, and thus the process is kinetically of zero order.

ZERO-POINT ENERGY. The energy possessed by a molecule at its lowest **energy level,** i.e., at a temperature of absolute zero. According to quantum mechanics this energy is finite, and it has been calculated for many molecules.

ZETA (Z OR ζ). The sixth letter of the Greek alphabet, used to denote the sixth carbon atom in a straight-chain compound, or a derivative in which a substitutent group is attached to that carbon atom (ζ-).

ZETA POTENTIAL. Modern theories of **electrokinesis** postulate the existence of a double layer between a charged surface and a liquid in contact with it. It is believed that there is, next to the metal, a very thin, possibly mono-molecular, layer of sharp potential gradient, and then a wider, diffuse layer of lesser potential gradient. The drop in potential across this wider, diffuse layer is the zeta potential.

ZETSCHE-NACHMANN REAGENT. An 0.1% solution of sodium or ammonium bis-p-chlorophenylphosphate, used in the quantitative determination of iron. Iron salts are precipitated by the reagent, the precipitate filtered off and washed with N hydrochloric acid and water, then decomposed with warm ammonia and ammonium chloride solution. Ferric hydroxide, which is weighed as the oxide, is obtained.

ZETTNOW TEST REACTIONS. Tests for tungstate made by acidifying a solution of a tungstate with sulfuric acid and (1) adding potassium ferrocyanide, forming a greenish-yellow to dark orange-yellow color, (2) adding stannous chloride, forming a white precipitate, or (3) adding zinc, forming a blue color.

ZIEGLER METHOD. A method of obtaining cyclic ketones from dinitriles by cyclization with metal amides, followed by hydrolysis and decarboxylation.

ZIERVOGAL PROCESS. A metallurgical process for the recovery of silver from sulfide ores, involving oxidation by roasting in air, solution of the silver sulfate in water, and displacement of the metallic silver from solution by treatment with metallic copper.

ZIMMERMANN REACTION FOR URANIUM. Curcuma paper is colored brownish to brown by slightly acid solutions of uranyl salts.

ZIMMERMANN REAGENT FOR BASES. Rufianic acid—1,4-dihydroxy-anthraquinone-2-sulfonic acid—which produces difficultly soluble salts with organic bases such as creatinine, histidine, arginine, betaine, choline, etc.

ZIMMERMANN-REINHARDT SOLUTION. A solution of 70 g. manganese sulfate in 500 ml. water, to which is then added 125 ml. concentrated sulfuric acid and 125 ml. 85% phosphoric acid, followed by dilution to 1 liter. This reagent is used in the determination of iron, by titration with permanganate in hydrochloric acid solution. This reagent prevents oxidation of the chloride.

ZIMMERMANN TEST FOR ARSENIC, ANTIMONY, AND PHOSPHORUS (AS THE HYDRIDES). Cover the test tube in which the gas is being evolved with a filter paper which has been treated with 1 drop of a 1% solution of gold sodium chloride or of gold chloride. A violet to violet-black spot is formed if the slightest trace of arsine, stibine, or phosphine is present. Pure hydrogen does not react, but hydrogen sulfide impairs the reaction.

ZIMMET REAGENT. A solution of 5 g. sodium nitroprusside and 50 g. sodium

$$
\begin{array}{ccc}
\text{CH}_2\!-\!\text{CH}_2 & \text{CH}_2\!-\!\text{CH}_2 & \text{CH}_2\!-\!\text{CH}_2 \\
| \quad\quad | & | \quad\quad | & | \quad\quad | \\
(\text{CH}_2)_n \quad \text{CN} \xrightarrow{\text{NaNR}_2} & (\text{CH}_2)_n \quad \text{C}\!=\!\text{NH} \xrightarrow[-2\text{NH}_3]{\;3\text{H}_2\text{O}\;} & (\text{CH}_2)_n \quad \text{C}\!=\!\text{O}. \\
& & \\
\text{CH}_2 & \text{CH} & \text{CH}_2 \\
| & | & \\
\text{CN} & \text{CN} &
\end{array}
$$

phosphite in 100 ml. water, used as a reagent for glutathione.

ZINC. Metallic element. Symbol Zn. Atomic number 30. Atomic weight 65.38. Density 7.14. Specific heat 0.0836. Melting point 419.4° C. Boiling point 907° C. Valence 2. Ores, franklinite, hydrozincite, zincite, etc. Oxides, ZnO, ZnO_2.

ZINCATE. The anion $ZnO_2^=$, $Zn_2O_4^{4-}$, $HZnO_2^-$, or ZnO_4^{6-}, or a compound containing one of these anions.

ZINCATE, HYDROXY-. The anion $Zn(OH)_3^-$, $Zn(OH)_4^=$, or $Zn(OH)_6^{4-}$, or a compound containing one of these anions.

ZINCIC. Containing **zinc.**

ZINCKE METHOD. A method for the production of sulfenyl halides by **halogenation** (with chlorine or bromine) of aryl disulfides, arylbenzyl sulfides, or thiophenols.

$$R.S.S.R + Br_2 \rightarrow 2RSBr.$$

$$RS.CH_2.C_6H_5 + 2Br_2 \rightarrow RSBr + C_6H_5.CHBr_2 + HBr.$$

$$R.SH + Br_2 \rightarrow RSBr + HBr.$$

ZINKE NITRATION REACTION. A method of preparing certain halogen-substituted **nitrophenols** by replacement of some bromine or iodine substituents by **nitro groups** by treatment with nitrous acid.

ZINCO-. Pertaining to or containing **zinc.**

ZIRCO-. Containing **zirconium.**

ZIRCONATE (META-). The anion $ZrO_3^=$, or a compound containing it.

ZIRCONIC. Pertaining to or containing **zirconium.**

ZIRCONIUM. Metallic element. Symbol Zr. Atomic number 40. Atomic weight 91.22. Exists in two allotropic forms: (1) Amorphous—density 4.15; and (2) Crystalline—density 6.54. Specific heat 0.936. Melting point 1857° C. Boiling point > 2900° C. Ore, zircon. Oxides, ZrO_2, Zr_2O_5. Valence 4, 3 and 2.

ZIRCONO-. Pertaining to or containing **zirconium.**

ZIRCONYL. The radical $=ZrO$.

Zn Symbol for the element **zinc.**

ZONE AXIS. The axis through the center of a crystal which is parallel to the edge of a zone.

ZONE, CRYSTAL. A set of crystal faces which meet in parallel edges.

ZONE, INTERFACIAL. The boundary area between two **phases,** consisting of the boundary particles of each phase if, in the particular case, they may be regarded as composed of particles.

ZORKIN CARMINE REAGENT. A solution of 0.05 g. carmine red in 100 ml. concentrated sulfuric acid, used in the detection of boric acid. A color change from red to blue indicates the presence of boric acid.

ZOUCHLOS SOLUTIONS. Two solutions, either of which is effective as a precipitant for albumin. One solution is prepared by mixing 60 ml. of a 1% aqueous solution of mercuric chloride with 10 ml. glacial acetic acid. The other solution is prepared by mixing 100 ml. of a 10% aqueous solution of potassium thiocyanate with 20 ml. glacial acetic acid.

Zr Symbol for the element **zirconium.**

ZSIGMONDY REAGENT. A reagent for colloids which is a red colloidal solution of metallic gold obtained by reducing auric chloride by formaldehyde in the presence of an alkali. When mixed with sodium chloride, this reagent becomes blue because of an agglomeration of the particles of gold, but this color change is prevented by the presence of an adequate amount of certain other colloids. They can be classified according to the amount required to prevent the color change.

ZULKOWSKY REAGENT. A reagent prepared by heating 6 g. starch with 100 ml. glycerol until the mixture is soluble in water. It is used as a reagent for iodine, which gives a deep blue color with it.

ZWIKKER REAGENT. A solution prepared by mixing 4 ml. of a 10% aqueous solution of cupric sulfate, 1 ml. pyridine, and 5 ml. water. It is used in testing for perchlorates, permanganates, chromates, thiosulfates, etc. Characteristic crystals are obtained.

ZWITTERION. An ion carrying charges of opposite sign. Many **amino acids,** for example, ionize as follows:

$$H_2N.CH_2.COOH \rightleftarrows {}^+H_3N.CH_2.COO^-.$$

ZYME. A **ferment.**

ZYMIC. Produced by **enzyme** action.

ZYMO-, ZYM-. (Greek, *zyme*, leaven) Relating to a **ferment** or fermentation, as zymophosphate, zymase.

ZYMOGEN. A progenitor of an **enzyme** in the organism; a substance from which an enzyme is supposed to be formed, as pepsin from pepsinogen, trypsin from trypsinogen, or thrombin from prothrombin.

ZYMOHYDROLYSIS. Hydrolysis catalyzed by an enzyme.

ZYMOLOGY. The science of **enzymes.**

ZYMOLYTIC REACTION. See **reaction, zymolytic.**